BRITAIN'S FIRST SPACE ROCKET

BRITAIN'S FIRST SPACE ROCKET

The Story of the Skylark

Robin H. Brand

NEW FOREST
ELECTRONICS

First published in 2014 by:

New Forest Electronics.
17 Park Road,
Fordingbridge,
Hants.
SP6 1EQ
UK

ISBN 978-0-9929896-0-6

Front cover photograph: An unidentified Skylark with Goldfinch boost motor leaves the tower at Woomera, South Australia c.1970. (WRE)

Back cover photograph: The snow capped peaks of the Andes with the Pacific Ocean beyond, taken by Skylark SL1182 in March 1973 from 200 km above Argentina. (See also figure 13.1) (RAE \ University of Reading)

Typeset by *wordzworth.com*

Indexed by Ann Parry FSocInd, Freelance Indexer, *www.parryindexing.co.uk*

Printed and bound by CPI Group (UK) Ltd, Croydon, CR0 4YY

Thence we came forth to rebehold the stars[1]

[1]   The Divine Comedy of Dante Alighieri – 'Inferno', Canto XXXIV, last line. (Translated by Henry Wadsworth Longfellow, c.1867+).

It is strange that we are not able to inculcate into the minds of many men, the necessity of the distinction of my Lord Bacon's, that there ought to be *Experiments of Light,* as well as of *Fruit.*

It is their usual word, *What solid good will come from thence?* They are indeed to be commended for being so severe *Extractors* of goodness. And it were to be wish'd, that they would not only exercise this vigour, about *Experiments,* but on their own *lives,* and *actions*: that they would still question with themselves, in all that they do; what *solid good* will come from thence?

But they are to know, that in so large, and so various an *Art* as this of *Experiments,* there are many degrees of usefulness: some may serve for real, and plain *benefit,* without much *delight*: some for *teaching* without apparent *profit*: some for *light* now, and for *use* hereafter; some only for *ornament* and *curiosity.*

If they will still persist in condemning all *Experiments,* except those which bring with them immediate *gain,* and a present *harvest*: they may as well cavil at the Providence of God, that he has not made all the seasons of the year to be times of *mowing, reaping* and *vintage.*

Thomas Sprat, *The History of the Royal Society*, 1667

(As displayed in many offices, workshops and laboratories of the WRE at Woomera and Salisbury, South Australia[2])

---

2   In the first instance from Southall (1962), *Woomera,* p.48, originally Thomas Sprat (1667), *The History of the Royal Society*, (p.245 of fourth edition).

CONTENTS

PREFACE

To my generation, during whose formative years space flight was science fiction, a book concerning the 'history' of space exploration seems a contradiction in terms. Yet here it is. Space flight began in the 1950s and 60s, when rocket technology came of age, and scientists started to use this new tool to help explore previously unreachable regions. Public interest was great. When the first space satellites were launched, the newspapers published the times when they could be seen overhead, and the sound of data transmissions were broadcast on the radio. Somewhere I hope I still have the tape recordings I made!

Mostly unheralded, Britain took a full part in this breakthrough, and had an active programme of upper atmosphere and space science research. Leading this programme was the 'Skylark' sounding rocket. Originally designed to carry payloads of 100-150 lb to heights of up to 100 miles, it was continually improved, and became an outstanding technical and commercial success. On its fourth launch in 1957 it became the first British rocket to reach space; this at a time when all space research was exploration into the unknown, and the sounding rocket was the only direct method of involvement. Skylark continued in use for decades, from the late 1950s, until its final flight 47 years later in 2005, becoming one of the most successful rocket projects of all time.

So why did I write this book? Because it was <u>not</u> there. Curiously, virtually nothing has been published for the more general reader on this activity. Hence, this account tells the story of this little known but advanced contribution to the early days of spaceflight technology and upper atmosphere scientific research. It brings together for the first time ever information from specialised articles and scientific journals from over the last 50 years; and uses archival research into original British Government documents and primary reference material to provide new information and historical photographs.

The political origins, design and flight-testing are all covered, as is the nearly 50 years of scientific results including eventual use by the European Space Agency. In general, it is an account told from the bottom up, rather than from the top down, tending to concentrate on the technology as evolved by the scientists, engineers and technicians directly involved.[3] This is where the action started; Skylark was in the vanguard of a disruptive technology that governments and administrations struggled to cope with for decades afterwards. The book includes details of the first scientific discoveries made about the then unexplored boundaries of space, and reproduces the first scientific paper published on the initial results.

Some may feel this book is a curious mixture of popular and academic, however this is deliberately so; the author's view is that a book that is first in its field does not have to appeal to only one niche in the market, the reader is invited to sample what they will and leave the rest.

---

[3] Well expressed by Terry Pratchett "… what was once considered impossible is now quite easily achieved. Kings and lords come and go and leave nothing but statues in the desert, while a couple of young men tinkering in a workshop change the way the world works". (The Patrician, "The Truth", p.48).

This book, then, is the first ever published that spans the complete history of Skylark, and will be of interest to all who are interested in how space science evolved, in the history of British technology and spaceflight, and those who wish to learn more of this aspect of post-war British engineering history.

Robin H. Brand

17 Park Road,
Fordingbridge,
Hampshire
SP6 1EQ,
UK

robin@nfel.co.uk

October 2014

ACKNOWLEDGEMENTS

I anticipated this book would take six months to write. In the event, it has taken over six years. Along the way, I have become indebted to many people for their help, encouragement and advice. Any errors and omissions are my own. Thanks to:

Phil Alner, John Battersby (Kemble), Anne Beadell (Australia), Markus Braun, John Coker (MSSL), Roger Cooper, Mike Cruise, Len Culhane, Bryan Day (FAST), Eric Dorling, Colin Frizzell, Barry Giles, Sven Grahn, Phil Guttridge (MSSL), John Hargreaves, John Hardy, Chris Hazell, Bruce Henderson (Australia), Roger Henwood (DSTO), J.A.(Jim) Hill (Australia), Nicholas Hill, Brian Luff (FAST), Jonathan McDowell, Doug Millard, Ashley Morgan (FAST), Peter Morton (Australia), Martin de la Nougerede (MSSL), Stephen Parsons, Tony Parsons, John Pitfield, Grant Privett, Chris Rapley (ScM), Hilary Savigear, Maurice Shakespeare (FAST), Susan Southall, John Townshend, Ian Tuohy (BAE Systems Australia), Alan Wakefield (IWM), Lauren Wilkins (ScM), Peter Willmore, Ivan Winter, Leslie Yakimishyn (Bristol Aerospace Canada), John Zarnecki, Stefan Zenker.

My thanks also to those from the following organisations who have helped me in the course of their work:

BFI, British Interplanetary Society, Cranfield University Library, Imperial War Museum London, Mullard Space Science Laboratory (MSSL), National Aerospace Library Farnborough, National Archives of Australia, The National Archives London, Royal Society London, Science Museum London & Wroughton, Swedish Space Corporation, University of Reading. Also - the unsung heroes who have built the databases and created the World Wide Web allowing most of the world's scientific literature to be accessed from my desk.

And special thanks to:

John Harlow - for his initial encouragement and continuing help

Roger Henwood - for indefatigable efforts in providing archive material from the early Woomera days - and to the unknown person who decided that the Skylark records at the Edinburgh Archives should not be destroyed in 1972, but preserved for use 40 years later!

Erika Meller – for saving the Skylark Remote Sensing archive (i.e. not throwing "that old rubbish" away!)

Carmel and Clive of the Cumberland Guest House at Gatwick, for the use of their dining room for many an evening of revision!

My family – for their help and patience!

My apologies to any person or organisation I may have omitted. I hope the publication of this book will lead to further information on Skylark; anyone able to help towards an improved second edition is invited to contact the author.[4]

---

[4] Contact details are provided at the end of the Preface.

Two explanations

Measurement units

At the start of the Skylark project (c.1955) both the UK and Australia used Imperial units (miles, feet and inches) for distance. However during the long life of Skylark, changes took place, Australia converted to the Metric system between 1970 and 1988, and in the UK conversion has been taking place since about 1965 – and still continues!

Thus at the start of this book the measurements are quoted in the original Imperial units with the metric equivalents in brackets afterwards, by the end the order has been reversed! An exception has been made in the case of altitude, as in space measurements, kilometres rather than miles are usually used.

In addition, the use of some scientific units has changed. In particular, the angstrom (used to specify the wavelength of electromagnetic radiation) has been replaced by the nanometre (nm), which is ten times larger. This also is reflected during the course of this book.

Footnotes on the page

These are referred to by superscript numbers in the text, they are either:

a. Local notes expanding on an aspect of the text
b. A handy simplified version (Harvard style) of an entry in the references section at the back of the book
c. A specific source reference, for which there will only be a generic reference in the references section

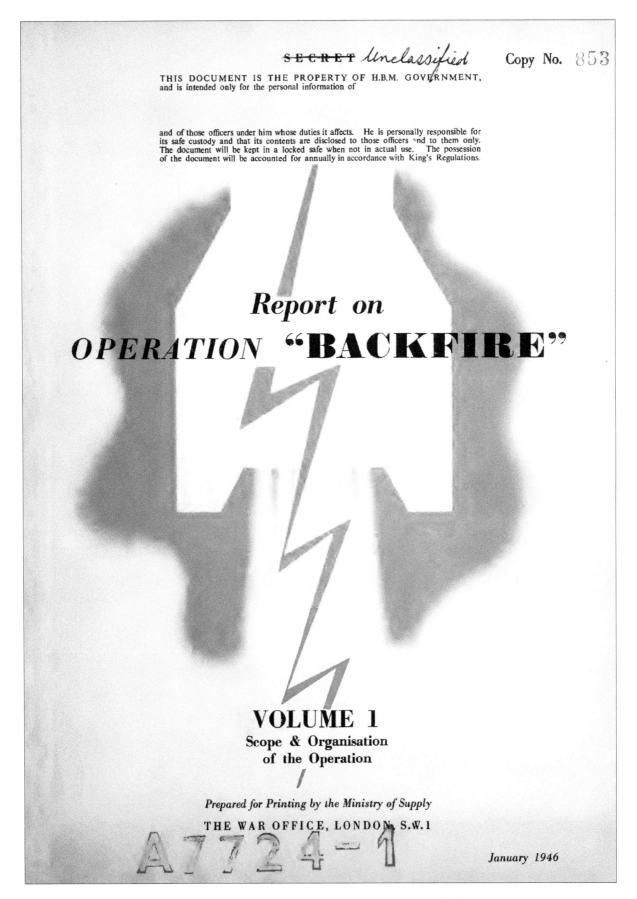

Figure 1.1 The cover of Volume 1 of the 1946 "Operation Backfire" report.[1]

---

[1]   Cameron (1946), *Report on Operation "BACKFIRE", Volume 1.*

CHAPTER 1

SKYLARK'S MILITARY ANCESTRY

The invention of the rocket is attributed to the Chinese; early records speak of "fire arrows", a simple form of solid-propellant rocket using gunpowder. It has been surmised the concept may have been accidentally discovered when bamboo tubes filled with gunpowder, thrown on bonfires to create explosions during celebrations, failed to explode, and zoomed out of the fire instead.

By the fifteenth century, rockets were being used for military as well ceremonial purposes. When visiting the National Museum in Seoul in South Korea some years ago, the author was surprised to come across a centuries old horse drawn multiple-rocket launcher!

The use of rockets spread to Europe, and from the 13th to 15th centuries, they were used for various military purposes, although in time such use greatly reduced as conventional artillery improved.

However, in 1792 and 1799, the British suffered heavily from rocket attacks in India[3], and so in 1801 the Royal Arsenal at Woolwich began a military rocket research and development programme. By 1805, Col. (later Sir) William Congreve had developed rockets which matched and exceeded the range of those used in India, and had produced a series of barrage rockets ranging in weight from 25 to 60 pounds. These were used in the Napoleonic wars (1803-15), and a barrage of 25,000 was used in 1807 against Copenhagen. They also saw use against the Americans in 1812 and 1814. The success of the first attack meant the British were able to advance on Washington, D.C., capturing and burning the city. The second, against Baltimore harbour was unsuccessful, but Francis Scott Key, inspired by the sight of the night engagement, wrote the words of the *Star Spangled Banner,* later adopted as the U.S. national anthem. The words "The rockets' red glare" and "bombs bursting in air" have continued to memorialise Congreve's rockets ever since.

Figure 1.2 A Korean 'Hwacha' replica in action.[2]

---

[2] This image appears on several dozen websites, but the author has not been able to trace its origin. See for instance the Korean website *www.arrow.or.kr/old/frame15.htm* (last accessed August 2014).

[3] See for instance *Encyclopaedia Britannica* (1962), Vol.19, p.366.

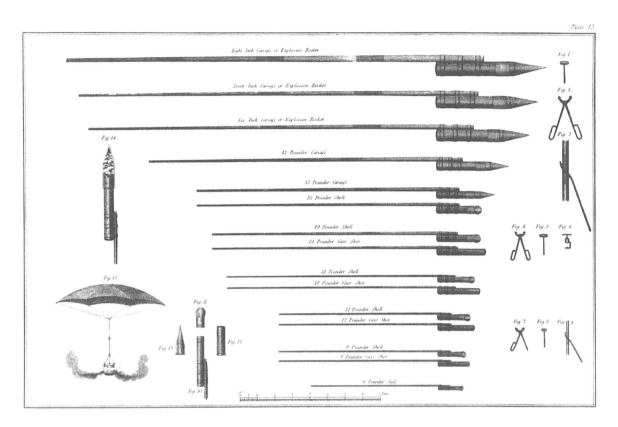

Figure 1.3 Congreve's rockets, an illustration from one of three books he published on the subject.

Congreve's rockets remained in service until the 1850s, when they were superseded by an improved spinning design by William Hale; however by then black powder rockets could no longer compete with artillery. Breech-loading cannon with rifled barrels and exploding warheads were far more effective weapons of war than the best rockets.[4] However in the 1870s rockets were adopted to carry rescue lines to vessels in distress. The Congreve rocket was capable of carrying a line over 1,000 feet to a stranded ship. By 1914, it was estimated that 1,000 lives had been saved by this technique.

Modern Rocketry and the V-2

In the early 1900s, Tsiolkovsky in Russia worked out many of the basic principles and formulas of rocketry, and although he never built any rockets, he has since become known as the "father of modern rocketry". In 1923 Hermann Oberth in Germany published a book about rocket travel into outer space, which inspired the formation of many German rocket societies. In the USA, Goddard carried out much rocket research, and in 1926 launched the first experimental liquid fuelled rocket. This was a much more complicated task than building a solid-propellant rocket, as fuel and oxygen tanks, pumps and a combustion chamber were all needed.

After the end of World War I, the Treaty of Versailles had in 1919 imposed restrictions on the use of conventional artillery

by the German army, and they became interested in the use of rockets as a possible substitute. In 1932, Wernher von Braun started rocket research for the army, and by December 1934 had achieved his first successes with an "A2" rocket, powered by ethanol and liquid oxygen. Two years later, as plans for the follow-on A3 rocket were being finalised, initial planning began for the A4 rocket – a version that would be a practical weapon, not a research tool. (For propaganda reasons, once in service it was designated the V-2.[5])

In 1934, the British War Office began to take serious notice of these activities. An intensive programme of research was started, and much technical progress was made on the design of two, three and five-inch diameter solid fuel rockets, which were introduced into service towards the end of WWII.

These UK developments were however overshadowed by the technical achievements of German rocket scientists and engineers. The German researchers had quickly outgrown their original facilities, and in 1936, operations were transferred to Peenemünde on Germany's Baltic coast. Between 1937 and 1941, von Braun's group launched some 70 A3 and A5 rockets, testing components for use in the proposed A4 rocket.

The A4 rocket was first launched in 1942, and the third, launched in October that year, flew 170 miles and was the first successful A4 in flight.

---

[4]   Although by the end of World War II, rockets had become extensively used once more.
[5]   *Vergeltungswaffe 2* = "Retaliation/Vengeance Weapon 2".

Figure 1.4 A diagram from a Peenemünde archive album, showing details of the first successful A4 firing on 3rd October 1942.[6]

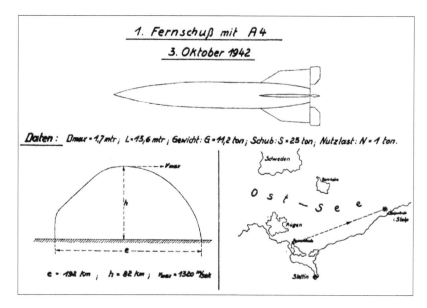

The A4/V-2 was 1.6 metres in diameter and 15 metres long. It weighed 12 tonnes and could deliver one tonne of high explosive over a range of at least 330 kilometres (205 miles).

It was the world's first long-range combat ballistic missile. During the war, British intelligence had deduced the existence of the A4/V-2, and in August 1943 Bomber Command carried out a major raid on Peenemünde. This had the effect of delaying the development and introduction of the V-2 by several months, and meant that London did not have to face V-2 attacks at the same time as the first V-1 attacks of 1944.[7] Two other factory sites were also heavily bombed, forcing the Germans to concentrate production of V-2s (and V-1s) in a huge underground factory at Nordhausen, which from August 1944 produced 600 rockets a month.[8] This used some 60,000 slave labourers as workers, and operated in conjunction with concentration camp 'Dora'. (It has been estimated that some 26,500 people died working on this facility, more than the V-2 killed as a weapon).

From 13th June 1944, a week after D-day, thousands of V-1 flying bombs fell on London. The effect of the V-1 on civilians is illustrated by this recollection[9] by the author's aunt, Betty Barber, who was 16 at the time:

A few days later after we had returned, on 17 June, I was getting ready to go to bed when I heard a most peculiar noise from outside. It sounded rather like an outboard motor or a high-powered lawn mower. I drew back the curtains and saw, what I thought was a plane in the sky, which was on fire and flying quite low. I was horrified. It was almost overhead and I hoped it wouldn't crash near us. I rushed downstairs to tell Mother and Dad, but it went over and out of sight, and I never thought any more about it.

The following day on the news, we heard that Germany had developed a new kind of bomb, which was able to fly unmanned for hundreds of miles, and it was being launched to target the South of England. It had the shape of a small plane and its main feature was that when the engine stopped the bomb glided to the ground and exploded. It had a great long flaming tail; this is what I had seen. It had great destructive power and was nicknamed 'doodle bug' or 'buzz-bomb'. If you heard the engine stop above, you knew it would be fifteen seconds before it could quite possibly fall on you, which was a very scary thought. After this we heard many of these things come over every night and often we heard them stop, some far away, but a few very near, and as it dropped we heard the door and windows rattle.

Epsom Down was lying in a direct path to London, where most of the bombs were headed. Most reached their target, but a few didn't make it so far and they fell near us. The worst part of all was that you never knew if the engine would stop or not, and you would listen to them with a great fear in your heart, just hoping it wound fly on. I remember one day, during daylight hours, the sky was filled with these buzz bombs, there must have been ten going over all at once. We couldn't take cover so we just had to try and carry on as usual. And surprisingly enough we did get used to them, mainly perhaps because few dropped near us [but] found their target in London itself. But it was nerve-wracking because you never really knew for sure if one would suddenly stop or not. The most ghastly moment was when you heard an engine cut out, and there was silence, and we had to wait and see where it landed. London was once more under fire and thousands of children were evacuated to the country again.

6   Jones (1978), *Most Secret War: British Scientific Intelligence 1939:1946*, p.456, Fig.31a.
7   Jones (1978), p. 346.
8   Jones (1978), p. 454.
9   Barber (2005), *My War Years 1938 -1947*, p.41.

German records (captured at the end of the war) show that 8,564 V-1s were launched against London from occupied France. In all, about 2,400 got through.[10] However, by the end of August 1944, most were being destroyed by UK defences.

Then, in September, the first V-2 landed, and by April 1945 German records show 1,190 had been successfully launched against London. Against this weapon, plunging at supersonic speeds from a height of about 50 miles, there was no defence once it had been launched.

"The rocket first rose vertically for six miles or so and automatic controls then turned it over to climb with increasing speed at about forty five degrees. When the speed was sufficient for the desired range, further controls cut off the jet, and the missile then flew in a gigantic parabola, reaching a height of about fifty miles and falling about two hundred miles away from the launching point." [12]

Other European towns and cities also suffered as the Germans were forced to retreat. Antwerp became the target for 1,610 rockets and 8,696 flying bombs.[13] In both London and Antwerp, thousands of civilians were killed and injured. The range of these weapons, although relatively substantial, meant that they had to be fired from occupied countries rather than Germany, and the attacks ceased once the Allies overran France.

Figure 1.5 On 11th November 1944 the Daily Herald broke the news about the V-2. Until then, the War Ministry had claimed the explosions were caused by ruptured gas mains, but civilians had become suspicious when they found metal debris in the ruins.

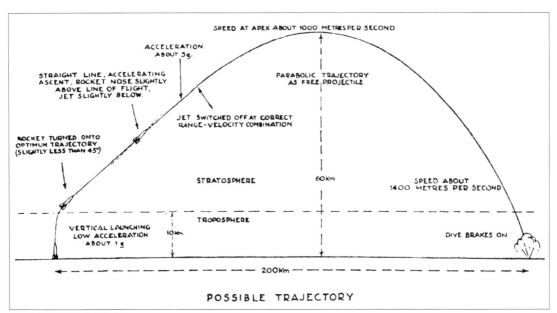

Figure 1.6 "Diagram from the Scientific Intelligence report of 26th August 1944, showing the guessed trajectory." This was later proved very accurate. (Vertical scale exaggerated).[11]

[10] Churchill (1954), *The Second World War*, Volume VI, p.43.
[11] Jones (1978), *Most Secret War*, p.456, Fig.31b.
[12] Churchill (1954), *The Second World War*, Volume VI, p.46, also Turnill & Reed (1980), *Farnborough: The Story of RAE* , p.66.
[13] Jones (1978), *Most Secret War*, p. 459, & Churchill (1954) p.49.

The spoils of war

In August 1944 Paris was liberated, and in January 1945, amidst hard fighting, allied troops entered Germany, which was subsequently was overrun by the Western Allies (Britain, France and the USA) approaching from the west, and the Russians from the east. As the forces swept on towards Berlin, an enthusiastic hunt began for the technical secrets of German weaponry. For the Western Allies, it soon turned into a race to get to the factories before the Russians. For the British, it also developed into a race to get there before the Americans. It so happened that in April 1945 the US Army was the first to come across the huge underground rocket factory at Mittelwerk near Nordhausen.

Despite orders confirmed in May by the Combined Chiefs of Staff that all V-2 equipment was to be frozen until the allocation for 'Operation Backfire' and other demands had been settled, US forces secured the cream of the rocket components, sufficient for over 60 rockets, and by May these had been transported to Antwerp and loaded aboard a fleet of 16 liberty ships bound for the USA.

Anglo-American friction was mitigated only by the fact that it soon emerged that what the Americans wanted most was rocketry; what the British wanted most was supersonic technology.[14] (The RAE at Bedford started existence by being equipped with several state-of-the-art wind tunnels from the Herman Goering Institute at Volkenrode). In May, just before the area was due to be handed over to the British, the Americans also managed to find tons of essential documentation hidden by the Germans.

As Germany crumbled, to prevent their capture, Hitler ordered von Braun and his whole V-2 development team to be executed. Naturally, they weren't too keen on this, and von Braun called a meeting at Peenemünde, at which they voted to try to surrender to the Americans, some fearing reprisals from the British who had been bombed by the weapons they had designed.

As the Russians overran Germany from the east, they gained the remnants of Peenemünde and some of the scientists; and as the V-2 factory at Nordhausen was located in what soon became East Germany, they also gained control of that facility.

Operation 'Backfire'

By the end of the war, more than 8,000 German rocket troops had been captured, along with hundreds of Peenemünde scientists. The Allies agreed on a proposal that the Germans be forced to demonstrate the V-2 handling and firing procedures by actually preparing and launching some V-2 rockets. The British were seeking thirty V-2s for this operation, and the Air Ministry had requested 120 more.

By June, the Backfire team had recovered an impressive 650 tonnes of equipment. However this was deceptive, as many of the complex sub-assemblies were missing. The team scoured northern Germany, and by September 1945, enough equipment had been collected, repaired and assembled to produce just eight V-2s to fire. The work of rebuilding and launching the V-2 rockets from Cuxhaven on the German coast was done by a 600 man German unit under British supervision comprising 2400 army and civilian personnel.

Figure 1.7 A partially assembled V-2 rocket inside Nordhausen Tunnel B in 1945, as discovered by the Allies.
(U.S. Army Signal Corps photo)

[14] Turnill and Reed (1980), p.92.

After several abortive attempts, three of the eight rebuilt rockets were fired into the North Sea. An excellent fully illustrated five-volume report followed in January 1946,[16] showing the technical secrets in full, and clearly revealing the potential of the long-range rocket concept.[17]

The information from Operation Backfire, both written and in the form of motion picture film was far more comprehensive than anything that existed in German records. The rocket project and deployment had been so secret during the war that very few operational photos were allowed by the Germans,[18] and many of the photographs and movie films produced by Operation Backfire were later thought to be German in origin.

Figure 1.8 The post-war divisions of Germany, showing the locations of Peenemünde and Cuxhaven.[15]

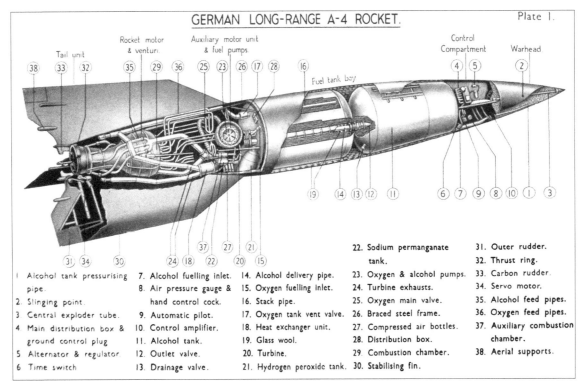

22. Sodium permanganate tank.	31. Outer rudder.	
23. Oxygen & alcohol pumps.	32. Thrust ring.	
24. Turbine exhausts.	33. Carbon rudder.	
25. Oxygen main valve.	34. Servo motor.	
26. Braced steel frame.	35. Alcohol feed pipes.	
27. Compressed air bottles.	36. Oxygen feed pipes.	
28. Distribution box.	37. Auxiliary combustion chamber.	
29. Combustion chamber.	38. Aerial supports.	
30. Stabilising fin.		

1 Alcohol tank pressurising pipe.
2 Slinging point.
3 Central exploder tube.
4 Main distribution box & ground control plug
5 Alternator & regulator.
6 Time switch
7 Alcohol fuelling inlet.
8 Air pressure gauge & hand control cock.
9 Automatic pilot.
10 Control amplifier.
11 Alcohol tank.
12 Outlet valve.
13 Drainage valve.
14 Alcohol delivery pipe.
15 Oxygen fuelling inlet.
16 Stack pipe.
17 Oxygen tank vent valve.
18 Heat exchanger unit.
19 Glass wool.
20 Turbine.
21 Hydrogen peroxide tank.

Figure 1.9 Plate 1 from Volume 3 of the 'Backfire' report provides this excellent cut-away diagram.[19]
(Cameron (1946))

[15] *www.v2rocket.com/start/chapters/backfire.html* (last accessed August 2014). Image reproduced by courtesy of website.

[16] Cameron (1946), *Report on Operation "BACKFIRE"*. (See Figure 1.1 The cover of Volume 1 of the 1946 "Operation Backfire" report.1 at the beginning of this chapter).

[17] The volumes are so detailed they resemble a car servicing manual!

[18] *www.v2rocket.com/start/chapters/backfire.html* (last accessed August 2014).

[19] Cameron (1946), *Report on Operation BACKFIRE*, Volume 3, Plate 1.

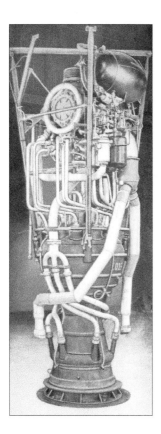

Figure 1.10 Left: Figure 2 from Volume 2 of the 'Backfire report', showing the 'combustion unit'.[20] (Cameron (1946))

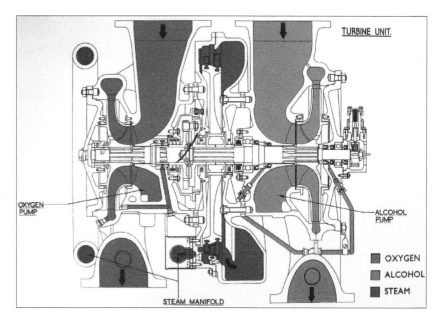

Figure 1.11 Above right: Plate 12 from Volume 2 of the 'Backfire' report, showing the important engine turbine in great detail.[21]

(Cameron (1946))

The turbine unit shown above was the heart of the V-2's liquid-propellant engine. The turbine was powered by super-heated steam derived from a hydrogen peroxide reaction unit, and in turn drove the two centrifugal pumps indicated in red and blue, one for the fuel (alcohol), and one for the oxidiser (liquid oxygen). The rating was nearly a thousand horsepower, and it pumped some four tons of fuel and five tons of oxidiser a minute. This concept has been used ever since on many liquid-propellant rocket engines.

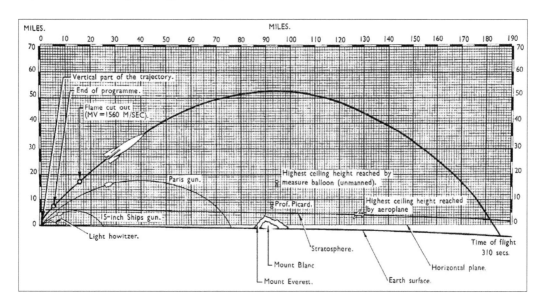

Figure 1.12 Plate 3 from Volume 3 of the Backfire report shows a typical V-2 trajectory to scale.[22]
The range was so great that the curvature of the Earth has to be shown. The "Paris gun" referred to was a 'super gun'
used by the Germans to bombard Paris in 1918. Its shells achieved a maximum altitude of 40 kilometres (25 miles) -
the greatest height reached by a man-made projectile until the first successful V-2 flight.

[20] Cameron (1946), *Report on Operation "BACKFIRE"*, Volume 3, figure 3.
[21] Cameron (1946), Volume 2, Plate 12.
[22] Cameron (1946), Volume 3, Plate 3.

The emergence of the long-distance missile age

Between August 1944 and February 1945, the Germans had manufactured some 3,000 rockets with a peak production of 30 in one day. Many of those landed on London and the home counties of England. Despite Hitler's hopes, the V-2 did not have time to be developed into a weapon of military significance. Notwithstanding the technical advances made, (for instance, use of inertial guidance), the accuracy of the rocket's guidance system meant that it could hit London as a city, but not a smaller target. (Time would show that accurate inertial guidance was a difficult goal to achieve). Like the V-1, it certainly affected the civilian population and politicians, but had relatively little military effect.[23] Antwerp, for instance, received twenty-six V-2s in one day, yet even this failed to bring the port to a standstill. Indeed, as a weapon the V-1 flying bomb achieved the same effect as the V-2, but far more cheaply, although unlike the V-2, effective countermeasures were possible. "I suspected that Hitler had been carried away by the romance of the rocket, just as our own politicians had been carried away by its threat: for some psychological reason they seemed far more frightened by one ton of explosive delivered by rocket than by five tons delivered by aircraft."[24]

The importance of the V-2 lay in the promise inherent in its design. Indeed when the first V-2 hit London, Wernher von Braun is quoted as saying "The rocket worked perfectly except for landing on the wrong planet."[25] This was not a facetious remark, even then he appreciated it was feasible to build a rocket capable of interplanetary travel, as he was to prove later on in the USA.

The Backfire report concluded:

> Whatever the future may hold, the A-4 is undoubtedly already a feasible weapon of war. Even if Britain and America do not wish to use it, they must at all costs be prepared to counter it. Efficient and up-to-date countermeasures cannot be produced without developing the weapon itself…For the sake of their very existence, Britain and the United States must be masters of this weapon of the future.[26]

At the end of the war, it was widely recognised that together, the atomic bomb and the ballistic missile had the potential to revolutionise strategic warfare. The ballistic missile was unstoppable once launched. If these two technologies could be combined, then the fleets of wartime bombers would be

obsolete at a stroke. If the rocket guidance system could be improved then specific military targets could be destroyed at will. Alternatively, if an atomic warhead could be fitted, then whole cities could be devastated, as had happened when the first atomic bombs had been dropped from aircraft on Hiroshima and Nagasaki in August 1945. With an atomic warhead, accuracy was not as important.

Even in 1944, R.V.Jones (in charge of British scientific intelligence during the war), concluded in an article "With a very long range rocket we may have to accept errors, and it may be easier to increase the radius of destruction by the use of explosive based on the fission of the uranium atomic nucleus".[27]

On the civil side, he was even more perceptive:

> There can be no doubt that with the A4 the rocket has come to stay for a long time, if only for its non-military applications; in no other way can we get free of the earth's atmosphere, with all that this freedom may mean to astrophysical studies. The attainment of the upper atmosphere will in itself be a major factor in experimental meteorology, and sooner or later someone will seriously try to reach the moon – and succeed….and have thereby made themselves leaders in a technique which sooner or later will be regarded as one of the masterpieces of human endeavour when it comes to the exploration of Space.[28]

Prophetic words indeed for 1944.

In the British War Cabinet, the potential of these new weapons was also appreciated, even if the technical details were not fully understood. In a report to the Cabinet, Duncan Sandys is quoted as saying, "The advent of the long-range, radio-controlled, jet-propelled projectile has opened up vast new possibilities in the conduct of military operations. In future, the possession of superiority in long-distance rocket artillery may well count for as much as superiority in naval or air power. High grade scientific and engineering staff, together with extensive research facilities, will have to be maintained as a permanent part of our peace-time military organisation." [29]

Exploiting captured V-2s

As the war ended, the USA had the resources to actively exploit these new possibilities. It was politically stable, had its expanding continental size economy intact, and negligible post-war reconstruction was necessary. It embarked upon its

[23] Albert Speer (Minister of Armaments and War Production for the Third Reich), "Even 5,000 long-range rockets, that is more than five month's production, would have delivered only 3,750 tons of explosives: a single attack by the combined British and American air forces delivered a good 8,000 tons". (Quoted by Jones (1978), p.438).
[24] Jones (1978), *Most Secret War*, p.455. Reproduced by permission of Penguin Books Ltd.
[25] Quoted on numerous websites.
[26] Cameron (1946), *Report on Operation "BACKFIRE"*, Volume 1, p.27, paras. 112 and 113.
[27] Jones (1978), *Most Secret War*, p.455. Reproduced by permission of Penguin Books Ltd.
[28] Jones (1978), *Most Secret War*, p.459-461. Reproduced by permission of Penguin Books Ltd.
[29] Churchill (1954), *The Second World War*, Volume VI, p.49.

own rocket development programme and had room to create a range to test them, having established the White Sands Proving Ground (now White Sands Missile Range) in New Mexico in 1945, as its principal site for rocket testing.

In addition, as noted above, the USA had significant amounts of captured hardware. In August 1945, 300 railway freight cars of captured V-2 components arrived in New Mexico. Every railway siding for a distance of 210 miles was full. The Army hired every flatbed truck in Dona Ana County to move the material. This included 215 combustion chambers, 180 sets of propellant tanks, 90 tail units, 100 sets of graphite jet vanes, and 200 turbo pumps.

Thus, the USA had a large supply of nearly complete rockets to use, and room to test them. In addition, they could afford to make good job offers to Dr Wernher Von Braun and other German rocket scientists, many of whom had surrendered to the Americans. Subsequently about 100 German rocket scientists and engineers were chosen to help, and glad to be able to continue their chosen profession in the USA.

Despite the abundance of V-2 material brought to White Sands, certain parts such as control hardware were in short supply, and no V-2s were received in flyable condition. The General Electric Company was contracted by the U.S. Army Ordnance Department to assemble, test and fire the V-2s. During the later stages of the firing programme, the company had to provide gyros, mixer-computers, wiring, servo-motors, and propellant piping to replace those German parts missing or which had deteriorated with age.

In all, 67 V-2 rockets were assembled and tested at White Sands between 1946 and 1952, providing the U.S. with valuable experience in the assembly, pre-flight testing, handling, fuelling, launching, and tracking of large missiles. The Army invited government agencies and universities to use the nose cone's 20 cubic feet of space for scientific research. Up to 2,000 pounds (907 kg, nearly 1 tonne) of scientific equipment, such as cameras, sensors, and on-board experiments, were carried aloft on each flight. The scientific experiments conducted aboard the V-2 yielded significant information about the upper atmosphere, and one series of tests, the "Blossom Project," carried out the first biological experiments in space. In 1946, the partaking scientists formed an ad-hoc scientific committee, which in 1948 took the title of "Upper Atmosphere Rocket Research Panel".

Landmark tests included:

V-2 No. 1: First firing, static test for 57 seconds; 15 March 1946
V-2 No. 2: First flight test, altitude 18,000 feet; 16 April 1946
V-2 No. 3: First high altitude flight, altitude 70 miles; 10 May 1946

V-2 No. 9: First separation of nose cone; 30 July 1946
V-2 No. 13: Motion pictures showing Earth's curvature: 24 October 1946

The Soviet Union and Europe

Although the USSR had suffered badly during the war, it survived politically intact, retained a large economic base, and had a communist government prepared and able to put military requirements before that of its population. With the help of captured German engineers they were able to revive V-2 production in the captured German factories, and probably a thousand or more V-2s eventually went back to Russia for experiments.

The first Soviet missile was the R-1, an exact copy of the V-2. Starting in October 1947, the Soviet-German team launched 11 R-1 rockets near the village of Kapustin Yar, north of the Caspian Sea. Not only was it a copy, but the R-1 was manufactured from scratch, as Stalin had ordered that no German-manufactured parts should be used. Once the Soviets had acquired the German knowledge, most of the German team was sent home. Work immediately began on larger missiles, the R-2 and R-5, based on extensions of the V-2 technology.

As a victor in the war, Britain was the only large western European country to emerge politically and economically intact. Despite this, the UK economy was in bad shape. At home, massive reconstruction was required; abroad, the war had drained the resources of the British Empire. Therefore, despite being in charge of 'Operation Backfire', and having discovered all the secrets and technology of the V-2, Britain was unable to spare the resources to exploit the information, or bid against the Americans for the services of the German rocket personnel. Indeed one of the Germans, after being asked to consider working in Britain, declined with surprising candour "We despise the French; we are mortally afraid of the Russians; we do not believe the British can afford us; so that leaves the Americans." [30]

Despite the constraints, the potential military threat of the nuclear-armed ballistic missile concept was keenly felt, as Britain's island status and traditional reliance on a large Navy would offer no protection. With no defence against ballistic missiles being possible, the concept of the nuclear deterrent emerged; the only hope was to deter an aggressor by the threat of swift and certain retribution, and soon the development of a British nuclear bomb began.

As far as long-range guided missiles were concerned, Britain had two problems. Firstly the country had very little to test in the way of ready-to-use captured V-2 rockets, and nowhere in the country was there room to carry out test launches. The best that might be done was to launch missiles hundreds of

30 Sharpe (1976), 'Operation Backfire: England launches the V2', p.131.

miles out to sea, which would make in-flight scientific measurements difficult and recovery of parts impractical.

By June 1947, the UK Ministry of Supply had twenty potential Guided Weapon designs 'on their books'. These included a V-2 type tactical missile, and a long-range strategic missile capable of reaching across Europe. These were codenamed 'Hammer' and 'Menace' respectively. Hammer was a ballistic missile intended to be developed from the V-2, and have a range of 20-150 miles[31]. Menace was Britain's first staff requirement for a ground to ground strategic weapon, it was to be either a rocket or pilotless aircraft with a range of up to 2000 miles, and equipped to carry an atomic warhead of 7000 lbs.[32]

To develop these new guided weapons, a unified approach was needed, one that combined aerodynamics, radio and radar, rocket motors, propellants and explosives. To support this requirement, resources were rationalised, and in 1946, a new Guided Projectile Establishment was set up at Westcott in Buckinghamshire to carry out work on rocket design. Here the chemistry of propellants was investigated, and test-firing stands built.[33] Also that year a Controlled Weapons Department was formed at the Royal Aircraft Establishment (RAE) at Farnborough in Hampshire, to study aerodynamics and structural design. This quickly grew, becoming the Guided Weapons (GW) Department as it assumed more responsibility in system assessment and design.[34]

Britain's rocket range would have to be overseas. Both Canada and Australia were considered, the choice being between Hudson Bay tundra and Australian desert. The balance tilted towards Australia, and after many months of negotiation and survey, agreement was reached in December 1946. The 'Joint Project' came into formal existence on 1st April 1947,[35] and construction soon followed. On the 24th April, the name 'Woomera' was adopted.[36]

However, even whilst Woomera was being established, the UK's post-war development of long-range strategic weapons was put on hold. The wealth of information generated from the 'Operation Backfire' V-2 trials had revealed that for the country to produce a weapon to meet the emerging 'Cold War' requirements, the V-2 design would have to be vastly upgraded. The payload of the existing design would have to be increased by a factor of five to carry the size of atomic weapon dropped by aircraft on Japan at the end of the war; and the range of the V-2 would have to be increased by at least a factor of six to reach Moscow, and a vast improvement in guidance control would be needed.

At that time, it was considered that Britain did not have the resources to spare for such developments. So in 1947, only just after the Joint Project had started, the requirement for Woomera to have a long-range capability was dropped, and in 1948 the UK government reluctantly decided to curtail any further research into long-range guided rockets, and concentrate on its defensive missile programme instead.[37] (Although within five years, this decision would be reversed).

Hence, unlike the USA and USSR, who capitalised on the German V-2 technology they had captured, and despite the British War Office having been told by experts that Operation Backfire would save Britain countless man-hours of research and testing in weapons technology,[38] the UK retreated from the opportunity available. This approach must have been encouraged by the UK economic situation as described above, but also helped by the fact that Sir Ben Lockspeiser, Chief Scientific Adviser to the Ministry of Supply, regarded a long-range weapons programme as both impractical and unnecessary.[39] (Although even by 1947 the Admiralty were complaining that his policy placed too much concentration on fundamental problems rather than developing weapons using the best techniques already available).[40] This slow and steady approach precluded any quick results, although in the end it may well have benefited both the Skylark and other British rocket projects, which, when they did eventually emerge, always worked more reliably from the start, compared to their American equivalents.

The future foreseen

One person who did have a clear idea of future possibilities was the illustrator, Frank Hampson, who had been under bombardment from V-2 rockets during the war, and had seen something of their internal construction. His artwork was outstanding, with a realistic engineering look to what he produced:

> I felt that prognostications were too gloomy. Attitudes were so pessimistic… I wanted to give hope for the future, to show that rockets and science in general could reveal new worlds, new opportunities. I was sure that space travel would be a reality – I had seen the innards of V-2 rockets while under attack in Antwerp, and had been taken by the beauty and precision of the working parts. It seemed to me, somewhat ironically, as we were under constant bombardment by these machines, that here was the birth of space travel.[42]

[31] Twigge (1993), *The Early Development of Guided Weapons in the United Kingdom* , pp. 136 and 246, also Morton(1989), pp. 19 & 21.
[32] Twigge (1993), pp.136, 188 & 247.
[33] Morton (1989), *Fire across the Desert,* p.10.
[34] Massey & Robins (1986), *History of British Space Science,* pp. 12 & 13.
[35] Morton (1989), *Fire across the Desert,* p.27.
[36] Morton (1989), p.117.
[37] Twigge (1993), p.186.
[38] Sharpe (1976), 'Operation Backfire: England launches the V2', p.122.
[39] Twigge (1993), p.61.
[40] Twigge (1993), p.117.

Frank Hampson became involved with a new type of comic for boys, where from the start he was responsible for writing and illustrating its front-page feature about Dan Dare, 'Pilot of the Future'. On the very first story, he had the help of Arthur C.Clarke, then scientific consultant to *Eagle*. Arthur C.Clarke is credited with having been the first to propose the idea of using geostationary satellites for telecommunications relays; and it interesting to see the concept illustrated in Dan Dare's first adventure, published in June 1951![43]

In 1975, Frank Hampson won an international award for his work, and *Dan Dare* was declared to have been the best written and drawn comic strip produced anywhere after the war. His declared intention in 1950 "to create the best strip-cartoon in the world" was officially accepted as having been fulfilled.

It was against this background that the first British space rocket emerged.

The gibber desert of Australia's interior is the site of the Empire rocket range. Lieut.-Gen. Evetts, chief executive officer, at left, with Brig. Edgar, plots the position of airfields, hangars, laboratories and workshops.

To Australia has been assigned the most spectacular role of the Empire's rocket project—that of firing and testing the rockets as they come from the laboratories and factories of Great Britain.

Specially written for "Wings"
by TOM FAIRHALL

OUT in the gibber desert of Australia's interior, scientists and engineers are establishing there the chief long-range weapons testing ground for the British Empire.

Significantly, they called it Woomera, after the device Australian Aborigines used to direct their spears and put greater force behind the throw.

And from Woomera in the not-too-distant future, new guided missiles, of which the Nazi "doodle-bugs" of World War II were merely the shape-of-things-to-come, will zoom into space in trials to find the ultimate in defensive—and offensive weapons.

Stretching across our Continent, in some of the loneliest and most remote country in the world, will lie a chain of stations equipped with the newest gadgets devised by science to photograph and record every pitch and roll, every movement and change in acceleration of a rocket in its flight.

The Empire's rocket project is necessarily a long-term plan, as expansive as its gibber-desert range-head. Australia, joint partners with the United Kingdom in the project, will pay its share of the work from the Commonwealth Government allocation of £32,000,000 to be spent over the next five years on scientific defence works. So far about £5,000,000 has been spent in Australia.

In the initial stages, most of the rocket research and development work will be centred in Britain, but it is expected that Australia will also play its part in assisting in both research and development. The reason for this is obvious: if war comes to Europe again, additional responsibilities can be taken more readily by Australian factories and will not dislocate or seriously delay rocket development.

Naturally, Britain's rocket story cannot be told yet. Here, as in England and in other parts of the

2 WINGS, September 1, 1948

Figure 1.13 This 1948 article from an Australian magazine captures the spirit and enthusiasm of the time. (On the left is Lieutenant General John Evetts who led the original diplomatic and survey mission.)
(Wings magazine, Volume 4, No.3, September 1948)[41]

[41] Reproduced courtesy of the RAAF 'Wings' magazine.
[42] Frank Hampson as quoted by James Slattery, Introduction to *Dan Dare, Pilot of the Future in The Man from Nowhere*, (Hampson & Slattery (1979)).
[43] Hampson (1951), 'Voyage to Venus', Eagle comic, Vol. 2 No.9 (8 June 1951), picture 16.

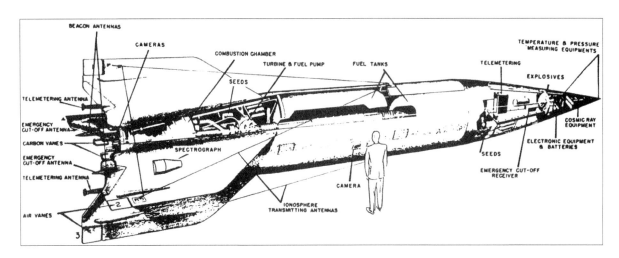

Figure 2.1 A captured V-2 equipped by the Americans for upper atmosphere study.[1] (Compare with Figure 1.9.)

(In order to maintain the stability of the rocket, the V-2 warhead was replaced by 2,200 lbs (1 tonne) of instrumented nose cone. This gave American researchers a very generous payload, allowing even ciné cameras to be installed.[2])

More than 1000 pictures were taken from V-2 flights between 1946 and 1950. "Results of these tests now are pointing to a time when cameras may be mounted on guided missiles for scouting enemy territory in war, mapping inaccessible regions of the earth in peacetime, and even photographing cloud formations, storm fronts, and overcast areas over an entire continent in a few hours....the entire land area of the globe might be mapped in this way."[4]

**Figure 2.2 A composite of four photographs of southwestern USA
and northern Mexico taken in 1947 by a V-2 rocket-borne camera.**
(US Naval Research Laboratory)[3]

---

[1]   Bergstralh and Krause (1975), 'Early Upper Atmospheric Research with Rockets', figure 2, p.137. (AAS History Series Volume 9, see bibliography.) Figure reproduced courtesy American Astronautical Society.

[2]   There was no parachute system; recovery was achieved by exploding the rocket on the way down, to reduce the impact speed of the various parts!

[3]   Originally Bergstralh, T.A. (1947), *Naval Research Laboratory Report R-3083*, later referenced by Bergstralh and Krause (1975), p.158.

[4]   Holliday (1950), 'Seeing the Earth from 80 Miles Up'.

CHAPTER 2
THE EVOLUTION OF BRITAIN'S FIRST SPACE ROCKET

The Royal Society and MoS collaborate

In 1951, the Gassiot Committee of the Royal Society invited the American Upper Atmosphere Rocket Research Panel to take part in a conference on rocket exploration of the upper air, to be organised by the Gassiot Committee in Britain.[5] The panel accepted, and the conference was arranged to take place in Oxford in 1953. During preparation for the conference, the first contact was established by the scientists with those working on the design and development of rockets at the UK Ministry of Supply; and these key figures were also invited to the conference. In May of that year, even before the conference had taken place, the chairman of the Gassiot Committee (H.S.W.Massey) was asked by the Ministry of Supply if the committee would be interested in using rockets available from the ministry for scientific research:

> Meanwhile, on the morning of 13 May 1953 when Massey was just preparing to leave his room at UCL for the annual departmental cricket match between staff and students at Shenley, he received a telephone call from a Ministry of Supply official asking whether he would be interested in using rockets from the Ministry for scientific research. Immediately he replied "Yes" and went in search of Boyd and repeated the question! Naturally Boyd welcomed the prospect of the direct application of his probes in the exploration of the ionosphere.[6]

This effectively marked the beginning of the British scientific rocket programme, and nearly fifty years later the then Sir Robert Boyd recalled:

> …Harrie Massey came into my lab and said to me, 'Boyd, how would you like to have some rockets for research?' So I replied that I would very much like that, and I went off into the library to find out what had been going on, using rockets to study the ionosphere.[7]

The conference duly took place at Oxford that August. It was well attended and very successful, the American Upper Atmosphere Rocket Research Panel being represented by 15 delegates. Their chairman was J. Van Allen, after whom the Earth's radiation belts would be named following their discovery by the first American space satellites in 1958. The Americans attending had been actively concerned in flying instruments in rockets, and provided first hand details of what had been achieved by their V-2 and Aerobee rocket programmes.[8]

Also during the time in Oxford, a meeting took place between prospective British scientific users that confirmed their desire to embark on a rocket programme, although it was realised that the funding for such a programme would be more than the universities themselves could afford. In February 1954, a meeting was arranged with Sir Arnold Hall of the RAE (Royal Aircraft Establishment), at which the scientists were delighted to hear of the development of the CTV.5 Series 3 rocket. They were told this would be capable of taking a payload of 100 lb (45 kg) to an altitude of 200 km (124 miles), much higher than the 30km they had been expecting, and well beyond the E region of the ionosphere.[9]

The prospects of collaboration seemed very good, and the Royal Society made a direct application to the Treasury for a sum of £100,000[10] for rocket research in the upper atmosphere to take place over a four-year period.

Referring to the Oxford meeting, Desmond King-Hele recalled:

> …and this can now be seen as the first British step on the ladder into space which we climbed for nearly twenty years. I cannot remember much about the meeting, except that it was held in a dark medieval lecture-room, lit by a few light bulbs with dusty white shades: it seemed paradoxical that these new ventures into space were being planned in such antiquated surroundings.[11]

---

[5] Massey & Robins (1986), *History of British Space Science*, p.7.

[6] Fox (c.1984), *From Lardner to Massey – A history of physics, space science and astronomy at University College London, 1826 to 1975*.

[7] Sir Robert Boyd in 2001, CCBH (2005), *Skylark Sounding Rockets 1957-1972*, p.28, & *Prospero* No.2. p.94. Note: this and all subsequent "CCBH (2005)" quotations are reproduced thanks to the Institute of Contemporary British History at King's College London.

[8] See the excellent Boyd & Seaton (1954), *Rocket Exploration of the Upper Atmosphere*.

[9] Massey & Robins (1986), p.19.

[10] Where £100,000 in 1954 was equivalent to £2.2 - £8.3 million by 2011. (2011 figures based on the "Historic Opportunity" and "Economic Cost" measures for a large project, from Lawrence H. Officer and Samuel H. Williamson, "Five Ways to Compute the Relative Value of a UK Pound Amount, 1270 to Present," MeasuringWorth, 2013, *www.measuringworth.com/ukcompare/*, last accessed August 2014).

[11] King-Hele (1992), *A tapestry of orbits*, p.4, © Cambridge University Press, reproduced with permission.

Skylark's family history

As explained in the previous chapter, immediately after WW II the UK had not proceeded with work on long-range rockets. However, the development of defensive guided weapons was being actively pursued by the Ministry of Supply on behalf of the armed forces. This was being done in conjunction with government establishments and industry, and would lead to various guided missiles being introduced into military service. The first of these would be the Bloodhound surface to air missile, the origins of which can be traced back to 1948, and which, after acceptance trials at Woomera in 1957, went into service with the RAF in 1958.[12]

In support of this development programme, various test missiles were being used for research and development, and these were designated with various three-letter prefixes. For instance, JTV was used for Ramjet test vehicles, XTV for development models of production missiles, RTV for liquid fuelled rocket test vehicles, and CTV for control test vehicles.[13]

Skylark was originally designated the CTV.5, Series 3. The CTV vehicles were originally used to investigate the aerodynamic control of missiles, particularly under tight manoeuvres. They were essentially unguided darts that were accelerated to

supersonic speeds by booster rockets. The dart could have movable fins or small rocket motors fitted to carry out programmed movements, hence the 'Controlled' part of the name.[14]

CTV.1

This was a supersonic beam riding test missile, which started life in the laboratory as 'Longshot' in 1944. It was redesigned under the code name 'Red Hawk' before being given the designation CTV.1, and in 1951 achieved the first supersonic guided missile flight in the UK.[15] It was a 'boost/coast' test vehicle, which comprised a dart or head, propelled by a three-rocket solid fuel boost assembly. It was the first British missile fitted with electronics, and the trials in 1947 and 1948 were used to see how glass thermionic valves (vacuum tubes) would cope with the shock and vibration of rocket flight. Subsequently, guidance, control and telemetering systems were successfully developed, using specially developed sub-miniature valves and components. By July 1948 the missile contained 22 thermionic valves, and later the guidance receiver alone contained 53 valves! The flight trials took place at Larkhill on Salisbury Plain in the UK, and by 1952 dozens of CTV.1 firings had taken place.[16]

Figure 2.3 A beam riding CTV.1 on the launcher at Larkhill in May 1951.
The similar looking 'sighter' rocket on the right was fired first, to check that the range instrumentation was set up correctly and able to follow the fully equipped beam rider vehicle in flight.
(Aspinall (1953b, figure 1)

---

[12]   See Twigge (1993), *The Early Development of Guided Weapons in the United Kingdom,* Chapter 2 onwards for a good explanation of the UK programme.
[13]   Designations – see for instance Twigge (1993), p.18.
[14]   See Everest (2006), 'An Armourer at Farnborough', p.18, for an introduction to these aspects.
[15]   Aspinall (1953a), *The development of the supersonic beam riding test missile CTV.1.* (TRE Malvern Report T2144).
[16]   The range is still in use 60 years later, and is now administered by the QinetiQ defence company.

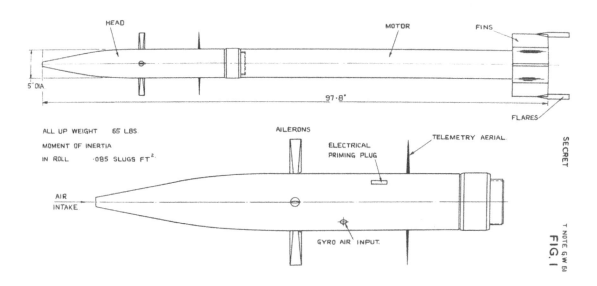

Figure 2.4 The CTV.2 Test Vehicle.
(Robins (1949), figure 1)

CTV.2

This was a supersonic control test vehicle used for the development of roll stabilisation systems, which were subsequently used on CTV.1. Firings took place at Larkhill in 1948 and 1949.[17]

CTV.3

This test vehicle was a little different, being a one-third scale model of the proposed 'Blue Boar' guided bomb.[18] The model carried no internal equipment, as it was only intended to provide a cheap and convenient means of obtaining 'free flight' data of a preliminary nature. Blue Boar was intended to be guided but unpowered, with a television camera in the nose to increase the accuracy of bombing from high altitudes. Originally, its development was accorded top priority status, and it was tested at Woomera from 1951 to 1954,[19] but in 1954 it was cancelled, as progress had remained slow and new methods of guidance had become available.[20]

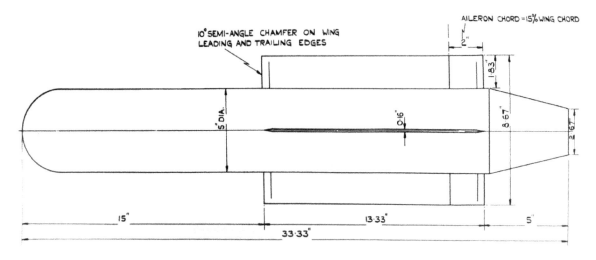

Figure 2.5. The layout of CTV.3.
(Deudney (1950), figure 1)

[17] Robins (1949), *Interim note on the Roll Stabilization of a Supersonic Control Test Vehicle C.T.V.2.* (RAE Technical note GW 61).
[18] Deudney (1950), *Flight Trials measurement on roll control characteristics of C.T.V.3.* (RAE Technical note GW 71).
[19] Morton (1989), *Fire across the Desert: Woomera and the Anglo-Australian Joint Project*, p.181.
[20] Twigge (1993), *The Early Development of Guided Weapons in the United Kingdom*, p.245.

CTV.4

This comprised a homing dart (similar to that on CTV.1), with a booster and homing receiver. It was developed with Ferranti for guidance, control and parachute development of the Red Duster/Bloodhound ground to air missile.[21] The idea was that it would be a lot cheaper to carry out trials using the CTV.4 rather than the large and expensive RTV.2 rocket.[22]

CTV.5, Series 1

The RAE was keen to further its knowledge of high altitude rockets. In December 1950, 'Technical Note GW.99' was written by N.K.Walker and J.F.Hazell, entitled *Preliminary discussion of a test vehicle for flight tests at high incidence and high altitude – C.T.V.5*.[23] This discussed two stage test vehicles launched at angles of 65 to 70 degrees from the horizontal and reaching altitudes up to 47,500 feet (9 miles / 14.5 km).

This resulted in a true guided weapon, the multistage CTV.5, Series 1, which was fired at Woomera in April 1953. It had a two stage Mayfly motor[24] and operated up to 50,000 ft.[25] The first stage boosted the test vehicle up to speed and then separated. Following a long coast up to heights of 10 to 15 kilometres, the second stage burnt then fell away too, leaving the unpowered dart to coast freely at supersonic speeds, initially at over Mach 2.[26] It was used mostly to explore different configurations, and small wing-like control surfaces were programmed to turn the dart sharply, to simulate a guided missile pursuing an evading quarry. The aerodynamic effects on the dart – drag, accelerations, roll and so on – were computed from trials records.

The first stage booster used the type GW 22 fins, later used in the first version of Skylark.[27]

CTV.5, Series 2

This was a single stage version of the CTV.5 Series I with an especially small low drag head with no wings or controls. It was initially used for preliminary aerodynamic heating measurements up to a Mach No of 4 at low altitudes, but was also suitable for experiments up to 100,000 ft. (19 miles / 31 km).[29] It was powered by a Mayfly sold propellant motor.

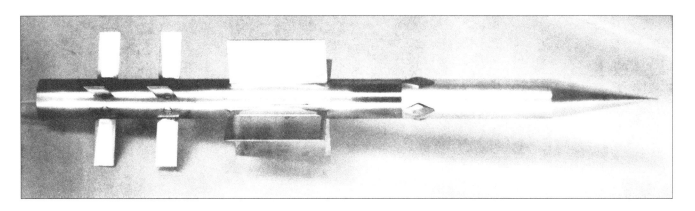

Figure 2.6 A scale model of the CTV.5, Series 1, unpowered dart, used for wind tunnel tests.[28]
(Deudney & Watts (1958), figure 2)

[21] Twigge (1993), *The Early Development of Guided Weapons in the United Kingdom*, p.17.
[22] Walker & Varker (1949), *Preliminary note on the proposed new test vehicle, the C.T.V.4.* (RAE Technical Note G.W. 57).
[23] Walker & Hazell (1950), *Preliminary discussion for Flight Tests at High Incidence and High Altitude – C.T.V.5.* (RAE Technical Note GW 99).
[24] Mayfly – an early British solid fuel motor with a burning time of about 2.7 seconds and a thrust of some 19,000 lbf (85kN). It was used on many different projects.
[25] RAE GW Dept. (1958), *A Brief Review of the C.T.V.5 Series III Programme*, p.1. (TNA: PRO AVIA 65/671).
[26] Morton (1989), *Fire across the Desert*, p.198.
[27] Dorling (1959), *The First Six Skylark Firings*, p.7. (RAE Farnborough Technical Note GW 530).
[28] Deudney & Watts (1958), *Wind tunnel tests of several configurations of a model C.T.V.5 at mach numbers 1.58 and 2.02*, figure 2. (RAE AERO 2596).
[29] Memorandum to the Ministry of Supply from M.B.Morgan, Deputy Director RAE, dated 20 August 1958, in document file "Upper Atmosphere Research Policy and Financial Control – Skylark". (TNA: PRO AVIA 65/671).

Figure 2.7 The CTV.5, Series 2 vehicle on its launcher. During flight, measurements were taken of the heating of the outer skin caused by the speed of the head through the air.

(Dawton, Knott & Barford (1959), figure 14)

CTV.5, Series 3

The Series 3 was designed to extend CTV.5 studies to greater altitudes, and is the vehicle that became 'Skylark'. As described below, the design evolved through a series of studies carried out by the Guided Weapons department of RAE over a two-year period between the end of 1953 and the end of 1955.

In December 1953, the RAE had issued a report written by D.G. King-Hele titled 'The Limitations of Upper-Atmosphere Research Vehicles Powered by Current British Solid Fuel Rockets'.[30] This investigation had been prompted by the 1953 Oxford conference, and referring to this, the report included "The visiting speakers' accounts of the extensive American work on this subject during the last few years served to emphasize the meagreness of the effort being devoted to it in Britain", which must have reflected British frustrations at the time. The purpose of the study was to find out if rocket motors then in production for guided weapon projects would be of value in propelling rockets for upper atmosphere research. The answer was negative, as the report concluded that a rocket design using existing solid fuel mo-

tors would at best attain a maximum altitude of 120,000 feet (23 miles / 37 km), scarcely above that of ordinary research balloons. It continued by saying that if such a vehicle was to be of value it would have to be launched from a high mountain or a balloon. (The Americans had launched many upper atmosphere research rockets from balloons – the 'Rockoons',[31] but a similar Anglo-Australian scheme (HARP) at Woomera would be abandoned in 1958.[32]) It suggested that the use of a new long burning motor designed specifically for high altitude research would provide a simpler approach.

In February 1954, representatives of the Gassiot Committee visited the RAE. King-Hele recalled:

> ...a few months later [i.e. after his report was issued] they came to visit the Director of the RAE, Sir Arnold Hall. To my surprise, I was called in, because they wanted a design study for a rocket to fly to high altitudes, and I was the obvious victim, having already done so many (abortive) design studies. But this new idea looked as though it might actually materialize.[33]

[30] King-Hele (1953), *The Limitations of Upper-Atmosphere Research Vehicles Powered by Current British Solid Fuel Rocket Motors.* (RAE Technical report GW 291).
[31] For an illustration, see Boyd & Seaton (1954), *Rocket Exploration of the Upper Atmosphere*, p.61.
[32] Morton (1989), *Fire across the Desert*, p.396.
[33] King-Hele (1992), *A tapestry of orbits*, p.5, © Cambridge University Press, reproduced with permission.

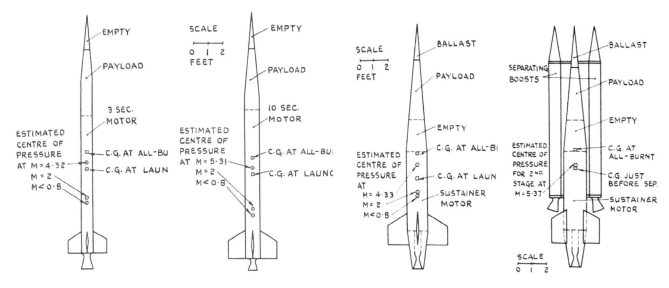

Figures 2.8, 2.9, 2.10 and 2.11. The four possible configurations (vehicles A to D) considered by D.G. King-Hele's RAE report in May 1954.

(King-Hele (1954a), figures 1 & 2)

His subsequent design study was issued in May, and was a revised and extended version [34] of his previous study. It explored the best design for a future vehicle by considering four possibilities, based on hypothetical motors with burning times of 3 to 30 seconds. It concluded that a single stage solid-fuel rocket vehicle (based on designs B or C above) weighing about 1000 lb and launched near sea level, should adequately cover the altitude band 100,000 to 250,000 feet (19 – 47 miles / 30 – 76 km). In addition, if solid fuel motor performance improved as expected, then carrying a payload of 50 lb [plus ballast of 50lb!] to 300,000 feet (57 miles / 91 km) should be consistently possible.

The more complicated two-stage version (vehicle D) would have been capable of rising to 510,000 feet (97 miles / 155 km), but would be more expensive, and he thought the design complications of boost motor attachment and separation would absorb technical effort and probably delay production.

It is interesting to note that when the representatives of the Gassiot Committee had met Sir Arnold Hall (the director of RAE) in February 1954 (i.e. before this new report was produced), they were told that the upper atmosphere rocket being considered would be capable of carrying a payload of 100 lb to 200 km. This was twice the altitude of the single stage vehicle that King-Hele thought best, and 30% more than the more ambitious two-stage vehicle. One wonders why they were told this figure – the answer seems to be that the director was jumping the gun a little, and providing internal RAE figures (see the 'Re-Entry Test Vehicle Panel Meeting No.4' minutes of March 1954 discussed below), which were

not 'officially' confirmed until the subsequent report of October 1954 – no wonder the scientists were pleased!

King-Hele's May 1954 report was excellently written, and clearly identified and quantified the various factors involved in achieving maximum altitude. It considered factors such as motor properties, vehicle length to diameter ratio, nose cone angle and drag. It included 18 graphs showing the effect of the various parameters, and as this was before the general use of computers, all these must have been produced from many hundreds of hand calculations - a feat in itself! (Indeed, referring to other reports of the time, King-Hele recalled "All the work on ballistic missiles was of course hand-calculation with electro-mechanical calculators, Friedens and Monroes, which took about half a minute to grind out a division." [35])

The report must be considered a landmark in British rocket design. It appears to be the first professional analysis undertaken in Britain of the factors involved in launching a rocket into space, and from it, the design of Skylark can be seen to be emerging. This, Britain's first civilian rocket application, must have been an interesting project to work on, presumably confirming the realisation that launching rockets into space was perfectly feasible with the new technologies then emerging. Science fiction was becoming true!

A little later, in January 1956, the RAE issued another report written by King-Hele, in which he assessed the feasibility of launching into Earth orbit a satellite of weight about 2000 lbs at an altitude of 200 miles (322 km),[36] and concluded that such an achievement was practicable using the liquid fuel rocket technology of the time:

---

[34]   King-Hele (1954a), *The Performance of Upper-Atmosphere Research Vehicles Powered by Solid Fuel Rocket Motors.* (RAE Technical Note GW 315).

[35]   King-Hele (1992), *A tapestry of orbits*, p.7, © Cambridge University Press, reproduced with permission.

[36]   King-Hele & Gillmore (1956), *Preliminary assessment of an Earth satellite reconnaissance vehicle.* (RAE Technical Note GW 393).

Like Blue Streak, the proposed satellite launcher relied on liquid oxygen and kerosene as propellants for the first stage. We tried to work out a near-optimum climb path, and the chosen trajectory was quite similar to those subsequently used by real satellites. The weight of its launcher came out as 60 tons, and it was rather similar to the later US Thor-Delta 1 launcher.[37]

This report was followed by others in August and September analysing the dynamics of re-entry - advanced work considering that it would be October 1957, another year later, before the USSR launched the first Sputnik! Equally impressive was the fact that King-Hele then used observations of the Sputnik 1 & 2 rocket cases to discover that the Earth was pear shaped, a classic scientific 'detective story'.[38]

However, we are getting ahead of things. King-Hele's report of May 1954 was classified as 'Confidential', but in June, an unclassified précis was released, in the form of "technical memo" no. GW225,[39] and presumably circulated to the Gassiot Committee and other interested parties. Also in May that year, the RAE produced an estimate for the cost of the proposed vehicle. This concluded that a vehicle of the "Type C" from the King-Hele report would have a development cost of £30,000 to £50,000,[40] with a subsequent cost per vehicle of £600 to £1000,[41] and the RAE could make up to six of these a year.[42]

Up to this point, a vehicle specifically for the Royal Society programme had been under consideration. However when the proposal reached the project group concerned it became apparent that it dovetailed into other proposals that were being formulated for an RAE vehicle, extending the scope of the CTV.5 Series 1 and 2. Moreover these other proposals were for a vehicle using a more advanced motor than that considered in King-Hele's report, one which would exceed in height and payload the Royals Society's specification. This was most satisfactory from all points of view, and the proposed Royal Society's vehicle was absorbed into the CTV.5 programme.[43]

This interest of the RAE in extending the CTV.5 programme was caused by a renewed British interest in long-range ballistic rockets. Unbeknown to the scientists, the government had decided that it needed a nuclear deterrent for the RAF,

and in June 1953, even before the Oxford conference, had issued a secret operational requirement OR 1139 for a Medium Range Ballistic Missile (MRBM).[44] Contracts were subsequently awarded to several companies, although overall project responsibility remained with the RAE as R&D authority. By 1954 the RAE were working hard on the project, and the concept of 'Blue Streak' with an associated 'Re-Entry Test Vehicle' emerged. In March 1955, the 'Re-Entry Test Vehicle Panel Meeting No.4' considered whether the re-entry test vehicle should be powered by solid fuel or liquid propellants, and decided, "...the four motor liquid fuel vehicle seemed the best solution".[45] Thus, the 'Black Knight' rocket (as it subsequently became known) took on its final form.

The same meeting also considered the high altitude vehicle for the Gassiot Committee. It recognised that the complexity and cost of the new re-entry test vehicle would be too much for that application, which "might best be met by a simpler easily made lower performance vehicle." This would consist of a single stage fin stabilised vehicle having a solid propellant motor, the motor of which would be an elongated 'Smokey Joe' with a burning time of 30 seconds. It was stated that an estimated height of 678,000 feet (128 miles / 207 km) should be attained with 100 lbs of instrumentation. (Slightly better than the figures of the presumably more considered report subsequently issued in October, see below).

This defence interest certainly helped the scientists, as in 1955 the funding for which the Gassiot Committee had applied for was finally granted. On June 29th, Treasury support, spread over four years, was agreed. This was to be divided into £50,000 to cover the design and provision of rocket vehicles by the Royal Aircraft Establishment, and £50,000 to be made available to the Gassiot Committee to cover the cost of the experiments.[46] In addition, in June 1955, two members of the RAE visited the USA to discuss the design and instrumentation of upper atmosphere research rockets, in particular with the CTV.5 Series 3 in mind. Here they visited several establishments, principally the Naval Research Laboratory at Anacostia, but also the White Sands Missile Range in New Mexico. It was this latter visit that led to the launch tower at Woomera, and the Skylark having three fins.[47]

---

[37] King-Hele (1992), *A tapestry of orbits*, p.8, © Cambridge University Press, reproduced with permission.

[38] King-Hele (1992), *A tapestry of orbits*.

[39] King-Hele (1954b), *Performance Estimate for Upper-Atmosphere Research Vehicles: Outline of Results.* (RAE Technical Memo GW 225).

[40] Where £40,000 in 1954 was equivalent to £0.8 -£3.3 million by 2011. (2011 figures based on the "Historic Opportunity" and "Economic Cost" measure for a large project, from Lawrence H. Officer and Samuel H. Williamson, "Five Ways to Compute the Relative Value of a UK Pound Amount, 1270 to Present," MeasuringWorth, 2013, *www.measuringworth.com/ukcompare/*, last accessed August 2014).

[41] Where £800 in 1954 would on a similar basis be equivalent to £18-£67 thousand by 2011.

[42] Minutes of the Royal Society Rocket Subcommittee meeting of 12th September 1958, response from RAE Control Division on 5th May 1954, to a memo from the RAE Director. Document file 'Upper Atmosphere Research Policy and Financial Control – Skylark'. (TNA:PRO AVIA 65/671)

[43] Correspondence from Sir Arnold Hall, Director RAE. Document file 'Upper Atmosphere Research Policy and Financial Control – Skylark', (TNA: PRO AVIA 65/671).

[44] Martin (2002), *De Havilland Blue Streak: an illustrated story*, p.1.

[45] Minutes of 'Re-Entry Test Vehicle Panel Meeting No.4' 21st March 1955, (document file TNA: PRO AVIA 49/110).

[46] Jones & Massey (1956), 'Rocket Exploration of the Upper Atmosphere'.

[47] Dorling (1975), 'Early History of the Skylark Rocket', p.164.

In September 1955, the RAE wrote to the Ministry of Supply regarding financial cover for the CTV.5 Series 3:

> The introduction of the ballistic missile into the defence programme has brought about an urgent need for research at much higher altitudes and speeds. The investigation of the physics of the upper atmosphere and the experience gained on previous C.T.V.5 work now allows the rapid development of a comparatively simple and cheap vehicle for this work.[48]

Regarding its use in Australia, another source stated:

> The immediate use of this vehicle will be to extend the aerodynamic investigations of skin heating, etc. up to Mach 6. This is regarded as a very important use in spite of the fact that a higher performance vehicle (Black Knight), which does not belong to this series, is in the design stage.
>
> The vehicle will be used to develop airborne and ground instrumentation suitable for high and nearly vertical trajectories. In this respect, it will bridge the gap in operational experience between C.T.V.5 Series II and the Black Knight vehicle.[49]

The work of D.G. King-Hele was extended in a subsequent report from the RAE in October 1955.[50] It was written by D.I.Dawton, and provided a performance analysis and design detail for a proposed single stage upper atmosphere research vehicle propelled by a solid fuel motor which would be capable of reaching altitudes in excess of 500,000 feet (97 miles / 152 km) carrying a payload of 100 lb (45 kg). In other words, this would be the first British rocket to reach space, a fact not even mentioned in the report!

In effect, this became the outline specification for the CTV.5 Series 3 / Skylark. Here (with the help of RPD,[51] Westcott), the crucial rocket motor specification was established with a burning time of 30 seconds and thrust of 12,000 lb, (53 kN). Its total impulse of 360,000 lb sec was over three times that assumed to be the best available by King-Hele, allowing the vehicle to be nearly three times as massive as his original single stage proposals, and achieving the performance that previously required a two stage vehicle. Here too the greater efficiency of a relatively slow burning motor is acknowledged, avoiding loss of performance due to aerodynamic drag in the lower atmosphere, one of the characteristics that ensured the longevity of the design.

This report set the scene for the development of Skylark, fully described in the next chapter.

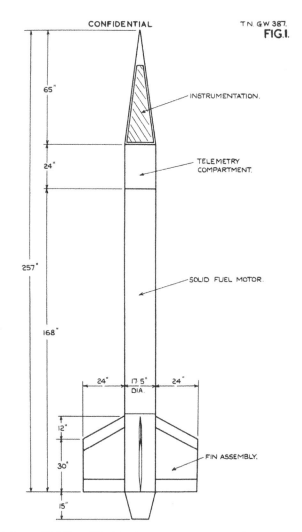

Figure 2.12 The proposed upper atmosphere vehicle begins to look like Skylark.
(Dawton (1955), figure 1)

FIG.I. UPPER ATMOSPHERE RESEARCH VEHICLE.

---

[48] Document file 'Upper Atmosphere Research Policy and Financial Control – Skylark', correspondence quoted. (TNA: PRO AVIA 65/671).

[49] RAE GW Dept. (1958), *A Brief Review of the C.T.V.5 Series III Programme*, p.1. (TNA: PRO AVIA 65/671).

[50] Dawton (1955), *Performance Estimates for a Single Stage Upper Atmosphere Research Vehicle Powered by a Solid Fuel Rocket Motor.* (RAE Technical Memo GW 387).

[51] RPD = Rocket Propulsion Department.

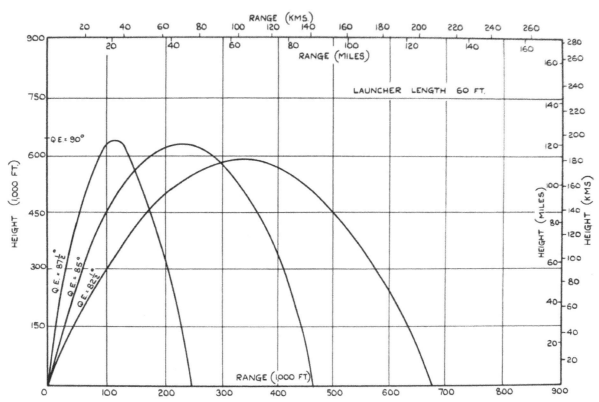

FIG. 9. ESTIMATED TRAJECTORIES FOR UPPER ATMOSPHERE RESEARCH VEHICLE.

Figure 2.13 Figure 9 of RAE report GW 387,[52] showing three estimated trajectories for the proposed upper atmosphere research vehicle. "Upper atmosphere" was a bit of a misnomer, as the rocket would leave the Earth's atmosphere altogether (at 100km) and spend about half its time in space!

(Dawton (1955), figure 9)

CTV.5, Series 4

This was the cover story for the start of Black Knight,[53] which although developed at the same time as Skylark, is another story altogether.[54]

---

[52] Dawton (1955), *Performance Estimates for a Single Stage Upper Atmosphere Research Vehicle Powered by a Solid Fuel Rocket Motor*, figure 9. (RAE Technical Memo GW 387).

[53] Dommett in 2001, CCBH (2005), *Skylark Sounding Rockets 1957-1972*, p.76, & *Prospero* No.2, p.139.

[54] See for instance Hill (2001), *A Vertical Empire*, Chapter 9, or Hill (2007), *Black Knight – Britain's first ballistic missile*.

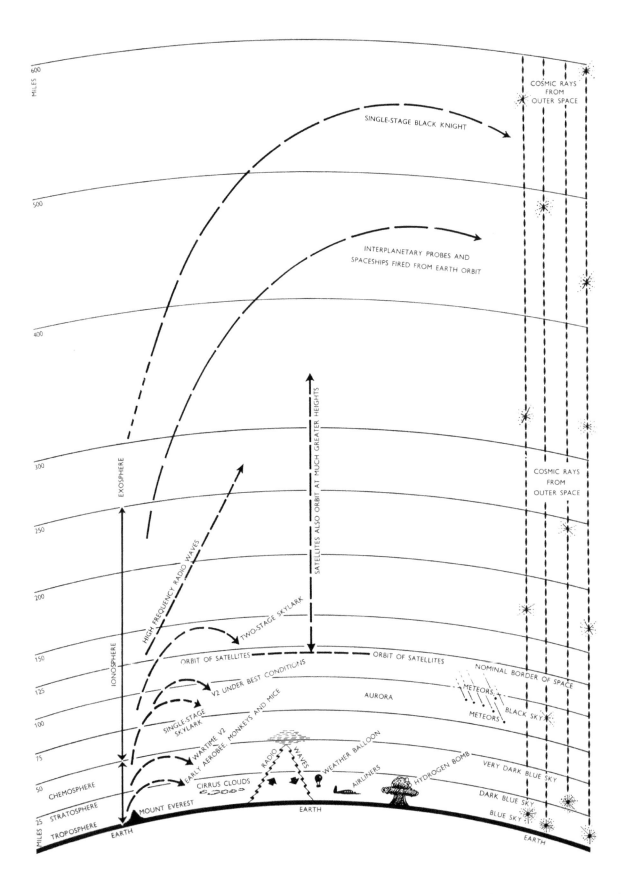

Figure 3.1 This scale diagram from 1964 shows the upper atmosphere and lower reaches of space, and includes the trajectory of a typical early single stage Skylark. However, the "Nominal Border of Space" is now internationally accepted to start at an altitude of 100 km (62 miles) (the Kármán line) rather than the 125 miles indicated here. (The "Single-Stage Black Knight" shown was Britain's second space rocket, first fired from Woomera in 1958, a year after Skylark).

(Southall (1964), *Rockets in the Desert*, p.47)

CHAPTER 3

(1955-57)

THE DESIGN AND DEVELOPMENT OF SKYLARK

Skylark was announced to the world in an article published in 'Nature' magazine on 7th April 1956,[1] (although then still called the 'Gassiot vehicle'). The authors were Dr F.E.Jones of the RAE,[2] and Professor H.S.W. Massey of UCL. The article, 'Rocket Exploration of the Upper Atmosphere', explained the evolution of the project and gave details of the proposed rocket vehicle and launch tower. The performance figures provided were based on those in RAE Technical Note GW 387 by D.I.Dawton, as discussed at the end of the previous chapter.

The vehicle described was a sounding rocket; and although it would reach space, it was not intended for launching orbiting earth satellites. Indeed, when first launched, there were no artificial space satellites.

> Sounding rockets are designed to explore the region of the upper atmosphere higher than balloons or aircraft can reach, and lower than an orbiting satellite can descend because of air drag. It is a region where much is going on – interactions between the earth's atmosphere and solar ultra-violet radiation, terrestrial magnetism, micrometeorites, cosmic rays – all of which repay scientific investigation. In 1957 when Skylark was first launched, these properties of the ionosphere were largely a mystery.[3]

Visible events in the upper atmosphere such as auroras and shooting stars had long been known if not fully understood, as were other phenomena such as the electrically conducting layers of the atmosphere that reflected radio waves and enabled long distance short-wave radio communication. One of Professor Massey's particular interests was promoting new areas of research on atomic and ionic collisions, particularly those in connection with studies of the upper atmosphere,[4] a field in which Skylark would be a revolutionary new tool. As his colleague R.L.F. Boyd expressed it:

> The upper atmosphere is a scene of great activity, where energetic radiations interact with the gas, where electric currents flow, where huge winds blow, and a fluorescent light is continually radiated. Here there are a multitude of problems still awaiting solution.[5]

By 1958 there was also felt a need for sounding rockets to reach altitudes at which the first satellites orbited, "partly to check data obtained by satellites, and partly to make a virtually instantaneous survey of the variation of some important quantity with height to very great heights".[6]

Starting the project

The following statement by Professor Massey conveniently summarised the start of the project:

> In April 1955 a programme of research on the properties of the upper atmosphere using instruments carried to high altitudes in rockets was initiated by the Gassiot Committee of the Royal Society, in collaboration with the [UK] Ministry of Supply through the Royal Aircraft Establishment. This programme was made possible by means of a grant of £100,000 over a four-year period paid through the Air Ministry. Half of this was to contribute towards the cost of the rocket vehicles and the remainder to the cost of employing scientific and technical staff and of equipment for the purely scientific work.[7]

The fact that the funding was made available via the Ministry of Supply is a reminder that Skylark also had a military purpose - it was also to be available for use in the research programme of the Royal Aircraft Establishment, particularly in connection with the ballistic missile programme.[8] "G.W. Department [RAE Guided Weapons Department] were very

---

[1]   Jones and Massey (1956), 'Rocket Exploration of the Upper Atmosphere'.
[2]   Dr F.E.Jones was Deputy Director of the RAE from 1953 to 1956, and had been one of the delegates at the Oxford conference in 1953. He left to join Mullard Ltd.
[3]   Morton (1989), *Fire across the Desert*, p.395.
[4]   See for instance Bates, Boyd & Davis (1984), 'Harrie Stewart Wilson Massey, 1908-1983', p.458.
[5]   Boyd (1960), *Space Research by Rocket and Satellite*, p.9.
[6]   Massey (1958), *Memorandum on Rocket Research*, p.2.
[7]   Massey (1958), p.1.
[8]   Dorling (1959), *The First Six Skylark Firings*, p.7. (RAE Farnborough Technical Note GW 530).

interested in this project from their own viewpoint and would assist in the design, manufacture, preparation and firing."[9]

Once the overall concept and funding had been agreed,[10] responsibility for running the project had to be decided. The University groups to be involved would be responsible for the design and construction of the scientific instruments and the analysis of the results, but the UK Ministry of Supply would be responsible for everything else: supply of the rocket vehicles, final integration of the instruments, firing the rockets at Woomera, and collecting the scientific data. Coordination of the programme would be carried out by a subcommittee of the Royal Society's Gassiot committee.

The RAE (the Royal Aircraft Establishment at Farnborough in Hampshire) was then the UK's principal research and development facility for aircraft and guided weapons, and as they were part of the Ministry of Supply,[11] the assignment fell naturally to them. "J.F. [Frank] Hazell, who had been the physicist and aerodynamicist in an earlier project in the series, was given overall responsibility for the Series III [Skylark] in September 1955, and much of the ultimate success of the new venture was due to him." [12]

The local newspaper, the Farnborough Chronicle,[13] provided the following information about those in figure 3.2:

> **Mr. J.F. Hazell** is head of the Air Dynamics and Upper Atmosphere Research section of the [Guided Weapons]

Department. A principal scientific officer, he joined the R.A.E. in 1945.

Mr. W. H. Stephens is the Deputy Director (Equipment) of the R.A.E., and has particular responsibility for rocket development. He is a former head of Guided Weapons Department.

Dr. E. B. Dorling, an upper atmosphere research expert and a senior scientific officer, has been able to devote all his time to Skylark, unlike the others, who have had to combine it with other responsibilities. He joined the R.A.E. in 1955.

Dr. T. S. Moss is the only "outsider" in the team. He is in Radio Department at the R.A.E. outstation at Ambarrow and is especially concerned with high altitude spectroscopy experiments which the R.A.E. is to carry out using Canberra bombers. He has been at the R.A.E. for three years and was also there during the war.

Mr. M. O. Robins, a senior principal scientific officer, is head of the Control Division of Guided Weapons Department. He has been at R.A.E. since 1940.

Mr. E. C. Cornford is the head of Guided Weapons Department. He has been in charge of the department since Mr. Stephens moved up last year, and has been at the R.A.E. since 1939.

Figure 3.2 Some of the Skylark design team at RAE Farnborough, 1955. (Left to right): J.F.Hazell, W.H.Stephens, E.B.Dorling, T.S. Moss, M.O.Robins, E.C.Cornford.

(Farnborough Chronicle)
(See also Figure 5.16)

---

[9]   Re-Entry Test Vehicle Panel Meeting No.4, 21st March 1955, item 8. (TNA: PRO AVIA 48/110).

[10] Jones & Massey (1956), 'Rocket Exploration of the Upper Atmosphere', (Nature, April 7 1956, p.643).

[11] At this time the RAE was still part of the Ministry of Supply, however from 1959 it became a part of the Ministry of Aviation, and from 1967 part of the new Ministry of Technology. At the time of writing (2014), after several further changes and mergers, its original activities are vested in two separate organisations, the state-owned *Defence Science and Technology Laboratory* (DSTL), and the privatised QinetiQ, a public-private partnership.

[12] Dorling (1975), 'Early History of the Skylark Rocket', p.165.

[13] Farnborough Chronicle, Friday February 15, 1957.

An ambitious target date of summer 1956 was set for the first proving rounds, in the hope of making a useful contribution to the International Geophysical Year.[14] The operation was undertaken in Q65 Building at the RAE, just across O'Gorman Avenue from Q134 Building.[15] It was one of the old buildings with a steel frame and clad in corrugated iron.[16]

The name of Frank Hazell occurs frequently throughout this book, as he was a pivotal figure in the development of Skylark, and would still be the RAE technical authority at Skylark meetings nearly twenty years later.[17] He was later to write:

> My part in the programme started with a memo from Sir Arnold Hall[18] asking for proposals to meet the Royal Society sounding rocket requirement at a cost of £50,000. I was indeed fortunate to be in a unique position to create a legitimate defence requirement, the only answer to a seemingly impossible problem.
>
> I still find it difficult to believe that without any formal priority but [unreadable word] instead an infectious enthusiasm that permeated industry, establishments and universities alike, the vehicle was ready to launch in an incredibly short time.[19]

The overall requirement

As described in the previous chapter, the design of Skylark was a continuation of the missile work carried out by the Guided Weapons department of the RAE since WW II. In particular, it was based on the studies carried out by D.G.King-Hele (GW 291 & 315) and D.I.Dawton (GW387) from 1954 to 1955.

These studies had demonstrated that drawing up the overall design requirement was an iterative process, where both 'top down' and 'bottom up' approaches had their place. Thus on the 'top down' side, Skylark had to be able to meet the scientists' need for a payload to reach hitherto unobtainable heights at a reasonable cost. From the 'bottom up' point of view, it was the capabilities of the technology of the day that mattered, together with a fine judgement on how far that capability could be improved at reasonable cost.

The performance it was considered possible to specify depended on the payload being considered, and the convenient figure "100 lb to 100 miles" was often quoted. The original article in 'Nature' magazine gave a figure of 150 lb (68 kg) to 550,000 feet (105 miles / 169 km). This was based on the 1955 study by D.I.Dawton,[20] in particular from the graph shown below.

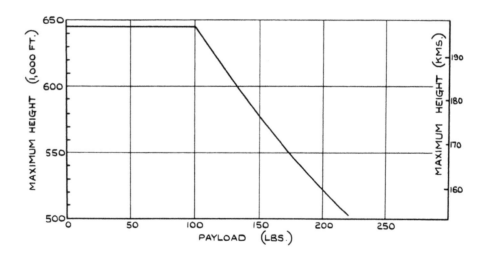

Figure 3.3 Maximum height – payload mass curve, vertical launch, for the proposed vehicle. (The maximum height is shown as constant below 100 lb since it was assumed all lighter instrumentation payloads would be ballasted up to that weight to ensure aerodynamic stability, i.e. the effective payload would never be less than 100 lb).
(Dawton (1955), figure 7)

---

[14] The IGY ran from July 1957 to December 1958, and in 1957, a static exhibit of Skylark was placed in the forecourt of Burlington House in London, home of the Royal Society. (See the start of the BBC documentary *The Restless Sphere* at *www.bbc.co.uk/archive/prince_philip/6012.shtml* (last accessed August 2014).

[15] Q134 then housed the RAE Guided Weapons Department, later the Space Department. The building has (surprisingly) survived the demolition of the old RAE site, has been refurbished, and amongst other uses now houses the National Aerospace Library.

[16] The poor condition of the building (it was built in 1915!) was to cause problems when assembling Skylarks. Q65 was eventually demolished in about 2005, but its frame, comprising as it did the lower part of a 1912 portable airship shed, has been re-erected and preserved as the centrepiece of a new development on the site. (See Figure A6.11).

[17] For instance, see the minutes of the 26th Skylark Policy Meeting held in London on 14th June 1973. (TNA: PRO AVIA 92/145).

[18] Sir Arnold Hall was Director of RAE from 1951 to 1955.

[19] Frank Hazell, draft letter written c.1978, personal correspondence from Chris Hazell, March 2011.

[20] Dawton (1955), *Performance Estimates for a Single Stage Upper Atmosphere Research Vehicle Powered by a Solid Fuel Rocket Motor.* (RAE Technical Memo GW 387).

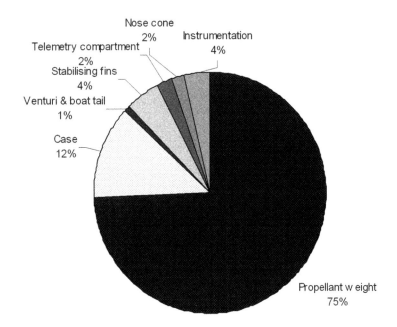

Nose cone
2%
Instrumentation
4%
Telemetry compartment
2%
Stabilising fins
4%
Venturi & boat tail
1%
Case
12%
Propellant weight
75%

Figure 3.4 This chart shows the original weight breakdown estimated by D.I.Dawton for the "all up weight at launch" of the proposed vehicle. The total estimated weight was 2689 lb (1220 kg), of which the payload (instrumentation) would be 4%.[21]

As concluded in the study, this showed that a lighter payload of 100 lb (45 kg) was anticipated to reach about 645,000 feet (122 miles / 197 km), a little higher than commonly quoted.

In this and other reports of the time (and hence later in this book), the term 'payload' is used a little loosely, but is usually shorthand for 'instrumented' or 'net' payload. In other words, the figures of 150 lb or 100 lb used above referred to the weight available for the scientific payloads, and excluded the rest of the vehicle head and telemetry instrumentation. As shown in the chart above, items such as the nose cone and telemetry compartment could weigh as much again.

General design considerations

As D.I.Dawton's report stated:

> The ideal upper atmosphere research vehicle should be easy to manufacture, prepare and fire and the total cost per flight should be kept as low as possible.[22]

These aspirations resulted in a proposed design for a single-stage uncontrolled rocket propelled by a solid-fuel motor, with the aim of achieving great height at reasonable cost. The final performance depended on the burning-time of the motor. A fast burning motor would produce high velocities in the lower atmosphere with resultant excessive drag. A slow burning motor would reduce the drag in the lower reaches in the atmosphere, but might mean a reduction in specific impulse,[23] and because of the lower accelerations involved, the dispersion[24] would increase. The optimum burning time seemed to be about 30 seconds, and this was the figure chosen.

A relatively low acceleration would also help reduce stress on the payloads. The use of 'solid state' electronics was still to come (the transistor had been invented in 1953, only a few years earlier), and all electronic circuitry was still thermionic valve (vacuum / electron tube) based. This could cause difficulties; for instance in 1953 at Woomera, problems had been identified with the guidance system of the experimental RTV.1 vehicle, which used a complex circuit employing many valves. "More than a hundred of them were packed into the small interior, five times as many as in a television set of the period, and they often failed under the strong acceleration and vibration".[25]

The decision was also made to design the vehicle so that it was capable of meeting the requirements from a ground level launch. The advantages of launching at a high altitude from a balloon were considered, but the complications were thought to outweigh the benefits.[26]

Skylark would be the first British rocket capable of reaching space, and its design involved entering the unknown. Indeed, as noted above, this was the very reason the Ministry of Supply was funding the project:

---

21 Chart by author, using data from Dawton (1955), p.5. (RAE Technical Memo GW 387). (TNA: PRO AVIA 6/19785).

22 Dawton (1955), *Performance Estimates for a Single Stage Upper Atmosphere Research Vehicle Powered by a Solid Fuel Rocket Motor*, p.3. (RAE Technical Memo GW 387).

23 Specific impulse is a measure of the efficiency of a rocket motor or jet engine.

24 Dispersion is the variation of the impact point from that predicted.

25 Morton (1989), *Fire across the Desert*, p.199.

26 Dawton (1955), p.3. Some early US sounding rockets using this technique ('rockoons') were launched from naval ships travelling with the wind to help avoid problems launching the large balloons required. (For an illustration of a rockoon see Boyd & Seaton (1954), *Rocket Exploration of the Upper Atmosphere*, p.61).

The introduction of the ballistic missile [Blue Streak] into the defence programme has brought about an urgent need for research at much higher altitudes and speeds. The work at much higher altitudes will include the investigation of the physics of the upper atmosphere and the experience gained on previous C.T.V.5 work now allows the rapid development of comparatively simple and cheap vehicles for the work.[27]

One technical aspect was that Skylark would be a supersonic vehicle which after some 40 seconds, would be at a height of 100,000 feet (19 miles / 30 km) travelling at up to 5000 feet per second (3500 mph / 5490 km/h).[28] This was Mach 5.1, i.e. it would be reaching hypersonic speeds. To calculate the trajectory under these conditions, estimates had to be made of the drag from the various body parts, and confirmed by observations of the first flights. As noted in the previous chapter, the first few trajectories had to be calculated by hand, until a "Pegasus automatic digital computer" became available.[29]

Eric Dorling has recalled other aspects of this early stage of the development:

> I arrived at RAE in 1955 at a propitious moment. Everything was ready for the start of the Skylark programme. Design work on the Raven motor at the then RAE Westcott had had still to begin and the massive launch tower for Woomera had yet to be designed and constructed. An important task by the late Frank Hazell, who was in charge of the project, and Peter Herbert, who is here today, was making the necessary aerodynamic and trajectory calculations, the latter lengthy tasks having to be done by hand. Two lady assistants calculated trajectories during motor burn, a quarter of a second by a quarter of a second; those quarters of seconds added up to two weeks of work. I imagine any of today's small calculators would make half a dozen to the minute, but in 1955 we were without that very important tool, the computer.
>
> My job amongst other things was to act as a kind of glue between the small team at Farnborough (and it was small) and the University experimenters. I had the pleasant task of go-between, visiting them to discuss with the group there how the requirements might be met.[30]
>
> The nominal characteristics of the motor were by then already decided, but the motor still had to be de-

signed and made, as had the rocket head and launcher... Best estimates had to be made for the actual weight of the motor case, propellant, unburned propellant (sliver), structure and payload. Dispersion of the rocket's impact point was of primary concern and much of Hazell's time was taken up, together with that of his assistants, in assessing the likely behaviour of the rocket once it left the launcher rails. Meanwhile, the design and engineering team got to work on the rocket head and launcher, whist at Westcott work began on the motor.[31]

Another important design factor was that, for simplicity, Skylark was stabilised only by fixed fins; it had no other form of flight control. Unlike more sophisticated vehicles (e.g. Black Knight), it was unable even to keep itself pointing in a particular direction. Thus, when it entered areas where wind speed varied with height, the variations would affect the lower fin area more than the upper body, and Skylark would tend to point in the direction the stronger wind was coming from. In addition, the use of three fins was a significant departure from that originally proposed by D.I.Dawton's original study, which had assumed four fins:

> ... I also ought to point out the big mistake we made right at the beginning when we were deciding what the configuration was. I was involved with Ted Phythian while we trying to sort out an optimum layout, and I was working on cone cylinders in those days, so I suppose my responsibility was only for the cone angle. But it was decided that three fins would be wonderful, it would save us a lot of trouble.[32] Unfortunately, the theory we were using didn't tell us the problems we were going to have, that when the body was at a combined pitch and yaw there were then rolling moments. So this combined pitch and rolling moment drove the thing into spinning up, and ending up in free space in a flat spin. It was alright if you were throwing out grenades [see Chapter 5], but it wasn't very helpful if you tried to point at things.[33]

The lack of active guidance also gave rise to the 'dispersion' problem, (common to most sounding rockets) whereby Skylark could impact many miles from its predicted position. Efforts to reduce the dispersion included taking several wind measurements before launch, and carefully setting the launch angle in order to compensate.

[27] Dawton (1955), *Performance Estimates for a Single Stage Upper Atmosphere Research Vehicle Powered by a Solid Fuel Rocket Motor*, p.3. (RAE Technical Memo GW 387).

[28] Dorling (1959), *The First Six Skylark Firings*, figures 28 and 29. (RAE Farnborough Technical Note GW 530).

[29] Dorling (1959), p.8. This was the Ferranti Pegasus, which used miniature thermionic valves (vacuum tubes) rather than transistors or integrated circuits. A gallery featuring this machine (the oldest working computer in the world) was opened at the London Science museum in 2001. See *www.sciencemuseum.org.uk/visitmuseum_old/galleries/computing.aspx* (last accessed August 2014).

[30] Dorling in 2001, CCBH (2005), *Skylark Sounding Rockets 1957-1972*, p.28, & *Prospero* No.2, p.95.

[31] Dorling (1975), 'Early History of the Skylark Rocket', p.165.

[32] One of the reasons for deciding on three fins was launch tower compatibility, see later in this chapter.

[33] Dommett in 2001, CCBH (2005), p.53, & *Prospero* No.2, p.119.

The origin of the name 'Skylark'

The name 'Skylark' was introduced by Eric Dorling:

> I was probably the only one to write articles about the programmes for general publication. When in 1957 [34] I was asked to write for the RAE's Magazine I was determined that the project name CTV5 Series III should give way to something more appealing; I wanted 'Skylark'. Frank Hazell being in Australia with Robert Boyd, I consulted our division head. From a list of names I had prepared, many quite hopeless, he lighted upon the right one. So leaving no time for second thoughts nor for Hazell's return, I got headquarters' agreement. 'But don't forget, it's to be a nickname only,' they warned me, 'not a project name'. The name took on at once, but alas, within a week Skylark was being written on orders instead of CTV5 Series III. When these orders were received in the ordering department they went into limbo; nothing was ordered, and there was a terrible pause. The worst consequence was that the ordering of the next batch of motor tubes was held up until suitable apologies had been made! [35]

Detailed design and making the prototypes

As far as the RAE was concerned, from both a design and funding point of view, Skylark was simply a continuation of earlier CTV work. The first Skylarks were assembled in RAE Farnborough's building Q65, which had been fitted out with equipment to measure mass properties of payloads, vibration tables and a whirling-arm acceleration tester: [36]

> Really it just continued on from the designs we were doing for the controlled test vehicle and things like that. Frank Hazell's group used to agree on something and then they fed the information down to us, and we just built the units and *Skylark* continued from those early controlled test vehicles.
>
> … We were [then] confronted, as you say, with getting some of the materials. The bodywork was made up out of magalloy[37] and these were quite solid sections all bolted together with twenty-four 5/16th BSF bolts, and it really formed a very solid assembly. But on the other hand it had problems in quick assembly and that sort of thing.
>
> … the instrumentation components had all been tried and tested on those early programmes. Then we re-engineered it for the *Skylark* heads. The only thing was the overall weight, because with the CTV1s we were using very solid support brackets and things for accelerometers so the weight was going up tremendously … But initially from March 1956 to the first one flying, we had about a year to get all these things on…
>
> We operated as small teams, in fact there were only a handful of people in 1956 really, and we had two mechanics loaned to us from the main workshop. There were about four or five of us working away… for that first year it was hard going, because of all the trying to get the bits and pieces together to get the thing to the first trial flight, and we were lucky to get it all assembled for the first trial firing in 1957. We were going to fire in December 1956, but the firing was based on the firing of six motors at Westcott and I think three had failed, so we couldn't continue then. There were Don Hawes and myself out there [Woomera] dealing with the programme and the paperwork and stuff like that and we had to return without flying and then they managed to fly it in February.[38]

The resulting design

Skylark comprised three main parts, an instrumented head, a Raven solid propellant motor, and a fin assembly. It was just over 25 feet (7.6 m) long, the body diameter was 17.4 inches (44 cm), and at 2500 lbs (1134 kg), it weighed just over a tonne. The motor formed the lower part of the rocket, and made up about 60% of the overall length, and 75% of the all up weight.

---

[34] Eric Dorling is speaking 'off the cuff' here. In fact, the article featuring the new name appeared in September 1956. (See RAE News, September 1956, page 43, also Dorling (1991), page 4.

[35] Dorling in 2001, CCBH (2005), *Skylark Sounding Rockets 1957-1972*, p.29, & *Prospero* No.2. p.96.

[36] Bryan Day, personal correspondence, May 2009.

[37] Magalloy – magnesium alloy, a lightweight metallic structural material.

[38] Spurr in 2001, CCBH (2005), pp.68-70, & *Prospero* No.2. p.133.

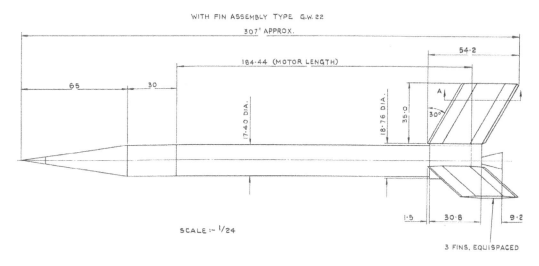

Figure 3.5 The original version of Skylark, with the larger type GW 22 fins.
(Dorling (1959), figure 1)

The head assembly

The head was designed to give the maximum flexibility in meeting a wide range of instrumentation additions and changes as the research programme developed:

The nose cone was some 65 inches (165 cm) long and formed one compartment, and a cylindrical telemetry bay 30 inches (76 cm) long formed a second compartment.

The original expectation was that university experiments would be carried under the nose cone, and telemetry and other equipment in the cylindrical compartment. However this arrangement was soon varied for particular missions,[39] and later on extra cylindrical bays were added.

In line with this, a 15° total cone angle was chosen to provide adequate instrumentation space (about 2.6 cubic feet /

74 litres), without too serious a penalty in nose drag. It was recognised that a reduction in drag and a slight improvement in overall performance could have been obtained by using a minimum nose drag profile, e.g. a secant ogive, but that would have been more difficult (and hence expensive) to manufacture.[40] From SL03 onwards, Skylark nose cones were made of 20-gauge stainless steel,[41] steel being chosen to cope with aerodynamic heating, stainless because of its non-magnetic properties.[42]

The nose cone and cylindrical bay were joined by 'an intermediate strong ring', which originally housed an 'M.T.S.' (Missile Tracking System) beacon and two large electrical (L.T.) battery containers. There was another strong ring between the head and the motor.

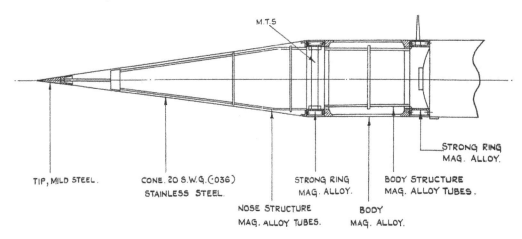

Figure 3.6 The original Skylark head assembly, with just one cylindrical bay.
(Dorling (1959), figure 2(b))

[39] The first being SL04 in November 1957.
[40] See Dawton (1955), (GW 387), p.4 and King-Hele (1954a), (GW 315), p.7.
[41] Dorling (1959), *The First Six Skylark Firings*, p.10. (RAE Farnborough Technical Note GW 530).
[42] See for instance Parker & Smith (1955), *Note on a visit to USA in June 1955*, p.3. (RAE Technical note RPD 134).

The strong rings included pressure bulkheads with pressurised connectors for the cables. Thus, the cone and the body could be pressurised if required, an arrangement that would prevent the high-voltage supplies to any thermionic valves present from sparking over at high altitudes, or air from the head polluting the environment in which sensitive scientific experiments might be taking place.[43]

The Raven solid propellant motor

The RAE at Farnborough did not carry out motor or propellant design work; this was done by the RPE (Rocket Propulsion Establishment) at Westcott in Buckinghamshire, by then being administered as a branch of the RAE. The RPE was a government research and development facility, established in 1946 after the war as the Guided Projectile Establishment (GPE), the first of many titles.[44]

The original studies in 1954 had concluded that the British solid propellant motors then available, not having been designed for the purpose, would not be able to meet the proposed vehicle requirements; but that the required performance should be attainable in the next few years.[45] Hence, the 'Raven'[46] motor was designed especially for Skylark, although for speed and cost reasons it was based on the development of existing designs.

> Frank Hazell worked in close co-operation with Dr Harold Crook and his team at RPE (Rocket Propulsion Establishment). The flexibility of the requirement made it possible to make maximum use of existing technology and materials at RPE, which was essential to meet the demandingly short timescales.[47]

However the Raven was still by far the largest solid fuel rocket motor then developed in the UK, being nearly three times the size of any previous design, and a critical part of the project. It made Skylark the first single-stage high performance solid propellant sounding rocket in the world.[48]

In October 1955, the initial specification agreed was:[49]

Total sea level impulse:	326,000 lb sec (1450 kN sec)
Burning time:	25 seconds
Initial thrust:	12,000 lbf (53.4 kN)

To put this in context, the total impulse was over twice that of the boosters used on various earlier US sounding rockets, (which typically provided 50,000 lb for 3 seconds). However, it was less than the 45,000 lb for 34 seconds of the Thiokol XM100 motor then being developed in the US for the *Sergeant* surface to air missile, and deployed a few years later in 1963.[50]

Motor Design

In principle, solid propellant rocket motors are very simple, requiring none of the complicated pumps, plumbing, and control systems of liquid fuelled engines. They basically comprise a steel case with a filling of solid propellant. John Harlow recalls:

> …we had a motor called Smokey Joe, which was the sustainer system really for the army ground-to-air anti-aircraft weapon [Red Shoes / Thunderbird I], and what we basically did to create the Raven motor was to weld three of these together. The Smokey Joe had about 330 kilogrammes of propellant in it and three of these obviously made one ton of propellant, and that was the basis of the Raven I motor.[51]

The other possibility had been to base the Raven on the original Goldfinch I motor, which had been developed for a cancelled military project. This was not done because its thrust was too high; instead, only the Goldfinch's proven nozzle design was used.[52]

[43] Parker & Smith (1955), p.3.
[44] It had originally concentrated on liquid propulsion, but from 1948 solid propellant work was undertaken. (Harlow (1992a), p.1).
[45] King-Hele (1954a), *The Performance of Upper-Atmosphere Research Vehicles Powered by Solid Fuel Motors*, p.13. (RAE Technical Note GW 315).
[46] Many motors developed at Westcott were named after birds – "… owing to the quiet persistence of an amateur ornithologist, later to become Superintendent of the Solid Propellant Laboratory at Westcott, the practice of using birds' name was accepted." (Harlow (1992a), p.2). Subsequently, an RPE document issued in March 1968 *Index to Solid Propellant Rocket Motors*, listed 73 motors, mostly with the names of birds, ranging from Albatross and Blackbird through to Woodpecker and Wren!
[47] Bryan Day, personal correspondence, May 2009.
[48] Hazell (1961), 'Skylark', p.526. *Journal of the Royal Aeronautical Society*, August 1961, Volume 65.
[49] Dorling (1959), p.9.
[50] See for instance *www.designation-systems.net/dusrm/m-29.html* , last accessed August 2014.
[51] Harlow in 2001, CCBH (2005), *Skylark Sounding Rockets 1957-1972*, p.57, & *Prospero* No.2. p.122.
[52] Harlow (1998), 'Sustainer propulsion for the UK air defence weapons – The early history', p.8.

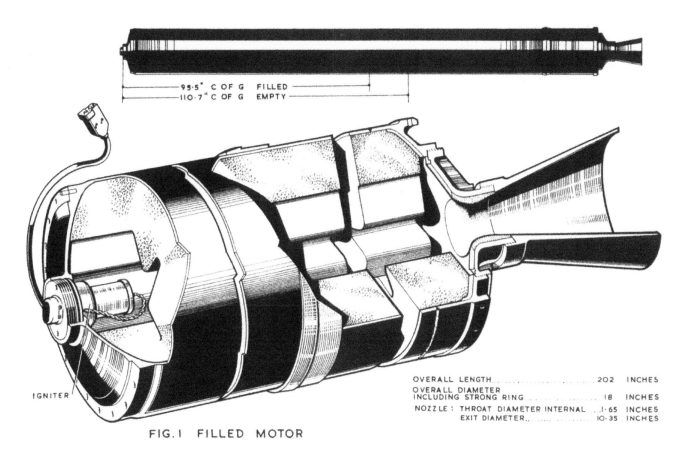

95.5" C OF G FILLED
110.7" C OF G EMPTY

IGNITER

OVERALL LENGTH . . . . 202 INCHES
OVERALL DIAMETER
INCLUDING STRONG RING . . . . 18 INCHES
NOZZLE : THROAT DIAMETER INTERNAL . . 1·65 INCHES
EXIT DIAMETER . . . . 10·35 INCHES

FIG. I FILLED MOTOR

Figure 3.7 This August 1961 drawing shows the later Raven Va, but earlier versions were very similar. The top view shows the true proportions.[53]

The Raven motor case and the Bristol Aeroplane Company

Neither the case nor the propellants were easy to make in the late 1950s. The steel case for the Raven motor was a cylinder 15 feet (4.6 metres) long and 17.4 inches (44 cm) in diameter. It had to be strong enough to withstand the combustion forces, and its manufacture required new techniques to be developed. The initial manufacturing contract for motor cases, forging, and nozzle[54] went to Bristol Aircraft (Weston) Ltd.

The background to this was that in 1956 the Bristol Aeroplane Company were setting up a rocket motor manufac-turing facility at a wartime shadow factory at Banwell, near Weston-super-Mare in Somerset. Here they were installing the required facilities, and together with the RPE Westcott and PERME[55] government establishments, developing new 'state-of-the-art' fabrication techniques. Manufacture of the Raven cases began early in 1956.[56]

(In 1959 the factory became a joint venture with the large Aerojet General company of the USA, and from then on the enterprise at Banwell was known as Bristol Aerojet, generally referred to as BAJ).

[53] RPE Westcott (1961), *Solid Motor Data Sheet for Raven Va*, figure 1.
[54] RAE GW Dept. (1958), *A Brief Review of the C.T.V.5 Series III Programme*, p.2.
[55] PERME = "Propellants, Explosives and Rocket Motor Establishment", then based at Waltham Abbey, previously the Royal Gunpowder Mills.
[56] Dorling (1959), The First Six Skylark Firings, p.7.

Figure 3.8 A deep pit furnace being excavated at Banwell in January 1956. Here large cylindrical heat treatment ovens were installed for motor case manufacture.

(Parsons (1993), p.16)

The Raven cases were made from high tensile steel, and designed for a working pressure of 1,250 psi (almost 100 kg/cm²). Two methods of fabrication were tried, and both proved successful:[57]

(a) Lengths of drawn steel tubing were produced and welded together to the desired length. The end fittings

consisted of machined forgings that were in turn welded to the tube.

(b) Lengths of sheet were wrapped on a former and seam welded. The resulting tubes were stretch formed and welded together as for method (a).

Figures 3.9 and 3.10 Left: Making a longitudinal weld using an automatic welding head running on a track parallel to the joint line. Right: Working on the stretch forming process.

(Parsons (1993), p.20)

---

[57] Hemphill (1957), *"Raven" Motor* report. For information on later improvements in the fabrication of rocket motor cases, see the three articles in the *Journal of the British Interplanetary Society*, Vol.20 No.5 (January-February 1965), pp.7-29.

Figure 3.11 Heat treatment of a Raven rocket motor case at Banwell, using a cylindrical oven installed in the pit shown in Figure 3.8.
(Parsons (1993), p.33)

The latter method of construction was encouraged because it was a more flexible technique, and could be useful for future larger diameter motors, such as might be required for Polaris.[58] However, at first there were some procurement problems:

> …when the Skylark project was getting under way, the country was still suffering from the effects of World War II. One of these was a steel shortage. Bristol Aerojet had to go to Eastern Europe in search of the right steel for

the motor case and were triumphant in finding one billet. Then they found that nowhere in the UK was there rolling equipment wide enough to thin a plate of steel to their requirement. Again they went to Eastern Europe.[59]

After fabrication, the cases were heat treated to ensure they remained straight and circular rather than becoming bowed and oval. Finally, items such as the fin-mounts were fitted to the outside.

---

[58] Harlow in 2001, CCBH (2005), *Skylark Sounding Rockets 1957-1972* p.67, & *Prospero* No.2, p.131. (Polaris was a US submarine launched nuclear delivery missile also fitted to specially built Royal Navy submarines).
[59] Dorling in 2001, CCBH (2005), p.62, & *Prospero* No.2, p.127.

Figure 3.12 Rocket cases in the main production hall at Banwell in the 1960s.
(Parsons (1993), p.26)

Filling the Raven cases

Once completed, the Raven rocket motor cases were originally sent to RPE at Westcott for the propellant to be added.

> Westcott had [recently] completed work on a large facility for producing plastic (uncured polymeric binder) composite solid propellants for boost and sustainer systems.[60]

The propellant was a plastic composition containing ammonium perchlorate, ammonium picrate and a polymeric hydrocarbon. This was injected into the case under vacuum at a temperature of about 60°C, and a former of the required "star" cross-section pressed into the charge and withdrawn after a "dwell" period. This gave the desired axial conduit – a seven-pointed star – and at the same time caused the propellant to bond to the walls of the motor tube.[61]

The star shaped conduit was designed to present a constant surface area for combustion, thereby ensuring even thrust when firing. This 'axial burning' (rather than from one end) also meant that the unburnt propellant helped reinforce the case.

After proof tests, the motor burning time was adjusted by machining the graphite throat of the expansion nozzle. Ignition

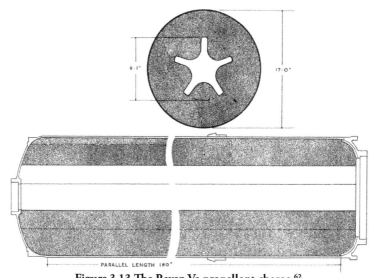

Figure 3.13 The Raven Va propellant charge.[62]

---

[60] Harlow (1992a), 'A History of the Early Solid Propellant Motors of Royal Ordnance plc Rocket Motors Division', p.1
[61] Hemphill (1957), *"Raven" Motor* report, RAE Westcott, (TNA: PRO document file AVIA 48/107).
[62] RPE Westcott (1961), *Solid Motor Data Sheet for Raven Va*, figure 2.

was by means of 150 grams of a standard pyrotechnic composition contained in a metallic housing screwed to into the head end closure of the motor.[63] An apparent variation was 300 grams of a standard composition, for which "There are no electrical connections for the igniter, which is itself fired by a separate primer unit which can be screwed in immediately before firing.[64]

ROF Bridgewater

In later years, Raven motors were filled at the Royal Ordnance factory at Bridgewater in Somerset:

Static testing

Stan Green – who was what I guess you might call a senior ballistician at Westcott at the time, although he was a lot more than that – relates the story that with the

first Raven motor they were so worried about the performance and capabilities that they produced the motor just with a one inch thick web around the outside and fired that for maybe two seconds, just to see if the case would stand up to it. And it did, so we then went forward with the first charge design with the full one ton.[65]

During development, test firing had not been without its problems:

At that time the rear-end forging of the motor was not insulated, and after about two-thirds of the expected burning time, the rear-end forging burnt through. The end of the motor was ejected and combustion ceased immediately so that it was possible to examine the remainder of the charge. Subsequent motors have had their rear-end insulated and a considerable number of firings have been completed without further trouble.[66]

Figures 3.14, 3.15 and 3.16 Top left: the fuel mixture to be inserted into the motor case. Right: For safety, filling was carried out by remote control. Bottom left: a filled case being moved so the filling can be pressed into the correct shape.
(BAC film (1967/68), *Skylark: Sounding Space*)

[63] Hemphill (1957), *"Raven" Motor* report, RAE Westcott, (TNA: PRO document file AVIA 48/107).
[64] *Progress report on the 'Raven' Motor*, dated December 1956, (TNA: PRO document file AVIA 48/107).
[65] Harlow in 2001, CCBH (2005), *Skylark Sounding Rockets 1957-1972*, p.58, & *Prospero* No.2, p.122.
[66] Hemphill (1957), *"Raven" Motor* report.

Type	Propellant	Total impulse	Charge weight	Initial thrust	Used on
Raven I	RD 2332	325,000 lb sec (1446 kN sec)	1850 lb (839 kg)	5,000 lbf (22.2 kN)	SL01
Raven IIA	"	"	1787 lb (811 kg)	10,000 lbf (44.4 kN)	SL02
Raven IA	RD2402	345,000 lb sec (1535 kN sec)	1853 lb (841 kg)	8,000 lbf (35.6 kN)	SL03,04,06
Raven II	"	"	1846 lb (837 kg)	12,000 lbf (54.4 kN)	SL05

Table 3.1 The early Raven motor variants.

(Data from Dorling (1959), p.9)

The first static firing was made in September 1956, but didn't meet the specification, and a re-design of the charge shape was begun at once to correct the low initial thrust. (The pressure must have been on in many ways, as Skylark was due to be fired in Australia in November!) Various propellants were also tried, resulting in four different versions being used on the first six Skylark flights.

To avoid delays in waiting for these modifications, Skylark 01 was fired with a Raven I motor. Raven II incorporated both the new propellant and modified charge shape, and in this form exceeded the requirement. The motor was used in this form for the first six years or so, until superseded by later improvements.

Fin Assemblies and other parts

The nose cones, parallel portions, fins and internal structure were manufactured by Hudswell Clarke Ltd. in Leeds, under an extension of the original CTV 5 contracts.[67]

Figures 3.17, 3.18 and 3.19 A Raven motor being batch tested at RPE Westcott.

(BAC film (1967/68), *Skylark: Sounding Space*)

---

[67] RAE GW Dept. (1958), *A Brief Review of the C.T.V.5 Series III Programme*, p.2.

The original GW 22 fins

It had been found convenient to use CTV.5 Series I 35-inch [90 cm] fins on the first six Skylarks. They were available, proven in flight, and gave ample stability margin, but being larger and more solidly constructed than necessary they were a little heavy.[68] (It is this version that is shown on the first Skylark diagram in this chapter).

The fins themselves were riveted to a casting that was slipped over and then fastened to the motor case. The total weight of this original GW 22 fin assembly was 145 lb (66 kg),[69] slightly more than the 120lb originally estimated.[70]

However, these too were not without their manufacturing problems:

> …we had great difficulties in keeping them [the fins] at the alignments…Even Clark[e]s, they did a very good job, but it was very difficult with a ribbelywoppely skin and things like that. Also the castings for supporting the fins, they were quite a problem, sorting those out. Even the people at Stirling Metals that did the castings at the time were having difficulty. We were fortunate in RAE in having our own foundry and the chap in charge of it was going up and down sorting out some of those problems. The whole fin assembly was rather difficult and we had to keep trying.[71]

Lighter GW 24 fins

Soon a new 29-inch (74 cm) fin was designed, and flight-tested on Skylark 05. The construction was similar, but lightened wherever possible. At 87 lb (40 kg), the weight of this fin assembly was 30% less than the previous version. These later versions of Skylark appeared as shown in figure 3.20.

In later years the weight and drag of the fins was reduced further; by 1970, it was found possible to reduce the weight by an additional 4.5 kg (10 lb), and the drag by 10%. The nose cone, which was a geometrical cone and not the optimum secant ogive form, also came under survey at the same time but it was still found that the engineering difficulties inherent in producing such a shape would not justify a drag reduction of less than 4%.[73]

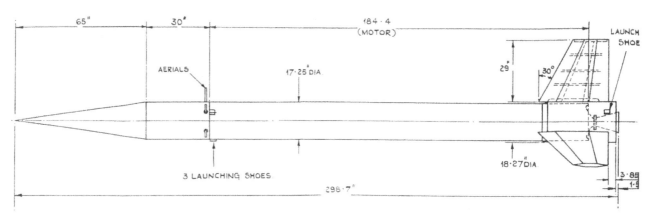

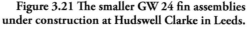

Figure 3.20 Skylark with the new GW 24 fin assembly.
(Hazell (1961), figure 1) [72]

**Figure 3.21 The smaller GW 24 fin assemblies
under construction at Hudswell Clarke in Leeds.**
('Flight' magazine, 6 July 1967, p.33)

[68] Dorling (1959), *The First Six Skylark Firings*, p.10. (RAE Farnborough Technical Note GW 530).
[69] Dorling (1959), p.19.
[70] Dawton (1955), *Performance Estimates for a Single Stage Upper Atmosphere Research Vehicle Powered by a Solid Fuel Rocket Motor*, p.5. (RAE Technical Memo GW 387).
[71] Spurr in 2001, CCBH (2005), *Skylark Sounding Rockets 1957-1972*, p71, & *Prospero* No.2, p.135.
[72] RAeS Journal Vol.65 (August 1961), p.526. Reproduced by kind permission of The Royal Aeronautical Society's Aeronautical Journal.
[73] Lewis (1972), 'Recent Developments in the Skylark Sounding Rocket', pp.179-180.

Instrumentation

As described in the next chapter, Skylark would be tracked in flight by various ground based optical instruments, but it also required two types of electronic instrumentation that had to be built into the vehicle itself.

The first type was for tracking, needed 'as standard' on all Skylarks, to meet both Woomera range operational needs and that of experimenters. The second type was telemetry provided for particular purposes, such as RAE proving trials or university experiments. Fortunately, Skylark was able to utilise instrumentation already developed for military missile use.

Missile Tracking System (MTS)

The Missile Tracking System had been developed to help solve the problem of tracking long-range military missiles at Woomera, a task for which the radar equipment of the time lacked range and accuracy. The MTS used a radar beacon installed in the missile concerned, which provided an extra strong signal for modified radar equipment to track.

The radar beacon was a simple reliable one-valve transmitter generating a CW (Continuous Wave) signal on the C-band (6-centimetre wavelength). It was small, light, economical on power, and unlike the multi-valve transponders then used on aircraft, would fit into most of the missiles fired at Woomera.[74]

On Skylark, the MTS beacon was carried in the intermediate strong ring, (located between the nose cone and the first bay), with wave-guides brought out to the maximum diameter and pressurised with mica diaphragms. (In SL02 and onwards the dielectric aerials were of PTFE instead of Perspex, to avoid trouble caused by aerodynamic heating).

On the ground, the MTS equipment used the dishes from a wartime No.3 Mk 7 anti-aircraft radar system. As the dishes automatically tracked the beacon, the elevation and azimuth angles were recorded in two ways. Firstly, for long-term use, at each radar station the scales were photographed in the light of a strobe lamp flashing four times a second, the film being developed and read back at the Woomera base at Salisbury.

Secondly, in a real time system installed at Range E (where Skylark was launched), coded data was transmitted by landline from each station to a central point (the instrumentation building), where the angular data was processed by an analogue computer which worked out, by triangulation, the co-ordinates of the missile. This information was passed to plotting tables that drew the height and plan position of the missile whilst still in flight, thus making the flight path immediately available to those in charge of the firing.

The Doppler transponder

A second sort of tracking instrument carried in all the early Skylarks was the 'Doppler transponder'. The receiving and transmitting aerials it used were 10 inch (25 cm) high tensile steel blades carried by the rear strong ring, and can be seen on many Skylark drawings and photographs.

The Doppler ground based equipment transmitted a 104 MHz signal to the vehicle, and received a 208 MHz signal back from its transponder. It could then work out the instantaneous velocity, using the Doppler Effect, in the same way as today's police radar speed equipment. In the early 1960's digital computers were introduced which could calculate position as well as velocity, but various inaccuracies meant that the Doppler transponder system never lived up to its early promise.[75]

Telemetry

The second type of instrumentation, Radio telemetry, was used to transmit live measurements from instruments onboard Skylark to ground stations. This was an essential feature, especially in the early days, as before the parachute recovery system was introduced the vehicle head was mostly destroyed on impact. Skylark utilised one of the standard telemetry systems used by the RAE, the 'Type 465', which had been developed by the SRDE (Signals Research and Development Establishment) at Christchurch in the UK. (It had for instance been used on the CTV.5 Series II test vehicles.[76])

This system sampled 24 channels[77] of data in turn and transmitted them to ground via a single 465 MHz radio link. The principle of operation was standard enough, but whereas in later versions the channels would be sampled and combined into one channel electronically, in the original equipment an electric motor was used to rotate a mechanical commutator to sample the 24 signals of interest. The channel sampling rate could be set between 40 and 120 per second - one of the development problems was working out how fast the miniature mechanical commutators could rotate and still have a reasonable life – 'reasonable' in this context meaning at least ten minutes!

The telemetry system used a pair of 8-inch (203 mm) steel blade radio aerials, for carried for structural reasons on the same rear strong ring as the Doppler transponder aerials.[78]

[74] Morton (1989), *Fire across the Desert*, p.292.
[75] Morton (1989), *Fire across the Desert*, p.291.
[76] Dawton *et al.* (1959), *The Technique of Kinetic Heating Measurement in Rocket Test Vehicles*, p.1. (RAE Farnborough Technical Note GW 509).
[77] Strictly speaking 23 channels of data and one synchronising channel.
[78] Dorling (1959), *The First Six Skylark Firings*, p.11.

Until 1956, all the telemetry information at Woomera had been recorded on film from the front of oscilloscopes, and reading and decoding the data was a long and tedious process.

It is extraordinary now to think that from rocket flights in those early days all that came to us were paper records. There were no computers, and only the simplest machines to help us. Instead, there was a room full of girls working on long rolls of photographic paper to predetermined instructions, taking off measurements of interest.[79]

However, by the time Skylark was first launched in 1957, magnetic tape recorders had been introduced, and various methods of advanced automatic data extraction were carried out by WRE at their Salisbury base near Adelaide. The final product was a printout of columns of figures of calibrated data.

The T5 sender

For use on Skylark, a contract was arranged with EMIED[80] Ltd. of Feltham, Middlesex, for the production of a unit combining these three standard electronic systems. It thus comprised a 465 MHz telemetry sender, a Doppler transponder, an MTS oscillator, and associated power supplies. It was known as the T5 sender, and was first used on Skylark 04:

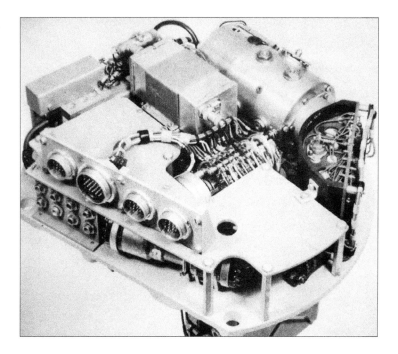

Figure 3.22 The original Skylark T5 telemetry sender (less MTS unit), as used in Skylark 04 onwards.
(Dorling (1959), figure 26)

Figure 3.23 Left: This view of the T5B version of the telemetry sender was photographed by the author at the Science Museum, Wroughton, some 50 years after the picture above was taken! It shows the sturdy construction of the 'electronics' used at the time.
(Science Museum object 1974-307, author 100_5005) [81]

79 Dorling in 2001, CCBH (2005), *Skylark Sounding Rockets 1957-1972*, p.77, & *Prospero* No.2 p.140. For an interview with one of the original female computers (Mary Whitehead), see *Prospero* No.1, p.19.
80 EMI Engineering Development Ltd.
81 Image taken at the London Science Museum (Wroughton), permission granted by Science & Society Picture Library.

Figure 3.24 Left: The serial number label of the T5B sender shown in Figure 3.23 above.
(Science Museum object 1974-307, author 100_5002) [82]

Figures 3.25 and 3.26 General and close-up views of a "Skylark telemetry ground station" receiving set, part of the "Type 465" telemetry system.
(Science Museum object 1981-875, author 100_5007 and 100_5008) [83]

On the ground, telemetry signals were received from Skylark by a corresponding cabinet of equipment. The 'Type 465' telemetry system was so called because it originally used a radio frequency of 465 MHz. In later years the frequency was changed, for instance the Skylark version shown here is labelled '455 Mc/s [MHz] Telemetry Test Set', but the general "465 Tele" name stuck.[84] (See Figure 12.26 for a view including this type of equipment in use).

Priming equipment

The 'Priming' equipment was another necessity that had to be designed and built. This test facility was used to power up and check Skylarks, both in the UK, and again before launch in Australia. Sets were constructed for use at the RAE, Salisbury and at Woomera. For range use at Woomera, a transportable set was built for operation in the preparation room or at the launcher, and a remote unit with a limited number of operations for the monitor room. (See Figure 12.26). The priming set provided 96 connections into the vehicle, with lines to supply external electrical H.T and L.T. voltages, to meter currents and voltages, and to carry out operations such as switching to internal supplies. Cooling air facilities were also incorporated.[85]

[82] Image taken at the London Science Museum (Wroughton), permission granted by Science & Society Picture Library.
[83] Photographs taken at the London Science Museum (Wroughton), permissions granted by Science & Society Picture Library.
[84] For an introduction to '465 Telemetry' see Everest (2006), 'An Armourer at Farnborough', p.19, and for greater depth Mallett *et al.*(1965), *Bramble, an Automatic Processing System for Telemetry Data*. See also Morton (1989), *Fire across the Desert*, p.309, for a good summary.
[85] Dorling (1959), *The First Six Skylark Firings*, p.11.

Figure 3.27 "Skylark priming plus power packs".
(Science Museum object no. 1981-873, author, 100_5009).[86]

A two pin snatch plug was provided, which pulled away as the rocket was launched, this enabled internal power supplies to be turned off if the firing was stopped after the main connection had been removed.

The launch tower

The use of launch towers for sounding rockets had been pioneered in the USA. For example, back in 1946-47, the early WAC Corporal experimental rocket had used a three-rail launching tower that was 100 feet high. The purpose of the tower was to keep the rocket steady until it had achieved sufficient speed for stability.[87] Similarly, the later Aerobee sounding rockets originally used a 50-foot tower.

Skylark was subject to the same limitations, the low acceleration of the original single stage version meant that when fired it would take a relatively long time before the guidance fins could take effect. Thus, the 80-foot launch tower came into being.

Some basic calculations for the first Skylark launch (SL01) indicate that this length of 80 feet (24.4 metres) mean that Skylark would clear the tower travelling at about 96 mph (140 feet/sec / 43 metres/sec)[88] after 1.1 seconds. The initial acceleration would only have been about 4g, giving the instruments a relatively easy ride.

The design of the launcher began late in 1955 [November]; the shortage of steel was largely overcome by incorporating steel Bailey bridge units into the structure. To enable adjustments to be made to the angular setting of the launcher as near as possible to the moment of launch, the 80 ft [24.4 metre] launching tower was designed to be supported on gimbals in a frame resting on three legs. The launcher was completed at the R.O.F. [Royal Ordnance Factory] Woolwich in April 1956, and was ready for use in Australia in November 1956. In late 1958, the length of the tower was increased to 100ft. [30.5 metres].[89]

The use of Bailey bridge units is interesting. The Bailey bridge was a portable pre-fabricated truss bridge design first used in 1943 during WW II. It was based on a modular concept, and could be assembled by army personnel on site to the size required. Some sources have suggested that using Bailey bridge parts in this way was an economy measure,[90] but steel was in short supply in Britain after the war, so using material in this way had more to do with availability than economy:

> There was an appalling steel shortage after the war and this was exacerbated by the relaxing of wartime building constraints in 1951. It was therefore decided that the launcher should be fabricated from redundant Bailey bridge sections. The design was done by the GW Drawing Office at Farnborough, and the construction at the Woolwich Arsenal.[91]

[86] Photograph taken at the London Science Museum (Wroughton), permission granted by Science & Society Picture Library.
[87] See for instance *www.designation-systems.net/dusrm/app1/rtv-g-1.html*, last accessed August 2014.
[88] This compares with an early estimated figure of 120 ft/sec assuming a 60-foot tower, Dawton (1955), p.7, and a 150 ft./sec figure for the 100-foot tower. (Hazell (1961), p.527).
[89] Dorling (1959), *The First Six Skylark Firings*, pages 8 and 18. (RAE Farnborough Technical Note GW 530).
[90] Morton (1989), *Fire across the Desert*, p.398.
[91] Bryan Day, personal correspondence, May 2009.

Shipping all the hardware to Australia was a major task and a special section in GW Department under Ken Porter was responsible for making the arrangements. Fortunately, it was safely shipped to Australia before the Suez incident.[92]

The tower's angular setting was designed to provide deviations of +15° to -5° in elevation, and of ±10° in azimuth, in order to allow for wind effects. Movement was carried out by remotely operated electric motors, and reading scales indicated the launcher setting.[93]

The tower had three vertical parallel rails to guide the rocket. Shoes were mounted on the body of the rocket to act as guides, and the fins fitted between the rails.

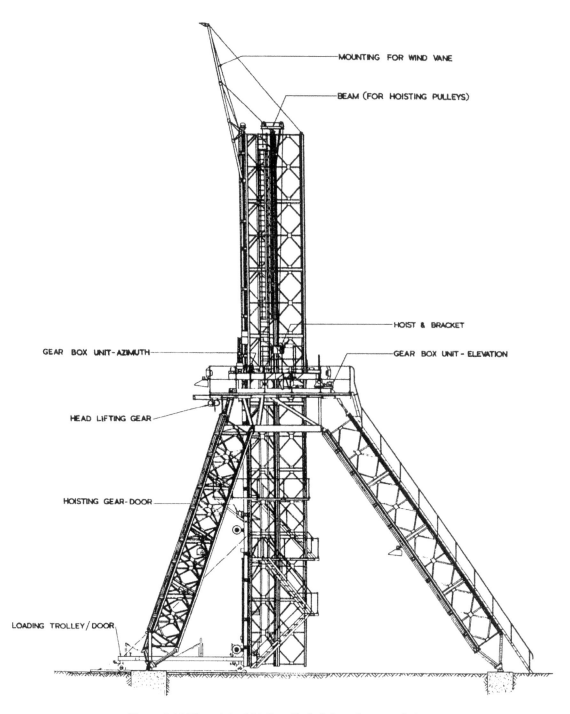

Figure 3.28 The original 80-foot Skylark launch tower design.
(Dorling (1959), figure 11)

[92] Stephens (1958), 'British Upper Atmosphere Sounding Rocket', p.28. During the 'Suez incident', the Suez Canal was closed from the end of October 1956 until March 1957.
[93] Dorling (1959), p.18.

Skylark was unusual in having three guidance fins rather than four. This came about after a fact-finding visit to the USA in 1955,[94] during which it was realised that the American Aerobee sounding rocket was similar in size to the proposed CTV.5 Series 3. Hence, it would be possible to bring the US and UK launcher designs into complete conformity. At the same time work in the UK was showing that a triangular cross section was desirable for the launcher beam. During the visit, the Americans agreed to make the Fort Churchill launcher[95] take a 17-inch diameter CTV.3, and the British agreed to design their launcher so it could take an Aerobee 15 inches in diameter.

The thinking was that the ability to interchange vehicles between Fort Churchill and Woomera could be very useful in the future.[96] In the event, no Skylarks were launched in North America, although attempts to sell it to NASA in 1992 might have been successful.[97] The only use the author knows of the use of the Skylark launcher by a North American sounding rocket is the launch of a Canadian Black Brant in November 1976, (see Chapter 14).

The Aberporth Launch Tower

As noted above, by November 1956 the Skylark launch tower had been erected at Woomera. In November 1957, this was followed by a second, 100-foot tower, erected at the RAE Aberporth base in Wales,[100] where at the end of the month it was viewed by the Duke of Edinburgh.[101] (See Chapter 5).

Figure 3.29 The ancestor of the Skylark launch tower? This vertical test chamber, 56 ft. high, was built after WWII at Cuxhaven in Germany for 'Operation Backfire'.[98] It is said to have been constructed out of a military Bailey bridge.[99]

(Cameron (1946), Volume 2, p.8)

---

[94] Parker and Smith (1955), *Note on a visit to USA in June 1955*, (RAE Technical note RPD 134).

[95] Fort Churchill was a sounding rocket launch site established in 1954 near Hudson Bay in Canada; afterwards it was used intermittently by the Canadians and Americans.

[96] Parker and Smith (1955), p.5.

[97] Harlow in 2001, CCBH (2005), *Skylark Sounding Rockets 1957-1972*, & *Prospero* No.2, p.147.

[98] Cameron (1946), *Report on Operation BACKFIRE*, Volume 3, page 8.

[99] "The Canadians had succeeded in constructing a vertical checkout stand for the launch system made from sections of a military Bailey bridge in two weeks." *www.v2rocket.com/start/chapters/backfire.html* , last accessed August 2014.

[100] Dorling (1959), *The First Six Skylark Firings*, p.18.

[101] 'Flight' magazine, 6 December 1957 p.8. See Chapter 5 of this book for photographs of the visit.

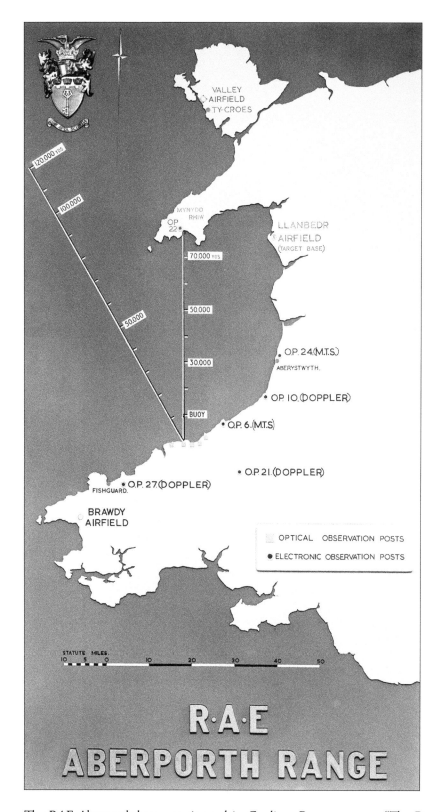

Figure 3.30 The location and extent of the Aberporth range on the Welsh coast, c.1957.
(© Crown Copyright. Imperial War Museums (ABRP 2029-1))

The RAE Aberporth base was situated in Cardigan Bay on the Welsh coast, and had been used for missile testing since WWII, the missiles sometimes directed at pilotless target drones (later the remote controlled Jindivik) flown from the RAE outstation at Llanbedr, some 50 miles (80km) up the coast.

"The Bay itself forms a great arc on the West coast of Wales, facing across the Irish Sea to Ireland, only about one hundred and fifty kilometres [90 miles] distant. The whole arrangement was a sort of Woomera-by-the-Sea, but with vastly more stringent geographical constraints, dictating that all operations had to be carried out over water."[102]

[102] Taylor (2000), *Flights of Fancy,* p.43.

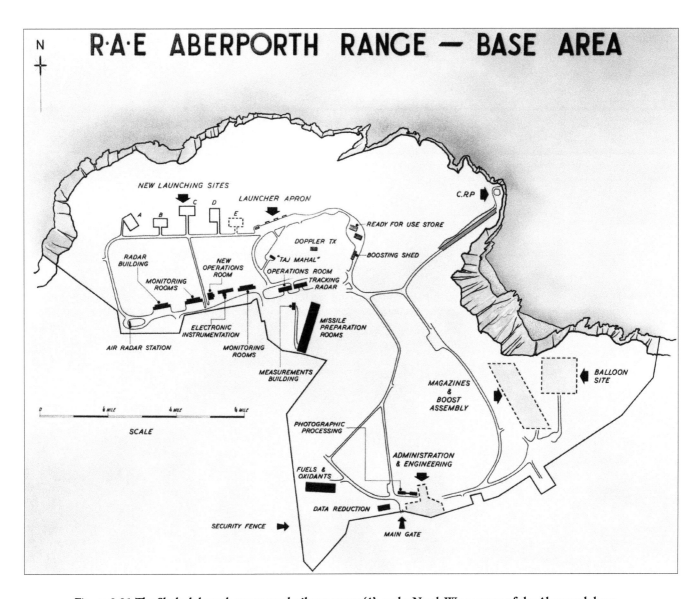

Figure 3.31 The Skylark launch tower was built on apron 'A', at the North West corner of the Aberporth base.

(© Crown Copyright. Imperial War Museums (ABRP 2028-1))

 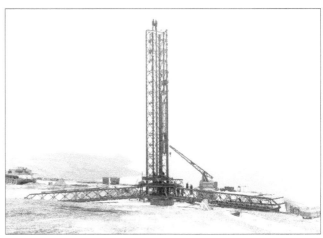

Figures 3.32, 3.33 and 3.34 Left: Assembly of the Skylark launch tower on a bleak looking Monday the 11th November 1957. Right: Progress by Friday 15th, with two brave workers standing on top!

(© Imperial War Museums (ABRP 1379 & 1388))

Figures 3.35 and 3.36 The tower legs were raised into position on Saturday 16th November by a pulley arrangement powered by the tracked vehicle shown on the left of the lower photograph.

(© Imperial War Museums (ABRP 1393 & 1394))

Figure 3.37 The tower legs in the final position, (Saturday 16/11/1957).

(© Imperial War Museums (ABRP 1397))

Figure 3.38 The "Skylark Monitoring Room" at Aberporth. Although the Aberporth launch tower was never to be used,[103] there were Skylark launches at Aberporth in 1971 and 1972 to test transportable single rail launchers. (See Chapter 12).

(© Crown Copyright. Imperial War Museums (ABRP 1656-01))

(This series of photographs has been reproduced from the original glass negatives of the Imperial War Museum DERA Aberporth collection, retrieved from Duxford after research by IWM staff.)

---

[103] Although towards the end of 1958, it was still anticipated that flights with an altitude limited to 60 miles (97 km) would be possible. (Massey (1958), *Memorandum on Rocket Research*, p.2).

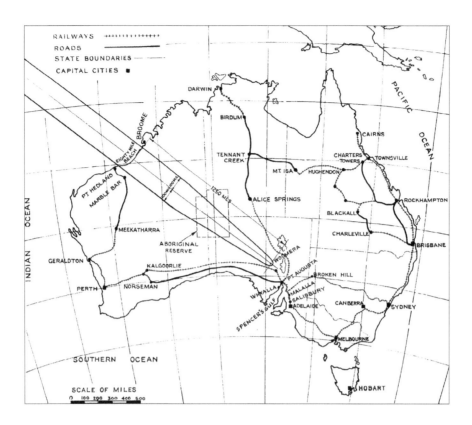

Figure 4.1 This 1949 map shows how the Woomera rocket range was planned to extend 1250 miles (2012 km) across Australia, with the option of continuing across the Indian Ocean.[1]

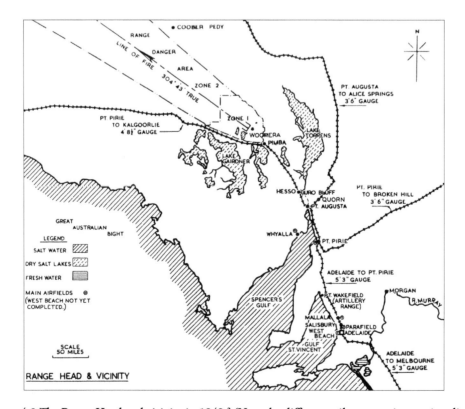

Figure 4.2 The Range Head and vicinity in 1949.[2] (Note the different rail gauges, since rationalised!)

---

[1]   Department of Supply and Development (DoSD), Commonwealth of Australia (1949), *The Joint United Kingdom – Australia Long Range Weapons Project in Australia,* p.2.

[2]   Ibid, p.3.

CHAPTER 4

(1957-58)

WOOMERA

A very convenient rocket range

Skylark and the Woomera rocket range were made for each other.

As mentioned in Chapter 1, Woomera was the very large land based experimental rocket range set up in 1947 under a "Joint Agreement" between the British and Australian governments. The UK did have its own missile range at Aberporth, near Cardigan in Wales, but this was a relatively small sea range, and it was not possible to recover expended parts or payloads. Therefore, despite being on the other side of the world from Britain, Woomera was the obvious choice as the original launch site for Skylark.

The establishment of the Woomera range is worthy of a book in its own right.[3] It had survived a temporary set back in 1947, when British post war enthusiasm for long-range missiles met economic and technical reality, and it was realised that the "Menace" and "Hammer" V-1 and V-2 equivalents couldn't be produced as anticipated.[4] (Menace was cancelled in 1947, all work on its large diameter (36") ramjet propulsion units was stopped, and the programme lapsed[5]). However the Woomera range survived, priorities were reset, and the bomb ballistic range was the first facility to come into use. By the time the Skylark project arrived in 1956, a considerable amount of military missile work had been undertaken, although Skylark became the rocket with the longest range tested until then.

Overview

The vast size of the Woomera range can be seen from the map opposite, the region chosen because of its remoteness, dry climate and clear atmosphere. The location was initially suggested and surveyed in 1947 by Len Beadell, who became well known throughout Australia from the talks he gave and the books he wrote about his experiences – he was regarded by many as the "last true Australian Explorer". His book of his Woomera surveying activities, "Still in the Bush",[6] makes fascinating reading. It describes his labours in deriving longitude and latitude from the stars, and exploring land beyond the most distant sheep stations, millions of square miles never before visited by white people:

> "We're looking for someone to start some sort of rocket range er...or something." Len Beadell cheerfully accepted the challenge in this apparently casual remark and thus began his involvement in what was to become a multi-billion dollar weapons testing project in the Australian outback - the Woomera Rocket Range.
>
> Laden with trig poles, theodolites – and porridge – Beadell and his team built roads, laid out town sites and undertook an enormous survey programme in order to prepare a test launching area in one of the most isolated parts of the world. The problems ranged from taking astrofixes in a cloudy sky and becoming surrounded by a sea of red mud, to patching a bald spot on a pet joey.[7]

The region was an arid desert-like area,[8] consisting mainly of a red sandstone surface stained with iron oxide, covered in rock fragments and pebbles called 'gibber', an aboriginal word. In the absence of defined watercourses, floods from the very occasional torrential rains spread over miles of country, distributing gravel mixed with sand. When blown by the wind the sand polished the gibber stones, resulting in a varnished appearance.[9] Animal and bird life included kangaroos, desert marsupial rats, wallabies, dingoes, emus, brush turkeys, parrots and galahs. After the range was established, it was said:

---

[3]   Len Beadell (1975), *Still in the Bush,* provides a good start, as does Morton (1989), *Fire across the Desert.*
[4]   Morton (1989), *Fire across the Desert,* p.31 and Chapter 1 of this book.
[5]   Harlow (1998), 'Sustainer propulsion for the UK air defence weapons – The early history'.
[6]   Beadell (1975), *Still in the Bush.*
[7]   Promotional material for 'Still in the Bush' - *www.beadell.com.au/our-products.html* (last accessed August 2014).
[8]   An 'arid' region is defined as having less than 250 mm (10 inches) of annual rainfall.
[9]   Australian DoSD (1949), *The Joint UK – Australian Long Range Weapons Project in Australia,* p.5.

Figure 4.3 Typical bush countryside near Woomera. The tall bushes are Mulga, a small tree native to the arid outback areas of Australia.

(National Archives of Australia: A6135, K11/10/74/130)

There was plenty of wildlife if one looked for it, particularly several types of lizard up to a metre or so long, although most were much smaller. The village boys made a speciality of carrying these creatures around in their shirts, notably to frighten little girls with. There were also kangaroos a plenty as well as the ubiquitous rabbit; almost in plague proportion in some areas.[10]

Despite this unpromising terrain, good seasons could produce grass "as if responding to the wave of a magician's wand",[11] and the territory west and north-west of Woomera carried sheep on some sixteen or more large sheep stations averaging 700 square miles (448,000 acres / 181,000 hectares) each. However, the total population in the first 250 miles of the immediate range was under 200.

Construction

The construction of the rocket range was a huge undertaking, the Australian contribution alone amounting to £ (A) 26 million for the first five years.[12] The total workforce engaged in rangehead construction was approximately 2,300,[13] plus 300 men engaged on the fresh water pipe line, which ran 280 miles from the River Murray.[14]

Figures 4.4 and 4.5 Woomera's main civilian construction camp, and part of the 280 mile (450 km) fresh water supply pipeline.[15]

---

[10]   Taylor (2000), *Flights of Fancy*, p.112.
[11]   Australian DoSD (1949), *The Joint UK – Australian Long Range Weapons Project in Australia*, p.5.
[12]   Australian DoSD (1949), Introduction. The equivalent figure would be at least 20 times that in today's terms (2014), i.e. $(A)1040 million. The original funding arrangements were amazingly informal (Morton (1989), p.17 onwards), and most of the Range infrastructure costs appear to have been borne by Australia. For further details See Morton (1989), p.38; and for the later agreements, Morton (1989), pp.544 and 553.
[13]   Australian DoSD (1949), p.22.
[14]   More accurately, the Woomera pipeline was a 170 km (106 mile) branch off an existing pipeline. (Morton (1989), p.124).
[15]   Australian DoSD (1949), p.23 & p.21.

Figure 4.6 This aerial view of the early bomb ballistic range (Range A) to the north of the Technical Area shows the vast open nature of the region. (The buildings in the foreground housed cameras).[16]

By the time Skylark was first tested, the WPA (Woomera Prohibited Area[17]) extended over a million square miles. This part of South Australia was so vast and empty there was even room to carry out atmospheric nuclear weapon tests. These had taken place at Emu Field and Maralinga, which were 300 miles (480 km) to the west of Woomera Village, and included in the WPA. (The last three major tests occurred at Maralinga in 1957, but associated minor experiments continued until 1963).

Even today (2014), over thirty years after the Joint Agreement ended, and with the range reduced in size, the facility remains one of the world's largest launch sites. The extent of the WPA remains about 127,000 sq km, almost exactly the size of England!

Figure 4.7 shows one of the signs on the edge of the WPA. The upper sign includes the words "A person shall not be in, enter or fly over this prohibited area without proper authorization. Penalty: Imprisonment seven years", and the lower "Whilst this sign is displayed permission is hereby granted the travelling public to use this road <u>at their own risk</u>".

Figure 4.7 This early 1960s photograph of a car parked by a 'Prohibited Area' sign near Woomera captures the spirit of the time.[18]

(Photo - Robin V. F. Smith)

[16]   Australian DoSD (1949), *The Joint UK – Australian Long Range Weapons Project in Australia*, p.52.

[17]   The 'Woomera Prohibited Area' was the name given under the Australian Defence Force regulations to the test range land area. It originally included the nuclear weapons test sites to the west of Woomera itself, and a large 'rocket landing area' in the north west of the country. It still exists today (2014), although reduced in area, and is currently managed under contract by BAE Systems Australia Limited

[18]   Smith, Robin 1960. "Car parked near a 'Prohibited Area' sign, near Woomera, South Australia, 1960-1964 [picture]" / Robin V. F. Smith *http://nla.gov. au/nla.pic-an24114228*.

The component parts of Woomera

'Woomera' was the general name[19] for what was originally termed the 'Long Range Weapons Establishment',[20] which comprised both the rangehead facilities and a separate administration and technical base, 270 miles (430 km) to the south east near Adelaide. By the time Skylark arrived in 1956, the 'rangehead' [21] comprised three main parts: Woomera Village, where most staff and their families lived, a 'Technical Area' with an airfield, just to the north of the village, and the actual missile range (Range E) 28 miles (45 km) to the north west.

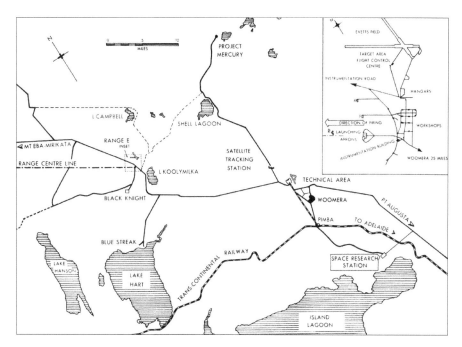

Figure 4.8 The rangehead and surrounding area in 1961, a few years after Skylark arrived. It shows Woomera Village, the Technical Area, and Range E, the actual missile range. (National Archives of Australia: A1200, L38160)

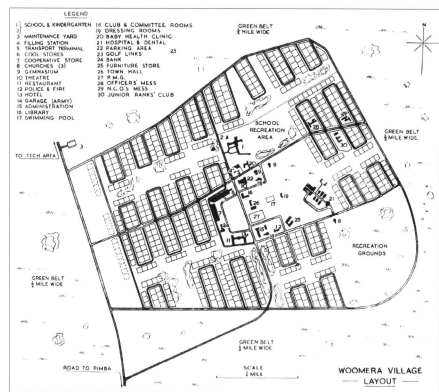

Figure 4.9 The original plan of Woomera Village.[22]

---

[19] Originally intended as the name for the village only, the name "Woomera" was soon used to refer to the Range as a whole. (Morton (1989), p.117).
[20] From 1955 to 1978 the Weapons Research Establishment (WRE). For further details of name changes, see Morton (1989), p.xvi.
[21] As explained here, the term "rangehead" originally referred to all the facilities away from the Salisbury base, but later on, the term came to refer to the Range E missile range/launch area.
[22] Australian DoSD (1949), *The Joint UK – Australian Long Range Weapons Project in Australia*, p.27.

Figure 4.10 Woomera Village in 1993, viewed from the NE. When Skylark arrived in 1956, the population was about 3000. The distant salt lake is Island Lagoon, ten miles away.

(WRE)

Theoretically the Woomera ranges lie a day's walk to the west of the village. In practice, few men could make the distance on foot in the time. That is the point where the main range begins – twenty-five miles west – but it doesn't end until the great beach reaches down into the Indian Ocean. The ocean is almost as far from the rangehead as the shores of the Black Sea are from London, yet not a village or a hamlet lies between. This again is the donga, the country in which they give a man nine hours to live if he runs out of water and can't find shade."[23]

The Missile Range comprised the Launching Zone and Observation Posts, the former including the heavily instrumented Launching Site, supporting airfield, and the local facilities at Koolymilka.

[23] Southall (1962), *Woomera*, p.87.

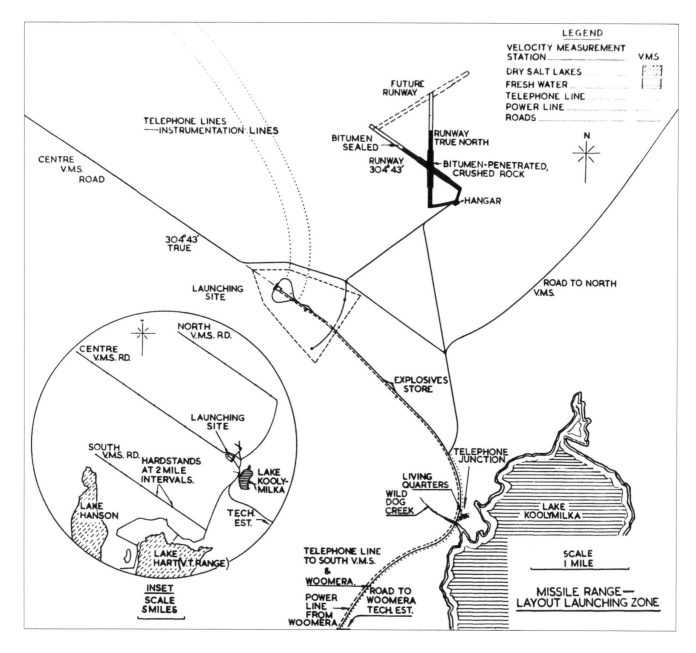

Figure 4.11 The Woomera Missile Range Launching Zone.
(DoSD Australia (1949), p.43)

The facilities at the rangehead changed considerably over the years. For instance, there was originally a bomb ballistic range to the north of the Technical Area, and several sites for testing relatively short-range military missiles. However by the time Skylark arrived all had fallen out of use except for the original Missile Range described above, by then known as Range E.[24] In later years additional launch sites for the larger liquid fuelled rockets were added.

Along the centre line of Range E (the original 'line of fire') were many observation and instrument posts. Most were located within the first 20 miles (30 km), the furthest away regularly used outpost being situated at Mirikata some 105 miles (170 km) downrange. The full 1250-mile (2012 km) capability of the range was not used until 1964 for the test firing of Blue Streak, in its role as first stage of the 'ELDO' satellite launcher.

24   Morton (1989), *Fire across the Desert*, p.261.

Figure 4.12 Mirikata c.1970, a major observation post 105 miles (170 km) downrange.
Two radar dishes and a kinetheodolite can just be made out mounted on the large structure on the left.
(WRE)

The HQ at Salisbury near Adelaide was a substantial facility. The site had originally been constructed as an explosives factory during WWII, and was so large a project that South Australia's entire production of bricks was appropriated for its construction.[25] By the time Skylark arrived, it had expanded to some seven square miles of laboratories, assembly shops and computing facilities, and included the nearby Edinburgh airfield. Here at Salisbury, the administration of Woomera was carried out. The HQ employed several thousand people, the combined total including the Rangehead rising to a peak of 6000 by 1964.[26]

The Australian government agency that managed the Woomera range for most of its operational life was the Weapons Research Establishment (WRE), "...effectively the country's first 'space agency', responsible not only for research and development in many fields of aerospace science and technology, but also managing Australia's international responsibilities in several space-related projects." [27]

The journey to work – the Road to Koolymilka

Except for a few staff living at Koolymilka, those working on the rocket vehicles had to travel daily from Woomera Village to the Launching Zone. In 1962, the journey to work from Woomera Village to Range E was graphically described as follows:[28]

> A roaring procession of giant buses, painted sky-blue, most of them seating about sixty passengers, streams out of Woomera at 7.10 am each day. If there's to be an early firing they might be on the road by four-thirty or five. Unless they are heading south to the Deep Space Instrumentation Facility on the shores of Island Lagoon, all the buses turn first to the north, and even at 7.10 am the air is hot enough for the blinds to be drawn on the eastern side... Near the Technical Area the buses begin to take their separate ways.... To the north of this point lies the Satellite Tracking Station and, still further to the

[25] Morton (1989), *Fire across the Desert*, p.44.
[26] Morton (1989), p.212.
[27] Dougherty (2006), *The Weapons Research Establishment: an Administrative History*, p.1
[28] Southall (1962), *Woomera*, p.93.

north the major installations at Red Lake for the American manned-space projects. For range E, Blue Streak and Black Knight, the buses head west into the red desert, down a long ribbon of bitumen, between the clean perspectives of telegraph poles and power lines. [29]

By day there is no unusual danger on these roads, but by night blue kangaroos and the giant reds, six feet high, loom in the headlights, transfixed by the glare. The careless driver can crash into them, and many kangaroos die. [30]

The first buses in the morning scare the crows away from squashed carcasses, and the ugly birds wheel overhead or shriek from the power lines.

For a few moments, far ahead, the iron rooftops of the rangehead heave up from the horizon and glare like polished silver. They vanish again as the buses roar into a long depression where Lake Koolymilka – a plain of hard clay and salt – dazzles the eyes on the sunny side. Here during the early years the men of Woomera sailed

yachts on a wide stretch of deep salt water, so wide and so deep that the prevailing easterlies and southerlies blew it into loping waves. Then the lake disappeared. In a couple of years it was a sticky mess of mud.

Koolymilka sits in a pocket beside the dry lake. It is hot and stifling...Koolymilka is a satellite village of Woomera. Kooly they call it, a small village with its own mess halls where the entire rangehead staff may eat, its own picture show once or twice a week, its own canteens and bars, and its own resident population – transport drivers, construction workers, cooks and stewards, and Commonwealth police.

The pull out of Koolymilka is steep enough for buses to slow down, even to shudder with a full load. They come over the top, and there's the business end of Woomera … a wide dispersal of buildings large and small, a multitude of strange aerials in the distance, launching towers and towers for observation, a huge airfield for radio controlled targets and service machines, and barring the way a man-proof fence[31] with a large guard-house, and a tall, wide iron gate, shut.

Figure 4.13 The road to Koolymilka.
(National Archives of Australia: A1200, L20772)

---

[29] Southall (1962), *Woomera*, p.91.

[30] Southall (1962), *Woomera*, p.91. "Kangaroos became a particular problem within the enclosed launching site, and a routine was developed to clear them by removing a section of fence, and forming a line of 'beaters' to drive them out". (Geoff Taylor, *Flights of Fancy*, p.122).

[31] Indeed, the launching site fence seems to have existed mainly to keep out kangaroos "It had been a dry summer again, and smelling the water and seeing green grass, every kangaroo within a radius of about 20 km or so had tried to get in. Many had succeeded by forcing their way under the wire or in the case of some of the biggest, jumping over the lower sections". (Taylor (2000), *Flights of Fancy*, p.122).

Figure 4.14 Range E as approached from the east.
(National Archives of Australia: A1500, K12427)

Figure 4.15 The Range E guard post.
(NAA: D874, N61/3437)

"All transport stops….In each bus, as it slows down, the Security policeman inspects every person's pass."[32]

[32]   Southall (1962), *Woomera,* p.95.

At the rangehead [strictly speaking the Launch Site] the biggest structure was the Instrumentation Building, housing the main control, communication and recording equipment for the trials. In front of it were the launching aprons with some fixed launchers and, to the side, the heavily armoured blockhouses of the equipment centres. These housed the monitoring apparatus and power and air supplies. Below ground were the test posts, where the last minute checks of the missiles out on their launchers could be carried out with safety. Behind the instrumentation building lay the test shops where the missiles were prepared after arriving from Salisbury or overseas, and various common facilities: a measurements shop, a liquid fuel and oxidant filling post and a magazine area for storing boosts and explosives.[33]

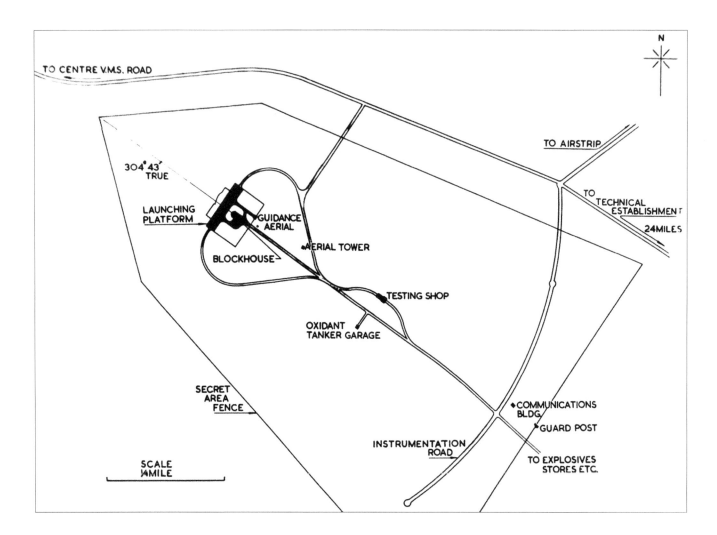

Figure 4.16 The detailed layout of the launching site as originally planned.[34]

[33] Morton (1989), *Fire across the Desert*, p.223.
[34] Australian DoSD (1949), *The Joint UK – Australian Long Range Weapons Project in Australia*, p.44.

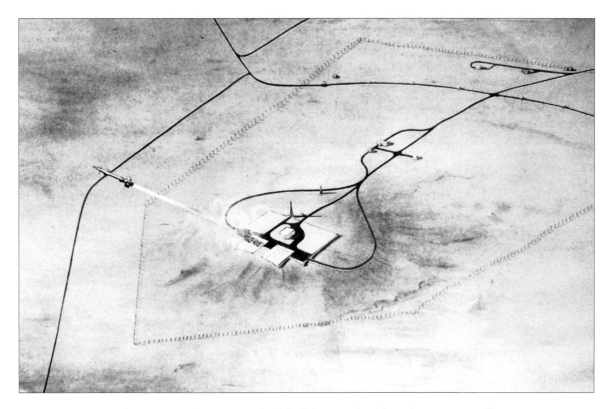

Figure 4.17 An artist's impression (1949) of the completed launch site in action.[35]

Figure 4.18 The launching site as implemented, viewed from the northwest. (The Sun is in the northeast!)
The tall Skylark launch tower is in its original 80-foot state, so this view must be dated 1957-58.
The instrumentation building is on the left in the mid-distance, and dry Lake Koolymilka in
the far distance. The layout is surprisingly close to that originally envisaged.

(WRE)

---

[35] Australian DoSD (1949), *The Joint UK – Australian Long Range Weapons Project in Australia*, p.45.

Beneath the concrete apron, invisible, are the control rooms, forbidden to visitors, where military personnel fire weapons under realistic conditions. Army weapons are fired from a replica of an underground base; naval weapons are fired from the replica of a ship.[36]

The Skylark launches were controlled from a similar underground control room (Equipment Centre 2 / EC2) built into the edge of the concrete apron. (See Figure 9.26 for an external view).

This part of the range is still in active use today (2014), and the launch apron including the distinctive curved road pattern is clearly visible from the air on Google Satellite Maps, and at the time of writing can be directly found at *www. satellite-sightseer.com/id/4753*.[37] This view (inaccurately called Woomera bombing range!) also clearly shows Lake Koolymilka and the airfield; and after zooming in, the in-strumentation and other buildings can be identified. The very technology Woomera was helping to develop has made privacy much more difficult!

The facility known as the Missile Range comprised two parts, the Launching Zone and the Observation Posts. The former included that region near the actual Launching Site that was heavily instrumented, but as can be seen from the map below, the Observation Posts reached out hundreds of miles along the line of fire:

To emphasise the distances involved in the map below, from the launching site to the top left is about 250 miles, nearly the length of England from London to the Scottish border! Further Observation Posts were built as required for longer-range missile projects, (e.g. Blue Streak). Skylark rockets would typically land some 30 to 100 miles (50 to 160 km) downrange.

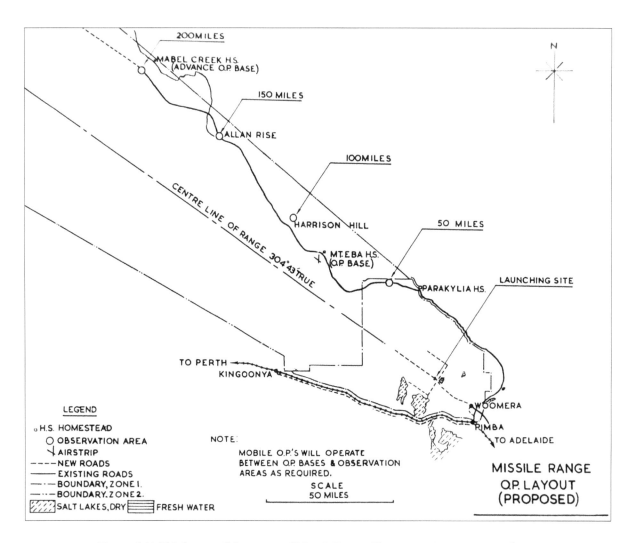

Figure 4.19 This layout of the proposed Missile Range Observation Post positions shows how they came to be distributed hundreds of miles along the line of fire.[38]

---

[36] Southall (1962), *Woomera*, p.110.
[37] *www.satellite-sightseer.com/id/4753* , last accessed August 2014.
[38] Australian DoSD (1949), *The Joint UK – Australian Long Range Weapons Project in Australia*, p.49.

Woomera the laboratory

Woomera was a giant open-air laboratory. Its main purpose was to measure the performance of the missiles and other items under test:

> It is not the firing of the rocket that takes the time or the skill, but the preparation for its measurement.[39] … We can say that the main inputs are the missiles from Britain or Salisbury, and the main outputs are trial data in the form of magnetic tape, paper tape, canisters of film, and the bits we manage to pick up.[40]

Ground based instruments – optical instrumentation

> When I first went to Woomera I was absolutely amazed at the infrastructure that was needed for the tracking and recording of all the data that was taken. That for me was a great surprise.[41]

Some of the facilities were general, some for specific projects. Each Tuesday a trials programme for the coming week was issued from the base at Salisbury, and each trial was allocated a time slot for its activities. "While a user is in his own time slot everything that he needs to conduct his own experiment is at his disposal, but once he's outside that slot, no matter who he is, he's got to accept the sad fact that there are only eight working hours in each day, and all the other range-users are lined up behind him yelling for their share." [42]

Like any laboratory, Woomera had to have instruments to observe measure and record the experiments. Of the quantities being measured, perhaps the most important was trajectory.

One of the reasons Woomera had been chosen for the range in the first place was the excellent visibility. The sky was usually a "dome of flawless blue". On average, the sky was completely overcast for only two or three days a month in summer and five or six in winter. Mornings were usually clearer than afternoons. At 8.30 a.m., the sky was essentially cloudless for 59% of the year. The transparent air and fierce light together gave superb visibility,[43] with an average of nine hours of sunshine a day.

In 1956 when Skylark first arrived, the range had been in operation for nearly ten years. Range E was equipped with two different types of kinetheodolites, an optical tracking instrument that included a recording cine camera, which photographed both the object being tracked and the azimuth and elevation scales of where it was pointing. By using at least two of these instruments and a locked timing system the position of the object at any one moment could be calculated. The tracking was done by operators who became very skilled at the task.

The kinetheodolite had been developed in Germany during the war, and the first ones used at Woomera were the Askania model KTh 41, booty taken by the British after hostilities. However by 1957 these had been replaced by the model KTh 52. Five were fitted at range E, numbered K2 behind the launch aprons to K6 on the right flank 4.5 kilometres away.[44]

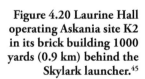

Figure 4.20 Laurine Hall operating Askania site K2 in its brick building 1000 yards (0.9 km) behind the Skylark launcher.[45]

[39] Southall (1962), *Woomera*, p.112.
[40] Southall (1962), p.114.
[41] Zarnecki in 2001, CCBH (2005), *Skylark Sounding Rockets 1957-1972*, & *Prospero* No.2, p.102.
[42] Southall (1962), p.117.
[43] Morton (1989), *Fire across the Desert*, p.267.
[44] Morton (1989), p.269.
[45] Southall (1964), *Rockets in the Desert*, p.29, Southall (1962), *Woomera*, p.129, & Morton (1989), p.269.

Figure 4.21 A twin Contraves kinetheodolite post, down range. After use, a protective shelter on rails was rolled back overhead.[46]
(WRE)

The Contraves kinetheodolite was a more modern and so-phisticated Swiss made instrument, which could measure to 20 seconds of arc. (About 10 metres in 100 km / 62 miles!). It had a power driven servo controlled mount, and could be put under the control of a distant radar, which pointed it in the right direction until the operators spotted the object and took over manually. By 1957, at least seven had been installed at Range E, designated K8 to K14. More were to follow.

A blonde in a blue summer dress and a bespectacled young man seated on opposite sides of the instrument, turned their steering wheels slowly, apparently gazing intently through the kinetheodolite into each other's eyes. In fact one was pivoting the instrument in eleva-tion, the other in azimuth.[47]

The Contraves kinetheodolites were favoured for measuring trajectory. The twin sites were originally installed for short-range military interception trials, where one instrument would track the missile, the other the target. When Skylark arrived, there were four such twin sites, situated from 9 to 28 km (6 to 17 miles) downrange. Later on, more instruments were installed, out to 70 km downrange.[48]

[46] Southall (1962), *Woomera,* p.128.
[47] 'Flight' magazine, December 1963, p.937.
[48] Morton (1989), *Fire across the Desert,* pp.271-72.

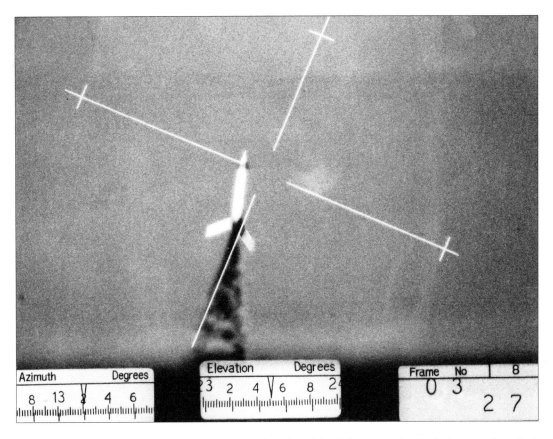

Azimuth   Degrees   Elevation   Degrees   Frame   No   8
8   13   4   6   3   2   4   6   8   2   0   3
                                                                              2   7

Figure 4.22 A Skylark captured on a cine camera frame by a Contraves kinetheodolite. The particular Skylark is not identified, but the shape of the fins, the fact that it is in daylight, and the date of the original record mean it must be one of SL01-03.
(National Archives of Australia: D880, D58/14)

Figure 4.23 One of the 'manned' high-speed cine cameras used at Woomera.
(National Archives of Australia: A1200, L20766 / W.Brindle)

As well as kinetheodolites, various special cine cameras were also used on the range. They all recorded timing pulses on the film to provide precise measurements of when events happened. The most common was the Vinten HS300, used with a 900 mm lens, which could expose up to 250 frames a second. Some were too close to the launchers to be manned, and were automatic, others at a safer distance were manned on tracking mounts to follow and record the flight of missiles.[49]

49 Morton (1989), *Fire across the Desert*, p.273.

Film processing was also required. "Woomera's optical instruments produced great quantities of exposed film, which poured not only from the many and various cameras but also from the telemetry system and in the early years from the Doppler and MTS recorders too. A single trial might produce 5 kilometres [3 miles] or so of 35-millimetre cine film. All of it had to be developed and printed at top speed, as the results were always wanted urgently; yet the films represented a large investment when they were the records of an expensive trial. Many of them were secret".[50] Thus, back at the Salisbury base, a complex film-processing laboratory was created over the years.

Ground based instruments – electronic instrumentation

Strictly speaking, these differed from the optical instruments not because they were electronic, but because they used radio waves rather than visible light to track vehicles or obtain data.[51] For tracking purposes radar was used, as well as the MTS and Doppler systems described in Chapter 3. In addi-

tion, there was a telemetry receiving system for the transmitters on the Skylark vehicle.

Radar had been invented and developed during the war, and when Woomera was founded soon afterwards, it was a relatively new technology. For the first ten years or so, the British 'No.3 Mk 7' set [52] was used. This had been designed late in the war as a mobile S-band (10 cm wavelength) radar for controlling anti-aircraft guns, and its mobile aerial and dish reflector were designed to track aircraft. At Woomera, the sets were used to track missiles instead, but adapted to provide real-time tracking information and with recorders added. They were no match for the optical instruments in terms of accuracy and took longer to lock-on, but once locked they had longer range and were usually able to track up to 90 kilometres (56 miles).

The MTS (Missile Tracking System) was used on range E from 1954 until about 1968. Its operation was described in the previous chapter. Like the kinetheodolites it measured only angles, from which trajectory was calculated, but unlike them, it could do so in real time, i.e. provide results during flight.

Figure 4.24 A tracking radar as originally used at Woomera.
(WRE)

Figure 4.25 MTS ground station P3, complete with a No.3 Mk 7 radar dish on top. P3 was installed at Range E in 1955.
(WRE)

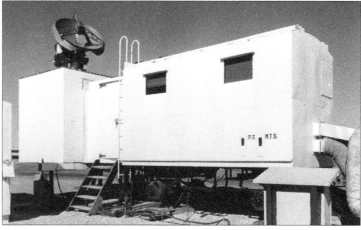

---

[50] Morton (1989), *Fire across the Desert,* p.281.
[51] Morton (1989), p.287.
[52] A web search reveals restoration projects for these radars in both the UK and Australia.

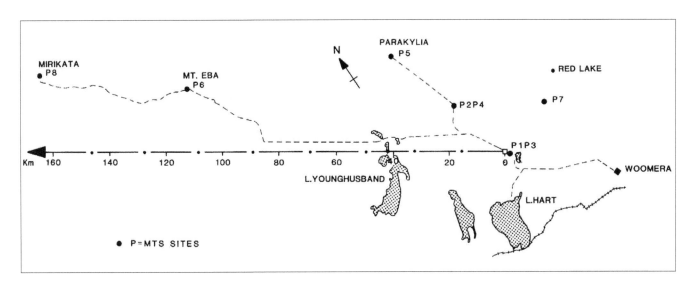

Figure 4.26 The MTS positions P1 to P8. This shows the maximum extent of the system, which at Mirikata was in position only from 1960 to 1962, after which more modern radars took over. The first MTS installations were operational in 1954, but in 1968 (11 years after Skylark arrived) the MTS system was phased out.[53]

As described in the previous chapter, early Skylarks were also fitted with a Doppler transponder. This system was based on a ground based 104 MHz transmitter and 208 MHz receiver, and this too had its own ground based installation at Range E.

Telemetry

Telemetry information from the Skylark type 465 system was received by equipment on the ground floor of the instrumentation building. As noted in the previous chapter, until 1956 all telemetry information had been recorded on film, and reading the many wiggly lines by eye from the lengthy records was a long and tedious process. However, in March 1956 the first fully integrated trials data-processing system was introduced, and the information was recorded on quarter inch magnetic tape. The tapes were sent to Salisbury for processing, where the information was read and processed by the specially designed and built WREDAC computer.

Figure 4.27 A 'Type 465' telemetry equipment installation in 1964.
(WRE)

53 Morton (1989), *Fire across the Desert*, p.293. Map reproduced courtesy Australian DSTO.

Figure 4.28 The telemetry aerials on the instrumentation building were spiral in form, because circular polarisation was used to avoid signal loss from a rotating missile.
(WRE)

The telemetry data was received from Skylark by aerials on the roof of the instrumentation building. In 1957, an improved custom-built self-tracking system was being introduced, which was operational by 1959. This used twelve helix aerials on a modified No.3 Mk 7 radar mount:[54]

The Instrumentation building

The instrumentation building overlooked the Skylark launcher from about two thirds of a mile (1 km) away. The nerve centre for operational purposes was a room where information from the instruments came together and was displayed for safety and navigational purposes, and acquisition data flowed out to instruments down-range to help them find their targets. This room was known at first as the Plotting Room, and later as the Tracking Data Centre.

Figure 4.29 The Instrumentation building at Range E. On the right can be seen the room from which the Trials Control Officer directed operations.[55] The building still exists, and received a major renovation when the Range E facilities were refurbished during 2000-2003.[56]

(WRE)

54   Morton (1989), *Fire across the Desert*, p.308.
55   Southall (1964), *Rockets in the Desert*, p.29.
56   *Gibber Gabber* community magazine 20 April 2007, 60th anniversary supplement.

**Figure 4.30 This unusual view from the roof of the instrumentation building shows the various 'test shops',
workshops to the north east. TS1 (where Skylark was prepared) is in the foreground.**
(WRE)

The 'real-time' information was used for monitoring missiles for safety purposes, or directing trials that involved aircraft. In 1957 when Skylark was introduced, the plotting tables were driven by valve (vacuum tube) based analogue computers, although in time, the equipment was updated considerably. This use of tracking information was separate from the longer term 'off-line' information produced for each trial, the processing of which took place back at the WRE base in Salisbury, using the photographic and magnetic tape records discussed previously.

Bringing Skylark to Woomera

The first Skylark rockets were assembled and tested by the RAE at Farnborough in England, then shipped to Woomera for firing. The first six firings (or 'rounds') were technology-proving flights, without university experiments on board. They were used to prove that the vehicle performed as expected, and to test the range facilities such as the launch tower, telemetry and tracking systems.

Skylark would fly higher and further than any British rocket before, and would be the first to go into space. As with all rocket and guided weapon projects at Woomera, a great deal of planning had to take place. Although each project used existing range facilities as far as possible, any new requirements introduced had to be especially catered for.

Thus, arrangements were made with WRE during 1955 for the firing of Skylark at Woomera, and Planning Specification WRE 155 was issued in December 1955.[57] This in turn was converted into a 'Project Planning Specification' by the planners at Salisbury,[58] which detailed for instance the workshops and test shops that had to be made ready, and covered the erection of the launch tower. New test instruments had to be designed and manufactured, and the accommodation for the scientists who would accompany each rocket from the UK had to be organised. Woomera was operated by Australian not British personnel, and new operational and safety procedures had to be devised and people trained in their use.

[57] Dorling (1959), *The First Six Skylark Firings*, p.7.
[58] Southall (1964), *Rockets in the Desert*, p.51.

One of the important sections of the master plan laid down the method by which the graziers and their families were to be protected from the bits that would be falling out of the sky, even though the extent of this danger was still guesswork… The only safe course was to direct all the graziers down-range to go to their shelters until the rocket worked out its own pattern of behaviour. At least three or four rockets would need to be fired before the planners could be sure of anything.[59]

The range was sparsely populated, but certainly not empty. When Woomera was first being considered, it was thought possible that those who did live there would have to be moved, but for political and practical reasons this never came about. In addition, it was considered that shelters would first

be required for the 'Black Knight' project, a military rocket that was first fired about twelve months after Skylark. However by August 1957 it was realised that Skylark would also require such protection. (Even if all went well, after returning from space its landing point might be many miles from its theoretically predicted position).

In the event, Skylark launches started in 1957 before the shelters were built; however, the first half dozen had been completed by the spring of 1958. Over the following years, forty-eight different locations were protected by shelters, and with a few minor exceptions every place of habitation on the range, whether temporary or permanent was physically protected and connected to the warning system.[60]

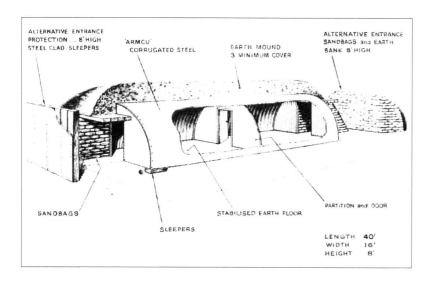

Figure 4.31 A cutaway sketch showing the type of shelter construction to be used.
(Southall (1964), p.52)

Figure 4.32 A shelter in front of the 'Twins Homestead', pictured in 1959. This settlement was some 95 miles (153 km) downrange, and in due course, several Skylarks impacted only a few miles away. (For instance SL361 in 1965 and SL328 in 1966.[61])
(WRE)

[59] Southall (1964), *Rockets in the Desert*, p.51.
[60] See Morton, *Fire across the Desert*, Chapter 4, for a good discussion of the evolution of the homestead protection and warning system.
[61] From the map "Skylark Impact Points 1964-1969", drawing T 2414 Issue 1 (WRE?\Henwood).

Figures 4.33 and 4.34 Then and now - Left: Billa Kalina shelter 1966. Right: Austral Downs shelter 2002.
(WRE)

Figure 4.35 "…I am told that the children usually used to, when they received this and heard that the rocket was coming near them, sit on top of the bunkers." [62]
(Drawing by Len Beadell, reproduced courtesy of Anne Beadell)

The launch tower

The 35-ton[63] tower had been completed at Woolwich in London in April 1956.

> Shipping all this hardware to Australia was a major task and a special section in GW [Guided Weapons] Department under Ken Porter was responsible for making the arrangements. [64]

The tower was shipped from the UK in May, [65] and installed on Launcher Apron 2 (LA2) of Range E, and ready for use by November, in time for the first launch of Skylark, originally scheduled for that month.

---

[62] Zarnecki in 2001, CCBH (2005), *Skylark Sounding Rockets 1957-1972*, & *Prospero* No.2, p.102.
[63] Southall (1964), *Rockets in the Desert*, p.51.
[64] Bryan Day, personal correspondence, May 2009.
[65] Dorling (1959), *The First Six Skylark Firings*, p.18.

Figure 5.1 Preparation two days before firing.
(Southall (1964), p.58)

Figure 5.2 Skylark being wheeled out of the test shop.
In the foreground is the crate in which it was brought to Woomera.
(Southall (1964), p.58)

Figure 5.3 Skylark being towed to the launch tower.
Later versions of the trailer were a little more sophisticated!
(Southall (1964), p.46)

CHAPTER 5

(1957-58)

JOURNEY INTO SPACE

13 February 1957   SL01

The first Skylark Launch

Wednesday 13 February 1957 dawned clear, with a light variable wind from the east, and the promise of another hot summer's day. (It had reached 29ºC / 84ºF by 11.20 am.[1]) As the Skylark team rode the one-hour bus ride from Woomera Village to the launching zone, hopes were high for a successful first launch - a proving flight to test both the rocket and the ground facilities. Would the years of development and theory be proved correct?

Previously, the development teams in the UK and the Australian launch team had worked hard to meet an ambitious target for launch in November 1956, but frustratingly this

had had to be postponed because of problems with the Raven motor,[2] a motor ignition problem encountered during proof tests at Westcott.[3]

Range closures over Christmas[4] had added to the delay, but it may have been on Monday 11th February the first Skylark rocket was placed in the launch tower at launcher apron LA2.[5] Here the instrumented payload head, weighing some 186 lbs (84 kg), had been lowered onto the motor and fin assembly, to give an all up weight of 2496 lbs (1132 kg).[6] The electrical priming unit had been attached, and the countdown checks begun.

For this first flight, things were kept simple. Test instrumentation was carried in the single parallel instrument bay, and the nose cone was empty apart from insulation and three thermocouples spot-welded inside.

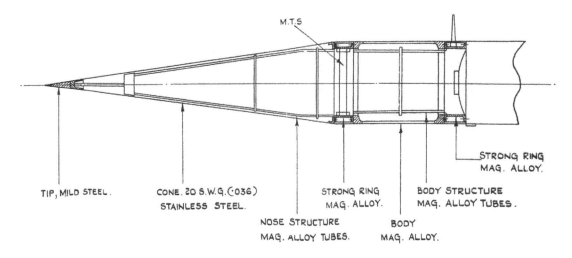

Figure 5.4 The head assembly as used on the first Skylarks.[7] After the nose cone was just a single instrument bay.
(Dorling (1959), figure 2(b))

---

[1]   Dorling (1959), *The First Six Skylark Firings*, p.22. The following day the temperature at nearby Woomera Aerodrome reached 40.6ºC (105ºF)! (*www. tutiempo.net/en/Climate/Woomera_Aerodrome/02-1957/946590.htm* , (last accessed August 2014).
[2]   Spurr in 2001, CCBH (2005), *Skylark Sounding Rockets 1957-1972*, & *Prospero* number 2, p.133.
[3]   Dorling (1975), 'Early History of the Skylark Rocket', pp. 168 & 174.
[4]   The range closed down entirely for a month at the end of each year. "The population fell to less than half in this period as families fled south to cooler and more sympathetic climes." (Taylor (2000), *Flights of Fancy*, p.112).
[5]   Southall (1964), *Rockets in the Desert*, p.58 indicates Skylark was finally assembled and ready two days before firing.
[6]   Dorling (1959), p.19.
[7]   Dorling (1959), figure 2 (b)

The vehicle carried no university experiments, only the RAE test instruments to monitor performance. These comprised accelerometers and rate gyros to measure vibration and movement, thermistors and thermocouples to measure temperature, and a pressure transducer to measure internal air pressure. Also included was an RAE sub-miniature[8] telemetry system to radio the instrument readings to the ground, and standard MTS (Missile Tracking System) and Doppler transponder electronic devices to help track the rocket during flight. However experiments to support the 'Black Knight' rocket development were included, these comprised thermocouples to measure temperature rise in two dummy aerials and the vehicle skin.[9]

Skylark was 'solidly built', in the style of the earlier CTV series, and at 186lb (84 kg) the instrumented head was no exception. The approximate breakdown for the rocket head was:[10]

Structure		Payload	
Nose cone	47 lb (21 kg)	Telemetry	17 lb (7.7 kg)
Body	17 lb (7.7 kg)	M.T.S. unit	13 lb (5.9 kg)
Intermediate ring	15 lb (6.8 kg)	Power unit	17 lb (7.7 kg)
Base ring	18 lb (8.2 kg)	Instruments	27 lb (12 kg)
Fittings	15 lb (6.8 kg)		
Total structure	**112lb (51 kg)**	**Total payload**	**74 lb (33 kg)**

Table 5.1 An approximate weight breakdown of the SL01 instrumented head, showing that the structure weighed more than the 'Payload' carried!

Figure 5.5 At the launch site, the Raven motor was transferred to the loading trolley (which incorporated a section of the third rail). Together they were raised by an electric winch and fastened into position, locating the main body of the rocket between the two fixed rails. The trolley and its section of the third rail remained in place, forming part of the tower.

(Southall (1964), p.59)

---

[8]   Sub-miniature only by the standards of the day! The first three flights carried an ad hoc telemetry system; SL04 onwards used the purpose built T5 sender described in the previous chapter.

[9]   RAE GW Dept.(1958), *A Brief Review of the C.T.V.5 Series III Programme*, p.4, and Dorling (1959), *The First Six Skylark Firings*, p.19.

[10]   Dorling (1959), *The First Six Skylark Firings*, p.20, table 3.

Figure 5.6 This view shows "Two young British Army technicians working on a Skylark rocket in its launcher". The top of the motor is visible, with the primer in position. The three guide rails can be clearly seen; that on the left with the binding still on, is part of the loading trolley.

(National Archives of Australia: A1200, L33569)

Next, the rocket head was hoisted by lifting gear to the loading platform above the loading trolley, and was passed into the tower by the head-loading door. It was then lowered into position on the motor and secured.[11] It was fastened by means of a magnesium alloy 'strong ring' and twenty-four 5/16 inch bolts.

Figure 5.7 Sometimes the head assembly would be raised into the tower first.
(WRE \ Southall (1964, p.59)

---

[11] Dorling (1959), *The First Six Skylark Firings*, p.18.

Figure 5.8 The launch tower with a Skylark ready inside, similar to its appearance to the team that morning.[12]
(National Archives of Australia: A1200, L33562)

---

[12] However, this view dates from 1959, after the tower had been extended from 80' to 100' high.

Preparation was resumed from where it had been held overnight, and the checks continued.

Skylark firings at Woomera were restricted to conditions of steady wind; turbulent gusty conditions even at low average wind speeds made wind predictions (and hence aiming Skylark) difficult or impossible. Hence, at 6 am that morning, a meteorological balloon had been released to provide high-level wind information at 50,000 feet. As the time for launch approached, this was followed by others at 9:55, 10:45, 11:00 and 11:15, to provide wind speed and direction at 3000 feet.

In future, these measurements would be used to point the launch tower to compensate for the wind.[13] However, this first launch was different. Instead of being fired straight up, for this proving flight, SL01 would be fired along a relatively low trajectory, in part because the low performing[14] Raven I motor was being used. Thus on that morning the Launch Officer set the tower elevation to 15° from the vertical, the maximum variation the tower was capable of. The azimuth was set to a bearing of 313°, along the launcher centre line. Precautionary jacks were used to stabilise the central tower for this and the next two firings.[15]

No doubt this first firing was as keenly watched as later launches:

> When an important missile is in sequence, and the amplified count-down, which may be heard almost everywhere, nears zero, the balconies may support forty or fifty observers who don't need to observe at all.
>
> Every man who fires a rocket, or officially watches it, or officially listens to it, has his channel of communication into the instrumentation building...but [unofficial] observers still leave their desks or benches for a few seconds to watch each one depart. It is difficult to work anyway, against the consuming inevitability of a count-down, unless one's work is associated with the count-down. It is on the public-address system, a blend of human voice and the soprano squeak of electronic peeps. By its very nature it commands attention and dominates the mind like a powerful theatrical performance or the tick of a clock in a quiet room.[16]

At 11:20, 60 seconds before launch, the Launch Officer, threw the switch that started the firing sequence.

At 11:21, the igniter fired the Raven motor, and the rocket accelerated steadily up the tower for the first time. After two seconds, it cleared the tower, and roared up into the sky:

> A blinding flash, an immense, all enveloping curtain of black smoke and an awesome roar rapidly becoming a scream – and Britain's first high-altitude rocket, "Skylark", left the launcher at Woomera, Australia, for the first time on Wednesday.[17]

As it left the launch tower, Skylark was tracked firstly by those instruments situated in a broad arc, 1000 yards (1 km) behind the launch apron.

After 10 seconds it had reached 341 mph (549 km/h), after 20 seconds 1023 mph (1646 km/h), and after 30 seconds 1773 mph (2853 km/h).[18] It reached a peak of 2318 mph (3731 km/h) at 34 seconds as the motor finished burning, but Skylark glided upwards for another 30 seconds, before starting to descend. Altogether, the flight lasted about two minutes.

---

[13] Or as Geoff Taylor expressed it "where exactly should the crew point the trainable launch tower in order to avoid being underneath the returning missile?" (Taylor (2000), *Flights of Fancy*, p.126).
[14] The initial thrust of Raven I was only 5,000 lbf, for Raven IIA (used on SL02) the figure was 10,000 lbf. (See Table 3.1).
[15] Dorling (1959), *The First Six Skylark* Firings, pp. 18 & 20.
[16] Southall (1962), *Woomera*, p.111.
[17] Farnborough Chronicle, Friday February 15th 1957, p.1.
[18] Dorling (1959), figure 14.

Figure 5.9 The first Skylark launch. SL01 is fired from Woomera at 11:21 am local time, Wednesday 13 February 1957.
(WRE\ Dorling (1959), figure 12)

Figures 5.10, 5.11 and 5.12 Although not of very good quality as stills, these three frames from a cine film of the launch of SL01 show the sequence well.[19]

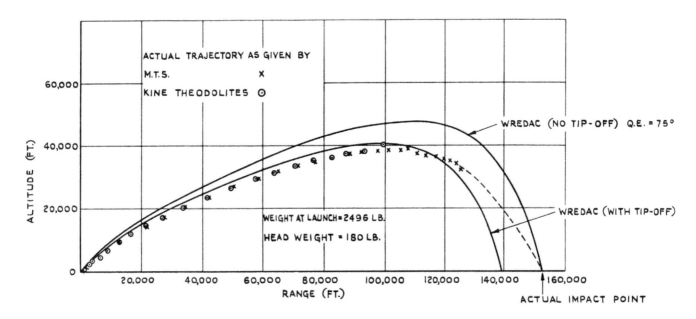

Figure 5.13 The trajectory of Skylark's first flight was close to that predicted.
(Dorling (1959), figure 13)

This first flight lasted only two minutes, during which Skylark travelled to a height of 40,000 feet (7.6 miles / 12 km) and downrange for a distance of 153,000 feet (29 miles / 47 km):[20]

It can be seen from the diagram that the kinetheodolites tracked it optically for a distance downrange of 100,000 feet (19 miles / 31 km), a remarkable achievement made possible by the clear atmosphere at Woomera. The radio based MTS (Missile Tracking System) tracked it about 25% further. The impact point was located, but SL01 was buried in the ground up to its motor nozzle, so no recovery attempt was made. The relatively low altitude obtained on this first test launch was caused by the combination of low initial thrust from the Raven I motor, and the depressed angle of firing.[21]

[19] 'Testing Rockets at Woomera Rocket Range' is a 2 minute 16 seconds excerpt from the film *Rocket Range Australia* (19 mins), produced in 1957. It may be viewed online at *www.australiansatwork.com.au/rocket/rocket_sc7-8.php* (last accessed August 2014). See also the List of References, section 5.2, for details of a BBC programme available online that includes the launch of SL01.

[20] Dorling (1959), *The First Six Skylark Firings*, p.20.

[21] Dorling (1959), p.20.

.Jnes). CLASSIFIED ADVERTISING: **M F 0 3 0 1** (30 Lines).

FEBRUARY 15, 1957   20 PAGES   PRICE 4d.

Saved from Fire

NEW ROCKET TESTED AT RANGE

CANBERRA, Thursday. — The first upper-atmosphere sounding rocket was successfully launched at Woomera rocket range yesterday.

The Minister for Supply (Mr. Beale) announcing this today, said the rocket had followed a flat trajectory as the firing was only experimental.

After further preliminary tests a vertical launching would take place later in the year.

When the rocket was fired vertically, it was estimated that it would carry 65 lb. of instruments to a height of about 100 miles.

Yesterday's rocket, which had not carried any instruments, had been launched at a low angle from the 80-foot long 30-ton launcher.

Following a flat trajectory it had risen to only about 50,000 feet and had travelled about 20 miles.

The rocket, which was named Skylark, was powered by a Raven solid-propellant rocket motor, producing 11,500 lb. thrust for 30 seconds.

Figure 5.14 The launch of SL01 was the first of many to make the front page of one of Australia's main newspapers.[22]

Figure 5.15 This still frame from a film clip provides a sideways view of the first launch, and shows the angle at which the tower was trained.[23]

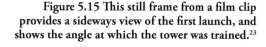

This first firing was regarded as most successful. The rocket travelled up the launch tower without problem, and was stable before and after powered flight. Telemetry reception was continuous for practically the whole flight, an essential requirement. Optical tracking using the Vinten cine cameras was good, although affected by the haze, and reliable data was obtained from the kinetheodolites for at least the first half of the flight. However radar tracking was soon lost, although the low trajectory meant it was not really a fair test. Doppler signals were received for about three quarters of the flight. The MTS system fared better, providing trajectory information for most of the flight.

In general, the ground and airborne tracking and telemetry instruments worked well, and useful heating measurements were returned from the nose and a dummy aerial, all agreeing satisfactorily with theoretical predictions. As expected, the heating effect caused by friction with the air was considerable, the inside of the nose cone reaching 220ºC (428ºF) and that of the dummy spike aerials 170ºC (338ºF).[24]

As noted in the newspaper article, for this first test firing, the vehicle was launched at a low angle, the Q.E. (Quadrant Elevation) of 75º [25] being the lowest the tower was capable of.

[22] 'The Age', Friday 15th February 1957, p.1. Reproduced with permission.
[23] The preparation and launch of SL01 are shown 1 hour 2 minutes into a BBC Television documentary of the time 'The Restless Sphere – the Story of the International Geophysical Year', archived & available online at *www.bbc.co.uk/archive/prince_philip/6012.shtml* (last accessed August 2014).
[24] Dorling (1959), *The First Six Skylark Firings*, p.22.
[25] Dorling (1959), p.20.

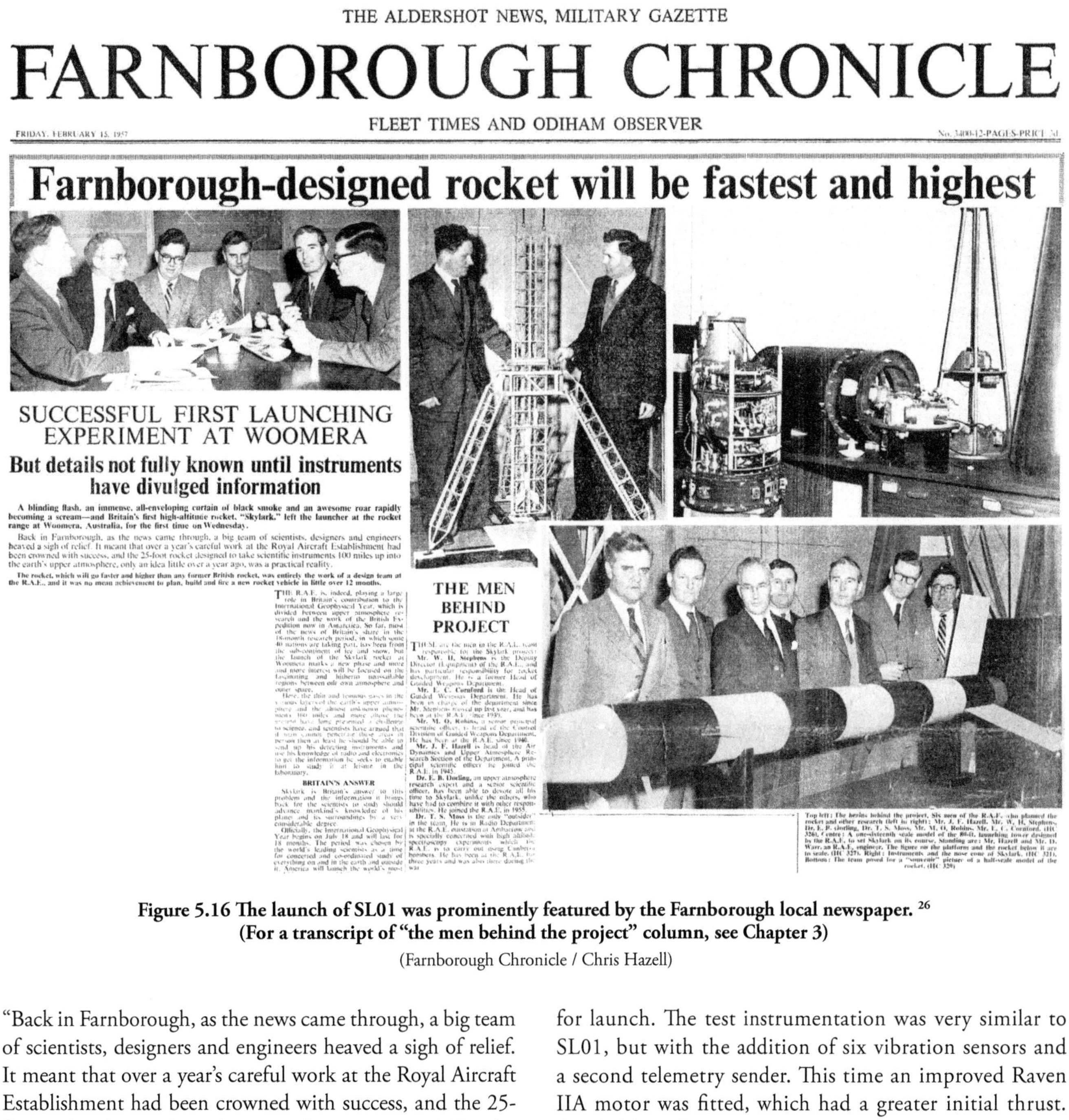
THE ALDERSHOT NEWS, MILITARY GAZETTE

FARNBOROUGH CHRONICLE

FRIDAY, FEBRUARY 15, 1957

FLEET TIMES AND ODIHAM OBSERVER

Farnborough-designed rocket will be fastest and highest

SUCCESSFUL FIRST LAUNCHING EXPERIMENT AT WOOMERA

But details not fully known until instruments have divulged information

A blinding flash, an immense, all-enveloping curtain of black smoke and an awesome roar rapidly becoming a scream—and Britain's first high-altitude rocket, "Skylark," left the launcher at the rocket range at Woomera, Australia, for the first time on Wednesday.

Back in Farnborough, as the news came through, a big team of scientists, designers and engineers heaved a sigh of relief. It meant that over a year's careful work at the Royal Aircraft Establishment had been crowned with success, and the 25-foot rocket designed to take scientific instruments 100 miles up into the earth's upper atmosphere, only an idea little over a year ago, was a practical reality.

The rocket, which will go faster and higher than any former British rocket, was entirely the work of a design team at the R.A.E., and it was no mean achievement to plan, build and fire a new rocket vehicle in little over 12 months.

THE MEN BEHIND PROJECT

Figure 5.16 The launch of SL01 was prominently featured by the Farnborough local newspaper.[26] **(For a transcript of "the men behind the project" column, see Chapter 3)**

(Farnborough Chronicle / Chris Hazell)

"Back in Farnborough, as the news came through, a big team of scientists, designers and engineers heaved a sigh of relief. It meant that over a year's careful work at the Royal Aircraft Establishment had been crowned with success, and the 25-foot rocket designed to take scientific instruments 100 miles up into the earth's upper atmosphere, only an idea a little over a year ago, was a practical reality."[27]

22nd May 1957 SL02

The Second Skylark Launch

Preparation for the second flight followed immediately, and three months later, the second Skylark was ready for launch. The test instrumentation was very similar to SL01, but with the addition of six vibration sensors and a second telemetry sender. This time an improved Raven IIA motor was fitted, which had a greater initial thrust. (See Table 3.1)

Wednesday 22nd May dawned fine with a moderate breeze from the south, and visibility at 30 miles. At 7 am, the Skylark head and motor were mounted in the launcher, and preliminary checks completed two hours later.[28] There was a delay waiting for the wind to die down, but final preparations started at 13:30, the firing sequence started at 14:35, and after a two-minute standby called because of excessive winds, firing occurred at 14:50.

[26] Models of the launch tower appear to have survived both in the UK (Science Museum object 1974-299) and in the South Australian Aviation Museum (see Appendix 6).

[27] Farnborough Chronicle, Friday February 15th, 1957, page 1. (Transcribed by Chris Hazell).

[28] Dorling (1959), *The First Six Skylark Firings*, p.25.

Figure 5.17 The launch of Skylark SL02 at 14:50 local time, 22 May 1957.
(WRE\Dorling (1959), figure 17)

After two and a half minutes, Skylark 02 reached an estimated peak altitude of 250,000 feet (47 miles / 76 km), over six times as high as Skylark SL01:

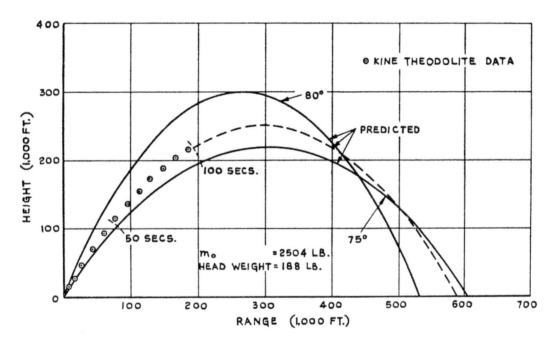

Figure 5.18 The trajectory of Skylark's second flight.
(Dorling (1959), figure 18)

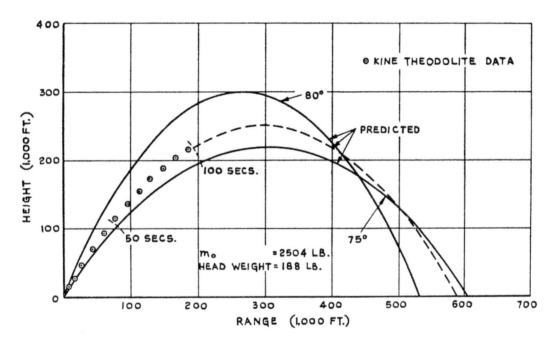

Figure 5.19 With the launch of SL02, Skylark again made the front page of Melbourne's 'The Age' newspaper, albeit a month after the event.[29]

---

[29] 'The Age', Friday 28 June 1957, p.1. Reproduced with permission.

A navigational error

Unfortunately, because of an error in setting the launch tower dial readings, Skylark 02 was not fired in the correct direction! The 'official' account states simply "…the launcher was not correctly trained to achieve the desired impact point on the range centre line".[30]

However, another account provides more details:

> …Skylark roared off far to the right of its intended path. Taken by surprise, few of the tracking instruments kept up with it, and its impact point was not calculated for some time; but it had obviously transgressed the northern range boundary. It was one of the very few occasions when this unforgivable sin was committed at Woomera; but fortunately, it did no harm in such a sparsely populated region. What had happened was that, when working out the procedures for setting the launcher to compensate for winds, one rather elementary calculation had been forgotten…. very wisely it was decided not to go and look for [the Skylark] because that would have drawn attention to it.[31]

Thus, the impact point could only be estimated; the figure arrived at being 111 miles (179 km) downrange. Later that day the launching officer wrote "I shot an arrow in the air, it fell to earth I know not where", convinced that Hazell's carefully devised technique of wind correction was quite ineffective.[32] Later, when it was realised what the true training angles were, he was able to show that the rocket had responded as predicted.

Telemetry and other records were satisfactory as far as they went. Optical tracking was good, the high trajectory and favourable position of the Sun making the results considerably better than with SL01. Useful heating measurements were again made on the nose cone (a maximum of 200°C at +50 seconds), and there was confirmation of the SL01 observation that internal pressure sealing was good.[33] The purpose of the extra vibration sensors was to help establish a vibration specification for Skylark, to which future experimental equipment could be tested. Unfortunately, no results were obtained because the vibration amplifier failed in flight. This was ironic, as the vibration environment in Skylark was later proved mild by missile standards![34]

At heaven's gate[35] - the third Skylark launch

Despite being mainly a proving flight, on the third launch the opportunity was taken to flight test two photometers (sensitive light detectors), of a type to be used in later experiments by Queen's University, Belfast, and three Pirani type[36] pressure gauges made by the RAE.

The standard flight test instruments and power supplies were in the main bay as before, and the additional test instruments were placed within the nose cone space. The photometers were mounted on the third bulkhead, the Pirani gauges on the fourth. This time the instrumentation part of the head weighed 123 lb (56 kg), the head structure 78lb (35 kg), and the all up weight of the assembled rocket was 2584 lb (1172 kg), i.e. just over a tonne.[37]

**Figure 5.20 The internal structure
of the SL03 instrumented head.**

(Dorling (1959), figure 22)

[30]   Dorling (1959), *The First Six Skylark Firings*, p.28.
[31]   Morton (1989), *Fire across the Desert*, p.398.
[32]   Dorling (1975), 'Early History of the Skylark Rocket', p.175.
[33]   Dorling (1959), p.28.
[34]   Dorling (1975), p.175.
[35]   *William Shakespeare* twice refers to the lark singing "at heaven's gate". *Sonnet 29*, and *Cymbeline*, Act II, scene 3, line 20.
[36]   The Pirani gauge is a robust thermal conductivity gauge used for the measurement of low air pressures.
[37]   Dorling (1959), *The First Six Skylark Firings*, p.30.

The first three attempts to launch SL03 had to be abandoned. The first on Thursday 17th July was cancelled because of the failure of the programme motor caused by a wiring error, and a subsequent deterioration in weather conditions. The second attempt on the following day was cancelled because of a fault in the range DTU (Doppler Trigger Unit) system, and a third on the 22nd July because of trouble with the range Doppler aerials. (In these circumstances the benefits of using a solid propellant motor were shown to advantage; the tanks of a liquid propellant based engine would have had to be emptied each time, a problem avoided with Skylark).

However, Tuesday 23rd brought better luck. The weather was mostly sunny, and the eight meteorological balloons released confirmed a moderate breeze from the east up to 5000 feet (1500 m). Stage II of the preparations was complete by 10 am, the countdown started at midday, and launch was at 12:32.

Unfortunately, SL03's run of bad luck continued. Although the rocket performed correctly in flight, a major mistake was made during the countdown:

> An error by the priming monitor shortly before launch caused all power supplies to fail at plug extraction and therefore no in-flight telemetry, Doppler or MTS data was obtained.[38]

As explained in Chapter 3, the priming set was used to power Skylark until just before launch. Before it was unplugged,

an isolation switch should have been thrown so that once launched, Skylark's electronic systems were powered from its internal batteries.

Dave Everest has a more revealing recollection:

> When it was fired, the ground crew forgot to switch the power supplies from the ground supplies to the airborne batteries. So, as soon as the Skylark disengaged from the umbilical, the rocket flew completely dead. When this firing was announced on the BBC, there was a statement that the firing went "exactly as expected". Well, if it is a dead missile, that is true enough, but it certainly is a bit Machiavellian. In fact the only true word in "exactly as expected", is the word "as".[39]

It has to be said that the countdown procedures initially used for Skylark appear to have been a little casual. Indeed, it may only have been when the Black Knight rocket was first fired from Woomera the following year (1958) that written trials procedures were introduced:

> I think I am right in saying that BK [Black Knight] was one of the first missiles handled by RAE which required written trials preparation procedures. Previously, any suggestion that trials teams needed written prompting was regarded as an insult – but of course many a missile failed miserably because of elementary forgetfulness in the stress of the moment…[40]

[38] Dorling (1959), *The First Six Skylark Firings*, p.31.
[39] Everest (2006), 'An Armourer at Farnborough', p.23.
[40] R.N.Reeds as quoted by Morton (1989), *Fire across the Desert*, p.422.

**Figure 5.21 The launch of Skylark SL03, 12:32 local time 23 July 1957.
After 21 seconds, it disappeared into the clouds, never to be seen again!**

(WRE\ASRI)

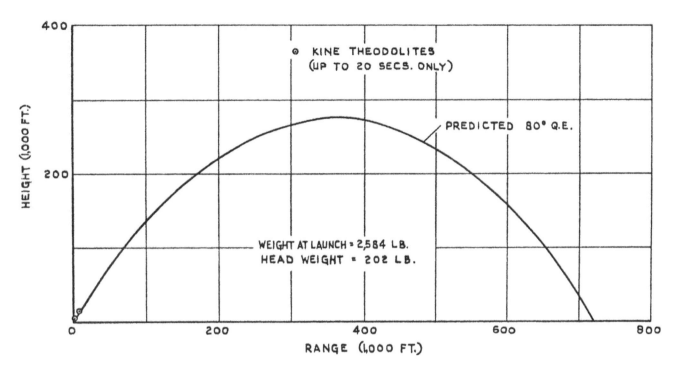

Figure 5.22 The estimated height versus range trajectory for Skylark SL03.
(Dorling (1959), figure 23)

The power supply error meant that no in-flight telemetry data was received, and that none of the on-board electronic tracking systems worked. Ground based optical tracking was lost after 21 seconds when the rocket became hidden in the clouds. As a result, Skylark SL03 was never found, although it was estimated to have reached an altitude of 280,000 feet (53 miles, 85 km) and landed some 136 miles (219 km) down-range.[41] The estimated trajectory is shown in figure 5.22.

13th November 1957   SL04

The fourth Skylark launch – journey into space!

In contrast to the third Skylark launch, the fourth was very successful, although there were similar technical problems before firing.

As the previous test flights had gone relatively well, on this occasion the opportunity was taken to trial three university experiments. These were a full-scale test of the University College London 'grenade' experiment, the Imperial College 'window'[42] experiment, and the University of Birmingham

dielectric experiment. In fact, the grenade experiments had a double purpose, they also supported flash detector and ballistic camera tests for the Black Knight programme.[43] In addition, a second flight test of Pirani pressure gauges was made.

The construction of SL04 differed a little from the previous versions; the normal flight instrumentation was moved to the nose cone, so that the instrumentation bay (the compartment below the tapered nose cone) could be replaced by a 'grenade bay' carrying eighteen grenades and ten 'window' cartridges.

The design and development of the grenade bay had taken some time, and a considerable amount of work on the grenades and detection work had been carried out at various locations in the UK. It was originally planned in some detail to carry out this experiment in Wales, from the RAE short-range launch site at Aberporth, but this was not to be.[44] The technique of using grenades to measure temperature and winds at altitude had been started in the USA in 1948, but with no success until 1950.[45]

---

[41] Dorling (1959), *The First Six Skylark Firings*, p.31
[42] 'Window' or 'Chaff' comprised clusters of metallic strips, originally used for radar deception in World War II.
[43] RAE GW Dept. (1958), *A Brief Review of the C.T.V.5 Series III Programme*, p.4, and Dorling (1959), *The First Six Skylark Firings*, p.34.
[44] Massey & Robins (1986), *History of British Space Science*, p.29.
[45] Stroud (1975), 'Early Scientific History of the Rocket Grenade Experiment', p.239, & Weisner (1954), 'The Determination of Temperatures and Winds above Thirty Kilometres'.

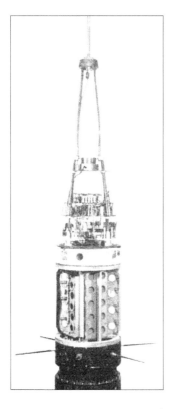 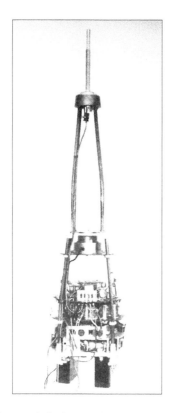 

Figures 5.23, 5.24 and 5.25 Skylark 04 flight instrumentation. Left: general view of the internal structure. Centre: the instrumented nose, with the Pirani pressure gauges and part of the University of Birmingham experiment. Right: the modified instrument bay with the 18 grenade positions, with one dummy grenade in place. The aerials emerging from the lower strong ring are those of the Doppler tracking transponder.

(Left: Hazell (1961), figure 6(b),[46] Centre & right: Dorling (1959), figures 25(c) & (d))

Ken Pounds recalls:

I remember for the first year of my PhD I worked with someone called Dr Gerry Groves on a Skylark experiment that involved throwing grenades out of the rocket as it rose through the atmosphere, and then measuring the flash from the ground and listening to the sound coming through the atmosphere, in order to get a temperature and density profile for the atmosphere. That was great fun. Robert Boyd, of course, was very much in the lead in those days and I recall going with him to Shoeburyness, to fire grenades into the air, to test the equipment before being allowed to put them on a Skylark.[47]

Figure 5.26 A Skylark grenade head on display at Cranfield College of Aeronautics in July 1957. The exhibition also included a model of the launch tower, and the completed head of SL04 ready for despatch to Woomera.

('The Aeroplane' magazine, 2 August 1957, p.162)

[46]   RAeS Journal Vol.65 (August 1961), p.528. Reproduced by kind permission of The Royal Aeronautical Society's Aeronautical Journal.
[47]   Ken Pounds in 2001, CCBH (2005), *Skylark Sounding Rockets 1957-1972, & Prospero* No.2, p.99. By then he had become Professor of Space Physics and Head of Department at the University of Leicester.

Sputnik 1

Whilst preparations for SL04 were being made at Woomera, the astonishing news came through that on the 4th October the USSR had launched the world's first artificial space satellite. Sputnik 1 was a sphere of 23 inches (58 cm) in diameter with a mass of 184 pounds (84 kg), and it broadcast its famous "beep beep beep" signal as it orbited the Earth every 96 minutes. The final stage of its launch rocket also went into orbit; this was much larger, and at night could easily be seen by the naked eye. The original impact of this event is difficult to convey, as these days we tend to take space satellites for granted, but at the time it seemed like science fiction coming true - which of course it was - a feeling that today could perhaps only be re-captured if aliens landed or time-travel was invented!

The technology within Sputnik 1 was similar to that being used on Skylark; for instance, its transmitter was similarly valve (vacuum tube) based. The difference was that the USSR had available (just) the powerful R7 rocket to launch it. (As described in Chapter 1 this rocket was originally developed from the V-2 and R1 for military purposes.) A fact not then known in the West was that the simply constructed Sputnik 1 had been built at the last moment, after it was realised that the scientific satellite originally intended had become too big and complicated to be ready in time.[48]

The launch of Sputnik 1 was a great surprise to Western observers. However, since 1949 the USSR had been active in the field of scientific sounding as well as military rockets. This had started with geophysical variants of the R-1 ballistic missile,[49] and during the 1950s continued with not only atmospheric experiments, but also biology experiments with dogs. At that time, the USSR was very secretive, and closed to outsiders, making progress difficult to judge. However what did become apparent only decades later, was that the launch had came about after a frantic political and technical battle by their chief designer Korolev, to try to achieve the first satellite launch before the USA.[50]

Sputnik 1's batteries ran out after three weeks, but it continued to orbit for a total of three months, finally burning up in the Earth's atmosphere on 4 January 1958. Meanwhile, the much larger Sputnik 2 had been launched on 2nd November, carrying the dog Laika. As its orbit decayed, in April it too re-entered the Earth's atmosphere and burnt up.[51]

Figure 5.27 A model of Sputnik 1, open to show its construction, as displayed in a Moscow museum.[52]

(Seiji Yoshimoto)

---

[48] Cadbury (2006), *Space Race*, p.157.

[49] Mirtov and Vedeshin (1975), 'Early Upper Atmospheric Research with Rockets', p.231.

[50] Cadbury (2006) *Space Race*, Chapter 10. For instance, the R-7 rocket had only ever worked once before, having failed after launch on five of the previous six occasions.

[51] The apparent demise of Laika in this way provoked a storm of abuse from British animal lovers. However, Laika had died of overheating after six hours in orbit. (Cadbury (2006), p.170).

[52] The RCS Energia museum near Moscow, see for instance *www.npointercos.jp/Energiamuseum.html* (last accessed August 2014).

Back at Woomera

Another more local launch also took place in October, that of the first successful Australian made upper atmosphere sounding rocket. The 'Long Tom' was 8.2 metres long, and put together entirely at WRE using surplus British solid propellant 'Mayfly' motors - a cluster of three to form the boost and a fourth one as the second stage. (Mayfly motors had been used on the CTV 5 series II and other earlier missiles tested at Woomera). It was first fired in October 1957, only ten weeks after the decision had been taken to make the rocket,[53] and at one stage, the main ambition was apparently to produce a vehicle that would fly higher than the first Skylarks.[54] Officially, Long Tom was designed to test the instruments that formed part of the Black Knight safety system.

Long Tom had three fins as did Skylark, and was first launched from the Skylark launcher,[55] reaching a greater height than had Skylark on its first flights. However the third flight, the following year, suffered a partial boost failure, which dam-

aged the launcher slightly and brought a request from RAE to refrain from using it again. One witness described this a little more colourfully:

> I always wondered if my work in setting up the timing fuses down the side of the Long Tom round had contributed to the failure. There was a most satisfactory bang in the control bunker whereupon we all ran outside to see the second stage doing cartwheels amongst the stars in the night sky. One of the first stage solid fuel cans had opened up and was wrapped around the beams of the Bailey Bridge sections of the launcher. The other two fuel cans, though unbalanced, had managed to propel the round out of the launcher, shaving metal off the guiderails, much to the disgrunt of the Range management.[56]

WRE subsequently put together their own launcher and 16 or so Long Tom rockets were launched before it was succeeded by later designs.

Figures 5.28 A Long Tom rocket on display at Canberra.

(National Archives of Australia: A1200, L35204)

Figure 5.29 The first Long Tom launch,[57] which took place from the Skylark launch tower.

(WRE\ Southall (1962), p.65)

Figure 5.30 On its own single rail launcher in April 1959.

(National Archives of Australia: D880, D59/71)

[53]   Australian DSTO (undated), *Innovations in Defence Science*, p.8.
[54]   Morton (1989), *Fire across the Desert*, p.402.
[55]   Some internet sources state this first launch occurred on 1st October 1957 and the altitude reached was 100-120km, but the author has been unable to find any documentary support for this.
[56]   Bob Chambers, "Memories of Woomera -2", *http://homepage.powerup.com.au/~woomera/memor2.htm* , (last accessed August 2014).
[57]   The tower was extended in October 1958, so this must be the first Long Tom launch, (October 1957), as the second appears not to have been launched until May 1959.

Skylark SL04

Meanwhile, preparations continued with Skylark SL04. The grenade experiment meant that the launch had to take place during a moonless night so the grenade flashes could be seen and photographed. As with SL03, the first three attempts to launch SL04 had to be abandoned. The first attempts on the 23rd and 24th October failed because of a fault in the priming set plug ejector mechanism, and the delay meant the launch had to be postponed until the next moonless period.

Three weeks later, another launch attempt was made. On the 12th November, the countdown was stopped when the grenade timing switch failed to start because of a wiring fault. However, on Wednesday the 13th all went well. The day itself was a fine and cloudless summer's day with visibility at 25 miles (40 km). At ground level, there was a gentle breeze from the south, but the meteorological balloons released towards the evening revealed it was calm above 3000 feet (914 metres).

The countdown was successful, launch occurred at 21:22 in the evening, and with a roar, the Raven IA motor powered SL04 into the night. After 10 seconds Skylark 04 broke the sound barrier, by 20 seconds had reached a speed of 1500 mph (2400 km/h), and entered the stratosphere at an altitude of some 6 miles (10 km).[58]

After a total of just over 40 seconds, the Raven motor finished firing, and at 'all burnt', the rocket had reached a maximum velocity of some 3300 mph (5260 km/h) at a height of 100,000 feet (19 miles / 30 km). At this point it was travelling at nearly a mile (1.6 km) a second!

The rocket continued upwards under its own momentum, soon passing the maximum height achievable by balloon.

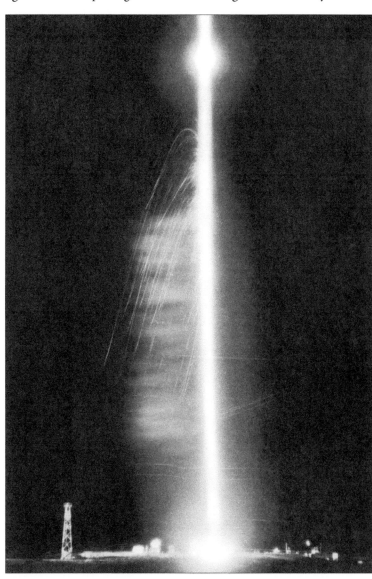

Figure 5.31 The RAE report on the first six Skylark firings[59] does not include a photograph of the launch of SL04, perhaps because it took place at night. However, this time lapse photograph of an unidentified Skylark launch shows what it must have looked like.
(WRE\Southall (1964), p.61)

[58] Figures derived from Dorling (1959), *The First Six Skylark Firings*, figures 28 and 29.
[59] Dorling (1959), *The First Six Skylark Firings*.

Next, the 'window' and grenade experiments began firing, starting those experiments at an altitude previously unobtainable. At +55 seconds and a height of 31 miles (50 km), the rocket cleared the stratosphere and entered the mesosphere, the region where meteors from space burn up when they enter the Earth's atmosphere.

Still Skylark 04 continued upwards, and after a flight time of 110 seconds crossed the nominal 100 km (62 miles)[60] border into space. Here it continued to climb for another minute or so through the region where the sporadic E layer of the ionosphere occurs, reaching an apogee of 420,000 feet (128 km / 79 miles) after a total of three minutes. Just over a minute later re-entry occurred, Skylark 04 having spent two and a half minutes in space.

Unlike SL03, there were no major electrical problems, and telemetry data was successfully received for most of the six minutes of the flight. Impact was 107 miles (172 km) down range, the impact point located, and parts recovered.

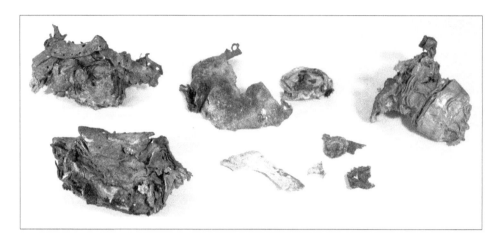

Figure 5.32 Instant archaeology, or "what can happen when a man-made object returns from space without a parachute!" The remains of Britain's first space rocket, the recovered parts of SL04.

(National Archives of Australia: D891, N58/170)

Figure 5.33 Skylark makes the front page again.

('The Age', Thursday 14th November 1957, p.1) [61]

Skylark IV Fired in Woomera Night Test

CANBERRA, Wednesday.—The fourth Skylark rocket was successfully launched at Woomera tonight, the Minister for Supply (Mr. Beale) announced.

Mr. Beale said the Skylark was fired at an angle of six deg. from the vertical and reached an altitude of 83 miles.

A maximum velocity of 3307 miles an hour was reached.

The point of impact was 107 miles down-range from the launching point, and the Skylark had already been found.

The firing was designed to check some of the instrumentation associated with the International Geophysical Year experiments being conducted by United Kingdom universities as part of the Royal Society programme.

Grenades were ejected at various altitudes, and the time intervals between the "flash" and the arrival of the "bang" on the ground will permit calculations of winds and temperature in the upper atmosphere.

Detection of the "flash" was an essential part of the experiments and the firing was therefore conducted on a cloudless and moonless night, Mr. Beale said.

In addition, a cloud of thin metal foil strips, known as "window," were released from the vehicle, and the drift of these strips had been recorded by radar.

This drift would be an additional check on the wind - speeds deducted from the grenades.

Electronic Instrumen-

tation carried by the vehicle included a special oscillator designed by Birmingham University to measure the concentration of electrically-charged particles in the atmosphere at various altitudes.

These ionised layers had a vital effect on radio communications.

Mr. Beale said the results of the firing were now being examined in detail.

---

[60] Where 100 km (62 miles) is 328,000 feet, and these times are derived from Figure 5.34.

[61] Reproduced with permission.

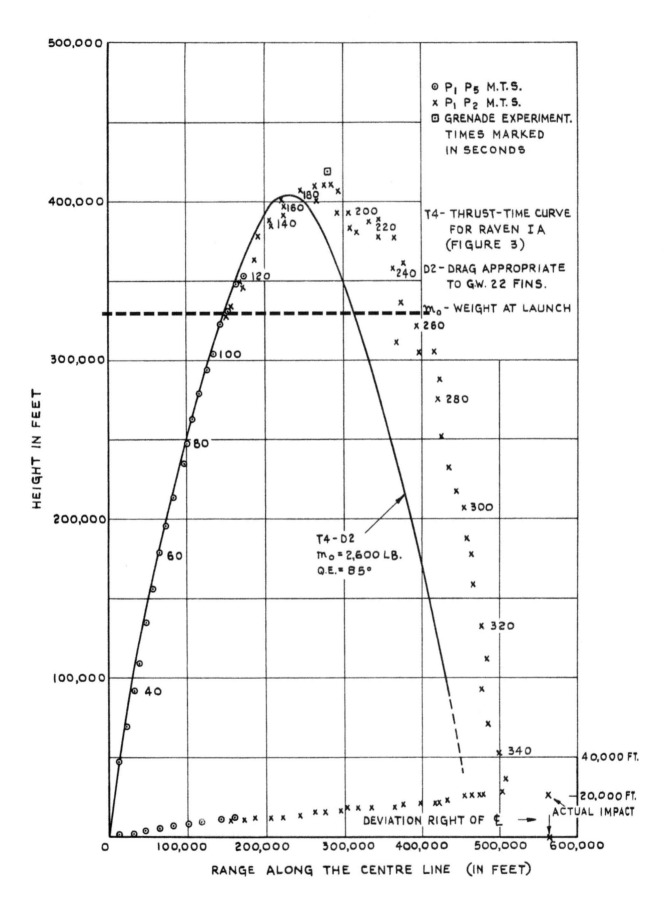

Figure 5.34 The trajectory and experiment release times for Skylark SL04. The apogee of 420,000 feet was 79 miles / 128 km, and the dashed line shows the nominal border of space at 100km (328,000 feet / 62 miles).

(Dorling (1959), figure 28)

The university and RAE experiments

Seq. Nos	Launch date	Ref. (sponsor) launch site	Config-uration	Apogee km (miles)	Experi-menters	Experiments	Result
4 (4)	13 Nov. 1957	SL04 (UK) Woomera	Un, Raven IA	128 (79)	RAE	Test – vehicle flight proving & Black Knight airborne flash detection	
					UCL	Neutral atmosphere – temperature, density & wind speed (grenades)	S
					IC	Neutral atmosphere – wind speed (window/chaff)	S
					Bir	Ionosphere - electron concentration by rf probe	F
					RAE	Test (scientific instrument) – Pirani gauges	S

Table 5.2 A summary of SL04.

One purpose of this Skylark flight was to test the experimental equipment under the real conditions of acceleration and vibration experienced during a supersonic flight into space. Complete sets of scientific data were not necessarily expected, the first full scientific flight (SL07) would not occur until the following April. Even so, good upper atmosphere wind and temperature data was returned.

Grenade experiment, University College London

The purpose of this experiment was to measure atmospheric temperatures and winds at high altitudes by means of sound propagation. At first sight, the use of grenades to do this seems a little odd, but it was a technique that had been proven by early American workers in the field.[62] Grenades are discharged at intervals during a rocket's flight, and the explosions observed by various flash detectors. Microphones on the ground record the time of arrival of the corresponding sound waves, and from these figures the temperature and wind velocities at height can be deduced.

The experiment required extensive ground facilities, including sensitive microphones and cameras to record the sounds and flashes from altitudes of up to 40 miles (70 km). Some were installed around the launch area as shown below; others were up to 37 miles (60 km) along the centre line. (The furthest microphone (H7J lower left below) of the near cluster was 17 miles (27 km) from the launch area). All had to be connected to the rangehead by specially installed telephone landlines, to provide the accurate timing information needed.[63]

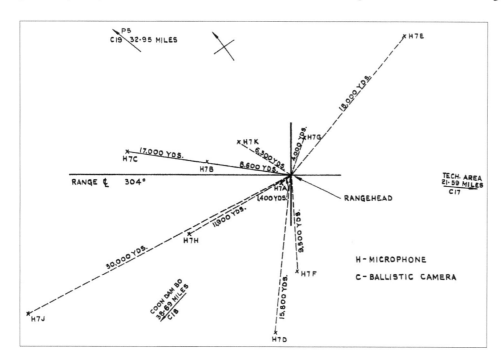

Figure 5.35 The cluster of microphone and ballistic cameras closest to the launch area, as used for SL04.

(Dorling (1959), figure 27)

[62] Newell (1953), *High altitude rocket research.*
[63] Timing signals originated from the range 'Central Timing Unit' in the launch area Instrumentation Building.

Figure 5.36 A microphone pit installed at Woomera for the grenade experiment.
(Bowen *et al.* (1963), figure 3) [64]

During the flight of SL04, eleven of the eighteen grenades successfully fired, and were observed from the ground. The flashes were recorded on three ballistic cameras, good star background calibrations were obtained and eight bursts were recorded by the sound ranging microphones.

During flight, the grenades were fired sideways in horizontally opposed directions, the sidewalls of the grenade bay being provided with copper foil windows through which each grenade cut its way out with the aid of a small four bladed cutter.[65]

The series of grenade experiments thus began very well, yielding good measurements even at this first attempt. A temperature profile of the upper atmosphere between 40 and 70 km (25 and 44 miles) high was obtained, with temperatures varying between 10 and -40°C.

**Figures 5.37 & 5.38 Left: A Skylark grenade bay, positioned with four window cartridges at the top.
Right: A close-up of the copper foil windows after the grenades have been ejected.**
(Science Museum object 1974-239, author 100_4975 & 100_4977) [66]

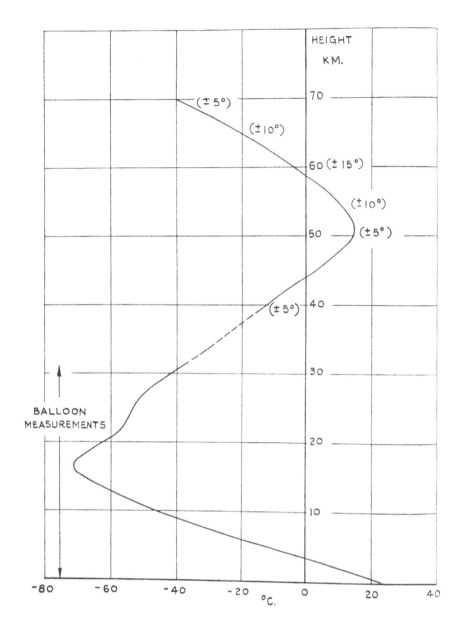

Figure 5.39 The atmospheric temperature profile prepared from Skylark 04's grenade experiment, using provisional data supplied by Dr G.V. Groves of University College, London. This clearly shows how atmospheric temperature increases in the stratosphere, reverses at the 'stratopause' (at 50 km) and decreases in the mesosphere above. This is now standard textbook information, but in 1957, Skylark SL04 revealed it to British researchers for the first time.

(Dorling (1959), figure 30)

Corresponding wind speeds were also obtained, from 10 to 40 metres/sec (22 to 88 mph).

'Window' experiment, Imperial College

This was designed to measure winds at high altitudes by measuring the drift of clouds of reflective metal ejected from the rocket. Fourteen cartridges of 'window' (chaff) were carried in the grenade bay, and ejected at high altitude.

Dave Everest recalls:

> We also had to ground test a Skylark fitted with "chaff" (that is aluminium strips) to be tracked by radar, for upper atmosphere wind velocity measurements…We

took the nose cone which was fitted with dozens of chaff cartridges to one of the tunnels at Ball Hill (within RAE Farnborough) and fired them all off. When we re-entered the tunnel, and turned the lights on, it was like Christmas – the tunnel sides, floor and ceiling were glittering with tinsel.[67]

Two salvoes of window cartridges were duly released from SL04, at heights of 145,000 feet (28 miles / 44 km) and 173,000 feet (33 miles / 53 km). They were successfully tracked by radar, and provided confirmation of the grenade experiment wind speed results at those heights. However, they floated down at only five metres per second, and had dispersed after falling three km, so the expected wind profiles were not obtained.

---

[67] Everest (2006), 'An Armourer at Farnborough', p.23.

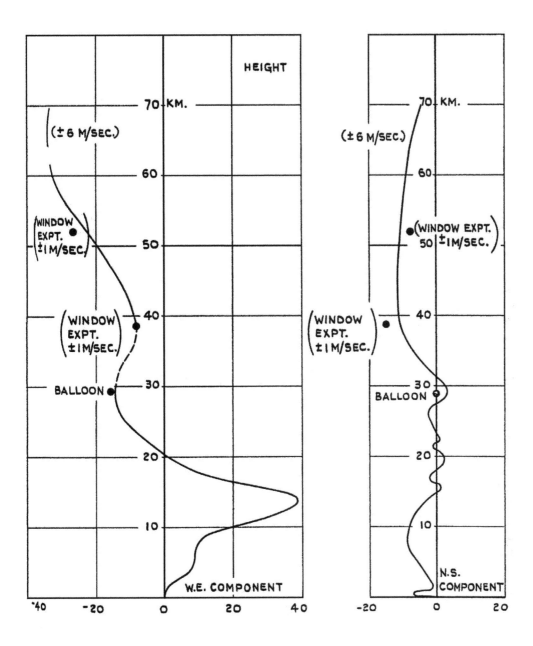

Figure 5.40 The atmospheric wind profile in m/sec prepared from Skylark 04's grenade and window experiments, using provisional data supplied by Dr G.V.Groves of University College, London and Professor P.A.Sheppard of Imperial College.

(Dorling (1959), figure 31)

The joint wind speed results (as shown above) revealed that the wind speed at height could be very high. The peak of 40 m/s (90 mph) at an altitude of 14 km is the westerly jet stream at the top of the troposphere, an example of wind shear that became known as the Sissenwine.[68] The structure of subsequent satellite launch vehicles had to be carefully designed to cope with the wind loads these caused, which otherwise could have easily destroyed them. For instance, the Blue Streak rocket (first launched from Woomera in 1964), was carefully designed and tested to ensure it could cope.[69]

These winds could also cause problems with the measurements made before Skylark was launched "Meteorological balloons could blow away over the horizon before reaching to the heights we needed." [70]

This was pioneering upper atmosphere research, and the results appear to have been the first ever obtained in the southern hemisphere above balloon height.

---

[68] Named after Norman Sissenwine, a pioneering American weather scientist.
[69] Martin (2002), *De Havilland Blue Streak: an illustrated story*, pp.27-29.
[70] Dommett (2004), 'The First Charles Martin Memorial Lecture', p.14.

Figure 5.41 A Skylark nose cone displayed at the London Science Museum. It is similar to that used on SL04, although it does not have the insulating ring 40 inches (1 metre) from the tip. (See Figure 6.10)

(Science Museum object 1975-569, author 100_2252) [73]

The dielectric experiment, University of Birmingham

This was the first Skylark experiment designed to measure the properties of the ionosphere, the layer of electrically charged particles on the edge of space that determines long-range radio transmission. Here at last was the first opportunity for British scientists to make direct measurements, rather than having to rely on ground–based techniques.

This ingenious experiment for measuring electron concentration as a function of altitude had been devised by Professor Sayers of the University of Birmingham. During the war he had been a member of the British team associated with the Manhattan atomic bomb project, and in 1946 had become professor of electron physics at Birmingham University, where he remained for 26 years. In 1949, he received a government award for his work on the cavity magnetron valve, which during the war had been of vital importance in the development of radar.[71]

For this experiment, the Skylark nose cone was modified by insulating part of it from the rest of the rocket by a 1.5 inch (38 mm) thick insulating ring at about 40 inches (1 metre) from the tip.[72] The electrical capacity between the insulated nose cone and the remainder of the rocket was measured by monitoring the frequency of an electrical circuit in which they were included. From this, the dielectric constant of the region through which the rocket passed could be measured, and the electron density derived mathematically.

Unfortunately, this first attempt failed to produce valid information because of power supply design problems. Afterwards it was also realised that the experiment would not have been sensitive enough to measure the low electron density at night. However it was repeated several times in the coming years, and once the teething problems were sorted out, its mechanical simplicity (no moving parts), meant it became one of the most reliable of the Skylark experiments. It was first successfully flown on SL09 in June 1958, (see the next chapter).

RAE experiments

The RAE included inductive and Pirani pressure gauges on this flight (used to obtain data on ambient pressures and temperature, and missile behaviour) as well as the usual accelerometers to measure longitudinal (acceleration) and lateral (vibration) forces. In addition, a Doppler Trigger Unit was under test. A voltage failure at +80 seconds limited the data returned, but until then most of the results had been satisfactory.

---

[71] And since used in all microwave ovens!
[72] Dorling (1959), *The First Six Skylark Firings*, p.32.
[73] Image taken at the London Science Museum, permission granted by Science & Society Picture Library.

Conclusion

Skylark SL04's apogee of 128 km was some 70% greater than the 85 km estimated for Skylark SL03, and it became the first British rocket to cross the nominal 100 km boundary and reach space, a tribute to the British who designed and manufactured it, and the Australians who launched it.

The University scientists and the Royal Society must have been delighted to see their first experiments carried through the upper atmosphere into space. Although the research programme was not due to start until the following year, to those taking part, Skylark 04 marked the real beginning of the British high altitude rocket programme.[74] It had become clear that there was no need to await the completion of the proving flights before starting the scientific programme, and planning for grenade and other experiments began for Skylarks 07, 08, 09 and 18.

Whilst the development of Skylark had been continuing, quite independently, preparations had been going on for the "International Geophysical Year" (IGY), the largest international co-operative scientific enterprise up to that time. This 'year' (actually 18 months) ran from July 1957 to December 1958, and by hard work from all involved, the Skylark programme came to fruition during this time. These scientific results from Skylark SL04 were therefore the first from the Skylark programme to contribute.

Aberporth

As described in Chapter 3, in November 1957 a second Skylark launch tower had been constructed at Aberporth on the Welsh coast. Soon afterwards, on Friday 29th November, HRH the Duke of Edinburgh made a five-hour visit to Aberporth, where he witnessed the firing of two Armstrong Whitworth Sea Slug missiles, watching from a roof-top about 150 yards away. He also inspected other developments, including the newly erected Skylark launch tower.[75]

Figure 5.42 HRH Duke of Edinburgh at Aberporth's Skylark launch tower, inspecting an example of the SL04 type Skylark head with grenade bay, with a Raven motor on the launch tower trolley.[76]

(© Imperial War Museums (ABRP 1403))

[74] Dorling (1975), 'Early History of the Skylark Rocket', p.176.
[75] 'Flight' magazine, 6 December 1957, p.858.
[76] Five months earlier, the Duke of Edinburgh had introduced the BBC television documentary "The Restless Sphere – the Story of the International Geophysical Year". The programme had shown Skylark outside Burlington House in London, home of the Royal Society, and included footage of the first Skylark launch. (See References, section 5.2, for access details).

Figure 5.43 This view includes the main section of the launch tower, and the Aberporth base in the background.

(© Imperial War Museums (ABRP 1405))

Skylark SL05

SL05 was first scheduled for firing on 4th December 1957, but was withdrawn for modifications designed to improve on the poor telemetry performance from SL04. Subsequent problems meant that the launch did not take place until 20th May 1958 (see below), and its launch was overtaken by Skylarks 06 and 07.

Meanwhile, in the outside world, the United States' first attempt to launch an Earth satellite failed on 6 December 1957, when the Vanguard rocket exploded on the launch pad. The next attempt during the night of 31 January 1958 was successful, when a modified Jupiter-C rocket launched the USA's first satellite, Explorer 1. Interestingly, the second, third and fourth stages of this launcher comprised 15 scaled down solid propellant Sergeant rockets, based on the design mentioned in Chapter 3. This heralded a total of 28 satellite and space probe launch attempts by the USA and USSR in 1958. Of these, only eight succeeded, resulting in six Earth-orbiting satellites and two attempted lunar probes that failed to reach escape velocity.[77]

2 April 1958	SL06

Skylark SL06

This was originally scheduled to be the last of the proving flights, but as SL05 had been delayed and the preparations for SL06 had proceeded without problem, it was launched beforehand.

The main purpose of SL06 was to test a device called the 'thrust interrupter unit', also known as the 'motor cut-down' device. Despite their many advantages, one of the problems with solid propellant motors is that, unlike liquid propellant engines, once fired it is very difficult to vary the thrust or stop them. Over the years, various methods have been adopted to overcome this problem. For instance on the US Army solid propellant 'Sergeant' missile (first tested in 1956, and deployed from 1963), range was controlled by drag-brakes, opened by the guidance system halfway through the planned flight path. The drag-brakes neutralised the motor thrust, causing the missile to follow a ballistic flight path back to the ground.[78]

---

[77] See for instance Jonathan McDowell's *Jonathan's Space Report,* at *http://planet4589.org/space/log/launchlogy.txt* (last accessed August 2014).

[78] *www.designation-systems.net/dusrm/m-29.html* (last accessed August 2014).

The technique being tested in SL06 was designed to disable the motor altogether, by blowing out a sealing plug at the opposite end of the motor to the exhaust throat. This was initiated by a command over a radio link, providing a method of aborting a flight if required. Skylark was one of the first missiles tested at Woomera which, if it accidentally headed in the wrong direction, could fly far enough to leave the range area altogether - as indeed had embarrassingly happened with SL02.

The larger missiles tested later at Woomera (such as Black Knight) had more sophisticated guidance and tracking systems, and a self-destruction capability. The thrust interrupter unit was developed to provide a similar function for Skylark, although in the event it was not required, as the measures used to control dispersion proved adequate in use.[79]

The interrupter device employed a sealing plug which closed the hole in the motor head, the plug being held in position with an 'O' ring seal by four radial wedges. The wedges themselves were held in position by a cylindrical locking plug, which could be ejected by an explosive charge so releasing the wedges. The pressure inside the burning motor would then blow out the sealing plug.

Because of the short duration of this test flight, Skylark 06 carried no experimental equipment, just basic instrumentation, although a third attempt was made to obtain vibration data. The opportunity was also taken to flight test a dummy nose cone probe some 5-foot (1.5 m) in length and 1 inch (25 mm) in diameter,[80] to be used for experiments in later flights. (Starting with SL14 in July 1959).

Wednesday 2 April 1958 dawned fine and cloudless with visibility at 15 miles (24 km). Work began early, with weather balloon releases starting at 6.45 am. These showed that the light south-easterly breeze was a little stronger at height.

Preparation was accomplished smoothly and quickly; the countdown was successful, and launch occurred at 8.02 am. The Raven IA motor powered the SL06 for just 26 seconds, and then the motor thrust was interrupted as planned. The head was separated from the motor by the cut-off operation and fell to the ground 15,700 feet (3 miles / 4.8 km) downrange, although unexpectedly the residual thrust from the motor meant the case travelled much further, to 183,000 feet (35 miles / 56 km) downrange, and reached a height of 140,000 feet (26.5 miles / 43 km).

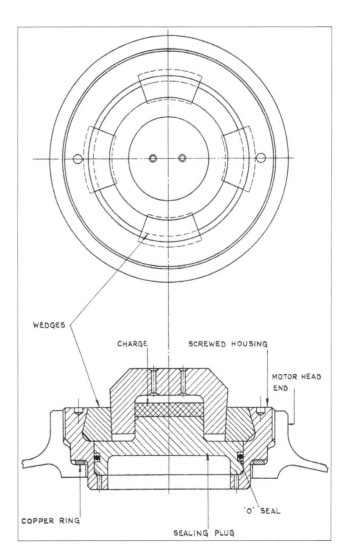

Figure 5.44 The Raven motor thrust interrupter unit, as tested on SL06.
(Dorling (1959), figure 43)

[79] Hazell (1969), *Spinning Skylark – To Reduce Dispersion and Avoid Roll Lock-in & Resonance,* three page technical document dated 28th August 1969 (TNA: PRO document file AVIA 65/1773).
[80] Dorling (1959), *The First Six Skylark Firings,* p.57.

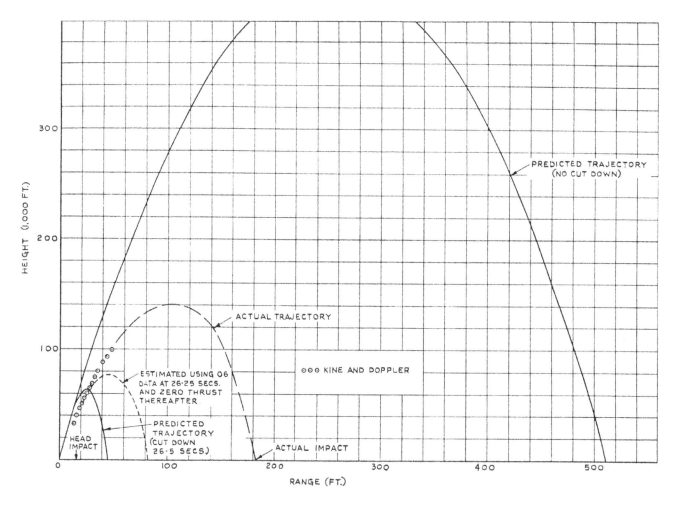

Figure 5.45 Comparison of the predicted and actual trajectories for SL06, with and without the thrust interrupter unit.
(Dorling (1959), figure 46)

It was later discovered that the launcher rails at the top of the tower had been bent as the rocket departed. The firing had taken place with the tower at its maximum depression, using the relatively low thrust Raven IA motor, worst case conditions that would not be repeated. WRE calculated that "tip-off" caused the damage, which was not serious and soon repaired. (In 1958 the tower would be extended in length).

This time the vibration experiment did produce 25 seconds worth of data, which provided a frequency spectrum of the vibration, although not its absolute amplitude.[81] Although the thrust interrupter worked well on this occasion, it was not long before it caused the first Skylark failure, when in June 1958 SL18 crashed after launch. (See the next chapter).

Figure 5.46 One of the pieces recovered from SL06.
(National Archives of Australia: D8891, N58/1363)

81 Dorling (1959), *The First Six Skylark Firings*, p.61.

Skylark SL07

SL07 was launched on 17 April 1958, just two weeks after SL06. It was the first purely scientific flight, and so is described at the start of the next chapter.

---
20 May 1958   SL05

Skylark 05 is finally launched

This launch tested a new lighter design of fin, the GW 24,[82] and was the first launch to use the new Raven II motor.

The payload included what was becoming the standard instrumentation for flight measurements, comprising accelerometers, rate gyros, and the combined telemetry, Doppler transponder and MTS beacon package. (The "T5" sender, see Chapter 3.)

There were two new instruments, a flux gate magnetometer and sun detecting photocell, which were being developed for use in measuring rocket attitude. The magnetometer was a type of compass, and its elements were installed in the fins to try to avoid disturbing magnetic fields from the rocket itself.

The sun detecting photocells were mounted in the intermediate strong ring, and had a 45° viewing angle. The circuitry included what was then the very latest in technology, a transistor amplifier.[83]

Two Queen's University of Belfast airglow photometers were again carried, (similar to the ill-fated instruments flight-tested on SL03). The airglow is the very weak emission of light by the Earth's atmosphere, an effect that means the night sky is never completely dark. Because it is a very faint phenomenon, it was not discovered until 1868, and we know now it is caused by a glowing layer of gas at an altitude of about 97 km. However in 1958, this fact, and the chemical reactions that caused the glow, were only a matter of speculation. The Belfast photometer experiments were an ambitious attempt to find out more, although it would be 1965 before success was achieved (See SL39 in Chapter 8).

Three years later, describing the view of the Earth from space in 1961, Yuri Gagarin would radio, "It has a very beautiful sort of halo, a rainbow." He was probably describing the airglow, the first person to see it from space.[84]

Figure 5.47 This photograph was taken from the International Space Station some 50 years after SL05, and shows the airglow well. The predominantly green colour is caused by the 5,577Å light wavelength from atomic oxygen atoms.

(Image STS099-355-24, courtesy of the Image Science & Analysis Laboratory, NASA Johnson Space Center)

---

[82] See Chapter 3 of this book, Figure 3.20 onwards.
[83] Dorling (1959), *The First Six Skylark Firings*, p.55.
[84] Quoted by several websites, but the author has been unable to find an authoritive source.

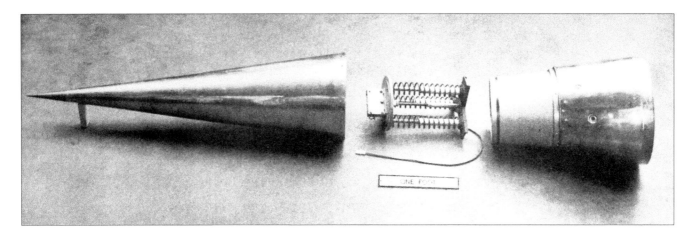

Figure 5.48 SL05 nose cone showing the upper (jettisonable) and lower (fixed) halves.
(Dorling (1959), figure 34)

The SL05 photometer experiment was designed to measure the variation with altitude of the green emission at 5,577Å (557.7 nm). It included an optical system with a rotating shutter, and electronic photomultipliers with associated circuitry. These were mounted under a jettisonable nose, which after release would allow the sky to be viewed.

The jettisonable nose cone was being tested for the first time. Overall, it was four and a half feet (1.4 metres) long, with the upper part designed to be released by a bomb release activated spring mechanism. To monitor the release a small cine camera was mounted alongside the photometers. The release was timed for +71 seconds, at an altitude of about 250,000 feet (47 miles / 76 km).

In addition, a break-up system was fitted, comprising a length of Cordtex arranged to sever a strong ring. This was designed to separate the entire rocket head from the motor at +215 seconds, so that the impact velocity of the separated head would be sufficiently low for recovery of the camera.

As noted above, Skylark 05 was had been scheduled for firing on 4 December 1957, but had been withdrawn for modifications. It was next scheduled for firing on 5 February 1958, but repeated attempts over a period of three weeks were unsuccessful because of unfavourable weather and difficulties with rocket instrumentation and batteries. In March, a cable loom was burned out in the rocket head when on the launcher because of an error when making connections to the priming set. Weather and other problems caused further postponements at the end of April and start of May, and it was not until 20th May that success was achieved.

On Tuesday 20th May, the weather was fine, the sky cloudless, and visibility 15-25 miles (24-40 km), the wind light and variable in direction. After two attempts when the priming set extractor plug and extractor gave trouble, launch was finally achieved at 13:56 local time.

The SL05 rocket itself performed well in flight, and in just over three minutes reached a peak altitude of 495,000 feet (94 miles / 151 km), a little lower than expected, but still nearly one fifth higher than SL04. As noted above, SL05 was the first to be fitted with the more powerful Raven II motor (See Chapter 3), which was to become the standard motor used on Skylark during the next few years.

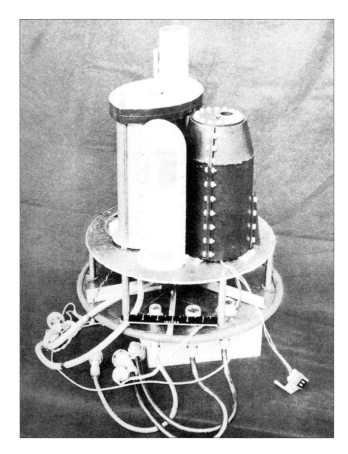

Figure 5.49 The SL05 upper bulkhead with pressurising ring, showing the cine camera with the photometers behind. The cine camera (on the right) was enclosed in rubber and bolted inside a steel container. The other structure, to the left of the camera, was a fibreglass container being tested to compare the impact resisting qualities with those of steel.
(Dorling (1959), figure 33(a))

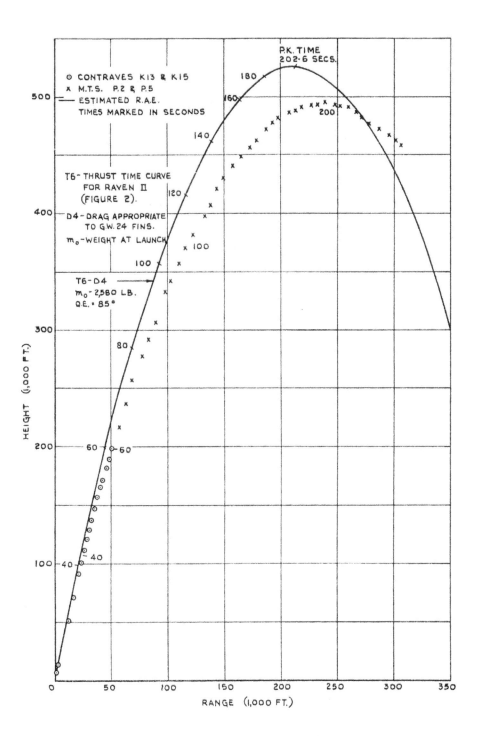

Figure 5.50 The trajectory for Skylark SL05.
(Dorling (1959), figure 36)

Unfortunately, no in-flight observations of the nose cone release took place because the camera did not start running, the reason never being discovered. In addition, the photometer that should have recorded daylight airglow on release of the cone gave no output, possibly because a protective shutter had not worked, and it was not clear if the nose cone had released correctly. However, the break-up charge did operate when expected, three and half minutes into the flight, just after the peak altitude was reached. At this point telemetry reception ceased sharply (probably because of the destruction of the aerial feeder cables), although the MTS (Missile Tracking System) system continued to operate at reduced performance. The motor case impacted 76 miles (122 km) downrange, where it was found embedded in the ground with the fins thrown forwards. The head was found a mile away, severely damaged and in three main pieces.

Figure 5.51 The SL05 motor case after impact 76 miles (122 km) downrange.
(WRE\ Dorling (1959), figure 38(b))

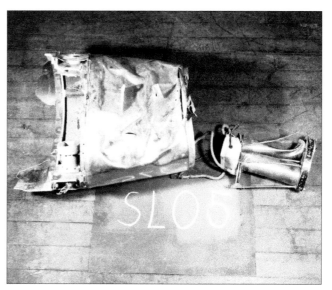

Figures 5.52 & 5.53 SL05 - the lower (fixed) part of the jettisonable nose cone.
Left: as found. (WRE \ Dorling (1959), figure 38(c))
Right: as recovered back at base (National Archives of Australia: D891, N58/1225)

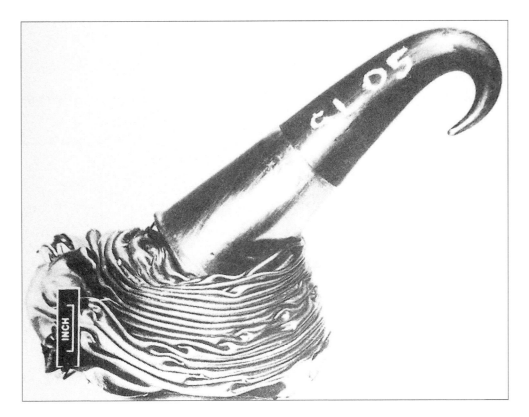

Figure 5.54 The upper (jettisonable) part of the nose cone of SL05 after recovery. It was fortuitously discovered by a homesteader sixteen miles (26 km) beyond the impact point of the motor and head.
(Dorling (1959), figure 38(a))

The armoured camera was recovered intact, but was wrecked by the impact because of the unsatisfactory nature of the heavy rubber packing.

During the flight, the magnetometer experiment succeeded in providing measurements of the angle between the rocket's axis and the Earth's field, and at one point clearly showed the roll of the rocket as being half a revolution a second. However, some of the readings were heavily affected by changes in the magnetic field of the rocket when the motor was firing.

The sun photocells functioned throughout the flight, although the quality of the records was not sufficient to provide the change of the Sun's position with time. The test of the photometers demonstrated that despite shutter and power supply problems, they would work correctly under flight conditions.

Overall, the flight yielded little in the way of positive measurements, and showed that the experiments would require much development before becoming reliable measuring devices.[85]

Conclusions from the proving flights

The flight of Skylark SL05 completed the series of six Skylark proving flights. The main purpose had been to flight test the rocket, check its performance against prediction, to test telemetry and tracking and obtain information on dispersion.

On the propulsion and structural side, all had gone well. No structural failures had occurred, and it was concluded that the design was robust and reliable. Indeed, it wasn't found necessary to await completion of the test programme before beginning the research programme proper, and the first firing for the Royal Society; (Skylark 07) had been made on 17 April 1958, just over a month before the flight of Skylark SL05.

The performance of the Raven motor had generally been most satisfactory, and this was the major factor in the success. The Raven II motor, though a little down on its expected performance in terms of peak height, had shown the required high initial thrust, and there was general confidence that as its development continued, it would fully meet all expectations.

In only two and a half years, and "on a rather low budget",[86] Skylark had become a reality, and flown through the upper atmosphere into space.

---

[85] Dorling (1975), 'Early History of the Skylark Rocket', p.178.
[86] Boyd (1961), 'The Scientific Programme of Skylark to Mid 1960', p.531.

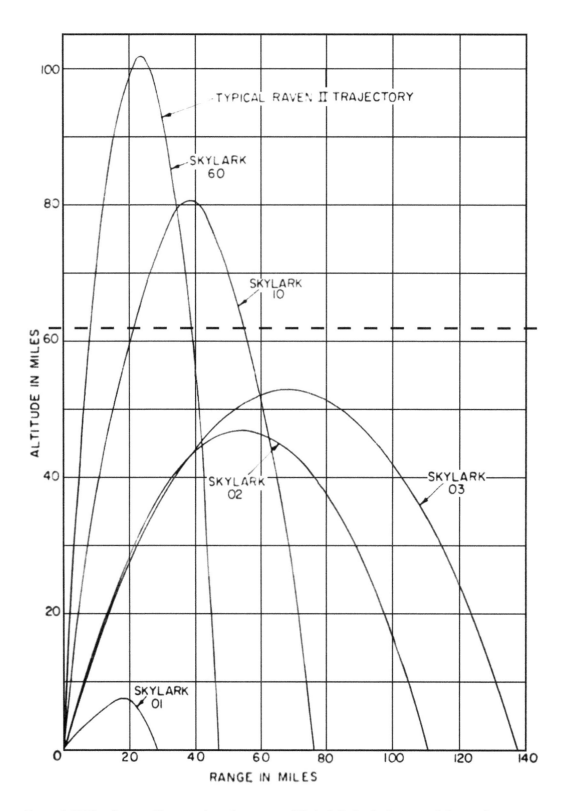

Figure 5.55 This diagram illustrates how the apogee of Skylark flights had increased during the proving programme. (SL04 was similar to SL10 (79 miles / 128km), SL05 close to SL60 (94 miles / 151 km). The dashed line represents the nominal border of space at 100 km (62 miles) (the Kármán line).

(After Hazell (1961), figure 2) [87]

[87]   RAeS Journal Vol.65 (August 1961), p.527. Reproduced by kind permission of The Royal Aeronautical Society's Aeronautical Journal.

On the ground, the priming facilities for monitoring and powering the payload through the umbilicals before launch had given trouble, and underwent various modifications because of experience during the firings. During flight, the telemetry performance had been below expectation, the signal strength being significantly lower than expected, and this was the main outstanding problem from the trials. (However during 1958 it was discovered that the problem had been in the ground equipment, rather than Skylark).

Dispersion of the point of impact of Skylark was always one of the major concerns, both during the original design phase and during the trials. This problem is common to any un-guided rocket, especially one re-entering from space. Despite the most careful preparations, minute variations in any one of many factors at launch can cause the point of impact to be tens of miles away from that predicted. For instance, during the trials, Skylarks 04 and 05 landed 8.3 and 25.7 miles (13.4 and 41.4 km) respectively away from their declared aiming points.[88] At best this meant that the recovery party needed to search hundreds of square miles of outback, at worst the rocket became a safety hazard. Indeed, this was one of the reasons that the idea of firing Skylark from the UK rocket range at Aberporth was postponed for many years, despite a complete launcher being built there.[89]

Some of the factors affecting dispersion were linked with Skylark's design and construction, such as the accuracy of fin and jet alignment, others were to do with inaccuracies in being able to predict performance because of errors in measuring the all-up weight, and in thrust and drag predictions.[90] In addition, external factors were introduced at launch, such as the accuracy of aligning the launch tower, and variations in the wind speed at different altitudes could occur. The wind speed especially could be difficult to determine, despite the many meteorological balloons used before launch, and of course, it could change before launch, after it had been measured. However, the concept of an adjustable launch tower to compensate for wind speed had worked.

[88] Dorling (1959), *The First Six Skylark Firings*, p.64.
[89] Spurr & Dorling in 2001, CCBH (2005), *Skylark Sounding Rockets1957-1972*, p.77, and *Prospero* No.2, p.140.
[90] By 1975 it had been shown that motor thrust misalignment, particularly as Skylark left the launcher, was the dominant cause of dispersion. A misalignment of 0.06 degrees would produce a dispersion of about 20 km (12.4 miles). Dorling (1975), 'Early History of the Skylark Rocket', p.183.

Figure 6.1 A time-lapse photograph of a Skylark night launch. From the date of the original, it is most likely to be that of SL18 or SL09. (18 and 19 June 1958.)

(National Archives of Australia: D880, D58/278)

CHAPTER 6

(1958-60)

THE ART OF EXPERIMENTS

In April 1958, Skylark officially started its operational programme. This chapter describes the successes, trials and tribulations of the first three years of operation, during which this revolutionary new tool was used to study regions of the upper atmosphere previously unattainable by British scientists.

Preparations for a typical Skylark launch

Most missile programmes carried out at Woomera were R&D proving trials; once testing was over and the weapon went into service, it would be used by armed forces elsewhere. For Skylark, once the vehicle proving trials were over, Woomera remained 'home', and for the first seven years, the only place where it was deployed.[1] Thus, once the user firing programmes started, a 'supply chain' was set up, stretching around the world from the UK to South Australia.

The original Skylark rockets travelled from the UK by plane, the Raven motors to Woomera, and the payloads arriving as a 'kit of parts' at WRE's Salisbury base. Here they were put together by the Australians with help from the British scientists involved. "When a rocket payload left this country [UK] in its boxes of bits and pieces, it was destined to be put into the hands of another organisation, there to be reassembled, checked and readied for flight".[2] "... [there] we unpacked, re-assembled and checked out the Skylark and experiments".[3]

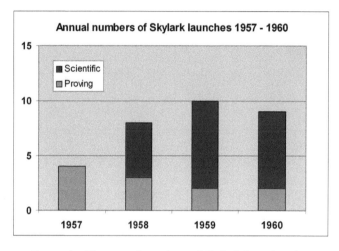

Figure 6.2 The annual numbers of Skylark launches during the first four years of operation. (All were of unstabilised payloads fired from Woomera.)

(Author)

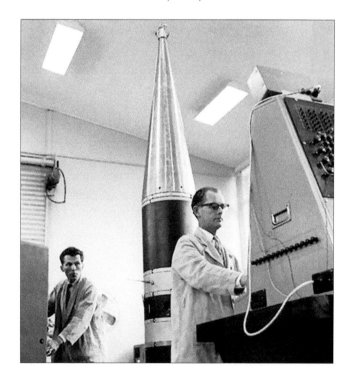

Figure 6.3 A Skylark payload being tested at Salisbury in 1964.

(National Archives of Australia: A1200, L49321)

---

[1]   The first Skylark fired outside Woomera was S01/1 at Sardinia, in July 1964.
[2]   Dorling in 2001, CCBH (2005), *Skylark Sounding Rockets 1957-1972*, p.70, & *Prospero* No.2, p.134.
[3]   Ibid, p.33, & *Prospero* No.2, p.100.

The payloads were then transported the 270 miles (435 km) to the actual range for final preparation and firing:

> The Skylark trials were handled in an unusual fashion, administratively speaking. Most of the other British Projects were prepared and launched by a Range user provided by the R&D authority and staffed by men from the British establishments, their contractors, or an appropriate services detachment. Skylark was different. For much of its Woomera career the Range user functions were carried out by a WRE team from the Weapons Research and Development Wing, just as if it had been an Australian-sponsored project. Normally the sponsoring UK university or other establishment sent out a small team to look after their experiment, but their enthusiastic activities were co-ordinated by an officer in charge appointed for that trial from the WRE team.
>
> Systems Assessment Division of WRE, which had earlier handled Range user aspects of the RTV1 and CTV1 series I firings, continued this for the first two firings of Skylark. Responsibility for the trials then passed to Research Vehicles Group in Aerodynamics Division (AD), who launched the third Skylark in July…Research Vehicles Group expanded subsequently and by 1963 was fielding four separate teams so several Skylarks could be prepared at once.[4]

Once at the range, each Skylark would spend about two weeks in the test shop at range E, being thoroughly checked and tested again.

After testing, the rocket would be hoisted onto a trailer and towed to the launcher, usually two days before launch. Here it came under the jurisdiction of the Launch Officer, whose duties included being responsible for fitting the rocket into the tower, adjusting the angle of launch, and during the final sixty seconds of the countdown, throwing the switch that started the firing sequence. He also had to put things right should the rocket fail to fire or there be a misfire. These last operations were carried out from an underground control room (Equipment Centre 2 / EC2) built into the edge of the concrete apron. (See Figure 9.26.)

Figure 6.4 Preparing an early Skylark in the Range E test shop. For later Skylarks, the payload head and rocket motor would only be brought together at the launch tower.

(Southall (1964), figure.5.1)

---

4 Morton, *Fire across the Desert*, p.399.

Mike Cruise recalls the launch procedure as it was a few years later:

> Normally the experimenters watched the launch proceedings from the blockhouse, EC2, a concrete building below ground level, built into the edge of the concrete launch apron. All the control connections to the vehicle came to EC2 and there were telemetry receivers to check data from the instrumentation and the experiment. In a separate room in EC2, an Australian military technician did the actual firing by starting an automatic sequencer two minutes before launch. This counted down and issued the firing pulse to the detonator in the booster motor at the pre-programmed time. Up to two seconds before launch the launch could be stopped using a line attached via a small snatch connector to the side of the instrumentation bay. Several people in EC2 had "Stop Action" buttons which could abort the launch via this route. The snatch connector was left in place as the launch proceeded and the wires literally snatched from the side of the vehicle as it departed.[5]
>
> …The launches of other peoples *Skylarks* were very spectacular, but you saw little of your own, being heavily occupied inside EC2 watching things happen on the telemetry.[6]

The early warning system comes into use

Skylark was the first of the long-range vehicles to be launched at Woomera, and the even longer range 'Black Knight' soon followed. Thus during 1958, the first homestead shelters were built, and the telephone warning system came into operation.[7] This required a specially built telephone network that stretched dozens of miles across the bush, using thousands of poles, and for most homesteaders was the first telephone connection they had ever had.[8]

Once in action, the first or 'preliminary' warning was given when a firing was first planned. This could be a week or more before the event. If it was postponed for any reason, 'intermediate' warnings were given, advising of the delay. Twenty-four hours before the programmed time the Range Overseer would issue an 'advance' warning'. During the last few hours up to three more warnings – 'main', 'intermediate' (if necessary) and 'final' would go out to all the pastoral stations downrange that would be affected. By the time of the final warning, every person was supposed to be under cover or making his or her way there. (See Chapter 4 for details of the shelters.)

SKYLARK LAUNCHES AND SCIENCE IN 1958

April 1958   SL06, SL07

Vehicle proving flights SL06 and SL05 have been described in the previous chapter, so this account starts with **SL07**, only a summary being provided for SL06. Although some scientific experiments had been flown on SL04 the previous November, SL07 in April 1958 was Skylark's first flight for primarily scientific purposes.

As shown in Table 6.2, SL07 had on board four main experiments, a similar set to SL04. Those from the universities included the 'grenade' and 'window' experiments from UCL and Imperial College, designed to measure atmospheric properties as SL07 rose through the upper atmosphere. However, for SL07 the ground network was upgraded with new pre-amplifiers using that latest invention, the transistor.[9] As before, the 'grenade' experiments were also useful to the RAE, allowing them to test Black Knight 'Type A' flashes and a new type of Ballistic Camera,[10] the new camera also

Jan.	Feb.	March	April	May	June	July	Aug.	Sept.	Oct.	Nov.	Dec.
			SL06	SL05	SL22			SL08			SL11
			SL07		SL18						
					SL09						

Table 6.1 The eight Skylark Launches that took place in 1958. (For full details, see Appendix 3)
(Key: black = test launches, blue = UK national programme (unstabilised)

[5]   Cruise (2008), *Skylark Ascending*, online article p.18, and *Prospero* number 5, Spring 2008, p.52.
[6]   Cruise (2008), p.19, and *Prospero* number 5, Spring 2008, p.53.
[7]   For more details of the early warning system, see Morton (1989), *Fire across the Desert*, p.65.
[8]   Morton (1989), *Fire across the Desert*, p.320.
[9]   Bowen *et al.* (1963), 'Upper atmosphere wind and temperature structure by Skylark rocket-grenade experiments…', p.174.
[10] RAE GW Dept. (1958), *A Brief Review of the C.T.V.5 Series III Programme*, p.4.
[11] Bowen *et al.* (1963), p.177.

Seq. Nos	Launch date	Ref. (sponsor) launch site	Config- uration	Apogee km (miles)	Experi- menters	Experiments	Result
5 (1)	02 April 1958	SL06 (UK) Woomera	Un, Rav.1A	43 (26.5)	RAE	Test (Skylark technology) – thrust interrupter	S
					UCL	Test – dummy nose cone probe	S
6 (2)	17 April 1958	SL07 (UK) Woomera	Un, Rav.2	153 (95)	UCL	Neutral atmosphere – (grenades)	S
					IC	" " - (window/chaff)	S
					Bir	Ionosphere - electron concentration	F
					RAE	Tests (instrument & Skylark technology) – Pirani gauges & B.K. flash & ballistic camera	?

Table 6.2 A summary of SL06 and SL07. SL07 was Skylark's first scientific flight proper, its apogee of 153 km meant it achieved an altitude of 20% more than SL04, and became Britain's second rocket to reach space.

APPENDIX II
GASSIOT PROGRAMME WITH SKYLAK AT WOOMERA

GW/2320/EBD

Round No.	Payload			Remarks
SL 07	1. Grenades 2. Window 3. B'ham Oscillator 4. U.C.L. Flash Detector	5. Long acceler. 13g. 6. Long acceler. 2g. 7. Lat. acceler. ±5g (2) 8. R.A.E. Piranis 2 cone 1 ram	9. R.A.E. 15 p.s.i. gauges 10. Flares 11. 12.	DC G IN N

DC...DC System   G...Grenade Bay   IN....Insulated Nose   N....Night Firing

Figure 6.5 An official list of the payload experiments on board SL07.
During the planning process, these lists were compiled for each payload.[12]

being used by UCL.[11]

The university experiments were mostly successful, and provided good results for the temperature and wind variation with altitude over Woomera. (Part of a paper including the results of the UCL Grenade experiment is reproduced in Appendix 4).

Thus, Skylark immediately allowed British scientists to contribute to international class IGY research on the upper atmosphere; for instance, the Woomera upper atmosphere temperature profiles were correlated with similar American results from White Sands and Guam, to help develop international standard models of the atmosphere. Such rocket grenade experiments "...made significant contributions to our understanding of the structure and dynamics of the atmosphere between 30 and 90 km".[13]

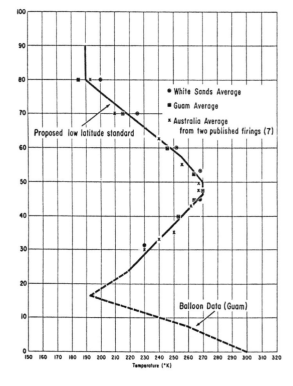

Figure 6.6 A temperature profile for the upper atmosphere derived by combining US and Woomera results. (The White Sand results were from 1950-53, the Guam & Australian ones from 1958 during the IGY.)

(Stroud (1975), figure 3)[14]

[12] RAE GW Dept. (1958), *A Brief Review of the C.T.V.5 Series III Programme*, Appendix II p.1. (TNA: PRO AVIA 65/671).
[13] Stroud (1975), 'Early Scientific History of the [US] Rocket Grenade Experiment', p.245.
[14] AAS History Series Volume 9 p.245, see bibliography. Diagram reproduced courtesy American Astronautical Society.

It was on the SL07 flight that a significant new discovery was made. One of the grenades exploded at 130 km, and produced a conspicuous bright glow of about 1 km radius. This was a valuable result, the persistence of the glow compared to the instantaneous flashes at lower altitudes allowed alternatives to the sound measuring technique to be used, and the range of the experiment to be extended well above the 80 km limit otherwise set by background noise in the microphones.[15]

The glow arose from photochemical reactions between the explosion products and atomic oxygen. It lasted for about 20 minutes, and observations of its motion through the air and rate of expansion enabled the wind speed and the diffusion coefficient of the glow gases through the local atmosphere to be derived, which gave an estimate of the local air density.[16] A year or two later, Robert Boyd, then a Reader in Physics at UCL, commented on this "By a very kind act of nature, which I think is quite exceptional, we discovered that grenades would provide data on wind above 110 km, because the products of the explosions glow photo-chemically, and their motion can be tracked."[17]

Figure 6.7 This dramatic view was taken at the beginning of April 1958, its purpose to show Skylark launch tower rail damage. The damage is not obvious, the vertical launcher rail may have pulled away from its support strut and been repaired, however it does provides an interesting (possibly unique) perspective of launch apron LA2 below.

(National Archives of Australia: D891, N58/692)

[15] Following this discovery, and the release of sodium vapour from SL11 that produced a similar effect, the creation of glows from contaminant release became a standard sounding rocket technique; see for instance SL761 and SL762 in May 1968. (Chapter 10).

[16] Fox (c.1984), *From Lardner to Massey – A history of physics, space science and astronomy at University College London, 1826 to 1975.*

[17] Boyd (1961), 'The Scientific Programme of Skylark to Mid-1960', *RAeS Journal Vol.65 (March 1961), p.531.* Quotation reproduced by kind permission of The Royal Aeronautical Society's Aeronautical Journal.

Also on board SL07 was the Birmingham dielectric experiment designed to measure the variation of electron density with altitude. This experiment had failed on SL04, and was only partially successful this time, but with SL09 in June, it would achieve full success. Hence, this flight was an example of how some of the scientific experiments were repeated many times in order to perfect the equipment, and to determine seasonal variations of the phenomena measured.

May 1958   SL05

In May 1958, a month after the launch of SL07, the last of the six initial scheduled RAE proving flights (SL05) took place. This is described in the previous chapter.

June 1958   SL22, SL18, SL09

SL22 – the first military flight

As has been described in Chapter 3, Skylark had been developed for military as well as scientific purposes, and once the original proving flights had been completed, a firing programme was drafted as follows:[18]

1. Programme in support of Black Knight
2. Programme in support of Ballistic Missile development [Blue Streak]
3. Gassiot programme [i.e. the Royal Society scientific experiments]
4. RAE research programme

In some cases the firing was to be primarily in support of a military programme, in other cases the military experiment was secondary to the main purpose, for instance Skylarks 01 to 03 had been primarily to prove the vehicle, but they also carried special aerials for heating measurement experiments devised by the RAE B.M.(Ballistic Missile) Division. At the beginning of June, the first launch for purely military purposes duly took place. See Table 6.3.

As described shortly, the Black Knight rocket vehicle was designed to obtain data on the behaviour of payloads during atmospheric re-entry from space. In 1958, the UK and Woomera were busy preparing for its first launch, and as part of this programme, SL22 tested the Black Knight command system, and a long burning high altitude flare.[19] The test of the command link was successful,[20] although SL22 may have subsequently broken up.[21]

SL18 - Disaster strikes

In 1957, the CSAGI[22] Rocket and Satellite Conference in Washington had recommended a special 'rocket' interval for June 1958.[23] In accordance with this, the next two scientific flights of Skylark were scheduled specially for the IGY programme, with firings planned for successive days. They were the object of official interest, the Australian Minister of Supply attending the launchings.[24]

Unfortunately the launch of the first, SL18, resulted in the first Skylark failure, a motor problem four seconds after firing causing it to crash.[25]

Seq. Nos	Launch date	Ref. (sponsor) launch site	Config-uration	Apogee km (miles)	Experi-menters	Experiments	Result
8 (4)	5 June 1958	SL22 (UK) Woomera	Un, Rav.2A	153 (95)	RAE	Test – Black Knight command system & long burning high altitude flare	S

Table 6.3 A summary of SL22.

Seq. Nos	Launch date	Ref. (sponsor) launch site	Config-uration	Apogee km (miles)	Experi-menters	Experiments	Result
9 (5)	18 June 1958	SL18 (UK) Woomera	Un, Rav.2	3 (1.9)	UCL IC Bir	Neutral atmosphere – (grenades) " " - (window/chaff) Ionosphere – electron concentration	Motor failed +4 s.

Table 6.4 A summary of the ill-fated SL18.

[18] RAE GW Dept. (1958), *A Brief Review of the C.T.V.5 Series III Programme*, p.3.
[19] RAE GW Dept. (1958), p.4.
[20] Dorling (1959), *The First Six Skylark Firings*, p.66.
[21] BAe (1990), *Record of Skylark Launches 1957-1990*.
[22] This committee had been formed to act as the governing body for all IGY activities. (CSAGI was an acronym derived from the French).
[23] 'Flight' magazine 26 February 1960, p.269.
[24] Massey & Robins (1986), *History of British Space Science*, p.46.
[25] Dorling (1959), p.62 and Jessen (1959), *Re-design of the Raven Interrupting Device*, p.3.

No. 32,175 (Registered at G.P.O., Melbourne, for) (Transmission by Post as a Newspaper)   MELBOURNE, THURSDAY, JUNE

BRITISH ROCKET TEST ENDS IN CRASH

Skylark Fails at Woomera

From "The Age" Special Reporter.

WOOMERA, Wednesday. — The British Skylark rocket test tonight ended in spectacular failure when the giant cylinder turned over after rising 10,000 feet and crashed about two miles from the launching site.

The Skylark shot away from the ground with a burst of purple flame and sped into the dark night sky trailing fire and emitting a series of reports.

At 10,000 feet it appeared to turn aside, and came down still trailing fire. When it hit the ground it sent up a pillar of burning pink flame, which died down and then rose again time and again.

Figure 6.8 Despite the claims later on in this newspaper article,[26] SL18 crashed because of a motor interrupter unit that inadvertently operated.

('The Age', Thursday 19th June 1958, p.1.) [27]

Figure 6.9 Some remnants of the SL18 grenade bay, after recovery from the crash site.

(National Archives of Australia: D891, N58/1234)

A subsequent RAE investigation concluded [28] that vibration had caused inadvertent interrupter operation, and recommended that interrupters should only be fitted[29] when needed (on SL18 an interrupter less gunpowder charge had been used instead of a normal pressure plug). The interrupter was also redesigned to avoid the problem in future.

---

[26] That all the grenades had accidently fired at the same time.
[27] Reproduced with permission.
[28] Jessen (1959), *Re-design of the Raven Interrupting Device*.
[29] As described in Chapter 5, the interrupter had been first tested on SL06, the fifth proving flight.

SL09 – second time lucky

Fingers must have been crossed for the similar launch the following evening. Fortunately, this time all went well, and SL09 reached an altitude of 149 km (93 miles).

As shown in the table below, the experiments carried were the same as for SL18, and although the grenade and window experiments failed, the dielectric method for measuring electron concentration worked well for the first time. This clearly showed the presence of a narrow shelf of ionisation near 100 km, caused by sporadic E ionisation. This result came in time for it to be reported by Sir Harrie Massey at an IGY conference the following month in Moscow.[30]

…one of the big questions was the sporadic E layer… We didn't know the thickness of it at all, we didn't know to what extent it was due to sheer forces compressing the ionisation, or what….Various folk were giving their reports, and the American delegate reported they had made measurements on the sporadic E layer. It just so happened that we had done so, and Harrie turned to me and said 'And what did you find?' and I said 'We measured it to be 0.8 kilometres'. That is of no particular significance … but I remember that Harrie Massey was immensely thrilled to have a figure to give the Americans on that occasion.[31]

Seq. Nos	Launch date	Ref. (sponsor) launch site	Config- uration	Apogee km (miles)	Experi- menters	Experiments	Result
10 (6)	19 June 1958	SL09 (UK) Woomera	Un, Rav.2	149 (93)	UCL	Neutral atmosphere – (grenades)	F
					IC	" " - (window/chaff)	F
					Bir	Ionosphere – electron concentration	S

Table 6.5 A summary of SL09.

Figure 6.10 A commemorative envelope celebrating Skylark's launches during IGY rocket week in 1958.
(J.A.Hill)

Figure 6.11 Left: A Skylark nose cone with isolating ring, as used for the University of Birmingham dielectric experiment.
(Science Museum object 1974-240 (probably), author 100_4987)[32]

---

[30] Massey & Robins (1986), *History of British Space Science*, p.47.
[31] Boyd in 2001, CCBH (2005), *Skylark Sounding Rockets1957-1972*, p.45, & *Prospero* No.2, p.110.
[32] Image taken at the London Science Museum (Wroughton), permission granted by Science & Society Picture Library.

Seq. Nos	Launch date	Ref. (sponsor) launch site	Config- uration	Apogee km (miles)	Experi- menters	Experiments	Result
11 (7)	19 Jun/ Sept. 1958	SL08 (UK) Woomera	Un, Rav.2	157 (98)	UCL	Neutral atmosphere – (grenades)	F
					IC	" " – (window/chaff)	F
					Bir	Ionosphere – electron concentration	Sf

Table 6.6 A summary of SL08.

19th Jun/Sep 1958   SL08

There is some confusion over the month of the launch of **SL08**, it appears that all 'official' sources [33] say it was the 19th September, but other sources [34] confidently report it was the 19th June! This is curious, as being primarily for scientific rather than military purposes, there would seem little need to be coy about the date.

The vehicle itself was successful, reaching an altitude of 157 km (98 miles), the highest yet achieved. The university experiments were the same set as before, but unfortunately the run of bad luck continued, the grenade and window experiments failed (the grenades failing to fire[35]), and there was no telemetry from the dielectric experiment. The lack of scientific results meant that the flight was not reported in any scientific papers, losing the chance to resolve the launch date ambiguity.

The launch tower extended

As noted in Chapter 3, the Skylark launch tower at Woomera was originally 80 feet (24.4 m) high. In October 1958, this was extended by 25% to 100 feet (31m).[36]

December 1958   SL11

Hence, in the final flight of 1958, Skylark **SL11** became the first to use the extended tower:

It had been intended to test the first Cuckoo boost motor on SL11, but this idea was abandoned when the Cuckoo motor was found to have an unsatisfactory filling.[37] It would be another year before the Cuckoo would be flight tested, on SL51 in April 1960.

SL11 was the first to carry a new type of scientific payload, a sodium vapour experiment that involved ejecting several kilograms of sodium at height. A bright yellow glow (as seen in street lamps) then occurred, caused by fluorescence in sunlight at the high altitude. The glow provided information about atmospheric density and wind speeds, just as for a grenade glow.[38] This experiment originated with David Bates, a distinguished professor at Queen's University of Belfast, whose early research papers with Harrie Massey had transformed the study of the terrestrial ionosphere into a quantitative discipline of enquiry.[39] The sodium glow experiment had been first suggested by Bates in 1946, long before the Gassiot Committee had any idea how it could be implemented!

Seq. Nos	Launch date	Ref. (sponsor) launch site	Config- uration	Apogee km (miles)	Experi- menters	Experiments	Result
12 (8)	3 Dec. 1958	SL11 (UK) Woomera	Un, Rav.2A	129-137 (80-85)	Belfast	Neutral atmosphere – density & winds > 60 km using sodium vapour	S
					RAE	Test – magnetometer & photocells	S

Table 6.7 A summary of SL11.

[33] Various RAE documents, for instance Dorling (1959), *The First Six Skylark Firings*, p.66, and BAe (1990), *Record of Skylark Launches 1957-1990*.

[34] Massey & Robins (1986), *History of British Space Science*, p.393, & McDowell (2009), *List of Skylark Launches*.

[35] Some initial unreliability of the grenades was traced to their delay fuses being unpressurised. (Dorling (1991), p.10.

[36] Dorling (1975), 'Early History of the Skylark Rocket', p.169.

[37] Dorling (1959), *The First Six Skylark Firings*, p.67.

[38] Massey & Robins (1986), *History of British Space Science*, p.30.

[39] Dalgarno (1997), 'Sir David Robert Bates 1916 – 1994', p.49.

Figure 6.12 The Skylark SL11 sodium burners, as positioned under the nose cone.
(National Archives of Australia: D891, N58/1361)

To observe the glow, Skylark had to be launched at twilight, when the Sun was at a depression of six degrees. This was achieved by SL11 within two minutes of the optimum time,[40] and was probably the first chemical release experiment from a rocket.[41]

Achieving a launch to such a tight timescale was not easy:

> This was a considerable feat when it was first performed at the Woomera range because the rocket had to be launched within a few minutes of a certain time, so that it would be twilight at the altitude wanted, between 60 and 100 kilometres or so.[42]

Fortunately, the experiment was a success:

> Bates' most celebrated experiment along these lines was conducted in 1955 [sic] and was certainly spectacular. The experiment was included as part of the UK space research programme and an impressive glow did indeed occur, much to the delight of the popular press, which ran headlines hailing the arrival of 'artificial moonlight'.

Of these press accounts, David, with his legendary dry wit and humour, reminisced as follows: "Nonsensical pieces were published about lighting up towns with sodium clouds. Photographers were sent to get pictures of me, reporters to interview me, or if that was a bother, to at least personalise the press release, which was easy because provincial professors could be assumed to be absent minded, untidy, and other-worldly. The folly stimulated Pravda to publish a skittish article entitled 'Moonshine Madness', according to the aged Irish Times reporter in St Petersburg, a correspondent whose very name was a guarantee of the authenticity of the report – I refer of course to Rory O'Snowinhisbooze." [43]

With others, Professor Bates went on to write papers "...that are the foundation of research on global change today as we seek to understand the response of the atmosphere to the damage we inflict upon it".[44]

A programme for the next three years

Meanwhile, in August 1958, the RAE Guided Weapons Department had issued a report that included a programme of Skylark launches planned for the next three years.[45] This included both "Gassiot" (scientific) and military missions, altogether it identified five separate programmes, rather than the four listed in the text of the report, an additional programme of "jet control development" being included:

---

[40] 'Flight' magazine 26 February 1960, p.269.
[41] Dalgarno (1997), p.64.
[42] Massey (1961), 'Upper Atmosphere Experiments with Particular Reference to Black Knight and Skylark', p.64.
[43] McCartney & Whitaker (2002), *Physicists of Ireland: Passion and Precision*, p.264.
[44] Dalgarno (1997), 'Sir David Robert Bates 1916 – 1994', p.49. (*Biographical Memoirs of Fellows of the Royal Society*, Vol. 43, Nov. 1997).
[45] RAE GW Dept. (1958), *A Brief Review of the C.T.V.5 Series III Programme*, Appendix III.

APPENDIX III

Programme of C.T.V. 5 Series III (Skylark) Firings
From June 1958 to June 1960

Date	(1) Gassiot Programme	(2) Programme in support of Black Knight	(3) Programme in support of B.M development	(4) Programme of jet control development	+(5) R.A.E.Research and Development programme
1958					
June	SL09, SL18	SL22			
July					
Aug.					
Sep.	SL08 SL10 SL11				SL19
Oct.		SL21			
Nov.	SL14 SL16	SL23			SL51[/] SL24
Dec.					SL52
1959					
Jan.	SL12 SL17		SL55[/]		SL53
Feb.	SL13 SL15		SL56		
Mar.		X	SL57		
Apr.			SL58		SL20
May					
June					XG
July				X	
Aug.		X			
Sep.			SL25		XG
Oct.			SL26	X	
Nov.			SL27		
Dec.					XG
1960					
Jan.		X	SL28	X	
Feb.			SL29		
Mar.			SL30		XG
Apr.				X	
May					
June					XG

/ - Rounds numbered 51 and above will be fired at Aberporth if possible.
X - Rounds planned but not yet detailed.
XG - Raven-Gosling rounds planned but not detailed.
+ - The rounds in column 5 are devoted exclusively to the R.A.E research
    Programme, but the rounds in column 1 carry experiments in the R.A.E.
    Programme as subsidiary payload.

Guided Weapons Department,
Royal Aircraft Establishment,
Farnborough, Hants.

14th August, 1958

Figure 6.13 The programme of Skylark firings for June 1958 to June 1960, as anticipated by the RAE.[46]

[46]   RAE GW Dept. (1958), *A Brief Review of the C.T.V.5 Series III Programme*, Appendix III.

1. The 'Gassiot' column showed the timescale for the completion of the first twelve firings agreed with the universities, which with those already launched, comprised SL07 to SL18.

2. The programme in support of Black Knight had already included secondary experiments associated with five earlier Skylarks, as well as the dedicated SL22 launched in June. These were to be followed by SL21, SL23 and three more rounds planned but not yet detailed.

3. The programme in support of "B.M. development" (Black Knight and Blue Streak) comprised ten rounds, with firing due to start in 1959. The intention at this time was that SL55 to SL58 would be launched from Aberporth in Wales, but for range safety reasons no standard Skylarks were ever launched from there, and SL55-58 were never flown as such. However, one of the aims of this programme was to obtain knowledge of the drift of high quality autopilot gyroscopes under conditions of prolonged acceleration,[47] and a comprehensive programme did take place from Woomera, starting with SL33 in 1960, and continuing over the next four years with SL25 through to SL32.

4. The RAE programme of jet control development concerned the control of missiles both inside and outside the atmosphere. A number of firings of a device to stabilise a separated head were planned for 1959, evolving into the fully stabilised head later used for scientific purposes.

5. RAE research and development experiments were carried in rounds belonging to other programmes wherever possible, for instance flight testing flux gate magnetometers and photocell devices to measure missile attitude. However the rounds in column 5 were exclusively for use by the RAE, for instance it was the intention to use SL24 to flight test two magnetic tape recorders, and devote SL20 to the measurement of atmospheric pressure using a variety of pressure gauges.[48]

The rounds marked "XG" were explained "To extend our field of investigations into the problems of very high speed flight along ballistic trajectories, Skylark will be modified to carry a Gosling motor and small payload, which will be projected to heights of 300-400 miles."[49] This did not come about in that form, but instead saw the light of day as the "Jaguar / Jabiru" hypersonic research programme. This used a research vehicle based on a Rook motor rather than a Raven, and the programme ran separately from Skylark for 15 years from 1959 to 1974.[50]

In the report it was admitted that delays in the Skylark programme would occur because of the 'Middle East Crisis'[51] and shortage of suitable motors. The programme was indeed optimistic; in the event, most of the Skylark launches listed were delayed by months, some by years. For range safety reasons, none were fired from Aberporth.

In later years, Skylarks being procured for the RAE tended to be classified simply as for RAE (Space Tech) or RAE (Motor/System proving).[52]

Black Knight - Britain's second space rocket

1958 was a busy year at Woomera. Whilst preparations were being made for the SL08 firing described above, the 7th September saw the first launch of a new and very different British rocket, Black Knight – the rocket for which the first Skylarks had been used to test components and systems.

Black Knight was the first of the 'big rockets' at Woomera, a ballistic research vehicle. Its purpose was to support the development of the even larger 'Blue Streak' medium range ballistic missile by obtaining data on the behaviour of test heads during atmospheric re-entry from space.[53] The design and development of Black Knight had been running in parallel with Skylark, and as noted in Chapter 2, during some of the early meetings both had been on the agenda. For instance in March 1955, one meeting had considered whether this re-entry test vehicle should be powered by solid fuel or liquid propellants, and concluded that "the four motor liquid fuel vehicle" seemed the best solution.[54]

Development contracts were awarded to Armstrong-Siddeley in Coventry for the Gamma 201 engine, and to Saunders Roe on the Isle of Wight for the airframe and integration. Although work started at the same time as Skylark, Black Knight was considerably more complex, and so development took longer. However, despite being Britain's first major liquid fuelled rocket, the development programme went very well. At Woomera a new launch area (LA5) situated 5 km (3.1 miles) southwest of the existing range head was

---

[47] RAE GW Dept. (1958), *A Brief Review of the C.T.V.5 Series III Programme*, p.4.
[48] RAE GW Dept. (1958), p.5.
[49] Ibid.
[50] Jabiru – see for instance Morton (1989), *Fire across the Desert*, p.405.
[51] In July 1958, a pro-Western government was toppled in Iraq and Lebanon was threatened by civil war. A large US force occupied Beirut, an action that was condemned by the Soviet Union, and for a time the situation threatened to escalate into full-scale war.
[52] For instance, see minutes of the Third Skylark Policy meeting, November 1966, Appendix 4. (TNA: PRO AVIA 92/144).
[53] The development of the appropriate atmospheric re-entry technology was essential to avoid the Blue Streak warheads being vaporised like a meteor by the intense heat of re-entry.
[54] Minutes of 'Re-Entry Test Vehicle Panel Meeting No.4' March 1955. (TNA: PRO AVIA 49/110).

designed and constructed by WRE. This included a water cooled exhaust duct and a launcher stand on massive foundations incorporating hydraulic jaws; and just 150 metres away a blockhouse and equipment centre (EC5) with a concrete roof two metres thick.[55]

Since 1956, equipment had been arriving from the UK for installation. This included an umbilical mast and an assem-

bly gantry that rolled back, all another step up from the relatively simple Skylark.

A successful static firing of the Gamma 201 engine had taken place on 2 September 1958. Black Knight was always launched during moonless nights, so that head re-entry could be optically tracked. (Hence the name from 'black night'?) Thus, it was at 8:03 pm on the warm spring even-

Figure 6.14 Testing the exhaust duct water-cooling at the new Black Knight launch pad, c.1959.[56]
(National Archives of Australia: A1200, L33563)

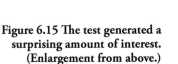

Figure 6.15 The test generated a surprising amount of interest. (Enlargement from above.)
(National Archives of Australia: A1200, L33563)

---

[55] Morton (1989), *Fire across the Desert*, p.416.
[56] Ivan Winter recalls, "We had to clean out the thousands of jets or orifices in a large, elbow-shaped, cylindrical duct, located directly beneath the rocket, to deflect hot exhaust gases away from the launcher. Huge volumes of high-pressure water blasted out of these orifices during firings preventing the metal duct from melting. But even wearing a jumper and duffle coat didn't keep me warm, with the cold wind from the donga blasting up the duct, right up my trouser legs and duffle coat!" (Winter (2010), *Those were the days!*, p.322).

Figure 6.16 Black Knight BK03 being prepared for launch at LA5, three miles south west of the Skylark launch pad.
(WRE)

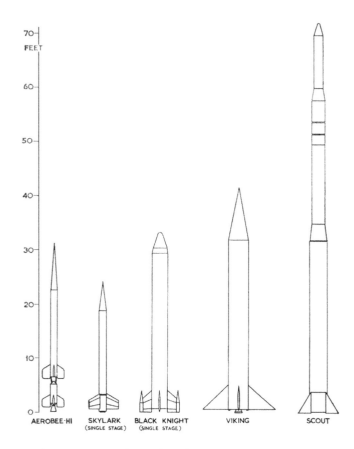

Right: Figure 6.17 This outline drawing compares various ballistic research rockets of 1960.
(Lyons (1961, figure 3)[58]
The four on the left are sub-orbital rockets, the Scout vehicle on the far right was a solid fuelled satellite launcher developed by NASA, and later used to launch several British scientific satellites.

ing of the 7th September that BK01 rose from its floodlit launching pad and disappeared into the darkness:

> All tests had previously been conducted at Highdown [IOW], except for the actual lift-off, and in view of the reported failures at lift-off in the US, we were inwardly apprehensive about how Black Knight would perform. Failures were expected and because of this as many as 12 launches per year were envisioned. Subsequent events proved this to be unnecessary. The count-down and lift-off went smoothly. We held our breath as the seconds of flight time accumulated. After the 120 seconds mark we knew success was at hand. In actual fact the engine shut down prematurely a few seconds before all-burnt. To almost get to all-burnt on the very first attempt was success indeed.[57]

The main proving trial objectives had been achieved, although a problem in the destruct command system resulted in an explosion at +132 seconds,[59] after 90% of the fuel was burnt, so the velocity achieved was only 70% of nominal.[60] Hence this first proving flight reached an apogee of 140 miles (225 km), only a little greater than that of the Skylarks to date, although subsequent flights would rise several times further.

BK01 had an all up weight of 13,000 lbs (5900 kg), compared to that of typically 2,600 lb (1179 kg) for Skylark, making it five times more massive.

However the original Black Knight Gamma 201 engine thrust of around 16,400 lbf (73 kN),[61] was only a little up on the 12,000 lbf (53 kN) of the solid fuelled Skylark, but at around 132 seconds[62] the burn time was four times as long, providing considerably more impulse.

[57]   Tharratt (1972), 'Personal Profile, Charles E. Tharratt, Rocket Engineer', p.306.
[58]   RAeS Journal Vol.65 (March 1961), p.173. Reproduced by kind permission of The Royal Aeronautical Society's Aeronautical Journal.
[59]   Post-flight analysis showed an aerial had picked up a stray signal and had inadvertently triggered the destruct system. (Hill (2007), p.12).
[60]   Gordon & Parkin (1964), *A summary of "Black Knight" flight data from 1958 to 1962*, p.3.
[61]   See for instance Millard (2001) *The Black Arrow Rocket*, p.36.
[62]   See for instance Hill (2007), *Black Knight – Britain's first ballistic rocket*, p.51.

Conclusions at the end of 1958 and the completion of the IGY

Although the first Skylark launching on 13 February 1957 was rather later than the optimistic target originally set (late 1956), a considerable number of experiments had still been carried out during the International Geophysical Year. As Frank Hazell described:

> The performance achieved has been very close to expectations, and far more than originally asked for by the Royal Society. There have been failures and disappointments – as in any rocket programme – but the results achieved are most gratifying, and the growing experience of all the teams concerned should ensure greater success in the future.[63]

Skylark funding renewal and associated complexities

As noted in Chapter 3, initial funding for a four-year Skylark programme had been granted in 1955, sufficient to carry the programme though to the middle of 1959. Half of the original

£100,000 grant had contributed to the cost of the rocket vehicles, the other half to the cost of staff and equipment for purely scientific work.[64]

Thus as 1958 and the IGY drew to a close, funding for both rocket manufacture and the scientific programme needed renewing, for what became known as the "extended programme". In September, the Royal Society Rocket Subcommittee met under its chairman Professor H.S.W.Massey.[65] They discussed and approved his proposed programme for upper atmosphere research for the four years beginning April 1959. This included experiments to investigate a set of nine different types of upper atmosphere phenomena, the experimenters to include the five original university groups, plus two new ones from Imperial College. The target launch rate was to be one a month.

The launching sites and types of Skylark rocket were also specified, and six launches from Aberporth in Wales were anticipated. The estimated costs appended to the minutes of the meeting were:

```
Estimated Expenditure

Cost of 48 rockets ...............................£192,000
Cost of 24 recorders  ..............................12,000
Subsistence expenses of representatives in Australia
(1½ present on average at any one time) ................7,000
Groups
Aberystwyth and Bangor(A)                        24,000
Belfast(Q)                                       19,000
Birmingham(B)                                    23,000
Imperial College(Geophys) (ICG)                  10,000
Imperial College(Meteor.)(ICM)                    9,000
University College (UC)                           36,000
Imperial College (Physics)(ICP)                  10,000
Research Laboratory (See(h)contamination)         8,000
                                    Total    £350,000
```

Figure 6.18 The Royal Society's proposed programme for Skylark upper atmosphere research for the four years beginning April 1959.[66]

[63] Hazell (1961), 'Skylark', *RAeS Journal Vol.65 (March 1961), p.530*. Quotation reproduced by kind permission of The Royal Aeronautical Society's Aeronautical Journal.

[64] Massey (1958), *Memorandum on Rocket Research*, p.1.

[65] Minutes of the 15th Royal Society Rocket Subcommittee D meeting of 12th September 1958, copy in UK Ministry of Supply document file 'Upper Atmosphere Research Policy and Financial Control – Skylark'. (TNA: PRO AVIA 65/671).

[66] Appendix to Minutes of the 15th Royal Society Rocket Subcommittee D meeting of 12th September 1958, copy in UK Ministry of Supply document file 'Upper Atmosphere Research Policy and Financial Control – Skylark', (TNA:.PRO AVIA 65/671). A similar but augmented estimate appears in Massey (1958), *Memorandum on Rocket Research*, p.3.

The total of £350,000 was considerably more than the £100,000 that had been granted in 1955. The expenditure on rockets had risen by about a factor of four (compared with the original £50,000 for 1955-59), because this time there would be a full four years worth of scientific launches and experiments, compared with the previous one year's worth, which had taken place after the RAE's original design, development and proving flights had been completed. A similar argument applied to the amount for university experiments.

Fifty years later, these estimated costs seem very low. However by 2011, £8000 was worth £145,000 to £496,000 and the total of £350,000 worth £6.4 to £22 million.[67] Even so, it was a bargain; the estimated cost to the scientists for each rocket was £4000, only half of the actual cost of £8000,[68] which rather begged the question of where the other half would come from.

It is also interesting to note that these estimates include no allowance for the WRE support facilities at Woomera, which came free of charge to the scientific users on the back of the existing military Joint Project.[69] This provision (together with the use of support facilities and staff) was of considerable benefit to the UK scientists and their budgets! (In the years that followed, this issue - the civilian use of military facilities funded mainly by Australia - had to be resolved.[70])

In Professor Massey's supporting memorandum in November, he acknowledged a new factor, that the advent of space satellites had changed the situation since last time around, but he made the following points:

> It is true that the introduction of artificial satellites must largely replace vertical sounding rockets for the study of atmospheric properties at altitudes greater than 150 miles or so. However, it is not possible to use satellites at lower altitudes because they would have too short a lifetime due to the high air drag. Vertical sounding rockets remain essential, therefore, for the study of the properties of the atmosphere at altitudes below 150 miles. Many very important phenomena occur in this part of the atmosphere…There is still a need for some vertical sounding rocket flights to altitudes at which satellites

can circulate, partly to check data obtained by satellites, partly to make a virtually instantaneous survey of the variation of some important quantity with height out to very great heights.[71]

A parallel RAE document[72] listed the benefits of Skylark to the RAE's military ballistic missile research in general and Black Knight in particular (recalling that it was originally the CTV.5 series III); and makes the point that if funding for the scientific flights was not forthcoming, RAE funded firings would have to continue anyway.

Another factor was that the IGY was due to finish in December 1958. Skylark had sometimes been known as the IGY rocket, but this name had led to concern that it might hinder further funding. As E.B. Dorling later explained:

> For why go on using the rocket once the IGY had ended? This misunderstanding competed, in what little attention was spared to the UK sounding programme in Britain, with a second, one widely conceived by scientists and non-scientists alike, because of the esoteric nature of the subject. The upper atmosphere was to them a still and inactive region beyond the furthest reaches of aircraft or balloon, unchanging and therefore readily characterised by one or two key measurements to be made from one rocket flight. The IGY rocket became to many in Britain *the* IGY rocket, one single rocket that would measure all there was to be measured. What justification could there be for two, let alone 200? [73]

The UK's Ministry of Supply were well aware of the apparent inconsistencies in the costs of the Royal Societies' proposal, one document responding with "The whole of the £192,000 that is included in the Royal Society's estimate, in respect of the rockets themselves, is highly fictitious." [74]

However it soon seems to have been recognised that the Royal Society proposal was for the scientific aspects only, it required 'matching funding' to meet the real costs, and a separate application to the Treasury by the RAE to fund their share of the Skylark programme in its "CTV.5 Series III" guise for three more years came to £500,000.[75] (£240,000 for supplying 23

[67] 2011 figures based on the "Historic Opportunity " and "Economic Cost" measures for a large project, from Lawrence H. Officer and Samuel H. Williamson, "Five Ways to Compute the Relative Value of a UK Pound Amount, 1270 to Present," MeasuringWorth, 2014, *www.measuringworth.com/ ukcompare/* , (last accessed August 2014).

[68] Burton, N.E.D, 'Letter to John Marshall, H.M.Treasury, requesting RAE Skylark funding', October 1958, p.4, and RAE GW Dept.(1958), *A Brief Review of the C.T.V.5 Series III Programme*, p.4, copies in UK Ministry of Supply document file "Upper Atmosphere Research Policy and Financial Control – Skylark" (TNA: PRO AVIA 65/671).

[69] Ibid.

[70] Discussed in some detail in 'Skylarks for Australia', Godwin (2007), p.197 onwards.

[71] Massey (1958), *Memorandum on Rocket Research*, p.2.

[72] Burton, N.E.D, letter to John Marshall, H.M.Treasury, re RAE Skylark funding, October 1958, (as above).

[73] Dorling (1975), 'Early History of the Skylark Rocket', p.165.

[74] Notes on Professor Massey's Memorandum (1958) about the Proposed Programme for 1959-1963, copy in UK Ministry of Supply document file 'Upper Atmosphere Research Policy and Financial Control – Skylark' (TNA:PRO AVIA 65/671)

[75] Burton, N.E.D., letter to John Marshall, H.M.Treasury, re RAE Skylark funding, October 1958. At some stage during the funding application process, the programme appears to have been reduced from four to three years.

vehicles a year and £260,000 for other contracts, motors, instrumentation, etc.). This came to a grand total of £862,000 to fund Skylark, an eight-fold increase on the £100,000 that had initiated the project some four years previously, and worth some £16 – £52 million in 2011 terms.

The outcome of all these machinations appears to be that although in December the Treasury agreed to continue funding Skylark on an annual basis, it refused to give authority for a full three-year programme.[76] These requests for funding were the first of several that had a profound effect on the machinery of UK government for funding scientific research, as it became recognised that the existing civil service procedures and organisation were no longer suitable for such "big science" spending.[77]

In May 1959, the British Prime Minister Harold Macmillan announced the start of a modest UK space programme, and a government Space Research Steering Group (SRG) was set up, under which the Skylark programme was brought in 1960.[78] Other countries set up space agencies to cope with this new field.[79] However, apparently because of a lack of political leadership, nothing similar was done in the UK, and funding applications as discussed above triggered years of tortuous in fighting and battles between the Treasury and other government departments about space related funding and control of expenditure.[80] Despite this, somehow the funding was granted for Skylark to continue, perhaps later on helped by the fact that it could provide the required test flights for UK instruments intended to be flown on US satellites.[81]

In parallel with all this, the Royal Society formed a new committee, the 'British National Committee on Space Research' (BNCSR), to help the scientific community cope with the rapidly developing field of space science. Initially this committee had been proposed just to provide UK liaison with the newly formed international Committee on Space Research (COSPAR)[82]. However, it was soon realised that it could also provide co-ordination and management of British post-IGY activities in space science, and take over from the Rocket and Artificial Satellite and sub-committees of the Gassiot Committee.[83] The BNCSR was therefore formed with three subcommittees:

1. TADREC – concerned with tracking, orbit analysis and data recovery.
2. DOE – Design Of Experiments – with a remit to continue the work of the Rocket Sub-committee in choosing experiments to be flown in sounding rockets, and soon artificial satellites.
3. The third sub-committee was set up to liaise with the World Data Centre at the Radio Research Station (RRS) at Slough. (The RRS was building a 25 metre diameter radio telescope at Chilbolton, deep in the Hampshire countryside, specifically for the tracking of satellites and deep space probes,[84] and would also launch its first experiment aboard Skylark in 1962).

The BNCSR first met in March 1959, and lasted for many years, although its relationship with the government and civil service for funding and approval purposes was complex and cumbersome.[85]

SKYLARK LAUNCHES AND SCIENCE IN 1959

In 1959, the Soviet 'Luna 2' became the first man made object to land on another celestial body, when it impacted on the surface of the Moon on September 14th.

Meanwhile, back at Woomera, 1959 started quietly for Skylark, although the second half of the year was quite busy. In July, SL14 provided the first solar physics experiment, the first of many to look beyond the Earth's atmosphere.

Jan.	Feb.	March	April	May	June	July	Aug.	Sept.	Oct.	Nov.	Dec.
		SL21				SL19	SL17	SL12		SL16	SL38
						SL14		SL15		SL60	
						SL24					

Table 6.8 The 10 Skylark Launches that took place in 1959. (For full details see Appendix 3.)

(Key: black = mainly RAE programmes, blue = mainly UK scientific programme (unstabilised)

---

76 Bissell, F.N.J., letter to Dr A.W.Lines at RAE Farnborough, 8 December 1958. (TNA: PRO AVIA 65/671). The reader may reasonably ask, "Does this mean the Treasury was controlling the UK space science programme?" The answer appears to be yes, see for instance Godwin (2007), *The Skylark Racket,* p.157.

77 See Godwin (2007), *The Skylark Rocket,* Chapter 7, for an in depth treatment of this subject.

78 Ibid, p.158.

79 For instance, NASA was set up in 1958 to coordinate American non-military space research, and the corresponding French agency, CNES, was established in 1961.

80 Godwin (2007) in *The Skylark Rocket*, Chapter 2, provides a good account of this Byzantine process. Not for the faint hearted!

81 Godwin (2007), p.65.

82 COSPAR's first meeting was in London in 1958, and in 2008 it celebrated its 50th anniversary.

83 Massey & Robins (1986), *History of British Space Science*, p.63.

84 This is now the Chilbolton Observatory (Chilbolton Facility for Atmospheric and Radio Research – CFARR !!), which celebrated its 40th anniversary of operation in 2007, see the excellent website *www.chilbolton.rl.ac.uk* (last accessed August 2014).

85 See for instance the description by Massey & Robins (1986), *History of British Space Science,* p.72, and the diagram by Godwin (2007), *The Skylark Rocket,* p.289.

The first launch took place on the 4th March, with three main experiments. The first was a repeat of the sodium vapour experiment of the previous flight; the other two were repeats of the grenade and window experiments. The RAE also included some equipment tests in support of the Black Knight programme.

Unfortunately, this 13th flight *was* unlucky. SL21 failed a short way into flight, and only reached an altitude of 30 km. High-speed film records showed a fin to have been torn away,[86] and the rocket broke up towards the end of the boost phase, when travelling at some 3000 mph (4800 km/h), near its maximum speed of a mile a second.

This came as an unpleasant surprise to the designers, who from the earlier proving flights had concluded that the rocket was stable in flight. Following this failure, theoretical and wind-tunnel investigations were undertaken,[87] with the result "It is now fairly well established that ... pitch-roll resonance occurred leading to a large amplification of an existing small malalignment and resulting in large lateral accelerations, which in the case of Skylark 21 were catastrophic".[88]

With hindsight, it was also realised that this incipient problem might have caused some of the dispersion anomalies observed in earlier flights. Similar problems were known to affect other sounding rockets. The 'roll-yaw' resonance effect occurs when the natural frequency of the yawing or pitching motion of a rocket (which varies with altitude) becomes close to the rate of roll. When Skylark was designed, no adequate theoretical treatment of the relevant aerodynamics existed,[89] and moreover in that pre-digital computer age, any calculations had to be laboriously done by hand.

SL21 appears to have been the first fitted with the GW 25 variation of the GW 24 fin as first used on Skylark 05, and investigation continued to find out why this might be more prone to the effect. To create the GW 25, the GW 24 fin assembly had been modified for future use with a Cuckoo booster, the fin mount being extended to enclose most of the exhaust cone and to accommodate the boost motor. The actual fins remained the same.

All this was of no consolation to the scientists. It had been a bad run for the UCL grenade and Imperial College window experimenters, the fourth successive failure, and a year had passed since the last success with flight SL07.

Skylark then appears to have taken a back seat for a few months, as Woomera concentrated on Black Knight launches. Firings of BK03, 04 and 05 took place on 12th March, 11th June and 29th June 1959 respectively. BK03 was the second proving flight, and BK04 the first to carry out the military re-entry experiment for which Black Knight had been designed. BK04 reached an apogee of 499 miles (803 km), five times the altitude Skylark had achieved so far. (For comparison, the International Space Station orbits at 217 miles / 350 km). From this vast height, the re-entry head fell earthwards, reaching a speed of 8000 mph (12,900 km/h) during atmospheric re-entry at 38 miles (70 km) high. This provided the required data on re-entry dynamics and heating, the head for instance reaching some 800ºC.[90] (The apogee of 599 miles can be seen to scale on the diagram at the start of Chapter 3).

Despite the great altitudes reached, the danger of Black Knight rockets colliding with any man-made space objects was negligible. By the end of June 1959, there were only eight such objects in Earth orbit (five satellites and three spent rockets),[91] although during the following 49 years a further 6000 have been launched, over half of which were still in orbit in mid 2008![92]

Seq. Nos	Launch date	Ref. (sponsor) launch site	Config-uration	Apogee km (miles)	Experi-menters	Experiments	Result
13 (1)	04 March 1959	SL 21 (UK) Woomera	Un, Rav.2	30 (19)	UCL	Neutral atmosphere – (grenades)	Vf
					IC	" " - (falling dipoles)	
					Bel	" " - (sodium vapour)	
					RAE	Test - Black Knight type A & B flashes	

Table 6.9 A summary of SL21.

86 Dorling (1975), 'Early History of the Skylark Rocket', p.181.
87 Merchant (1959), *Pitch Roll Resonance - with reference to Skylark 21.* (RAE Technical Memorandum No. G.W. 364).
88 Dorling (1959), *The First Six Skylark Firings* (GW 530), p.63.
89 Massey & Robbins (1986), *History of British Space Science*, p.23.
90 Hill (2001), *A Vertical Empire*, p.165.
91 See for instance Boyd (1960), *Space Research by Rocket and Satellite,* Table 1, p.70.
92 Even so, active satellites are said to comprise only 7% of orbital objects, the rest being space debris!

July 1959   SL19, SL14, SL24

SL19 was part of the RAE research and development programme,[93] which typically tested new forms of instrumentation. This may have been the second attempt to fire SL19, as one source[94] indicates a failed Skylark launch attempt in April. If so, even this firing was not a success as it reached only 50 km, and the same source says, "suffered a propulsion problem":

The new science programme starts

The new science programme for 1959-64 now began. The experiments could be divided into four groups: [95]

1. Study of winds, temperature and densities - the neutral atmosphere

Grenade method and falling sphere experiments	UCL
Radar reflecting foil (window, falling dipoles)	IC
Sodium cloud (temperatures)	QU
Sodium cloud (winds)	QU & UCL
Pressure gauges	RAE

2. Study of Ionosphere – the electrically charged atmosphere

Dielectric experiment and ion cage	BU
Langmuir, sporadic E and mass-spectrometer probes	UCL
Radio Doppler and radio pulse	UCW & RAE

3. Solar radiation experiments – astronomy, effects from outside the atmosphere

Photometry of green line and OH bands	QU
Lyman-alpha ionisation chamber	UCL
X-ray counters and emulsion detectors	UCL

4. Other Experiments

Micrometeorite microphones	QU
Proton precession magnetometers	IC

UC = University College, London; IC = Imperial College, London; QU = Queen's University, Belfast; RAE = Royal Aircraft Establishment; BU = Birmingham University; UCW = University College of Wales (Aberystwyth and Bangor).

SL14 was the first, launched just a week after SL19. The two main experiments were measuring electron and ion concentration by a Langmuir probes,[96] and solar X-ray detectors.

The rocket launch itself was only partially successful, reaching an altitude of just 93 km (57 miles): - "Skylark 14 developed a large incidence during boost and reached only 300,000 feet".[97] This was ascribed to the same resonance that had affected SL21 in March.

The experiments were correspondingly only partially successful. This was the first time a Langmuir probe had been used on Skylark, and it was carried on a five-foot (1.5 m) spike mounted on the Skylark's nose.[98] The purpose of this was to minimise the effect of disturbances caused by the passage of the vehicle.

Seq. Nos	Launch date	Ref. (sponsor) launch site	Config-uration	Apogee km (miles)	Experi-menters	Experiment	Result
14 (2)	01 July 1959	SL19 (UK) Woomera	Un, Rav.2	50 (31)	RAE	Test - probably of new instrumentation. "Suffered propulsion problem"	Ps?

Table 6.10 A summary of SL19.

Seq. Nos	Launch date	Ref. (sponsor) launch site	Config-uration	Apogee km (miles)	Experi-menters	Experiments	Result
15 (3)	08 July 1959	SL14 (UK) Woomera	Un, Rav.2	93 (57)	UCL	Ionosphere – electron & ion concentration (Langmuir probes)	Ps
					UCL/Lei	Solar physics – X-ray detectors	Ps

Table 6.11 A summary of SL14.

[93] RAE GW Dept. (1958), *A Brief Review of the C.T.V.5 Series III Programme*, Appendix III.
[94] Space Lists website, sounding rocket launches 1955-1959, *www.rocketservices.co.uk/spacelists.php*, (last accessed July 2010) (sic).
[95] This list has been compiled from (i) Appendix of the minutes of the Royal Society Rocket Subcommittee meeting of 12th September 1958 (TNA: PRO AVIA 65/671), (ii) Massey (1958), *Memorandum on Rocket Research*, and (iii) 'Flight' magazine 26 Feb.1960, p.270.
[96] The Langmuir probe is named after Nobel Prize winning physicist Irving Langmuir, and is used to measure the electron temperature, electron density, and electric potential of plasma.
[97] Dorling (1959), *The First Six Skylark Firings*, p.63.
[98] The spike had been tested on SL06 in April 1958.

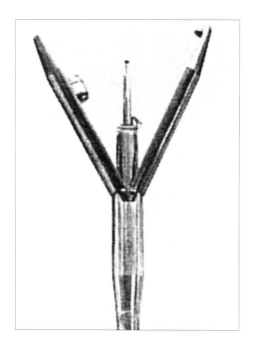

The X-ray detection experiment was the first solar physics experiment launched on Skylark, i.e. the first designed to look beyond the upper atmosphere rather than into it. It was also the first with University of Leicester involvement, and the forerunner of a major application for Skylark.

Interest in extra-terrestrial X-radiation had stemmed from pre- and post-war theories that it could be responsible for the maintenance of the daytime E-layer of the ionosphere.[99] As shown by Figure 6.20, X-rays cannot pass all the way through the Earth's atmosphere, and rockets or space satellites have to be used to observe them. In 1948, the Americans had used captured V-2 and early sounding rockets to demonstrate for the first time that such X-rays did indeed exist.[100]

Figure 6.19 The tip of a Langmuir probe as carried by the probe on the front of SL14.

(Flight magazine, 26 Feb 1960, p.270)

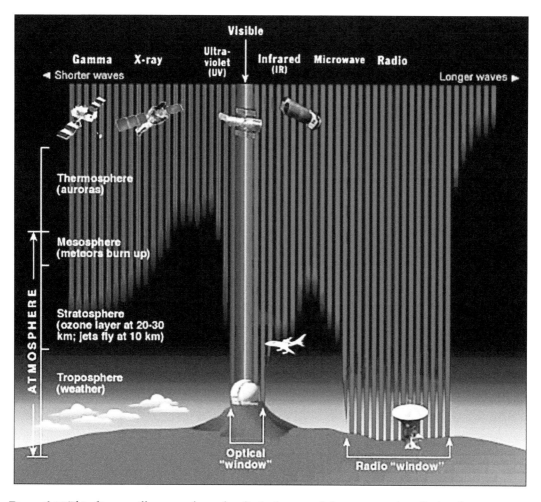

Figure 6.20 This diagram illustrates that only a limited range of electromagnetic radiation from space can penetrate all the way through the Earth's atmosphere. (Not to vertical scale!)

(Image courtesy NASA)

---

[99] See for instance Boyd (1965), 'Techniques for the Measurement of Extra-Terrestrial Soft X-Radiation', p.35.

[100] Boyd (1965), p.36.

Seq. Nos	Launch date	Ref. (sponsor) launch site	Config- uration	Apogee km (miles)	Experi- menters	Experiment	Result
16 (4)	23 July 1959	SL24 (UK) Woomera	Un, Rav.2A	91 (57)	RAE	Test (Skylark technology) - flight test of two magnetic tape recorders	Ef

Table 6.12 A summary of SL24.

Figure 6.21 A tape recorder as flown on Skylark. It is not known when this design was used, but it is a substantially built reel-to-reel affair!

(FAST \ author 100_6111) [106]

Scientists at UCL took up this work, and there K.A.Pounds developed a simple and robust X-ray "emulsion detector" that used special photographic film capable of detecting X-rays.[101] Unfortunately, the SL14 apogee of only 93 km meant it probably did not fly high enough to detect X-rays, and in any case, both emulsion detectors/cameras were destroyed on impact.[102] However, the equipment was designed to be used as a standard measurement device on Skylark rockets, and as such was flown again on SL12 a couple of months later. That launch was fully successful and so the equipment is described in more detail below.

Two weeks after SL14, **SL24** was launched, the second RAE research and development programme flight. See Table 6.12

It is known the intention was to flight test two magnetic tape recorders,[103] but these appear to have failed to work.[104] However within a few months tape recorders had

been successfully flown on Black Knight rockets, (the first flight test being on BK06 [105] in October 1959), so presumably this Skylark trial served its purpose in ironing out 'bugs' in the design.

August 1959   SL17

The next flight, **SL17** on the 19th August, was completely successful, and marked the end of a poor six months for Skylark.

SL17 reached a height of 144 km (89 miles). The experiment on board was designed to study the ionosphere, and was another UCL Langmuir probe experiment. It followed on from that launched on Skylark 14 just over a month before; only this one was completely successful. This probably led to similar equipment being orbited on the Ariel I satellite, see SL38 and the next chapter.

---

[101] Pounds and Bowen (1962), 'A simple rocket-borne X-radiation monitor'.

[102] Pounds and Bowen (1962), p.354.

[103] RAE GW Dept. (1958), *A Brief Review of the C.T.V.5 Series III Programme*, p.5.

[104] Space Lists website, sounding rocket launches 1955-1959, *www.rocketservices.co.uk/spacelists.php*, (last accessed July 2010) (sic).

[105] Gordon and Parkin (1964), *A Summary of "Black Knight" Flight Data from 1958 to 1962*, p.14.

[106] The tape recorder was on show when the author visited the 'FAST' museum at Farnborough UK in May 2011. Image reproduced courtesy of FAST (Farnborough Air Sciences Trust).

Seq. Nos	Launch date	Ref. (sponsor) launch site	Config- uration	Apogee km (miles)	Experi- menters	Experiment	Result
17 (5)	19 Aug. 1959	SL17 (UK) Woomera	Un, Rav.2	144 (89)	UCL	Ionosphere – electron & ion concentration (Langmuir probes)	S

Table 6.13 A summary of SL17.

September 1959   SL12, SL15

SL12 on 17th September included two new experiments. The most radical used a wide aperture (1000 sq cm) mass spectrometer from Birmingham University. The measuring head of this instrument, with its associated part of the electronic circuit, was ejected from the rocket vehicle on a long cable as soon as the vehicle had passed above the major atmospheric drag region. The purpose of this was to obtain measurements remote from any possible gas contamination from the pressurised sections of the rocket or from the hot motor shell.[107] This first attempt failed, but was repeated successfully on the next flight, see SL15 below. The experiment marked the university's move to study the composition of the positive ions that accompany electrons in the ionosphere.[108]

The solar X-ray experiment was the same as that carried on SL14 in July, but this time was completely successful – although as SL12 was not equipped with a parachute[109] the payload was eventually found buried to a depth of 16 feet (4.9 m) in the Woomera desert, having impacted at some 2900 mph (4680 km/h)! Surprisingly, the two cameras on board survived the impact and produced usable data.[110]

Seq. Nos	Launch date	Ref. (sponsor) launch site	Config- uration	Apogee km (miles)	Experi- menters	Experiments	Result
18 (6)	17 Sept. 1959	SL12 (UK) Woomera	Un, Rav.2	132 (82)	Bir	Ionosphere - ion mass spectrometer	F
					UCL	Solar physics – Lyman α detectors	Ps
					UCL	" " - X-ray detectors	S
					RAE	Test (Skylark technology) - magnetometers & aspect photocells	?

Table 6.14 A summary of SL12.

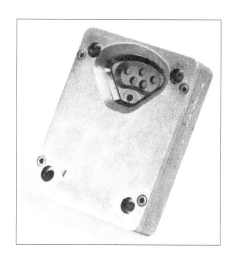

Figure 6.22 The rugged X-ray camera as used on SL12 to measure X-rays in the region 8-20Å (0.8nm-2nm). The shutter is shown open, exposing five filters of metal foil.[111] Below is the single aperture of the optical pinhole camera. The cases of the first cameras were made from duralumin, later changed to steel to reduce impact damage.[112]

[107] Sayers (1959), *Self-Contained Measuring Equipment for Electron Density and Ionic Mass Spectrum*.

[108] Willmore (1987), 'Thirty Years of Space Research', p.147.

[109] There is conflicting evidence regarding the introduction of parachute recovery. Pounds & Bowen (1961) state that parachute recovery on both SL14 (July 1959) and SL12 (September 1959) failed, however as described in the next chapter, the relevant RAE report states that the first parachute test did not take place until Skylark SL16 (November 1959). It is true that some of the Skylarks launched earlier in 1959 (e.g. SL15) were originally scheduled to be fitted with parachute recovery (GW/2320 Appendix II), so it appears the programme ran late.

[110] Pounds & Bowen (1962), 'A simple rocket-borne X-radiation monitor', p.354.

[111] The method of detecting solar X-rays through thin metal foil by means of X-ray sensitive film had first been used on a V-2 rocket in the USA in 1948. (Pounds & Bowen (1962), p.348).

[112] Boyd (1960), *Space Research by Rocket and Satellite*, p.64.

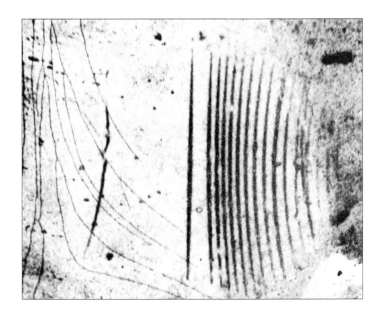

Left: Figure 6.23 The optical pinhole camera aspect monitor record from the flight of Skylark SL12, showing 19 passages of the Sun's image.

(Pounds and Bowen (1962), plate 8(b).)

The X-ray camera was mounted on the outside of the rocket, the base being sealed permanently into the 'strong ring'. It was able to produce measurements of the X-ray spectrum, despite being used on these early non-stabilised Skylarks that were rotating in space. X-ray images were achieved by exposing the film behind various thin foils of aluminium and beryllium, each transparent to X-rays but with different transmission properties. The total exposure of the camera to the Sun was monitored by means of the optical pinhole camera aperture that recorded each passage of the Sun's image across the face of the camera on the same piece of film.

Also in 1959, it was agreed that an instrument to measure solar X-rays would be included on the forthcoming British Ariel I satellite. (See the next chapter.) However, despite the fact that satellites were coming into use, sounding rockets continued to have an important role in this field. In 1962, three years later, an experiment aboard an American sounding rocket would discover X-rays emanating from outside the solar system, and open up a major new branch of astronomy. For this, Ricardo Giacconi would be awarded a share in the Nobel Prize for physics in 2002.[113]

The other new experiment on SL12 was a solar physics experiment. Originating from UCL, it was a "solar Lyman-α detector", designed to measure the strength of a particular ultraviolet wavelength of light from the Sun, "a good measure of the way the sun is behaving, not so much in the corona, but a little lower down, in the chromosphere".[114] As well as being of importance for solar physics, this latter experiment had an immediate importance as part of an investigation into the formation of the D region of the Earth's ionosphere, a layer that could cause complete blackouts in radio communication in times of strong solar disturbance.[115] This was to be followed over the next few years by many such experiments being launched not only by Skylark, but also on British scientific satellites.

Skylark SL15

Only a week later **SL15** was launched, reaching what was (just) a Skylark record altitude of 158 km, 1 km more than SL08 the previous September. As far as is known this mission was completely successful, the mass spectrometer experiment worked on this second attempt, and the "Sporadic E probe" was also successful:

Seq. Nos	Launch date	Ref. (sponsor) launch site	Config- uration	Apogee km (miles)	Experi- menters	Experiments	Result
19 (7)	24 Sept. 1959	SL15 (UK) Woomera	Un, Rav.2	158 (98)	Bir	Ionosphere - ion mass spectrometer	S
					UCL	Ionosphere - sporadic E probe	S
					RAE	Test (Skylark technology) - magnetometers, photocells, reflectometer	?

Table 6.15 A summary of SL15.

[113] Awarded for "pioneering contributions to astrophysics, which have led to the discovery of cosmic X-ray sources". He later became the first director of the Space Telescope Science Institute, the science operations centre for the Hubble Space Telescope.

[114] Boyd (1961), 'The Scientific Programme of Skylark to Mid -1960', p.532.

[115] See for instance Massey & Robins, *History of British Space Science*, p.32.

Figures 6.24 The measuring head of a Birmingham University wide aperture mass spectrometer.

(Hazell (1961), figure 6(a))[117]

Figure 6.25 As recovered after free fall without parachute from a height of 158 km (98 miles).

(Flight magazine, 26 Feb 1960, p.270)

The mass spectrometer was an "experiment of remarkable complexity and ingenuity…a piece of instrumentation fired out on the end of a cable some hundred feet long to make sure that it is well away from the rocket".[116] This had a measuring head consisting of a cylindrical cage having closed ends and a fine outer grid of wires. The transmit times of ions between the grid and central collecting rod provided information on ionic masses.

The Sporadic E probe was a simpler version of the Langmuir probe used before, probably employing a flush electrode in the rocket skin,[118] designed primarily to look for rapid changes in sporadic ionisation at 100 km, but also found useful to provide an ionosphere profile.[119]

At the end of December a short paper by Professor Sayers of Birmingham University appeared, describing the insulated nose cone and the ion mass spectrometer experiments first successfully flown on SL09 and SL15 respectively. It was published (appropriately) by the Royal Society.[120]

Nov. & Dec. 1959	SL16, SL60, SL38

Following a COSPAR recommendation on the value of near simultaneous launchings of rockets with related experiments in different parts of the world, and in connection with the resulting International Rocket Week, a triple Skylark firing

Seq. Nos	Launch date	Ref. (sponsor) launch site	Config-uration	Apogee km (miles)	Experi-menters	Experiment	Result
20 (8)	30 Nov. 1959	SL16 (UK) Woomera	Un, Rav.2	151 (94)	Bel	Neutral atmosphere – (sodium vapour)	S
					RAE	Test (Skylark technology) - first parachute recovery system proving flight	F
21 (9)	30 Nov. 1959	SL60 (UK) Woomera	"	163 (101)	UCL	Neutral atmosphere – (grenades)	S
					IC	" " - (falling dipoles)	F
22 (10)	01 Dec. 1959	SL38 (UK) Woomera	"	159 (99)	UCL	" " - (grenades)	Ps
					IC	" " - (falling dipoles)	F
					Bir	Ionosphere - dielectric probe	S

Table 6.16 A summary of the 1959 triple firing.

[116] Boyd (1961), p.531.
[117] RAeS Journal Vol.65 (August 1961), p.528. Reproduced by kind permission of The Royal Aeronautical Society's Aeronautical Journal.
[118] 'Flight' magazine, 26 February 1960, p.270.
[119] Boyd (1961), p.531.
[120] Sayers (1959), *Self-Contained Measuring Equipment for Electron Density and Ionic Mass Spectrum*.

was made during a 36-hour period on November 30 / December 1. Indeed, Skylark was one of the few rockets to be fired during the international rocket weeks.[121]

This was the first time that two Skylarks had been launched in one day, requiring a special effort by the WRE launch team. The first, **SL16**, carried a successful Belfast 'sodium vapour' experiment, as originally flown on SL11 the previous December and the ill-fated SL21 in March. It was also the first flight trial of the new RAE parachute based instrument head recovery system. Unfortunately it failed, the parachutes being severely damaged and the head becoming a total wreck. This proved a most intractable problem, and investigations and development continued for many years.

The story is begun in the next chapter.

SL60 was fired later the same night (at 22:05 local time), **SL38** the following night (at 21:06), the idea being to measure wind speeds and characteristics 24 hours apart. Despite the fact that over half the grenades failed to detonate, the grenade experiments were at least partially successful on each flight, (an improvement as the vehicle or experiments had failed altogether on the previous five attempts!), and the results were published by UCL as described in detail in a paper,[122] some of which is reproduced in Appendix 4. SL60 achieved the greatest Skylark altitude so far, beating the previous highest (SL15) by a few kilometres, and becoming the first to exceed 100 miles (163 km).

Figure 6.26 Ballistic camera record of SL60 grenade bursts and glow trails. Twelve bursts were fired at an average height of 110 km (68 miles).[123] Thus, this photograph is remarkable because the flashes were that distance from the ground based camera. The streaks in the background are star trails recorded by the long time exposure.

(Bowen *et al.* (1963), figure 8) [124]

[121] Hazell (1961), 'Skylark', p.530. (*Journal of the Royal Aeronautical Society*, August 1961, Volume 65).
[122] Bowen *et al.* (1963) 'Upper atmosphere wind and temperature structure by Skylark rocket-grenade experiments at Woomera, Australia, 1957-59'.
[123] Bowen *et al.* (1963) 'Upper atmosphere wind and temperature structure by Skylark rocket-grenade experiments...', p.178.
[124] Reproduced courtesy Royal Society London.

Figure 6.27 The provenance of this exhibit is a little uncertain. The label simply reads, "Langmuir probe – this probe travelled aboard a Skylark rocket in 1960 and measured the temperature of electrons in the ionosphere … The success of this mission allowed a modified instrument to be flown on Ariel I, the UK's first satellite."

(Science Museum object 1975-569, author, 100_2242) [125]

On flight **SL38**, the last Skylark launched in 1959, the "Dielectric Probe" from Birmingham University was a new type of instrument to measure electron density, and must have been similar to the gridded probe shown in Figure 6.27.

In fact, as with many Birmingham experiments, this apparatus comprises two slightly different probes. On the left is the Langmuir probe for measuring electron temperature. In this implementation, it comprises two spheres with associated electronics, and was similar to experiment R106 that would be flown on ESRO Skylark payloads S26 in 1967 and S43 in 1968.[126] On the right is a double RF electron grid type probe for measuring electron density, similar to experiment R105 that would also be flown on ESRO payloads S26 and S43.

The instrument shown had (and may still have) the distinction of being one the few Skylark artefacts easily accessible to the public, because in 2011 it was on view in the Space Gallery of the Science Museum in London.

Black Knight and university experiments

As noted above, Black Knight rockets BK03 to BK05 had been launched from Woomera during the first six months of 1959. These were followed by BK06 on 30th October. Although Black Knight was very much a military project, sometimes scientific experiments were included. As shown below, the first of these was on BK06, which reached an altitude of 732 km (455 miles). Thus the Imperial College Geiger counter experiment, which measured cosmic ray intensity,[127] was carried over four times higher than Skylark was capable of at the time.

Black Knight
Upper Atmosphere Experiments

Experiment	BK.06	BK.09	BK.07	BK.13	BK.14	BK.17	BK.15	BK.16	BK.18
Imperial College, London									
Geiger counter	√		√			X			
Scintillation counter			√		X		√		
Proportional counter								√	
University College, London									
Sporadic E		√	√				√		
Positive ion spectrometer				X					√
Electron temperature					X	√	√		
Balloon experiment					X				
Manchester and Cambridge Universities									
Galactic radio noise				X		X			
W.R.E./R.A.E.									
Controlled outgassing							√	√	√
Faraday rotation				X		√	√	√	√

√ Successful   X Not successful

Figure 6.28 The university experiments carried on Black Knight rockets launched during the three years from October 1959 to November 1962. The failures were caused by problems with telemetry and other systems rather than the experiments themselves.

(After Gordon and Parkin (1964), table 10)

[125] Image taken at the London Science Museum, permission granted by Science & Society Picture Library.
[126] See this book Chapters 10 and 11.
[127] 'Flight' magazine, 26 February 1960, p.267.

Jan.	Feb.	March	April	May	June	July	Aug.	Sept.	Oct.	Nov.	Dec.
			SL51		SL10		SL61			SL33	SL50
			SL62				SL13			SL67	
										SL49	

Table 6.17 The nine Skylark Launches that took place in 1960. (For full details see Appendix 3.)

(Key: black = mainly RAE programmes, blue = mainly UK scientific programme (unstabilised))

SKYLARK LAUNCHES AND SCIENCE IN 1960

There were fewer Skylark launches in 1960 than 1959, with just seven scientific flights and two RAE proving flights. However, these did include the first two Skylark experiments to try to detect micrometeorites.

In February, it was announced that a "multilateral" sounding rocket programme would take place involving the USA, Australia and Britain. For this, NASA would buy some Skylark rockets, fit them with American instruments, and the Australians would launch them from Woomera.[128] This duly took place, and four were launched on this basis in 1961, as described in the next chapter.

A more significant event in general terms occurred in April, when, for complex political and military reasons, the Blue Streak rocket was cancelled as a weapon by the UK government. This had major implications for Woomera, as all Blue Streak test firings were to have been carried out there, and the launch facilities (which been funded by Australia) were nearing completion. However, the UK government said it would consider if Blue Streak could be used as a satellite launcher, in the meanwhile funding for the project was reduced to a 'tick-over'.[129]

Nevertheless, Woomera remained busy, with for instance Black Knight launches in May, June and July. These began with the launch of the first 2-stage version, BK08. The second stage of this used a version of the Cuckoo motor (also being introduced on Skylark) to boost the payload back into the atmosphere at great speed, in order to test its re-entry properties.

April 1960   SL51, SL62

The year started with the launch of **SL51**, the first two-stage Skylark, and first major upgrade to the vehicle. It was implemented by fitting a Cuckoo boost motor[130] to the rear of the standard Raven motor as shown in figure 6.29.

SL51 was a proving flight to check the two-stage launch and separation phases, and the subsequent dispersion and trajectory. It used a new GW25 fin assembly that included a

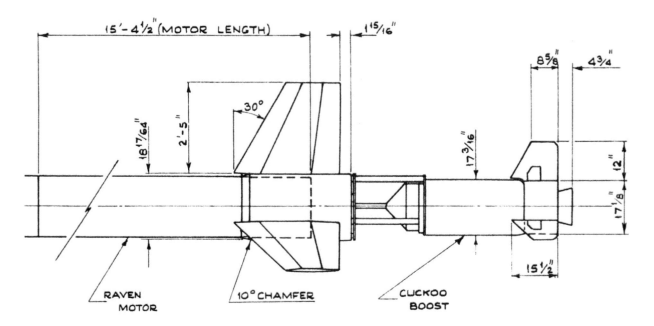

Figure 6.29 This diagram shows how the Cuckoo boost motor was added to the rear of the main Raven motor.

(WRE (1960), Trials Instruction No. B50 (SL51).)

---

[128] For instance, see 'Flight' magazine, 26th February 1960, p.267.

[129] For a good analysis of these events, see Hill (2001), *A Vertical Empire*, Chapters 6 and 7.

[130] The design and development of the Cuckoo boost motor is described at the start of the next chapter.

Seq. Nos	Launch date	Ref. (sponsor) launch site	Config-uration	Apogee km (miles)	Experi-menters	Experiment	Result
23 (1)	12 April 1960	SL51 (UK) Woomera	Un, Rav.2 +C	219 (136)	RAE	Test (Skylark technology) - first 2-stage vehicle, used Cuckoo booster	S

Table 6.18 A summary of SL51.

Raven timing and firing mechanism, and a special separation monitor connected to the telemetry.[131] To maintain stability, the head of SL51 included 90 lb (41 kg) of ballast instead of scientific instruments.[132]

The planned sequence was that the Cuckoo would be ignited by the launch facility at zero time,[133] and the Raven ignited at about 3000 feet, by the rocket-borne timer at +6 seconds or by separation should it occur first. The Cuckoo would be

Figure 6.30 SL51 loaded into the Skylark launch tower. The Cuckoo boost can just be made out.
(WRE (1960), SL51 Trials Results file J5555/3/51)

---

[131] *OISC Report SL51(B50)*, p.1. (WRE (1961) SL51 Trials Results file (J5555/3/51), Australian Defence Archives (Edinburgh)).

[132] *Summary of Firing for Skylark 51*, RAE document GW/2324/51/EBD dated 30 Aug 1960. (WRE (1961) SL51 Trials Results file (J5555/3/51), Australian Defence Archives (Edinburgh)).

[133] "On Skylark we attach it to the tail and fire it first. On Black Knight we attach it to the nose and fire it last". (Southall (1964), *Rockets in the Desert*, p.63).

blasted away and impact separately at about +20 seconds, some 1000 feet (305 metres) downrange.

During the previous week, a rehearsal had been carried out to practise loading the round in the launcher; following this, the Raven sustainer motor had been left in the tower over the weekend. On Monday the 11th April, the Cuckoo boost and the vehicle instrument head were refitted, and a GIMIC (Ground Instrumentation, Missile Instrumentation, Check) carried out.

On Tuesday the 12th, after various minor delays, and despite the sky being overcast with only occasional patches of blue,

SL51 was fired at 12:48 hours local time.[134] The flight was very successful, with the boost phase, separation, motor ignition and motor phase all operating as planned. The main part of the vehicle impacted about 108 miles (174 km) downrange, within the estimated impact circle. Excellent tracking and telemetry data was obtained, although the cameras could not follow after about 30 seconds of flight because the cloud base was only 10,000 feet. However the boost separation was well covered, and the apogee calculated from the MTS (Missile Tracking System) was 136 miles (219 km), by far the highest for Skylark.[135]

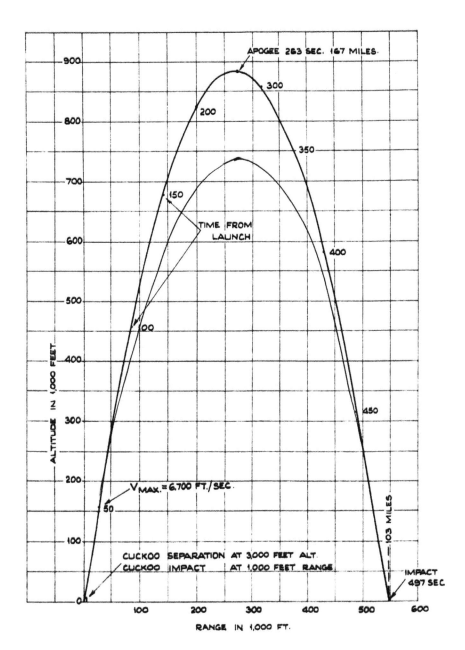

Figure 6.31 The anticipated and actual trajectories for SL51. The actual apogee of 136 miles (lower curve) fell short of the 167 miles expected, but was still a record.

(WRE (1960), Trials Instruction No. B50)

---

[134] *OISC Report SL51 (B50)*, p.1. (WRE (1961) SL51 Trials Results file (J5555/3/51).
[135] This was 30% higher than the previous best of 163 km (101 miles) achieved by SL60 the previous November.

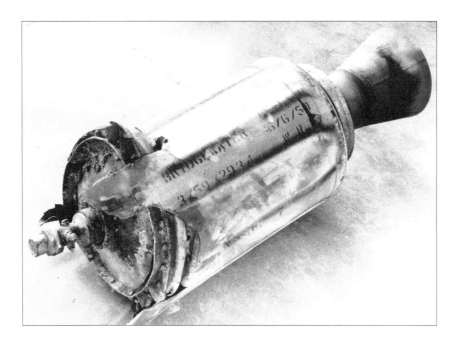

Figure 6.32 The compacted remains of the Cuckoo boost motor from SL51. As predicted, after separation it had impacted 300 yards down range. The stencilling "Bridgewater" and "16/6/59" on the case indicate where and when the propellant was added.
(WRE (1960), SL51 Trials Results file J5555/3/51)

The minutes of the WRE trial follow-up meeting provide an interesting glimpse into conditions at the busy multi-user Woomera range:

> The priming accommodation in EC2 [the underground room at the launch site] is still in the same unsatisfactory condition as we experienced last year. We are waiting for the installation of cables and partitions which have been held up until just recently by Army occupation. In the firing sequence of SL51 the trials team in EC2 had difficulty in hearing the intercom because of the background noise.[136]

The first scientific flight of the year followed just over a week later. **SL62** was a single stage Skylark, the experiments a repeat of SL 60 the previous November. It was a simple grenade and 'window' round fired to determine temperature from 'window' and luminous clouds, and did not carry telemetry, Doppler or MTS.[137]

After a dummy run at 16:30, launch took place at 20:05 local time. Unfortunately, only four grenade flashes were observed, and the radars did not locate any 'window'. It was concluded that most of the grenades and the window cartridges had failed, and tests were subsequently carried out on the stocks held by WRE, who were also working on a more reliable ejection and delay system for grenades in future Skylarks.

Seq. Nos	Launch date	Ref. (sponsor) launch site	Config- uration	Apogee km (miles)	Experi- menters	Experiment	Result
24 (2)	21 April 1960	SL62 (UK) Woomera	Un, Rav.2	141 (88)	UCL	Neutral atmosphere – (grenades)	Ps
					IC	" " - (falling dipoles)	F

Table 6.19 A summary of SL62.

---

[136] Minutes of a meeting held at WRE Salisbury 10 May 1960 to discuss the firings of SL51 and SL62. (WRE (1961) SL51 Trials Results file J5555/3/51), Australian Defence Archives (Edinburgh)).

[137] Ibid.

June1960   SL10

There was then nearly a two-month gap until the next flight in June. This included a repeat of Belfast's sodium vapour experiment as flown on SL16 the previous November, and for the first time, a micrometeorite detector.

Unfortunately, both these experiments failed,[138] but they were to be repeated more successfully two months later on SL13, see Table 6.22.

August 1960   SL61, SL13

Next was **SL61**, similar to SL62 and SL60 launched the previous April and November. It was part of the continuing series from UCL and Imperial College, designed to measure seasonal variations in the upper atmosphere. See Table 6.21.

Both experiments were partially successful, which for the Imperial College group was good news, following four failures; it was the first time their falling dipole experiment had even partly worked.

SL13 was a repeat of SL10, launched in June, but much more successful, as this time Belfast's sodium vapour glow experiment worked. See Table 6.22.

SL13 also included a micrometeorite detector.[139] At the time, knowledge of the composition and concentration of micrometeorite material was very uncertain,[140] and there was concern that the continual impact of these tiny particles might have an erosive effect on critical parts of space satellites and rocket experiments. However, taking measurements of micrometeorites proved difficult, various techniques were tried, and this Belfast experiment used a microphone detector, probably feeding a transistorised amplifier tuned to select the high frequency tone of an impact.[141]

Seq. Nos	Launch date	Ref. (sponsor) launch site	Config- uration	Apogee km (miles)	Experi- menters	Experiments	Result
25 (3)	16 June 1960	SL10 (UK) Woomera	Un. Rav.2	129 (80)	Belfast	Neutral atmosphere - (sodium vapour)	F
					Belfast	Micrometeorites – (microphone detector)	F

Table 6.20 A summary of SL10.

Seq. Nos	Launch date	Ref. (sponsor) launch site	Config- uration	Apogee km (miles)	Experi- menters	Experiments	Result
26 (4)	10 Aug. 1960	SL61 (UK) Woomera	Un. Rav.2	176 (106)	UCL	Neutral atmosphere – (grenades)	Ps
					IC	" " - (falling dipoles)	Ps

Table 6.21 A summary of SL61.

Seq. Nos	Launch date	Ref. (sponsor) launch site	Config- uration	Apogee km (miles)	Experi- menters	Experiments	Result
27 (5)	26 Aug. 1960	SL13 (UK) Woomera	Un, Rav.2	109 (68)	Belfast	Neutral atmosphere - (sodium vapour)	S
					Belfast	Micrometeorites – (microphone detector)	Ps
					RAE	Test (space technology) – magnetometer	?

Table 6.22 A summary of SL13.

---

[138] Apparently an "Instrumentation failure" ('Flight' magazine, 26 February 1960, p.270).

[139] Meteors are 'medium' sized particles from space that burn up at about 80 km (50 miles) high as 'shooting stars'. If large enough to reach the ground, they are called meteorites. However if small enough, they are rapidly slowed down by the atmosphere and do not burn up, but fall as a very fine dust. Hence, they too are correctly named micrometeor*ites* because, ultimately, they arrive at the surface of the Earth.

[140] See for instance Boyd (1960), *Space Research by Rocket and Satellite*, p.32.

[141] Boyd (1961), 'The Scientific Programme of Skylark to Mid-1960', p.531, also 'Flight' magazine, 27 April 1961, p.552, and Boyd (1960), *Space Research by Rocket and Satellite*, p.118.

SL33 was the first Skylark in a programme designed to investigate the performance of autopilot gyroscopes required for inertial navigation of the ballistic missiles Black Knight and Blue Streak.[142] There must have been a considerable budget for this, as nine Skylarks were fired in support of the programme over a four-year period. Indeed, in 1966, the final report on the results stated it was the largest single investigation carried out by the [then] Space Department of the RAE using the Skylark rocket.[143] It involved the development of several instrumentation systems, the construction of special range installations at Woomera such as transmitter sites and ground marker sites, and the development of gyroscope test equipments. This all required close co-operation between the RAE and several specialised industrial companies.

During flight, the performance of the gyroscopes under test within the rocket was compared with two external reference systems. The main reference comprised a sophisticated vehicle attitude measuring system with three radio interferometers fitted to the rocket, and two corresponding interferometer transmitter vans on the ground. A secondary reference system used a camera on board the rocket.

Three Skylarks (SL33, 25 and 26) were fired before the main programme was started, in order to test the instrumentation systems to be used in the trials proper.[145] The first of these was SL33, the main purpose of which was to test the photographic method of measuring rocket attitude. A secondary aim was to prove the head roll control unit, a module being used for the first time, and a third aim was to run a second parachute recovery system trial.[146]

Figure 6.33 The Reid and Sigrist GW.5 Mk.3 gyroscope as used for the drift experiments. The cover has been removed to show the gimbals, mirror and caging mechanism.[144]

(Knott (1966b) figure 2)

Seq. Nos	Launch date	Ref. (sponsor) launch site	Config-uration	Apogee km (miles)	Experi-menters	Experiments	Result
28 (6)	16 Nov. 1960	SL33 (UK) Woomera	Un, Rav.2	105 (65)	RAE	Test (space technology) - photographic method of measuring attitude	Ps
					"	Test (Skylark technology) - head roll control	Ps
					"	Test (Skylark technology) – 2nd parachute trial	F
					UCL	Ionosphere – positive ion probe	S

Table 6.24 A summary of SL33.

[142] Accurate guidance was essential for inter-continental range missiles. Inertial navigation systems were proof against jamming, but with the technology of the day, very difficult to make sufficiently accurate. See Hill (2001), *A Vertical Empire*, p.81, regarding the dire inertial equipment situation for Blue Streak in 1956.

[143] Knott (1966), *The Drift of an Auto-Pilot Gyroscope due to prolonged acceleration in the Skylark Rocket, Part 4*, p.3. The RAE Space Department was formed in January 1962.

[144] Knott (1966), *The Drift of an Auto-Pilot Gyroscope Due to Prolonged Acceleration in the Skylark Rocket, Part 4: Results from Skylarks SL31/32 and general conclusions from programme.* (RAE Farnborough Technical Report No. 66133), figure 2.

[145] Knott (1964), *The Drift of an Auto-Pilot Gyroscope due to prolonged acceleration in the Skylark Rocket, Part 1*, p.24.

[146] Shepherd (1961), *A Recovery System for the Skylark Instrument Head*, p.9.

SL33 was fired at night because an open-shutter cine-camera in the head was arranged to photograph flashing lights mounted at ground marker positions. The flashing lights were electronic flash units fired by a complicated system initiated from the Skylark flying overhead.[147]

The roll control unit was introduced to compensate for the fact that in flight a Skylark could roll up to one revolution per second. The unit's purpose was to provide a more stable platform for gyroscope operation in the forthcoming trials, and allow an on-board camera to continuously point to the ground. The roll control unit consisted of a bay mounted between the head and rocket motor, the whole head being

supported on roller bearings secured to a stub axle secured to the front end of the Skylark motor. An electrically operated servomotor controlled the rotation, using reference signals from one of the gyros under test.

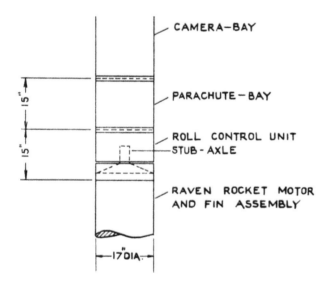

Figure 6.34 The position of the roll control unit between the motor and instrument head on SL33.

(From Knott (1964), figure 17)

Figure 6.35 The roll control bay with the top bulkhead removed. It was substantially built, and the servo amplifier circuit included at least five electronic valves! (Vacuum tubes).

(Biltcliffe *et al.* (1962), figure 11)

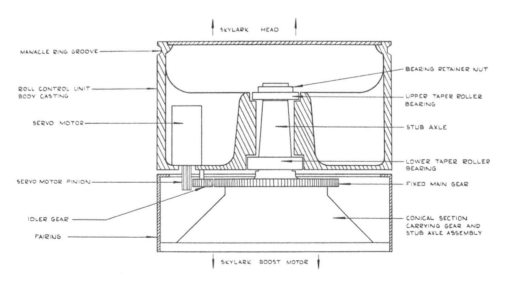

Figure 6.36 A cross-sectional view showing details of the roll control unit and axle assembly.

(Biltcliffe *et al.* (1962), figure 1)

---

[147] Knott (1964), p.24.

At first, all went well after the launch of SL33, with roll control operation beginning successfully at plus three seconds.[148] However, an abnormal build up of vehicle oscillations in pitch and yaw caused roll control to be lost after 38 seconds. This instability meant that head separation on the way down, which was on a timed basis (at 295 seconds), occurred at a relatively low altitude (70,000 feet / 21 km), and may have been why the parachute failed to deploy. [149]

Because of a fault in the camera film wind mechanism only nine photographs of the flashing lights were obtained.[150] Overall, this was not a very successful flight, and as a result, the open shutter camera and flashing light system was abandoned in favour of daylight firings using a camera fitted with a high-speed shutter.

Being part of a military programme, the UK Ministry of Aviation described the SL33 mission simply as for "RAE research purposes", however the Australian Minister for Supply was more forthcoming, openly describing it as "the first experiment to test drift and precision of the gyros",[151] see figure 6.37.

Skylarks SL67 and SL49

Only a day after SL33, the second two-stage Skylark was launched. Using the new 'Cuckoo' boost motor as on SL51 in April, SL67 achieved a new record altitude of 247 km, one eighth greater than previously. See Table 6.25.

The experiments themselves were standard, being repeated to determine the seasonal variations in temperature, pressure, density and wind speeds. It was the first time the Imperial College falling dipole experiment had been completely successful, the bugs appear to have been cured, and it would be successfully repeated many times. However, despite having succeeded in August, this time the Belfast Sodium vapour experiment failed.

Rocket Soars to 86 Miles at Woomera

CANBERRA. Thursday.— A Skylark single-stage rocket was fired to a height of 68 miles at Woomera late last night.

The upper atmosphere research rocket landed 40 miles from the launching site.

The Minister for Supply (Mr. Hulme) said today it was the first gyro-drift experiment to test drift and precision of the gyros. The results would be of interest in navigation.

Skylark, he said, was designed to examine a wide range of upper atmosphere phenomena, including temperature and meteoric dust.

The United States intended to buy a number of Skylarks from Britain for firing at Woomera in upper atmosphere research.

Figure 6.37 The launch of SL33 is reported in the Melbourne newspaper.
('The Age', 18 November 1960, p.7) [152]

Seq. Nos	Launch date	Ref. (sponsor) launch site	Config-uration	Apogee km (miles)	Experi-menters	Experiments	Result
29 (7)	17 Nov. 1960	SL67 (UK) Woomera	Un, Rav.2 +C	247 (153)	UCL	Neutral atmosphere – (grenades)	S
					IC	" " - (falling dipoles)	S
					Belfast	" " - (sodium vapour)	F

Table 6.25 A summary of SL67.

---

[148] Biltcliffe, Thirkettle & Kedar (1962), *A Roll Control System for Skylark*, p.12.
[149] Shepherd (1961), *A Recovery System for the Skylark Instrument Head*, p.10.
[150] Clearly, the camera at least was recovered from the instrument head.
[151] 'Flight' magazine 2 December 1960, p.866.
[152] Reproduced with permission.

The single-stage **SL49** was launched was exactly a week later. See Table 6.26

It is particularly interesting because it appears to be the Skylark involved[153] in the launch and recovery operation described in some detail in a 1964 Australian book by Ivan Southall.[154] As this is the only such account the author has found, it may well be a unique recollection, and an extract is reproduced at the end of this chapter.

The solar X-ray detector experiment from the University of Leicester was probably the first from their new university group. Speaking 50 years on, K.A.Pounds, originally at UCL, recalls:

> By 1959 the research was going well [at UCL], and it was decided to establish a new university group to specialise in X-ray observations from space. Leicester was by then the obvious place and I was offered an assistant lectureship, to come here and lead the project. The salary of £700 was too good an offer for a research student to refuse. So I came in January 1960, and in July we were awarded a grant of £13,006 from DSIR 'to study solar and stellar X-ray emissions'.[155]

Dec 1960   SL50

The final launch that year was **SL50**, another spectacular failure when it broke a fin and crashed to earth a few miles down-range. See Table 6.27.

Ivan Southall also appears to have seen this launch:

> Everything seemed to be under control as it left the launcher, but as it roared into the heavens, almost straight up, one could see through binoculars that it was rocking from side to side in a strange way, almost like a dog wagging its tail, and that pieces of metal were breaking away from one of its fins. It rose to a height of about 100,000 feet [30km] and crashed a few miles away down the centre line.[156]

Investigation revealed that structural failure had occurred in the fin because of distortion; subsequent flights used more carefully aligned fins of stronger build.[157] A failure like this could bring many years of hard work to nothing. Ivan Southall again:

> In the ruins of that Skylark on the rock hard plain lay the broken hopes of a group of scientists from a British university. They had waited years for that day, then everything had been destroyed through no fault of their own. They had to go back to the beginning to build their experimental equipment all over again. As I write they are still waiting their turn for the use of another rocket, and some day they will travel once more all the way from England to Australia for the firing. And there is no certainty that the next rocket will succeed either. The risk of failure remains, and it is the risk that makes life very trying as the clock advances towards the instant of firing.[158]

Seq. Nos	Launch date	Ref. (sponsor) launch site	Config- uration	Apogee km (miles)	Experi- menters	Experiments	Result
30 (8)	24 Nov. 1960	SL 49 (UK) Woomera	Un, Rav.2	158 (98)	RAE/UCW	Ionosphere - CW radio propagation	S
					Lei	Solar physics - soft x-ray detector	S
					UCL	Ionosphere – positive ion probe	S

Table 6.26 A summary of SL49.

Seq. Nos	Launch date	Ref. (sponsor) launch site	Config- uration	Apogee km (miles)	Experi- menters	Experiments	Result
31 (9)	7 Dec. 1960	SL 50 (UK) Woomera	Un, Rav.2	35 (21)	RAE/UCW	Neutral atmosphere – (sodium vapour)	Vf (fin came off)
					Lei	Solar physics – soft solar X-ray detector	

Table 6.27 A summary of SL50.

[153] The next most likely possibility seems to be SL35 in November 1961. (Although the extra time in flight indicates it may have been SL67 with Cuckoo boost motor, see figure 7.6).

[154] Southall (1964), *Rockets in the Desert,* Chapters 9 – 11.

[155] University of Leicester Department of Physics & Astronomy website, *www2.le.ac.uk/departments/physics/research/space/timeline* , last accessed August 2014. Reproduced with permission.

[156] Southall (1964), *Rockets in the Desert,* p.54.

[157] Dorling (1975), 'Early History of the Skylark Rocket', p.182.

[158] Southall (1964), p.54.

This is also a reminder that Skylark launches did not necessarily occur in a neatly planned order. Woomera was very busy with military missile testing, and Skylark firings were the result of a complex series of events and jockeying for position, as experimenters struggled to get their experiments ready on time, and flight slots became available.

A typical recovery operation

As mentioned before, Skylark was unguided, and the "dispersion" factor meant it could land up to 20 miles (32 km) from the theoretical impact point. Thus, locating and recovering hard or even soft-impacted parts could be quite an exercise. In addition, right from the beginning, it had been recognised that in some areas terrain would be a problem:

> The problem of "recovery" in mulga forest country is likely to give rise to some difficulty. There are large areas on the Range which vary from "spars[e]" to "very dense" mulga scrub. In particular, the area north-west of the 200 mile point is exceptionally dense. There are also numerous sandhills.[159]

In later years a helicopter was used, but before then an exclusively land based recovery team had been employed. As noted above, the author Ivan Southall accompanied one of these recovery expeditions, probably that for SL49 on 25 November 1960, and his subsequent account brings the process to life. It is reproduced here (with permission) from his book *Rockets in the Desert*.[161] This was written for young people and published in 1964, which explains the slightly formal style:

"At 7.30 a.m. we arrive at the 44-mile post, and a post is exactly what it is: a telephone pole bearing the usual little red box into which Mr Hawkins pokes his head and speaks to Control. At the same time two or three of the "Indians" scout round for sticks and get a fire going and put the billy on. The 44-mile post has obviously served this purpose before: here and there are the ashes of other fires, and a discarded tea-chest stands ready to serve as a table for cups and biscuits.

While we enjoy morning tea Mr Hawkins gives us his final plan of action. Apparently the meteorologists have reported unusual wind variations at high altitudes, and though the angle of the launching tower has been adjusted it is possible that the rocket will go a few miles farther down-range than at first believed. Because of this the crew of one Land Rover gulp their scalding tea and bolt for their vehicle. They will have to hurry if they are to reach their new observation post before the rocket lands. Mr Hawkins has pushed that post five miles farther on to allow for the corrected impact point, though with Skylark's behaviour so difficult to guess in advance it may well come down five or ten miles away in some other direction.

By 7.50 a.m. - ten minutes to launching time - all recovery vehicles, except ours and Mr Hawkins's, have gone off in one direction or another, and we are left to count off the remaining minutes. There is no sign of the aeroplane, but according to Control at the rangehead it had taken off from Woomera and is on the way. "He'd better hurry," says Mr Hawkins. "He's cutting it fine."

Figure 6.38 A ground view of mulga country taken during the original survey for the Woomera range. The partially visible vehicle trailer provides scale.[160]

[159] Australian DoSD (1949), *The Joint UK – Australian Long Range Weapons Project in Australia*, p.13.
[160] Ibid, p.7.
[161] Southall (1964), *Rockets in the Desert*, pp.68-76.

"Where is the Skylark expected to come down?" I ask.

"Here", he says.

"But what about the change of wind?"

"We've spread out to allow for it, but this is the impact point and I still think it'll be pretty close."

"So we'll be standing underneath it?"

He gives me that squint of his. "It's better that we should be close to it.[162] It's easier to see. If you're nervous you can always hide under the Land Rover. I've done it myself at times."

"And what sort of protection does a Land Rover provide?"

"None, but you think it does, and that's all that matters."

I get to thinking that death should be pretty sudden, anyway, and probably I won't feel it.

Back at the rangehead, the Trials Control Officer broadcasts the passing of time. "Minus 8 minutes."

"Minus 7 minutes."

"Minus 6 minutes."

Up and down the range, over hundreds of square miles, operators and technicians hear his voice but remain at their places and say nothing. Apart from the voice of Control not a sound is to be heard. Never has time seemed to pass more slowly. I can imagine how agonizing it must be for Mr Watson and for the men from England - for the OISC and his fellow scientists. For them so much depends upon the events of the next few minutes.

"Can't hear that aircraft," says Mr Hawkins. "Can you?"

I shake my head.

"Minus 3 minutes," broadcasts Control. "On yellow light."

Then another voice is heard: "Launcher clear."

From the white Land Rover nearby more voices are coming through on a different radio frequency. The "Indians", one after another, are reporting to Mr Hawkins that they have reached their positions.

"Minus 60 seconds."

"Looks as though she'll be off on time," says Mr Hawkins. "You'll be able to see it from here if you watch the horizon to the right of the Instrumentation Road."

"From forty-four miles away?"

"Certainly. Not with all missiles, but you can see Skylark from a much greater distance than this, Smoky Joe, some call her."

"Minus 40 seconds."

Mr Bruce explains the importance of that signal. "The barrel's alive now and she's ready to go. Every person in the probable area of impact has gone underground to shelter and reported the fact to Control."

"Except us?" "That's right," he admits, a little ruefully. Again the calm voice of the Trials Control Officer: "Minus 20 seconds,"

"If everything goes well," Mr Bruce continues, "that's the last you'll hear from him. Time from now on is counted out electronically with peeps. There won't be another voice until Plus 10 seconds, and that will be a different person - the Instrumentation Control Officer."

The count reaches zero. There is an almost breathless pause for a few seconds as we all stare into the eastern sky, into the glaring expanse of brilliant blue that lies beyond the bright red earth and the dusty greens of salt-bush and mulga scrub.

Suddenly it is there, a dark score mark against the flawless sky, a thrusting finger of black smoke. It seems to reach up from beyond the ends of the world like the arm of a drowning man. It is not a straight but a curved thrust, from which one seems to sense the curvature of the earth itself.

It thrusts to a tremendous height, a height I cannot even guess, and suddenly cuts out.

We hear the voice of the Instrumentation Controller: "Plus 40."

Skylark has burnt its fuel; all has gone except the persisting smoke trail which already is beginning to warp and twist in the blasting winds of the upper atmosphere. Of the rocket there is no sign; it has vanished; it is streaking towards space, still upwards, at thousands of miles an hour.

"Looks like a pretty good launching," says Mr Bruce. "If we give it about seven more minutes we'll hear it hit."

But Mr Hawkins is scratching his chin. He has watched the smoke trail of many Skylarks, and what to us is merely a wonderful sight in the sky is to him a pointer to future events. "I don't know," he says. "It was moving into the north away from the Centre Line - just enough into the north to put it down over this road. . . . Perhaps," he adds, turning to me, "you'd better get under the Land Rover after all and leave room for the rest of us."

For no reason apparent to me he then makes a dash to the cabin of his vehicle and begins poring over a large and detailed map of the impact area. "Where's that aeroplane?" he suddenly demands. "Lost, or gone to Adelaide for the weekend?" His "Indians", from points east and west, begin calling him on the radio, drawing his attention to the angle of the smoke trail - which, of course, he has noted already - though from each observation post the path of the smoke trail appears

---

[162] Percy Hawkins also recovered Black Knight re-entry heads, one of which is said to have missed him by only a few metres. (Morton (1989), *Fire across the Desert*, p.430).

to be different: One thing they decide for certain: it will not land on the Centre Line, forty-four miles from the launcher. Mr Hawkins goes to the telephone and discusses this opinion with the Trials Control Officer. He is told that there is no doubt that the missile is veering to the north. This is clearly shown on the screen of every radar set that is tracking it.

At last we hear the aeroplane. It comes in from the north - not from the east as we had expected - at a height of about 3,000 feet. It's a Winjeel, a small but fast single-engined monoplane usually used for flying training, and the pilot's voice is added to the static issuing from Mr Hawkins's radio. He requests instructions. Mr Hawkins tells him to maintain his present height and fly a circle ten miles wide with the 44-mile post in the middle of it. Mr Hawkins concludes his message with a question: "Where have you been?"

"Nowhere," says the pilot. "And probably," growls Mr Hawkins, "he's never spoken a truer word."

The time count from the rangehead has by this time reached Plus 380 seconds, which should mean that the rocket has long since passed its apogee - or highest point - and is now rapidly approaching the earth. It is supposed to hit at Plus 410, which gives us another half-minute. I must confess I'm looking at the sky a little anxiously and I'm thinking that it would be tough luck to have come so far from home only to be hit on the head by a falling rocket.

"All right," says Mr, Hawkins, "at this stage we have absolute quiet. The idea is to listen carefully and decide from which direction the sound of impact comes."

We listen. A few miles away we can see the aeroplane, and back towards Woomera the fantastically twisted smoke trail still writhes in the sky. Elsewhere there is nothing except a great blank emptiness of blue; no insects, no birds, nothing. It seems that all life has departed from the air to clear the way for the tumbling Skylark, but here we stand with heads bare in the open, listening, waiting, watching.

Plus 410 comes and goes, and nothing happens.

Plus 420 passes, and still nothing. Mr Hawkins sighs, but doesn't speak. The sky remains vastly empty and silent.

At Plus 440 I believe I can feel the first stirrings of concern. Skylark should be down, but apparently it isn't.

Mr Hawkins is now looking directly down-range. Obviously he no longer believes that it will land close to us.

Plus 480 comes and goes. Skylark is more than a minute late. "Funny," Mr Hawkins says, and makes the first move back towards the cabin of his vehicle. He changes his mind and gets down on his knees and puts his ear to the ground; and there he stays, listening, while the time count runs on past 500.

Mr Bruce gives us a glance, and shrugs. "Must be down," he says in an undertone. "For some reason we haven't heard it."

Still the seconds tick away and the great silence of the desert seems to press upon us; it seems to beat against our ears with a strange rhythm. Mr Hawkins has become distinctly restless, because now it is certain that the rocket cannot impact within sight of any of his watching posts or within sight of the aeroplane pilot either. The longer the Skylark stays in the air the farther away it must get. It cannot be lost, of course, because dozens of radio tracking instruments are following it, but it is a matter of professional pride with Mr Hawkins to trace the crashed rocket by his own calculations and to be on his way towards it or even to have reached it before the range head has signalled its precise position to him.

Finally he slides into the cabin of his Land Rover and calls his "Indians" one by one. None has heard it; nor has the pilot in the air seen it.

"What has happened?" the pilot asks. No one, except the radar operators and the tracking stations, knows the answer. I even start thinking about my nose cap. Perhaps I won't get it after all. Perhaps the rocket will never be found.

Suddenly, we feel a distinct thump. "That's it," shouts Mr Bruce. "It's down."

Mr Hawkins peers out from his cabin in amazement. "Are you sure?"

"Absolutely." "How far?"

"Very far and to the south of the road." Mr Hawkins turns to me. "And would you say that?" "I'd say dead ahead and a very long way off."

A voice calling Mr Hawkins issues from the radio transceiver, and in turn his watching posts report. The post in the east has heard nothing, and the men there are instructed to return to the 44-mile post as quickly as they can. Both posts in the west have heard it, but they do not agree upon the direction of the sound, except that it came from somewhere farther down-range. Both posts are told to wait for further instructions. The pilot above us has seen nothing, but Mr Hawkins, with that uncanny instinct of his, orders the aircraft to fly to Mount Eba sheep station about forty miles farther on. "That's where it is," he says. "It's on Mount Eba."

We wonder how on earth he could know that, but he knows. Mr Hawkins is famous for many things, not the least being his ability to smell out a missing rocket from incredible distances. But it's not guesswork, it's an ability that comes from long experience, from an understanding of the way sound waves travel, from his knowledge of the country itself, and from his close study of the performance of each rocket tested. This incident, however, has surprised him. It seems that the new fuel in the Skylark motor is more powerful than its designers believed, for this Skylark has certainly travelled much higher and much farther downrange than expected. At first sight it seems that it has gone double the distance intended. If it is indeed more than forty miles from where we stand, how strange it is that we have managed to hear it at all.

Soon the white Land Rover that has been stationed in the east speeds down the road towards us, and our little convoy - this time of three vehicles only - re-forms and heads west at about fifty miles an hour.

In the next section the road is not of bitumen but of gravel and dirt, and billowing clouds of dust roll away behind us. Unfortunately, our vehicle is at the rear and in almost no time we're eating dirt and breathing it and visibility is reduced to a few feet. This doesn't worry Mr Bruce in the least; he's used to it, and roars on at fifty miles an hour; but I'm almost frozen stiff with fright, despite the heat of the morning and all the sweat that goes with it. We slow down twice as the other vehicles rejoin the convoy, but they only make it worse. The dust they all raise looks like a bush fire in the desert. Needless to say, by this time the signal has come in from the rangehead stating definitely that the ruins of the Skylark lie on Mount Eba station close to the position worked out by Mr Hawkins, though as I'm sure we won't be alive when we get there it doesn't seem to matter any more. Who wants a nose cap, anyway? I'd rather just grow old, quietly.

In due course, to my astonishment, the convoy pulls in to the side of the road and stops beside a wire fence. All crew members are still alive and all vehicles are undamaged, I

heave an immense sigh of relief when I discover that we have reached the outskirts of Mount Eba station - a property of 800 square miles that runs about 18,000 sheep.

My relief comes too soon. A still more hazardous drive is ahead of us. From here, it seems, we are to leave the road and strike across open country littered with gibber stones, boulders, holes, saltbush, mulga, myall, and many fierce and thorny bushes. This country is so rough, Mr Bruce explains, that if we manage to get through without spiking our tyres it will be a miracle. We have two spares, he says, but we may need more. Perhaps we'll be mending tyres before long, and even he admits that trying to patch up blow-outs in the suffocating heat of a morning like this may not be entirely a picnic.

Mr Hawkins spreads his map on the ground and starts drawing lines across it while a few of us listen for the aeroplane. There is neither sight nor sound of it, though the pilot has called us on the radio several times in the past hour. He hasn't found the Skylark. This seems to suggest that it must be lying in scrub country, and Mr Hawkins is clearly hopeful that he still may find it first.

A peculiar sort of gate, which I had failed to notice, is opened and our vehicles stream through one after another, Mr Bruce's Land Rover still bringing up the rear. It is my job to shut the gate – a gate that does not swing on hinges because it consists of wire-netting anchored to a single

Figure 6.39 Mr Hawkins spreads his map on the ground and starts drawing lines across it.
(Southall (1964), p.72)

stout pole. This pole has to be dragged up to the nearest fence post, dropped into a hole at the bottom and fixed with an iron loop at the top. It's the sort of "gate" that is very easy to open. One merely raises the iron loop and leaps for safety while the gate, under great tension, twangs like a breaking spring and collapses in a heap - for this reason it is called a "drop-gate". To shut it, however, is quite a different matter. One needs nerves of steel and the strength of an ox, and I have neither. In the end Mr Bruce comes to my rescue. He picks up the guide pole, cracks it against the fence post, slams down the loop, dusts his hands and says, "Nothing to it." I, meanwhile, limp back to the Land Rover in disgrace.

We set off in pursuit of the convoy that is now strung out in a weaving line across the harsh and arid land. The drivers cannot steer a straight course and neither can we. We make our track as we go, winding between obstacles, lurching and bumping violently, and listening to the machine-gun clatter of countless gibbers, swept up by the tyres, striking the bottom of the vehicle. Mr Hawkins is making for a ridge of high land at astonishing speed, considering the nature of the country. He is in a hurry and he makes no secret of it. Perhaps he fears that the nose cone will melt in the sun or that a flock of sheep may eat it or that a passing crow may snatch it up and take it home to build a nest. For the life of me I can't imagine what all the rush is about.

"It's very simple," says Mr Bruce. "It's a matter of principle. The nose cone *must* be found as soon as possible."

"But why?"

"Why? Does there have to be a reason? All nose cones must be found as soon as possible. It's a matter of principle."

Which, of course, takes us back to where we started from, so I give up.

At last we reach the ridge - not a mountain by any means - simply higher ground than most, perhaps higher than the plain by fifty or sixty feet. From here we can see a very long way across the fantastically shimmering wastes of red and purple earth (the air actually seems to be boiling) and the dusty green of sparse vegetation. This is a form of green so dark that it is almost a pale hue of black, if such a thing can be. We can see the aeroplane, a tiny spot in the distance, perhaps six or seven miles away, a shimmering spot that scarcely seems to be real.

The pilot has found the Skylark. Mr Hawkins has lost his race, for which I thank my stars. Perhaps now we will drive a little slower.

The nose cone, the pilot says over the radio, is in saltbush and thorn country lying on gibbers, the main body is about a mile farther on in the sandhills. Mr Hawkins notes the

Figure 6.40 We come out onto a barren, sun-blistered clearing.
(Southall (1964), p.74)

Figure 6.41 "Mr Hawkins takes his pictures while I take mine."
(Southall (1964), p.75)

position, and the pilot goes off the air, stating that he will land at Mount Eba homestead to refuel.

Soon we're bumping and shuddering and lurching into the west again, each vehicle on the tail of the other, swooping and weaving through scrub and rocks, just as though the rocket hadn't been found at all, and the race was still on. Again and again, despite my fierce hold on everything within reach, I rise bodily into the air and crack my head against the roof. It's probably just as well that the roof is there to stop me, for where would I end up if it were not there? Mr Bruce, of course, is unperturbed. He has the steering-wheel to hang onto, and he seems to be using it less for its intended purpose than for securing himself to his seat.

As we enter the area reported by the pilot, the convoy changes formation. All vehicles are in radio contact with the leader, and Mr Hawkins orders them to advance in line abreast for the search. (We, too, can hear these orders because our Security vehicle is specially equipped for long-range patrols. Several very rugged wireless sets for different jobs are built into the cabin and into the luggage compartment at the rear.)

We all fan out until we're spread across more than a mile of countryside, and slowly (Heaven be praised) move in a broad line until we run into a belt of scrub. Here all vehicles pass from the sight of the others, and naturally it is Mr Hawkins who finds the nose cone. Having suffered so much (I feel as though I have been dragged through a bush backwards), I have been hoping that we might find the rocket first, but I suspect we haven't a chance. Mr Hawkins, knowing by instinct exactly where it is, has driven straight towards it.

We turn to the right, pick our way through the thinning vegetation and come out onto a barren, sun-blistered clearing where practically nothing grows except the cruellest thorns I have ever seen. Several vehicles are moving in across the face of this weird area, converging on Mr Hawkins. He has parked a short distance from the ruins of the nose cone, and as we approach we see that he is examining it, treading carefully around it, almost as though he expects it to jump at him.

We join him and tread with equal care, remembering his warning given back at the rangehead that nothing is to be disturbed until he has taken his photographs.

The camera is an important part of the Recovery Officer's equipment. He must photograph from every useful angle, in colour, the wreckage of each rocket before a hand has touched it. Much can be learnt from the way the wreckage lies, though one would not think so when one sees it.

Our Skylark nose cone has broken into two main pieces a few yards apart with numerous fragments scattered here and there. It is a sad sight, crushed, dented and torn, apparently useless for evermore. But Mr Hawkins says that one particular part has survived the impact well, that the OISC will be delighted with another part, and that the little radiation cameras are completely undamaged.

Not wishing to appear too eager, I start hunting furtively for the nose cap. It is nowhere to be seen. It is not on the nose cone. It has broken off. It may even have broken off in space and landed fifty miles away. A feeling of gloom descends upon me. Perhaps the OISC is going to be happy, but I'm not.

While Mr Hawkins takes his pictures I take a few myself, and hope that no one notices. "What are you creeping round like that for?" says Mr Bruce. "It's not secret. Take as many pictures as you like."

Somehow or other it doesn't seem to be my day. I can't even make a success of being sneaky.

"Right," says Mr Hawkins, "while we're loading it on, some-one can get the fire going for lunch."

This revives my spirits. I've heard so much about the meals that Mr Hawkins cooks that I can hardly wait. A couple of the "Indians" begin the preparations while the .rest of us carefully load the main pieces of the shattered Skylark into the back of the nearest vehicle. When we lift the main sec-tion the middle almost falls out of it and many pieces dangle pathetically from the wiring which once connected them to batteries or electric motors. Each of us is then given a small card- board box and we crawl round on hands and knees through the gibbers searching for tiny fragments of metal, fibre, nuts, bolts, clips, and wire. And thus the nose cap is found, undamaged, lying fifty feet away.

"Jolly good," says Mr Hawkins, and drops it into the back of his Land Rover. "You've no idea how important that little piece of metal is."

At this remark 1 find myself grinning rather sheepishly, but once again it's not my day. "You can't have it," says Mr Hawkins, "at least, not yet. There's another Skylark to fire next week, but a piece of it is missing. . . . Yes," he says, "this piece, the nose cap. So if we're lucky enough to find it a second time it will be an unusually distinguished lump of metal, it will have travelled into space twice."

What an odd turn of events this is - or is it? Perhaps I never really expected to get my hands on it, anyway.

We continue picking up our bits until nothing is left except a few scratches on the surface of the ground. Despite the speed of the nose cone at impact – and its weight - the ground is so hard that not the slightest indication of a crater has been formed. When all the pieces have been recovered one would never guess that the nose cone of a rocket once almost thirty feet tall had crashed on the spot.

The excitements of the day are not yet over. When Mr Hawkins prepares, with ritualistic care, to grill our dinner over the red-hot coals of mulga and myall wood, he discov-ers that the catering officer at Koolymilka has provided him not with fillet steak but with stewing steak, not with eggs but with potatoes, and not with onions but with carrots. The things he has to say about the catering officer are unprint-

Figure 6.42 "Later we find the main body of Skylark in the sand hills."
(Southall (1964), p.75)

able. "Stew," he fumes in frustration and disgust. "How can I cook a stew?" And when we open our personal food packs the final blow is struck. Each packet contains a ration of tomato sauce, a small envelope of salt, a little bag of sugar, two slices of bread made as crisp as toast by the heat of the morning, a piece of cake, and an apple.

"I'll kill him," says Mr Hawkins.

Later in the day, after we find the main body of the Skylark in the sand hills and load it onto the big truck, we turn for the 110 mile drive back through the range head to Woomera village. Everything goes beautifully for about a thousand yards; then the Land Rover carrying the nose cone (and Mr Hawkins) coughs violently, splutters, and stops.

We all crowd round, peer into the engine, under it and round it, but no matter what we do we cannot induce it to run for more than a few seconds at a time. "I don't believe it," Mr Hawkins declares. "Nothing stops my Land Rover."

Everything smells strongly of petrol and Mr Bruce thoughtfully fetches a fire extinguisher, for the temperature in the open is at least 130 degrees.

"Fuel line cracked," someone says. "Blown head gasket," says another. "Dirty jets," says another.

"More like a blocked air cleaner," says another.

"It's a punctured float," says another. Mr Hawkins considers these helpful suggestions, then runs a chain between his bumper bar and the rear axle of the truck. "Nothing stops my Land Rover," he says, and we all head for home.[163]

There is a sequel to this story. The next Skylark was fired about ten days later, the Skylark that carried my paperweight into space for the second time. This was the Skylark that broke its fin in the launcher and crashed to earth a few miles down-range." [SL50, launched 7th December 1960, see above].

---

[163] It is said that under these conditions, even Land Rovers lasted only six months! (Professor Len Culhane, Charterhouse Space Conference, 2010).

Figure 7.1 The launch of an unidentified two-stage Skylark, c.1965. The Cuckoo boost motor (one of the earliest enhancements) can be clearly seen at the rear of the vehicle, and the exhaust is a lot less smoky than before!

(WRE, still photography section, negative E1651)

CHAPTER 7

(1961-62)

ENHANCEMENTS AND LIGHT

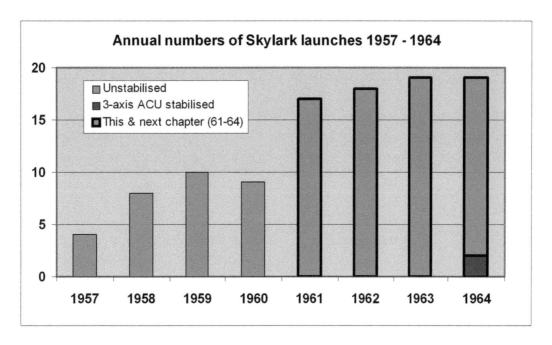

Figure 7.2 By the end of 1964 the annual launch rate had doubled, and the stabilised flights had begun.

Over the four years covered by this and the next chapter, the number of Skylark launches doubled to an average of just over eighteen per year. Skylark settled into a steady working life, launching dozens of experiments into space. The expansion followed British Prime Minister Harold Macmillan's announcement in May 1959 of a modest space research programme. Skylark was included in this in 1960 when brought under the supervision of the new Steering Group on Space Research (SRG),[1] an event that seems to have facilitated funding. Another helpful factor was that in 1961 a report on science versus space expenditure from the British government's Advisory Council on Scientific Policy (ACSP), gave the Skylark sounding rocket programme a clean bill of health, concluding:

> The UK sounding-rocket programme has already produced important information about the atmosphere (including the ionosphere) and this has had direct effects on important areas in applied science e.g. radio research and meteorology. This information cannot be obtained in any other way.[2]

However, the RAE recognised that the expansion of the Skylark programme was causing logistical problems. Analysis carried out by the beginning of 1961[3] had shown that the overall success rate (in terms of experimental results) was only 40%, although the basic rocket vehicle - excluding range instrumentation and payload - had a success rate of about 90%. Their view was that the Skylark programme was operating with inadequate staffing and finance, and in order to satisfy the ever growing demand and to improve the success rate, a more formal administrative structure should be created; one with an external executive committee to assess technical feasibility, plus a better structure with more resources within the RAE itself. It also recommended that there should be a permanent representative at Woomera, and at least one of the preparation team should accompany each round to Australia.

---

[1] Godwin (2007), *The Skylark Racket*, p.158.
[2] Quoted by Godwin (2007), *The Skylark Racket*, p.67. Chapter 2 provides a good explanation of the intricacies of the political and funding process.
[3] RAE (1961), *Organisation of the Royal Society Upper Atmosphere Research Programme using Skylark*, p.1.

It is not clear what resulting changes were made within the RAE,[4] but as explained in the next chapter, capacity was increased by "outsourcing" an increasing amount of assembly, testing and launching to a large industrial organisation, the British Aircraft Corporation. In addition, in due course, rounds were accompanied to Woomera by a dedicated member of the preparation team.

Woomera and space rocket logistics

The establishment of the Joint Project in 1947 meant that a logistics chain had been created which stretched 10,000 miles (16,000 km) from the UK to Woomera. Operating this was not an easy task before the advent of direct dial international phone calls or emails, and when Telex[5] provided the most reliable long distance communication. However, with the Woomera operation in place, Skylark was able to take increasing advantage of this facility.

Originally, of course, all transport from Britain to Australia was by sea. However, between the wars, air travel had begun. The first airmail service between the UK and Australia had started in 1934, followed the year after by the first passenger service. By 1938 more comfortable flying boat services were in operation; although even these flights had an elapsed time of over nine days, with passengers sleeping in comfort at overnight stops along the way in places such as Rome, Beirut, Karachi, Calcutta, Singapore, Jakarta and Darwin.

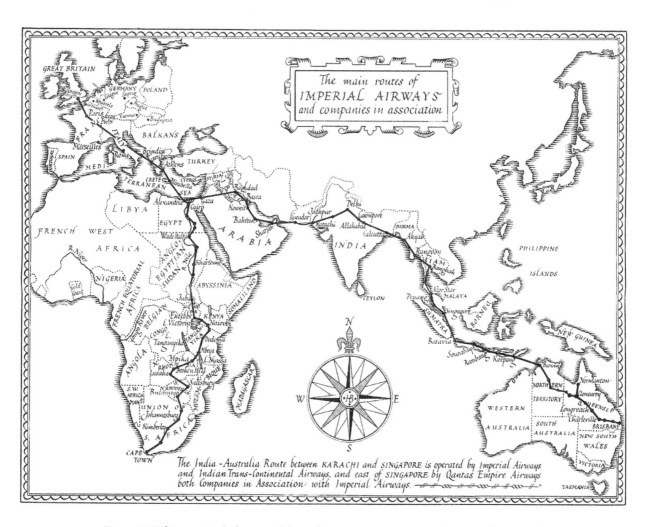

Figure 7.3 This map includes one of the earliest passenger air routes between the UK and Australia. It appeared in an April 1935 timetable.[6]

---

[4] Although the formation of the RAE Space Department in January 1962 may have been a consequence.

[5] Telex (TELeprinter EXchange) was the forerunner of email and texting. Electro-mechanical typewriters (teleprinters) could dial each other up via dedicated data telephone systems, providing a cheap and reliable world wide text messaging system. Telex started in the 1960s and lasted until ousted by fax and emails in the 1980s and 1990s.

[6] From the collection of Björn Larsson, see *www.timetableimages.com/ttimages/iaw.htm* (last accessed August 2014). In 1935, the single fare from London to Brisbane was £195 (equivalent to £12,000 - £48,000 by 2011!). (2011 figure derived using the measures for a "Commodity", from Lawrence H. Officer and Samuel H. Williamson, "Five Ways to Compute the Relative Value of a UK Pound Amount, 1270 to Present," MeasuringWorth, 2014, *www.measuringworth.com/ukcompare/* , last accessed August 2014).

During the very early days, senior members of the Joint Project staff used the newly resumed post-war commercial air service for urgent visits. Other staff travelled by ocean liner to Adelaide, which took about five weeks. Cargo went by sea, or was specially air freighted. However, from 1952 to 1975, the British Ministry of Supply ran a regular courier service. For the first five years this comprised a fortnightly flight provided by RAF Transport Command for freight and passengers; plus some extra flights for freight only and explosive cargoes, the latter generally landing directly at Woomera.[7] The regular service used piston engined Handley Page Hasting aircraft, and was primitive by modern standards. A typical load was twelve passengers at the rear with freight in the front. Flights were slow, so noisy that conversation was next to impossible, and the cabin was not pressurised so when the plane rose above 14,000 feet the passengers had to wear oxygen masks.[8] However, as Ted Chambers recalled:

> Those were the days when the British Raj still had some influence in the Middle East. Each night we spent the dark hours on terra firma, cosseted in one of the RAF bases which were once scattered like pearls across the world. Magic names like Changi, Colombo, Katenika, Tripoli, Ben Adam, Ghan and Nicosia, to name but a few. … There is no doubt that Changi [Singapore] was the preferred stopover place. The shopping was legendary, the RAF barracks were comfortable and the food good. If the RAF had an ailing aircraft, if humanly possible, it would be nursed to Changi airstrip for any repairs to be effected. The shopping there was so popular that there seemed no limit to what one might buy and lug on board. Like large wicker baskets, crates of Noritaki china, radios and the host of other items bought at bargain basement prices. On one flight I was on, the RAF pilot, noting the numerous passengers struggling on board with their booty, demanded all and their purchases off the aircraft so that they might be weighed. He needed to be confidant that takeoff could still be safely achieved!
>
> The record flight for longevity between England and Australia in the Woomera years was twenty three days from start to finish. A series of delayed departures from the U.K. and Ceylon, as it was then known, caused some of the passengers to have financial problems. Before leaving for Singapore more shopping money had to be remitted to them to carry on as they had originally planned.[9]

However, aircraft improved rapidly, and in 1957 RAF Comet II jet transports were introduced for passengers and small

items of cargo. The Comet could cover the route in only two days, with a day and a night stop in Singapore. From 1960 onwards, transport responsibilities were shared, with contracts being given to various charter airlines. As the Comet had no wide freight doors, big freight continued to go by Hastings aircraft, supported by six Avro Traders belonging to Air Charter Ltd owned by Freddie Laker, later famous for his no-frills walk-on transatlantic airline - the Laker Skytrain.

To support the flights to Woomera, a new airfield had been built next to the Joint Project HQ at Salisbury near Adelaide. It was named after the Duke of Edinburgh, who opened it in 1954,[10] and although the Joint Project is no more, Edinburgh airfield lives on as a major RAAF base.[11]

Skylark shares the Joint Project Facility

The UK Ministry of Supply was originally responsible for the supply of Skylark rocket vehicles. It acted through the RAE, and as the initial development ended, the RAE started a "production line", capable of making about ten Skylarks a year. Various university groups were responsible for the design and construction of the scientific instruments, and for analysing the results. Coordination of these activities was originally carried out by a subcommittee of the Royal Society Gassiot Committee, the "Rocket Committee".

By means of the Joint Project courier air service, Skylark payloads would arrive at the WRE's main base at Salisbury near Adelaide. Here they would be assembled and checked by the University or other sponsor, before being transported the 270 miles (430 km) northwest to Woomera itself. The rocket motors, with nearly a ton of solid propellant, were usually flown directly to Woomera's airstrip; RAF transport command ran flights for freight and explosive cargoes until at least 1957, and probably until 1960, after which charter flights took over.[12]

From 1963 to 1975 two Britannia aircraft were used, first by British Eagle then Monarch Airlines, one the passenger charter, the other the 'explosives' Britannia that carried the motors and the heavy payload items. The explosives plane had special doors to accept the long Raven motors.[13]

Enhancements

Once the original proving trials had been completed in early 1958, resources could be expended on improving Skylark. For instance, the Raven motor was being continuously developed, with the case being lightened and the nozzle performance improved. On the ground, the priming arrangements

[7] Morton (1989), *Fire across the Desert*, p.148.
[8] Morton (1989).
[9] Chambers (2000), *Woomera, Its human face*, pp.38 & 40.
[10] Morton (1989), *Fire across the Desert*, p.138.
[11] A web search reveals comprehensive details.
[12] Morton (1989), *Fire across the Desert*, pp.148 – 152.
[13] Cruise (2008), *Skylark Ascending*, online article p.11, and *Prospero* number 5, Spring 2008, p.45.

for monitoring and powering the payload through the umbilicals were re-engineered.

However, there were several major enhancements already under development by the end of the original flight-testing. These included the Cuckoo boost motor and a system for instrument head recovery by parachute.

Enhancement 1 - The Cuckoo Boost Motor

The Cuckoo boost motor was a relatively small solid fuel motor, which could be added to the rear of a Skylark vehicle. (The engineering drawing Figure 6.29 in the previous chapter shows how it was fitted).

As described in Chapter 2, in May 1954 Dr King-Hele's original design study had concluded that adding strap-on boost motors to the then CTV 5 series III rocket would add complication, absorb technical effort and delay production. In the event, the improved performance from the Raven motor made the idea unnecessary.

However, adding a single boost motor in tandem was simpler, thus the Cuckoo motor was developed. Its purpose was to increase Skylark's velocity off the launcher, and to carry heavier payloads to a greater height. Its name stretched the ornithological analogy further than most - it was named the "Cuckoo" because it "kicked the Raven out of the nest"! [14] As with the original Raven motor, the Cuckoo was designed and tested by the Rocket Propulsion Establishment at Westcott. It was initially (Series A) developed for Skylark, later the external shape was modified (as Series B) to enable it to provide a second propulsion stage for the Black Knight test vehicle. [15]

The Cuckoo motor comprised a plastic propellant charge pressed into a steel body. The available space on the Skylark launcher at Woomera restricted the parallel length of the body to only 29 inches (74 cm), and the diameter to 17 inches (43 cm). In March 1957, test firings had started at Westcott, and in 1959 an initial six were supplied to Woomera for Skylark, followed by four for Black Knight.

The Cuckoo I had a total impulse of 81,200 lb.sec (360 kN sec), delivered in a nominal four point one seconds, and provided a thrust of 18,000 lbf (80 kN), some 50% more than the Raven motor.

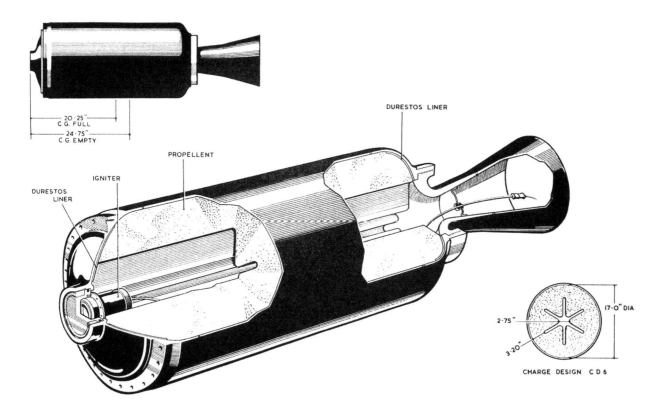

Figure 7.4 The Cuckoo solid fuel motor assembly and charge design.
(White (1960), figure 1)

---

[14] Journal of the Royal Aeronautical Society 1961, Volume 65, p.549.
[15] White (1960), *The development of the 'Cuckoo' rocket motor*, p.1. The Cuckoo was very versatile, as well as being used in the atmosphere and in space, it was also used underwater! (Harlow (1992a), p.7).

Motor	Cuckoo IA
Propellant mass	400 lb (181 kg)
Total mass	534 lb (242 kg)
Total impulse	81,200 lb-secs (361 kN-secs)
Mean thrust at 18ºC	18,000 lbf (80 kN)
Burning time at 18ºC	4.1 seconds

Table 7.1 The main characteristics of the Cuckoo I Series A motor.

(White (1960), Appendix 1)

Proving launches

As noted previously, the original plan to fire the first Cuckoo motor on Skylark SL11 in December 1958 was cancelled when the Cuckoo was found was found to have an unsatisfactory filling. Propellant RD 2311 was replaced by RD 2409 with better wetting and lower flame temperature,[16] and modified motors became available in March 1959.[17] In due course, the Cuckoo motor was first used on SL51 in April 1960. As described in the previous chapter, this achieved a 30% increase in peak altitude, to 219 km (136 miles). This was further improved on at the next launch with the Cuckoo booster, (SL67 in November 1960), which reached 247 km (153 miles). (The photograph at the start of this chapter shows such a launch).

Figure 7.5 A Cuckoo boost motor propelling a Skylark from the launch tower.[18]

(WRE)

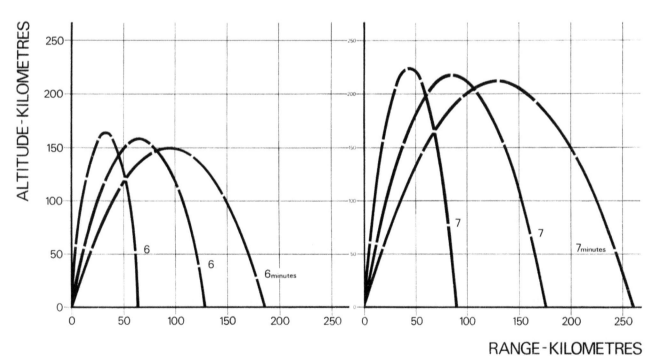

Figure 7.6 This diagram shows the greater altitude provided by the Cuckoo motor. The left hand side set of trajectories is for the Raven VIA sustainer motor with a 200 kg head, the right hand side for the same configuration with the Cuckoo boost motor fitted. (The breaks in the trajectory lines indicate one-minute intervals.)

(BAC (c.1966), p.21)

[16] White (1960), *The development of the 'Cuckoo' rocket motor*, p.5.
[17] Dorling (1959), *The First Six Skylark Firings*, p.67.
[18] The WRE photograph from which this enlargement was taken does not identify the launch.

The Black Knight version of the Cuckoo motor (series B) was used for the first time soon afterwards. This was as the second stage of the Black Knight rocket BK08, launched on 24th May 1960, when the Cuckoo boosted the payload back into the atmosphere at very high speed.

Enhancement 2 - Payload Recovery

The second enhancement was a parachute system for Skylark payload recovery. Recovery of man-made objects from space is a difficult task. For instance, the Black Knight rocket described earlier had been created primarily as a relatively cheap and practical way to develop and test atmospheric re-entry techniques and technology for nuclear warheads.

The recovery task for Skylark was much easier, because a sounding rocket re-enters the atmosphere at a far lower speed than that of an orbiting satellite or a sub-orbital ballistic missile.[19] However recovery was difficult to perfect when tackled for the first time, and even after it had been made to work, it was to be many years before it became reliable.

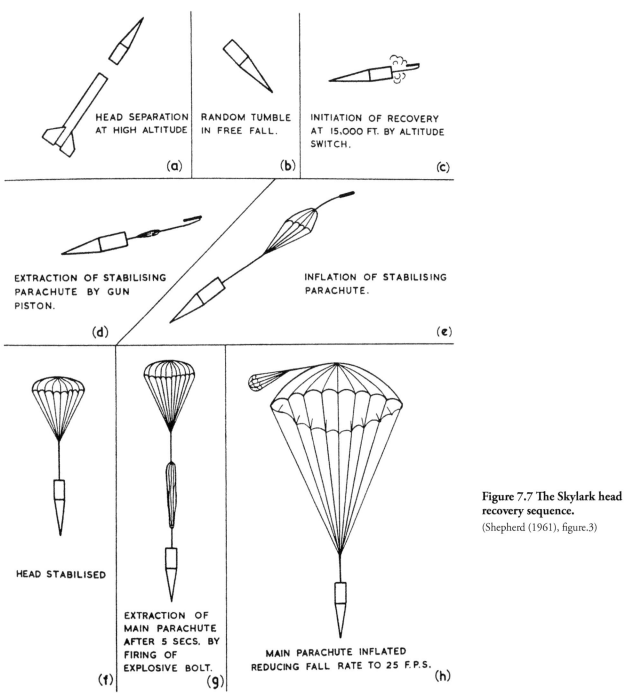

Figure 7.7 The Skylark head recovery sequence.

(Shepherd (1961), figure.3)

Figures 7.8 and 7.9 The original recovery parachute bay. In use, it was located between the instrument head and the Raven motor, one of many options to come that would extend the length of Skylark.

(Shepherd (1961), figures 6 and 9)

At the end of a flight, a Skylark payload would normally impact the ground at high speed and destroy itself. The objective of this exercise was to soft-land a typical 250 lb (113 kg) Skylark instrument head at 25 feet per second (17 mph / 27 km/h). The solution adopted by the RAE was to separate the head from the rocket close to apogee and then deploy a parachute below 20,000 feet (4.7 miles / 7.6 km), when it was estimated that the speed would be only about 340 mph (547 km/h). The system was based on that used for aircraft pilot ejector seats, and used two parachutes as shown in figure 7.7.

The design was successfully tested using aircraft dropping trials at the Imber range on Salisbury plain in the UK, and all seemed well. A small number of recovery bays were manufactured for fitting to Skylarks.

The first test at Woomera had been on Skylark SL16 on 30th November 1959. Disappointingly, the recovery system did not work, and in the words of RAE project leader J.V.Shepherd "When the head was located it was seen to be a total wreck with the parachutes torn and seared, and the straps severely melted".[20]

This was a severe setback, although a sign of things to come, and it was deduced that the parachutes had deployed early.

Several modifications were made to the initiation system, and it was not until twelve months later that the next test was carried out at Woomera. This was on Skylark SL33 in November 1960, an RAE proving flight. Again, the parachute system failed to deploy correctly, although this was blamed on a head separation problem.

The next try was three months later; this time the head was fully instrumented to check parachute operation. This was Skylark SL36, launched on 13 February 1961. For the first time the recovery system worked insofar as the head was recovered in an undamaged condition, although it was clear that the main parachute had again escaped prematurely.[21]

A few months later this was followed by SL34, launched on 1st August 1961 as described later. To quote the technical report "With the incorporation of the modifications to the securing of the main parachute cover, the functioning of the recovery system on this round was entirely successful and valuable equipment was recovered in an undamaged condition".[22]

There seems to have been an element of wishful thinking regarding the recovery system. Even before the next fully

[20] Shepherd (1961), *A Recovery System for the Skylark Instrument Head*, p.8.
[21] Shepherd (1961), p.10.
[22] Shepherd (1961), p.11.

Figures 7.10, 7.11, 7.12 and 7.13. A set of recovery site Polaroid photographs of SL36. Although the parachute system failed to deploy properly, this was still the first Skylark payload to be successfully soft-landed after re-entry from space.

(WRE (1961), Trials Result file J5555/3/36) [23]

instrumented proving flight (SL37 in October), it was stated that development of the recovery system was complete.[24] Even without hindsight, this seems to have been a premature conclusion, as the system had had numerous teething problems during development and the first flight trials,[25] and on only one Skylark, SL34 just mentioned, had it worked properly. Unfortunately, as Skylark became more powerful and the payloads larger, it proved very unreliable, and it was to be nearly ten years before a cure was introduced.

Consequently, by the late sixties the recovery system had gained a poor reputation "Parachutes seldom worked on

Skylarks and so the payload was usually badly smashed... (although at least the parachutes made good markers for finding the landing site!)". Similarly, "The parachute failures dented the effectiveness of the whole programme and were a factor in letting the US pull ahead in many scientific fields. As the payloads became heavier and longer, the parachute design remained the same and success rates suffered."[26]

It was eventually worked out that a phenomenon that took place before the recovery sequence was initiated was to blame. As the rocket head re-entered the atmosphere, it could be driven into a propelling motion so fast that the main parachute would be torn from its bay by centrifugal

---

[23] This set of SL36 site of recovery photographs also appears as "Shepherd (1961), *A Recovery System for the Skylark Instrument Head*, figure 13", but the better quality set shown here has been sourced from the original photographic prints in the WRE (1961) SL36 Trials Result file J5555/3/36.

[24] Shepherd (1961), p.12, "Conclusion".

[25] Even the dropping trials on Salisbury Plain in the UK had had a 20% failure rate; despite this, it had still been thought that no specific flight trials would be necessary. (Shepherd (1961), p.8).

[26] Cruise (2008), *Skylark Ascending*, online article pp.21 & 26, and *Prospero* number 5, Spring 2008, pp.55 & 60.

force. The solution adopted was to restrain it with strong wires that were freed before deployment by explosive cutters.[27] This modification had been introduced by 1971,[28] but it tackled only the symptoms, not the underlying cause. It was not until 1977 that the German DFVLR calculated that if the centre of gravity of the returning payload was within 5% of the centre of the payload, oscillation and dynamic forces were kept within bounds.[29]

Enhancement 3 - The Skylark head evolves

This 'enhancement', the increase in size and complexity of the payload head, evolved steadily rather than being introduced all at once. As shown in earlier chapters, the Skylark payload head had originally consisted of four main parts: (1) a nose cone, (2) an intermediate strong ring, (3) a parallel walled (instrument) bay and (4) a rear/base strong ring. At first these were bolted together, but later quick release 'manacle rings' were used. The intermediate strong ring (2) originally held the

MTS (Missile Tracking System) beacon and two large electrical batteries, the rear strong ring (4) included vehicle services, mainly the 'T5 sender', comprising the 465 MHz telemetry sender, a Doppler transponder, MTS oscillator and associated power supplies with ground connectors.

However, as even from the start the head assembly tended to be custom built, the experiments could be either in the nose cone or instrument bay, or both. In time, the original instrument bay became used only for standard instruments carried on every flight, the university experiments being carried in their own parallel bays. (The standard instruments included magnetometers, rate gyros, accelerometers and a programmer switch that provided timing pulses).

As explained above, new bays such as the parachute bay and roll control unit were soon added between the original head and the motor, and as shown below, other bays were added under the nose cone as required for particular experiments. Later versions of Skylark had up to half a dozen extra bays.

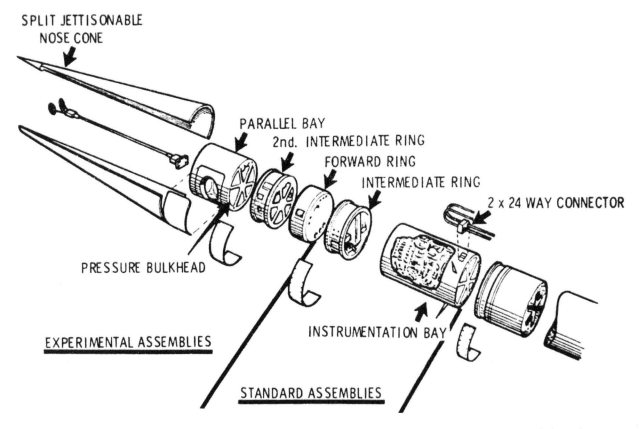

Figure 7.14 This exploded view shows an example of how the Skylark instrument head was expanded. In this implementation, a parallel bay, second intermediate ring and forward ring have been inserted between the nose cone and standard assemblies. (Lewis (1972), figure 2) [30]

[27] Dorling (1975), 'Early History of the Skylark Rocket', p.179.

[28] The cable retaining system with cutters had been introduced by December 1971. (Minutes of 20th Skylark Policy Meeting, December 1971, p.4, item 4).

[29] See TEXUS 1, Chapter 15 of this book.

[30] Journal of the British Interplanetary Society, Vol.25 No.2 (February 1972), p.176. Reproduced with permission.

Figure 7.15 The 'standard' instrument bay, mounted on the base ring with the telemetry and Doppler system aerials.

(BAC (c.1966), p.10)

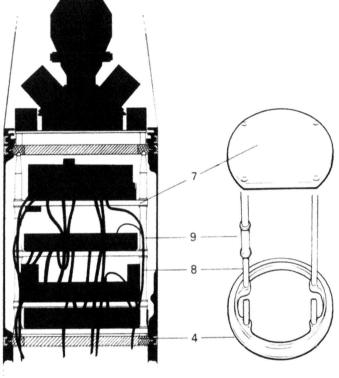

Figure 7. 16 This diagram shows how university experiments (solid black) could be mounted in an instrument bay and under the nose cone.

(BAC (c.1966), p.8)

Meanwhile - the first manned space flight

In 1961, the Soviet Union astounded the world when they launched the first man into space; when on the 12th April Yuri Gagarin became both the first human in space and the first to completely orbit the Earth. His 108-minute flight in the Vostok 1 craft became a sensation, and made headline news. He became a celebrity, visiting Italy, the UK, Germany, Canada and Japan; everywhere he was welcomed by vast crowds.

Yuri Gagarin had been braver than was generally realised. Of the previous 16 launches of the version of the R-7 rocket that used the same engines that put Gagarin in space, eight had failed.[31] Indeed, a few days before, he and his fellow cosmonauts had witnessed at first-hand a launch pad disaster when such a combat missile had exploded on takeoff.[32]

However, with the resources that had been made available, the newly formed NASA was able to start catching up, and on 5th May that year, Alan Shepard became the first American to fly into space, when he rode his Mercury capsule on a 15-minute suborbital mission.

[31] Cadbury (2006), *Space Race*, p.236.
[32] Ibid, p.240.

The Black Brant sounding rocket emerges – cousin and rival to Skylark

Back in the sounding rocket world, details of a new vehicle, the 'Black Brant', were revealed in the UK in 1961.[33] In appearance, it was very similar to Skylark, and was based on a similar 17-inch (43 cm) motor case. An initial acceleration of about 10g enabled the vehicle to be fired from a 15-foot (4.6 metre) launcher. The rear structure weighed 145 lb (66 kg), somewhat heavier than Skylark and the launching velocity and hence kinetic effects were greater than in Skylark.

The Black Brant sounding rocket had a complicated evolution. It effectively began in a 1957 Canadian government requirement to test a new solid rocket fuel. To do this, they acquired from Bristol Aerojet in England details of the 17-inch diameter 'Skylark' motor, and what became known

Figure 7.17 The original Black Brant 2 sounding rocket.
(Beadle (1961), p.550) [37]

as the 'Propulsion Test Vehicle' was born.[34] As the "PTV", the first four were launched from the Fort Churchill army range[35] on the edge of Hudson Bay in September 1959. The Canadian Armament Research and Development Establishment (CARDE) then turned its attention to long-distance communications research, and they found the PTV useful as a sounding rocket, being capable of lifting 149 lb (68 kg) to typically 100-130 km (67-81 miles). To better suit this role, the manufacturer (the Canadian division of the UK's Bristol Aeroplane Company) re-designed it to be a dedicated sounding rocket.[36]

This 'Black Brant' was first launched in October 1960 from Fort Churchill, and could send 68 kg to an altitude of 200km. Like Skylark, the name Black Brant was ornithological, being that of a goose indigenous to Western Canada.

This version subsequently became known as the Black Brant 2. It had a diameter of 43 cm (17 inches), the same as Skylark, whereas the earlier PTV (subsequently called the Black Brant 1) had a smaller diameter of 26 cm (10.25 inches). Other versions were soon made, for instance in 1962 these designs were followed by the smaller Black Brant 3.

The Black Brant rocket family went on to become extremely successful in North America, and later versions have outlived Skylark. They were mostly used by NASA, and by the year 2010 over 1000 had been made and launched. However, its origins and success were the subject of some controversy, because the manufacturer in Canada was at the time part of the same British Company that made Skylark's Raven motor.[38] "I should say that Bristol Aerospace of Canada ...obtained the plans for Raven II through their connections with Bristols, of which Bristol Aerojet was of course a common partner. And they took that design, which as far I was aware was really Her Majesty's government's design, and actually exploited it in North America at no cost."[39]

---

[33] Journal of the Royal Aeronautical Society, August 1961 (Volume 65, No. 608), p.550.

[34] Newey & Carlson (1980), *Bristol Aerospace Limited: 50 Years of Technology 1930-1980, Volume 2*, p.65.

[35] Fort Churchill had been the Canadian location originally considered for the British overseas rocket range when the choice had been made between Canada and Australia.

[36] A decision made with the essential backing and support of Sir Reginald Verdon Smith, Chairman of the then British parent, the Bristol Aeroplane Company. (Newey & Carlson (1980), p.66).

[37] RAeS Journal Vol.65 (August 1961), p.550. Reproduced by kind permission of The Royal Aeronautical Society's Aeronautical Journal.

[38] The Canadian company itself had a complicated history. In 1954 "MacDonald Brothers Aircraft" had been purchased by the UK based Bristol Aeroplane Company, and became its Canadian division. In March 1962, at least part became a joint enterprise, Canadian Bristol Aerojet Ltd., a parallel to the Bristol Aerojet joint venture operating at Banwell in Somerset. In 1965, Aerojet of California withdrew, and in 1966/67, the Canadian company became Bristol Aerospace Limited after it was acquired by Rolls-Royce Industries.

[39] John Harlow in 2001, (CCBH (2005) *Skylark Sounding Rockets1957-1972*, p.83. & *Prospero* No. 2 (Spring 2005), p.146.

However, the Canadian company (which remained part of Rolls Royce Industries until 1997) had put a large amount of development work into Black Brant and its motors, much of it in parallel to that carried out on Skylark. Hence, in 1968, the following observation was made:

> …one soon realises that the only vehicle that offers any competition over Skylark is the Canadian Black Brant. This is most interesting because the Canadians started from the basic Skylark design and proceeded to develop further and by using a faster burning propellant and packing more propellant in the same tubes have achieved a higher efficiency but of course at the expense of a harder ride with increased vibration and higher temperatures. It does, however, demonstrate the fact that because of the small amount of money available for development in this country [UK] over the last few years only small improvements to the basic vehicle have been possible compared to what could have been done.[40]

The RAE becomes more involved in space matters

In June 1961, the RAE hosted the well-known annual SBAC (Society of British Aircraft Constructors) aviation trade show at Farnborough in the UK. Reports reveal that the RAE was becoming increasingly involved in space related activities. On the 15th June, "Flight" magazine reported:

> Amongst the Guided Weapons Department exhibits were items depicting Blue Streak, Black Knight and Skylark developments. In the main concourse, the "space" stand included models of an astronomical and a communications satellite described as "possible designs",[41] a full-scale model of the second stage and re-entry head assembly in the two stage version of Black Knight, and a model of the Skylark launcher installed at Woomera. Outside one of the GW Department buildings were two rockets – a two-stage Black Knight and a Skylark fitted with a Cuckoo boost motor.

Skylark exhibits also included a fully instrumented Skylark head identical to that of Skylark No 43 [launched May 1961] which carried stellar ultra-violet light measuring equipment; a working model of the servo-controlled roll-stabilization of the nosecone; and some of the methods employed in determining the attitude of the rocket with reference to the Sun and to the Earth's magnetic field. Test rigs for sensitive jet control systems such as those for Skylark and for other rocket and satellite applications were demonstrated.[42]

SKYLARK LAUNCHES AND SCIENCE IN 1961

Meanwhile, Skylark's fifth year of operation was the busiest so far, with a record 17 launches from Woomera, nearly twice as many as in 1960. The first astronomy[43] experiments were launched, four of them by NASA.

Back in the UK, 1961 saw the BNCSR (British National Committee for Space Research) involved in an increasing range of activities, including the establishment of a co-operative European programme, and the development of stabilised Skylarks and new small research rockets (see the next chapter). The possibility of satellite space for British experiments contributed to an increase in the number of interested university scientists, and March saw recommendations for research grants to no less than fifteen groups for the development of instrumentation in sounding rockets and/or Earth satellites. In addition to the five main groups who had been involved from the outset (Belfast, Birmingham, Leicester, Imperial College and UCL), new groups from Cambridge, Leeds, Leicester, Imperial College, Manchester, Reading, Sheffield and Southampton arrived on the scene.[44]

At Woomera, the Black Knight programme continued, with BK13, 14 and 17 all being launched during the year.

Jan	Feb.	March	April	May	June	July	Aug.	Sept.	Oct.	Nov.	Dec.
	SL36	SL63	SL64	SL43	SL26	SL65	SL34	US01	US02	US03	SL42
				SL25				SL40	SL37	SL35	
										US04	
										SL83	

Table 7.2 The 17 Skylark launches in 1961. (For full details see Appendix 3)

(Key: black = RAE gyroscope test programme, blue = mainly UK scientific programme (unstabilised), pink = NASA southern sky survey programme)

[40] Thomas (1968), 'Suborbital probes', p.248.
[41] King-Hele & Gilmore (1956), *Preliminary assessment of an Earth satellite reconnaissance vehicle*. (RAE Technical Note GW 393) may have applied. The RAE carried out a great deal of pioneering work on Earth satellites, for instance later on the *List of Technical Papers Issued by Space Department January 1962 – December 1965* listed hundreds of technical reports on matters such as satellite design and orbital calculations. (TNA: PRO AVIA 6/21301).
[42] 'Flight' magazine, 15 June 1961, p.826. (See figure 7.26, and also figure 13.3 showing a Skylark exhibited with a later version of the boost motor).
[43] In this context, astronomy is used to mean observations beyond the Sun, solar physics experiments are excluded.
[44] Massey & Robins (1986), *History of British Space Science*, p.194.

1961 began with the launch of **SL36**, an RAE vehicle designed to test the Skylark recovery system for a third time. After the malfunction of the parachute on SL33 the previous year, a metal strip was added to retain the main chute cover plate. In addition, in order to help find out what was really happening during parachute release, the operation of the drogue gun, drogue, explosive bolt, main chute cover plate and pressure switches were monitored by telemetry.

As a secondary experiment, the vehicle carried a grenade and 'window' bay. Its purpose was to measure temperature and winds by the "flash and bang" method and compare the wind result with wind determination from radar tracked window clouds.[45] It was the first of four such grenade experiments that would be flown in 1961.

The round[46] had arrived in Australia in September 1960, but was withheld from firing because of the high priority rounds SL33, SL49 and SL50, which had required all the available effort at the end of the previous year.[47]

It was eventually prepared for firing the week commencing Monday 6th February 1961, but did not get an opportunity that week as BK13 was fired on the Tuesday and the weather on Wednesday and Thursday was unsuitable.[48]

It may appear from accounts so far, that by now launching Skylark was a routine activity that merely required the firing button to be pressed. However, the following detailed account for SL36 reveals the many difficulties that could occur when launching even a relatively simple sounding rocket into space:[49]

Figure 7.18 The SL36 payload being prepared. It can be seen that for this assembly, the base ring with aerials has been positioned above the parallel bay.
(WRE (1961), Trials Preparation file J5555/2/36)

---

[45] SL36 OISC report, 23/2.61. (WRE SL36 Trials Results file J5555/3/36).

[46] In WRE / Woomera parlance, each missile or rocket to be fired was known as the 'Round'.

[47] SL33 was the first full test of the autopilot gyroscope investigation, SL49 and SL50 had carried joint RAE and scientific payloads. From the recovery point of view, it would have been better if SL36 had been fired first, because it was the first to be fully instrumented. (Shepherd (1961), *A Recovery System for the Skylark Instrument Head*, p.9).

[48] BK13 reached an impressive 427 miles (687 km). In addition to the re-entry head, it carried three upper atmosphere experiments but these were unsuccessful. For further details of BK13, see Hill (2001), *A Vertical Empire*, p.173.

[49] E.M.I.E. Trial Notes (March 1961) for Skylark Round SL36, pp.1&2. (WRE SL36 Trials Results file J5555/3/36).

6/2/61		Round loaded in launcher
7/2/61	1500 hours	GIMIC called off. Intercommunication was faulty between Priming Hut and E.C.2 monitor and between E.C.2 and M3
8/2/61	0900 hours	GIMIC commenced. Fluctuating telemetry signals received by M3 and fluctuating signals of M.T.S. received by P3. In addition intermittent signals were received on Doppler. Pogo motor failed to start. GIMIC was cancelled. Pogo motor faults was traced to intermittent connection on terminal strip and leads to Ledex switch in grenade bay. Telemetry was proved to function correctly on E.C.2 Monitor and M.T.S. was checked on launcher with a wavemeter and proved to function correctly. The Doppler Modulator Box on the launcher was investigated by the range and was thought to be the cause of the intermittent signals received during the GIMIC.
	1300 hours	GIMIC recommenced. Telemetry channels 6 and 7 were found to be open circuit. This was traced to connectors between Grenade Bay and parachute bay and the fault was cleared.
	1400 hours	Firing was cancelled because of excessive wind forecast.
	1500 hours	GIMIC recommenced and a successful run at M3 was completed followed by a successful recording run.
9/2/61	1400 hours	Firing was cancelled because of adverse weather forecast.
13/2/61	1145 hours	Firing sequence commenced.
	1640 hours	Clock run completed.
	2058 hours	Second clock run completed (following repatching after a B.K. static firing.
	2152 hours	Firing sequence entered
	2201 hours	Standby by M3 due to low 24 volt supply.
	2202 hours	Sequence restarted
	2211 hours	Stop action taken at -4 sec by Priming Monitor owing failure of extractors. Another clock run was made and proved to be successful. In addition connections to extractor control box were checked and found to be correct.
	2311 hours	Sequence recommenced
	2317 hours	Doppler standby -9 mins.
	2319 hours	Sequence re-started.
	2328 hours	Round fired.

(GIMIC = "Ground Instrumentation, Missile Instrumentation, Check". EC2 = Equipment Centre 2 (under the edge of the Skylark launcher apron). P3 = an MTS ground station near the launcher, see photo Figure 4.25 and map Figure 4.26)

Fortunately, the flight itself went well. The science experiments were highly successful, which must have been a relief, as there had been some concern beforehand that the grenade experiment might jeopardise the parachute trial.[50]

[50] In a Telex from WRE to RAE dated 2/9/60 it was suggested the grenade experiment be abandoned and the bay removed. "I consider further firings with result similar to SL61 would only destroy confidence of all concerned". (WRE SL36 Trials Preparation file J5555/2/36).

Seq. Nos	Launch date	Ref. (sponsor) launch site	Config- uration	Apogee km (miles)	Experi- menters	Experiments	Result
32 (1)	13 Feb. 1961	SL36 (UK) Woomera	Un, Rav.2	146 (91)	RAE	Test (Skylark tech.) – third parachute trial	Ps
					UCL	Neutral atmosphere – (grenades)	S
					IC	" " - (falling dipoles)	S

Table 7.3 A summary of SL36.

This time the parachute recovery did basically work for the first time, and so SL36 was distinguished as having the first Skylark payload to be successfully soft landed after re-entry from space. It was recovered in excellent condition; see Figures 7.10, 7.11, 7.12 and 7.13 earlier in this chapter. However, the telemetry records revealed that the main parachute had deployed early yet again, this time at +421 seconds (at about 35,000 feet / 10.7 km). After this, the payload had floated down for a good six minutes before it reached 15,000 feet

(4.6 km) when the release mechanism had worked correctly as intended. It was concluded by WRE that the main chute had been forced out by aerodynamic loads in a similar manner to the malfunction in SL33.[51]

The recovered payload (less parachute bay) appears to been have subsequently exhibited on the WRE stand at the Singapore Air Show that April, before being returned to the UK, where in turn it was going to be exhibited.[52]

Figure 7.19 SL63 complete with Cuckoo booster being prepared at the launch tower. This view is from the 'front' (North West) of the launcher. Behind on the right can be seen the top of the EC2 equipment centre/control room.

(National Archives of Australia: D874, N61/653)

[51] Telex dated 14/2/61 from WRE to RAE. (WRE SL36 Trials Preparation file J5555/2/36).
[52] Telex dated 24/2/61 from WRE to RAE. (WRE SL36 Trials Results file J5555/3/36).

Seq. Nos	Launch date	Ref. (sponsor) launch site	Config- uration	Apogee km (miles)	Experi- menters	Experiments	Result
33 (2)	06 March 1961	SL63 (UK) Woomera	Un, Raven 2 +C	231 (144)	UCL	Neutral atmosphere - (grenades)	S
					UCL	" " - grenade glows	Ps
					IC	" " - (falling dipoles)	S
					Bel	" " - (sodium vapour)	S

Table 7.4 A summary of SL63.

The next round designed to test the recovery system was SL34, launched on 1 August 1961 as described later in this chapter.

6 March 1961   SL63

In March, SL63 successfully launched a similar atmospheric physics payload. This time the payload included a Belfast sodium vapour experiment, which, as shown in figure 7.20, gained its fair share of publicity:

The glow cloud was indeed seen over a wide area:

A sodium cloud …was seen by people over an area of 10,000 sq.miles. More than 100 miles above the Earth, the cloud appeared to be 50 times the size of the Moon, and was observed from southern Australia, Victoria, New South Wales and parts of southern Queensland.

The timing of the experiment was arranged so the Sun would illuminate the cloud for ground observers in regions where the Sun had already set. In north-west Queensland, the cloud was seen low above the horizon as a fiery red ball, but in west New South Wales it appeared well above the horizon as a golden colour. In west and north Victoria, the cloud appeared oval shaped and a bright orange.[54]

5 April 1961   SL64

SL64 was launched on the 5th April, with the third in the year's series of grenade and falling dipole experiments from UCL and Imperial College. The experiments were the same as for SL63, but without the sodium vapour experiment from Belfast. It reached an altitude of 158 km, and was completely successful.

WOOMERA ROCKET LIGHTS UP THE WESTERN SKY

Thousands See Man-made 'Moon'

WOOMERA scientists last night shot a giant man-made moon of glowing vapor high over Australia.

People over a vast area of the continent reported sighting the "moon."

The brilliant reddish glow was from a Skylark rocket fired from Woomera at 7.25 p.m. Central Australian time (7.55 Melbourne time).

Flares emitted by the rocket on its climb were seen in Victoria, New South Wales, Queensland, South Australia and The Northern Territory.

Figure 7.20 The Queen's University of Belfast sodium vapour experiment continued to make headlines. On the day following its launch, the results from Skylark SL63 appeared on the front page of the Melbourne based newspaper "The Age".

(The Age, 7 March 1961, p.1) [53]

---

[53] Reproduced with permission.
[54] 'The Aeroplane' magazine, 17 March 1961, p.300.

Seq. Nos	Launch date	Ref. (sponsor) launch site	Config- uration	Apogee km (miles)	Experi- menters	Experiment	Result
35 (4)	01 May 1961	SL43 (UK) Woomera	Un, Rav.2	155 (96)	UCL	Astronomy - stellar UV detection (photometer)	S

Table 7.5 A summary of SL43.

May 1961	SL43, SL25

SL43 was significant because it carried the first Skylark astronomy experiment that observed the stars rather than the Sun. It made pioneering measurements in ultraviolet light, the first ever of stars in the southern sky.[55]

The experiment originated from the Physics Department of University College London, and although carried out before a stabilised payload facility was available for Skylark, still succeeded in making observations of 22 stars. A number of ultraviolet photometers were mounted on the payload, each with a limited field of view, and the sky was scanned by the uncontrolled spin of the vehicle. The signals from the photometers were transmitted to the ground over a radio telemetry link, together with those from several devices for measuring the attitude of the rocket. Analysis of the records enabled the signals from the photometers to be associated with known stars.

SL43 preceded the similar NASA Skylark UV experiments launched a few months later, all of which emphasised the need for a stabilised version of the payload platform, the development of which is described in the next chapter.

Figure 7.21 This cutting from the 'The Age' newspaper anticipated the flight of SL43.
(The Age, 16 February, 1960, p.12) [56]

"Flying Telescope" to be Sent Up

CANBERRA, Monday. — A "flying telescope" is to be launched from Woomera rocket range in a Skylark rocket soon.

It will take pictures of the sky and measure the intensity of ultra-violet light.

Five scientists at London's University College have been working on the telescope for nine months.

The United Kingdom High Commissioner's office said today the flying telescope would soon be flown to Australia.

The research team hopes to "find out more about the stars and the atmosphere, and perhaps even discover new astronomical objects radiating ultra-violet light at present invisible to us."

It is not a telescope in the conventional sense, but consists of six amplifiers, each set into a cast metal framework at different angles to the verticle so as to look at a low angle of degree at the sky and measure the intensity of the ultra-violet light.

Six photo-multipliers work by building up a television-type picture of the sky.

This is then transmitted via a radio-telemeter back to the earth.

Scanning of the picture is achieved from the "yawing" rotary action of the rocket itself.

The Skylark rocket will reach a height of up to 100 miles above the surface of the Earth before the pictures are taken.

It is purely a research rocket, originally developed and built for carrying instruments into the upper atmosphere during the geophysical year.

---

[55] Massey (1966), *Space Travel and Exploration,* p.71. (As discussed in the previous chapter (see Figure 6.20), most UV light is blocked by the Earth's atmosphere, so such observations cannot be made from the ground).

[56] Reproduced with permission.

Work had started on the SL43 experiment in March 1959,[57] and must have been very thorough, as an early model of the Skylark rocket includes the SL43 payload, see figures 7.22 and 7.23

The experiment apparatus comprised five 'telescopes', each consisting of 10 cm lengths of aluminium honeycomb, which were fixed at different angles in the rocket head. Photocells with sharply peaking sensitivity at c. 1900 Å (190 nm) detected radiation collimated by the telescopes as the rocket rolled and changed attitude during flight. The attitude of the rocket was measured by means of a Moon detector, a magnetometer, and a camera photographing the star background.[58]

Continuous determination of the attitude was essential for the payload, because it was not stabilised, and the experimenters needed to know which stars their experiment was pointing at whilst rotating. In all, four separate attitude-measuring devices were fitted. As noted above, a magnetometer system and a lunar detector using photoconductive cells were supplied by the RAE as vehicle services. In addition, a second lunar sensor using a photomultiplier tube behind a pair of crossed slits was mounted on a platform above the photometer system. Finally, an automatic 35mm film camera was also mounted on this platform, and was intended to record the axial star field during flight.[59]

Figure 7.22 This splendid 1/4 scale model of an early Skylark motor assembly on its launching trolley is preserved in the London Science Museum collection at Wroughton, Wiltshire. On the right are models of the Cuckoo boost motor (painted red) and the SL43 UV astronomy payload (the "flying telescope").
(Science Museum object 1974-300, author 100_4963) [60]

[57] Alexander, Bowen & Heddle (1963), 'Southern hemisphere observations of ultra-violet radiation from celestial objects', p.512.
[58] Fox (c.1984), *From Lardner to Massey – A history of physics, space science and astronomy at University College London, 1826 to 1975.*
[59] Alexander, Bowen & Heddle (1963), p.513.
[60] Image taken at the London Science Museum (Wroughton), permission granted by Science & Society Picture Library.

Figure 7.23 A close-up of the model above, showing the "flying telescope" that would be mounted under the nose cone.

(Science Museum object 1974-300, author 100_4970) [61]

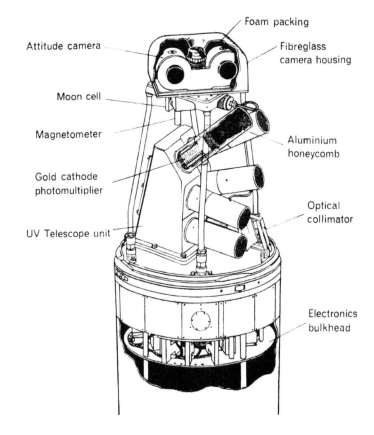

Figure 7.24 The parts of the payload of SL43.

(Massey & Robins (1986), p.195) [62]

Labels on Figure 7.24:
- Attitude camera
- Moon cell
- Magnetometer
- Gold cathode photomultiplier
- UV Telescope unit
- Foam packing
- Fibreglass camera housing
- Aluminium honeycomb
- Optical collimator
- Electronics bulkhead

[61] Image taken at the London Science Museum (Wroughton), permission granted by Science & Society Picture Library.

[62] Massey & Robins (1986), *History of British Space Science,* © Science and Engineering Research Council 1986, published by Cambridge University Press, reproduced with permission.

Figures 7.25 and 7.26 Left: The stellar UV detector payload as used for SL43 in 1961, as stored in the Science Museum at Wroughton in 2010. This is a prototype or flight spare, because in 1961, the Skylark parachute recovery system was not yet available, and "The vehicle was very severely damaged on impact…and little of the experimental assembly was recognizable." [63] Right: the original fairing has been cut away to show the electronics in the parallel bay, so this may well be that exhibited at the 1961 Farnborough show, as referred to at the start of this chapter.

(Science Museum object 1974-518, author 100_4983 & 100_4982) [64]

Flight Details

The time of launch of a Skylark could have many constraints, and for SL43 was complicated by three conditions:

1. The Sun should be below the horizon as seen from the vehicle.
2. The Moon should be nearly full.
3. The Moon should make an angle of not less than 30° with the horizon, and with the Earth's magnetic field.

Figure 7.27 shows the launch windows available.

Despite the restrictions, preparations went well, and the launch took place during the evening of 1st May at 21:40 local time. The vehicle was observed to roll in the sense of a right-handed screw, and was tracked by kinetheodolites until 38 seconds after firing (flares were fitted to the fins).

After passing through the denser part of the atmosphere the split nose cone was successfully jettisoned at some 80 km.,

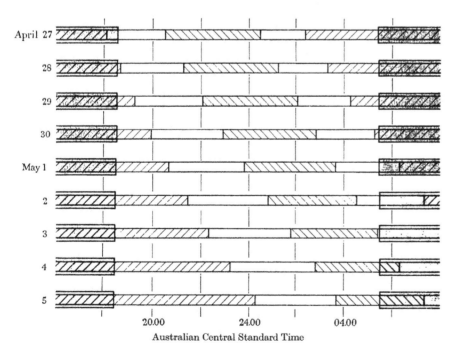

Figure 7.27 The launch windows day by day for SL43. The unshaded portions show when it could be fired.

(Alexander, Bowen & Heddle (1964), figure 9) [65]

---

[63] Alexander, Bowen & Heddle (1963), 'Southern hemisphere observations of ultra-violet radiation from celestial objects', p.521.
[64] Images taken at the London Science Museum (Wroughton), permission granted by Science & Society Picture Library.
[65] Reproduced courtesy Royal Society London.

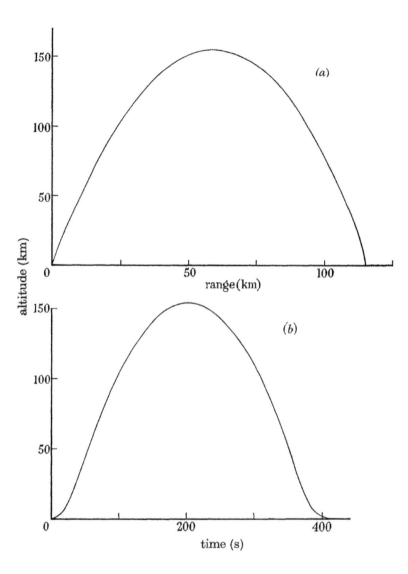

Figure 7.28 The trajectory of SL43 plotted against (a) range and (b) time.
(Alexander, Bowen & Heddle (1964), figure 10) [67]

and the vehicle continued upwards and reached an apogee of 150 km after three and a half minutes. Whilst in space the vehicle rolled at a rate of once every four seconds,[66] the experiment worked well, and telemetry from the two senders was received. The payload was successfully tracked by the MTS system until impact after nearly seven minutes. (+412 seconds).

Unfortunately, during descent, the motor and the payload did not separate at +292 seconds as intended. No parachute recovery system was fitted, and the payload velocity was greater than if separation had occurred. Hence, during re-entry, a considerable amount of vibration began at 360 seconds, and at 370 seconds the various systems began to fail. The legs supporting the forward structure and camera failed at 373 seconds, and 40 seconds later, the vehicle was "very

severely damaged on impact as a consequence of this too rapid descent". The 35mm star field camera carried a reinforced take-up cassette, and it had been anticipated that at least the exposed film would survive the landing impact. However, no trace of the camera was found in the landing area and little of the experimental assembly was recognisable.[68]

However, overall, the experiment was successful, the ultraviolet irradiances of the stars was measured, and it was concluded that early models of the stars had over-estimated the UV emitted. It also provided the first reported measurements of lunar ultraviolet irradiance to be made from rockets.[69] SL43 thus took its place amongst the pioneering UV astronomy missions, a field where sounding rockets could still make original contributions.[70]

[66] Alexander, Bowen & Heddle (1963), p.510.
[67] Reproduced courtesy Royal Society London.
[68] Alexander, Bowen & Heddle (1964), 'Southern hemisphere observations of ultra-violet radiation from celestial objects', p.521.
[69] Heddle (1962), 'Observations in the Southern Hemisphere of Ultra-violet Light from Celestial Objects'.
[70] The first such stellar spectra in the ultraviolet from sounding rocket observations had been obtained in the USA only in November 1960, (Stecher *et al.* (1962), *Stellar Spectrophotometry from above the Atmosphere*), and the first satellite-based measurements did not take place until 1964. (Wilson & Boksenberg (1969), 'Ultraviolet Astronomy', p.449).

SL25 and **SL26** were RAE programme proving flights, successors to SL33 (November 1960), being used to investigate the performance of auto-pilot gyroscopes as required for inertial navigation of the ballistic missiles Black Knight and Blue Streak. These three Skylarks were fired before the main programme was started in order to test the instrumentation systems.

The purpose of both SL25 and SL26 was to test the interferometer method of measuring missile attitude.[71] This technique used three radio receivers on Skylark to monitor radio signals from two transmitters on the ground, the results of which allowed the attitude of the Skylark to be calculated. The principle was simple, but the accuracy required[72] and the high frequency used (X-band, approximately 9.5 GHz), meant the radio equipment was quite sophisticated.

SL25 was launched on the 30th May and performed as required. All three interferometer receivers worked, and the

corresponding telemetry results were successfully received. SL26 followed on the 7th June, it too performed satisfactorily, although the reference gyroscope stopped working after ten seconds when the caging mechanism struck the outer gimbal of the instrument, a defect subsequently eliminated by a modification.[73]

Limited gyro-drift information was obtained from SL25, but this was not the purpose of these initial flights, the main programme would start a year later with the launch of SL28 in August 1962.

SL65 continued the series of UCL and Imperial College grenade and falling dipole experiments, following on from SL64 launched in April. However it only reached an altitude of 70 km (44 miles), less than half that of SL64, and the grenade glow experiment was unsuccessful, presumably because the vehicle did not rise high enough.

 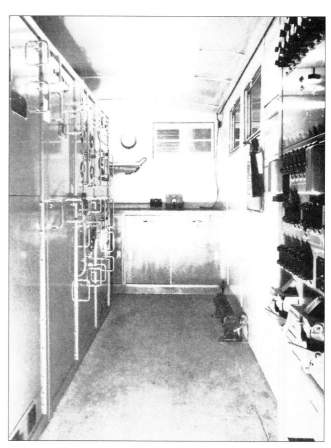

Figures 7.29 and 7.30 Left: The interferometer bay with receivers, waveguides and aerials (A0 – A3), as mounted on Skylark flights SL25 and SL26. Right: The interior of one of the two Interferometer Transmitter vans. These six-ton air-conditioned trailers were positioned 25 miles (40 km) down-range from the Skylark launcher, about 25 miles either side of the range centre-line.

(Knott (1964), figures 9 and 10)

---

[71] Knott (1964), *The Drift of an Auto-Pilot Gyroscope due to prolonged acceleration in the Skylark Rocket, Part 1*, p.25.

[72] It was estimated the radio interferometer technique could measure attitude in pitch, yaw and roll to an accuracy of ±3, ±3 and ±5 arc minutes respectively, i.e. to about one fifteenth of a degree. (Knott (1966), part 4, p.4).

[73] Knott (1964), p.25.

Seq. Nos	Launch date	Ref. (sponsor) Launch site	Config-uration	Apogee km (miles)	Experi-menters	Experiments	Result
39 (8)	01 Aug. 1961	SL34 (UK) Woomera	Un, Rav.2	124 (77)	UCL	Astronomy? - UV camera	F
					RAE	Test (Skylark technology) - fourth parachute trial	S

Table 7.6 A summary of SL34.

1 August 1961   SL34

As noted at the start of this chapter, SL34 was used for the fourth parachute recovery test:

> With the incorporation of the modifications to the securing of the main parachute cover, the functioning of the recovery system on this round was entirely successful and valuable equipment was recovered in an undamaged condition.[74]

This was therefore the second successful recovery of a Skylark payload from space, the "valuable equipment" recovered must have been UCL's UV camera. Despite the recovery, this unfortunately failed, and although nothing more about it is known, it may have been similar to the stellar UV experiment flown on SL43 in May.

Sept. 1961   US01, SL40

Skylark and NASA

The next Skylark launch of 1961 was the first sponsored by NASA, the first from outside the UK. The US government had formed NASA (the National Aeronautics and Space Administration) only three years earlier, by merging several existing organisations. Even at the start, it was a large enterprise, with 8,000 employees and an annual budget of $100 million.

Project Mercury (the first US manned space flight project) was NASA's original high-profile space programme, but NASA still had other activities in the background. These included an active sounding rocket programme; which after 40 years of activity continues to provide low-cost access to space today (2014), with some 20 flights a year.[75] The USA was also keen to co-operate with other countries on the peaceful uses of space,[76] and from 1959 had been working with the UK towards launching the first international satellite, Ariel I, (see 1962 for details). Meanwhile, towards the end of 1960, NASA had placed an order for four Skylarks to be launched in a co-operative programme with the Australians. This programme was administered by the Goddard Space Flight Center in Maryland USA, a laboratory for developing and operating unmanned scientific spacecraft, and which at the time of writing (2014) still plays an important role in the NASA sounding rocket program.

The purpose of NASA's Skylark programme was to carry out an ultraviolet astronomical survey of the southern skies, to complement similar observations already made in the northern hemisphere. The presence of features that could only be viewed from the south, such as the Magellanic Clouds and the more pronounced structure of the Milky Way, suggested that these observations would be of particular interest

The NASA payloads launched by Skylark were quite sophisticated. Each contained ten telescopes, six with electron multiplier phototube detectors filtered for sensitivity to energy bands at 2600 and 2100Å (260-210 nm); and four with ionisation chamber detectors responsive to selected ranges between 1050 and 1500Å (105-150 nm). At this time, the Skylark payload was still unstabilised, and so a spin rate control system was included to reduce the spin rate from a possible 0.5 rev/sec to 0.05 rev/sec., so that as the payload spun, each star would be viewed in each telescope's two-degree field of view for at least 0.1 seconds. This control system consisted of a nitrogen storage bottle in the nose feeding opposed pairs of roll jets, controlled by a gyro system.

Rather than use the standard Woomera range telemetry system, NASA used their own transmitter on the payload, equipped a receiving van in the United States, and shipped it to Australia for the firings.

---

[74] Shepherd (1961), *A Recovery System for the Skylark Instrument Head*, p.11.
[75] NASA Sounding Rocket Program details can be found at *http://rscience.gsfc.nasa.gov/index.html* and *www.nasa.gov/mission_pages/sounding-rockets/index.html* . (Both last accessed August 2014).
[76] For background, see Godwin (2007), *The Skylark Racket*, p.110.

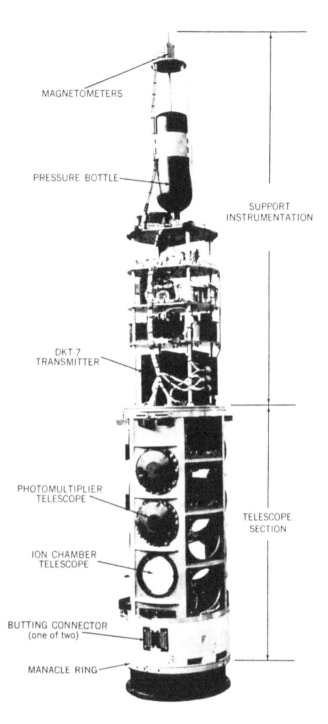

MAGNETOMETERS

PRESSURE BOTTLE

SUPPORT
INSTRUMENTATION

DKT-7
TRANSMITTER

PHOTOMULTIPLIER
TELESCOPE

TELESCOPE
SECTION

ION CHAMBER
TELESCOPE

BUTTING CONNECTOR
(one of two)

MANACLE RING

Figure 7.31 Left: The NASA Southern Sky Survey payload used on Skylark, shown with protective covers mounted over the telescope apertures.

(Windsor (1963), figure 4)

NASA also provided their own test console for pre-flight checkout:

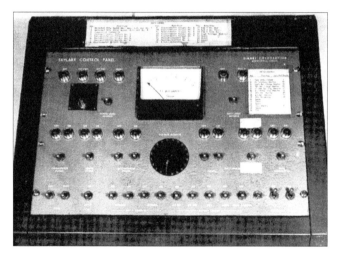

Figure 7.32 Above: The NASA Skylark pre-flight test console panel.

(Windsor (1963), figure 13)

The NASA report from which the above details have been obtained was published in February 1963, and provides interesting information about the loading of the payload and Skylark into the tower: [77]

"Depending on whether or not a booster is used, two different working levels are provided. A removable rail permits access to the payload. Attached to the launcher is a pneumatically operated system for extracting the umbilical connectors. The land lines run from these connectors to the Equipment Center some 500 feet away.

Upon arrival at the launcher, the payload was hoisted to the appropriate level and mounted in the firing position on a temporary plate set between the rails. The final pre-flight check was then made. After this check the payload was swung clear of the rails, and the launcher was released to the launcher officer for installation of the motor and booster.

[77] Windsor (1963), *The Southern Sky Survey Payload,* NASA Technical Note D-1719.

Figure 7.33 This slightly later (c.1964) photograph shows a Skylark payload being loaded into the Woomera launch tower as described above.

(National Archives of Australia: A1500, K12426)

The motor was backed up to the tower base on a railed dolly, and the dolly was pivoted into the tower. The motor was then hoist-held about 10 feet up in the tower while its dolly was removed and a second dolly holding the booster was erected into the tower. (The booster dolly is part of the tower structure during launch.) The motor was lowered onto the booster, and mating was completed. Finally the payload was swung back in line and permanently bolted onto the forward skirt of the motor. A removable service plate at the forward end of the motor permits access for connection of the service lines. After the motor is placed in the tower, range safety regulations require that no voltage sources (i.e. ohmmeters) be on the tower and that no personnel remain on the tower after 8 hours of duty in any 24 hour period."

The first of these NASA Skylarks was duly launched on the 18th September 1961, the second in October, and the final two in November. All four missions were mostly satisfactory, and despite various technical problems with the payload instruments, good observations were obtained. The photomultipliers

Seq. Nos	Launch date	Ref. (sponsor) launch site	Config- uration	Apogee km (miles)	Experi- menters	Experiments	Result
41 (10)	27 Sept. 1961	SL40 (UK) Woomera	Un, Rav.2	152 (95)	UCL/Lei	Solar physics - X-ray photos & spectra	S
					IC	Geomagnetic - proton magnetometer	S
					UCL	Ionosphere - sporadic E probe	S

Table 7.7 A summary of SL40.

in the telescopes caused some problems; on the first flight only two of the six worked, and in addition, the spin control failed. However, the Skylark spun naturally at only 0.08 rev/sec and useful data was returned. Parachute recovery was not used, and "Skylark 9.01 came in streamlined and, while the motor was found beside a hole in the desert, no part that could convincingly be identified as payload was ever found." [78]

The problems were addressed on the subsequent three flights, the spin control problem was cured, and good data from both stars and extended sources was obtained.

SL40 was launched just over a week after the first NASA Skylark, its experiments were all successful, and may have been related to those being designed for Ariel I.

October 1961   US02, SL37

US02 was the second NASA Skylark, launched on the 4th as referred to above. **SL37** was fired three weeks later, and

as noted earlier in this chapter, was the second fully instrumented proving test for the parachute recovery system.

The launch of SL37 had taken over a year to come to fruition. The payload head had arrived in Australia in September 1960, but in October it was decided not to fire it because the experimental telemetry ground equipment was not ready, and "the team effort was required for SL49 and 50". [79] Some of the parts were used on other Skylarks (in October both X-ray cameras were removed and used on SL49, fired on November 24th). However integration of SL37's payload continued, and it seems that practically every sub-assembly and experiment had to be modified to get it to work - one report lists over four pages of technical problems that needed to be solved! [80]

The primary aim of SL37 was to flight test the airborne and ground equipment of the "Scheme A S.R.D.E. broadband telemetry equipment" for the first time at Woomera. [81] Secondary experiments included flight tests of the Skylark parachute recovery system, and two new types of micrometeorite detectors developed by Jodrell Bank. Also fitted were two

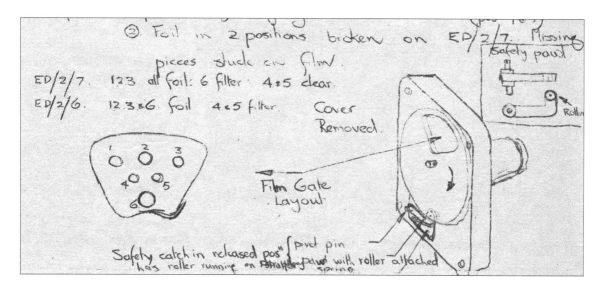

Figure 7.34 The replacement X-ray cameras for SL37 gave a considerable amount of trouble, and had to be returned to the UK. This sketch comes from a short report on the initial diagnosis and attempted repair at Woomera. (Compare with the photograph of the camera shown in Figure 6.22).
(WRE (1961), SL37 Trials Preparation file J5555/2/37(PT.1))

---

[78] Windsor (1963), The Southern Sky Survey Payload, p.11.
[79] *MPO's report for SL37*, WRE (1961), SL37 Trials Results file J5555/3/37.
[80] Ibid.
[81] WRE (1961), *Advance Summary of Firing for SL37 (B56/1)*. (SL37 Trials Results file J5555/3/37). (The SRDE was the Signals Research and Development Establishment at Christchurch in the UK).

X-ray cameras, and a sporadic E detector probe, these latter two experiments having being flown previously.

The SRDE 'Scheme A' appears to have been the first attempt at providing an electronic rather than mechanically based telemetry system for Skylark. However, with solid-state electronics in its infancy, the valve (vacuum tube) based airborne equipment weighed in at a hefty 90 lbs (41 kg),[82] which together with the base ring with aerials, accounted for about half the weight of the payload.[83]

The micrometeorite detectors were a first from Jodrell Bank,[84] and were carried under a split nose cone to be jettisoned at a height of 57 miles (92 km), in order to expose the detectors to the space environment. The principle of operation was different to the microphone detectors flown on SL10 and SL13

the previous year. This time 'penetration detectors' were used, a precursor to the type that would be flown on the Ariel II satellite in 1964. These were based on the principle that a thin metal foil would be exposed in flight, and any micrometeorites encountered would puncture the foil leaving small holes.

On SL37, these penetration detectors were of two designs. In one, the holes were to be recorded by an optical detector viewing the Sun through the foil and monitoring the signals during flight (as would be implemented on Ariel II). In the other, the foil was in the form of a stretched roller blind, to be released before re-entry and wound into an armoured cassette so it could be examined after recovery.[85] There were four of these roller blinds, in size about one metre long and ten centimetres wide, and these were erected before launch.[86]

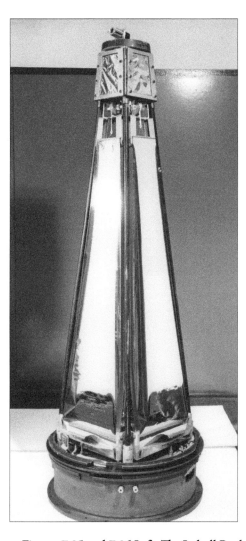 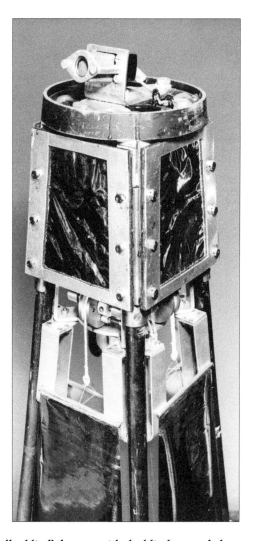

Figures 7.35 and 7.36 Left: The Jodrell Bank micrometeorite 'roller blind' detector with the blinds extended. Right: a close-up of the top of the mechanism, with above, presumably the optical detector foils.
(WRE (1961), SL37 Trials Preparation file J5555/2/37)

[82] Apparently, mainly because of the power supplies which included a rotary converter and 3–phase transformer to generate multiple voltages up to 300 Vdc.
[83] RAE (1960), *Round Specification for Skylark SL37*. (WRE SL37 Trials Preparation file J5555/2/37).
[84] More correctly the "Space Research Group at the Nuffield Radio Astronomy Laboratories of the University of Manchester".
[85] WRE (1961), *Advance Summary of Firing for SL37 (B56/1)*, para. 5.2. (WRE SL37 Trials Preparation file J5555/2/37).
[86] Jennison (1967), 'Some Penetration and Charge Detection Techniques', p.253.

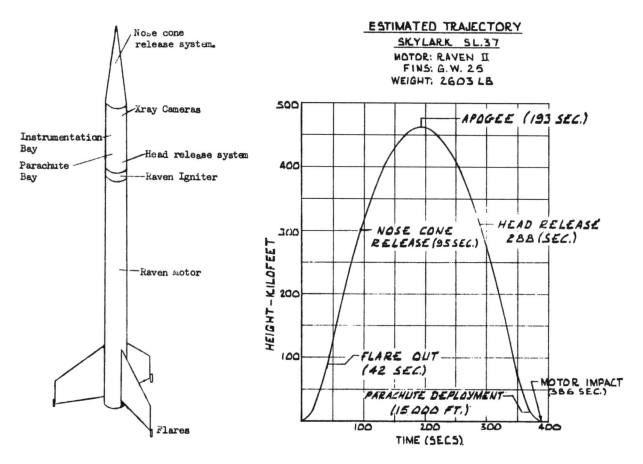

Figures 7.37 and 7.38. Left: This sketch of SL37 was produced for trials purposes at Woomera.
Right: The estimated trajectory, the result was close to that predicted.
(WRE (1961), WRE Trials Instruction Appendices A/2 & B/2, (SL37 Trials Preparation file J5555/2/37)

As the experiment required the foils to be examined afterwards for possible holes caused by micrometeorites, they had to be recovered in good condition, hence the use of the parachute recovery system.

Further delays ensued when in February 1961 the round was withdrawn from the launch programme once more; this time work was suspended until September 1961, when an SRDE support team arrived from the UK.[87]

Seq. Nos	Launch date	Ref. (sponsor) launch site	Config-uration	Apogee km (miles)	Experi-menters	Experiments	Result
43 (12)	24 Oct. 1961	SL37 (UK) Woomera	Un, Rav.2	142 (88)	RAE/SRDE	Test (Space technology) – SRDE broadband telemetry	S
					RAE	Test (Skylark tech.) – parachute recovery	S
					JB	Micrometeorite – penetration detectors	Ps
					UCL/Lei	Solar physics – X-ray flux	S
					UCL	Ionosphere – sporadic E probe	S

Table 7.8 A summary of SL37.

[87] EMI Electronics (1961), *Engineers Trial Notes for Preparation and Firing of Skylark Round SL37*, p.4. (WRE SL37 Trials Results file J5555/3/37).

The launch

At last, SL37 was ready. On the 13th October 1961 the payload arrived at the Woomera launch area, and on the 19th, it was placed in the launcher. On Monday the 23rd, the motor and parachute bay were added, and finally, on Tuesday the 24th, the launch procedures took place. Details were recorded in a WRE report, which gives an interesting insight into the process: [88]

> The micrometeorite blinds were raised into position by T.McDonnell.
>
> The air bottle pressures for the split nose cone were checked and one had to be recharged. A programme motor run was done to check if a pulse was received at the parachute bay. The X ray cameras were reset and covers removed.
>
> The flight plugs were inserted into the nose cone release system, and the micrometeorite blind system. The cover over [the] sporadic "E" plate was removed, and the plate cleaned with carbon tetrachloride.
>
> The parachute bay was checked and armed by the Range Launcher Officer (RLO). The raven motor was armed by the RLO. The cooling air pipe was manually extracted. The sequence was commenced at -7 minutes, at 0946 hours and continued without any delays. SL37 was fired at 0953 hours.

The flight

Fortunately, despite all the previous problems, the flight of SL37 went well, the new telemetry system and experiments all worked, and the parachute deployed satisfactorily.

Results

The head was recovered in such good condition that after its return to Salisbury, it was switched on and the telemetry signals monitored to check their calibration.[90] During flight the main telemetry test had provided strong signals until +840 seconds, well after the parachute had deployed at +476 seconds. Preliminary results indicated that the experiments had worked satisfactorily, with the nose cone being jettisoned at +102 seconds, leaving the micrometeorite detectors exposed. The separate photocell unit also functioned satisfactorily from this time until re-entry. It was monitored by the telemetry system, but no micrometeorites appeared to have been detected. During descent, the four roller blinds were restored to the cassettes as programmed, ready for examination after recovery.[91]

Figure 7.39 The recovery of SL37's payload. "This was the first completely successful test of the parachute recovery system, and the head was recovered in good condition".[89] Although some of the micrometeorite assembly was lost on re-entry, the blinds had successfully retracted into the storage cassettes.
(WRE (1961), SL37 Trials Results file J5555/3/37)

[88] WRE (1961), *Skylark SL37 MPO's Report*, p.5. (WRE SL37 Trials Results file J5555/3/37).
[89] WRE (1961), *Advance Summary of Firing for SL37 (B56/1)*, para.4.1. (WRE SL37 Trials Results file J5555/3/37).
[90] EMI Electronics (1961), *Engineers Trial Notes for Preparation and Firing of Skylark Round SL37*, para.4.4, (WRE SL37 Trials Results file J5555/3/37).
[91] WRE (1961), *Advance Summary of Firing for SL37 (B56/1)*, para.5.2. (WRE SL37 Trials Results file J5555/3/37).

The author has been unable to find any further results from this first micrometeorite experiment from Jodrell Bank, except for the enigmatic comment:

> Unfortunately, these early experiments were mounted on an ill-fated series of rockets that came to grief for a variety of reasons.[92]

This seems a curious conclusion, as despite its problems during preparation, SL37 appears to have performed perfectly during flight. With the benefit of hindsight, the experiment may in fact have worked, but demonstrated that the number of 'larger' micrometeorites was not as great as had been conjectured.[93] In fact, later on, a supporting conclusion re the micrometeorite experiment on Ariel II was reached by the scientist involved in both experiments.[94]

November 1961	US03, SL35, US04, SL83

US03 and **US04** were the last two NASA Skylarks, as referred to above.

SL35 was similar to SL37, the main difference being that the main experiment was from the Meteorological Office:

> Skylark 35 was fired from Woomera on 8th November, 1961 at 1830 hours CST (0900 hours GMT). This was the 45th Skylark to be fired. The primary aim of the trial was to measure the variation with height of ozone concentration in the atmosphere. The equipment was developed by the United Kingdom Meteorological Office and is to be used later in satellite experiments.[95] Jodrell Bank micrometeorite detectors were carried under a split nose cone which was to be jettisoned on ascent at a height of 57 miles leaving the equipment exposed to the atmosphere. Also carried in the vehicle was a U.C.L. probe to measure the density profile of the positive ions in the atmosphere, and in particular to detect patches of Sporadic-E ionisation.

A knowledge of the attitude of the vehicle was essential to the Meteorological Office Experiment. The attitude with reference to the sun was to be measured by R.A.E. sunslits and the attitude with respect to the earth's magnetic field by means of the R.A.E. fluxgate magnetometers. The head was to be separated from the motor at 91 seconds after launch at a height of 54 miles. Four seconds later the nose cone was to be jettisoned. The parachute was to be deployed on descent by the operation of a barometric switch set to function at 15,000 feet. [2.8 miles].[96]

The ozone[97] experiment was the first of many to be flown on Skylark by the Meteorological Office. It comprised an array of photomultipliers and photocells mounted in additional strong ring between the intermediate ring and the nose.[98]

SL35 had arrived at the Salisbury base in South Australia on September 14th. It was the first RAE built vehicle using a new standardisation system, and manacle rings were fitted throughout, replacing the flanges and bolts that had been used before.[99] Once in Australia, it had fewer teething problems than SL37, but it still had its own share of difficulties:

> October 19th.20th.21st.
> Programming motor test run O.K. but smoke poured out of blind release ledex.[100] Many wires and ledex damaged due to relay contacts having seized.[101]

This took two days of valuable time from a busy schedule to repair.[102]

Preparations at Woomera

SL35 arrived at the Woomera range on October the 30th, where last minute testing took place in the test shop. The launch tower became free a couple of days later, after Skylark US03 had been fired at 03:26 local time on November 2nd, and later that day SL35's head was placed in the tower with

[92] Jennison (1967), p.253, although Massey & Robins (1986), *History of British Space Science*, p.394 indicate the experiment was a partial success.
[93] A sounding rocket had been fired from White Sands, New Mexico, USA, on 6 June 1961 (only a few months before SL37), with a "Venus Flytrap" micrometeorite detecting experiment. Approximately seven particles/mm² were collected and extensively analysed. Only three of the particles had sufficient momentum to rupture an exposed Mylar film. (Hemenway & Soberman (1962), 'Studies of Micrometeorites Obtained from a Recoverable Sounding Rocket'.
[94] "…the lifetime for the survival of thin surfaces is many orders of magnitude greater than that expected when the experiment was designed". (Jennison (1967), 'Some Penetration and Charge Detection Techniques', p.253).
[95] For instance on Ariel II in March 1964.
[96] WRE (1961), *Skylark 35 (B66/1) Advance Summary of Firing*, (WRE SL35 Trials Results file J5555/3/35).
[97] We now know the ozone layer removes about 95% of the power of the Sun's ultraviolet rays, which would otherwise be lethal to Earth's inhabitants.
[98] RAE (1961), *Provisional Round Specification for Skylark No.35*. (WRE SL35 Trials Preparation file J5555/2/35).
[99] RAE (1961), *Skylark 35 Assembly Instructions and Information*. (WRE SL35 Trials Preparation file J5555/2/35).
[100] Ledex were (and are) a US company that made solenoids and other electromechanical assemblies.
[101] WRE (1961), *Skylark SL35 MPO's Report*. (WRE SL35 Trials Results file J5555/3/35).
[102] Telex SAL 15911 from Cartwright of WRE to Gait of RAE. (WRE SL35 Trials Preparation file J5555/2/35).

Figure 7.40 A 'Ledex' motorised switch assembly. (This example was used on SL1306 in 1976, 15 years after SL35).
(Barry Giles)

a dummy parachute bay.[103] Testing was interrupted by Sea Slug preparations,[104] but work continued, and the motor was loaded on the 3rd. Unfortunately, during preparation, one of the micrometeorite detector blinds was totally damaged and another partly damaged.[105]

A clear sky was an essential condition for firing, and the method used by the ozone experiment was most accurate when the Sun was near the horizon, so SL35 was planned to be launched during the 20 minutes before sunset.[106] However, at 13:00 hours on Monday 6th the trial was cancelled because of poor weather. It was rescheduled for the following day but again weather caused postponement. By Wednesday conditions had improved, but because of a following trial, the slot was restricted to seven minutes. However, the countdown sequence was entered at 18:15 and the vehicle was successfully fired at 18:30.

Final preparations on Wednesday November 8th included:[107]

13:35 hrs:	Cone removed and bottles charged up to 1500 p.s.i. MMD foils fitted and roller blinds drawn up into position. One roller spring U/S but no time to replace. MSU relay operations checked.
16:05	Cone replaced. Flight plugs fitted. On account of other trials unable to have GIMIC[108] or clock run between 1300 and 1630 hrs.
17:30-18:00	Round armed, protective covers removed from detectors, prepared for firing.
18:15	Entered firing sequence
18:30	Round fired

---

[103] WRE (1961), *Skylark SL35 MPO's Report*. (WRE SL35 Trials Results file J5555/3/35).

[104] Sea Slug was a first generation surface-to-air missile designed for use by the Royal Navy. It came into operational service in the 1960s and was still in use at the time of the Falklands War (1982).

[105] WRE (1961), *Skylark 35 (B66/1) Advance Summary of Firing*. (WRE SL35 Trials Results file J5555/3/35).

[106] WRE (1961), *W.R.E. Trials Instruction No.B66*, p.1. (WRE SL35 Trials Preparation file J5555/2/35).

[107] WRE (1961), *Skylark SL35 MPO's Report*. (WRE SL35 Trials Results file J5555/3/35).

[108] GIMIC = Ground Instrumentation Missile Instrumentation Check.

Figure 7.41 SL35 being prepared in the launch tower.
(WRE (1961), SL35 Trials Preparation file J5555/2/35)

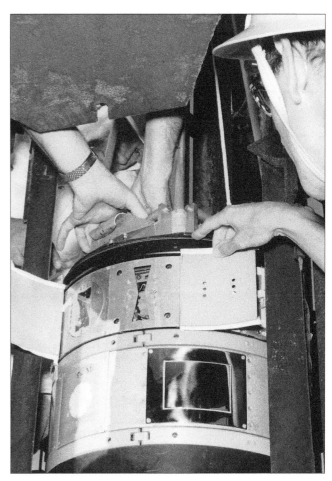

Figures 7.42 and 7.43 These rare close-up views show SL35's payload in the tower about four hours before launch. At this stage the micrometeorite detector foils were fitted and the roller blinds drawn up to their final position.

(WRE (1961), SL35 Trials Preparation file J5555/2/35)

The flight

The launch took place 20 minutes before sunset. The flight went to plan, with the head separating after 105 seconds and the nose cone jettisoning a few seconds later.

Good telemetry signals were received, indicating that most of the instruments were working, but revealing that one of

the micrometeorite photocell detectors had failed after only nine seconds, followed by the other two soon after.

However, the recovery system worked correctly and the head was recovered in good condition.

Seq. Nos	Launch date	Ref. (sponsor) launch site	Config-uration	Apogee km (miles)	Experi-menters	Experiments	Result
45 (14)	08 Nov. 1961	SL35 (UK) Woomera	Un, Rav.2	152 (95)	MO	Aeronomy - ozone distribution	S
					JB	Micrometeorite – penetration detectors	F
					UCL	Ionosphere - sporadic E probe	S
					RAE	Test (Skylark technology) – parachute recovery	S

Table 7.9 A summary of SL35.

Figures 7.44 and 7.45 SL35 successfully soft-landed 100 miles downrange some eleven minutes after launch. Ironically, this time the framework of the Jodrell Bank blind detectors survived mostly intact.

(WRE (1961), SL35 Trials Results file J5555/3/35)

Results

The micrometeorite detector roller blind containers were recovered intact but there was only a small section of blind in each. It was concluded that the blinds had suffered the same fate as the photocell detectors, and had been ruptured by the inflow of air through a gap between the nose cone halves during ascent,[109] and that this occurred because there was no asbestos seal between the nose cone halves, as has been fitted on SL37. The WRE telexed:

```
DISTURBED THAT YOU FAILED TO FIT SEAL
STRIPS TO NOSE CONE OF SL35 AND THAT WE
FAILED TO NOTICE THEIR ABSENCE.[110]
```

To which the RAE's response was:

```
WE DISCONTINUED FITTING THE SEALING
STRIPS AFTER SL37 BECAUSE WE FELT THE
RATE OF INFLOWING OR THROUGH FLOWING AIR
WAS INSUFFICIENT TO CAUSE TROUBLE. WE
WILL NOW FIT A SEAL TO FUTURE CONES.[111]
```

Clearly there was no computer simulation providing supersonic shock wave analysis; these were pioneering times, and a 'suck it and see' approach was the order of the day!

However, the Met Office's first ozone experiment worked reasonably well, although there were some instrument anomalies that were resolved after the equipment had been returned to the UK and recalibrated.[112] Similar equipment was subsequently flown on SL114 (1962) and SL 115 (1963). The SL35 results may have been the first direct measurements of vertical ozone concentration made outside the USA,[113] and most probably the first such in the southern hemisphere.

The UCL Sporadic E probe appeared to have functioned correctly but no high levels of ionisation were detected during the flight.[114]

The SL35 instrument head was refurbished in Australia and launched again as SL35B the following February.

[109] Telex from Whiteside of WRE to Hazell *et al.* of RAE, 9.11.61. (WRE SL35 Trials Results file J5555/3/35).
[110] Telex from Cartwright of WRE to Warr *et al.* of RAE, 14.11.61. (WRE SL35 Trials Results file J5555/3/35).
[111] Telex from RAE to WRE, 16.11.61. (WRE SL35 Trials Results file J5555/3/35).
[112] Letter dated 19/10/62 from Dr K.H. Stewart of the Met Office to R.Cartwright of the WRE. (WRE SL35 Trials Results file J5555/3/35).
[113] "Agreement with results obtained at White Sands by Johnson, Tousey and others is quite good". Letter 19/10/62 from K.H.Stewart of Met. Office to R.Cartwright of Aerodynamics Division, WRE. (WRE SL35 Trials Results file J5555/3/35).
[114] WRE (1961), *Skylark 35 (B66/1) Advance Summary of Firing*. (WRE SL35 Trials Results file J5555/3/35).

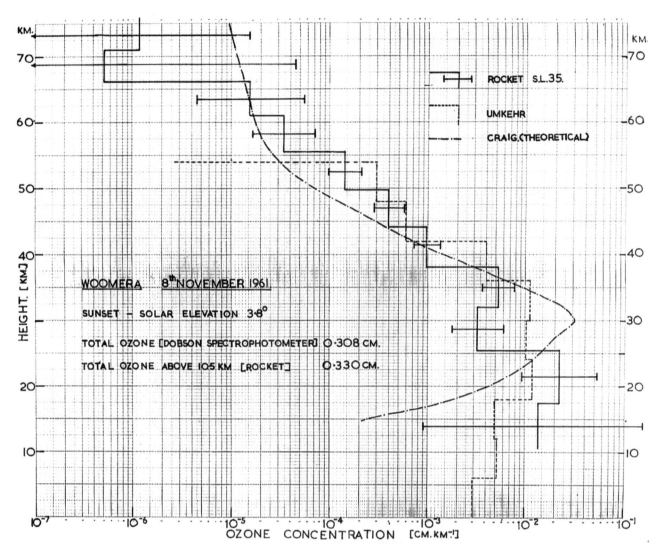

Figure 7.46 Ozone concentration measurements from the lower part of the flight of SL35, showing the expected peak at 30 km.

(K.H.Stewart \ WRE Trials Results file J5555/3/35)

SL83 was the first Skylark powered by a new, more powerful version of the Raven motor, the Raven V, which had 16% greater total impulse. (The Raven V is described later in this chapter).

Unfortunately, SL83 came to grief early on when the vehicle broke up, although large parts of the payload were recovered;

see figure 7.47. The break-up was caused by structural failure linked to the use of the Raven V/VA with the Cuckoo booster.[115] It turned out to be a serious problem that stopped this motor combination being used on scientific flights for several years, and many test flights were to take place to prove the resulting structural modifications. (The first was SL35B in February 1962).

Seq. Nos	Launch date	Ref. (sponsor) launch site	Config- uration	Apogee km (miles)	Experi- menters	Experiments	Result
47 (16)	24 Nov. 1961	SL83 (UK) Woomera	Un, Rav.5 +C	-	UCL/Lei	Solar physics - X-ray photos	Vf, broke up
					UCL	Ionosphere – sporadic E	
					RAE/UCW	" - CW radio experiment	

Table 7.10 A summary of SL83.

[115] WRE (1963), *Advance Information on Skylark SL87A*, para.1.1. (WRE SL87A Trials Preparation file J5555/2/87A).

December 1961   **SL42**

Fortunately, no such problem occurred with **SL42,** which completed the year in fine style by reaching a respectable altitude of 226 km, and with all the university experiments a success. (See table 7.11).

SKYLARK LAUNCHES AND SCIENCE IN 1962

The demand for Skylark was increasing:

> By 1962 there was a long waiting list for payload space. Over twenty universities and organisations in Britain and Australia wanted to fly their experiments and instruments, and it fell to the British Science Research Council and the Space Research Management Unit to sort out and allocate the experiments to particular vehicles; several went in each Skylark when their functions were compatible.[116]

During 1962 18 Skylark rockets would be launched, 14 with scientific experiments (4.2 experiments per round on average[117]), and four "proving" rounds, a term which appears to have come to mean any RAE or government sponsored test. This was mainly a year of consolidation, with the same universities continuing their experiments, a series of eight being launched to measure the upper atmosphere through the year. However three new organisations, (the RRS (Radio Research Station), the University of Sheffield and the University of Cambridge Cavendish Laboratory), did launch their first experiments.

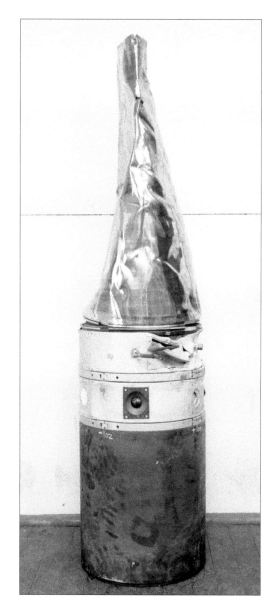

Figure 7.47 The recovered nose cone and head from the crashed SL83.

(National Archives of Australia: D874, N62/431)

Seq. Nos	Launch date	Ref. (sponsor) launch site	Config-uration	Apogee km (miles)	Experi-menters	Experiments	Result
48 (17)	06 Dec. 1961	SL42 (UK) Woomera	Un, Rav.2 +C	226 (140)	Bir	Ionosphere – RF electron probe	S
					UCL/Lei	Solar physics - X-ray photos	S
					UCL	Ionosphere - sporadic E probe	S

Table 7.11 A summary of SL42.

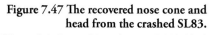

Jan.	Feb.	March	April	May	June	July	Aug.	Sept.	Oct.	Nov.	Dec.
	SL35B	SL66	SL163		SL35C	SL164	SL109	SL44	SL82	SL114	SL166
		SL160	SL162		SL45		SL28	SL108	(SL81)	SL27	
		SL161								SL165	

Table 7.12 The 18 Skylark launches in 1962. (For full details see Appendix 3)

(Key: black = test launches, blue = UK national programme (unstabilised)

---

[116] Morton (1989), *Fire across the Desert*, p.399.
[117] 'Flight International', 15 August 1963, p.240. ('Flight' became 'FLIGHT International' in 1962).

In addition, the Black Knight programme was now well into its stride, with BK15, 16 and 18 all being launched. As before, these included university experiments[118] (see Chapter 6) similar to those flown on Skylark, but being carried to an altitude three or four times greater. (For instance BK15 reached 494 miles / 795 km).

In the wider world, the first active communications satellite "Telstar" was launched by NASA in July 1962, as part of a multi-national agreement to develop experimental satellite communications over the Atlantic Ocean. It acted as a relay station high in the sky, and transmitted the first live television signals between America and Europe. This achievement created huge interest at the time, not least because the results could be seen in the ordinary home. Telstar's transmission power was only 14 watts, which necessitated huge ground-based receiving aerials; the British installation being at Goonhilly Downs in Cornwall. Although limited in its capability, Telstar helped pave the way for the international telephone, television and internet communications now taken for granted. Over the years, Goonhilly developed until at one time it was the largest Earth station in the world, with over 60 dishes pointing into space.

The Formation of the RAE Space Department

In January 1962, the RAE created a Space Department, to which was allocated more than half the staff from the increasingly misnamed Guided Weapons Department. One of the staff, Desmond King-Hele, recalled "These changes were most helpful: we were now officially working on space research and not renegades slinking away from guided weapons." [119]

Raven improvements

1962 also saw several improvements introduced to the Skylark's Raven motor. As noted in the various tables, the Raven II motor had become standard for the first few years of Skylark use. However, motor development had continued at RPE, with the aim of lightening the case, increasing the total thrust, improving the nozzle to eliminate uneven erosion, eliminating uneven burning and reducing the unburnt propellant.[120]

November 1961 had seen the first launch using the Raven V (SL83), and during 1962, other variations were tried. The evolution of these variations was a little complicated, the numbering in particular being obscure, and the following table tries to clarify the sequence:

Main variations		Minor structural changes
Raven II (1958)	▶	Raven VII (1962)
▼		
Raven V (1961)		
▼		
Raven VA (1962)	▶	Raven VIA (1964)

Table 7.13 The evolution of Skylark's Raven sustainer motor.

With an initial thrust of 13,000 lbf (58 kN) and a total impulse of 420,000 lb sec (1877 kN sec),[121] the Raven VA was a little more powerful than the Raven V, and provided some 22% more performance than the Raven II. This was particularly needed for solar and astrophysics missions, although not all applications needed the extra power. Hence, after minor structural changes the Raven II was renamed the Raven VII, in which new form it continued for a number of years. The same structural changes applied to the Raven VA resulted in the Raven VIA/VI.

October 1962 saw the last of the Raven II launches, as the Raven VII took over and the V and VA versions were introduced.

Skylark and the World's first international space satellite

In April 1962, just four and a half years after Sputnik I, the first Earth satellite with British scientific experiments on board was placed in orbit. This was Ariel I, the first international space satellite, the result of two years cooperative effort between the UK and the USA. Writing four years later, Sir Harrie Massey stated:

> The successful launching and operation of Ariel I, the first international satellite, marked a new era of international cooperation in space research. Although the scientific goals aimed at were ambitious, and made severe demands on the scientific, technological and managerial skill of all concerned, there is no doubt that, as a pilot project to establish a pattern of international cooperation, Ariel I was an unqualified success.[122]

As with many of the Skylark flights, Ariel I was designed to contribute to knowledge of the ionosphere and its complex relationship with the Sun, and in many ways could be regarded as "Skylark in orbit":

> The value of the experience gained from preparation of the instrumentation for the early Skylark flights for the development of British experiments flown in artificial satellites cannot be exaggerated.[123]

---

[118] Gordon & Parkin (1964), *A Summary of "Black Knight" Flight Data from 1958 to 1962.* (RAE Technical Note Space 57), table 10.

[119] King-Hele (1992), *A tapestry of orbits*, p.77, © Cambridge University Press, reproduced with permission.

[120] Dorling (1975), 'Early History of the Skylark Rocket', p.180.

[121] RPE Westcott (1961), *Solid Motor Data Sheet for the Raven Va.* (TNA: PRO document file AVIA 48/130).

[122] GSFC (1966), *Ariel I The First International Satellite, Experimental Results, NASA SP-119*, foreword by Sir Harrie Massey.

[123] Massey & Robins (1986), *History of British Space Science*, p.33. © Science and Engineering Research Council 1986, published by Cambridge University Press, reproduced with permission.

ARIEL I
The First
International
Satellite

Figure 7.48 Part of the cover of the NASA Ariel I project summary report.[124] Even this summary is 76 pages long, indicating the complexity of the project.

Background

Since 1958, British scientists had been actively considering how their experiments could find space in artificial Earth satellites. In the USA, scientists could utilise the massively funded government sponsored space programme being implemented by NASA, but in the UK, there was no such centralised satellite launching facility or space agency. Even sounding rockets were expensive in scientific budgetary terms; although as described in earlier chapters Skylark itself was a spin off from UK military rocket activities and developments, and for instance was able to share the Woomera launch facilities without charge. The UK was developing a major military rocket (Blue Streak), which although capable of being adapted for launching satellites, was originally designed to fire nuclear warheads at the USSR.

However in 1958 estimates and recommendations were produced for the cost of adapting and using the Blue Streak and Black Knight rockets to produce a British satellite launching system; and a total cost of £10 to £11 million was thought sufficient cover the launch and tracking of four or five British satellites, with British rockets, by the mid-1960s.[125] Then in 1959, these considerations were overtaken by the USA

making an offer to launch, without charge, scientific experiments or complete satellites prepared by scientists of other nations. There would be various technical conditions to be satisfied, for instance, the equipment would have to meet stringent environmental tests, and have operated satisfactorily in vertical sounding rockets.

This offer came at an opportune time for the five groups of British Scientists who had been active in the use of Skylark for upper atmosphere experiments, and promised early access to scientific satellite experiments.[126] However, it was still recognised that this should not preclude the development of a British launching capability,[127] although it could be argued that the US offer compromised the possibility of an all-British launcher.

Events moved quickly. Anglo-American co-operation began, and a complicated UK government space science organisation arrangement was set up around the BNCSR (British National Committee for Space Research). The UK project scientist was R.L.F. Boyd, and the UK Project Manager and UK Coordinator were M.O. Robins and E.B. Dorling respectively, both of whom had been on the original Skylark team in 1955.

[124] GSFC (1963), *Ariel I The First International Satellite, The Project Summary*, NASA SP-43, front cover.
[125] Massey & Robins (1986), *History of British Space Science*, p.66.
[126] Massey & Robins (1986), p.69.
[127] Massey & Robins (1986), p.70.

Solar Emission / Ionosphere		Cosmic Ray
Ionosphere	**Solar Emission**	
1. Electron Density-Plasma Dielectric Constant	4. X-ray Emission-Corona Radiation	
2. Electron Temperature and Density-Modified Langmuir Probe	5. Solar Lyman-α Emission-Chromospheric Radiation	6. Cerenkov Detector-Analysis of Energy Spectrum vs. Magnetic Field
3. Ion Mass Composition and Temperature-Mass Spectrometer		

Table 7.14 Ariel I Experimental Functional Groups.

(After GSFC (1966), Table 2-1)

Experiments

By the end of 1959 the experiments to be carried in the Ariel I payload had been agreed.[128]

> In determining the experiments to be carried out by Ariel I, every effort was made not to duplicate experiments already performed or underway by the U.S. and Russia. Simultaneously, experiments were selected to (1) take advantages of the techniques developed in the U.K. as part of the Skylark sounding rocket program, and (2) provide an integrated assault on unknowns connected with the sun-ionosphere relation.[129]

As indicated by table 7.14, of the six specific experiments carried on board, five were closely interrelated, and provided concurrent measurement of two important types of solar emission and the resulting changing states of the ionosphere. Four of the six (numbers 1, 2, 4 and 5) were very similar to those developed for earlier Skylark flights.[130]

The experiments listed below can be identified in the illustration of Ariel I, figure 7.50.

Ionosphere Experiments:

1. At the bottom right is the radio frequency plasma probe (with circular discs of wire mesh) to measure electron density. (Sayers, University of Birmingham), (Similar to those flown on Skylarks SL38 and SL42).
2. Opposite that, at the top left, is the Langmuir probe to determine electron density and temperature using a complementary technique to that used in '1.' above.

(Boyd and Willmore, University College London), (Similar to those on Skylarks SL14 and SL17)
3. At the top is the spherical probe to determine ion composition and temperature, (Boyd and Willmore, UCL). This was first flown (unsuccessfully) from Woomera on a Black Knight rocket, BK13 in February 1961, also after Ariel I, on BK18 (successfully) in November 1962.[131] (A version appears also have been flown on NASA's Explorer 20 satellite, launched 25 August 1964).[132]

Solar emission Experiments:

4. An X-ray spectrometer to measure emission from the Sun in the 3 to 12Å (0.3 to 1.2 nm) band. (Boyd, Pounds and Willmore, UCL and University of Leicester). It used two proportional counters mounted either side of the spin axis of Ariel I,[133] and appears to have been a development of the X-ray detection techniques used to date on Skylark.[134]
5. Detection of solar Lyman alpha radiation (University College London). This can be seen at the upper right hand side of the diagrams. (A UCL Lyman alpha detector had been flown on Skylark SL12).

Primary cosmic ray analyser:

6. Cosmic ray detector (Imperial College). This was designed to measure the way the spectrum changed because of modulation by the interplanetary magnetic field.[135]

[128] Massey & Robins (1986), p.75.
[129] GSFC (1963), *Ariel I The First International Satellite, The Project Summary*, (NASA SP-43), p.11.
[130] Massey & Robins (1986), p.76.
[131] GSFC (1963), *Ariel I The First International Satellite, The Project Summary*, NASA SP-43, Figure 4-4, and Gordon and Parkin (1964), *A Summary of "Black Knight" Flight Data from 1958 to 1962*, table 10.
[132] The NASA NSSDC (National Space Science Data Center) database has details. (*http://nssdc.gsfc.nasa.gov/*, last accessed August 2014).
[133] Pounds (1986), 'British X-ray astronomy', p.437.
[134] Pounds (1986), describes how the counter used was specially developed for Ariel I.
[135] Durney *et al.* (1964), 'The Energy Spectrum of the Heavy Primary Cosmic Rays'.

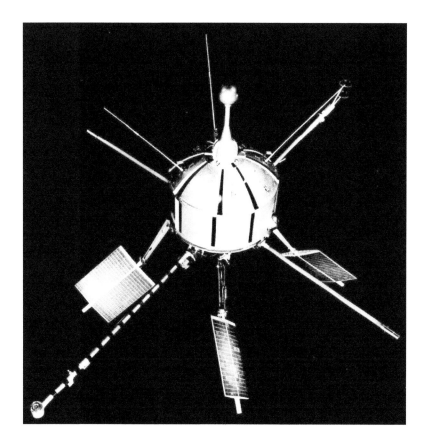

Figure 7.49 Ariel I in flight configuration.
(GSFC (1963), frontispiece)

The detailed design of this first satellite was a joint venture with NASA, who designed the satellite structure and services that supported the UK experiments. A complex system for collecting and processing telemetry data also had to be established.

In due course, launch took place on 26 April 1962, and placed the satellite into a near-Earth elliptical orbit with an apogee of 1212 km (753 miles), a perigee of 390 km (242 miles), and an orbital period of 101 minutes. Beforehand it had been designated "UK1" in the UK, and "S-51" by NASA, but on entering orbit it became known as Ariel I, starting the British tradition of using Shakespearean names for satellites.

After launch, Ariel I was deployed successfully, although unfortunately the Lyman alpha detection experiment failed.[136] However all the other experiments operated correctly, and the scientific observations began to pour in, even though the data processing requirements pushed British computing capabilities to the limit.[137] Telemetry data was received via the US "STADAN" network (which included a tracking station

at Woomera), and two British operated tracking stations, one at Singapore and one in the South Atlantic.[138]

Ariel I continued to operate for over two years, despite being damaged by the American high altitude "Starfish" hydrogen bomb explosion three months after launch. (The explosion also damaged the first Telstar communications satellite.) In November 1964, it was judged that the performance no longer justified the efforts required for data reception and analysis. By then, a total of 11,910 data tapes had been received from the tracking and data acquisition stations; from these tapes no less than 3,307 hours of data were successfully processed, representing 595 million data points).[139] The orbit finally decayed, and Ariel I was destroyed on entering the atmosphere on 24 May 1976.

As a pilot exercise it was a great success, most of the scientific aims were achieved, and the techniques of design and testing were to become standard practice for many years. The instruments provided data of much interest for atmospheric, solar and cosmic ray physics.

---

[136] See Massey & Robins (1986), p.82, for a fuller account, which also explains the use of a Royal Navy ship for tracking in the South Atlantic.
[137] Massey & Robins (1986), p.80.
[138] GSFC (1966), *Ariel I The First International Satellite, Experimental Results*, (NASA SP-119), pp.98-99.
[139] Fox (c.1984), *From Lardner to Massey – A history of physics, space science and astronomy at University College London, 1826 to 1975*.

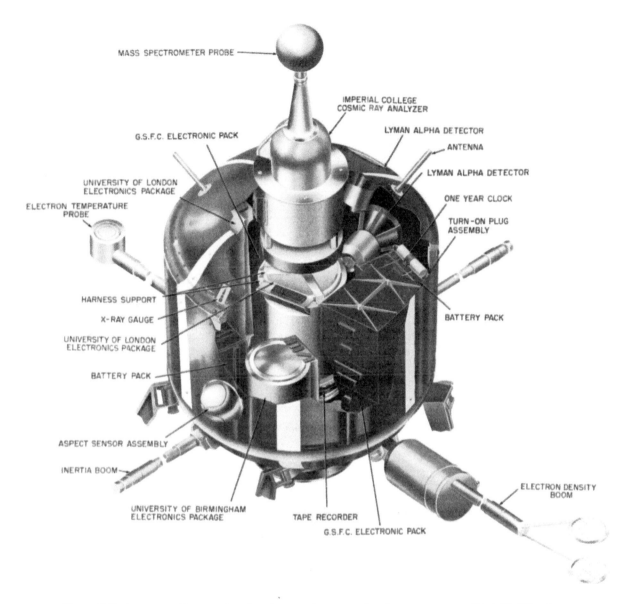

Figure 7.50 A cutaway diagram showing the experiments and major components of Ariel I. (The electron density boom (bottom right) is similar to the Skylark version shown in Figure 6.27)

(GSFC (1966), figure 1-2)

---

6 February 1962   SL35B

Meanwhile, back at Woomera, Skylark's year had begun with an RAE proving launch to further test the new Raven VA motor (described above) with a Cuckoo booster:

> SL35B is a Skylark Test Vehicle to investigate the aerodynamic behaviour and propulsion system performance of a Cuckoo boost and Raven 5A motor. This round has been added to the Skylark programme because of the failure of SL83 when this propulsion system was used for the first time. SL35B is a local rebuild using parts recovered from SL35. [140]

At this time, the reason for the breakup of SL83 was a complete mystery, and so the head of SL35B was instrumented to record the flight behaviour to try to determine what went wrong. The instruments included airborne cameras, gyros, accelerometers, sun cells and magnetometers; supplemented on the ground by kinetheodolites, Vinten cameras [141] and radar. For good measure, one scientific experiment was also included, a UCL Sporadic E probe.

The most interesting additional airborne equipment was the use of the 35mm 'movie' cameras in a special bay. These were designed to view backwards, one to view each fin.

---

[140] WRE (1962), *Trials Instruction No.B71/B66*, p.1. (WRE SL35B Trials Preparation file J5555/2/35B).
[141] The 'Vintens' were special high speed cine cameras, see Figure 4.23.

Preparation

Work had begun on 1 December 1961, when it was agreed to use the recovered head of SL35 to test the Raven VA – Cuckoo propulsion system. Over the next few weeks, the design was finalised by the WRE at their base in Salisbury, by Christmas the hardware was being tested, and the cameras had been set to run at 17 frames/sec.

However, there was still time to exchange seasonal greetings:

THE NUMBER FIRED AND SUCCESS RATE OF
SKYLARK THIS YEAR IS MOST IMPRESSIVE,
THE REPUTATION OF SKYLARK IN AUSTRALIA
HAS NEVER BEEN HIGHER, ALL THE BEST FOR
XMAS AND NEW YEAR TO YOU AND THE SKYLARK
GROUP.[142]

After the Christmas break, more detailed electrical measurements were carried out, and on 26th January the head was packed and despatched to the range. On the 2nd February, it was loaded into the launch tower, but pressure testing revealed a leak in the camera bay bulkhead, which was only finally sealed by pouring in Araldite near the leak.[143]

The Launch

Two requirements influenced the time of firing, in general with all Skylarks the time of day was chosen to give a good probability of suitable stable winds (in summer at Woomera the probability decreased rapidly after 09:00); also the conditions had to be suitable for ground based camera observations for the first 60 seconds. Thus, it was preferable to fire before 09:00.[144] This aim was met, but the unfortunate result was reported as follows:

SL35B FIRED 0827 HRS.6TH FEB....
CONDITIONS STEADY – SKIES CLEAR CUCKOO
PERFORMANCE CORRECT. ROUND CORRECT UNTIL
32 SECS WHEN ALL SIGNALS CEASED AND
PIECES WERE OBSERVED FALLING OFF. HEAD
OBSERVED TO COME OFF AT 45 SECONDS.[145]

At +32 seconds SL35B would have been travelling at about 2000 mph (3220 km/h) at an altitude of some 23 km (14 miles).

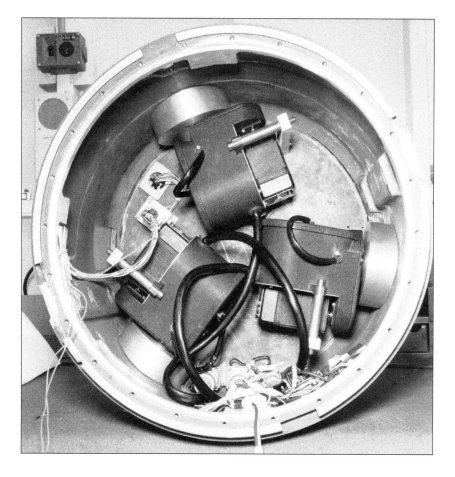

Figure 7.51 SL35B's camera bay during assembly.

(National Archives of Australia: D874, N62/251)

---

[142] Telex from WRE to RAE Farnborough 15/12/61. (WRE SL35B Trials Preparation file J5555/2/35B).

[143] WRE (1962), *SL35B MPO's Report*, (SL35B Trials Results file J5555/3/35B).

[144] WRE (1962), *Trials Instruction No.B71/B66*, p.1. (WRE SL35B Trials Preparation file J5555/2/35B).

[145] Telex from Cartwright AD Weapons (WRE) to Hazell Space Dept. RAE Farnborough, 6/2/1962. (SL35B Trials Results file J5555/3/35B).

Figure 7.52 A photomontage of the instrument bay and head of SL35B. The bottom right-hand photograph shows one of the protective fairings through which the cameras viewed rearwards to the fins in periscope fashion.

(WRE (1962), Trials Preparation file J5555/2/35B)

Figure 7.53 The broken remains of SL35B's camera bay, as found a few miles downrange. Amazingly, the bulk of the film was recovered and successfully processed. (Compare with Figure 7.51!)
(WRE (1962), Trials Results file J5555/3/35B)

Results

The instrument head came down in one piece, and was found about 4.6 miles (7.4 km) downrange. It had apparently landed on the camera bay, which broke off and broke up, spilling out one camera and damaging the others:[146]

The cameras had started six seconds before launch, and all gave good pictures of the vehicle leaving the launcher,[147] but unfortunately, none recorded the break-up at 31 seconds because the battery powering them had been damaged. Figure 7.54 shows how this was later reported.

Conclusions

All observations and times indicated that the failure of SL35B was a repeat of that of SL83, and the recovered nose cone showed a remarkable similarity to that from SL83. It was concluded that distortion of the nose cone before it broke off was the only cause that could explain the observations, in particular a change of angle of flight during the event.[148] Subsequently, a specially strengthened nose cone was built and successfully tested on SL35C in June, see later in this chapter.

Thus, although SL35B had failed, the trial achieved its primary purpose in indicating what had gone wrong with SL83. After the failure at 32 seconds the Raven motor would have continued firing for another ten seconds or so, but by then the telemetry had ceased and tracking was limited to radar only, and the documentary records do not reveal the results. Without the weight of the head, the rocket may well have travelled higher than the 133 miles / 214 km originally estimated. Over a month later, the motor had still not been located.[149]

Seq. Nos	Launch date	Ref. (sponsor) launch site	Config-uration	Apogee km (miles)	Experi-menters	Experiments	Result
49 (1)	06 Feb. 1962	SL35B (UK) Woomera	Un, Rav.5A +C	215 (133) (est., motor only)	RAE	Test (Skylark tech.) - Raven 5A motor & Cuckoo	Ps
					"	Test (Skylark technology) – parachute recovery	Vf
					"	Test (") – cameras & flight instruments	Ps
					UCL	Ionosphere - sporadic E	Vf

Table 7.15 A summary of SL35B.

---

[146] WRE (1962), *Skylark SL35B MPO's Report*, p.10. (SL35B Trials Results file J5555/3/35B).
[147] WRE (1962), *Skylark 35B B71/1 Advance Summary of Firing*, 8th March 1962. (SL35B Trials Results file J5555/3/35B).
[148] Letter "Skylarks SL35B and SL83", 22 Feb.1962. (WRE SL35B Trials Results file J5555/3/35B).
[149] WRE (1962), *Skylark 35B B71/1 Advance Summary of Firing*, p.3. (SL35B Trials Results file J5555/3/35B).

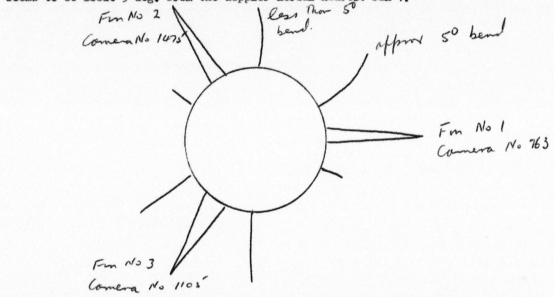

5.   The camera motor monitors indicate that the cameras stopped just before failure. Unfortunately some of the film was lost in processing and one film goes to 30 sec., one film has the last 10 sec. missing and the third was badly cut and exposed due to impact damage. Consequently, the state of the round in the last second cannot be seen. Up to then there is no sign of distortion. I will get a print of these films and send you a copy.

6.   The cameras would stop when their battery which was under the nose cone was damaged. This must have happened when the nose cone came off. When I decided on the layout of the camera bay I did not suspect a nose cone failure otherwise I would have put a guard over the battery. Also an attempt would have been made to observe the nose cone during flight.

7.   The films show cuckoo separation and the ground very clearly. After raven light up some of the doppler aerials bent slightly. The greatest bend seems to be about 5 deg. from the doppler aerial nearest fin 1.

Figure 7.54 This letter describes how most of the exposed SL35B camera film was saved. Unfortunately the results have not come to light; the photographs would have made fascinating viewing!

(WRE (1962), SL35B Trials Results file J5555/3/35B)

March 1962   SL66, SL160, SL161

On the 5th March, **SL66** continued the experiments to measure the properties of the upper atmosphere, the first of a series of eight such Skylarks to be launched in 1962.

The following day **SL160** was launched with a similar set of experiments, but without the Cuckoo booster or sodium vapour experiment.

SL161 followed a few weeks later on the 29th, with the same set of experiments as SL160; all were successful.

April 1962   SL163, SL162

Next in the series, on the 6th April, was **SL163** with an identical payload, but using a Cuckoo booster to gain more altitude. Again all the experiments were successful.

Seq. Nos	Launch date	Ref. (sponsor) launch site	Config- uration	Apogee km (miles)	Experi- menters	Experiments	Result
50 (2)	05 Mar. 1962	SL66 (UK) Woomera	Un, Rav.2 +C	233 (145)	UCL	Neutral atmosphere – (grenades)	S
					UCL	" " - grenade glows	S
					IC	" " - (falling dipoles)	Ps
					Bel	" " - (sodium vapour)	F

Table 7.16 A summary of SL66.

Figure 7.55 "View from Long Tom missile at 100 mile altitude". The geographical feature in the middle distance may be the south coast of Australia. (See SL1081 in Chapter 12).
(National Archives of Australia D880, D62/257)

It was followed by **SL162** on the 11th. Unfortunately, this time disaster struck, and SL162 failed to gain any altitude, having presumably suffered a motor failure.

Pictures from Space

In May 1962 there were no Skylark launches, but an Australian 'Long Tom' sounding rocket (LT14) was launched on the 31st, and appears to have taken this photograph (figure 7.55) from an altitude of 100 miles (161 km). At the time of writing, the author has been unable to discover any more information, but this photograph is of similar quality to that taken from an unknown Skylark around this time, shown as Figure 7.57 later in this chapter.

Hence, it is possible these photographs were part of a 'space exploration' initiative undertaken at Woomera by the WRE.[150] This Long Tom was fitted with a parachute recovery system,[151] which allowed the recovery of the camera.

June 1962	SL35C, SL45

June began with an RAE proving launch on the 6th, to investigate the Raven VA and Cuckoo motor combination for a third time. The particular purpose was to flight test a strengthened split nose cone, this type taking priority over testing a one-piece cone, because a large number of the rounds scheduled for 1962 were to be fitted with split cones and powered by the Raven VA/Cuckoo combination.[152]

The "C" suffix indicates this was a "recycled" payload head from SL35B (February 1962), although little of the original was used, the head comprising parts from several sources. The assembly was designed and put together locally at WRE,[153] using an existing nose cone that had been strengthened by the addition of longitudinal stiffeners riveted on the inside. The cone was to be monitored in flight by a camera mounted in a specially made camera bay designed to view

it from inside, the interior being illuminated by a ring of six lights. The camera bay was 14 inches (36 cm) long and sealed at each end with a bulkhead to form a pressure tight compartment. The camera was mounted on the after bulkhead, with the lens facing a glass window in the forward bulkhead.[154] There were no upper atmosphere scientific experiments carried.

The Flight

The launch of **SL35C** was postponed for several days because of unfavourable weather, but eventually took place at 12:30 local time on Wednesday June 6th. In order to reduce the range but still account for the wind, the launcher was trained almost vertically, which resulted in the vehicle achieving the one of the highest Skylark altitudes to date (estimated at 234 km (146 miles), with impact only 56km (35 miles) downrange.[155] As usual, the homesteads that might be affected were warned to take cover, and the list of outback properties has an almost poetic ring to it:

[150] For instance, Skylark SL35B was fitted with a locally made camera bay, see figure 7.51.
[151] Roger Henwood, personal correspondence, October 2013.
[152] WRE (1962), *Skylark SL35C MPO's Report*, p.1. (WRE SL35C Trials Results file J5555/3/35C).
[153] WRE (1962), *Skylark 35C Round Specification*, compiled by P.R.Malcolm. (WRE SL35C Trials Preparation file J5555/2/35C).
[154] Ibid, p.2.
[155] WRE (1962), *Skylark 35C (B77/1) Advance Summary of Firing*, p.3, (SL35C Trials Results file J5555/3/35C).

Mulga Hut, Nth.Well, Big Tank, Myall Hut, Koual Well, Locks Well, Parakylia, Mt.Vivian, Sth.Vivian Bore, Vivian Well, Bon Bon, Whymlet, No.7 O.S., Mt.Eba, Millers Creek, Billakallina, Sloanes Bore, Mintabyng, Mentor, Bulgannia, Bald Hill, The Twins, Ealbara, Johns, Goode, McDouall[sic] Peak, Carne, Gina, Pharlap, Ingomar, Lake Wirrida, Gosse Well.[156]

The Trials Instruction also rather formally included "The O.I.S.C. and M.P.O. may observe the flight from +5 secs. onwards from the walled approach of E.C.2 within 15 feet of the door. In the event of flight failure they will return to E.C.2" [!]

Fortunately, this time the payload survived the powered ascent, and the trial became the first successful launch using the Raven VA and Cuckoo motor combination. The vehicle was tracked optically for up to 70 seconds. Although only mentioned in passing in the Telex concerned,[157] this duration of tracking was a considerable feat, a tribute to the skill of the Australian operators and the clear air of Woomera - because the trajectory of SL35C reveals that by this time it had reached an altitude of 102 km (63 miles), i.e. the edge of space! The head had been fitted with the new T5E telemetry sender and good signals were received until impact at 680 seconds. This revealed that the nose cone aerodynamic heating was more than expected, and between 40 and 50 seconds into the flight, all seven sensors on the inside of the nose cone exceeded their limit of 300°C.

Unfortunately, during descent the parachute failed to deploy because the supply leads to the explosive bolt were badly burnt, and the head broke apart on impact.

In a masterpiece of understatement an official report stated "...the head and airborne camera were in poor condition...",[158] but astonishingly the photographic film was recovered undamaged. This had run at 33 frames per second for the first minute of flight, and a good image was visible

Figure 7.56 Part of the mangled remains of SL35C after falling over 100 km (63 miles) from space.
(WRE (1962), SL35C Trials Results file J5555/3/35C)

up to about 30 seconds, after which it became progressively blurred until at about 40 seconds the interior of the nose cone could not be distinguished. It was deduced that this was probably caused by smoke from the vaporisation of temperature sensitive paints that had been applied to the inside of the cone.[159] Hence, after this trial, extra thermal insulation was provided to protect the parachute and wiring. (See SL87 in the next chapter).

The nose cone modification was deemed successful, and was soon used on **SL45,** which followed two weeks later on the 20th:

Seq. Nos	Launch date	Ref. (sponsor) launch site	Config- uration	Apogee km (miles)	Experi- menters	Experiments	Result
56 (8)	20 June 1962	SL45 (UK) Woomera	Un, Rav.5A +C	216 (134)	RAE	Test (Skylark technology) – strengthened nose cone	F
					UCL/Lei	Solar physics – X-ray photos	F
					UCL	" " - Lyman α detectors	Ps
					UCL	Neutral atmosphere - (grenades)	Ps
					UCL	" " - falling sphere	F
					UCL	Ionosphere - positive ion probe	S

Table 7.17 A summary of SL45.

---

[156] WRE (1962), *Skylark No. SL35C , Trials Instruction No.B77*, p.12. (SL35C Trials Preparation file J5555/2/35C).
[157] Telex from WRE to RAE, 8 June 1962. (SL35C Trials Results file J5555/3/35C).
[158] WRE (1962), *Skylark 35C (B77/1) Advance Summary of Firing*, para.4.1. (SL35C Trials Results file J5555/3/35C).
[159] Telex from WRE to RAE 9/7/62. (SL35C Trials Results file J5555/3/35C).

Unfortunately, this time the new strengthened nose cone failed,[160] and the trials had to be resumed. The next in the series was SL86, over a year later in August 1963, see the next chapter.

The SL45 payload had comprised a mixture of five university experiments, mostly from UCL, but as table 7.17 shows, they were not very successful, presumably because the nose cone failed during ascent. The falling sphere experiment was a first for Skylark, this time it failed, but it would succeed when repeated on SL167 the following April.

---

5 July 1962   SL164

SL164 followed a couple of weeks later, the sixth in the series of upper atmosphere measurement flights which included both a grenade experiment from UCL and a falling dipole experiment from Imperial College. Both were successful.

August 1962   SL109, SL28

The RRS and Sheffield experiments

In August, two new organisations, the RRS (Radio Research Station) and the University of Sheffield, became Skylark users when they flew a successful joint experiment on SL109. This experiment appears to have been the first rocket study specifically of the D region of the ionosphere.[161] SL109 reached the relatively low altitude of 111 km (69 miles), probably by design, as the D region of the ionosphere is lower than the E and F layers, and varies between 55 and 90 km in height.

Understanding the behaviour of the D-region was important (especially before the advent of satellite and optical cable communications) because it absorbed radio waves in a variable way, causing long distance radio communication blackouts. The Skylark experiment was just part of a wider programme of investigation of the D region by the RSS.

The RRS/Sheffield University Skylark experiment was launched on SL109 at night, and successfully repeated on SL108 in September during daylight (see the next page). It was designed to determine the height distribution of electrons in the lower D-region of the ionosphere, using a radio technique. A continuous radio wave of frequency 202 kHz was transmitted from the ground to generate a wavefield in the lower ionosphere, and the field strength was measured using receivers connected to three orthogonal dipole aerials carried on the rocket.[162] Very satisfactory results were obtained, from which variations in the electron concentration were deduced.[163]

The RRS had had a distinguished history in radio research, and since 1918, pioneering work had been carried out at their Ditton Park base near Slough in southern England. In the 1920s, early researchers such as E.V.Appleton, R.L.Smith-Rose and R.A.Watson-Watt had worked on atmospherics, direction finding and field strength measurements. During this time, Appleton and his co-workers had proved the existence of an ionised reflecting layer at a height of about 100km, and later discovered a second layer at 200 km.[164] Watson-Watt (the radar pioneer) coined the name "ionosphere" in 1926. The direction finding activity resulted in the invention and development of RADAR, of major importance during World War II and ever since. In addition, at the start of WWII an Ionospheric Forecasting Service to aid long distance communication was introduced, which became very important to the Services during the conflict.

In 1957, a new laboratory was opened at Ditton Park, and during the IGY, the World Data Centre for the collection and exchange of ionospheric information was established there.[165] The launch of Sputnik 1 in 1957 marked the beginning of extensive research, involvement and contribution to space science. The RRS has since evolved into the Rutherford Appleton Laboratory.[166]

Seq. Nos	Launch date	Ref. (sponsor) launch site	Config-uration	Apogee km (miles)	Experi-menters	Experiments	Result
58 (10)	15 Aug. 1962	SL109 (UK) Woomera	Un, Rav.2	111 (69)	Shf/RRS	Ionosphere - electron density by effects on lf radio waves	S
					UCL	Solar physics – Lyman α detector	S
					UCL	Ionosphere - positive ion probe	S

Table 7.18 A summary of SL109.

[160] WRE (1963), 'Skylark 86' document. (SL86 Trials Preparation file J5555/2/86).

[161] Massey & Robins (1986), *History of British Space Science*, p.303.

[162] For a definitive description of the dipole system, see Bradley, Bullough & Jenkins (1965), 'A Dipole Aerial System for Rocket Experiments'.

[163] Massey & Robins (1986), *History of British Space Science,* p.303, 'Flight International', 18 June 1964, p.1040, and Hall & Fooks (1965), 'The energy distribution in the quiet D-region derived from rocket measurements'.

[164] In 1947, Appleton was awarded a Nobel Prize for his confirmation in 1927 of the existence of the ionosphere.

[165] See *www.ukssdc.ac.uk/ditton_park_archive/history.html* (last accessed August 2014). Now a WDC for Solar Terrestrial Physics, see *www.wdc.rl.ac.uk/wdc/europe/solar.html* (last accessed August 2014).

[166] The Rutherford Appleton Laboratory website provides further information at *www.stfc.ac.uk/76.aspx* (last accessed August 2014).

Vehicle No.	Firing date	Camera bay	Doppler transponder	M.T.S. beacon	Roll control unit	
					Max. torque lb ft (nom.)	Max. roll rate rev/sec
SL28	29th Aug'62	Not Fitted	Fitted	Fitted	9	1.0
SL27	22nd Nov'62	Not Fitted	Not Fitted	Fitted	18	0.5
SL29	25th Jul'63	Fitted	Not Fitted	Fitted	18	0.5
SL30	20th Feb'64	Fitted	Not Fitted	Fitted	18	0.5
SL31	15th Jul'64	Fitted	Fitted	Fitted	27	0.33
SL32	17th Jul'64	Fitted	Fitted	Fitted	27	0.33

Table 7.19 SL28 was the first launch of the main gyro drift test programme.

(From Knott (1964), p.16)

SL28 followed on the 28th August, and was the first of the main RAE programme of six firings designed to investigate the performance of autopilot gyroscope drift. It followed on from earlier Skylarks SL33, 25 and 26 (launched in 1960 and 1961), which had been used to prove the system and instruments.

SL28 reached an altitude of 110 km (68 miles), and the impact point of the motor and head was about 89 km (54 miles) down range, the head successfully landing by parachute. It carried no camera, just the radio interferometer reference system to monitor the vehicle attitude during acceleration. The flight was not a complete success, because the roll control system lost control between +7 seconds and +25 seconds.[167] As a result, on SL27 (launched in November, see below), the roll control unit torque was increased.

September 1962   **SL44, SL108**

SL44 on the 11th was a straightforward ionosphere measurement mission with three successful experiments from UCL, and **SL108** on the 20th was a successful repeat of the SL109 ionosphere mission described above, this time carrying just the Sheffield/RRS experiment to investigate the D region, but launched during daylight.

October 1962   **SL82, (SL81)**

SL82 saw the first experiment from another new player on the Skylark scene, the Cavendish Laboratory of the University of Cambridge.[168] Their experiment used a long wire aerial, consisting of two ten metre lengths of stranded wire, intended to be deployed after SL82 was launched, by being unwound from a drum under the control of an electric motor. The purpose of the experiment was to investigate the D and E layers of the ionosphere during the night using a VLF (Very Low Frequency) radio technique, apparently using receivers in a Dakota aircraft.[169] It was also a precursor to a similar experiment to be flown on the forthcoming Ariel II satellite. The launch of SL82 was successful, but unfortunately, the aerials failed to deploy. (A task difficult to achieve when the vehicle was rotating in flight).

Skylark SL81 made it all the way to Woomera but was never fired! It was a companion to SL82, but as subsequently explained, its launch was cancelled:

In October 1962, a system for deploying long wire aerials in the upper atmosphere was tested in Skylark 82. The test was to have been repeated in an identical round, Skylark 81, but when the aerials failed to deploy in Skylark 82 the firing of Skylark 81 was cancelled. Skylark 81 was sent back to the United Kingdom where modifications

---

[167] Knott (1965), *The Drift of an Auto-Pilot Gyroscope Due to Prolonged Acceleration in the Skylark Rocket*, Part 2, p.9.
[168] The Cavendish Laboratory can claim to be the world's most famous physics laboratory. It was opened in 1874, and Professor James Clerk Maxwell, the developer of electromagnetic theory, was a founder and became the first Cavendish Professor of Experimental Physics. The electron was discovered by J.J.Thomson working there in 1897. By 1990, 29 Cavendish researchers had won Nobel prizes.
[169] Letter dated 9/1/62 and documents in WRE SL81 Trials Preparation) file J5555/2/81.

Seq. Nos	Launch date	Ref. (sponsor) launch site	Config- uration	Apogee km (miles)	Experi- menters	Experiments	Result
62 (14)	15 Oct. 1962	SL82 (UK) Woomera	Un, Raven 2	154 (96)	Cam	Ionosphere - deployment of long wire aerial	F
					Cam	" - measurement of electron density	F
					UCL	" - sporadic E probe	S

Table 7.20 A summary of SL82.

were carried out. The modified vehicle has been returned to Australia (Skylark 81A) and another attempt is to be made to test a system for deploying long wire aerials.[170]

SL81A was duly launched in October 1963, see the next chapter.

Figure 7.57 This photograph has the intriguing title "Cloud formation taken from Skylark missile [Mr Boswell's lecture]". The date is given as 01 Oct 1962, but it is not known from which Skylark it was taken. 'Mr Boswell' must have been R.W. (Bill) Boswell, who from 1958 was Director of WRE.[171]

(National Archives of Australia: D880, D62/577)

A photograph of a cloud formation taken from the new TIROS weather satellite[172] also appears to have been included in Bill Boswell's lecture that day, so he may have selected that taken from Skylark to show how similar work was being carried out from Woomera.

---

[170] WRE (1962), 'Skylark 81A' document, folio 57 of WRE SL81 Trials Preparation file J5555/2/81.

[171] As controller (director) of the Weapons Research Establishment from 1 December 1958, Bill Boswell became known as "Mr Rocket Range". For a good biography of him as scientist and public servant, see T. F. C. Lawrence, 'Boswell, Robert William McGregor (1911–1976)', Australian Dictionary of Biography, National Centre of Biography, Australian National University, *http://adb.anu.edu.au/biography/boswell-robert-william-mcgregor-9547/text16815* , last accessed August 2014.

[172] The first weather satellite to be considered a success was TIROS-1, launched by NASA on 1 April 1960.

Seq. Nos	Launch date	Ref. (sponsor) launch site	Config-uration	Apogee km (miles)	Experi-menters	Experiments	Result
63 (15)	13 Nov. 1962	SL114 (UK) Woomera	Un, Raven 7 +C	206 (128)	UCL/Lei	Solar physics - X-ray counter spectrometer	F
					JB	Micrometeorites – penetration detectors	F
					MO	Aeronomy - ozone measurements	Ps

Table 7.21 A summary of SL114.

November 1962 SL114, **SL27**, SL165

SL114 was the first to use the new Raven VII motor, the version created by minor structural changes to the Raven II, and which became the most commonly used motor for missions that did not require the greater power provided by the Raven V and variants.

Although the vehicle performed satisfactorily, the experiments did not do well, and only the Meteorological Office's second ozone measurement experiment achieved some success. The Jodrell Bank micrometeorite experiment was similar to those launched a year before on SL37 (October 1961) and SL35 (November 1961), but again appears to have failed.[173] The UCL/Leicester spectrometer may have been a new type of device, but no details are known.

SL27 was the second of the main series of firings of the RAE programme to investigate the performance of autopilot gyroscopes.

It was fired on the 22nd November, and reached an altitude of 115 km (71 miles), the impact point of the motor and head (which landed by parachute) being some 97 km (60 miles) down range. As with SL28, it carried no camera, but instead used the radio interferometer reference system to monitor attitude. Increasing the maximum torque of the roll control system worked; the flight was a success and measurements of gyro drift were successfully determined by comparing attitude information obtained with the interferometers with that indicated by the gyroscopes on board.

November concluded with the launch of **SL165** on the 28th. The payload comprised the standard set of upper atmosphere experiments (grenade and falling dipole), and was the seventh of the series of eight such Skylarks to be launched in 1962.

Vehicle No.	Firing date	Camera bay	Doppler transponder	M.T.S. beacon	Roll control unit	
					Max. torque lb ft (nom.)	Max. roll rate rev/sec
SL28	29th Aug'62	Not Fitted	Fitted	Fitted	9	1.0
SL27	22nd Nov'62	Not Fitted	Not Fitted	Fitted	18	0.5
SL29	25th Jul'63	Fitted	Not Fitted	Fitted	18	0.5
SL30	20th Feb'64	Fitted	Not Fitted	Fitted	18	0.5
SL31	15th Jul'64	Fitted	Fitted	Fitted	27	0.33
SL32	17th Jul'64	Fitted	Fitted	Fitted	27	0.33

Table 7.22 SL27 was the second in the gyro drift test programme.

(Knott (1964), p.16)

[173] Jennison (1967), 'Some Penetration and Charge Detection Techniques', p.253, and Massey & Robins (1986), *History of British Space Science*, p.395.

Figure 7.58 The instrument head of SL27 after landing by parachute 97 km (60 miles) down range.
(WRE (1962))

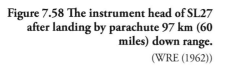

4 December 1962	**SL166**

A week later SL166 successfully completed 1962's comprehensive programme of upper atmosphere measurements. Providing so many grenade experiments had been a major operation for UCL, "…almost the entire staff of the department concerned with space research in 1962 co-operated in the development of the grenade programme. Groves[174] then took over the responsibility for the whole programme…" [175]

This 1962 programme of eight Skylark launches was designed to investigate the seasonal and daily variations of winds and temperature in the upper atmosphere. The results revealed a surprising amount about the global aspects of the upper atmosphere, including atmospheric oscillations and tides:

The Woomera experiments showed that seasonal variations of atmospheric parameters generally predominated below 70 to 80 km (Groves 1966) and that variations of a wavelike nature on a time-scale of the order of a day or less became increasingly important above 45 km. The wavelike nature of the wind velocity is apparent in figure 1 (Groves 1985). The downwards progression of the oscillation from one launching to the next corresponds to an obliquely upwards propagation of energy when interpreted as an internal gravity wave…[176]

---

[174] G.V.Groves had been a pioneer in the field since working with Professor Massey in 1954. Originally with the RAE, he had joined UCL in 1956, where he became a professor in 1968. He carried out research on the properties of the upper atmospheric for many years, producing numerous scientific papers on the subject.

[175] Fox (c.1984), *From Lardner to Massey – A history of physics, space science and astronomy at University College London, 1826 to 1975*.

[176] Groves (1976), 'Rocket Studies of Atmospheric Tides', p.437.

The experimental results were summarised as follows:

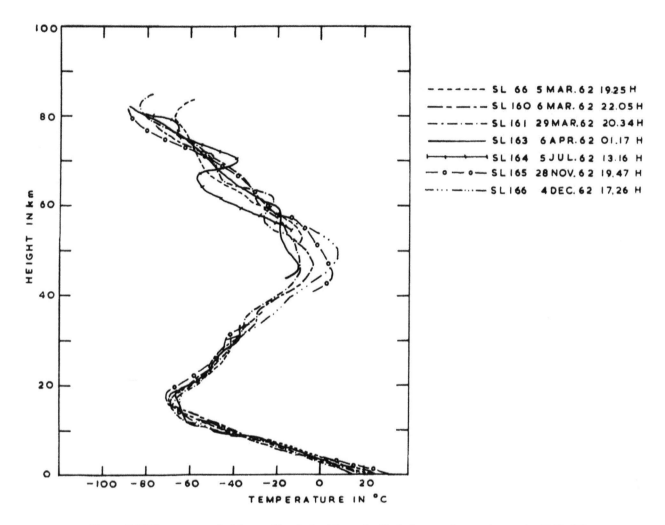

Figure 7.59 Temperature-height profiles derived from the Skylark grenade experiments in 1962. (These were similar to those obtained by SL04 in 1957, see Figure 5.39.)

(Massey & Robins (1986), p.274) [177]

---

[177] Massey & Robins (1986), *History of British Space Science,* © Science and Engineering Research Council 1986, published by Cambridge University Press, reproduced with permission.

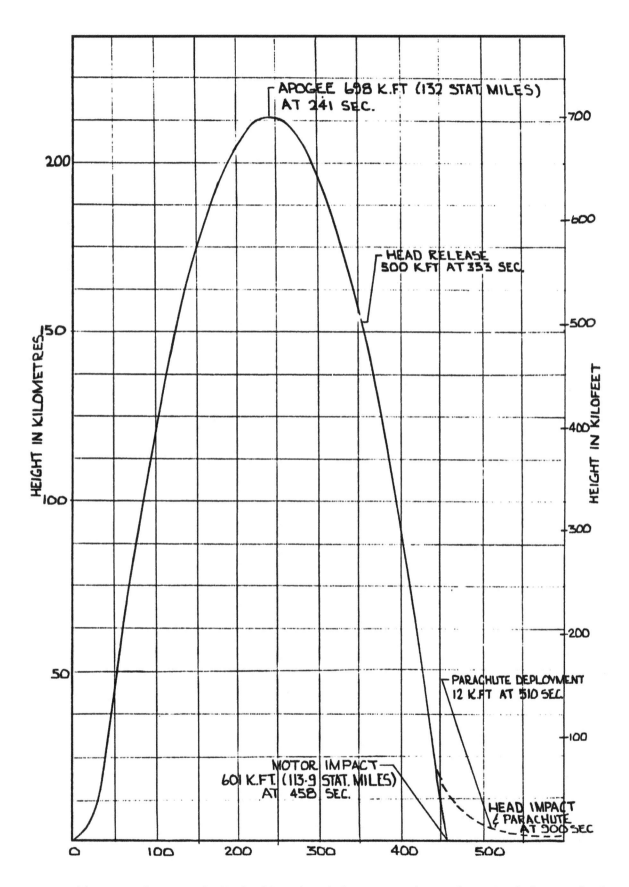

Figure 8.1 The estimated trajectory for SL86 and SL87, launched in August and September 1963. The horizontal scale is in seconds. These diagrams were included in the WRE Technical Instruction file for each Skylark project, this one shows the altitude expected from the new Cuckoo boost and the Raven VA motor combination.

(WRE (1963), Trials Instruction No.BS95, p.5, SL86 Trials Preparation file J5555/2/86)

CHAPTER 8

(1963-64)

WOOMERA BLOSSOMS

SKYLARK LAUNCHES AND SCIENCE IN 1963

1963 was a heady time at Woomera, when the range in general and the British space effort in particular, were reaching their peak. The scene was captured by the following report in 'Flight International' magazine:

> Woomera welcomed its visitors with a fresh face this year. The rainfall had been relatively high, and the broad, flat landscape surrounding the town and the rangehead had sprouted a healthy fuzz of grey saltbush over the red desert soil. The trees in and around the town, tens of thousands of them now where there was literally none before the rocketmen came, looked young and healthy, but careful staking, individual watering pipes and irrigation ditches hinted at the painstaking and continuous effort that was needed to achieve this premeditated oasis.
>
> Fifteen miles south of the town, near a dried salt lake called Island Lagoon, is the big dish of the of the deep-space tracking station set up by NASA – one of three such stations set up at roughly 120° intervals around the globe. Nearby is the Minitrack satellite tracking station, also provided by the US space agency and almost identical to the Minitrack installation at Winkfield, Berkshire (and to those at 11 other locations throughout the world).
>
> Thirty miles to the north of the town is Range E, the rangehead including four launch areas and the main

instrumentation building – control centre and data-collection centre for the range. The rangehead is served by one airfield, Evetts Field, the town by another airport used by the regular Airlines of South Australia services from Adelaide. Four miles from the rangehead are the two Black Knight pads of Area 5; ten miles away in another dried salt lake, on the edge of which is Woomera's largest, most complicated, and most expensive launch site – the Blue Streak pad is Area 6, now being adapted to serve the ELDO vehicle.[1]

Amidst these new activities, Skylark launches continued at a steady rate. During 1963 "14 Skylark rockets containing 59 scientific experiments were launched and, of the main and subsidiary experiments combined, about 54 per cent were successful and 15 per cent were partially successful."[2] This makes an average of 4.2 experiments per Skylark (the same as for the previous year). These included 14 solar physics experiments, a surprisingly large number considering the stabilised payload was not yet available. In addition, as shown in Table 8.1, there were also five 'proving' or test rounds:

As an aside, in March 1963, Donald Campbell arrived at nearby Lake Eyre[3] in an attempt to beat the world land-speed record. Although it had not rained there for many years, in 1963 it flooded, and in May the attempt was abandoned. (However, there was a successful attempt there in July 1964.)

Jan.	Feb.	March	April	May	June	July	Aug.	Sept.	Oct.	Nov.	Dec.
		SL84	SL167	SL115	SL126	SL29	SL86	SL87	SL81A	SL103	SL135
		SL85		SL127	SL46				SL171		SL104
									SL169		
									SL170		
									SL168		
									SL134		

Table 8.1 The 19 Skylark launches in 1963. (For full details see Appendix 3)

(Key: black = UK test launches, blue = UK national programme (unstabilised))

---

[1] 'FLIGHT International', 21 November 1963, p.846.

[2] British national report to COSPAR meeting in Florence May 1964, as reported by 'Flight International' 11 June 1964, p.992.

[3] Lake Eyre is only about 300 km (200 miles) north of Woomera, see for instance Figure 12.39.

Seq. Nos	Launch date	Ref. (sponsor) launch site	Config-uration	Apogee km (miles)	Experi-menters	Experiments	Result
67 (1)	01 Mar. 1963	SL84 (UK) Woomera	Un, Rav.7 +C	197 (122)	Bir	Ionosphere - RF probe	S
					UCW/RAE	Ionosphere - CW propagation	Ps
					Lei	Solar physics - X-ray counters	S
					Lei	" " - X-ray cameras	S
					UCL	" " - Lyman-α telescope	S
					"	Ionosphere - sporadic E spike probe	F

Table 8.2 A summary of SL84. The same set of experiments was repeated on SL85 ten days later.

March 1963   SL84, SL85

The 1963 Skylark 'season' opened with the launch of **SL84** on the 1st March. This was successfully followed by the similar **SL85** ten days later, both had on board the same comprehensive set of university ionosphere and solar X-ray experiments shown in the Table 8.2.

17 April 1963   SL167

SL167 was launched at twilight, carrying a set of four atmospheric physics experiments. One of these was the 'falling sphere' experiment which had failed when first tried on SL45 the previous June, but which worked on this second attempt.

A report of a later attempt at this experiment (SL361) was described thus:

> University College used a special rocket section from which their self-inflating 6ft sphere was ejected. This was tracked by radar and high-precision cameras, to give the rate of fall of the sphere and so the air densities encountered during the descent.[4]

This experiment was probably flown on the same mission as the sodium vapour experiment because falling sphere experiments tended to be carried out at evening twilight, because if the radar had trouble acquiring the sphere, visual acquisition was also possible. In all, only six falling sphere experiments were flown on Skylark, and only two worked:[5]

> The UCL falling-sphere experiment was not a success. It relied on the same ballistic camera technique as did the grenade experiment, with coded shutter operations for timing. Bowen and his team spent a lot of time producing the inflatable balloon package, but there must have been problems with its deployment. After a number of abortive trials the experiment was abandoned. It was to be many years and many failures with separable heads and recovery parachutes before it was realised that once outside the effective atmosphere the rocket, which for many years was not spun up to give it stability, gyrated far more wildly than suspected, sometimes even throwing a parachute out of its bay prematurely. It is just possible, I suppose, that something on these lines caused the balloon failures.[6]

However, on Australian sounding rockets the falling sphere experiment was repeated as nearly as possible at monthly intervals.[7] Because of the large number of years over which these were conducted, they became a prime source of upper atmospheric data for the southern hemisphere.

Seq. Nos	Launch date	Ref. (sponsor) launch site	Config-uration	Apogee km (miles)	Experi-menters	Experiments	Result
69 (3)	17 April 1963	SL167 (UK) Woomera	Un, Rav.7 +C	235 (146)	UCL	Neutral atmosphere - (grenades)	S
					"	" " - grenade (glow cloud)	Ps
					"	" " - falling sphere	S
					Bel	" " - sodium vapour	F

Table 8.3 A summary of SL167.

4   'FLIGHT International', 3 June 1965, p.890.
5   The falling sphere experiments on SL45 (1962), SL171, SL168 (1963), SL362 (1965) all failed, only SL167 (1963) and SL361 (1965) succeeded.
6   Dorling (1991), *Reminiscences of the Mullard Space Science Laboratory to 1991*, p.11.
7   Lloyd (1978), *Upper Atmosphere Research at WRE – a Review*, p.6. Upper atmosphere research by sounding rocket was actively supported by the Australian Weapons Research Establishment (WRE) from 1960 until 1976.

Figure 8.2 A falling sphere as used on Australian sounding rockets. That released from SL167 would have been similar.

(Lloyd (1978), figure 2)

For some of the other experiments on SL167 it was reported "… so a number of grenades, sodium vapour and chalk powder…were ejected, in experiments to determine physical properties of the upper atmosphere including wind speed and direction at various levels".[8] In general, all the grenade glow clouds were produced by the explosion of standard 1 lb (437 gram) grenades, although on SL167 two 25-gram grenades were exploded simultaneously as a scale experiment.[9]

May 1963   SL115, SL127

SL115 was a successor to SL114, launched six months earlier (November 1962), and carried the same three experiments, at least two of which required a parachute landing.

That from Jodrell Bank (JB) was notable, as at this fourth attempt their micrometeorite experiment was apparently successful for the first time, although the results were ambiguous:

Seq. Nos	Launch date	Ref. (sponsor) launch site	Config- uration	Apogee km (miles)	Experi- menters	Experiments	Result
70 (4)	23 May 1963	SL115 (UK) Woomera	Un, Rav.7 +C	207 (129)	MO	Aeronomy - ozone distribution	S
					JB	Micrometeorites - penetration detector	S
					Lei	Solar physics - X-ray cameras	S

Table 8.4 A summary of SL115.

[8] 'Flight International' magazine, 25 April 1963, p.616.
[9] Lloyd & Sheppard (1966), 'Atmospheric Structure at 130–200 km Altitude from Observations on Grenade Glow Clouds during 1962-63', p.324.

In this experiment six holes were found in the foils when they were recovered and removed from the sealed cassettes. These holes were extensively examined by high-powered microscopes. None of them was of the type that had been anticipated from hypervelocity impacts, for the holes were of various shapes, ragged and elongated, and it could not be definitely established that they were formed through the impact of dust particles in space. Nevertheless, the holes were not there on the foils before launching and identical control foils, which were subject to similar treatment at Woomera, but were not flown in the rocket, did not show any holes....The foils were exposed in space for less than 10 min, so that if the holes were true dust-particle punctures the impact rate would be very high, commensurate with that claimed for the Venus Flytrap experiment.[10]

The Jodrell Bank results may not have been helped by British Railways, as the cutting figure 8.3 shows.

A similar but more sophisticated experiment from Jodrell Bank would be launched into orbit on Ariel II in March 1964. The research group was later disbanded, so it was not possible to follow up the Skylark results with further experiments.

On SL115, the X-ray 'camera' from the University of Leicester may have been a successful flight of the X-ray spectrometer that failed on SL114, but nothing further is known.

Six days later SL127 was launched.

On this launch, the RRS consolidated their work that had used SL109 and 108 the previous year, by providing two of the four experiments. Both were successful, as was the Leicester X-ray experiment, a repeat of that flown the week before. However, the UCL sporadic E experiment failed.

The RAE vehicle attitude tests were subsequently repeated on SL121 and SL48; the results are described with SL48 in the next chapter.

Odyssey Of A Box Of Dust

LONDON, July 16 (A.A.P.). – There were only two slight spelling errors on the address label of the grey box lost by British Railways on its way from Australia's Woomera rocket range to Britain's Jodrell Bank.

The box, missing since June 12, was delivered to Jodrell Bank, Cheshire, yesterday.

It contained dust samples collected by a Skylark rocket from the outer atmosphere on June 5.

The "Daily Telegraph" says the box was addressed to "Jodrell Bank Experimental Station, Lower Whittington, Maccelsfield, Cheshire", instead of "Lower Withington, Macclesfield."

British Railways had said earlier that it had been wrongly addressed to "Nuffield Research Laboratories, Macclesfield, Yorkshire."

A Jodrell Bank spokesman said the box was intact. As far as they could see no damage had been done.

Today, a British Railways official said: "It is just one of those things. We simply don't know where the box has been, but we are making inquiries."

The "Guardian" today asked this question: "Why did the rocket cone, which flew 150 miles in space in 10 minutes, and travelled by plane from Australia to Britain in two to three days, take 33 days by rail from Hayes, Middlesex, to Stockport, Cheshire?"

The box arrived at Stockport yesterday and was immediately delivered by road.

Figure 8.3 This cutting from an Australian newspaper reveals that Jodrell Bank's micrometeorite experiment results got lost on the way home.

(Sydney Morning Herald 17 July 1963, p.1) [11]

Seq. Nos	Launch date	Ref. (sponsor) launch site	Config- uration	Apogee km (miles)	Experi- menters	Experiments	Result
71 (5)	29 May 1963	SL127 (UK) Woomera	Un, Rav.7 +C	207 (129)	RRS	Ionosphere - LF propagation	S
					"	" - resonance probe	S
					UCL	" - sporadic E	F
					Lei	Solar physics - X-ray cameras	S
					RAE	Test (Skylark technology) – vehicle attitude determination using solar and magnetic sensors	S

Table 8.5 A summary of SL127.

[10] Jennison (1967), 'Some Penetration and Charge Detection Techniques', p.253. The "Venus Flytrap" experiment was on a micrometeorite collector sounding rocket fired from White Sands, New Mexico, USA, on 6 June 1961. Approximately seven particles/mm² were collected and extensively analysed. Only some of the larger particles had sufficient momentum to rupture exposed films. (Hemenway & Soberman (1962), 'Studies of Micrometeorites Obtained from a Recoverable Sounding Rocket', (ADS).

[11] Reproduced with permission.

Seq. Nos	Launch date	Ref. (sponsor) launch site	Config-uration	Apogee km (miles)	Experi-menters	Experiments	Result
73 (7)	20 June 1963	SL46 (UK) Woomera	Un, Rav.7 +C	232 (144)	UCL	Ionosphere - Langmuir probe	Ps
					"	Ionosphere - electron temperature probe	S
					"	Solar physics - Lyman-α chambers	Ps
					"	Ionosphere – Sporadic E grid probe	S
					Lei	Solar physics - X-ray cameras	S

Table 8.6 A summary of SL46.

June 1963   SL126, SL46

SL126 was launched on the 18th June, an exact repeat of SL127 three weeks before. This time the second RRS experiment was only partially successful, but the UCL sporadic E experiment worked.

SL46 was successfully launched two days later, a year to the day after its numerical predecessor, SL45.

As with SL45, SL46 carried five geophysics experiments from UCL and Leicester, but this time most were concerned with measuring the ionosphere rather than atmospheric winds and temperature.

25 July 1963   SL29

SL29 followed a month later, the third in the RAE programme of six firings designed to investigate the drift of gyroscopes under acceleration. It was first to be fitted with the complete experiment, i.e. using radio interferometry and photography, so included the aerial survey camera as well as the two gyroscopes and three interferometer receivers:

Vehicle No.	Firing date	Camera bay	Doppler transponder	M.T.S. beacon	Roll control unit	
					Max. torque lb ft (nom.)	Max. roll rate rev/sec
SL28	29th Aug'62	Not Fitted	Fitted	Fitted	9	1.0
SL27	22nd Nov'62	Not Fitted	Not Fitted	Fitted	18	0.5
SL29	25th Jul'63	Fitted	Not Fitted	Fitted	18	0.5
SL30	20th Feb'64	Fitted	Not Fitted	Fitted	18	0.5
SL31	15th Jul'64	Fitted	Fitted	Fitted	27	0.33
SL32	17th Jul'64	Fitted	Fitted	Fitted	27	0.33

Table 8.7 SL29 was third in the gyro-drift test programme.
(From Knott (1964), p.16)

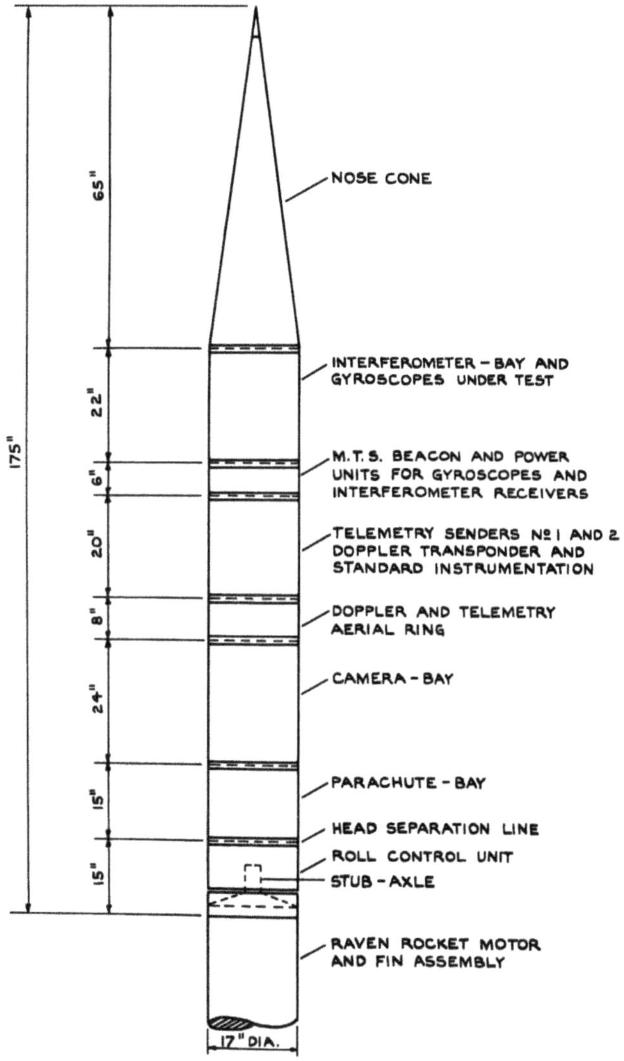

NOSE CONE

INTERFEROMETER — BAY AND
GYROSCOPES UNDER TEST

M.T.S. BEACON AND POWER
UNITS FOR GYROSCOPES AND
INTERFEROMETER RECEIVERS

TELEMETRY SENDERS Nº 1 AND 2
DOPPLER TRANSPONDER AND
STANDARD INSTRUMENTATION

DOPPLER AND TELEMETRY
AERIAL RING

CAMERA — BAY

PARACHUTE — BAY

HEAD SEPARATION LINE
ROLL CONTROL UNIT
STUB — AXLE

RAVEN ROCKET MOTOR
AND FIN ASSEMBLY

17" DIA.

65"
22"
6"
20"
8"
24"
15"
15"
175"

Figure 8.4 The instrument head configuration for gyro drift test vehicles SL29 and SL30. On these Skylarks, the number of parallel bays has grown to three, and the head has reached 14.6 feet (4.5 m) long.

(Knott (1966a), figure 1)

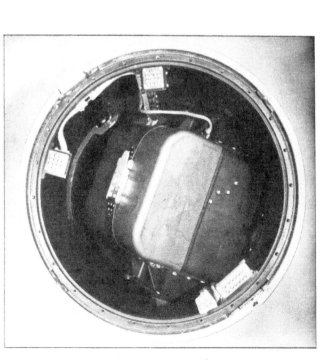

6 inches

Figure 8.5 The Williamson F117B aerial-survey camera fitted in SL29's camera bay. This was a standard aerial camera and quite hefty – about 9 inches (23 cm) wide. It had an auto wind mechanism that took approximately 110 4.5 x 4.5 inch pictures (one every 0.5 seconds) through an aperture in the side of the vehicle. It used Kodak Plus X Aerographic film at f.22, with a shutter time of 1/400th of a second.

(Knott (1968), figure 15)

Launch and Results

SL29 was originally due to be fired on the 11th July, but repeated launch attempts were thwarted because of a series of events worth including here, because they show the problems that had to be overcome during these pioneering times:

> Skylark 29 was first scheduled to be fired on Thursday 11th of July, but the trial was cancelled due to cloud and there was no attempt the following day due to the continued bad weather. The trial was reprogrammed for the following week and on 17th July the sequence was entered, but stopped at minus twenty seconds due to an E.H.T. trip failure at the GEC transmitter at Coondambo. After resetting the programme motor and E.H.T. supply and recaging gyros a second sequence was entered but stop action was taken when the indicator failed to monitor gyro uncage. The trial was then cancelled for the day and bad weather prevented any further attempts that week. The next attempt to fire was made on 24th July and the sequence was stopped at minus two minutes due to a fault in the range firing leads. The fault was cleared and a second sequence entered, but stop action was taken when there was no indication

of airborne camera operation. Unfortunately the stop action was taken too late to prevent the ignition of the ground flares. The trial was cancelled for the day and re-programmed for the following afternoon. On Thursday 25th July the vehicle was fired at 1429 hours.[12]

During this process, the camera bay was replaced by that intended for SL30.[13] Unfortunately, even after the launch, not all went well:

> The vehicle operated correctly until +21.5 seconds when the roll control unit appeared to lock the head to the rocket motor. At +24 seconds when the missile had reached an altitude of about 35000 ft [11 km / 6.6 miles] the rocket broke up and all telemetry signals ceased. The head of the vehicle broke into three parts but the parachute deployed at about 10000 ft landing the camera undamaged. The rocket motor continued to an altitude of about 160 000 ft [49 km / 30 miles] and landed about 26 miles [42km] down-range. Irregular burning of the motor was observed shortly before break-up and inspection of the venturi after impact showed that it had burnt through at the throat causing a lateral thrust which initiated the failure in flight.[14]

Figures 8.6 and 8.7 Left: the camera bay from SL29 fortuitously remained connected to the parachute bay and successfully soft-landed. Right: the remainder of the payload was found shattered near Evetts Field,[15] the airstrip that served the Woomera rangehead.
(WRE (1963), SL29 Trials Results file J5555/3/29)

[12] WRE (1963), *Advance Summary of Firing for Skylark 29 (B92/2)*, p.2. (SL29 Trials Results file J5555/3/29).
[13] Telex SAL 12373 from Whiteside to Hazell *et al.*, July 1963. (SL86 (sic) Trials Preparation file J5555/2/86).
[14] Knott (1965), *The Drift of an Auto-Pilot Gyroscope Due to Prolonged Acceleration in the Skylark Rocket, Part 3*, p.8.
[15] Named after Lieutenant General John Evetts who led the original Woomera diplomatic and survey mission, see Figure 1.13.

Figures 8.8 and 8.9 SL29's motor suffered a very different fate when it plunged into wet sand further downrange - the buried motor was over 15 feet (4.7 m) long! (The clothing worn by the observers and water in the crater are reminders that this was the Australian winter).

(WRE (1963), SL29 Trials Results file J5555/3/29)

Examination of the film from a Vinten high-speed cine camera revealed a:

> …large glowing cloud about 5-10 feet diameter suddenly appear at nozzle at 23.66 sec…[16]

Hence, it was realised that the spent motor could solve the mystery of why SL29 broke up.

However, physically recovering the motor was a different matter.

```
FURTHER INFORMATION REGARDING CONDITION OF MOTOR AND MOTOR
HARDWARE AFTER IMPACT WOULD BE MOST VALUABLE IN CONSIDERING
ALLEGED MOTOR FAILURE ON SL29.  PLEASE URGE ALL REASOOABLE
STEPS TOWARDS RECOVERY AND RETURN ANY PARTS OF RECOVERED
MOTOR TO RPE WESTCOTT.
```

Figure 8.10 Part of a Telex from RPE Westcott to WRE, 11 September 1963.

(WRE (1963), SL29 Trials Results file J5555/3/29)

Figure 8.11 The response from WRE to RPE.

(WRE (1963), SL29 Trials Results file J5555/3/29)

```
14245 TO KNOTT OF SPACE DEPARTMENT?. IN SHORT, RECOVERY
EXTREMELY DIFFICULT.
EVIDENCE INDICATES SEVERE IMPACT DAMAGE AT FRONT OF MOTOR BUT
ASSUME THAT THE VENTURI IS THE AREA YOU ARE MOST CONCERNED
ABOUT AND THERE IS SOME CHANCE THAT EXCAVATION MAY UNCOVER IT.
ACCORDINGLY, WE PROPOSE EXPENDING SOME EFFORT ON EXCAVATING TO
AT LEAST THE VENTURI AND PHOTOGRAPHING IT. THE DECISION TO PROCEED
FURTHER WILL BE TAKEN AFTER EXAMINATION OF EXPOSED EVIDENCE BUT
I AM EXTREMELY PESSIMISTIC ABOUT THE CHANCES OF EVER
EXTRACTING IT FROM THE MUD. WE ARE INVOLVED IN A BUSY FIRING
PROGRAMME AT PRESENT AND IT WOULD BE THE WEEK COMMENCING OCTOBER 7
AT THE EARLIEST BEFORE I WOULD BE ABLE TO ATTEMPT THE EXCAVATIONS.
```

---

[16] Telex from Whiteside of WRE to Hazell *et al.* at RAE, early September 1963. (WRE SL29 Trials Results file J5555/3/29).

Figures 8.12 and 8.13. The venturi of SL29's Raven motor during and after recovery. The recovery operation revealed that most of the expansion cone was missing before impact. (WRE (1963), SL29 Trials Results file J5555/3/29)

It was indeed October before the venturi was recovered. The motor was buried in wet salty sand, and inclined at a slight angle to the vertical. Recovery was achieved by cutting the motor tube about four inches from its rear. The expansion nozzle was badly damaged and distorted away from its axis, with approximately two thirds of it missing, although the fins were in good order and showed no impact damage, despite being nearly two feet below the surface.[17] It was concluded that the failure of the nozzle had caused SL29 to fail.

Results

By the time SL29 broke up, it was most of the way though its acceleration phase, and so via telemetry and the fortuitously recovered camera, a reasonable amount of data was obtained. A total of 41 frames were exposed by the camera,[18] and gyro drift data was calculated using a computer programme to compare the attitude of the head obtained from the gyroscopes with the attitude obtained from the interferometers.

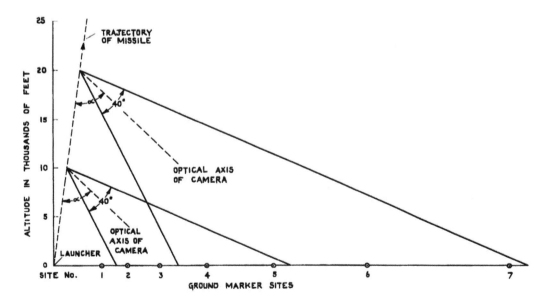

Figure 8.14 This scale diagram shows how the ground markers were photographed as SL29 ascended.
(After Knott (1968), figure 16)

17 Telex from WRE to RAE 23 October 1963. (WRE SL29 Trials Results file J5555/3/29).
18 Ibid, p.9.

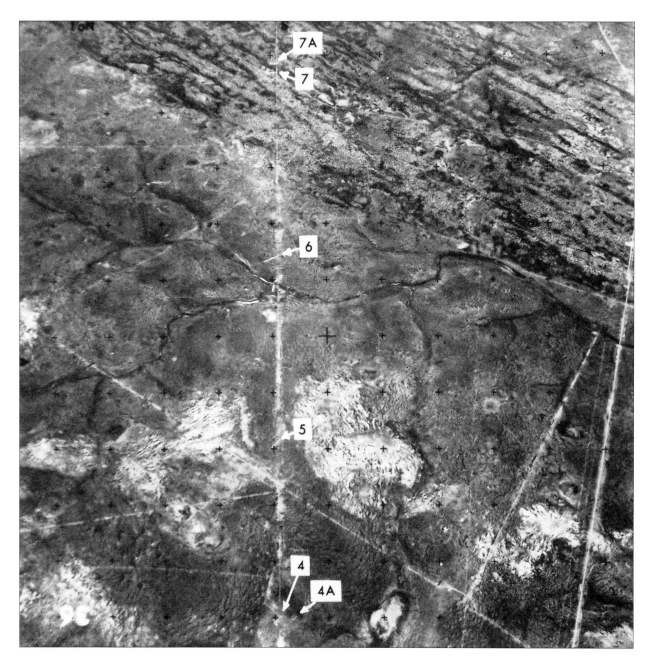

Figure 8.15 Photograph of ground markers taken from Skylark SL29 from an altitude of about 27,600 feet (5.2 miles, 8.4 km), reached 15-20 seconds after launch. The distance on the ground from marker 4 to marker 7 was just over six miles (9.8 km).[19]

(Knott (1966a), figure 13)

---

2 August 1963   SL86

SL86 was a proving flight to test measures designed to overcome nose cone problems arising from the higher performance of the Cuckoo boost and the Raven VA motor combination,[20] part of a continuing investigation into the structural failure with this motor combination:

This motor combination was first flown in November 1961 (Skylark 83), and the equipment failed early

in flight. In an attempt to reproduce and investigate the failure the motor combination was flown again with the head of the vehicle instrumented to record the flight behaviour (Skylark 35B). It was found that the nose cone failed structurally in flight. A specially strengthened nose cone was built, and after a successful flight-test of the vehicle fitted with this nose cone (Skylark 35C) it was decided to continue the Skylark programme using the high performance motor combination. Unfortunately, the failure was repeated in the

---

[19] Knott (1968), *The Drift of an Auto-Pilot Gyroscope Due to Prolonged Acceleration in the Skylark Rocket (Abridged Version)*, Appendix A.

[20] WRE (1963), *Skylark 87* (sic). (WRE SL87 Trials Preparation file J5555/2/87).

first firing of the Skylark carrying the upper atmosphere experiment (Skylark 45).[21]

Following the previous failures, the investigation was taken over by the RAE and SL86 was built in the UK. [22] It was fitted with extra instruments to record its flight behaviour, and the cone modifications included a linear displacement device to measure possible distortion during flight (see the SL87 photographs below), gauges to measure differential pressure across the cone wall, and thermistors and thermocouples to measure cone wall temperatures.[23] Overall, the payload head was similar in length and weight to that to be used for the

forthcoming "A.E.R.E. Solar Physics experiment".[24] A secondary purpose was to test the parachute recovery system under the higher temperature re-entry conditions arising from the use of the Raven VA/Cuckoo.[25] (Although in the event a Raven V rather than VA appears to have been used).

There used to be stories from those who went on the launch campaigns telling of how prized the nose cone half shells were to Aborigine chiefs who it seems liked them either side of their hut entrance! - but I don't know if that was true. [26]

Figure 8.16 The two halves of the "non-separating split nose cone" for SL86. The photograph is one of a series "Modifications on Skylark 86", and close examination reveals the riveted fastenings for additions on the inside of the cone.

(National Archives of Australia: D874, N63/2442)

---

[21] WRE (1963), *Skylark 86*. (WRE SL86 Trials Preparation file J5555/2/86).

[22] WRE (1963), *Skylark 86*. (SL86 Trials Preparation file J5555/2/86).

[23] WRE (1963), *Skylark Nos. 86 & 87 Round Specification*, (document SP/2324/86/DAW), para.1.4 "General Physical Measurements". (WRE SL86 Trials Preparation file J5555/2/86).

[24] Ibid.

[25] Ibid.

[26] John Coker, personal correspondence, February 2013.

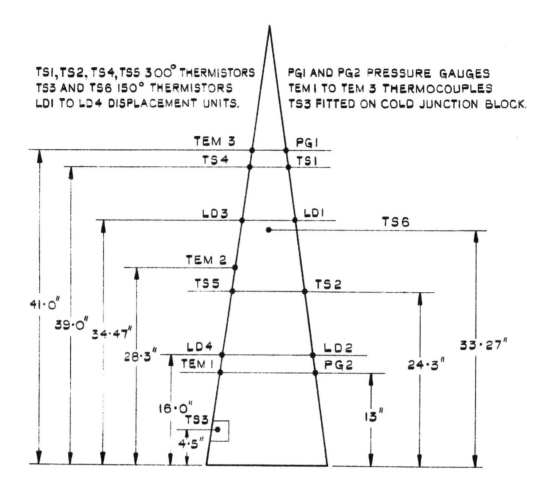

TS1, TS2, TS4, TS5 300° THERMISTORS
TS3 AND TS6 150° THERMISTORS
LD1 TO LD4 DISPLACEMENT UNITS.
PG1 AND PG2 PRESSURE GAUGES
TEM 1 TO TEM 3 THERMOCOUPLES
TS3 FITTED ON COLD JUNCTION BLOCK.
TEM 3
PG1
TS4
TS1
LD3
LD1
TS6
TEM 2
TS5
TS2
41·0"
39·0"
34·47"
28·3"
LD4
LD2
TEM 1
PG2
33·27"
24·3"
16·0"
TS3
4·5"
13"

Figure 8.17 This engineering drawing shows the position of the extra instrumentation that was fitted inside the nose cones of SL86 and SL87.
(WRE (1963), drawing "Position of Instruments SL.86/87", SL86 Trials Preparation file J5555/2/86)

Unfortunately, the launch compounded failure upon failure, because the second stage failed to ignite, and SL86 crashed into the desert:

SL86 FIRED APPROX 1200 HRS 2ND AUGUST. CUCKOO OPERATION
APPARENTLY CORRECT. NO EVIDENCE THAT RAVEN IGNITED
CUCKOO WAS OBSERVED TO SEPARATE AT END OF BURNING RAVEN AND HEAD
THEN CONTINUED IN AN UNPOWERED FLIGHT AND IMPACTED NOSE FIRST AT
500 YDS DOWN RANGE AND 500 YDS RIGHT AT 40 SEC. THE RAVEN
APPARENTLY EXPLODED AT IMPACT THE CRATER IS ABOUT 10 FEET ACROSS
AND MOST OF THE ROUND IS BURIED. AROUND THE CRATER ARE SCATTERED
PIECES OF MOTOR CASE, HEAD AND LARGE SECTION OF UNBURNT RAVEN
PROPELLANT.

Figure 8.18 Part of a Telex from WRE dated 2nd August 1963, providing the RAE in the UK with the first news of the failure of SL86.
(WRE (1963), Telex SAL 12737, SL86 Trials Results file J5555/3/86)

Seq. Nos	Launch date	Ref. (sponsor) launch site	Config-uration	Apogee km (miles)	Experi-menters	Experiments	Result
75 (9)	02 Aug. 1963	SL86 (UK) Woomera	Un, Rav.5A +C	0	RAE	Test (Skylark technology) – test of Cuckoo/Raven 5A combination and strengthened nose cone	Mf

Table 8.8 A summary of SL86.

Close examination of the cine film and telemetry evidence from SL86 supported the view that the Raven second stage igniter had failed to operate, but insufficient physical evidence could be recovered, and the reason for the failure remained unexplained.[27]

---

5 September 1963   SL87

Fortunately, not all the design effort had been wasted, as the next Skylark, **SL87,** was identical to SL86. Its purpose was

the same, to test measures designed to overcome the problems arising from the higher performance of the Cuckoo boost and Raven VA motor combination.

SL87 had arrived from the UK at the WRE's Salisbury base on 29th July and just over a month later was fired from Woomera at 13:11 local time on the 5th September. This time the launch was successful, although the Cuckoo boost landed in an unexpected place.

Figure 8.19 Part of the SL87 payload, the linear displacement-measuring device that fitted under the nose cone.
(WRE (1963), SL87 Trials Preparation file J5555/2/87)

---

[27] WRE (1963), *Summary of Firing of Skylarks 86 and 87*, (WRE SL87 Trials Results file J5555/3/87).

```
A SOUTH AUSTRALIAN CROW TOOK UP RESIDENCE IN THE LAUNCHER JUST

BEFORE FIRING AND SUFFERED IN THE ENGAGEMENT WITH THE BRITISH

RAVEN AND CUCKOO. THE CUCKOO LANDED ON THE ROOF OF THE PRIMING

HUT KNOCKING THE CEILING IN. THIS IS MINOR DAMAGE AND WILL NOT

EFFECT FIRINGS.
```

Figure 8.20 This extract from a Telex reveals the unexpected landing place of SL87's Cuckoo booster. On SL86, the Cuckoo had landed 300 yards from the launcher, this time the distance was only 20 yards. The reason for this may have been that SL87 was launched only 3 degrees from the vertical into a light wind from the west, whereas for SL86 there had been practically no wind at all.[28]
(WRE (1963), SL87 Trials Results file J5555/3/87)

Four minutes later SL87 reached the respectable altitude of 214 km (133 miles), and ten minutes after that the payload head landed 225 km (140 miles) downrange. Full telemetry was received, and even before recovery, the duration of tracking indicated that the parachute had operated correctly. The telemetry indicated no evidence of nose cone distortion, although its maximum temperature did reach approximately 650ºC.[29]

The payload head as in Figures 8.22 and 8.23 landed about 30 miles (48 km) short of the Opal mines at Coober Pedy, in terrain that looks more like Mars than Earth! As the head included the MTS (Missile Tracking System), it was tracked to the ground by radar and relatively easy to locate. However, the Raven VA motor separated from the payload before re-entry, and impacted separately without tracking aids. Although required for investigation, it appears never to have been found.[30]

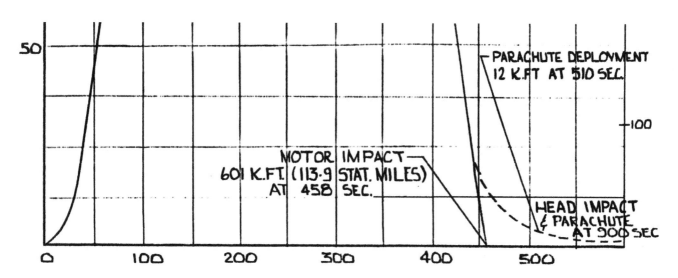

Figure 8.21 The lower part of the estimated trajectory for SL87 shows how (if all went well) the head and motor would reach the ground separately, the head taking over seven minutes longer to land. The left hand vertical scale is in km, the horizontal scale in seconds.
(WRE (1963), drawing "Estimated Trajectory: Skylark – SL86 & SL87", SL86 Trials Preparation file J5555/2/86)

---

[28] WRE (1963), *Summary of Firing of Skylarks 86 and 87*, (WRE SL87 Trials Results file J5555/3/87).
[29] Telex 14652 5/9/62 from Whiteside of WRE to Hazell *et al.* of RAE. (WRE SL87 Trials Results file J5555/3/87).
[30] WRE (1963), *Summary of Firing of Skylarks 86 and 87*. (WRE SL87 Trials Results file J5555/3/87).

Figures 8.22 and 8.23 The payload of SL87 landed in excellent condition with only minor impact damage.
(WRE (1963), SL87 Trials Results file J5555/3/87)

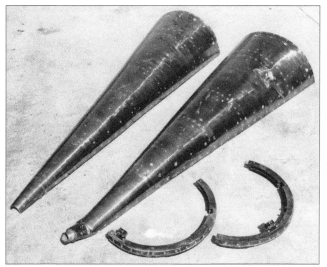

**Figures 8.24 and 8.25 Left: SL87's recovered parachute bay, showing the undamaged straps.
Right: SL87's recovered nose cone halves, with hardly a dent!**
(WRE (1963), SL87 Trials Results file J5555/3/87)

Following the parachute system failure the year before on SL35C,[31] extra thermal insulation was provided on SL87 to protect the parachute and wiring. Clearly this was successful, and the payload was recovered in such good condition it was re-used on Skylark SL87A the following year.

October 1963	SL81A, SL171, SL169, SL170, SL168, **SL134**

Scientific flights resumed in October, a particularly busy few weeks for Skylark, and the first time that six had been launched in one month.[32] Firings started with **SL81A**, carrying a repeat of the Cambridge long wire experiment on SL82. SL81A was an upgraded version of SL81; the Skylark that had been returned to the UK for modification after the long wire experiment on board SL82 had failed twelve months earlier. This time the experiment was at least partly successful.

---

[31] WRE (1963), *Advance Information on Skylark SL87A*. (WRE SL87A Trials Preparation file J5555/2/87A).
[32] The previous maximum launched in one month was four in November 1961.

Seq. Nos	Launch date	Ref. (sponsor) launch site	Config- uration	Apogee km (miles)	Experi- menters	Experiments	Result
77 (11)	3/2 Oct. 1963	SL81A (UK) Woomera	Un, Rav.7	146 (91)	Cam	Ionosphere - long wire aerial impedance	Ps
					UCL	" - Sporadic E	S

Table 8.9 A summary of SL81A.

Unusual Test of Atmosphere By Rocket

CANBERRA, Thursday. — A Skylark rocket fired from Woomera early today carried out an unusual test in the upper atmosphere.

The Minister for Supply (Mr. Fairhall) said the rocket, which reached a height of 91 miles, was primarily used to check the release of a long wire aerial.

Mr. Fairhall said: "This is a difficult problem when the rocket is rotating in flight, but its solution is necessary if experiments are to be conducted using low frequency radio waves.

Figure 8.26 This Melbourne newspaper article reported the launch of SL81A.

(The Age, Friday 4 October 1963, p.14) [38]

SL81A was launched just after midnight, at 00:40 local time on the 3rd October (2nd October GMT).[33] The rocket head was released from the motor at a height of 75 km, and unusually, the roll rate was then accelerated to 1.2 rev/second,[34] presumably to help deploy the aerial. As on SL82, the aerial was a simple dipole comprising two ten metre lengths of stranded nylon copper braided wire, released from a drum at a rate of about one quarter of a metre per second, using a mechanism based on that designed for Ariel II.

The Cambridge University experiment was intended to help in the interpretation of measurements using radio-receiving equipment in space vehicles, such as the radio astronomy experiment on the forthcoming British scientific satellite Ariel II.[35] In particular, it was designed to test various theories predicting the electrical properties of aerials situated in the ionosphere.[36]

Results

Measurements were transmitted by telemetry as the aerial was deployed, which was fortunate, because at the end of deployment the feeding drum rotated 180° too far, which had the effect of short-circuiting the aerial, so that no readings were obtained above a height of 128 km.[37]

The payload was recovered in reasonable condition 80 miles (129 km) downrange; this allowed some recalibration, and the cause of the fault to be determined.[39] The experimental results obtained resulted in a fair agreement with theory.

---

[33] Hugill (1965) states that the launch was on the 4th local time, but a telex from WRE to RAE announcing the launch not only states the 3rd, but is also date stamped the 3rd. 'The Age' newspaper report on the launch also indicates it took place on Thursday the 3rd.

[34] Apparently using a gyro spin-up mechanism (Various telexes from WRE to RAE., WRE SL81A Trials Results file J5555/3/81(sic)).

[35] Satellite S-52 / UK-2 / Ariel II was the second joint UK-USA satellite, launched on 27th March 1964.

[36] Hugill (1965), 'Some Measurements of Aerial Impedance in the Ionosphere', p.345.

[37] Hugill (1965), 'Some Measurements of Aerial Impedance in the Ionosphere', p.346.

[38] Reproduced with permission.

[39] Hugill (1965), p.346

Four in one night

Two weeks later, four Skylarks were fired during one night, the purpose being to study how upper atmosphere properties varied over a period of just a few hours, rather than month by month. This event was described as "one of the most comprehensive series of upper-atmosphere probes yet made from this range".[40] One of the visitors from the UK commented:

It was necessary to face the considerable problems in launching a number of Skylark rockets with grenade payloads during one night. Those of us who had witnessed rocket firings on occasional visits were astonished at the courage of those who would attempt such a task ...[41]

Figure 8.27 Right: The head from SL81A being recovered, showing an aerial wire and what is probably the silver-coated brass cone from which it was released.

(WRE (1963), SL81A Trials Results file J5555/3/81(sic))

Figure 8.28 The Skylark 'grasshopper' or gate trolley, with a typical grenade head.

(WRE \ J.A.Hill)

---

[40] 'Flight International' magazine, 24 October 1963, p.701.
[41] Massey & Robins (1986), *History of British Space Science,* p.274. © Science and Engineering Research Council 1986, published by Cambridge University Press, reproduced with permission.

The launch sequence that night was as follows:

Vehicle	Local Time	Local Date
SL171	19.21 CST	15.10.63
SL169	21.18 CST	"
SL170	00.39 CST	16.10.63
SL168	04.52 CST	"

Table 8.10 Launch data for the night of 15/16 October 1963.[42]

The two single stage Skylarks (SL169 and SL170) reached 130 km (80 miles), and the two two-stage versions (SL171 and SL168) around 200 km (125 miles).

Despite the hectic schedule, all the actual launches were successful. A total of fourteen typical upper atmosphere experiments from UCL, Belfast and Imperial College were carried. Those on SL171 and SL168 were the same set as on SL167 the previous April, those on SL169 and SL170 the same as on SL165 and SL166 twelve months before. The resulting grenade glow clouds were tracked by a scanning photometer and several specialised cameras.[43] Unfortunately, only half the experiments were completely successful, with four, the UCL falling sphere and Belfast sodium vapour experiments failing completely.

The recovery team must have been busy the following day!

However, on balance, the campaign was very successful, revealing information on the density and temperature of the upper atmosphere at the edge of space, as well as wind speed information as shown below. In April 1965, an even more ambitious one-night programme would follow, as described in the next chapter.

Congestion at the Launch Tower

By now, the WRE Research Vehicles group at Woomera had expanded substantially, and was fielding four separate teams so that several Skylarks could be prepared at once.[44] This allowed them to be launched within a week or so of each other, or even several on one day, as above. This method helped keep up the launching rate, which in 1963 reached a new peak of 19 firings. However, the following extract from a later report reveals that this brought its own problems, as the limitations of having only one Skylark launch tower became apparent:

> SL103 was put on the launcher on 21st October, but the conditions were not suitable. On 25th October, it was removed from the launcher and replaced by SL134 which required full moon conditions. SL134 was fired

Figure 8.29 A recovered part of the "balloon assembly" from SL171. It may have been recovered to try to find out why the falling sphere experiment failed.
(National Archives of Australia: D874, N63/4124)

on 30th October and SL135 was inserted, but the conditions for it were not suitable. It was removed on 6th November to make way for SL103, as no ionosphere storms were predicted, and WRE hoped for a stable ionosphere. However, SL103 could not be fired until 19th November. During this time there were many days when SL135 could have been fired had it been in the launcher.

> SL104 was then prepared for firing, but was removed on 24th November to give SL135 a chance again. SL135 was fired on 2nd December, and by a special effort, SL104 was fired on 3rd December. The number of working days that various rounds were not in a position to be fired because of this conflict are shown below; they total 29.[45]

The report also concludes that the extra 'waiting time' spent in Australia by supporting UK personnel during this time was 22 man weeks. It might also have added that the launcher activity and associated delays may well have reduced the reliability of the Skylark and/or the launch preparations, as the last three to be launched in 1963 (SL103, SL135 and SL104) all suffered vehicle failures.

[42] Data from Lloyd & Sheppard (1966), 'Atmospheric Structure at 130-200 km Altitude from Observations on Grenade Glow Clouds during 1962-63', p.327.
[43] Ibid, p.324.
[44] *Case for a Second Skylark Launcher at WRE Woomera*, document reference DS/55/01, (TNA: PRO document file AVIA 92/146).
[45] Morton (1989), *Fire across the desert*, p.399.

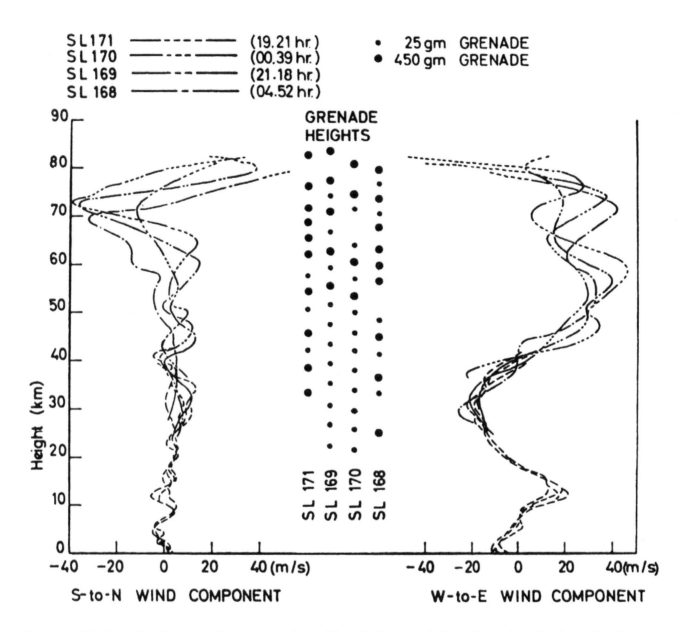

Figure 8.30 Height profiles of wind speed components obtained from the four grenade flights during the night of 15-16 October 1963.
(Massey & Robins (1986), p.275) [46]

During 1964 this launch rate continued, and the RAE and WRE put forward a proposal for a second Skylark launch tower, as discussed at the start of the next chapter.

Measurements of the Earth's Infra-Red Radiation

Skylark **SL134** was an RAE space technology mission, its main experiment to check the feasibility of using the Earth's horizon for attitude control of an orbiting satellite. A number of infrared detectors were mounted underneath the nose cone, which when exposed, were designed to measure the radiation gradient at the Earth-space interface. The payload also carried secondary experiments to test an RAE Moon sensor system, a magnetic tape recorder, and an RAE Moon scanner.[47]

[46] Massey & Robins (1986), *History of British Space Science,* © Science and Engineering Research Council 1986, published by Cambridge University Press, reproduced with permission.

[47] WRE (1963), *Skylark No.134 Round Specification*, (document SP/2324/134/SOS). (WRE SL134 Trials Preparation file J5555/2/134).

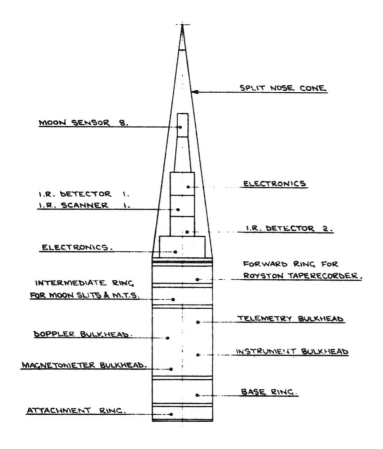

SPLIT NOSE CONE

MOON SENSOR 8.

I.R. DETECTOR 1.
I.R. SCANNER 1.

ELECTRONICS

ELECTRONICS.

I.R. DETECTOR 2.

INTERMEDIATE RING
FOR MOON SLITS & M.T.S.

FORWARD RING FOR
ROYSTON TAPERECORDER.

DOPPLER BULKHEAD.

TELEMETRY BULKHEAD

MAGNETOMETER BULKHEAD.

INSTRUMENT BULKHEAD

ATTACHMENT RING.

BASE RING.

ESTIMATED HEAD WEIGHT 240 lb   HEAD LENGTH 111·15 INS.

HEAD FOR SKYLARK No. 134

Figure 8.31 This sketch shows the original layout for the head of SL134.
(WRE (1963), Skylark No.134 Round Specification, WRE SL134 Trials Preparation file J5555/2/134)

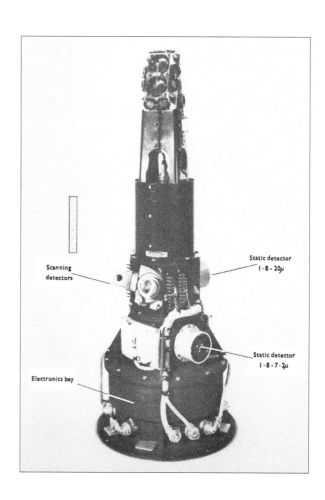

Figure 8.32 The SL134 nose cone assembly showing the infrared detectors.
(Moore (1965), figure 10)

Scanning detectors

Static detector 1·8 - 20µ

Static detector 1·8 - 7·2µ

Electronics bay

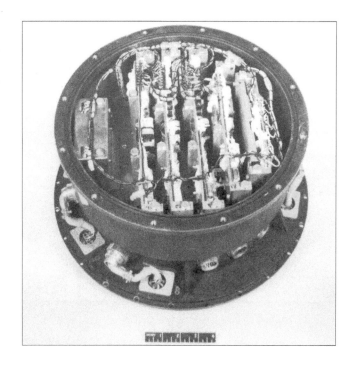

Figure 8.33 A view of the transistorised amplifiers forming the electronics bay of the main experiment on SL134. These included then state of the art silicon transistors, a type first made in 1954, only nine years previously. The bay would have been perhaps ten times bigger if transistors had not been used.

(Moore (1965), figure 13)

SL134 was one of two similar vehicles. It was designed to be launched at night, after the Earth had had time to cool, whereas the second (SL135) was intended to be launched in the afternoon, when the temperature of the Earth's surface at the launching point had reached its maximum value. (The launch of SL135 is described below).

By now Skylark's original valve (vacuum tube) based electronics was making way for the latest and much smaller transistor technology.[48]

Despite the availability of transistors, the Royston magnetic tape recorder[49] remained a substantial piece of equipment, which in its bay weighed some 40 lb (18 kg) and required a full one Amp of battery current.[50] However much of the weight must have been accounted for by the fact it was a "black box" flight data recorder in a metal box, substantial enough to survive landing in a Skylark payload not fitted with a parachute recovery system. In this application, it was intended to make a back-up record of data from the experiments, with wider bandwidth than possible using the radio telemetry system alone.

SL134 was required to be launched at night once the local Earth's surface had cooled down, and also within three days of full moon. In addition, information on the cloud cover and type was required up to 800 miles (1290 km) radius. After displacing SL103 in the launcher as described above, firing was achieved at 23:56 local time on Wednesday 30 October.[51] The flight was generally successful, although the tape deck stopped running at launch.[52] The nose cone was correctly jettisoned at about 70 seconds, and after about three and a half minutes, an apogee of 115 miles (186 km) was achieved, with impact 65 miles (105 km) downrange. The head was recovered in relatively good condition; ironically, the tape deck box was intact with only light damage. Curiously, for safety reasons the photographer was not permitted close enough to take worthwhile photographs,[53] the reason for this is not known.

Telemetry from the experiments was good, although the results were devalued because the attitude information recovered from SL134's standard attitude instruments was poor - "the unfortunate motion of SL134 in space caused a paucity of information in the standard Skylark attitude instrumentation, resulting in poor attitude definition".[54]

However all the infrared detectors from the main experiment showed Earth and space levels clearly, and an infrared chart of the region was derived, as shown in Figure 8.34.

---

[48] The first transistor radio had appeared in 1954, less than ten years earlier.

[49] Aircraft flight data recorders were becoming mandatory at this time. Royston Instruments Ltd was based at Byfleet in Surrey, and their flight recorders were fitted to the VC-10, BAC 1-11 and similar aircraft. The company went into liquidation in 1968, but their MIDAS range of data recorders appear to have continued for many years afterwards.

[50] WRE (1963), *Skylark No.134 Round Specification*, (document SP/2324/134/SOS). (WRE SL134 Trials Preparation file J5555/2/134).

[51] Moore (1965), *The Measurement of the Earth's Infra-red Radiation from a Skylark Rocket*, p.6.

[52] Telex dated 31/10/63 from WRE to RAE. (WRE SL134 Trials Results file J5555/3/134).

[53] Telex dated 27/11/63 to Skylark Project Officer. (WRE SL134 Trials Results file J5555/3/134).

[54] Moore (1965), *The Measurement of the Earth's Infra-red Radiation from a Skylark Rocket*, Summary.

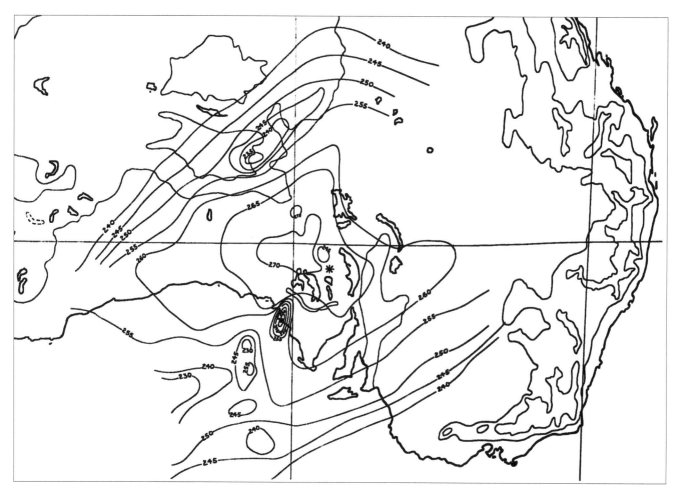

Figure 8.34 The infrared chart of night-time southern Australia produced from the data returned by SL134.
The contours mostly corresponded with the cloud cover.
(Moore (1965), figure 8)

As well as the chart shown above, it was found possible to assess the radiation gradient at the Earth-space horizon, but it was concluded that the small signal levels produced by the detectors indicated this method would be unlikely to be suitable for satellite horizon sensing under these night-time conditions.[55]

19 November 1963	SL103

Originally, **SL103** had been put on the launcher on 21st October, but conditions were not suitable (it required a stable ionosphere) and on 25th October it was removed and replaced by SL134, which as described above, was launched on the 30th. Next, SL135 was placed in the launcher, but was in turn displaced by SL103, which was finally launched on the 19th November. The SL103 payload carried the same set of ionosphere and solar X-ray measuring instruments as flown on SL84 and SL85 the previous March.

Unfortunately, a major motor failure occurred at +9 seconds,[56] the vehicle reached no appreciable height, and must have been mostly destroyed when it crashed. The Australian National Archives contain four photographs of the motor fragment shown in figure 8.35, presumably significant, but the author has no further information on the cause of the crash.

December 1963	SL135, SL104

After the launch of SL103, **SL135** was returned to the launcher, but unlike its predecessor SL134, not all went smoothly. As with SL134, the main experiment was designed to measure the Earth's infrared radiation in order to help design horizon sensors for use in a space vehicle. However as SL135 was designed to make these measurements during daylight, its secondary experiments included solar cells and a solar scanner rather than Moon sensors. It still

[55] Moore (1965), *The Measurement of the Earth's Infra-red Radiation from a Skylark Rocket*, p.9.
[56] *WRE All Projects Review No.24*, para.12.2, p.16. (National Archives of Australia, digitised item D174, SA5409/4/3 PART4, page 101).

Seq. Nos	Launch date	Ref. (sponsor) launch site	Config- uration	Apogee km (miles)	Experi- menters	Experiments	Result
83 (17)	19 Nov. 1963	SL103 (UK) Woomera (BS94/1)	Un, Rav.7 +C	-	Bir	Ionosphere - RF probe	Vf (MF)
					UCW/RAE	" - CW propagation (I)	
					Lei	Solar physics - X-ray counters	
					"	" " - X-ray cameras	
					UCL	" " - Lyman-α telescope	
					"	Ionosphere – sporadic E spike probe	

Table 8.11 A summary of SL103.

Figure 8.35 The recovered port end of the motor from SL103.
(National Archives of Australia: D874, N63/4491)

certain periods of the Sun's cycle.[58] However as noted above, SL103 could not be fired until 19th November. SL104 was then prepared for firing, but in turn was removed from the launcher on the 24th to give SL135 another chance.

The first SL135 firing attempt was made at about 14:00 local time on the 26th November, but was stopped at minus 15 seconds when a monitor light failed to show the extractor arms had correctly stowed.[59] (It turned out the priming cable had caught up preventing one arm from operating the microswitch). On Wednesday the 27th, SL135 remained on standby, the weather was ideal but because of other priority trials, there was no opportunity to start the launch sequence. A slot was made available on Thursday the 28th, but high winds and extensive cloud made the weather unsuitable, and as the weather forecast remained poor, the team returned to Adelaide.[60]

Monday the 2nd December dawned with brighter prospects, and the team must have thought their luck had turned when at 13:45 local time SL135 was finally fired. Unfortunately, their hopes were soon dashed when disaster struck and the nose cone came off 13 seconds into the flight. The vehicle however continued on its way and reached a maximum velocity of 5200 ft/sec [61] (3545 mph / 1 mile per second / 5705 km/h) after one minute; but the resulting aerodynamic heating resulted in all the infrared equipment being burnt out

included a Royston magnetic tape recorder, which after the failure on SL134 was improved by the RAE's Peter Sumpster, who modified the motor drive circuit so full start voltage was provided throughout running.[57]

SL135 launch delays

It was originally intended to launch SL135 within a few days of SL134, but unsuitable cloud cover and surface winds prevented this, and on the 6th November it had been removed from the launcher to make way for SL103, which required precise ionospheric conditions only likely during

[57]   Telex dated 31/10/63 from WRE to RAE. (WRE SL134 Trials Results file J5555/3/134).
[58]   Telex ref. SAL 18906 from WRE to RAE. (WRE SL135 Trials Preparation file J5555/2/135).
[59]   Telex dated 27/11/63 from WRE to RAE. (WRE SL135 Trials Preparation file J5555/2/135).
[60]   Telex dated 28/11/63 from WRE to RAE. (WRE SL135 Trials Preparation file J5555/2/135).
[61]   WRE (1964), *Summary of Firing of Skylarks 134 and 135*. (WRE SL134 Trials Results file J5555/3/134).

during ascent through the atmosphere.[62] SL135 did reach an apogee of 167 km (104 miles), but the reduced altitude, maximum velocity and impact time were all consistent with high drag resulting from loss of the nose cone.

One source states that all signals ceased shortly after the nose cone was lost,[63] but this must refer to the main experiment only, as another source states that the Sun scanner and static detector slits operated until re-entry, and some telemetry was

Figures 8.36 and 8.37 The motor case of SL135 being recovered 38 miles (61 km) down range. The close-up shows impact damage to a fin, possibly caused when the nose cone came away.
(WRE (1963), SL135 Trials Results file J5555/3/135)

Figures 8.38 and 8.39 The scattered remains of SL135's payload were found a short distance from the motor case. The right hand photograph shows the burnt out experiment from under the nose cone.
(WRE (1963), SL135 Trials Results file J5555/3/135)

[62] Moore (1965), *The Measurement of the Earth's Infra-red Radiation from a Skylark Rocket*, p.6.
[63] WRE (1964), *Summary of Firing of Skylarks 134 and 135*. (WRE SL134 Trials Results file J5555/3/134).

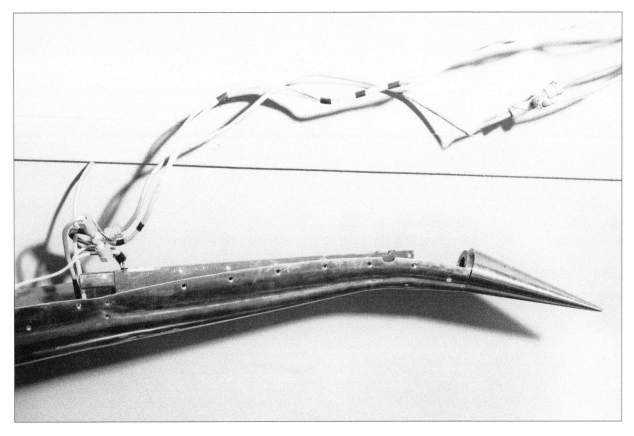

Figure 8.40 The tip of the first SL135 nose cone half to be recovered.
(WRE (1963), SL135 Trials Results file J5555/3/135)

obtained.[64] The motor and head were programmed to separate at re-entry and were recovered near each other 38 miles (61 km) downrange:

Astonishingly, the magnetic tape recorder was recovered intact from the wreckage of the instrument head:

> A Midas type MIR-7 missile recorder was recently fired in a Skylark rocket from Woomera, Australia, on a high altitude test. The rocket reached a height of 104 miles and subsequently impacted 50 miles down-range on a rock surface. No parachute or other recovery aids were employed. It is stated that not only was the tape record undamaged, but that the recorder itself was still operative when picked up, an event considered to be unique in the history of missile development.[65]

Just after launch the pieces of the nose cone had been observed separating and on Tuesday the 3rd one half was recovered 500 yards down range where it had fallen, and on the following day the other half was found 800 yards down range.[66]

The damage to the nose cone halves showed that the cone had separated at the base first, then forced open the latch at the top. The photograph above shows how one half was bent back about five inches (125 mm) from the base of the nose cone tip by leverage from the other half when it broke away. Both sections at the base of the cone onto which the manacle ring fitted were found with the head. It appeared that the nose cone halves had failed under normal loading for reasons that were not certain, and the nose cone parts, recovered head section and telemetry records were returned to the UK on the next charter flight for investigation.

Meanwhile, on Tuesday the 3rd, "after a special effort" SL104 was launched, a repeat of SL103 launched a fortnight previously. Unfortunately, disaster struck yet again, and the vehicle broke up on the edge of space, at a little above 100 km. Following the failure of SL103, this must have been doubly disappointing for the experimenters, who had to return to the UK empty handed for Christmas.

Following the recovery of SL104, marks caused by the launcher rails were found on the vehicle, and although these appeared only superficial, all the rails were removed for checking and refurbishing.[67]

---

[64] Telex ref. SAL 20954 from Whiteside of WRE to Barnes *et al.* of RAE. (WRE SL135 Trials Results file J5555/3/135).
[65] 'FLIGHT International', 20 February 1964, p.299.
[66] Telex dated 05/12/63 from WRE to RAE. (WRE SL135 Trials Results file J5555/3/135).
[67] Telex ref. SAL 20658 from WRE to RAE. (WRE SL135 Trials Results file J5555/3/135).

Jan.	Feb.	March	April	May	June	July	Aug.	Sept.	Oct.	Nov.	Dec.
	SL88	SL129	SL136	SL20		S01/1	SL301	SL137	SL47		SL302
	SL30	SL128				S01/2	SL121	SL87A			
						SL31		SL120			
						SL32		SL133			
								SL132			

Table 8.12 The 19 Skylark launches in 1964. (For full details see Appendix 3)

(Key: black = test launches, blue = UK national programme (unstabilised), plum = UK (stabilised), pink = ESRO programme)

SKYLARK LAUNCHES AND SCIENCE IN 1964

1964 would see several milestones in the history of Skylark. Firstly, in July, was the start of its use by ESRO, (the European Space Research Organisation), which resulted in the first launches outside Australia. Then, in August, came the first flight of the new stabilised payload system (on SL301), followed in September by the launch of the 100th Skylark from Woomera (SL132). This was also the year when activity at Woomera reached a peak, and the Australian Weapons Research Establishment staff numbers reached over 6000.[68]

After the year had ended, it was reported that the eleven UK scientific launches of Skylark had involved 42 experiments,

approximately 71 per cent of the main subsidiary experiments were successful, and 15 per cent were partially successful.[69]

February 1964   SL88, SL30

SL88 was another Raven VA/Cuckoo motor test, continuing from SL87 the previous September. The head was similar in weight and length to the forthcoming stabilised payloads,[70] and as with its predecessors, included a linear displacement unit to measure possible nose cone distortion. Although the vehicle was ready in January, launch was delayed several times, initially because of repairs to the launch tower following the problems with SL103, but later because of unsuitable

Figures 8.41 and 8.42 The instrument head of SL88 being recovered 61 miles (98 km) down range. In general it was in excellent condition, although the close-up shows the sun slit assembly bay where one detector had "lost its filter and mask because of the failure of adhesive holding the cover".[71] To the right of this bay the nose cone assembly has mostly gone, leaving just a tail of electrical cable - "The hollow bolts securing pillar have snapped flush with forward bulkhead and every thing forward of this bulkhead is missing [although the] nose cone half rings were still attached".[72]

(WRE (1964), SL88 Trials Results file J5555/3/88)

[68] Morton (1989), *Fire across the Desert*, p.212.
[69] BNCSR figures, as reported in FLIGHT International, 20 May 1965, p.806.
[70] WRE (1964), *Advanced Summary of Firing for SL88*. (WRE SL88 Trials Results file J5555/3/88).
[71] Telex ref. SAL 2760 Feb.1964 from Fenton of WRE to Warr of RAE, p.3. (WRE SL88 Trials Results file J5555/3/88).
[72] Ibid, p.1.

weather.[73] Eventually it was fired at 10.35 local time on the 4th February, even though the visibility was only about four miles because of dust haze, and the temperature was 95°F (35°C) in the shade.

The motor thrust was higher than expected, and it appeared that at 31 seconds roll-yaw lock-in occurred, and "The conditions at 35 seconds put SL88 into the class where some Skylarks break up and some don't".[74] What was certain was that at 34 seconds the head release mechanism operated and the nose cone was torn off whilst the vehicle was travelling at its maximum of 4400 mph (1.2 miles per second).[75] Nevertheless, after three minutes the head reached an altitude of 74 miles (119km), and soft-landed some eight minutes later 61 miles (98 km) down range.

Good telemetry was received, and the MTS tracked the payload to impact. Even so, it took a week to find the head, which was not recovered until the 11th.

So why had the head release mechanism operated early at +34 seconds? (Which should only have happened during re-entry at +353 seconds). The reason appeared linked to an override micro-switch inside the nose cone, fitted so that head release would occur should the nose cone be lost in flight (as had happened for instance on SL135). However,

this switch had been set so that a deformation of 0.25 inches at the displacement-measuring unit was required to trigger it, and the telemetry showed that the maximum displacement in flight had been less than 0.1 inches.[76]

The answer appears to have been deduced some months later, after the RAE had measured the deformation of the split nose cone in heating tests; following which the WRE responded "This type of deformation would explain why SL88 [Fired Feb 1964] separated head from motor during thrust phase. We were mystified because displacement gauges showed very small movements." It seems that the aerodynamic heating effect was sufficient for the nose cone to have lost its rigidity, and it deformed unequally over the distance between the measuring gauge and the switch.[77]

Meanwhile the search had continued for the nose cone parts and the motor. The nose cone may never have been found, but the motor at least was located on the 26th, some three weeks after firing.

The payload was refurbished and later flown again as SL88A, and over the next couple of years, launches also took place of SL88B and SL88C, so it became the most frequently reused of all Skylark payloads!

Figures 8.43 and 8.44 SL88's motor was located three weeks after launch on the 26th February, broken into two main parts.
(WRE (1964), SL88 Trials Results file J5555/3/88)

---

[73]   Telex 31/1/64 from WRE to RAE. (WRE SL88 Trials Preparation file J5555/2/88).
[74]   Telex ref. SAL 1502. (WRE SL88 Trials Results file J5555/3/88).
[75]   WRE (27/2/64), *Advanced Summary of Firing for SL88*. (WRE SL88 Trials Results file J5555/3/88).
[76]   Telex ref. SAL 3064 Feb.1964 from Fenton of WRE to Hazell *et al.* of RAE, p.2. (WRE SL88 Trials Results file J5555/3/88).
[77]   Telex ref. SAL 3104 from Malcolm of WRE to Hazell of RAE. (WRE SL88 Trials Results file J5555/3/88). (Although the author would rather like to ask, "had switch bounce at high temperatures and vibration at 4400 mph been taken into account?")

Vehicle No.	Firing date	Camera bay	Doppler transponder	M.T.S. beacon	Roll control unit	
					Max. torque lb ft (nom.)	Max. roll rate rev/sec
SL28	29th Aug'62	Not Fitted	Fitted	Fitted	9	1.0
SL27	22nd Nov'62	Not Fitted	Not Fitted	Fitted	18	0.5
SL29	25th Jul'63	Fitted	Not Fitted	Fitted	18	0.5
SL30	20th Feb'64	Fitted	Not Fitted	Fitted	18	0.5
SL31	15th Jul'64	Fitted	Fitted	Fitted	27	0.33
SL32	17th Jul'64	Fitted	Fitted	Fitted	27	0.33

Table 8.13 SL30 was fourth in the gyro drift test programme.
(From Knott (1964), p.16)

SL30 followed on the 20th, and was the fourth in the RAE programme to investigate the performance of autopilot gyroscopes. As with its predecessor SL29, it was fitted with the complete gyro experiment, and fortunately this time the vehicle operated correctly (SL29 had broken up after 24 seconds), and SL30 reached an altitude of 345,000 feet (105 km / 65 miles) after 166 seconds.

However, the payload did not perform very well, and at +15 seconds the roll control stopped working. After the vehicle passed through the apogee position, the head correctly separated from the motor and landed about 37 miles (60 km) down-range. The parachute recovery system failed to operate, but surprisingly the photographic film record was recovered from the camera magazine, albeit in a badly damaged condition,[78] and some gyro drift measurements were obtained.

March 1964   SL129, SL128

On the 10th and 12th March, **SL129** and **SL128** were launched at 11:36 and 11:37 local time respectively. Each carried the same payload of four varied experiments: including a galactic gamma ray detector, a new type of experiment from a new Skylark user, the University of Southampton.

The University of Southampton was developing apparatus for searching from a satellite for energetic primary gamma rays in the cosmic radiation, and SL129 appears to have provided a flight test.[79]

The magnetometer experiments

An unusual experiment was included by Imperial College. This was a proton magnetometer, designed to measure the

Seq. Nos	Launch date	Ref. (sponsor) launch site	Config- uration	Apogee km (miles)	Experi- menters	Experiments	Result
88 (3)	10 Mar. 1964	SL129 (UK) Woomera (BS106/2)	Un, Rav.7 +C	175 (109)	Soton	Astronomy – galactic γ-rays (spark chamber)	S
					IC	Geomagnetic - field (magnetometer)	S
					Lei	Solar physics – X-rays (non-imaging cameras)	S
					UCL	Ionosphere - sporadic E (probes)	F

Table 8.14 A summary of SL129.

[78] Knott (1965), *The Drift of an Auto-Pilot Gyroscope Due to Prolonged Acceleration in the Skylark Rocket, Part 3*, p.9.
[79] FLIGHT magazine, 15 August 1963, p.258.

strength of the Earth's magnetic field at height.[80] This magnetometer was specially designed to be flown in Skylark rockets, and may have been similar to that flown on SL40 in September 1960. The experiment helped to investigate the 'dynamo theory' which postulated that observed ground level variations in the Earth's magnetic field were caused by sheet electric currents flowing through the upper atmosphere, maintained by the combination of the action of solar tidal winds and the effects of solar radiation. The advent of the first high altitude sounding rockets had allowed the Americans to test and develop the dynamo theory, starting with the first rocket experiment in 1951, and further experiments of this nature had been advocated by Chapman at the Oxford conference in 1953.[81]

Both SL129 and SL128 successfully reached 175 km (109 miles) high, thus flying through the E region of the ionosphere situated just above 100km. In order to reduce the effects of rocket magnetism and audio frequency interference, a pneumatic system was developed to deploy the proton magnetometer sensor from the rear of the head of the Skylark:

> After the rockets had passed through the dense atmosphere the spent motor was ejected, by means of three pneumatically operated plungers, and the probe was deployed to its full length of 20 feet [6 metres], at which range the residual magnetic fields associated with the rocket were negligible.[82]

On both flights, the proton magnetometers functioned satisfactorily and produced data continuously from the time of probe deployment until the sensing head was torn off as the rockets re-entered the Earth's atmosphere.[83] The first flight simply observed a decrease of magnetic field with height, but on the second flight, a significant magnetic discontinuity was recorded. These results were consistent with ground observations at the times of the two flights, and they established experimentally the existence of an electric current system in the *E* region of the ionosphere over South Australia.

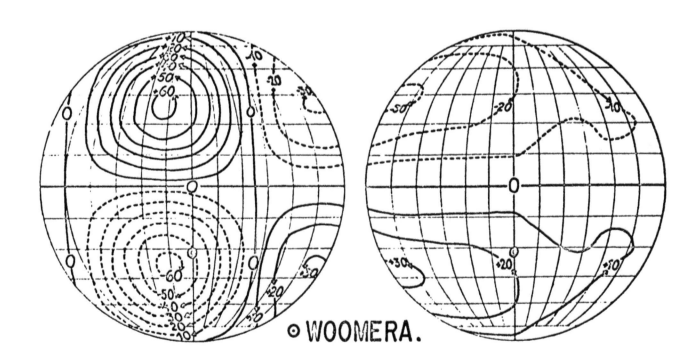

Figure 8.45 The position of Woomera at local midday and midnight relative to the world Sq (Solar quiet) current system at midday (left) and midnight (right). Woomera's position is shown by the small circle with the dot. The left hand map shows how the focus of the southern midday pattern passed very close to Woomera.

(Burrows & Hall (1965), figure 1) [84]

---

[80] Burrows & Hall (1965), 'Rocket Measurements of the Geomagnetic Field above Woomera, South Australia'. For a historical perspective, see Massey & Robins (1986), *History of British Space Science*, p.304.

[81] Chapman (1954), 'Rockets and the Magnetic Exploration of the Ionosphere', p.292.

[82] Burrows & Hall (1965), p.8.

[83] Ibid, p.11.

[84] Although clearly based on the upper half of Chapman (1954), 'Rockets and the Magnetic Explorartion opf the Ionosphere', figure 1.

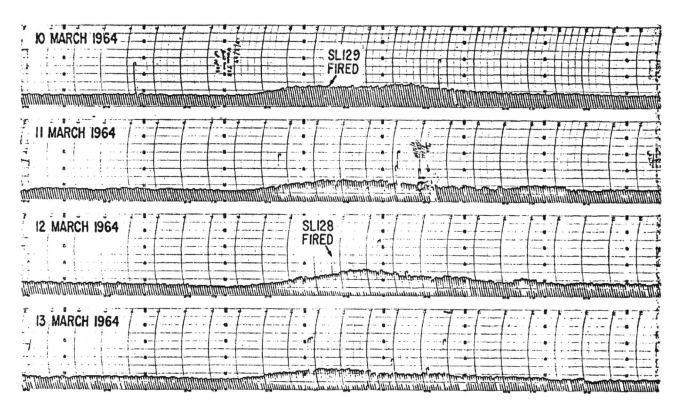

**Figure 8.46 Ground Proton Magnetometer records taken at Woomera,
indicating the local time and conditions when SL129 and SL128 were fired.**

(Burrows & Hall (1965), figure 4)

Ariel II

Also in March, on the 27th, the second joint UK/USA scientific satellite was launched into orbit by NASA. Its construction was similar to Ariel I, using the same components and sub-systems wherever possible, and as before the experiments were provided by the UK.

It had three main experiments on board, based on proposals not accommodated on Ariel I:

1. Measurements of galactic and extra-galactic radiation (Cambridge/Manchester Universities)
2. Measurement of ozone distribution in the high-atmosphere (Meteorological Office)
3. Detection of micrometeorites (Manchester University / Jodrell Bank)

All three of these experiments had been supported by earlier work on Skylark. For instance, the measurement of galactic and extra-galactic radiation (cosmic radio noise) used similar apparatus to that flown on SL82 and SL81A in 1962 and 1963. However on Ariel II the aerial used was 40 m, twice as long as that used on Skylark, and the rotation rate of the satellite had to be slowed from 55 rpm to 5 rpm to allow it to be deployed.[85]

The Ariel II ozone experiment was the responsibility of the British Meteorological Office at Bracknell. The ozone layer is situated at the relatively low altitude of about 25 km (15 miles), through which all Skylark rockets passed, and the Meteorological Office had launched their first ozone experiment on SL35 in November 1961. This had been followed by others on SL114 and SL115 in 1962 and 1963, and, as explained below, would be followed by another in two week's time.

The Space Research Group at the Nuffield Radio Astronomy Laboratories of the University of Manchester (Jodrell Bank) had developed a number of techniques for the investigation of the dust particles in space. Their Ariel II micrometeorite detection system used the same 'puncturing of thin aluminium foil' method that they had used on Skylark missions from 1961 to 1963 (SL37, SL35, SL114 and SL115). For Ariel II, four units were arranged around the equator of the satellite and utilised the light from the Sun and the spin of the satellite to scan the holes in the foil. Preliminary results indicated no micrometeorite-generated holes occurred, it was concluded the penetrating power of the average particle was very low, and the mass and density smaller than expected, hence "…the lifetime for the survival of thin surfaces is many orders of magnitude greater than that expected when the experiment was designed." [86]

---

[85] Hugill & Smith (1965), 'Cosmic Radio Noise Measurements from Satellite Ariel II', p.138.
[86] Jennison (1967), 'Some Penetration and Charge Detection Techniques', p.256.

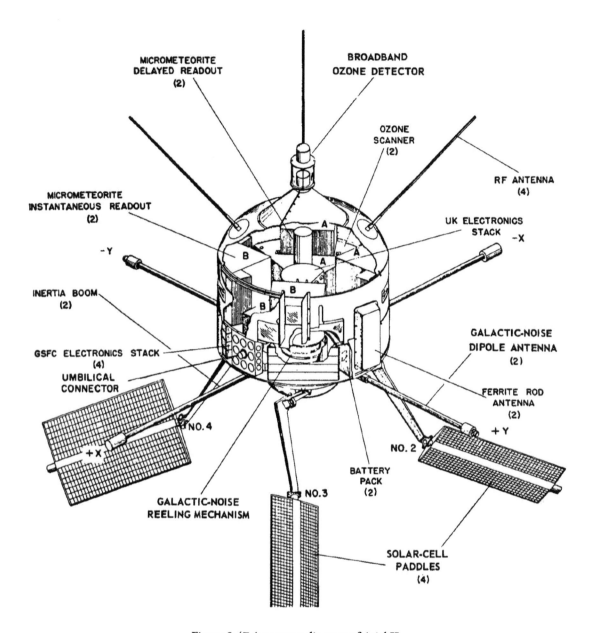

MICROMETEORITE
DELAYED READOUT
(2)

BROADBAND
OZONE DETECTOR

OZONE
SCANNER
(2)

RF ANTENNA
(4)

MICROMETEORITE
INSTANTANEOUS READOUT
(2)

UK ELECTRONICS
STACK
-X

-Y

INERTIA BOOM
(2)

GALACTIC-NOISE
DIPOLE ANTENNA
(2)

GSFC ELECTRONICS STACK
(4)

UMBILICAL
CONNECTOR

FERRITE ROD
ANTENNA
(2)

+Y

NO. 4

NO. 2

+X

GALACTIC-NOISE
REELING MECHANISM

NO. 3

BATTERY
PACK
(2)

SOLAR-CELL
PADDLES
(4)

Figure 8.47 A cutaway diagram of Ariel II.
(Mandell & Leverone (1964), figure 2-1)

The group involved also developed a charge-detection technique that had considerable possibilities. Unfortunately, although a rocket payload was prepared, the closing down of the group's activities in space research resulted in the premature abandonment of the project.

Useful data was received from Ariel II up to the end of September 1964, but in October, the satellite tape recorder ceased to work, and at about the same time the rotation of the satellite became so slow and irregular that no further useful results were obtained.[87]

11 April 1964   SL136

SL136 was launched on the 11th April 1964, two weeks after the Ariel II satellite. It had onboard just one experiment, a broadband ozone detector, a type used on Ariel II.

The launch of SL136 took place at 18:49 local time, and was timed to coincide with the passage overhead of the recently launched Ariel II satellite, which was taking similar ozone distribution measurements from further out.[88] The Skylark measurements helped calibrate those on Ariel II,[89]

---

[87] Miller & Stewart (1965), 'Observations of atmospheric ozone from an artificial Earth satellite', p.540.
[88] Morton (1989), *Fire across the Desert*, p.401.
[89] Massey & Robins (1986), *History of British Space Science*, p.95.

Seq. Nos	Launch date	Ref. (sponsor) launch site	Config-uration	Apogee km (miles)	Experi-menters	Experiments	Result
90 (5)	11 April 1964	SL136 (UK) Woomera (BS108)	Un, Rav.7 +C	202 (126)	MO	Aeronomy - ozone vertical distribution (broad-band detector)	S
					RAE	Test (Skylark technology) – vehicle attitude determination using solar and magnetic sensors	S

Table 8.15 A summary of SL136.

an example of how the new technology of satellites could be combined with that of sounding rockets.

The RAE attitude measurements revealed that unexpected attitude changes were probably caused by air-leakage from a compartment in the instrument head once in free space, although this does not appear to have caused a problem during ascent.[90]

---

14 May 1964   SL20

As noted in Chapter 6, as part of their research and development programme, it was the intention of the RAE to devote SL20 to the measurement of atmospheric pressure using a variety of pressure gauges.[91] This may have been done, however it is known it did have on board an RAE experiment to investigate the properties of liquid propane under conditions of zero gravity, part of a study of the suitability of liquid propane in satellite guidance systems.[92] In due course, the system developed was used to control the British X4/Miranda satellite launched in 1974.[93]

5th June - Blue Streak F1

There were no Skylark launches in June 1964, but at Woomera, another and very much larger rocket project was taking shape. The military version of the British Blue Streak rocket had been cancelled in 1960, but the vehicle had found a new role as the first stage of the 'Europa' satellite launch vehicle, under the auspices of the newly formed European Launcher Development Organisation (ELDO).[95] The military version of Blue Streak was originally due to have been launched in mid 1960 (the first had been on its way to Woomera at the time of the cancellation!), since then the project had been maintained at a tick over rate. Thus once the go ahead for Europa had been given, it was ready for flight-testing long before the corresponding French second and German third stages. Hence, it was decided to have a first phase of three launches of Blue Streak in its original configuration, as a proving exercise. These were designated F1, F2 and F3.

Blue Streak was a major rocket vehicle in its own right, the equivalent of the American Atlas.[96] Atlas had been the first stage booster for the vehicle that had launched the first US astronauts into orbit in 1962, and had also launched various

Figure 8.48 A propane 'boiler' as tested on Skylark.
(FAST \ author 100_6112)[94]

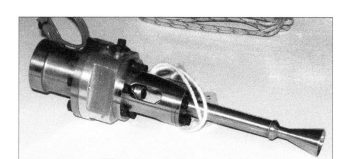

---

[90] Herbert (1967), *Determination of the Attitudes of the Skylark Rocket in Free Space*, p.6.

[91] RAE GW Dept. (1958), *A Brief Review of the C.T.V.5 Series III Programme*, p.5.

[92] 'FLIGHT International', 28 May 1964, p.911. In 1965, an article was published in the Journal of the British Interplanetary Society, concluding that propane was the best of 17 different vaporising liquids considered for a satellite cold gas propulsion and control system. (Briscoe (1965)).

[93] See Fearn (2005), 'Orbit-Raising Past and Present – the X-Series of Spacecraft and Artemis', pp.5 & 6.

[94] The propane boiler was on show when the author visited the 'FAST' museum at Farnborough UK in May 2011. Image reproduced courtesy of FAST (Farnborough Air Sciences Trust).

[95] For a good readable account of ELDO and Europa, see Hill (2001), *A Vertical Empire*, Chapter 8.

[96] Like Blue Steak, the United States Atlas had started out as a military rocket. Some 350 were built, many of which were converted to orbital launch vehicles after they had been removed from service as missiles.

	Skylark (SL02)	Black Knight (BK01)	Blue Streak (F1)
Take off weight	2,584 lb	13,000 lb	185,000 lb
Nominal Thrust	10,000 lbf (Raven IIA)[97]	15,600 lbf	270,000 lbf (RZ-2 x 2)

Table 8.16 A comparison of the Skylark, Black Knight and Blue Streak rockets.[98]

Moon missions. The Europa launcher was designed to place around one tonne into low Earth orbit, and the Blue Streak first stage was in a different league to Skylark, as Table 8.16 shows.

The launch facility for Blue Streak (Area 6) was on a correspondingly large scale. It had been built some ten miles (16 km) south of the Skylark launch area, on a steep cliff side overlooking a large dry salt lake, Lake Hart.[99] Following his appointment as operational "Officer In Charge of Area 6" (OIC6), Geoff Taylor recalls how he "… looked up in awe and some apprehension at the 42-metre tower looming above me, as high as a twelve-storey building…"[100]

Blue Streak F1 was installed in the tower in early March 1964, after which followed some three months of intensive preparation including a static firing. (The entire count down consisted of some 8000 operations and took nearly 48 hours, assuming no major hold-ups!)

This first launch was scheduled for Monday 25th May, but was postponed because of heavy cloud and then technical problems.

The whole town was by now aware of the impending launch of Woomera's biggest and most spectacular rocket to date. More especially, this event, unlike those of the past, would not be shrouded in secrecy from the wider public. A press party with UK representation had already visited the range; and unprecedented insight into our heretofore mostly clandestine activities.[101]

Figure 8.49 A Blue Streak being raised into its tower at Woomera.

(National Archives of Australia: A1200, L45080)

[97] See this book Table 3.1.
[98] SL02 figures from Table 3.1, BK01 from the data next to Figure 6.16, F1 from Hill (2001), *A Vertical Empire*, p.148.
[99] See the map Figure 4.8.
[100] Taylor (2000), *Flights of Fancy*, p.108.
[101] Taylor (2000), *Flights of Fancy*, p.114.

Figure 8.50 Liftoff for Blue Streak.
(National Archives of Australia: A1200, L48408)

To quote from an ESRO report:

> On the evening of 6 July 1964 ESRO went into space for the first time when the Skylark sounding rocket S01/1 was launched from the range at Salto di Quirra in Sardinia in the Mediterranean. By comparison with later payloads, the scientific and technological complexity was not great, consisting of ammonia and barium releases at altitudes of up to 200 km, but, in its own way, the payload was a microcosm of what ESRO was for and the way in which it was to work.
>
> The two experiments came from Germany and Belgium, the rocket used was British, the Project Scientist Austrian, the Project Engineer, Campaign Manager and Launch Team Leader French, the payload was integrated in the Netherlands, and the launch range, including most of the operational personnel, was Italian. It was, therefore, in the most real sense of the word, an international project.[104]

This first ESRO launch took place from Salto di Quirra on the Mediterranean island of Sardinia, an existing Italian military facility, used because ESRO's purpose built range at Kiruna in Sweden would not be ready until the end of 1966. At some time before March 1966 ESRO had been offered the free loan of the spare launcher at Aberporth,[105] but in the event, an existing launch tower at Sardinia was modified to accommodate Skylark rockets using Cuckoo boosters.[106] Here the first and second ESRO launches took place on the 6th and 8th July, the experiments on board were from the University of Liège in Belgium, and a Max Planck Institute in Germany. The altitude reached was nearly 200 km, and so Skylark became the first rocket launched into space by co-operative European effort.[107]

Finally, on 6th June 1964,[102] success was ours. Some thirty-five years later, I still remember the tremendous sense of excitement and relief as the great flaming rocket rose majestically off the launcher on our television screens and its roar, soon almost overhead, faded slowly away. I turned to see my own people and the twenty or so members of the trials team in the control room quite overcome with emotion, cheering, laughing hysterically and hugging one another, with many openly weeping. I rather think I shed a few tears myself as I congratulated my own crew and then went to shake hands with the Team Leader. A rare moment, indeed, the like of which I cannot remember either before or since. [103]

July 1964   S01/1, S01/2, **SL31, SL32**

On the 6th July 1964, the first launch of Skylark outside Australia took place.

---

[102] All other sources give this date as 5th June, so Geoff Taylor appears to have made an error here.

[103] Taylor (2000), *Flights of Fancy*, p.115.

[104] ESRO (1972), report SP-76, Introduction.

[105] See for instance the briefing document ref. DS/55/01dated 28 March 1966 circulated before the first Skylark Policy meeting in April 1966, para. 11.3, p.10. (TNA: PRO AVIA 92/144).

[106] Seibert (2006), *The History of Sounding Rockets and Their Contribution to European Space Research*, p.49.

[107] The firing of Blue Streak F1 the month before had been essentially a British and Australian operation.

Seq. Nos	Launch date	Ref. (sponsor) launch site	Config- uration	Apogee km (miles)	Experi- menters	Experiments	Result
92 (7)	6 July 1964	S01/1 (ESRO) Sardinia	Un, Rav.7 +C	198 (123)	Liège	Aeronomy – spectroscopic study of released ammonia cloud (experiment R12)	S
					MPI	Aeronomy – study of ion cloud produced by release of barium in sunlight (experiment R33)	S

Table 8.17 A summary of S01/1.

Skylarks **S01/1** and **S01/2** (launched two days later) were launched during evening twilight and carried identical payloads. "No problems were encountered during the design and integration of the payload except those which would normally be associated with a relatively inexperienced team working together for the first time".[108] (ESRO had only formally come into being less than four months previously). Both launches were successful, and released barium and ammonia vapour into the ionosphere at the nominal altitudes of 160 km (99 miles) and 200 km (124 miles). The ammonia releases produced brilliant torus shaped clouds that lasted about ten minutes, the barium releases less intense clouds that lasted 30 minutes.[109] There was no telemetry on the vehicle; these simple experiments had the advantage that only ground observations were needed.

Figure 8.51 Skylark S01/1, Europe's first cooperative space launch, clears the launch tower in Sardinia.[110]

[108] ESRO (1972), report SP-76, p.8.
[109] ESRO (1972), report SP-76, p.9.
[110] Photograph from ESA Bulletin Nr. 80, published November 1994, available online from *www.esa.int/esapub/bulletin/bullet80/inbrief80.htm*, last accessed August 2014.

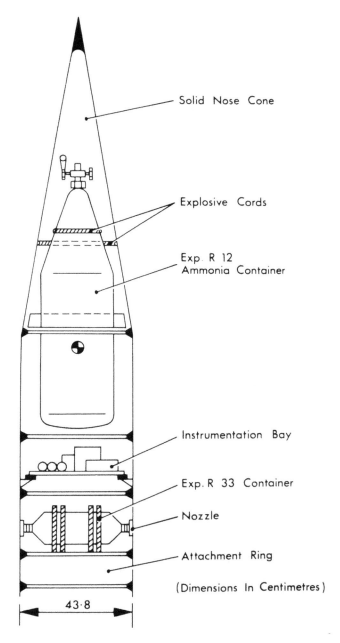

Figure 8.52 A diagram of payload S01, (as flown on both S01/1 and S01/2).
(ESRO (1972), report SP-76, p.11, figure 1)

The formation of ESRO

The concept of a European Space Research Organisation had been born in 1958, the idea being to create an organisation analogous to CERN, the European organisation for nuclear research. CERN was an institute devoted to research in high-energy nuclear physics, providing facilities too expensive to be funded by individual European nations. Its first major facility had come into operation in 1953 and had proved surprisingly successful. As a result, high-energy physicists in Europe were no longer at a disadvantage compared with their colleagues in America.

Within Europe, the UK was the most advanced in space science and launch capabilities, and British scientists in particular embraced the idea of European co-operation in these fields.[111] Professor H.S.W Massey, the original promoter of Skylark, played a key role in bringing about ESRO.[112] In 1960, meetings had been held in London and in Paris to move the concept forward. A Preparatory Commission was set up, chaired by Massey, and in 1962, ESRO was initiated at an inter-governmental meeting. Also in 1962, in parallel, a separate organisation, ELDO (the European Launcher Development Organisation) was established to develop a European space satellite launch facility based on the British Blue Streak rocket.

Unlike CERN, ESRO had to cover a wide range of scientific and technical disciplines, and did not have to be located at one single site (CERN's facility was on the Swiss – French border), and so ESRO could have an HQ and several individual centres. When NASA had been formed in 1958, there had been much political horse-trading between American States as to where the facilities would be situated, and in the same way, the selection of sites for the ESRO establishments caused considerable debate.

In the end the three main establishments, ESTEC (European Space Technology Centre), ESDAC (European Space Data Analysis Centre) and ESLAB (a Scientific laboratory) were located in Holland, Germany and Italy respectively,

[111] Massey & Robins (1986), *History of British Space Science*, Chapter 6.
[112] Fox (c.1984), *From Lardner to Massey – A history of physics, space science and astronomy at University College London, 1826 to 1975, (Space Research 1953-78).*

with the headquarters in Paris. The UK proposal that ES-TEC should be situated in Bracknell (35 miles southwest of London), was turned down on political rather than scientific grounds, because it was feared that such a location would give the UK too great an advantage, as it was already much further advanced in space science and technology than other member states.[113]

This decision was ironic given the subsequent lack of UK government support for ELDO and ESA.[114] This was elsewhere expressed as "The shadow of ELDO has fallen over ESRO in that Britain's "large share" of the ELDO launcher was the prime reason why the European Space Technology Centre had to be located elsewhere. History may show that we lost on the deal."[115] Indeed, it may be argued that the lack of an ESRO/ESA facility on British soil was a factor in the British political establishment subsequently turning its back on European cooperation in space activities.[116]

Meanwhile, the proposed scientific programme for ESRO comprised three parts: a sounding rocket programme with about 20 firings a year, a light satellite programme at the rate two or three a year, and a heavy satellite and space probe programme to start two years later at a rate of one to two a year.[117] Whilst ESRO was being established, a survey of available sounding rockets had been made, and a decision was taken to use the French Centaure and British Skylark rockets for the initial programme.[118]

SL31 and SL32 - The Skylark Gyroscope Drift Experiments conclude

July saw the completion of the RAE programme to investigate the drift characteristics of a typical autopilot gyroscope when subjected to prolonged acceleration. SL31 and SL32 were launched on the 15th and 17th July, each fitted with the complete gyro drift experiment comprising two gyroscopes, three X-band radio interferometers and an aerial survey camera. Both flights worked perfectly, SL31 reached an altitude of 264,000 feet (80 km / 50 miles) at +150 seconds and landed about 58 miles (93 km) downrange, SL32 reached 294,000 feet (90 km / 56 miles) and landed about 41 miles (69 km) downrange.[119] (Previous launches in the series had been SL28 and SL27 in 1962, SL29 in 1963, and SL30 in February 1964).[120]

Vehicle No.	Firing date	Camera bay	Doppler transponder	M.T.S. beacon	Roll control unit	
					Max. torque lb ft (nom.)	Max. roll rate rev/sec
SL28	29th Aug'62	Not Fitted	Fitted	Fitted	9	1.0
SL27	22nd Nov'62	Not Fitted	Not Fitted	Fitted	18	0.5
SL29	25th Jul'63	Fitted	Not Fitted	Fitted	18	0.5
SL30	20th Feb'64	Fitted	Not Fitted	Fitted	18	0.5
SL31	15th Jul'64	Fitted	Fitted	Fitted	27	0.33
SL32	17th Jul'64	Fitted	Fitted	Fitted	27	0.33

Table 8.18 SL32 was the final launch of the main gyro-drift test programme.
(From Knott (1964), p.16)

[113] Massey & Robins (1986), *History of British Space Science*, Annex 11, p.480, reproduces Dr O.Dahl's report on the location of ESRO establishments.

[114] ESRO evolved into ESA (the European Space Agency) in 1975.

[115] 'FLIGHT International' editorial, 7 June 1962. ('Flight' became 'FLIGHT International' in 1962).

[116] See Godwin (2007), Chapter 10 & Conclusion, for the political background.

[117] Massey & Robins (1986), *History of British Space Science*, p.120.

[118] Godwin (2007), *The Skylark Rocket*, p.196. In addition, Chapter 9 chronicles the surprisingly complex commercial, industrial and political factors that resulted in Skylark being used by ESRO.

[119] Knott (1966), *The Drift of an Auto-Pilot Gyroscope Due to Prolonged Acceleration in the Skylark Rocket, Part 4*, p.7.

[120] Knott (1968), *The Drift of an Auto-Pilot Gyroscope Due to Prolonged Acceleration in the Skylark Rocket (Abridged Version)*.

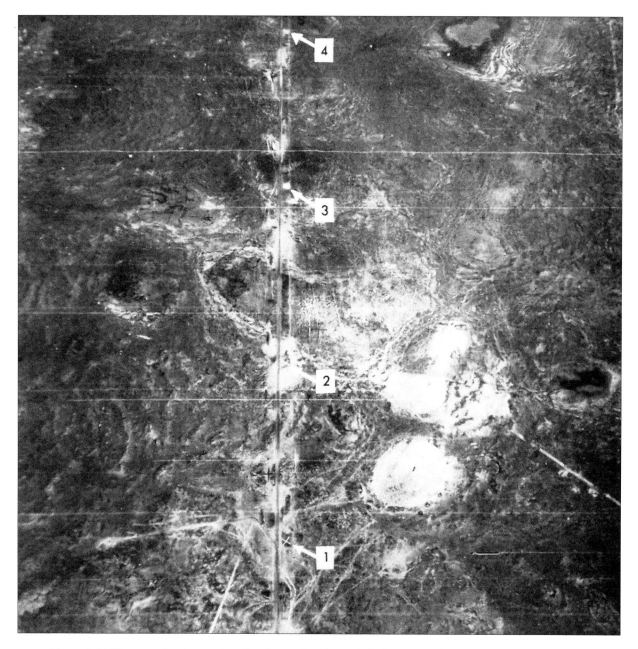

Figure 8.53 Photograph of ground marker flares taken from Skylark SL32 at about 7000 feet (2100 metres).
(Knott (1966b), figure 21)

The parachute recovery system operated correctly in both cases, allowing the cameras and film to be recovered. Photographs were taken at intervals of 0.5 seconds during the first minute of flight, that shown in figure 8.53 from SL32 must have been taken within ten seconds of launch. The white marker crosses were 80 feet (24 metres) across, the cross for marker 1 can be clearly seen. The distance between markers 2 and 3 was about three quarters of a mile (1.2 km). The camera is pointing down range at an angle of about 45 degrees, producing a foreshortening effect; markers 3 and 4 were in fact further apart than 2 and 3.

About 110 frames were exposed on each launch, the last from an altitude of about 180,000 feet (34 miles, 55 km) after some 75 seconds.[121] These pictures from half way to space would have been most interesting to see, but the author has not been able to locate them. The circular shapes in the photographs look like craters, but are dry lakebeds and other features of the local landscape. Surprisingly these features are still clearly visible on today's satellite imagery, although Google Maps for instance will not allow plain images to be reproduced in print – so finding the corresponding view of the ground features is left as an exercise for the reader!

---

[121] Knott (1968), *The Drift of an Auto-Pilot Gyroscope Due to Prolonged Acceleration in the Skylark Rocket (Abridged Version)*, figure 16.

(Hint - at the time of writing (2014) entering 'Woomera' into Google, and clicking on "Maps" at the top of the page will produce a map showing its location. Next, tracking North West past Lake Koolymilka and changing to satellite view will find the rangehead (still looking amazingly similar to that shown in Chapter 4) and continuing a short way along the centre line of the range will reveal a colour version of the view seen from SL32.)

Overall Results

The final report gave results for SL32 and SL27. For instance during the 34 seconds SL27 was accelerating, gyro drift in the yaw, pitch and roll axes was about 20 arc minutes in each case, equivalent to mean drift rates between 31 and 86 degrees per hour.[122] Results for SL32 were similar but showed slightly greater drift.[123] It was concluded that drift rates could be predicted from ground tests, and appeared to be controlled mainly by friction torques.

August 1964   SL301, SL121

The new stabilised payload system

In August 1964, **SL301** was launched from Woomera, its main purpose to test the new stabilised payload system. This was one of the most important enhancements to be made available for Skylark, its development had been expensive and taken several years, and is described in the next chapter.

The instruments flown had to be especially designed for the purpose. The Leicester equipment was mounted in the apex of the nose cone, and comprised a crystal X-ray spectrograph and a number of X-ray pinhole cameras for solar photography. The Culham experiments included two grazing incidence spectrographs, and a normal incidence spectrograph on gimbal mounts with a secondary stabilisation system of its own, aligned on the solar image.[124]

The UK Atomic Energy Authority's Culham Laboratory in Oxfordshire was a newcomer to Skylark, but they would soon become an important user of the new stabilised platform. Their laboratory at Culham was engaged in controlled thermonuclear research,[125] and by 1961, they had "…formulated a programme for carrying out observations of the solar corona by ultra-violet spectrographs carried above the Earth's atmosphere on rockets".[126] The idea was to augment their laboratory experiments by observing the naturally occurring plasma of the Sun,[127] however this hinged entirely on the provision of a stabilised Skylark payload, and it is apparent from the files that this was one of the reasons the Skylark ACU (Attitude Control Unit) development was funded in the first place.[128]

On the university side, the Leicester group included two instruments for solar X-ray studies, a pinhole camera to obtain X-ray images of the Sun, and a Bragg crystal spectrometer to study the detailed coronal X-ray spectrum. The pinhole camera in fact consisted of seven separate cameras, with a range of plastic and metal filters to yield images in different wavebands.[129]

Seq. Nos	Launch date	Ref. (sponsor) launch site	Config- uration	Apogee km (miles)	Experi- menters	Experiments	Result
96 (11)	11 Aug. 1964	SL301 (UK) Woomera	Sun, Rav.7 +C	145 (91)	RAE	Test (Skylark tech.) – first stabilised (Sun sensors)	S
					Cul	Test (instrument) - solar image control	S
					Cul	Solar physics – 2 grazing, 1 norm. incidence spectrograph	Ps
					Cul	Solar physics - UV (pin-hole camera)	F
					Lei	" " - X-rays (pin-hole camera)	S
					Lei	" " - solar X-rays (spectrograph)	S

Table 8.19 A summary of SL301.

[122] Knott (1968), *The Drift of an Auto-Pilot Gyroscope Due to Prolonged Acceleration in the Skylark Rocket (Abridged Version)*, figures 25 and 26, and table 5, p.27.
[123] Ibid, figures 27 and 28.
[124] Wilson (1965), 'First Launching of the British Stabilized Skylark', p.769.
[125] Of which the ZETA (Zero Energy Toroidal (or Thermonuclear) Assembly) device (which operated from 1954-58) at Harwell was best known.
[126] Letter dated 17 August 1961, from Cole of UKAEA to Goodson of Ministry of Aviation. (TNA: PRO document file AB 16/4342).
[127] The programme of stabilised Skylark rockets led to the discovery of many important emission lines and gave new information on the structure of the solar transition region. (Jordan (2004)).
[128] See for instance the letter dated 18 September 1961, from Clifford at the Ministry of Aviation to Cole of UKAEA. (TNA: PRO document file AB 16/4342).
[129] Pounds (1986), 'British X-ray Astronomy', p.438.

SL301 was launched from Woomera at 15:10 local time, and during the flight, the stabilisation worked well, acquiring the Sun 25 seconds after the separation of the motor and the detachment of the split nose cone, and pointing the payload towards the Sun throughout the flight to an accuracy of better than 10 minutes of arc. One of the Culham experiments included its own fine alignment system that in addition maintained the solar image to within 10 seconds of arc. Thus the primary purpose of the launch, to test the new stabilisation system, was achieved.[130]

Although the parachute failed to open, the photographic cassettes were recovered intact, although a number of films were fogged. Despite a camera jam, a successful sample spectrum was obtained, as well as X-ray solar photographs obtained with the Leicester pinhole cameras. Unfortunately, the Culham pinhole camera returned no useful results, although SL302 in December would be very successful.[131]

To sum up, the stabilised platform was essential for detailed solar observations in the ultraviolet and X-ray regions of the spectrum, and this flight marked the beginning of a series of state-of-the art studies in this new field.

SL121 followed nine days later. It had had a difficult time since arrival in Australia with SL120 in February. The two vehicles were identical, and were originally due to be fired in April a few days apart. However, after six weeks of technical problems with their payloads, they were finally withdrawn from firing because of problems in modifying ground equipment.[132] Having missed their launch slot, congestion at the launcher meant it was several months before a new firing date could be scheduled, although this did at least gave time

for the technical problems to be investigated further. Hence, on the 4th August, one of the instrumentation bays was lifted by helicopter to 1500 feet in order to assess the performance of the vehicle radio receivers in a relatively noise free environment.[133] The test proved satisfactory, but the firing of SL121 had to be postponed from the 13th August because of damage to the launcher caused by SL301 two days previously.[134] A week later, SL121 was finally launched.

The experiments

SL120 and SL121 were the first to carry a new pulse radio propagation experiment, as well as a continuous wave radio experiment that had been flown five times previously, (the last being the failed SL103 and SL104 in November / December 1963). Both experiments used an established method of ionospheric radio sounding, adapted for vertical sounding rockets, as an alternative to direct measurements of the ionosphere by rocket mounted probes.

The aim was to measure electron density and layer heights by two methods, and compare them with each other, as well as with a ground based ionospheric sounder.[135]

Although only partially successful this time, full success was achieved when the experiment repeated on SL120 a month later (see below), and the results led to similar observations being carried out on SL118 and SL119 in 1967.

The RAE vehicle attitude experiments would be repeated on SL48 in July 1965, as described in the next chapter, where a diagram showing a sample of the SL121 magnetometer output is included.

Seq. Nos.	Launch date	Ref. (sponsor) launch site	Config-uration	Apogee km (miles)	Experi-menters	Experiments	Result
97 (12)	20 Aug. 1964	SL121 (UK) Woomera (BS109)	Un, Rav.7 +C	192 (119)	UCW/RAE	Ionosphere - electron density (pulse propagation)	Ps
					UCW/RAE	Ionosphere - electron density (cw propagation)	Ps
					Lei	Solar physics – X-rays (2 pin-hole cameras)	S
					RAE	Test (Skylark technology) – vehicle attitude determination using solar and magnetic sensors	S

Table 8.20 A summary of SL121.

[130] Wilson (1965), 'First Launching of the British Stabilized Skylark Rocket', p.79.

[131] Burton (1969), 'Solar Photography in the Extreme Ultraviolet', p.63

[132] Telex from WRE to RAE, 22 April 1964. (WRE SL120 (sic) Trials Preparation file J5555/2/120).

[133] WRE (1964), *Trials Instruction BS113*. (SL120 Trials Preparation file J5555/2/120).

[134] Telex ref. SAL 13497 from WRE to RAE. (WRE SL120 Trials Preparation file J5555/2/120).

[135] WRE (1964), *Trials Instruction BS109*, p.22. (WRE SL120 Trials Preparation file J5555/2/120).

September 1964	SL137, **SL87A**, SL120, SL133, SL132

September was another busy month at Woomera, with five launches.

First away on the 1st was SL137, a repeat of SL136 in April, with another broadband detector for observing ozone distribution. Observations were probably linked to those from Ariel II, as indicated by this note in a Telex: "SL87A removed from launcher to allow SL137 to fire in conjunction with satellite Tuesday pm 1 Sept." [136]

SL87A was part of the continuing programme to develop a more powerful version of Skylark,[137] an exercise that was pushing the existing Skylark technology to the limit. The main purpose of this flight was to test the Raven VIA/Cuckoo motor combination carrying a head similar in length and weight to that of the forthcoming rounds designed for stabilised solar physics experiments.[138] It was the first flight of the Raven VIA, a version of the Raven VA with minor structural changes. The SL87A payload head was refurbished by WRE in Australia from that flown on SL87 twelve months previously, and as before (and with SL88 in February) included a linear displacement unit and full nose cone instrumentation. This time an

"ordinary 16 SWG full cone" was fitted,[139] the steel used was nearly twice as thick as the 20 SWG gauge used in the early days,[141] but when the change was introduced is not known.

The first attempt to launch SL87A was on Friday 28th August, but was abandoned because of low cloud. As noted above, it was then removed from the launcher to allow SL137 to be launched on Tuesday 1st September, but was returned to the launch tower and successfully fired at 10:50 local time on Friday the 4th.

The flight began normally, but at +32.8 seconds, an abrupt disturbance was seen on the telemetry records, followed by a sudden swing in direction to 34 degrees to the left of the existing flight path.[141] Despite this, after three minutes and forty seconds SL87A reached an apogee of 113 miles (182 km), and the head achieved a successful parachute landing 60 miles (96 km) down range - albeit on the southern edge of the range 31 degrees to the left of the aiming point and half the distance originally predicted.[142]

The head with nose cone attached was relatively quickly recovered and showed no flight damage.

However, the recovery of the payload head posed a mystery – if the head or nose cone had not caused the change of

Figures 8.54 and 8.55 The head of SL87A was recovered with only minor impact damage.
(WRE (1964), SL87A Trials Results file J555/3/87A)

[136] Telex from WRE to RAE, 28/8/64. (WRE SL87A Trials Preparation file J5555/2/87A).
[137] "…would like to keep priority on SL87A as sponsors are continually requesting greater altitudes." (Telex from RAE Space Dept. to WRE, 27/7/64, WRE SL87A Trials Preparation file J5555/2/87A).
[138] WRE (1964), *Advance Information on Skylark SL87A*. (WRE SL87A Trials Preparation file J5555/2/87A).
[139] WRE (1964), *Skylark No.87A Round Specification*. (WRE SL87A Trials Preparation file J5555/2/87A).
[140] As noted in Chapter 3, from Dorling (1959), *The First Six Skylark Firings* (GW 530), p.10.
[141] WRE (1964), *Skylark 87A (BS105/1), Summary of Firing*. (WRE SL87A Trials Results file J5555/3/87A).
[142] Ibid, p.4.

Seq. Nos.	Launch date	Ref. (sponsor) launch site	Config- uration	Apogee km (miles)	Experi- menters	Experiments	Result
99 (14)	04 Sept. 1964	SL87A (UK) Woomera	Un, Rav.6A +C	182 (113)	RAE	Test (Skylark technology) – first trial of Raven 6A / Cuckoo combination. First test of FPS16 radar transponder.	Ps

Table 8.21 A summary of SL87A.

```
SAL 17577

RECOVERY OF 8A MOTOR E E E OF 87A MOTOR AND FINS.

CONSIDERABLE AIR AND GROUND SEATCH HAS BEEN EMPLOYED TO RECOVER

REMAINDER OF 87A BUT TO DATE NO PIECES HAVE BEEN FOUND.

RADAR TRACKING OF TRANSPONDER IN HEAD GAVE GOOD INFROMATION

FOR ESTIMATION OF MOTOR IMPACT POINT AND I AM CONVINCED THE

CORRECT AREA IS BEING SEARCHED.

OUR PROJECTS PEOPLE HAVE AUTHORISED A FURTHER SEATCH OF

THE AREA ON OUR REQUEST I WILL KEEP YOU INFORMED.
```

Figure 8.56 A Telex from WRE to RAE, reporting on the continuing search for the motor and fins of SL87A.
(WRE (1964), Telex SAL 17577, SL87A Trials Results file J5555/3/87A)

direction during flight, then what had? The search was on for the motor and fins of SL87A, but this was not without its problems, as indicated in figure 8.56.

It appears to have been several weeks before the motor was eventually found, only a couple of miles short of where the head had landed.

The firing report concluded, "Most of the expansion cone was missing and the fibre-glass was loose and separated into its constituent filaments. The only reason found for the sudden disturbance at 34.8 secs was a failure of the motor when the thrust was close to the maximum." [143]

Thus, the advantage of a land range with its ability to recover evidence was demonstrated once more. In due course the expansion cone design was replaced by one made of steel, but apparently not until after a similar failure on SL322 two years later.[144]

SL120 was the second of the pair of rounds built to flight test the joint University of Wales/RAE Pulse experiment,

designed to measure electron densities in the ionosphere, and, as in the first round SL121 fired one month earlier, also included a C.W. (Continuous Wave) experiment to measure the same quantities simultaneously.[145]

The main difference between the two round configurations was the replacement of the normal Skylark metal nose cone by one made of fibreglass and the addition of a four foot long aerial for the Pulse receivers, mounted inside the nose cone.[146]

SL120 was fired on the 17th September, successfully reaching an altitude of 197 km (122 miles). All the equipment worked correctly and good signals were recorded throughout the flight, and so this time (unlike SL121), the radio experiments were successful. They showed that SL120 passed through the upper E layer at an altitude of 107 km (66 miles) and probably the F layer at around 183 km (114 miles).[147]

[143] WRE (1964), *Skylark 87A Summary of Firing*, p.6. (WRE SL87A Trials Results file J5555/3/87A).

[144] Minutes of the 4th Skylark Policy Meeting, February 1967, p.6, para. 3.3.1. (TNA: PRO AVIA 92/144).

[145] The pulse propagation experiment involved the reception at the rocket of hf and vhf radio signals from ground based transmitters. Comparison of the observed time delays of the hf (2-5 MHz) signals (refracted and reflected by the ionosphere) and those of the vhf (104 MHz) signals (effectively uninfluenced by the ionosphere) enabled the electron density/height profile in the ionosphere to be deduced. (Massey & Robins (1986), *History of British Space Science,* p.300).

[146] RAE Space Department (Feb.1965), *Radio Propagation Experiments using Skylark, Interim Report on Round SL.120*. (WRE SL120 Trials Results file J5555/3/120).

[147] Ibid, p.3.

Figures 8.57 and Figure 8.58 The Raven VI motor case of SL87A impacted vertically. The cause of the flight problem was revealed when the remains of the expansion cone were examined.

(WRE (1964), SL87A Trials Results file J555/3/87A)

After some ten minutes of flight the motor casing landed about 55 miles (89 km) downrange, where it was quickly found, but the payload proved more elusive. It needed to be located to recover Leicester's solar X-ray cameras, but two months later, it still had not been found despite extensive ground and air searches. Active searching was abandoned, although the recovery officer was instructed, "Head still needed however so will you please note to look in area specified when a recovery team is in that vicinity." [148]

Figures 8.59 and 8.60 SL120's spent motor casing was soon located 55 miles / 89 km downrange, although curiously, two months later the payload had still not been found.

(WRE (1964), SL120 Trials Results file J555/3/120)

[148] Correspondence 17 & 18 November 1964. (WRE SL120 Trials Results file J5555/3/120).

Century of Skylarks

CANBERRA. — T h e Weapons Research Establishment h a s launched its 100th Sky-lark rocket from Woomera.

The Acting Minister for Supply (Mr. Freeth) said yesterday the event was an important milestone in the space-research project.

It would be celebrated by Skylark men in Woomera, Adelaide and the United Kingdom.

The 100th Skylark performed successfully and reached a height of 109 miles, he said.

The first Skylark was launched in February, 1957, and since then firings have continued steadily, with a high success rate.

British

The Skylark is a British rocket used mainly for scientific observations and experiments in the upper atmosphere.

Solid propellant motors are used to carry instrumented heads, weighing a few hundred pounds, to heights of 70 to 150 miles.

The Royal Aircraft Establishment in the United Kingdom initiated the project and is responsible for vehicle design and many other aspects, such as co-ordination, planning and some of the manufacture and testing.

The Australian Weapons and Research Establishment is a partner in the project and is responsible for preparing and firing the rockets, conducting the trials and for other activities such as data reduction of the trials, records, buildings and some of the payloads.

Figure 8.61 The 100th Skylark made the main Melbourne newspaper.
(The Age, Thursday 1 October 1964, p.5) [151]

Woomera launches its 100th Skylark

September ended with the launches of SL133 and SL132 on the 24th and 29th respectively. Both carried identical payloads, which continued the Radio Research Station's investigation into the physics of the ionosphere.[149]

SL132 had the honour of being the 100th[150] Skylark launched from Woomera, a significant achievement since the first had been fired seven years earlier in 1957.

The following comment subsequently appeared in a letter from Space Department RAE in the UK to the Controller of WRE in Australia:

The firing of the 100th Skylark is an event which has not gone unnoticed here and we intend to hold a celebration at the end of this month. Needless to say, you and all the WRE Skylark team are invited! You can be with us in spirit if not in body.[152]

15 October 1964	SL47

Although the night-time launch of SL47 appears to have been successful, the astronomy experiments did not fare too well, see table 8.22.

Seq. Nos.	Launch date	Ref. (sponsor) launch site	Config-uration	Apogee km (miles)	Experi-menters	Experiments	Result
103 (18)	27 Oct. 1964	SL47 (UK) Woomera	Un, Rav.7 +C	146 (91)	UCL	Ionosphere - sporadic E (probes)	Ps
					UCL/Lei	Astronomy – non-solar X-ray Background (telescope)	F
					UCL	Astronomy – stellar UV emission (camera)	F

Table 8.22 A summary of SL47.

---

[149] Bramley, Bain & Davies (1965), 'Rocket Studies of aerial admittance and resonance rectification'.
[150] Although the 102nd overall, counting the two launched by ESRO from Sardinia in July 1964.
[151] Reproduced with permission.
[152] Letter dated 6 October 1964 from J.J.Gait to The Controller WRE. (TNA: PRO document file AVIA 92/147).

Figure 8.62 The Australian WRE Research Vehicles Group and others gather to celebrate the 100th Skylark launch.
(WRE \ Chris Hazell)

Seq. Nos.	Launch date	Ref. (sponsor) launch site	Config-uration	Apogee km (miles)	Experi-menters	Experiments	Result
104 (19)	17 Dec. 1964	SL302 (UK) Woomera	Sun, Rav.7 +C	167 (104)	RAE	Test (Skylark tech.) – attitude control (sun sensors)	S
					Cul	Solar physics - (spectrographs)	S
					Cul	" " - UV (pin-hole camera)	S
					Lei	" " - X-rays (pin-hole camera)	S
					Lei	" " - X-rays (spectrograph)	S

Table 8.23 A summary of SL302.

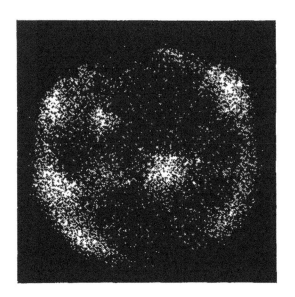
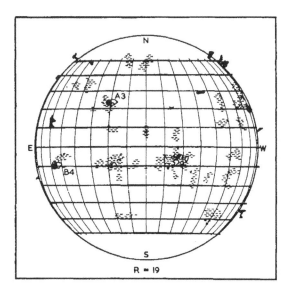

Figure 8.63 Left: A solar XUV image recorded by the Culham laboratory pinhole camera aboard SL302, together with (right) the Fraunhofer Institute solar map for the same day. The Culham laboratory images complemented those of the University of Leicester, as they included longer (XUV) wavelengths up to 230 Å [23 nm].[153] Although crude by today's standards, these were pioneering state of the art at the time, the Culham and Leicester photographs were the first non-smeared X-ray images ever obtained of the Sun.

(Burton (1969), figure 7)

---

17 December 1964   SL302

SL302 was the second launch of a stabilised payload. Not only was the stabilisation again a success, this time the parachute worked, and valuable scientific information was obtained.

These X-ray and XUV images of the Sun from the first stabilised Skylarks represented an important step in space science and provided new scientific information. They were the first such true images of the solar corona (outer atmosphere) because previous (US) photographs were obtained from sounding rockets whose roll was uncontrolled so the image was smeared over a circular arc. "Skylark ... was being used to obtain the first good-quality X-ray images of the solar

corona"[154] This was indeed the era when sounding rocket flights might make new discoveries.

Although the stabilised flights were primarily for spectroscopic solar physics studies, pinhole cameras were also included as experiments in these first stabilised Skylark payloads. Using these, soft X-ray photographs of the Sun were also obtained from the second and third flights, by both the Culham group and a group from Leicester University led by K.Pounds, pioneers in the new field of X-ray astronomy.[155]

The quality of such solar images from Skylark would soon improve, as described in the next chapter. Whilst the short observation time meant that sounding rockets were not the ideal platform for obtaining such astronomical images from

---

[153] Roughly speaking, UV (Ultraviolet) wavelengths are < 4000 Å (400 nm), XUV < 200 Å (20nm), soft X-rays < 100 Å (10nm), hard X-rays < 10 Å (1nm). (See Figure 6.20 for an overall view of the spectrum received from space).

[154] Pounds (2002), 'Forty Years on from Aerobee 150: a personal perspective', p.1905.

[155] See Massey & Robins (1986), *History of British Space Science,* p.339 onwards for further details.

space, they were the only method available until the launch of the first dedicated stabilised X-ray satellites from 1970 onwards, and they did have the significant advantage of being able to return exposed photographic film. From 1965 onwards the Stage 1 stabilised Skylark played an important part in the overall British space science programme, and until 1972 an average of four Stage 1 stabilised payloads were launched annually, as described in the next two chapters.

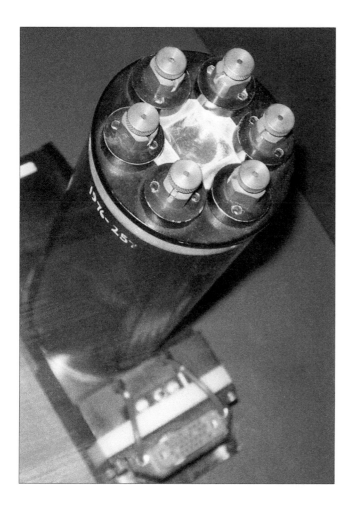

Figure 8.64 This design of X-ray pinhole camera from the University of Leicester flew on the first stabilised Skylarks, and successfully produced pioneering X-ray images of the Sun. The technique formed the basis for later, more sophisticated, missions.
(Science Museum object 1974-257, author 100_5203) [156]

Figure 8.65 A soft X-ray image of the Sun (in the 10-40 Å (1-4 nm) band) taken by such a pinhole camera on the Sun-stabilised Skylark SL302.[157]
(University of Leicester)

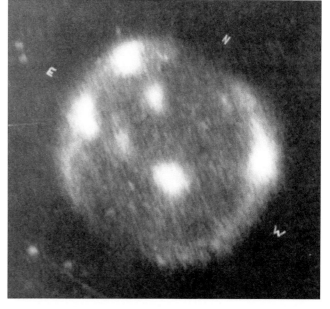

---

[156] Image taken at the London Science Museum, permission granted by Science & Society Picture Library.
[157] Image from University of Leicester (2010), *Fifty Years of Space Science at Leicester – A brief history*, p7, used with the kind permission of Professor Ken Pounds, University of Leicester. Details from Massey & Robins (1986), p346.

Figure 9.1 Using the 'grasshopper' [1] **(gate trolley) to load an unidentified Skylark instrument head at Woomera c.1966.**
(National Archives of Australia: A1500, K15122)

Figure 9.2 An unusual view - the launch tower shadow with the EC2 blockhouse on the left.
(WRE)

[1]   See for instance WRE (1974), *Trials Instruction No. BS217 (SL1012)*, p.79.

CHAPTER 9

(1965-66)

MANY DEGRESS OF USEFULNESS

In 1965, the annual number of Skylark launches jumped by 50% to a record of 28, before temporarily declining over the following three years. However, the numbers of stabilised flights increased steadily:

During 1965 and 1966, work on improving the Skylark rocket vehicle continued and a new rocket range was introduced by ESRO. As the programme matured (1967 would see the tenth anniversary of the first Skylark launch), the number of users increased. By 1966, there were active space science groups in about 17 UK universities and some nine SRC and government establishments.[2] Towards the end of this four-year period, the UK also introduced two smaller and cheaper sounding rockets.

Proposals for a second Australian launch tower

As noted in the previous chapter, operational pressure on the Skylark launch tower had increased significantly as the number of Skylark launches at Woomera had grown. In 1964, the WRE (responsible for launching Skylark), had confirmed that in the near future they would like to take up their option on the surplus Skylark launcher at Aberporth.[3] This proposal was supported by the RAE, and in January 1965, a comprehensive document was issued by the UK Ministry of Aviation supporting the case.[4] This cited improved operational flexibility, lack of time for mending firing damage and carrying out preventative maintenance, and mentioned "minor damage, mainly to the rails, put the launcher out of action for six weeks in the past year". It also revealed that the original cost of the launcher had been £45,000, and the cost of a new one would be some £60,000, the installation of which WRE hoped to be able to fund.

The proposal was dated 7 January 1965, and was due to be tabled in March, but despite the increase in the numbers of launches at Woomera in 1965 (23 compared to 17 in 1964) the matter dragged on. The minutes of the Fourth Skylark Policy meeting (February 1967) reveal it was eventually rejected on financial grounds, "...this could not be supported by Space 1 under the present financial climate and firing programme."[5] The temporary decline in the annual numbers of Skylark launches (as shown in above), contributed to this decision.[6]

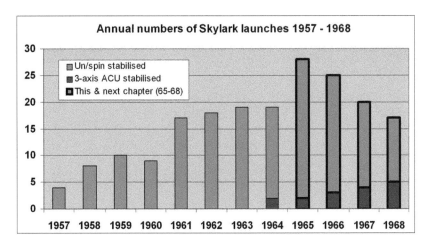

Annual numbers of Skylark launches 1957 - 1968

Figure 9.3 The annual numbers of Skylark launches up to 1968, that is until the end of the next chapter.

---

2   Massey & Robins (1986), *History of Space Science,* p.220.
3   Report on visit to Australia 12 February – 4 March 1964 (Secret) by R.Anderson of the UK MoA, p.5. (TNA: PRO document file AVIA 92/147).
4   "Case for a Second Skylark Launcher at WRE Woomera", document reference DS/55/01. (TNA: PRO document file AVIA 92/146).
5   Minutes of the 4th Skylark Policy Meeting, February 1967, p.15, para.3.13.3. (TNA: PRO document file AVIA 92/144).
6   Ministry memo dated November 1964. (TNA: PRO document file AVIA 92/146). Sir Humphrey (of 'Yes Minister' fame) would have been proud of this memo, containing as it did phrases like "After reading your draft case my immediate reaction to the second launcher proposal is that while it is obviously desirable it cannot be described as essential", and "On motor proving rounds he questioned the need for new types of Raven Motor"[!] ("... the very viability of Skylark as a research tool has rested on the production of ever better motors." (Dorling, 1975)).

Funding changes

Meanwhile, a major administrative change for Skylark scientific research funding had occurred in the UK, when at the start of 1965, the new Science Research Council (SRC) was created.

The background was that in the late nineteen fifties and early sixties governments were struggling to come to terms with the problem of 'big science'[7]. Typical of these was the field of physics, where military work during the Second World War had accelerated the trend towards large-scale scientific and industrial research projects too expensive for individual universities, companies, or even countries to afford. Thus, the pan-European CERN particle physics project came into being in 1954, and at the national level in the UK, various nuclear physics facilities were established.

Space research was a similar activity. Like many significant and disruptive new technologies, this had started from small beginnings, and like the development of aircraft before the First World War in the UK, had grown outside any single government organisation.

Hence, by 1961 the structure that had been set up to deal with the management and financial administration of the British space research programme had become quite complex and the establishment of ESRO threw a greatly increased burden on the system.[8] In 1962, the UK government had set up the 'Trend' committee to examine the question of support for civil science in Britain. This had resulted in the creation of the Science Research Council (SRC).

The SRC was part of the Department for Education and Science, through which the UK's budget for pure scientific research (now centralised) would flow. The SRC became responsible for allocating funds between space research, nuclear and particle physics and astronomy. This replaced the previous arrangement, whereby space science research funding had been directed via the Office of the Minister of Science to the Space Research Steering Group and then the BNCSR.[9]

As a non-civilian facility, the RAE remained under the Ministry of Aviation (itself absorbed by the Ministry of Technology in 1967); however Woomera continued to be funded directly by the British and Australian Governments, under successive Joint Project financial agreements.

The stabilised payload system

As noted in the previous chapter, the stabilised payload system was one of the most important enhancements to be made available for Skylark:

> Attitude stabilisation transformed the vehicle from a carrier of equipment to high altitudes to a sophisticated facility allowing astronomical instruments ... to be aligned accurately on the sun and selected stars. This capability led to Skylark becoming the forerunner of the astronomical satellites Ariel 5, Ariel 6, and the International Ultra-violet Explorer (IEU).[10]

For simplicity and cheapness, Skylark had originally been designed as a fin stabilised rocket. This meant that once out of the atmosphere in the near vacuum of space it had no guidance, and could spin and tumble. Thus, it was of limited use for those who wanted to study the Sun and stars.[11] However, the need for attitude control had been evident to scientists from the earliest days in 1955, even before Skylark was first launched.[12] By 1959, several scientific proposals for solar and astronomical observations had been made, all of which required a stabilised observation platform. These included astronomy experiments to photograph the Sun in X radiation and ultraviolet light, and the detection of ultraviolet emissions from stars.

The first steps had already been taken by the RAE by 1960, as during that year they had exhibited an attitude control set using gyroscopes, designed to control the head of the Skylark about three axes by compressed air jets:[13]

> The control system was built by Keith Goddard in Earl's section. It used thermionic valve amplifiers with a phase advance network to drive the control valves from the signals derived from two gyroscopes. Although the amplifiers (completed in 1958) still used thermionic valves, the inverter to produce the high tension was a self-oscillating transistor type. This was a curious mixture, which marked the amazingly rapid rise of transistors in the guided-weapons field. The inverter was built and tested by Cliff Woodcock in room 301 of Q134 building....

> Two of these control systems were launched on Skylark before 1961. Unfortunately, on the first occasion the Skylark head, which was the part to be controlled,

---

[7]   "Big science" is a convenient and descriptive term then coming into use, for instance by Massey & Robins (1986), *History of British Space Science,* p.211.

[8]   See for instance Massey & Robins (1986), *History of British Space Science,* p.210.

[9]   For details, see Massey & Robins (1986), Chapter 10, and Godwin (2007), *The Skylark Rocket,* Chapter 8. There are some useful diagrams in Godwin pages 289 and 290.

[10] Massey & Robins (1986), *History of British Space Science,* p.192. © Science and Engineering Research Council 1986, published by Cambridge University Press, reproduced with permission.

[11] SL43 (May 1961) had used uncontrolled sky scanning, but painstaking analysis of the data had been required.

[12] Interested scientists had met at Massey's rooms at University College London (UCL); see Massey & Robins (1986), p.192.

[13] Massey & Robins (1986), *History of British Space Science,* p.194.

failed to separate, and, with the whole rocket case attached, the torque-to-inertia ratio was too low for control to be achieved before exhaustion of all the nitrogen. On the second attempt, premature opening of the recovery parachute caused a similar failure. However, telemetry records indicated that the control system had, within the constraints imposed on it, performed well.[14]

It was a complex device, and it became clear that a considerable amount of development work was still required. The gyro had to be caged during boosted flight in order to prevent it tumbling, and it therefore 'pointed' in an arbitrary direction when released, and in the subsequent development it was replaced by sensing elements which detected the position of the payload with respect to various heavenly bodies.[15]

Following subsequent consultation and analysis, in 1961 a staged development programme was proposed. This started with the simplest form of stabilisation, and proceeded to stages that were more refined.[16] Each stage would be complete in itself, and capable of meeting a particular scientific need, although contributing to the development of the next. The stages were:[17]

Stage 1 – To achieve pointing at the Sun with errors of less than two degrees, using the existing RAE air jet control system.

Stage 2 – Using more sensitive detectors to allow pointing at the Moon.

Stage 3 – Increase of Sun and Moon-pointing accuracy to minutes of arc rather than degrees.

Stage 4 – The use of horizon detectors to allow alignment to the local vertical, to facilitate Earth and atmospheric observations.

Stage 5 – Using a combination of techniques to lock on to preselected stars.

In late 1961, a design study contract was place with Elliott Bros. Ltd.,[18] which marked the start of a major collaborative effort between that company, the RAE, and groups of interested scientists:

Prior to the decision the programme was in the doldrums. Thereafter it went ahead with new vigour. Many new possibilities were opened up for the experimenters, and a potent new group had joined them. Perhaps as important was the change to a customer/contractor relationship on Skylark between the BNCSR and the Ministry of Aviation, with the placing of the contract with Elliot Bros. The relationship was to grow, eventually leading to the placing of a contract by the Ministry with BAC (Filton) for the construction of all Skylark payloads.[19]

Subsequently a full development contract for Stages 1 and 3 was placed with Elliotts. Work started in 1962 and the first prototype system was flight tested on Skylark SL301 in August 1964.

Flight proving

As discussed at the end of the previous chapter, the SL301 Stage 1 proving flight had also included experiments from the Culham Laboratory of the UK Atomic Energy Authority,[20] and from Leicester University. Although the parachute system failed, photographic cassettes from the experiments on board survived the impact, allowing some recorded observations to be recovered.[21]

A lot of hard work had gone into the design and development of the stabilisation system, those involved were delighted that it had worked first time, and the following comment appeared in a letter from Space Department RAE in the UK to the Controller of WRE in Australia:

> The success of the sub-stabilised [sic] round SL301 has acted like a shot-in-the-arm to all concerned at this end and the Royal Society has even set up a small panel to discuss the possibility of developing a star-pointing system.[22]

This first launch was soon followed by SL302 and 303 in December 1964 and April 1965 respectively, both of which were completely successful – including the parachute landing! As described below, SL303 was particularly successful.

[14] Bryan Day, personal correspondence, May 2009.

[15] Cope (1964), 'The Attitude Control System of the Skylark Sounding Rocket', p.285.

[16] Ibid, p.198.

[17] For an interesting account of how this list was derived by J.Hosie, see see Dorling (1991), *Reminiscences of the Mullard Space Science Laboratory to 1991*, pp.69-70.

[18] Elliott's Frimley establishment was just up the road from RAE Farnborough. Elliott were a then large organisation in their own right (35,000 employees and over 100 specialised companies), and produced mainframe computers as well as avionics. Through a complex series of corporate takeovers and mergers (English Electric -> GEC-Elliott-Automation -> Marconi Avionics -> etc), the company has in effect been absorbed into BAE Systems.

[19] Dorling (1991), p.70.

[20] This aspect of UKAEA research was aimed at eventual control of nuclear fusion (the process that powers the Sun and stars), including a detailed understanding of the behaviour of plasmas in the laboratory and by extension in the solar corona. (Massey & Robins (1986), p.197). Fusion research continues at Culham to this day, see *www.ccfe.ac.uk* . (Last accessed August 2014).

[21] Massey & Robins (1986), *History of British Space Science*, p.201.

[22] Letter dated 6 October 1964 from J.J.Gait to The Controller WRE. (TNA: PRO document file AVIA 92/147).

A typical stabilised flight

During flight, stabilisation of the payload head occurred after separation from the main body of the Skylark vehicle. Usually this occurred about 77 seconds after launch, at an altitude of some 84 km (52 miles). The control system then came into operation, and the attitude was stabilised by about

111 seconds from launch. It was held for some 270 seconds (4.5 minutes) during which the altitude of the head rose to about 193 km (120 miles) and fell back to 72 km (45 miles). Finally, the attitude control unit was separated from the scientific part of the payload, which alone was parachuted to the ground. (In later missions, the rather expensive ACU was also recovered).

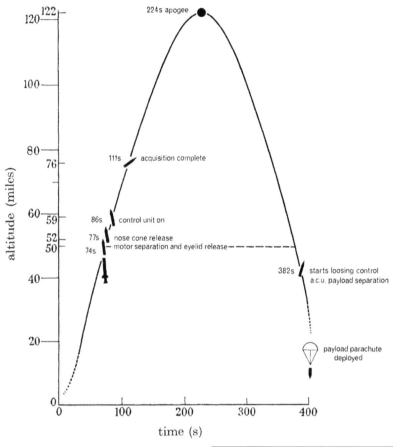

Figure 9.4 A typical stabilised Skylark trajectory.

(Thomas (1969), figure 7) [23]

Figure 9.5 The Skylark 'Stage 1' attitude control unit, designed as a standard Skylark bay. (The large sphere is the pressure vessel containing not only the propellant gas but also the poppet valves for the control jets.)

(Elliott Bros (1964), plates 1 & 2)

[23] Reproduced courtesy Royal Society London.

The attitude control unit in its bay on the separated payload worked as follows. The deviation from alignment with the Sun was detected by silicon solar cells mounted on its side. Signals from these, together with stabilising signals from rate measuring gyroscopes, controlled on/off poppet valves. The valves released high-pressure nitrogen thorough pairs of jets to align the axis of the head with the Sun. Stability about the third axis, longitudinal roll, was controlled by separate gas jets operated by a rate gyro and a magnetometer, which detected the Earth's magnetic field.

The pointing accuracy of the Stage 1 system exceeded that expected, in both absolute terms and steadiness in operation. For instance during the first flight, the head was kept pointed towards the Sun with an accuracy of better than 10 arc minutes,[25] a factor of about 10 better than the 1 to 2 degrees originally specified. (An arc minute is 1/60 of a degree). This success was a significant milestone in the enhancement of Skylark, which appears to have had the first 3-axis stabilised sounding rocket payload system available anywhere.

Attitude Control Unit Stage 3

Meanwhile, development of the Skylark attitude control unit continued. Stage 2 was skipped, and work started on the development of Stage 3, the version for more accurate Sun and Moon pointing. The first launch of this took place on SL403 in July 1968 (described later in this chapter). However, continuing work on Stage 1 improvements made it clear that Stage 3 accuracy could be achieved without the complexity of the Stage 3 system, and development was terminated after only four units had been produced. The last of these was flown on SL402 in October 1972.

In order to improve pointing accuracy, the Stage 3 version introduced the idea of moving the 'fine sun sensors' forward from the skin of the ACU bay to be adjacent to the scientific equipment in the nose.

This concept was subsequently introduced to the Stage 1 system, and the first flight that included this upgrade appears to have been SL601 in December 1968.[27]

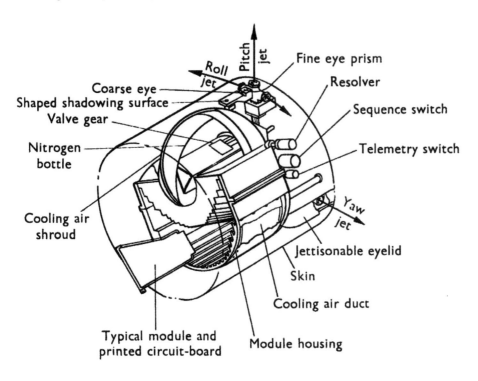

Figure 9.6 The Stage 1 attitude control bay.
(Cope (1964), figure 7a.) [24]

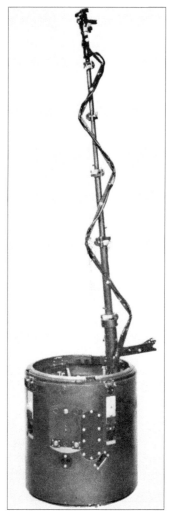

Right: Figure 9.7 The Skylark Stage 3 Attitude Control Unit.
(Thomas (1969), figure 10) [26]

[24] Journal of the British Interplanetary Society, Vol.19 no.7 (Jan.-Feb.1964), p.290. Reproduced with permission.
[25] Dorling (1975), 'Early History of the Skylark Rocket', p.184.
[26] Reproduced courtesy Royal Society London.
[27] BAe (1990), *Record of Skylark Launches 1957-1990*.

Attitude Control Unit Stage 5

Once more, a development stage was omitted,[28] and in 1967, a contract was signed with Elliott Bros. for the development of Stage 5, the version that could point to specified stars. The first prototype was flown on SL811 on 16 July 1970, and so Stage 5 is discussed at the start of Chapter 11.

The BAC [29] role expands

As explained in previous chapters, the first Skylarks had been individually built at RAE Farnborough using, wherever possible, proven and readily available missile components. Later the design was developed along the lines of unit construction and the main components standardised to facilitate their supply by industry.[30] However, the growing rate of Skylark launchings (from four in 1957 to nineteen in 1963) had placed an increasing burden on the RAE and Ministry of Aviation departments. The arrival of ESRO as an additional customer, and the possible need to release staff for new space projects at RAE, accelerated the decision to transfer as much as possible of the routine side of the work to industry. [31]

The assembly of 'fore bodies' with payloads for the Royal Society rounds (excluding grenade heads) had already been placed with BAC in 1960,[32] and by the end of 1964 they had prepared 17 Skylarks.[33] Also in 1964, it had been agreed that the then operational standard of vehicle build (Mk.I) should be transferred to BAC who would act as Design Authority, Prime Contractor and MoA (Ministry of Aviation) Industrial Agent for sales.

Formal contacts to this effect were placed in 1965,[34] although the RAE kept its role as the Skylark Research and Development Authority. The RAE also retained responsibility for the stabilised design (the Mk.II vehicle with an attitude control unit), then under continuing development, until that too would be ready for transfer to industry.

By then BAC had released the news, as in November 1964 it was reported:

British Aircraft Corporation announced on October 22 that a contract had been received from the Ministry of Aviation under which BAC assumed responsibility for the Skylark research sounding-rocket project. The announcement continued:-

"Hitherto the Royal Aircraft Establishment, Farnborough, has been responsible for Skylark, the manufacture of components having been sub-contracted to industry, including British Aircraft Corporation, which has assembled some of the rounds carrying Royal Society experiments.

Under the new contract, British Aircraft Corporation will take over the responsibilities undertaken by the Royal Aircraft Establishment and will be able to provide a complete service to customers for their Skylark sounding rocket, including advice on the engineering of their experiments, supply and assembly of the rockets, analysis of trajectory and attitude during flight, and delivery of the raw experimental data. It is hoped that at a later date the Corporation will be able to arrange for launch preparation and firing...The Skylark project will be based on the Bristol works of the British Aircraft Corporation's Guided Weapons Division" [35]

---

[28] This simple statement hides a complicated background; the decision was in fact the culmination of a complex series of cost, timescale, technical and scientific factors. For details, see Godwin (2007), *The Skylark Rocket,* p.209.

[29] The British Aircraft Corporation (BAC) had been formed in 1960 from English Electric Aviation, Vickers-Armstrong, the Bristol Aeroplane Company and Hunting Aircraft.

[30] At Farnborough, final assembly of most Skylarks had been carried out by the Space Department in building Q65 (built in 1915!), from a multitude of components supplied by some 20 subcontractors.

[31] See for instance the briefing document ref. DS/55/01 dated 28 March 1966, circulated before the first Skylark Policy meeting in April 1966, p.1, (TNA: PRO document file AVIA 92/144).

[32] Contract placed 29 December 1960; the first BAC prepared round (SL45) was launched 20th June 1962.

[33] BAe (1990), *Record of Skylark Launches 1957-1990.*

[34] Briefing document ref. DS/55/01, p.2. (TNA: PRO document file AVIA 92/144).

[35] 'FLIGHT International' 12 November 1964, p.840.

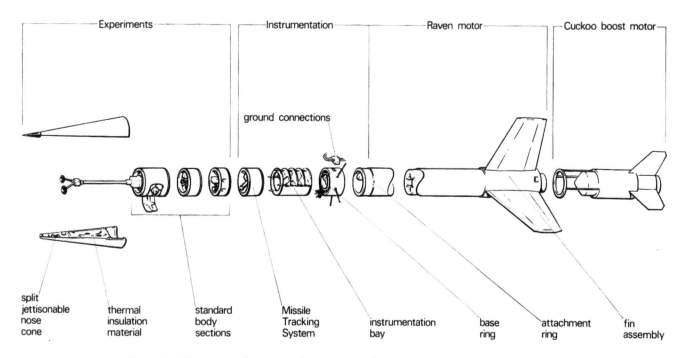

Figure 9.8 To support their new role, BAC started to produce sales and user literature, a brochure produced a little later included this exploded view of Skylark with Cuckoo boost.
(BAC (c.1966), p.6)

SKYLARK LAUNCHES AND SCIENCE IN 1965

1965 was the busiest year to date for Skylark, with 28 launches, nearly 50% up on the previous year, with the numbers of both UK and ESRO funded launches increasing. This was a launch rate of just over one every two weeks, which must have kept the worldwide supply chain busy, and was only possible because BAC had now taken over the manufacturing from the RAE. On the university side, the number of astronomy experiments began to increase, although most flights were still concerned with the physics of the upper atmosphere through which Skylark travelled.

On 22 February 1965 BAC announced they had received an order worth some £200,000[36] for the supply of 20 Skylarks, their first order since being appointed selling agents the previous October.[37]

In the wider world, on May 12th 1965, Luna 5 became the second Soviet spacecraft to reach the surface of the Moon, following Luna 2 in 1959. It was intended to be the first lunar soft-landing, but the retro-rockets failed to operate, and it crashed onto the surface.

Jan.	Feb.	March	April	May	June	July	Aug.	Sept.	Oct.	Nov.	Dec.
	SL88A	SL87B	S03/2	SL361		SL106	S05/1	SL88B	S04/2	SL130	SL131
		SL140	SL303	SL139		SL48		S04/1	SL39		
		SL141	SL464	SL138		SL105			SL306		
		S03/1	SL363								
			SL364								
			SL461								
			SL462								
			SL463								
			SL362								

Table 9.1 The 28 Skylark launches in 1965. (For individual details see Appendix 3.)
(Key: black = test launches, blue = UK national programme (unstabilised), plum = UK (stabilised), pink = ESRO programme)

---

[36] Where £200,000 in 1965 was worth £3 to £8.4 million by 2011, i.e. each of the 20 vehicles cost the equivalent of £150,000 to £420,000. (2011 figure derived using the "Historic Opportunity" and "Economic Cost" measures for a large project, from Lawrence H. Officer and Samuel H. Williamson, "Five Ways to Compute the Relative Value of a UK Pound Amount, 1270 to Present," MeasuringWorth, 2014, *www.measuringworth.com/ukcompare/* , last accessed August 2014).

[37] FLIGHT International, 4 March 1965, p.349.

---
25 February 1965   SL88A

SL88A and the Raven VI motor

1965 began with the **SL88A** proving flight, a trial very similar to SL87A the previous September, and the second to test the new Raven VIA sustainer motor.

This new version of the Raven motor was officially called the Raven VIA, but it appears to have been more generally known simply as the Raven VI, perhaps because no Raven VIB appeared. Having evolved from the Raven V, it was more powerful than the higher numbered Raven VII. With the same burning time of 30 seconds, it had a nominal thrust of 15,000 lbf (66.5 kN), compared to some 10,000 lbf (44.5 kN) for the Raven VI.[38]

The greater height it could achieve for a given Skylark payload was of particular benefit for astronomy experiments, because significant attenuation of some wavelengths of interest took place even at 150 km and above.[39] In addition, the weight of the new stabilisation system was an unwelcome overhead, so beginning with the fourth stabilised flight, (SL306 in October 1965), the Raven VI became used as standard on all stabilised payload launches. In due course, it became the most popular Raven version,[40] with 138 successful flights by August 1990.[41]

The SL88A payload head had been re-built by the RAE in Farnborough from the recovered head of SL88 that had been fired in February the previous year.[42] SL88A was mainly intended to prove the structural modifications carried out to convert the Raven VA to a Raven VIA,[43] and as noted above, was the second such flight trial. Launch at Woomera took place on schedule,[44] on the 25th February, at 11:32 local time, preceded by only a minor delay. See Figure 9.10.

Main variations		Minor structural changes
Raven II (1958)	▶	Raven VII (1962)
▼		
Raven V (1961)		
▼		
Raven VA (1962)	▶	**Raven VIA/VI (1964)**

Table 9.2 The evolution of Skylark's Raven sustainer motor.
(**Bold** = more powerful variants)

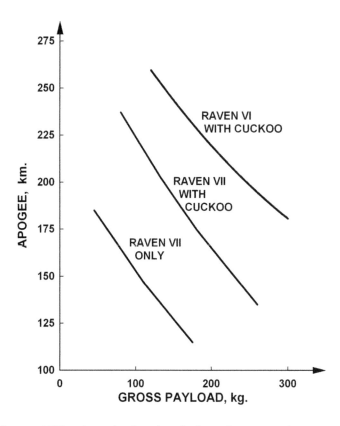

Figure 9.9 This diagram shows how the more powerful Raven VI motor could enhance Skylark's apogee, compared to the earlier Raven VII. The time above 80 km typically increased from 300 to 350 seconds.
(After Hazell, Cope & Walker (1968), fig.1)

---

[38]   RPE Westcott, (1968), *Index to Solid Propellant Motors*, p.15. (The figures for Raven VII have been taken from those for the similar Raven VIII).

[39]   At 150 km the atmospheric transmission factor for the XUV wavelength of 400Å (40nm) was only 0.3, for discussion of the figures involved see the paper by Burton (1969),'Solar Photography in the Extreme Ultraviolet', section 4, p.58.

[40]   See for instance the proposal "Standardisation on the Raven Mk.VI A Motor for Skylark", Appendix 2 of the minutes of the 3rd Skylark Policy Meeting November 1966. (TNA: PRO document file AVIA 92/144).

[41]   BAe (1990), *Record of Skylark Launches* 1957-1990.

[42]   WRE (1965), *Press Release Skylark 88A*. (SL88A Trials Preparation file J5555/2/88A).

[43]   WRE (1965), *Advance Information on Skylark SL88A*, p.1, (SL88A Trials Preparation file J5555/2/88A).

[44]   The week commencing 22/2/65, according to p.2 of WRE (1965), *Trials Instruction No.BS116*. (SL87B Trials Preparation file J5555/2/87B (sic)).

SEQUENCE WAS HELD AT MINUS 3 MIN 45 SEC FOR 15 MIN DUE BUTTING

CONNECTOR 4 PIN IN HEAD RELEASE AND MONITOR LINES NOT MAKING

CONNECTION. THIS NEARLY COST US SLOT.

LAUNCHER APPEARS IN VERY GOOD ORDER. CUCKOO SHOES RECOVERED

AND HARDLY WORN. LAUNCHER BEING GAUGED. ATTEMPT SL87B WEDNESDAY.

Figure 9.10 Part of a Telex reporting on the launch of SL88A.
(WRE (1965), Telex ref. SAL 2598, SL88A Trial Results file J5555/3/88A)

The reference in figure 9.10 to the "launcher being gauged" referred to a procedure carried out between firings, where a large rail and shoe gauge was hoisted up inside the launch tower to test the dimensional clearances. This checked not only for damage caused by the previous launch, but also that the desert temperatures had not caused the metal structure of the tower to expand or contract too much:

> … the launcher, owing to its great bulk, tended to expand and contract under the influence of the heating effect of the sun or its absence. An in spec. launcher in the morning could be out of spec. in the afternoon...[45]

Otherwise, the launch of SL88A was remarkable only for the fact that nothing went wrong! An apogee of 137 miles (220 km) was achieved, during re-entry, the nose cone wall reached a maximum of 228°C,[46] and nose cone displacement reached a maximum of only 0.06 inches (1.5 mm) during maximum velocity whilst ascending. After re-entry, the instrumentation showed the head appeared to be tumbling, but after a total of 14 minutes, it successfully soft-landed 133 miles (214 km) down range. After recovery, it was refurbished for a second time, and flown seven months later as SL88B.

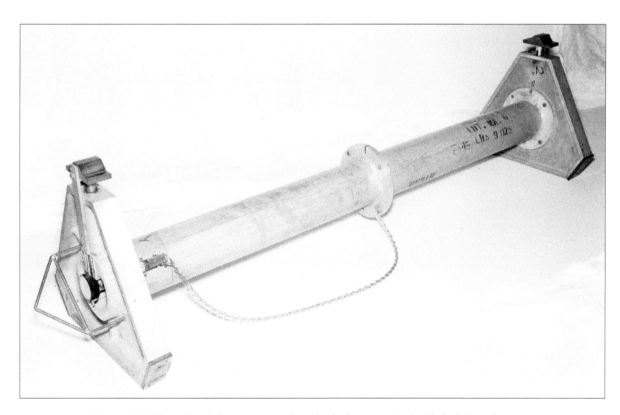

Figure 9.11 The rail and shoe gauge used to check clearances in the Skylark launch tower.
(National Archives of Australia: D874, N63/4618)

[45] Chambers (2000), *Woomera, Its human face*, p.109.
[46] WRE (1965), *Skylark 88A (BS116/1) Summary of Firing*, p.4. (SL88A Trials Results file J5555/3/88A).

Figures 9.12 and 9.13 The soft-landed head of SL88A was virtually undamaged, with only a slightly bent nose cone tip.
(WRE (1965), SL88A Trial Results file J5555/3/88A)

The motor landed only a couple of miles away, where it apparently impacted on fine gravel and partly disintegrated before falling back against a tree:

Figures 9.14 and 9.15 The motor of SL88A impacted a couple of miles short of the payload.
(WRE (1965), SL88A Trials Results file J555/3/88A)

March 1965   SL87B, SL140, SL141, S03/1

SL87B on the 3rd was a successful repeat of SL88A. It had originally been intended to launch it a week before SL88A,[47] but in the event, it was fired a week afterwards. Because the vehicles were so similar, both had the same WRE Trials Instruction document, No.BS116. A minor difference was that like SL87A, SL87B tested the new FPS16 radar transponder, designed to help plot the trajectory more accurately.

The flight was generally uneventful, except for a sudden deviation to the left just after launch, at +2 seconds. No technical reason could be found, and it was concluded:

WHAT WAS REFERRED TO AS A GUST WAS I BELIEVE IN THE NATURE OF A WILLY-WILLY. THESE ARE OF COURSE QUITE PREVALENT HERE ON HOT DAYS [48] WHEN WINDS ARE OTHERWISE

LIGHT AS IN PRESENT CASE. NATURALLY WE WOULD NOT FIRE IF ONE WAS VISIBLE NEAR THE LAUNCHER BUT THEY ARE NOT ALWAYS MADE VISIBLE BY DUST. [49]

The head of SL87B was recovered in good condition, and refurbished. "If re-furbishing is satisfactory, we will retain as a contingency round for use at short notice." [50] However it appears never to have been used, as there is no record of an SL87C having been fired.

Two weeks later the night firing of **SL140** on the 17th was a failure, the vehicle reaching an altitude of only 19 km (12 miles), and landing about 6.5 km (4 miles) downrange[51] – a record of sorts?

Fortunately, the mission was one for which this eventuality had been allowed for, and the repeat flight of SL141 a week later was successful. See Table 9.3.

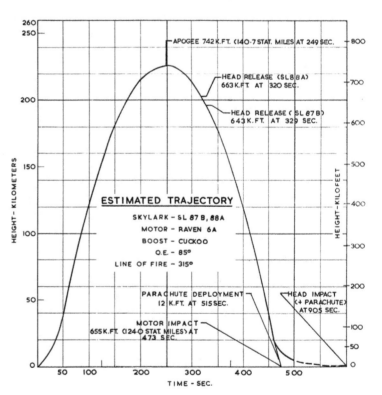

Figure 9.16 The estimated trajectory for SL87B and SL88A. The actual flights were similar.
(WRE (1965), *Trials Instruction BS116* p.8, SL87B Trials Preparation file J5555/2/87B)

Seq. Nos	Launch Date	Ref. (sponsor) launch site	Config-uration	Apogee km (miles)	Experi-menters	Experiments	Result
108 (4)	25 Mar. 1965	SL141 (UK) Woomera	Un, Rav.7 +C	174 (108)	UCL	Ionosphere - sporadic E (positive ion probes)	S
					Shf	Ionosphere - aerial impedance (probe)	S
					ROE	Astronomy - stellar UV radiation	Ps

Table 9.3 A summary of SL141.

---

[47] WRE (1965), *Trials Instruction No.BS116*, p.2. (SL87B Trials Preparation file J5555/2/87B).
[48] The ambient temperature when SL87B was launched was 100.9°F (38°C)! It was switched off during a hold before launch, to prevent overheating.
[49] Telex from OICRO (Officer In Charge Range Operations) to "Safety Weapons", (WRE (1965) SL87B Trials Results file J5555/3/87B).
[50] J.F.Hazell, Telex 10/6/65. (WRE SL88B Trials Preparation file J5555/2/88B).
[51] "Skylark Impact Points 1964 – 1969", WRE Drg. No. T 2414, Issue 1. (Via R.Henwood).

Seq. Nos	Launch Date	Ref. (sponsor) launch site	Config- uration	Apogee km (miles)	Experi- menters	Experiments	Result
110 (6)	03 April 1965	S03/2 (ESRO) Sardinia	Un, Rav.7	172 (106)	Breisach	Ionosphere – electron density in the D-layer (Radio spectrometer) (experiment R19)	S
					Breisach	Ionosphere – electron density in the E-layer (Variable frequency probe) (experiment R21)	Ps
					UCL	Ionosphere – electron temperature profile (Langmuir probe) (experiment R44)	Ps

Table 9.4 A summary of S03/2.

The payload comprised one astronomy and two ionosphere experiments. The Sheffield experiment involved transmissions through the ionosphere using jointed rod aerials, folded for launch, which extended during flight after the nose cone was jettisoned.[52]

The astronomy experiment was from a new Skylark user, the Space Research Division of the Royal Observatory, Edinburgh. It was the start of a programme of pioneering rocket experiments aimed at observing the absolute stellar fluxes of early-type stars in the UV region at wavelengths of 1000Å – 3000Å (100nm – 300nm).[53] The equipment comprised a Cassegrain telescope optical system with photomultiplier detectors, which because of the non-availability of a stabilised payload, scanned the sky using the motion of the rocket. This first attempt was only a partial success, but later flights on ESRO Skylarks from 1967 onwards (S11/1, S05/2, S47/1, S27/1) would be very successful, and are described later.

More ESRO launches

On the 31st March and the 3rd April, ESRO Skylark launches three (S03/1) and four (S03/2) took place in Sardinia. The payload was the same in each case, its purpose to perform measurements of the D and E regions of the ionosphere. Unfortunately, S03/1 suffered from vehicle failure, reaching only 45 km (27 miles) because the nose cone jettisoned prematurely at +29 seconds, and telemetry ceased three seconds later. Despite a search by helicopter, the nose cone was never found.

Fortunately a few days later S03/2 was successful, with an apogee of 172 km (106 miles), see table 9.4.

The UCL Langmuir probe on S03/2 was the first of many British sounding rocket experiments to be flown by ESRO.

April 1965	S03/2, SL303, SL464, SL363, SL364, SL461, SL462, SL463, SL362

April 1965 was the busiest ever month for Skylark launches, with nine taking place, albeit seven were over one night. S03/2 from Sardinia has been discussed just above, less than a week later; it was followed by **SL303** launched from Woomera. See Table 9.5.

This, the third stabilised flight, was particularly successful, and provided significant scientific results, including new data on the Sun's ultraviolet spectrum.[54] This was captured on photographic film on which about 300 emission lines were recorded, of which about three-quarters could be identified. These included several transitions that had not been previously reported in the solar spectrum, and also new lines not observed in the laboratory.[55] Some of these results were presented to the international meeting of COSPAR (the International Committee of Space Research) in Argentina in May 1965. It is worth emphasising that some of these results were new to science. At the time, sounding rockets, with their ability to return photographic film from space, were the most significant sources of such information, a position held for several years until the advent of stabilised astronomical satellites.[56]

During its approximately 100 mile (160 km) journey through space, the servo-controlled primary mirror stabilised an image of the Sun relative to the spectrograph slit with an accuracy of about three seconds of arc (one twentieth of a degree). The primary mirror was six cm in diameter and made of polished fused quartz. A six-position camera provided a series of exposures on Kodak-Pathé SC5 and SC7 film. At the end of the sequence, a protective shutter closed

---

[52] FLIGHT International, 1 April 1965, p.509.

[53] Campbell (1970), 'Absolute Stellar Photometry in the Region 1200 Å – 3000 Å'.

[54] Burton & Wilson (1965), 'Observations of the Sun in the Extreme Ultra-violet made from a Stabilized *Skylark* Rocket'. This seems a suitable point to mention that Auguste Comte, the 19th-century social theorist and philosopher, confidently predicted in 1825 that one thing we would never know is the chemical composition of the stars, because they are too far away to sample. This may have appeared reasonable at the time, but was totally wrong. Even when he made the remark, Fraunhofer in Germany was taking the first steps toward modern spectroscopy - the analysis of light to reveal the chemical composition of its source. In 1859, Gustav Kirchhoff used spectrographic methods to prove the existence of sodium in the Sun.

[55] Burton, Ridgeley & Wilson (1967), 'The Ultraviolet Emission Spectrum of the Solar Chromosphere and Corona', p.207.

[56] Such as ESRO's TD-1 (1972), and the larger IUE (International Ultraviolet Explorer) (1978). Both had significant British managerial and technical input from some of those (e.g. Wilson, Boksenberg) who had worked on Skylark. (Massey & Robins (1986), p.146 onwards).

Seq. Nos	Launch Date	Ref. (sponsor) launch site	Config- uration	Apogee km (miles)	Experi- menters	Experiments	Result
111 (7)	09 April 1965	SL303 (UK) Woomera	Sun, Rav.7+C	161 (100)	RAE	Test (space technology) – attitude control (sun sensors)	S
					Cul	Solar physics – corona (normal incidence spectrograph)	S
					Cul	Solar physics - corona (grating pin-hole camera)	S
					Cul	" " - XUV (pin-hole camera)	S
					Lei	" " - X-rays (pin-hole camera)	S
					Lei	" " - X-rays (crystal spectrograph)	S

Table 9.5 A summary of SL303.

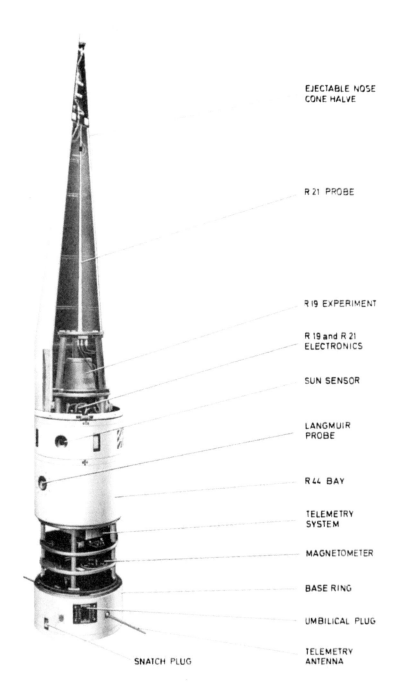

EJECTABLE NOSE CONE HALVE

R 21 PROBE

R 19 EXPERIMENT

R 19 and R 21 ELECTRONICS

SUN SENSOR

LANGMUIR PROBE

R 44 BAY

TELEMETRY SYSTEM

MAGNETOMETER

BASE RING

UMBILICAL PLUG

TELEMETRY ANTENNA

SNATCH PLUG

Figure 9.17 A general view of ESRO payload S03.
(ESRO (1972), report SP-76, p.26 figure 2)

and the films were subsequently removed from the rocket
payload after parachute recovery.[57]

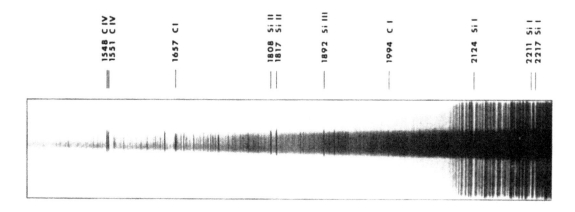

**Figure 9.18 This solar limb spectrum obtained by the Culham Laboratory group during
the flight of SL303 from Woomera on 9 April 1965 was of outstanding quality.[58]**

(After Burton, Ridgeley and Wilson (1967), figure 2)

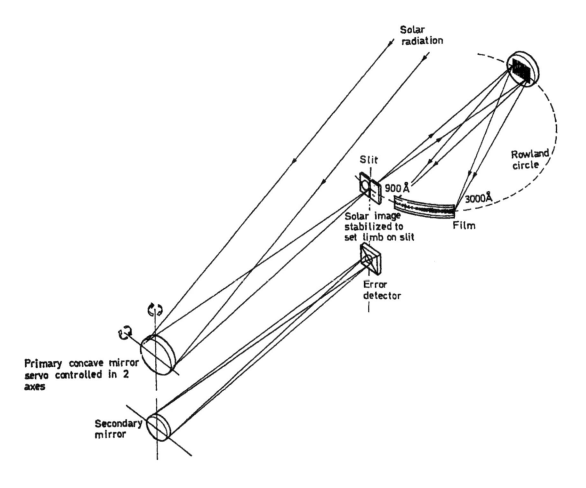

Figure 9.19 The sophisticated secondary optical alignment system used on SL303.

(Burton, Ridgeley and Wilson (1967), figure 1)

---

[57] Burton, Ridgeley & Wilson (1967), p.208.
[58] Dorling (1975), 'Early History of the Skylark Rocket', p.184.

An exaltation of Skylarks [59]

Three weeks after the launch of SL303, an attempt was made to launch no less than seven Skylark grenade rounds in one evening. This took place at Woomera on the night of 29-30th April, and whilst the first and last flights were unsuccessful, good results were obtained from the other five.

The grenade and falling dipole experiments were designed to augment the earlier work carried out on the previous multiple launch night of 15-16 October 1963. As before the launches were all on one night in order to measure how the wind speed and temperature varied over a relatively short time, because earlier work had revealed that not only did the properties of the upper atmosphere vary according to season, but also in an oscillating fashion on a much shorter timescale.[60]

The launches took place through the night approximately every two hours:

	Vehicle	Local Time	Local Date	Apogee (km)
1	SL464	18:33 CST	29.4.65	0
2	SL363	20:39 CST	"	137
3	SL364	21:55 CST	"	132
4	SL461	23.26 CST	"	124
5	SL462	01:49 CST	30.4.65	140
6	SL463	03:26 CST	"	135
7	SL362	06:10 CST	"	175

Table 9.6 The seven Skylarks launched between dusk and twilight on the night of 29-30th April 1965.

As before, it required a considerable effort to carry out such an operation. Geoff Taylor recalled:

The night of the seven launches was nonetheless a major effort for all concerned. There were several launcher crews involved, but for many of the range staff, including myself, it was a wearisome, all night exercise. I forget what the payloads were, but I remember the press the following day being full of public observations from as far away as Adelaide speaking of great multi-coloured lights and flashes in the sky. Skylark experiments seldom went unnoticed![61]

Despite the overall success, the evening did not get off to a good start, because the first launch (SL464) failed to reach any altitude after the Raven sustainer motor apparently failed to ignite:

The next five launches during the night were all successful. Unfortunately, despite reaching 175 km, the final flight was also a failure, as neither experiment was successful. However the five successful flights provided good results,[62] and showed that seasonal variations of atmospheric parameters generally predominated below 70 to 80 km. They also showed that variations of a wavelike nature on a time-scale of the order of a day or less became increasingly important above 45 km,[63] thus helping reveal how the global atmosphere varied with tidal and heating effects.

Seq. Nos	Launch Date	Ref. (sponsor) launch site	Config-uration	Apogee km (miles)	Experi-menters	Experiments	Result
112 (8)	29 April 1965	SL464 (UK) Woomera	Un, Rav.7 +C	0	IC	Neutral atmosphere - wind profile (falling dipoles)	Vf
					Bel	" " - wind velocities (lithium vapour)	
					UCL	" " - wind structure (grenades)	

Table 9.7 The first Skylark of the evening (SL464) carried three experiments; the remaining six Skylarks had only two each, not being fitted with the Belfast lithium vapour experiment.

[59] According to the OED, "exaltation" is the collective noun for Skylarks!
[60] Massey & Robins (1986), *History of British Space Science,* p.373.
[61] Taylor (2000), *Flights of Fancy,* p.126. Adelaide was some 300 miles (483 km) from the rangehead!
[62] See for instance Massey & Robins (1986), the figure on p.276.
[63] Groves (1976), 'Rocket studies of atmospheric tides', p.439.

However although these experiments admirably revealed details of vertical atmospheric structure, there were practical limits to the number that could be launched in less than 24 hours. In addition, the fact they were limited to night-time observations (to see the grenade glow), meant that to explore these variations in the upper atmosphere in greater detail, new methods were needed. Thus in December 1964, the BNCSR had decided there would be no more firings of grenade rounds from Woomera after this event in 1965,[64] and so these seven Skylark launches concluded the series of 28 such experiments in the UK national Skylark programme.[65] In the future, smaller and cheaper meteorological rockets came to be used for these type of experiments - although as they were only able to produce useful results up to 65 km (using radar tracked parachute sensors), observations in this field of research became more difficult to come by.[66]

SKYLARK LAUNCHER

Figure 9.20 Where's my rocket? – all that remained of the ill-fated SL464.
(WRE)

---

[64] "Loose minute" from R.A.Clifford dated 11 January 1965. (Ministry of Technology document file, TNA:PRO AVIA 92/146).
[65] Although at the end of September UCL did make use of ESRO Skylarks S04/1 and S04/2 to carry out grenade experiments in Europe (Sardinia), and later on, back at Woomera in 1968, SL761 and SL762 were launched with different grenade experiments to a higher altitude.
[66] Groves (1976), p.465.

SL361 was launched on the 11th May, and although it carried no grenades, it did have two alternative experiments to observe the upper atmosphere.

The first was a repeat of that from Queen's University, Belfast on SL464, the Skylark that had crashed less than a fortnight before, fortunately this time all went well. The experiment involved optical observations of a release of lithium vapour, leading to the measurement of high-altitude winds and temperature. The second experiment was from UCL, a revival of the falling sphere experiments of 1963. This used a special rocket section from which their self-inflating 6ft sphere was ejected, and this sixth attempt provided their second success. The sphere was tracked by radar and high-precision cameras, to give the rate of fall, and so the air densities encountered during the descent.[67]

SL139 and **SL138** followed successfully on the 14th and 19th May respectively. SL139 carried two ionosphere experiments from the RSRS;[68] SL138 flew the same two experiments plus a non-imaging solar X-ray camera from the University of Leicester.

**Figure 9.21 Loading an unidentified Skylark payload into the launch tower at Woomera c. 1965.
(This photograph is related to Figure 7.33 and Figure 9.1).**

(National Archives of Australia: A1200, L50178)

---

[67] FLIGHT International, 3 June 1965, p.890.
[68] In 1965 the RRS (Radio Research Station) was renamed the RSRS (Radio and Space Research Station).

There were no Skylark launches in June, but on the 1st July, SL106 successfully launched a selection of solar X-ray, ionosphere and rocket environment experiments, see table 9.8.

SL106 was followed on the 14th by **SL48**, which is particularly well documented, mainly because of the recollections of John Raymont from UCL/MSSL, who accompanied SL48's UCL payload to Australia.[69] The following extract is reproduced by permission:[70]

"In the Physics Department was a group, called the 'Rocket Group' and a friend of mine was a technician in this group. He was leaving and I decided to ask Dr Boyd [the Head of the Group] if I could be considered as the replacement. 'On trial' was the answer and I started in September 1961 in the electronics workshop. I never received formal confirmation that my 'trial' period was completed. I built electronic units for sounding rockets and worked on spare parts for UK1. First big step was to lay-out and wire a rocket payload for a recently graduated PhD student (Alex Boksenberg[71]).

Immediately after this wiring task Alex said I should do the testing, my first ever testing! Testing in UCL was followed by day trips to RAE Farnborough for testing on the whole payload (we were the only instrument) and then much to my surprise Alex said that I should go to Woomera, Australia, for the launch. The return flights were every 2 weeks and my stay was for 6 weeks. There was no freedom or choice in how you flew, it was London to Adelaide on a Government

charter flight. I had never been on a plane before and a 3 day propeller plane flight to Adelaide was quite an experience. Work was done in Adelaide and then weekly flights to Woomera for the launch.

Accommodation in Australia was good. In Adelaide, where we worked at the Weapons Research Establishment (WRE) for the post-transportation tests, we lived in private house accommodation and the remarkable lady who owned the house would almost not let you out in the morning without a huge fried breakfast (with many eggs). We were driven each morning to WRE Salisbury and returned in the evening by a WRE government driver. When the launch campaign was under way we would fly to Woomera at 05:30 / 06:00 on Monday mornings and back to Adelaide on Friday evenings. The flights to and from Woomera were on Convair Metropolitan or Douglas DC3 planes. The DC3 was quite an experience.

Accommodation at Woomera was in fairly basic ex British forces quarters. Evening meal, if work finished early enough at the 'Range Head', was in the officers' mess where you had to wear a tie to gain entry (it was called 'dress code'). If work did not finish early then it was to eat at Lake Koolymilka village. That is where we had daily lunch. It was a small village approx. 6 or 7 miles from the Range Head. Later, the ELDO (European Launcher Development Organisation) mess was more like a large hotel, but with 'self-service type' eating. Driving from Woomera Village to the Range Head was done in Government-allocated cars or vans and was strictly controlled. The distance was approx. 20 - 25 miles. The main hazards here whilst driving very late at night were kangaroos!!"

Seq. Nos	Launch Date	Ref. (sponsor) launch site	Config-uration	Apogee km (miles)	Experi-menters	Experiments	Result
122 (18)	01 July 1965	SL106 (UK) Woomera	Un, Rav.7 +C	130 (81)	Lei	Solar physics – X-rays (non-imaging camera)	S
					UCL	Ionosphere - electron & ion concentration (Langmuir & positive ion probes)	S
					"	Ionosphere- electron temperature (probe)	S
					"	Aeronomy - effect of rocket on local environment	S
					"	" - effect of rocket motion & photoemission on probe currents	S

Table 9.8 A summary of SL106.

[69] John Raymont had joined University College London (UCL) in September 1960 as a technician and retired at the end of March 2004 as Experimental Officer. He spent essentially all his career working at the Mullard Space Science Laboratory (MSSL), which was originally part of the Physics Department, and later became the UCL's Department of Space and Climate Physics.

[70] For the complete version, visit *www.ucl.ac.uk/mssl/about-mssl/heritage/archive-documents* , click on "John's Retirement Speech", and "John's Memoirs". (Last accessed August 2014).

[71] Since his Skylark days, Alex Boksenberg has had a most distinguished career. By 1970, he was the inventor of the Image Photon Counting System (IPCS), a groundbreaking instrument that came to be universally used in astronomy. By 2009 he was Professor Alexander Boksenberg CBE FRS FinstP PhD Dhc(mult), a Fellow of the Royal Society, Chair of the UK National Commission for UNESCO and Chair of its Natural Sciences Committee, Honorary Professor of Experimental Astronomy in the University of Cambridge, Extraordinary Fellow of Churchill College in Cambridge, Visiting Professor of Physics and Astronomy and Fellow of University College London, and Executive Editor of Experimental Astronomy (Springer). Formerly Director of the Royal Greenwich Observatory and the Royal Observatory, Edinburgh, he was responsible for the design and construction of major UK astronomical telescopes and operation of the UK Observatory facilities in the Canary Islands and Hawaii. He has even had an asteroid named after him! (3205 Boksenberg).

"The flight [SL48] was successful and Alex [Boksenberg] got his data. The pleasures and problems of rocket/satellite integration after the sometimes years of building and testing at MSSL were challenging, but they were good. Many events stick in my mind, but my 'first' rocket launch was an experience, the sheer noise, mixed with the emotion of your 'first' launch, then on to a satellite launch, quite different but still a huge experience."

The author has been unable to discover the results of the experiments on board SL48, although two aspects were significant. Firstly the use of photomultipliers (Boksenberg was soon to develop the revolutionary Image Photon Counting System),[72] and the secondly the fact that the experiment was directed towards obtaining ultraviolet spectra. Only four years later, Alex Boksenberg was to co-author a significant review of UV astronomy, which noted:

> The scientific importance of ultraviolet astronomy has been recognised since the rocket initiated the era of space research…an important factor being that the ultraviolet region is much "richer" than the visible in resonance lines of the common elements in their neutral and ionized states. Since these lines are the most sensitive pointers to the physics and chemistry of the media under observation, their study is of paramount importance.[73]

Figure 9.22 John Raymont and the SL48 'UV Skyscan' payload at Woomera in 1965.
(WRE \ MSSL)

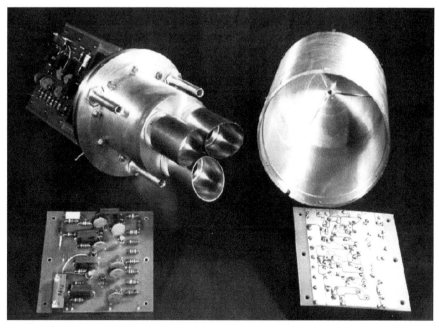

Figures 9.23 and 9.24 Left – the SL48 UV telescope, Right – the UV photomultipliers, housing and electronics cards.
(WRE & MSSL)

---

[72] Boksenberg (1972), 'Performance of the UCL image photon counting system'.
[73] Wilson & Boksenberg (1969), 'Ultraviolet Astronomy', p.421.

Seq. Nos	Launch Date	Ref. (sponsor) launch site	Config-uration	Apogee km (miles)	Experi-menters	Experiments	Result
123 (19)	14 July 1965	SL48 (UK) Woomera	Un, Rav.7 +C	182 (113)	UCL	Astronomy – stellar UV spectra (photometers)	S
					"	Test (scientific instrument) – attitude measurement (Moon detectors/horizon detectors/fluxgate magnetometers)	S
					RAE	Test (Skylark technology) – (i) vehicle attitude determination using solar and magnetic sensors (ii) Nose cone gap measurement.[74]	S

Table 9.9 A summary of SL48.

The other aspect of SL48 that is documented is the RAE test to determine vehicle attitude. This was the final trial in a programme to properly measure the motion of Skylark in free space. (Similar tests had been carried out on a large number of Skylarks, including SL127 (May 1963), SL136 (April 1964), and SL121 (August 1964) :

Before the Skylark firing programme started, it was anticipated that the rocket motion in free space would consist mainly of roll about the longitudinal axis with, in addition, a much slower precession of this axis about

a small angle cone. It soon became evident that Skylark is subject to the aerodynamic phenomena known as 'lock in' and can, if the roll rate is critical, fail structurally due to roll-yaw resonance…The precession cone semi-angle is frequently close to 90º, i.e. a tumbling motion.[75]

The trial validated the method for determining the rocket attitude in free space using intermittent data from instruments such as solar and magnetic sensors, and revealed the actual motion of Skylark during ascent and in space:[76]

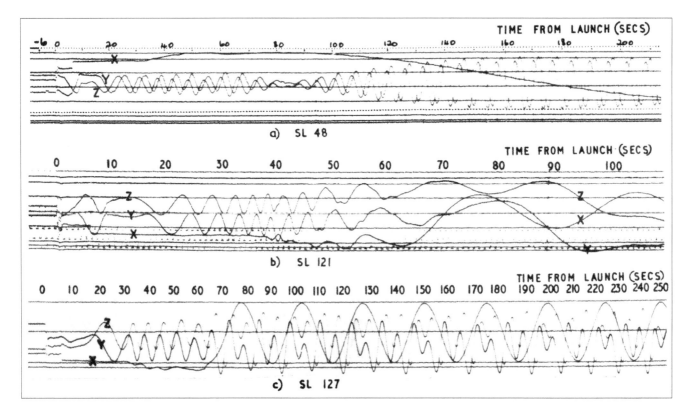

Figure 9.25 Magnetometer records for SL48, SL121 and SL 127. These measured the attitude of Skylark during ascent and in space.

(Herbert (1967), figure 3)

[74] Telex from WRE to RAE, June 1965. (WRE SL88B Trials Preparation file J5555/2/88B).
[75] Herbert (1967), *Determination of the Attitudes of the Skylark Rocket in Free Space*, p.3.
[76] Ibid, p.17.

Skylark was a reasonably reliable vehicle, but there were still many failures. SL105 followed SL48, and carried an identical payload to SL106 (successfully launched at the beginning of the month), but unfortunately disaster struck. Geoff Taylor, (at the time "OIC [Officer in Charge] Range Operations", at Woomera) recalled:

> ...one day I elected to watch a Skylark firing from the launcher officer's concrete blockhouse, quite close behind the launcher itself. There was a small, very thick glass observation window, from which the first hundred metres or so of flight could be seen. The small 'Cuckoo' boost, the first stage of the rocket, was intended merely to give it some acceleration out of the launcher, only burning for a few seconds. It fired satisfactorily, the rocket disappearing from our view, and our covered ears waited for the roar of the second stage to follow. To our horror, the launcher officer and I heard no sound. Seconds later, the main body of the rocket reappeared, hitting the ground only just in front of the launcher with a tremendous roar as its tonne of propellant exploded before our startled eyes.
>
> I think that this was the first time and last time in the history of the project that the second stage had failed to ignite [if only!]. Fortunately the rocket had tilted forward and hit the ground far enough in front of us to avoid damage to the launcher. Fortunately also,

the nature of the propellant was such that it was not 'high' explosive, burning rather than detonating. If it had been, the launcher and quite possibly the blockhouse would have been a writeoff. As it was, the explosion left a considerable crater in the earth. It was for me a salutary lesson, not to say a considerable fright![78]

August 1965   S05/1

S05/1 was an ESRO UV astronomy mission launched from Sardinia, carrying two stellar UV astronomy experiments from the Royal Observatory in Edinburgh. The payload was unstabilised, so it included magnetometers and Moon sensors as auxiliary equipment to determine the attitude of the payload as it scanned the stars through natural spin. Launch had to take place with a clear sky and within one day of full Moon, and this was achieved at 01:13 local time on the 11th. The payload reached an apogee of 215 km, well above the 190 km expected.[79]

Unfortunately, no scientific results were obtained at all. The first experiment failed because its hatch cover (there to protect the instrument from aerodynamic heating) failed to eject. This was compounded by failures of the rocket telemetry, timing system and the Moon sensor. This meant that very little attitude information was obtained, so the observations from the experiment that did work were of virtually no value.

Figure 9.26 The launch officer's concrete blockhouse from where Geoff Taylor viewed SL105's demise. (Figure 12.26 shows a later interior view). SL63's Cuckoo boost motor can be seen in the launch tower.[77]

(National Archives of Australia: D874, N61/653)

---

[77] This photograph is an enlarged part of Figure 7.19, which shows SL63 with Cuckoo boost motor in the tower in March 1961.
[78] Taylor (2000), *Flights of Fancy*, p.126.
[79] ESRO (1972), report SP-76, p.40.

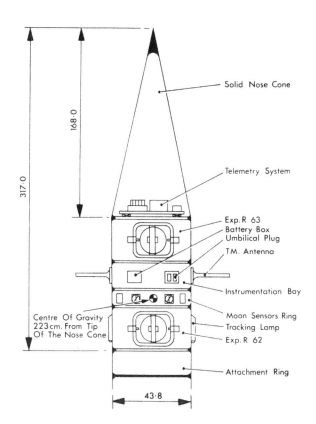

Figure 9.27 A diagram of ESRO payload S05/1. It was the lower hatch, the one for experiment R 62, that failed to eject.
(ESRO (1972), figure 1)

Following this failure, it was decided to cancel the second flight (S05/2), and return its payload to ESTEC for a complete redesign. This was done, and it was eventually launched over a year later, as described in the next chapter.

September 1965   SL88B, S04/1

SL88B was an RAE proving flight, the main purpose being to flight test the Raven VIA/Cuckoo combination with a 430lb (195 kg) head and modified split nose cone Type 2.[80] It was a continuation of the testing carried out by SL88A and SL87B at the beginning of the year. It was the fourth test of the Raven VIA sustainer motor, and the third flight of the instrument head from SL88, which as before had been re-furbished at WRE in Australia. The mission was a precursor to the first use of the Raven VIA on a scientific flight – "SL307 must have a 6A motor, and depends on SL88B. A Raven 7A can be used for SL306, but only as a last resort." [81]

The split version of the Skylark nose cone used on this flight had been redesigned by RAE with steel stringers and provision to avoid serious distortion during heating. The prototype was tested at RAE in June, before being shipped to Woomera to be flight tested on SL88B.[82]

After a day's delay because of cloud, SL88B was launched from Woomera on Thursday the 9th September at 13:50 local time. It was the 121st Skylark to be fired from there, although the 126th overall.[83] The flight itself was successful, reaching an apogee of 221km (137) miles , and landing 202 km (126 miles) down range. However, at this point things went a little awry. SL88B included a new radio recovery aid,

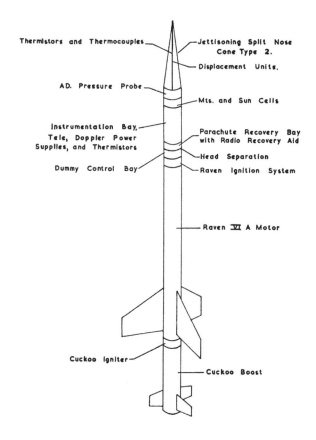

Figure 9.28 The configuration of SL88B.
(WRE (1965), *Trials Instruction BS123*, fig.1, SL88B Trials Preparation file J5555/2/88B)

---

[80]   "Skylark No.88B Round Specification", (WRE (1965), SL88B Trials Preparation file J5555/2/88B).
[81]   J.F.Hazell, Telex 10/6/65, (WRE (1965), SL88B Trials Preparation file J5555/2/88B).
[82]   Telex from "Hazell Space RAE Farnborough" to WRE, 26/5/65, (WRE (1965), SL88B Trials Preparation file J5555/2/88B).
[83]   By this time, five Skylarks had also been launched by ESRO in Europe.

a radio beacon fitted in the parachute bay. This should have helped the recovery process, but:

> Ground recovery did not function smoothly for SL88B and the head was not recovered until three days after firing. The Recovery Aid battery was then flat and could not be used to locate the head. The delay occurred partly because the ground party, who had a Recovery Aid receiver, was badly positioned for impact and no immediate ground search was made and because helicopters, which were also fitted with receivers, were not available. New batteries were fitted after recovery and the Recovery Aid Transmitter operated correctly.[84]

The trial had been an important one for testing the Recovery Aid, the second of two scheduled tests (the first being unsuccessful because the araldite holding the aerials melted on re-entry), and it was the first using a parachute descent. Those involved in its development were not amused:

> I am advised that the Recovery Team was assembled at Mt. Eba, on both Wednesday and Thursday (50 miles or so from the impact point) and it appears that they were not briefed to expect the impact at 132 miles and neither were they aware that visual aids in the form of dayglow streamers were fitted to the parachute. I am

given to understand that the Recovery Team set up the Rx [receiver] at Mt. Eba with a view to locating the Tx [transmitter] during descent. The distance of 50 miles, may be outside the range of the Tx, as no tests simulating the height/range conditions at the time (i.e. 12K ft./50 + miles) have been carried out.

> The decision seems to have been taken immediately after the firing that there would be no down range search on the day and the team returned to base. There was also no helicopter available, so no evaluation of the Recovery Aid was attempted.

> The recovery transmitter is designed to operate for 24 hours, so a search the following morning should have still been possible to prove the instrument…I think that OICRO's comment that "this was not one of our best recovery efforts" is somewhat of an understatement.[85]

The SL88B nose cone was jettisoned before re-entry at an estimated height of 107 km (66 miles) and the two halves fell to the ground independently. Despite this descent from the edge of space, one half was found virtually undamaged only 500 metres from SL88B; but the other half may not have been recovered – "Recovery of the other half cone is desired for evaluation here and in UK if it can be recovered quickly at reasonable cost."[86]

Figures 9.29 and 9.30 The soft-landed head of SL88B and its recovery aid radio beacon transmitter. The motor was found nearby.
(WRE (1965), SL88B Trials Results file J5555/3/88B)

[84] WRE (1965), *Skylark 88B (BS123/1) Summary of Firing*, p.4. (WRE (1965), SL88B Trials Results file J5555/3/88B).
[85] T.L.Cardnell, letter dated 21/9/1965. (WRE SL88B Trials Results file J5555/3/88B).
[86] Telex 29/9/65. (WRE SL88B Trials Results file J5555/3/88B).

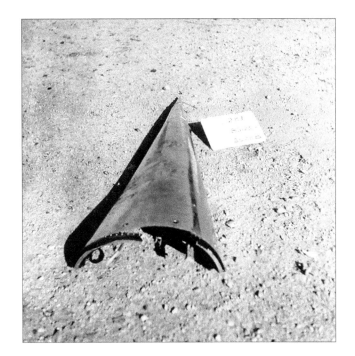

Figures 9.31 and 9.32 One half of the split nose cone from SL88B in remarkably good condition after falling from the edge of space. The right-hand close-up includes the nose cone tip that was a popular souvenir,[87] which after this photo was taken seems to have 'disappeared' - "Also require nose cone tip recovered with first half but not yet received by RV."[88]

(WRE (1965), SL88B Trials Results file J5555/3/88B)

Despite the recovery problems, SL88B was basically successful, and the following month SL306 was also successfully launched using a Raven VIA. The SL88B flight trial also proved that the new reinforced design of the split nose cone was successful, and it was cleared for future use.[89]

S04/1 was an ESRO mission designed to make measurements of the ionosphere and neutral atmosphere, experiments with the demanding requirements of excellent visibility, a low ground wind, and a launch at sunset or dawn within two minutes of the specified launch time. The vehicle was originally loaded into the Sardinian launch tower on the 19th September, but the launch was abandoned one minute before firing when an instrument failed at one of the observation posts. Bad weather and more technical problems repeatedly delayed further attempts, and the hazardous nature of the experiments (explosive barium coating mixture, spontaneously combustible TMA (trimethyl aluminium) and grenades) meant that great care had to be taken.[90] Finally, at dawn on the 30th, success was achieved:

Seq. Nos	Launch Date	Ref. (sponsor) launch site	Config-uration	Apogee km (miles)	Experi-menters	Experiments	Result
127 (23)	30 Sept. 1965	S04/1 (ESRO) Sardinia	Un, Rav.7+C	250 (probably) (155)	MPI	Aeronomy - study of ion cloud produced by release of barium in sunlight (experiment R33)	S
					UCL	Neutral atmosphere - grenades (experiment R48a)	S
					"	" " - wind profile by TMA release (expt.R48b)	S

Table 9.10 A summary of S04/1.

[87] See for instance Southall (1964), *Rockets in the Desert*, p.79.
[88] Telex 29/9/65. (WRE SL88B Trials Results file J5555/3/88B).
[89] See for instance WRE (1965), *Advance Information on Skylarks SL88C & SL581*, p.1. (SL88C Trials Preparation file J5555/2/88C).
[90] ESRO (1972), report SP-76, p.30.

The launch of S04/1 was successful - in fact almost too successful, as it reached about 250km instead of the 192 km expected. The apogee could not be confirmed because the tracking radar failed to lock onto the rocket. However all the experiment releases went as planned.

One of the conclusions from the subsequent ESRO report is a timely reminder that in 1965, everyday communications were much more difficult than in today's satellite and internet era:

> Communications with the outside world had been much improved through the provision of a teletype machine at the Perdas de Fogu post office, making it possible to send a message to Holland or Germany and to receive a reply the same day. Civil telephone communications were, however, still very poor.[91]

| October 1965 | S04/2, SL39, SL306 |

S04/2 was a repeat of S04/1, this time there was little delay, and the launch took place successfully into the clear skies of a Sardinian dawn at 06:22 local time on 2nd October.

SL39 was launched at night from Woomera, at 20:53 local time on the 18th October. It had one main experiment on board, a night airglow photometer from Queen's University, Belfast. It was the first successful Skylark flight in which measurements of the natural night airglow emission were achieved.[92] (Not to be confused with the artificial glows produced by the Belfast sodium release experiments). As described in Chapter 5, the first such attempt had been made by SL05 in 1958, but had failed, possibly because a shutter had not worked.

This time all went well, and the experiment was very successful, providing a wide range of observations at altitudes between 85 and 205 km, but particularly from 94 to 98 km.[93] These observations "... were particularly important because the results of ground-based observations …were completely incompatible with the theory to which Bates[94] had made major contributions. In retrospect the theory turned out to be correct".[95]

SL306 followed just two days later, and was the fourth successful launch with a stabilised payload. It was also the first scientific round to use the more powerful Raven VIA motor:

ROUND NO. SL	BUILT BY	RAVEN MOTOR	DATE FIRED	NOSE CONE	FLIGHT FAILURE OR SUCCESS	PURPOSE
83	BAC	5A	24/11/61	One-piece	F	Experiments
35B	AD	5A	6/2/62	" "	F	Investigate SL83 failure
35C	AD	5A	6/6/62	Split. Extra stringers	S	Vehicle development
45	BAC	5A	20/6/62	" "	F	Experiments
86	RAE	5A	2/8/63	IGNITION SYSTEM FAILURE		
87	RAE	5A	5/9/63	Split. Panels reinforced	S	Veh. development
88	RAE	5A	4/2/64	Split. Thick skin	F	" "
87A	AD	6A	4/9/64	MOTOR FAILURE		
88A	RAE	6A	25/2/65	Split. Thick skin	S	Veh. development
87B	AD	6A	3/3/65	" "	S	" "
88B	AD	6A	9/9/65	Split. Type 2	S	" "
306	RAE	6A	20/10/65	" "	S	Experiments

Table 9.11 A list of the eleven (twelve including SL306!) trials of the boosted Raven 5A and 6A motors that took place before the 6A was considered suitable for use on the SL306 scientific flight. The table is a bit rough and ready (for instance SL87A was mostly successful), but it does reveal the amount of work carried out on upgrading Skylark.

(WRE (1965), *Advance Information on Skylarks SL88C & SL581*, p.1, WRE SL88C Trials Preparation file J5555/2/88C)

[91]   ESRO (1972), report SP-76, p.31.
[92]   Massey & Robins (1986), *History of British Space Science,* p.290.
[93]   Greer & Best (1967), 'A rocket-borne photometric investigation…'.
[94]   David Bates, the distinguished professor at Queen's University of Belfast, and worldwide authority on this subject, see also Chapter 6.
[95]   Massey & Robins (1986), *History of British Space Science*, p.31. © Science and Engineering Research Council 1986, published by Cambridge University Press, reproduced with permission.

Seq. Nos	Launch Date	Ref. (sponsor) launch site	Config- uration	Apogee km (miles)	Experi- menters	Experiments	Result
130 (26)	20 Oct. 1965	SL306 (UK) Woomera	Sun, Rav.6A +C	213 (132)	Lei	Solar physics – X-rays (pinhole cameras)	S
					Cul	" " - spectra (grating pinhole camera)	S
					Cul	" " - image in XUV (pinhole camera)	S

Table 9.12 A summary of SL306.

Using the new more powerful Raven VIA motor, SL306 successfully achieved an apogee of 213 km, over 25% greater than its stabilised predecessors. This greater altitude had the benefit that the Earth's atmosphere absorbed less of the XUV radiation from the Sun.

On board were astronomy instruments prepared by the Culham Laboratory and University of Leicester groups for study of X-ray and UV emissions of the Sun. The Leicester Group flew an X-ray camera array similar to those flown on previous stabilised payloads, but with technical improvements to improve the resolution.[96]

The Culham Laboratory included two experiments based on those from the previous stabilised flight. (SL303, April 1965), these were the simple pinhole camera, and the grating pinhole camera. The latter, in addition to providing an image, was also able to provide spectral information.[97]

identical payloads, each with one neutral atmosphere, one solar X-ray and three ionosphere experiments, see table 9.13

The wind velocity experiment was linked to the ionosphere experiments, in order to test the wind shear theory of sporadic E formation.[98]

Between them, the flights made at least four encounters with sporadic E ionisation. A magnetic field minimum was detected on only one of these encounters, and the minimum was found to be 2–3 km below the observed ion layer. Although the vapour release experiment failed on SL130, it worked on SL131, and the wind measurements deduced from observations of the vapour trails indicated that the sporadic E layer occurred in a region of ion divergence.[99] The conclusion was that the results were consistent with the wind shear theory.

The results of the solar X-ray experiment are not known.

November – December 1965   SL130, SL131

SL130 and SL131 were launched from Woomera on the 19th November and 13th December respectively. They carried

Seq. Nos	Launch Date	Ref. (sponsor) launch site	Config- uration	Apogee km (miles)	Experi- menters	Experiments	Result
131 (27)	19 Nov. 1965	SL130 (UK) Woomera	Un, Rav.7 +C	138 (86)	Belfast	Neutral atmosphere - wind velocities (lithium vapour)	F
					Bir	Ionosphere - electron density & temperature (rf probe)	S
					Lei	Solar physics – X-rays (non-imaging camera)	?
					IC	Ionosphere - sporadic E field discontinuities (proton precession magnetometer)	S
					UCL	Ionosphere – sporadic E ionisation (positive ion probes)	S

Table 9.13 A summary of SL130.

[96] Russell & Pounds (1966), 'Improved Resolution X-ray photographs of the Sun'.

[97] Burton (1969), 'Solar Photography in the Extreme Ultraviolet', p.67.

[98] The wind shear theory of sporadic E formation is generally credited to J.D. Whitehead of the University of Queensland, Australia. In its simplest form, it holds that gaseous ions are accumulated and concentrated into small, thin, patchy sheets by the combined actions of high-altitude winds and the Earth's magnetic field in the E region of the ionosphere.

[99] Hall et al. (1971), 'Rocket observations of middle latitude sporadic E, magnetic fields, winds and ionization'.

The end of the 'Black Knight' rocket programme.

As 1965 came to a close, the Black Knight rocket test programme also ended. The last four launches, BK21, 23, 24 and 25, had taken place at two-month intervals from April to November during the year, with each vehicle head varying in material and shape to provide a range of data on radiation and wakes.

The last six firings comprised 'Project Dazzle', which brought to an end a most successful programme; one that had expanded from the relatively simple study of re-entry heads for Blue Streak, to a sophisticated international study of space vehicle re-entry wakes and related high altitude phenomena.[100]

Geoff Taylor, then OIC Range Operations, recalled:

> Dazzle involved both the UK and USA, as well as Canada, and there was a considerable amount of US observation equipment involved in the trials. For the intrigued South Australian population witnessing from time to time brilliant vertical steaks of light in the night sky, it was no doubt passed off as more of the upper atmosphere research which WRE was separately doing for quite peaceful purposes, using Skylark and other high altitude rockets. Black Knight was fired at night to get the most out of optical observations. It was a very reliable and well-tried rocket; its only problem, for range personnel, being their lack of sleep.[101]

From 1958 to 1965, a total of 22 Black Knight rockets were launched.[102] During the programme, its performance had been enhanced with a more powerful motor and the Cuckoo second stage, but it had been stretched to the limit. Thoughts had turned to a successor, using a larger diameter version called 'Crusade'. However, this was cancelled in favour of developing the 'Black Arrow' satellite launcher, to which the RAE turned its attention.[103] (Black Arrow was subsequently flight tested at Woomera from 1969 onwards, as described in the next chapter.)

However, although the UK no longer actively supported a re-entry physics project, the USA was still interested in using the Woomera range for more studies, and carried out further tests in a project codenamed 'Sparta'. This used three-stage launch vehicles, the first stage being the highly successful Redstone rocket, the second and third stages being solid propellant based. Nine 'Sparta' launch vehicles, plus one spare, were sent to Australia for the tests.[104]

Figure 9.33 A 'Sparta' vehicle being prepared for launch at Woomera.
(WRE)

---

[100] For a good description of the Black Knight programme, see Hill (2001), *A Vertical Empire,* Chapter 9.
[101] Taylor (2000), *Flights of Fancy,* p.125.
[102] BK02, BK10 and BK 22 were never fired.
[103] See for instance Morton (1989), *Fire across the Desert,* p.431.
[104] See for instance Morton (1989), *Fire across the Desert,* Chapter 24.

SKYLARK LAUNCHES AND SCIENCE IN 1966

1966 saw a small drop in the annual number of Skylark launches, down to 25 from the record 28 in 1965. However, it was still a busy year, and the number of ESRO launches increased from five to seven. See Table 9.14.

---

2 February 1966	SL307

After the Christmas break at Woomera, 1966 began with the launch of **SL307**, the fifth stabilised Skylark. See Table 9.15.

The launch vehicle again used the more powerful Raven VIA motor; the stabilisation system worked well, and provided more than four minutes of stabilised flight for solar photography. Elliott-Automation reported that the instrument package was stabilised within 30 seconds of arc[105] – a greater accuracy than ever achieved in any previous rocket firing.[106]

On board from Culham were three separate pin-hole camera experiments, including a prototype mirror filter pin-hole camera designed to obtain improved XUV images of the Sun in the wavelength region above 170Å (17nm).[107] The purpose of these XUV observations was to study the coronal features above the high temperature regions of the Sun's disc, thus revealing the three dimensional structure of these active regions.[108]

However, the recovery operation was not without its problems:

> Unfortunately the rocket nose cone was not recovered until late on the day following the flight and the exposed film was found to be badly fogged, probably as a result of severe solar heating while the instruments were exposed in the desert for two days at an ambient temperature of about 40ºC [104ºF]." [109]

One wonders about the story behind the lost nose cone – it seems the recovery aid radio beacon transmitter would have been really useful! This problem meant that two of the four experiments on board were only partly successful, but some images and results were obtained. However, in general the series of results being obtained were excellent:

> Meanwhile, the rocket programme reached fruition with the launch of the first stabilised Skylark rocket … Other flights followed, which, owing to Wilson's clear scientific objectives, competed well with the more established and larger programme in the USA.[110]

Jan.	Feb.	March	April	May	June	July	August	Sept.	Oct.	Nov.	Dec.
	SL307	SL581	SL582	SL304	SL327	S18/1			SL321	SL481	SL405
			SL583	SL422	SL328	S18/2			SL322	S11/1	SL581A
					S17/1	SL88C			SL324S		
					S17/2				SL323		
					S08/1				SL324		
					SL421						
					S08/2						

Table 9.14 The 25 Skylark launches in 1966. (For full details see Appendix 3)

(Key: black = test launches, blue = UK national programme (unstabilised), plum = UK (stabilised), pink = ESRO)

Seq. Nos	Launch date	Ref. (sponsor) launch site	Config-uration	Apogee km (miles)	Experi-menters	Experiments	Result
133 (1)	02 Feb. 1966	SL307 (UK) Woomera	Sun, Rav.6A +C	216 (134)	RAE	Test (Skylark technology) - attitude control unit (Stage 1)	S
					Lei	Solar physics – X-rays (pinhole camera)	S
					Cul	" " - spectra (grating pinhole camera)	Ps
					Cul	" " - image in XUV (pinhole camera)	Ps
					Cul	" " - image at very XUV (mirror filter pinhole camera)	S

Table 9.15 A summary of SL307, the fifth stabilised Skylark to be launched.

[105] 30 seconds of arc is 120th of a degree.
[106] FLIGHT International, 17 February 1966, p.282.
[107] Burton (1969), 'Solar Photography in the Extreme Ultraviolet', p.68.
[108] Burton (1968), 'Extreme Ultraviolet Observations of Active Regions in the Solar Corona', p.395.
[109] Burton (1969), p.69.
[110] Jordan (2004), *Sir Robert Wilson CBE...* p.371.

Indeed, it was reported, "Already scientists at Leicester University and the Culham Laboratory have obtained better X-ray and ultra-violet photographs of the Sun using the stabilised Skylarks than have been obtained anywhere else in the world." [111]

This was emphasised by the Space Science Board of the US National Academy of Sciences. In a study entitled *Space Research: Directions for the Future*, it commented:

> The United States has neglected much-needed vehicle development for solar work. The only new vehicle for solar research to appear on the scene since OSO-1 (1962) is the UK stabilised recoverable Skylark rocket... The tri-axially stabilised Aerobee 150 is greatly needed. Even with 1' [minute] of arc, pointing it would be valuable, but 5" [seconds] of pointing is required for much of the work. If this is not made available soon, the British will leave us behind in X-ray and ultra-violet solar research. [112]

| March – April 1966 | SL581, SL582, SL583 |

March and April 1966 saw three successive RAE proving rounds. **SL581** had originally been reserved as the back up for SL88B. [113] However, after the success of SL88B in proving the Raven VIA, it was not needed for that purpose, so was used instead to examine ignition system reliability following the failures at Woomera over the previous three years. The evidence from the launch showed "the systems and its units to be quite satisfactory". [114] Meanwhile the RAE continued to develop an improved motor ignition unit where all critical components were duplicated, a new type of battery was used, and improvements made to the plugs, sockets and wiring. [115] SL581 was probably also used to help clear the Raven VIA for lower head weight (unstabilised) rounds. [116]

The Raven VIII motor

The next two launches, those of **SL582** and **SL583** provided the first flight tests for the new Raven VIII motor. This was an upgrade to the Raven VII, and introduced the more stable aluminised Raven VI propellant in an attempt to cure a problem where erratic burning of the propellant had resulted in two in-flight tube bursts. [117] However, despite these two proving flights certain doubts on performance remained, which needed to be examined further. [118]

It appears that these doubts were soon resolved, and by November 1966, the Raven VII was restricted to Cuckoo-boosted firings whilst being phased out, because of the danger of a motor explosion near the launcher. [119]

The Skylark Policy Meetings

In April 1966 the first of many 'Skylark Policy Meetings' took place. These were organised by the UK Ministry of Aviation (MoA), successors to the Ministry of Supply. The minutes of these meetings have survived, [120] and provide a fascinating 'fly on the wall' account of the complex technical, managerial and financial issues encountered during procurement of a technically advanced product to be used across the world.

The meetings were held at the Ministry of Aviation in London, the first on the 4th April. About 28 people were invited,

Main variations		Minor structural changes		Propellant change
Raven II (1958)	▶	Raven VII (1962)	▶	Raven VIII (1966)
▼				
Raven V (1961)				
▼				
Raven VA (1962)	▶	**Raven VIA/VI (1964)**		

Table 9.16 The continuing evolution of Skylark's Raven sustainer motor.
(**BOLD** = more powerful variants.)

---

[111] FLIGHT International, 17 February 1966, p.282.
[112] As also reported by FLIGHT International, 17 February 1966, p.282.
[113] Telex from RAE to WRE, 10/6/65, (WRE SL88B Trials Preparation file J5555/2/88B).
[114] Minutes of 4th Skylark Policy Meeting, February 1967, para. 3.4.1, p.7. (TNA: PRO document file AVIA 92/144).
[115] Ibid, para. 3.4.2.
[116] Ministry of Aviation, Space 1(c) (1966), 'Skylark Policy and Programme', clause 3.3.1.
[117] Dorling (1975), 'Early History of the Skylark Rocket', p.180, and review document DS/55/29, Appendix 2 of the minutes of the 3rd Skylark Policy Meeting, November 1966. (TNA: PRO document file AVIA 92/144).
[118] J.F.Hazell, Minutes of the 2nd Skylark Policy Meeting, August 1966, p.5 clause 3.3.3. (TNA: PRO AVIA 92/144).
[119] Review document DS/55/29, Appendix 2 of the minutes of the 3rd Skylark Policy Meeting, November 1966. (TNA: PRO document file AVIA 92/144).
[120] TNA: PRO document files AVIA 91/144 & AVIA 92/145.

including representatives of industrial contractors (BAC, Elliott Bros), Government agencies (RAE, RPE Westcott), the Science Research Council and the MoA themselves.

The agenda covered all aspects of the project, including the R&D programme, the launching programme, supply, management and finance. The meetings continued quarterly, however, in the background a range at least eight types of more specialised regular progress meetings were also held, covering matters ranging from propulsion to management and supply. The liaison required between the disparate organisations involved must have been formidable and irksome at times, but the paperwork tabled and the minutes produced were of high quality. The meetings continued for about eight years, and have left a clear record of the Skylark project management process and the issues involved at the time.

A briefing paper[121] tabled at the first policy meeting clarified that there were three customers for Skylark, the Science Research Council (SRC), the RAE and ESRO. The MoA's responsibility was to ensure that as far as possible the technical needs of all three were looked after. As described earlier in this chapter, the SRC had by now taken over the civilian and scientific role of the Royal Society and represented what in general terms was called the 'British National Programme'. This paper therefore also clarified that in addition to its role as R&D and Design authority, (e.g. for the stabilisation system), the RAE was also a customer in its own right for defence and space technology experiments. ESRO had ordered 20 Skylarks via BAC, and another order for 26 more was being negotiated.

The document also reveals that the MoA had made the offer of a free loan to ESRO of the Skylark launcher at Aberporth, but BAC's tender to re-erect this at Kiruna in Sweden had not been accepted, instead ESRO had invited tenders for a new launcher to be ready by the summer of 1967.

Further correspondence[122] reveals that in 1966 the RAE was still assembling about fourteen Skylarks a year. The building used was 'Q65' at Farnborough, however the facilities were inadequate, and the RAE were:

> … working under great handicap at Farnborough. Space Department is required to work with close tolerance equipment stabilising the payload of scientific instruments and carrying out optical measurements to high accuracies. …The shortcomings of their existing facilities include large doors with no air lock which open on to a propeller test rig on the opposite side of the road; a leaking roof; a floor which requires repeated renewal of linoleum because of damp; and laboratories with individual glass roofs which are a major cleaning problem, and which, when cleaned, shower benches and equipment with dust and dirt coming through the joints between glass and frame. This state of affairs is largely explained by the fact that the building was constructed in 1915.[123]

Special treatment (at an extra cost of 10%) was requested from the Treasury because of the urgency, and it appears that the building was suitably improved and extended. [124]

Figure 9.34 Park at your own risk! This warning sign was used by the RAE at Farnborough, presumably when the propeller test rig described above was in operation. The sign is now preserved by the London Science Museum.
(Science Museum, author 100_5220) [125]

---

[121] Ministry of Aviation, Space 1(c) (1966), 'Skylark Policy and Programme', para. 3.3.1.

[122] "Extension of Q.65 Building at R.A.E. Farnborough, for Skylark". MoA letter from K.W.N. George to Dr P.F. Hicks, dated 13th April 1966. (TNA: PRO AVIA 92/144).

[123] Over its long life, Q65 had many uses. In the early days, it was the Fabric Shop, where an all-female workforce cut, stitched, fitted and doped the linen covering for airframes. By the 1970s, after various other uses including Skylark, Q65 housed the model making shop where all kinds of highly sophisticated aerodynamic models, carved out of solid steel and embedded with instrumentation, were prepared for testing in the Transonic wind tunnel. Despite being a listed building Q65 was demolished in about 2005, but its frame, comprising as it did the lower part of a 1912 portable airship hanger, has been re-erected and preserved as part of the centrepiece of a new business park. (See figure A6.11).

[124] Minutes of the first Skylark policy meeting April 1966, p.7 para. 6.2. (TNA: PRO AVIA 91/144). The matter appears not to have been discussed again, so was presumably resolved satisfactorily.

[125] Image taken at the London Science Museum, permission granted by Science & Society Picture Library.

[126] The Bragg Crystal Spectrometer (BCS) is an instrument that uses a crystal to split X-rays according to energy, just as a prism splits white light. In 1965,

By now the stabilised Skylark flights were getting into their stride, **SL304** was the sixth stabilised payload, and the second in 1966. See Table 9.17.

This solar physics payload concentrated on solar X-ray rather than the solar ultraviolet observations of previous stabilised flights. It included two types of instruments new to Skylark. The first was a pair of "plane crystal Bragg-type spectrometers"[126] from Leicester University.[127] These pointed in a fixed direction, and carried out relatively high resolution spectral analysis, whereas the second type of instrument, the scanning spectroheliograph, had moderate spectral resolution, but scanned the complete solar disc.

The background to the crystal spectrometer instruments was that in 1964 the NRL group[128] in the USA had obtained a good Bragg crystal spectrum of the Sun's corona. The Leicester group developed a similar Bragg spectrometer, which was first flown on SL304. Four separate spectral scans were carried out, and absolute intensities for 28 identified and four unidentified solar X-ray emission lines in the band 11-22 Å (1.1-2.2 nm) were measured. From these results, which were amongst the first obtained in this spectral region, it was possible to derive information about temperatures in both quiet and active regions of the corona.[129] The amount of neon, iron[130] and nickel relative to oxygen were derived. (The results were still proving useful nearly 40 years later.[131]) The second type of instrument, the scanning X-ray spectroheliograph, was a joint design by UCL and Leicester.[132]

Seq. Nos	Launch date	Ref. (sponsor) launch site	Config- uration	Apogee km (miles)	Experi- menters	Experiments	Result
137 (5)	05 May 1966	SL304 (UK) Woomera	Sun, Rav.6 +C	203 (126)	Lei	Solar physics – X-rays (2 crystal spectrometers)	S
					UCL/Lei	" " - X-rays (scanning spectroheliograph)	S
					RAE	Test (space technology) - silicon solar cell performance	S

Table 9.17 A summary of SL304.

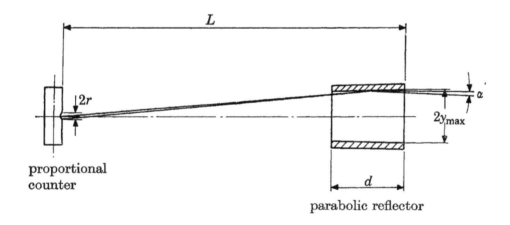

Figure 9.35 The principle of the X-ray spectroheliograph flown on SL304. It used a grazing incidence mirror and proportional counter as shown.
(Negus, Glencross & Pounds (1970), figure 1)[133]

it was the latest technology, but there were technical difficulties to overcome in making practical instruments suitable to fly in space.
[127] Evans and Pounds (1968), 'The X-ray spectrum of a solar active region'.
[128] The US Naval Research Laboratory had been at the forefront of rocketry and space science since the V-2 days after WW II. Many of the personnel had been transferred to NASA when it was created in 1958.
[129] Pounds (1986), 'British X-ray Astronomy', p.439.
[130] When the first spectroscopic observations of the corona were made over a hundred years ago, the results indicated the presence of an unknown element, dubbed *coronium*. Later work identified this as iron and other heavy elements at an extraordinary high temperature. See for instance Charles & Seward (1995), p.95.
[131] Shmelz *et al*, (2005), 'Neon lights up a Controversy: the Solar NE/O abundance', p.L199.
[132] Negus, Glencross & Pounds (1970), 'A Scanning X-ray Spectroheliograph'.
[133] Reproduced courtesy Royal Society London.
[134] Reproduced courtesy Royal Society London.

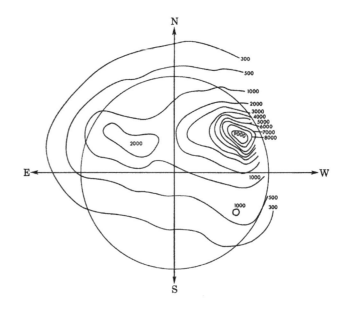

Figure 9.36 An X-ray map of the Sun produced from SL304 observations, showing a dominant active sector on the north west of the disc (Negus, Glencross & Pounds (1970), figure 6) [134]

The spectroheliograph was designed to overcome the limitations of previous imaging instruments using pinhole cameras with filters; instead, it produced an 'image' by using the Skylark Attitude Control Unit (ACU) to scan the Sun; which allowed contoured maps to be produced. It scanned the Sun in a number of only relatively narrow wavelength bands, thus compared to the Bragg crystal spectrometers; it traded resolution for 'image' capability.

The silicon solar cell performance experiment from the RAE may have been linked to their development of Moon or star sensors for future versions of the ACU.[135]

SL422 followed on the 31st May. It carried just two experiments, one from MSSL to study plasma waves in the rocket wake, and one from the University of Sheffield to measure aerial impedance. The latter may have been the same as they had flown on SL141 the previous year.

Meanwhile at Woomera, the launches of Blue Streak were continuing. On the 24th May, F4/Europa 1 was fired. One participant later recalled his part in the preparations:

> Then I had the very memorable job of maintaining gaseous nitrogen pressure to telemetry and guidance canisters on top of the LOX tank. Volunteers were sought for this job because it meant climbing into the guidance

bay of the rocket and staying there whilst the gantry or servicing tower was rolled back, leaving the rocket sitting like a big fat pencil in the midday sun, so that testing of telemetry and guidance systems could be carried out. Peering out of the porthole of this twelve-foot diameter rocket, about 65 feet above the ground and gently swaying from side to side in the light afternoon breeze, was a sight and sensation to behold. I hoped that the vehicle tanks didn't lose pressure and collapse beneath me! And what a view looking out over the control room, the surrounding donga, and Lake Hart for about twenty or thirty miles! And that's as close as I have ever been – and ever want to be – to flying in a rocket![136]

June 1966	SL327, SL328, S17/1, S17/2, S08/1, SL421, S08/2

June was a busy month for Skylark, starting at Woomera with **SL327** and **SL328** on the 2nd and 9th respectively:

Seq. Nos	Launch date	Ref. (sponsor) launch site	Config-uration	Apogee km (miles)	Experi-menters	Experiments	Result
139 (7)	02 June 1966	SL327 (UK) Woomera	Un, Rav.7 +C	176 (109)	MO	Aeronomy - ozone concentration (solar absorption detector)	S
					MO	Solar physics – solar intensity (photo-cells)	S
					UCW	Ionosphere – electron density profile (cw propagation)	S

Table 9.18 A summary of SL327.

[135] See for instance Cope (1964), 'The Attitude Control System of the Skylark Sounding Rocket', p.291.
[136] Ivan Winter (2010), *Those were the days!*, p.370.

They were launched at twilight just after 18:00 local time, and carried identical payloads, including experiments continuing the Meteorological Office's observations of the ozone layers. These produced useful results at altitudes from 55 to 70 km (34 to 44 miles) of the ozone concentration in the mesosphere and lower thermosphere.[137] One flight revealed a secondary ozone layer between 72 and 92 km. A third experiment in the series was launched later from Fort Churchill in Canada in 1969, but not on a Skylark rocket.

The UCW electron density experiment was a repeat of that flown on SL121 and SL120 two years before.

ESRO use continues

In June and July, the ESRO Skylark launches resumed after a break of seven months. Six Skylarks were successfully launched from Sardinia, starting with S17/1 and S17/2. See Figure 9.19.

The scientific purpose of the S17/1 and S17/2 payloads was to create an artificial ion cloud in the upper atmosphere. These experiments were part of a series in preparation for a more ambitious experiment, to create a similar ion cloud to be ejected from space probes or satellites with highly eccentric orbits to simulate an ionized cometary tail.[138] The ion cloud also allowed wind velocities and electron densities in the upper atmosphere to be measured.

S08/1 and S08/2 were launched soon afterwards, on the 20th and 28th June respectively. Each had on board two experiments. The first was a barium release similar to that on S17, and the second was from the UK's Meteorological Office, and designed to measure the vertical distribution of ozone in the upper atmosphere. The Meteorological Office instrument appears to have been very similar to that flown from Woomera on SL327 three weeks earlier (see above), and thus part of their active programme that had included experiments first flown on SL35 in 1961, and an instrument on aboard the Ariel II satellite in 1964.

Unfortunately, although the launch and flight of S08/1 were mostly satisfactory, all communications were lost at +34 seconds, the barium release did not take place and no scientific results were obtained. It was deduced that excessive vibration prior to the Raven VII burnout had resulted in failure of the common power supply package,[139] so extensive modifications to S08/2 were then carried out, to provide separate power-supply lines to the various systems. After a day's delay during which a heating system was installed in the tower to keep the ozone experiment dry, S08/2 had a successful flight.

Meanwhile, back at Woomera, SL421 was launched on the 23rd, and was a successful repeat of the SL422 aeronomy and ionosphere mission the month before.

July 1966   S18/1, S18/2, SL88C

The S18 payloads were similar in purpose to the S17 payloads, except that ammonia was released rather than barium. The main piece of equipment was a large tank containing 35 kg (77 lb) of liquid ammonia at a pressure of 11 atmospheres. S18/1 and S18/2 were launched from Sardinia during twilight on the 8th and 13th July, and near apogee, the tops of the containers were removed by the detonation of a shaped charge, thus instantly liberating all the contents. Both missions were completely successful.

July concluded with the launch of **SL88C** from Woomera on the 28th. This used the refurbished head from SL88B, the fourth time it had been used, the most for any Skylark payload. The main purpose of the flight was to flight test the Raven VIA/Cuckoo combination carrying a slightly lighter head (400 lb instead of 430 lb) and a modified Type 3 split nose cone. The previous September SL88B had cleared for use the Type 2 split nose cone, which had been modified to reduce in-flight distortions. SL88C was intended to prove the Type 3 cone, which had been modified in the same way. (Type 2 was a 5'6" (1.7 m) cone, and Type 3 was the same plus a cylindrical skirt about 1'3" (0.4 m) long.)[140]

Seq. Nos	Launch date	Ref. (sponsor) launch site	Config-uration	Apogee km (miles)	Experi-menters	Experiments	Result
141 (9)	16 June 1966	S17/1 (ESRO) Sardinia	Un, Rav.7 +C	231 (144)	MPI Garching	Aeronomy/Ionosphere – barium release (experiment R.33)	S
142 (10)	18 June 1966	S17/2 (ESRO) Sardinia	Un, Rav.7 +C	220 (137)	MPI Garching	Aeronomy/Ionosphere – barium release (experiment R.33)	S

Table 9.19 A summary of S17/1 and S17/2.

[137] Miller and Ryder (1973), 'Measurement of the ozone concentration from 55 to 95 km at sunset'.
[138] ESRO (1973), report SP-77, p.81.
[139] ESRO (1973), report SP-77, p.15.
[140] WRE (1965), *Advance information on Skylarks SL88C & SL581.* (SL88C Trials Preparation file J5555/2/88C).

There were also ten secondary experiments on SL88C, these included instruments to measure the internal pressure of the Raven motor, the temperature of the nose cone, and attitude and vehicle performance. They also included equipment flight tests such as the nose cone jettison system, a WRE ionisation gauge to measure atmospheric pressure at high altitudes, and the WRE Recovery Beacon.[141] (This was the fourth attempt to test the WRE radio beacon, previous trials on SL48 (July 1965), SL88B (September 1965) and SL306 (October 1965) had all failed).

On the 27th July, firing was delayed because of high winds,[142] but at 10:21 local time on the 28th launch took place. All went well at first, the telemetry streamed back, revealing for instance that pressure within the Raven motor reached a maximum of nearly 1000 psi at +34 seconds.[143] The vehicle successfully reached an apogee of approximately 220 km (136 miles), and the Type 3 nose cone jettisoned correctly at about 140 km before re-entry. Unfortunately,

soon afterwards the head failed to separate from the motor, the parachute was therefore unable to deploy, and the entire vehicle plunged nose first into the ground 141 miles (227 km) down range "Still burning when located three hours after firing".[144] The recovery aid (radio beacon) exercise had therefore failed a fourth time, once more for no fault of its own, and the remaining helicopter time was used instead for a nose cone search.

After recovery, it was reported:

> HAVE RECOVERED REMAINS OF SL88C. ONLY CONCLUSIVE EVIDENCE IS THAT HEAD WAS IN SAME HOLE AS MOTOR. THERE IS NO HOPE OF FINDING THE REASON FOR NON-SEPARATION.[145]

However, the same Telex concluded that the probable cause of failure was an open circuit along the head separation circuit, following a vibrational joint failure in flight.

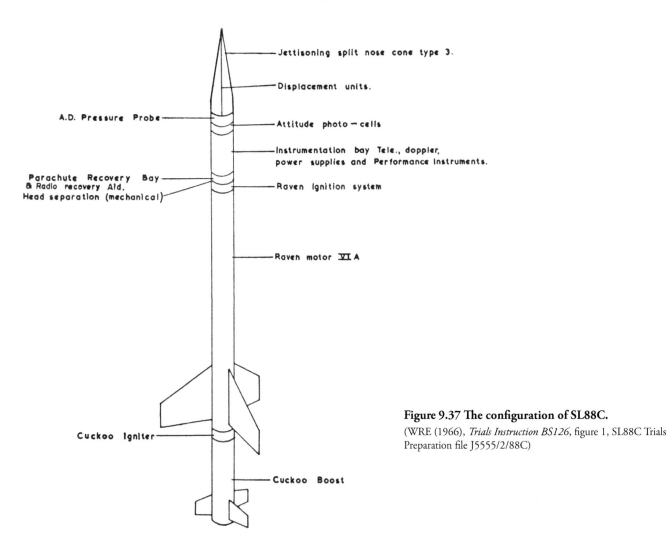

Figure 9.37 The configuration of SL88C.
(WRE (1966), *Trials Instruction BS126*, figure 1, SL88C Trials Preparation file J5555/2/88C)

[141] WRE (1966), *Trials Instruction No.BS126*, p.1, (SL88C Trials Preparation file J5555/2/88C).
[142] Telex 27/7/66. (WRE SL88C Trials Preparation file J5555/2/88C).
[143] Telex from WRE to RAE 29 July 1966. (WRE SL88C Trials Results file J5555/3/88C).
[144] Telex ref. H1879, 2 Aug 1966. (WRE SL88C Trials Results file J5555/3/88C).
[145] Telex ref. J8095 from WRE to RAE. (WRE SL88C Trials Results file J5555/3/88C).

**Figure 9.38 Part of SL88C being recovered from the crater formed at impact.
There would be no fifth flight for this payload!**
(WRE (1966), SL88C Trials Results file J5555/3/88C)

There was naturally disappointment over the failure, especially as it "…would have been good to display head which had flown four times".[146] The authorities were keen to recover the jettisoned nose cone halves, even though it was a seven-hour return travel journey for the crews. Over a month later, it was reported:

> SEARCHED AREA FROM 0900 TO 1600 HRS ON
> 14 SEPT 66 WITHOUT SUCCESS. VEGETATION
> AVERAGES 2 FEET AND HEAVY TIMBER COVERAGE
> AGGRAVATED SEARCH. SIX PUNCTURES AND NO
> MORE SPARES FINALLY STOPPED PLAY. HAVE
> BRIEFED OCCUPANTS OF LOCAL OUTSTATION
> AND THEY WILL INFOR[M] THE RANGE TOGETHER
> WITH LOCATION INFO SHOULD THEY FIND
> DURING THEIR WORKING ACTIVITIES.[147]

October 1966 SL321, SL322, SL324S, SL323, SL324

There were no Skylarks launches in August or September, but at the end of October five were launched over a period of three days, each with the same pair of ionosphere experiments from the University of Birmingham.

The first was **SL321** at 18:36 local time on the evening of Thursday the 25th. See Table 9.20.

The electron density probe continued the series of measurements made over the years (latterly with SL130 and SL131 the previous November and December). The second experiment appears to have been a new one from Birmingham, a double Langmuir probe.

---

[146] Telex ref. H1844, 29 Jul 1966. (WRE SL88C Trials Results file J5555/3/88C).
[147] Telex dated 15 Sept 1966. (WRE SL88C Trials Results file J5555/3/88C).

Seq. Nos	Launch date	Ref. (sponsor) launch site	Config-uration	Apogee km (miles)	Experi-menters	Experiments	Result
149 (17)	25 Oct. 1966	SL321 (UK) Woomera	Un, Rav.7 +C	211 (131)	Bir	Ionosphere - electron density (39 MHz probe)	S
					Bir	" - electron temperature (double Langmuir probe)	S

Table 9.20 A summary of SL321.

SL321 was followed by the launch of **SL322** only two hours later, the first scientific flight powered by the new Raven VIII motor. It had no Cuckoo boost, and only reached 119 km (74 miles), so presumably was meant to study a lower layer of the ionosphere than SL321. However a contributory factor was the failure of the Durestos expansion cone very near to the end of burning,[148] a problem that led to the Durestos cone being replaced by one made of steel.[149]

There was then a one-day gap, after which three more Skylarks were launched on Thursday the 27th. First was the curiously numbered **SL324S**,[150] launched at 18:17 local time, a repeat of SL321. Just over an hour and a half later, **SL323** was launched, this time a repeat of SL322. Finally, at 23:05, came the launch of **SL324.** Unfortunately, it failed when the Raven VII motor burst in flight, and although the payload may have reached 200 km, the experiments produced no results. The cause was thought to be unstable propellant, and the event reinforced the warning from the RAE that this type of motor should only be fired in conjunction with boosted rounds.[151] The reason for this

was the danger of a motor explosion in or near the launcher, the problem the new Raven VIII was designed to avoid.

November 1966   SL481, S11/1

SL481 was an RAE Skylark technology round,[152] apparently the first non-scientific flight with the Stage 1 stabilised payload.

It was also the first Skylark Mark II build to be launched; a version primarily developed for use with the Stage 3 attitude control system, but ultimately intended to completely replace the Mark I build.[153] The payload may have included a propane propulsion experiment (as with SL20 in 1964, described in the previous chapter).[154] However, it appears that something went wrong on the flight of SL481, as an altitude of only 142 km was achieved.

Next, **S11/1** was launched from Sardinia during the evening of the 26th. (see table 9.22)

Seq. Nos	Launch date	Ref. (sponsor) launch site	Config-uration	Apogee km (miles)	Experi-menters	Experiment	Result
154 (22)	18 Nov. 1966	SL481 (UK) Woomera	Sun, Rav.6 +C	142 (88)	RAE	Test (Skylark technology) - 1st Mk.II build. Failure? – certainly didn't get very high!	F

Table 9.21 A summary of SL481.

Seq. Nos	Launch date	Ref. (sponsor) launch site	Config-uration	Apogee km (miles)	Experi-menters	Experiments	Result
155 (23)	26 Nov. 1966	S11/1 (ESRO) Sardinia	Un, Rav.6 +C	2.5 (1.6)	PIB	Ionosphere/Astronomy – study of low energy (X-ray) proton component of cosmic X-rays (expt. R73)	Mf
					ROE	Astronomy – night sky random stellar UV survey (experiment R65)	

Table 9.22 A summary of S11/1.

[148] Minutes of the 3rd Skylark Policy meeting, November 1966, p.5, para. 3.3.3. (TNA: PRO AVIA 92/144).

[149] Minutes of the 4th Skylark Policy Meeting, February 1967, p.6, para. 3.3.1. (TNA: PRO AVIA 92/144).

[150] One source calls this SL325 (McDowell (2009), *List of Skylark Launches*).

[151] Minutes of the 3rd Skylark Policy meeting, November 1966, para. 3.3.2, p.5. (TNA: PRO AVIA 92/144).

[152] Ibid, Appendix 4.

[153] Briefing document ref. DS/55/01, para. 1.5, p.1. (TNA: PRO AVIA 92/144).

[154] From SL481 reference in a letter from MoA to J.F.Hazell, 3 August 1966. (TNA: PRO AVIA 91/144).

Unfortunately, S11/1 was the third failure in a row for Sky-lark, this time the Raven VI second stage failed to ignite. It was decided to postpone launching the second flight unit (S11/2) to await the outcome of further investigation, and as some problems had appeared on the payload, the second unit was returned to BAC for modifications in the light of experience preparing for this flight.[155] (Subsequently the RAE discovered from recovered motor parts that the ignition unit had been incorrectly assembled,[156] and an incorrect Raven arming plug had been used.[157])

December 1966   SL405, SL581A

On the 8th December, **SL405** was launched from Woomera, the seventh Skylark with a stabilised payload. It included a set of six mostly astronomy experiments from Culham, the Meteorological Office and the University of Leicester. This Skylark may have been designated SL405 rather than SL305 to indicate the vehicle was built to the new Mk.II standard.[158]

Unfortunately yet again another failure occurred, this time caused by a catastrophic motor problem of some kind. Fortunately, it was possible to fly the mission again, when SL406 was launched three months later. This was the fourth Skylark failure in a row (the third in a row at Woomera), so

it was a difficult time, as recognised in a letter written a few days later from the SRC in London:

> There has been a dreadful run of failures of various sorts and you must all find it very depressing. There is little I can say about them at present until R.A.E. and R.P.E. have had a chance to look at the bits and form some conclusions.[159]

SL581A had originally been scheduled for Raven VI and ignition proving tests in August,[160] but in December it was launched using a Raven VII:

This flight-tested one of the improved motor ignition units,[161] but, perhaps more significantly, was also used to test the new idea of using 'canted' fins to spin the vehicle during flight. This was done to try to counteract a tendency towards increased dispersion from both boosted and unboosted Skylark rounds, a problem that increased the danger of Skylarks landing outside the Woomera range safety limits.[162] Hence, this proving trial tried spinning the first stage (by means of the canted fins) as a contribution to the solution. The mission was successful, and the head was soft-landed in such good condition that as SL581B it was re-used for similar tests the following August.[163]

After the run of three failures, the success of SL581A must have been most welcome at Woomera.

Seq. Nos	Launch date	Ref. (sponsor) launch site	Config-uration	Apogee km (miles)	Experi-menters	Experiments	Result
157 (25)	14 Dec. 1966	SL581A (UK) Woomera	Spin, Rav.7 +C	164 (102)	RAE	Test (Skylark technology) – improved Raven ignition system & canted fins	S

Table 9.23 A summary of SL581A.

---

[155] ESRO (1973), report SP-78, p.25.
[156] Minutes of 4th Skylark Policy Meeting, February 1967, para.4.4, p.16. (TNA: PRO AVIA 91/144).
[157] ESRO (1973), report SP-77, p.35.
[158] Listed as such in Appendix 4 of the minutes of the 3rd Skylark policy meeting. (TNA: PRO AVIA 92/144).
[159] Letter dated 12 December 1966 from G.W.Eastwood of the SRC in London to H.W.Whiteside of the WRE in Adelaide, (WRE SL521 Trials Preparation file J5555/2/521).
[160] Letter dated 3 August 1966 from the Ministry of Aviation (Space 1(c)) to the RAE and SRC. (TNA: PRO document file AVIA 92/144).
[161] WRE (1967), *Advance information on Skylark SL581B.* (SL581B Trials Preparation file J5555/2/581B), also minutes of 4th Skylark Policy Meeting, February 1967, p.7, para.3.4.1.
[162] Minutes of 2nd Skylark Policy Meeting, August 1966, p.6, para.3.3.4 (b). (TNA: PRO AVIA 91/144).
[163] Telex from WRE to RAE 1st Feb.1967. (WRE SL581B Trials Preparation file J5555/2/581B).

Figure 10.1 The motor case from SL581B being recovered in August 1967, an unusual view taken at sunset. The tripod-like shadow on the right must be from the photographer's legs!

(WRE (1967), SL581B Trials Results file J5555/3/581B)

CHAPTER 10

(1967-68)

EXPERIMENTS OF FRUIT

The second decade

February 1967 saw the tenth anniversary of the first Skylark launch at Woomera. During those ten years, Skylark had been very successful, 157 had been launched, and it still had nearly another 40 years to go!

During this first decade a great many technology and scientific experiments had been launched aboard Skylark, the scientific experiments alone totalling over 300.

The chart below reveals the increasing numbers of solar physics and astronomy experiments, i.e. those observing beyond the upper atmosphere Skylark was originally designed to explore. Surprisingly, many of these were launched before the stabilised payload became available in August 1964.

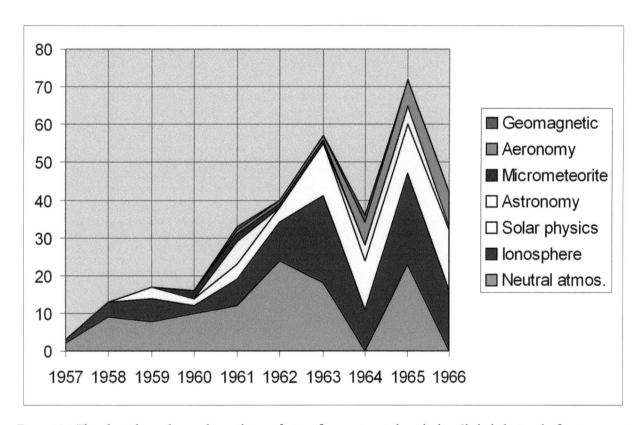

Figure 10.2 This chart shows the number and type of scientific experiments launched on Skylark during the first ten years. [1]

---

[1] Based on an analysis of the experiments as listed in Appendix 3, excluding RAE Skylark technology experiments and those flown on ESRO flights.

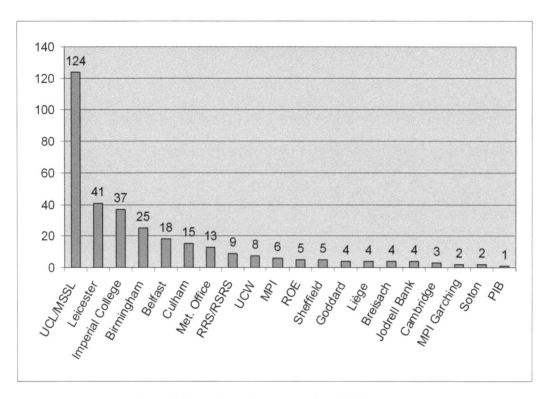

Figure 10.3 An analysis of the number of experiments launched per institution/organisation during the first ten years of Skylark operation (1957 to 1966).[2]

The establishment of MSSL

As the chart above shows, the University College London (UCL) was the largest provider of Skylark experiments. Thus, a significant event in 1967 was the formal opening of the new Mullard Space Science Laboratory (MSSL) on the 3rd May. The laboratory was a branch of the UCL physics department, and had originated in 1965 with a donation from the Mullard company, which enabled the College to purchase a country mansion at Holmbury St.Mary, near Dorking in Surrey. MSSL had come into full operation in October 1966, and housed the largest scientific space research group in Britain, which undertook some 25% of total British University space research.[3]

The opening ceremony was attended by several of the founders of British space science who were also responsible for the instigation of the Skylark project. This included Dr F.E.Jones (by then Managing Director of the Mullard Company) and was presided over by Sir Harrie Massey. In his opening speech, Professor R.L.F.Boyd (the first head of the laboratory) mentioned the early days:

> I recall, for example, our visit to see Dr. Jones at Farnborough at the very start of the programme, and the

excitement of discovering that we were to get not just a little rocket reaching 80 Km, but one that, when fully developed, would reach about 300 Km – Skylark as it became known, is still one of the best vertical sounding rockets in the world.[4]

By the time of the formal opening MSSL had a staff of 67, and is still (in 2014) busier than ever. Appendix 6 includes some more details, including photographs of Skylark SL1302 on display there.

Skylarks and Australian Experiments

As explained earlier, the Woomera range was run for military purposes under a succession of joint agreements between the UK and Australia. However it had soon become apparent that Skylark's main application was for civilian use, and for several years the Australians had been making representations that if they were to continue launching Skylark 'free at the point of use' then it was only fair they should be assigned the use of some Skylark payload space for their own national scientific purposes.[5] By June 1965, they were asking for the provision of two to three rounds per year for their exclusive use.

---

[2] Based on an analysis of the Institutions as listed in Appendix 3 – joint experiments have been counted as a half!

[3] MSSL (1967), *MSSL general information*, and other documents related to the opening, available online at *www.ucl.ac.uk/mssl/about-mssl/heritage/archive-documents/mssl-opening* (last accessed August 2014).

[4] Ibid.

[5] See for instance the TNA document file AVIA 92/147 "Proposals to Supply Australian Government – Skylark" for correspondence between 1962 and 1965 on this tricky subject.

Jan.	Feb.	March	April	May	June	July	Aug.	Sept.	Oct.	Nov.	Dec.
		SL406	SL426	S11/2			SL305	S26/1	S19/1	SL407	SL422A
			SL118	S05/2			SL581B		S26/2	SL423	
			SL119				SL521		S19/2	SL424	
			SL425				SL522				
			SL682								

Table 10.1 The 20 Skylark Launches in 1967. (For full details see Appendix 3)

(Key: black = test launches, blue = UK national programme (unstabilised), plum = UK (stabilised), pink = ESRO programme)

This position was fully understood in the UK by parties such as the RAE, who were in favour of establishing by such means more enthusiasm for the Skylark project by the Australian WRE.[6] The problem as always was money. The UK Office of the Minister for Science (OMS) "opposed wholeheartedly any suggestion that their [the Australian] programme should be financed in part from our very rigidly controlled scientific space research budget",[7] but instead supported the view that if such provision was deemed necessary for the overall benefit of the Joint Project, then it should be charged to the UK Ministry of Aviation in general terms.[8]

The problem was complicated by the fact that the Australian requests were informal, as they apparently had no budget for such research anyway. Furthermore, no formal requests could be made, as an extensive review was being was being carried out on Australian Government funding for research, particularly in the way it affected Australian Universities.[9]

In the end, a compromise was found by the provision of payload space on board Skylark rounds that were being used by the RAE for motor and system proving purposes, and which in general did not carry UK scientific experiments. These RAE rounds tended to use payload heads assembled in Australia by the WRE mainly from surplus or re-claimed

parts, so could conveniently have local experiments added. This cleared the way for Australian scientific experiments to be flown on Skylark, the first of which was flown on SL426 in April 1967 as described below.[10]

SKYLARK LAUNCHES AND SCIENCE IN 1967

For a summary of the year's launches, see table 10.1 above

March 1967   SL406

After the Christmas break at Woomera, Skylark's 1967 season (and second decade of operation) opened with the launch of **SL406**. This was a repeat of SL405 that had suffered motor failure the previous December, thus it had a stabilised payload with the same six experiments on board. See Table 10.2.

The Culham solar physics UV and XUV experiments resumed the use of spectrographs as flown on SL301-303. The first experiment from the Meteorological Office used the same detectors that would be used on the forthcoming Ariel III satellite. The second measured molecular oxygen at the high and very rarefied altitude of 100 to 150 km (within the thermosphere) using ionisation chambers as ultraviolet detectors.[11]

Seq. Nos	Launch date	Ref. (sponsor) launch site	Config-uration	Apogee km (miles)	Experi-menters	Experiments	Result
158 (1)	14 Mar. 1967	SL406 (UK) Woomera	Sun, Rav.6 +C	200 (124)	Cul	Solar physics – XUV spectrum 10-500Å (grazing incidence spectrograph)	Ps
					Cul	Solar physics - UV spectrum 500-3000Å (normal incidence spectrograph)	S
					Cul	Solar physics - XUV image	F
					Lei	" " - solar disc X-ray spectrum	S
					MO	Aeronomy - solar radiation flux (Ariel III sensor)	S
					MO	" " - molecular oxygen concentration	S

Table 10.2 A summary of SL406.

6   Letter from J.J.Gait of RAE dated 22nd April 1965. (TNA: PRO document file AVIA 92/147).
7   Letter dated 13 September 1963 from J.F.Hosie of RAE to R.Anderson of UK Ministry of Aviation (MoA). (TNA: PRO document file AVIA 92/147).
8   For further reading on this issue, see Godwin (2007), *The Skylark Rocket*, p.197 onwards.
9   Secret Report on a visit to Australia in February – March 1964 by R.Anderson of the UK MoA. (TNA: PRO document file AVIA 92/147).
10   For a more informal Australian perspective, see McCracken (2008), *Blast Off*, pp. 208-209.
11   Wildman *et al.* (1969), 'Molecular oxygen measurements from 100 to 150 km at Woomera, Australia'.

SKYLARK PERSONNEL, TAKEN MARCH 1967
TO MARK THE FIRING OF THE 150TH. SKYLARK

TOP ROW : A. MATTHEWS, L. HEAD, J. TEAGUE, M. BURES, M. TAYLOR, D. CONGDON,
           B. HOWELL, D. SUTHERLAND, B. RALPH, H. SHUTT, G. BRASLINS, D. STEVENS.

2ND. ROW : C. FENTON, R. COOPER, B. UMLAUF, D. BRENNAN, M. SAJ, K. WILSON,
            J. SMITH, P. HOBBS, E. WATSON, B. CHANEY, DR. B. COOKE.

3RD. ROW : H. BARNARD-BROWN, J. MCKELLAR, P. MALCOLM, M. SHAW, M.T. BROCK,
            D. GRIFFITHS, D. HARDS, K. ROLPH, B. HALLIWELL, L. CARDNELL, (MRS.) Z. MARTIN.

SEATED : (MRS.) J. WHITTING, DR. F. BYRNE, S. BENNETT, H. WHITESIDE, B. GORDON,
          L. FRANCE, P. O'BRIEN, D. CLARKE.

Figure 10.4 A group photograph to mark the 150th Skylark launched from Woomera. [12]
Many of those present had also been there for the 100th celebration three years earlier. (See Figure 8.62).

(WRE \ Chris Hazell)

April 1967   SL426, SL118, SL119, SL425, **SL682**

A new branch of astronomy

From the earliest days of Skylark, British Scientists had considered the possibility that X-rays emitted from cosmic sources (i.e. from beyond the Sun) might be observable.[13] It was known that the Sun (then the only known astronomical source) emitted X-rays, but only at such a strength that if the same was true for stars in general, by the time their X-ray

emissions had reached Earth they would be far too weak for the equipment of the time to measure.

However, undeterred, a UCL group under Boyd and Willmore had proceeded with the design of a measuring system that could be included in a satellite. They also considered the design of detectors that could be used in the proposed Stage 3 stabilised Skylarks. Then, in 1962, a small sounding rocket borne detector fired in the USA made the unexpected discovery of an astonishingly powerful X-ray source in the

---

[12] Although the author's calculations make the 150th Skylark launched from Woomera as SL305 in August 1967! (The 150th overall was SL322 on 25th October 1966, see Appendix 3).
[13] Massey & Robins (1986), *History of British Space Science*, p.366.

direction of the constellation Scorpio. This first cosmic X-ray source was named Scorpius X-1, and was quickly followed by the discovery of a second, Taurus X-1, identified with the Crab Nebula.

These discoveries were of great scientific interest, and soon led to an entirely new branch of astronomy. As part of this, independent proposals were made by UCL and Leicester groups to carry out complementary explorations of the southern sky from Woomera using Skylark, and in due course April 1967 saw the launch of four significant galactic X-ray experiments. [14]

The first Skylark to include a cosmic X-ray detector was **SL426** in April 1967, although in the event, its experiment was from the Australian "UAT" group (Universities of Adelaide and Tasmania),[15] rather than a British institution.

However the main experiments on board SL426 were to measure properties of the ionosphere, and the UAT X-ray equipment formed an ancillary experiment. This resulted in the firing conditions for SL426 being quite particular, requiring the E and F layers of the ionosphere to be formed in virtual absence of Sporadic E.[16] However Tuesday 4th April brought suitable conditions, having dawned bright and clear with visibility at 30 miles (48 km). There was a light wind from the North West, and a trace of cloud at 12,000 feet. Despite being the middle of the Australian autumn, the temperature had risen to 84ºF (28.8ºC) by 10 am, when SL426 was fired.[17]

The flight was successful, the vehicle penetrating the E (100-120 km) and F layers (200+ km) of the ionosphere, reaching an apogee of 220 km. There was no parachute fitted, and the separated head and motor impacted a long way downrange, at about 150 miles (241 km).

The UCW hf pulse radio propagation experiment was unusual for Skylark, because it included a special aerial mounted inside a glass fibre nose cone, and despite the novelty the overall experiment worked well.[18] Unfortunately, no useful information was obtained from the corresponding cw radio propagation experiment, because the signal at the ground receiver faded away after only 20 seconds.

However good results were obtained from the UAT celestial X-ray experiment. The main discrete X-ray sources observed were the Sun, Sco XR-1 and Cen XR-2,[19] the last of which was identified as a new X-ray source in the constellation of Centaurus.[20] Professor Ken Pounds of Leicester later recalled "… I remember it was a bit frustrating for us that they managed to fly the first X-ray astronomy experiment on a Skylark…" [21]

Next SL426 was followed only six days later by **SL118,** on which one of the main experiments was an X-ray survey of the Southern sky using a high sensitivity proportional counter spectrometer - a University of Leicester experiment to scan the sky a with a much larger detector, one of 295 sq.cm area. Similar surveys had been carried out in the northern hemisphere, and it had originally been anticipated that that this experiment would be the first such galactic X-ray survey in the southern hemisphere.

Seq. Nos	Launch date	Ref. (sponsor) launch site	Config- uration	Apogee km (miles)	Experi- menters	Experiments	Result
159 (2)	04 April 1967	SL426 (UK) Woomera	Un, Rav.6 +C	220 (137)	UCW	Ionosphere - electron density profile (cw prop.)	F
					UCW	" - electron density profile (hf pulse prop.)	S
					UAT	Astronomy - celestial X-ray scan	S

Table 10.3 A summary of SL426.

[14] For more background, see Pounds (1986), 'British X-ray astronomy', p.439.

[15] The advanced X-ray apparatus did not come out of the blue - the initial UAT X-ray detector hardware development was performed at the Southwest Center for Advanced Studies, Dallas, Texas, under a NASA contract (Francey *et al,* (1968) 'The Variability of Centaurus XR-2', p.109).

[16] BAC Round Spec. for Skylark No. SL425 and SL426, October 1966.

[17] WRE Research Vehicles Group *Skylarks 425 and 426 (BS141/2 and BS141/1 Summary of Firing,* August 1967, p.3.

[18] Ibid, p.6.

[19] Harries and Francey (1968), 'Observations of CEN XR-2, SCO XR-1, and Terrestrial X-rays', p.716.

[20] Harries (1968), *Variable X-ray fluxes from Celestial Objects,* also Harries and Francey (1968), and Pounds (1986), 'British X-ray Astronomy', p.439.

[21] Pounds in 2001, CCBH (2005) *Skylark Sounding Rockets1957-1972',* p.46, & *Prospero* No.2 p.112. The author cannot but wonder about the fact that SL426 was launched the week before SL118!

Figures 10.5 and 10.6. Left: The Leicester X-ray detector instrument as used on SL118 & SL119. It was an early form of collimator and proportional counter, using the principle explained a little later in this chapter. The gridded collimator in front was officially described as "… an aluminium egg box-array mounted before the counter." [22] Right: One of the infrared horizon detectors, used to help determine payload attitude.

(Roger Cooper)

The other main experiment on board SL118 was from Queen's University Belfast, and designed to measure the intensities and altitude profile of the two night-time airglow molecular bands,[23] a similar experiment to that first carried out successfully on SL39 in October 1966.[24] On SL118 and SL119, the equipment was mounted under a special pressurised nose cone, which had a glass tip and two three inch (76 mm) diameter portholes to allow observations. The photometer detectors used were very sensitive, and even required the range headlights to be switched off to allow the light tight covers to be removed from the nose cone before firing.[25]

As launch had to be on a moonless night, the usual photocells could not be used to help determine the vehicle's attitude in space. Instead, attitude with respect to the horizon was measured using a new infrared detection system from the University of Leicester. The Belfast photometer data was also used to help determine the attitude.

After the SL118/119 project had been initiated, an ancillary experiment was added, designed to measure the disturbance to the ionosphere caused by the passage of the rocket vehicle. It arose because of some unusual results obtained from the UCW (University College of Wales Aberystwyth) radio propagation experiments on SL120 and SL121 in 1964. This experiment was also carried out by UCW, and comprised only ground based measurements taken using a 3.6 MHz radio transmitter and receiver, and an Ionosonde[26] operated from 1-20 MHz.[27]

SL118 was duly launched at 20:21 local time on Monday 10th April 1967, and apogee was successfully reached about three and a half minutes later. See Table 10.4.

[22]   Cooke *et al*, (1967), 'A Cosmic X-ray Survey in the Southern Hemisphere', p.L189.
[23]   Round Specification for SL118 and SL119, Issue 2, December 1966. (WRE SL118 Trials Preparation file J5555/2/118).
[24]   "Advance information on Skylarks SL118/119". (WRE (1966), SL118 Trials Preparation file J5555/2/118).
[25]   Para.15.1 of the Round Specification for SL118 and SL119, Issue 2, December 1966. (WRE SL118 Trials Preparation file J5555/2/118).
[26]   An ionosonde is a ground-based instrument that transmits radio pulses upwards to measure the height of the ionosphere.
[27]   Amendment No.2 to Round Specification Skylark SL118 and SL119, 20 Jan 1967. (WRE SL118 Trials Preparation file J5555/2/118).

Seq. Nos	Launch date	Ref. (sponsor) launch site	Config-uration	Apogee km (miles)	Experi-menters	Experiments	Result
160 (3)	10 April 1967	SL118 (UK) Woomera (BS140)	Un, Rav.7 +C	167 (104)	Bel	Aeronomy - altitude & intensity of molecular oxygen (photometers)	S
					"	Aeronomy – attitude (airglow horizon)	S
					Lei	Astronomy - cosmic X-ray survey southern sky	S
					"	Test (space technology) – infrared horizon detector	Ps
					UCW	Ionosphere - rocket induced ionosphere disturbance	S

Table 10.4 A summary of SL118
(WRE \ Chris Hazell)

During flight, the head of SL118 was left attached to the motor to provide greater inertia, so that the whole assembly would only slowly tumble in space.[28] Thus, although the head was uncontrolled, natural spin allowed the X-ray detector to scan the sky. (In the event, every point in the sky was scanned at least twice.[29])

The payload did not include a parachute, as soft-landing was not a requirement. However, before re-entry, the head was separated from the Raven motor case, and so the impact of the head was not as bad as it might have been. (See figures 10.7 and 10.8.)

The Leicester experiment was very successful, and during the period of observation, from 80 to 350 seconds after launch, 50 scans across the sky were obtained.[30] Several cosmic X-ray sources were observed, the most outstanding being that in Centaurus (Cen X-2), which by now had brightened to outshine Sco X-1. Overall, the experiment was deemed an outstanding success – sufficient for the UK Science Research Council to grant another pair of flights with bigger and better detectors.[31] (SL723 launched in June 1968).

These were the days when missions often had two Skylarks assigned to insure against the possibility of failure. Thus, SL118

Figures 10.7 and 10.8 The head of SL118 fell over 160 km (100 miles) from space without a parachute. Even so, the remains are surprisingly recognisable.
(WRE (1967), SL118 Trials Results file J5555/3/118)

[28] Cooper (2006), *Rocket Man*, p.4.
[29] Cooke *et al*, (1967), 'A Cosmic X-ray Survey in the Southern Hemisphere', p.L189.
[30] Cooke *et al*, (1967), p.L189.
[31] Cooper (2006), *Rocket Man*, p.4.

was followed two days later by a repeat payload aboard **SL119**, launched at 22:02 local time on Wednesday 12th April. The vehicle successfully reached 160 km (99 miles), although there were problems with the Leicester X-ray experiment. (See figure 10.9)

Hence, this time the Leicester X-ray experiment appears to have been unsuccessful, as observations for SL119 are missing from the scientific papers for SL118, SL426 or SL425.[32]

Finally in this series, **SL425** was launched on the 21st

April, a duplicate of SL426 with similar results, including a successful repeat of the UAT X-ray experiment.[33] Overall, the UAT experiments on SL426 and SL425 were particularly successful, revealing for the first time the extreme variability of an X-ray source. The new source in Centaurus (Cen XR-2) was measured and compared to the existing known Sco X-1 and Tau X-1. During the span of these four Skylark missions it had brightened to outshine Sco X-1, a result that led to it being the first X-ray object to be unambiguously identified as variable.[34]

```
UNCLAS J3624 J5555/3/119 AD 67/115
FURTHER INFO ON SL119. AIRGLOW RESULTS VERY GOOD.
ONE FORWARD AND ONE SIDE VIEWING PHOTOMETER SAW HORIZON AND
TOPSIDE OF MOLECULAR OXYGEN LAYER SEVERAL TIMES. APPARENT
FAILURE OF ZX-RAY COUNTER EQUIPMENT NOT YET EXPLAINED.
ALL SECTIONS OF ROUND HAVE BEEN RECOVERED. MOTOR WAS 81 MILES
ON 334 DEGS. HEAD 77.7 MILES ON 335 DEGS.
RECOVERY TEAM SAW NO TRACE OF GLASS NOSE CONE TIP EXCEPT FOR
METAL BASE RING WHICH WAS IN SEVERAL PIECES. PERHAPS IT SHATTERED
DURING RE-ENTRY.
```

Figure 10.9 Part of a Telex from WRE reporting on SL119.
(Telex ref. J3624 WRE (1967), SL119 Trials Results file J5555/3/119)

Figures 10.10 and 10.11 The head of SL119 appears to have descended horizontally with a relatively low terminal velocity. On the right is a close-up of the broken bay of the Leicester X-ray electronics, with on its right the horizon sensor bay.
(WRE (1967), SL119 Trials Results file J5555/3/119)

---

[32] See for instance Cooke *et al*, (1967), 'A Cosmic X-ray Survey in the Southern Hemisphere', p.L189.

[33] The slide presentation at *www.chemphys.adelaide.edu.au/about/physics/history/symposium/ken-mccracken.pdf* (last accessed August 2014), contains a little more on SL425 and SL426.

[34] Francey, Fenton, Harries & McCracken (1968), 'The Variability of Centaurus XR-2'.

Now designated Centaurus X-2, this was the first of a new class of objects, the 'X-ray transients', which might not flare up again for years. (They are now known to be binary systems where one companion is a black hole).

By this time (1967), at least 30 discrete cosmic X-ray sources had been discovered,[35] and a new branch of astronomy was being opened up, in which Skylark would play a very useful part. Table 10.5 reveals the pace of new discoveries during the next 40 years.

Early cosmic X-ray observing equipment

X-ray sources are difficult to observe because X-rays from them pass though non-metallic materials, and so, unlike visible light, cannot be focussed by glass lenses. One instrument used on the early Skylarks to overcome this difficulty was the pinhole camera, which having no lens, could be used to form an X-ray image. This was fine for the study of the Sun, where there was plenty of energy available, but detecting more distant sources required instruments with greater sensitivity.

Early American sounding rockets (c.1946) had used the Geiger counter as a detector, but this was an 'all or nothing' device, and so the 'proportional counter' was devised. This was a variation of the Geiger counter that comprised a metal container filled with gas and with a thin plastic window to allow the X-rays to enter. The individual X-ray photons interacted with the gas in manner proportional to their energy, allowing their strength to be measured electrically as a series of voltage pulses.

To provide directional capability a 'collimator' was added (not shown below), which allowed X-rays within a restricted angular range to pass to the proportional counter. The simplest type of collimator consisted of a set of parallel metal plates, the "aluminium egg box-array". (See for instance figure 10.5).

Year	No. X-ray Sources known	Based on
1960	0	(excluding the Sun)
1962	1	Rocket experiments
1965	10	Rocket experiments
1970	60	Rocket & balloon experiments
1974	160	3rd Uhuru Catalog
1980	680	Amnuel et al. (1982) Catalog
1984	840	HEAO A-1 Catalog
1990	8,000	Einstein & EXOSAT source catalogs
2000	340,000	ROSAT source catalogs
2010	780,000	above + XMM-Newton & Chandra detected sources
2013	1,100,000	above + XMM-Newton & Chandra detected sources

Table 10.5 The rapidly increasing number of cosmic X-ray sources discovered since 1960.[36]

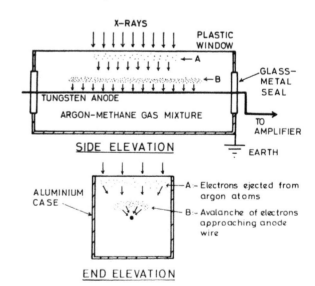

Figure 10.12 The principle of the proportional counter.
(Griffiths (1971), figure 4)[37]

---

[35]   Friedman, Byram & Chubb (1967), 'Distribution and Variability of Cosmic X-Ray Sources'.

[36]   Figures from NASA website *http://heasarc.gsfc.nasa.gov/docs/heasarc/headates/how_many_xray.html* , (last accessed August 2014).

[37]   Journal of the British Interplanetary Society, Vol.24 no.3 (March 1971), p.134. Reproduced with permission.

The terms 'collimator' and 'proportional counter' have been explained here because they appear frequently in descriptions of Skylark payloads and instruments in this book. Later on, more sophisticated instruments were developed, including the crystal spectrometer and X-ray telescope.

SL118 was followed by **SL682** on the 27th April. This was an RAE test flight that reached 203 km (126 miles); however, the author has been unable to find out its purpose. The payload was stabilised, so it was probably a 'special', as it was the only Skylark to be given a 68x series number. It is possible it was a modified version of SL482, (a successor to SL481), which was due to be launched with a stabilised payload in May 1967,[38] but no round with that number was ever launched.

Ariel III

This third joint UK/USA scientific satellite was launched into orbit by a NASA Scout rocket from the Vandenberg Air Force Base in California on 5th May 1967. This time, as well as providing the scientific experiments, the UK undertook all the engineering, design, construction and testing of the satellite itself, these responsibilities being undertaken by the then Ministry of Technology, acting through the RAE and British Industry.[39] Overall, Ariel III looked similar to its predecessors, and there were five scientific experiments on board:

1. Measurements of electron density and temperature (Langmuir and capacitance probes) (J.Sayers, Birmingham University)

2. Measurement of galactic and ionospheric noise (F.G.Smith, Cambridge (later Manchester) University/Jodrell Bank)
3. Measurement of natural VLF radiation (T.R.Kaiser, Sheffield University)
4. Measurement of HF noise from thunderstorms (Radio Research Station)
5. Distribution of molecular oxygen (K.Stewart, Meteorological Office)

Three of these were linked to or extended from experiments carried in Ariel I and Ariel II, the other two (numbers 3 and 4) were new.[40]

The Space department of the RAE at Farnborough played a major role in the design of the spacecraft; the main industrial contractors were the British Aircraft Corporation and the General Electric Company:

> The scientific success of Ariel III was important but of equal significance was the fact that the UK had, for the first time, successfully designed and developed a complete satellite. That the necessary technology and design techniques had been available was very largely due to the research and development programme undertaken at RAE in the immediately preceding years and concerned with the many individual systems required by satellites – power, attitude control, telemetry, command, data handling and so on – and with their mechanical and thermal design.[41]

Thus the Skylark programme had contributed both directly (as with the Meteorological Office sensors tested aboard SL406) and indirectly by building up the skills of the RAE Space Department.

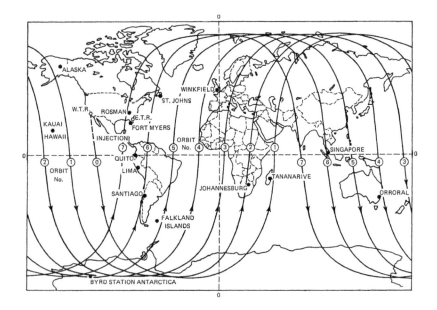

Figure 10.13 The first eight orbits of Ariel III.
(Ladd and Smith (1969), figure 1) [42]

---

[38] From SL482 reference in a letter from MoA to J.F.Hazell, 3 August 1966. (TNA: PRO AVIA 91/144).
[39] Massey & Robins (1986), *History of British Space Science*, p.97.
[40] Ladd and Smith (1969), 'An introduction to the Ariel III Satellite Project', p.480.
[41] Massey & Robins (1986), *History of British Space Science,* p.100. © Science and Engineering Research Council 1986, published by Cambridge University Press, reproduced with permission.
[42] Reproduced courtesy Royal Society London.

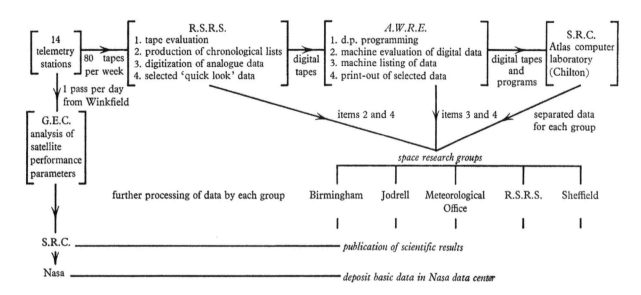

Figure 10.14 Ariel III data processing.

(Ladd and Smith (1969), figure 2) [43]

Scientific satellites produce orders more data than sounding rockets,[44] and the figure above illustrates the complex arrangements that had to be put in place to handle the data from Ariel III. The fact that 80 data tapes a week were received from the telemetry stations highlights the difference. That this might be too much of a good thing is indicated by the fact that eleven months after Ariel III had been launched, only 40% of the low speed and 30% of the high speed data had been processed in the form required by the individual space research groups.[45]

Of particular interest is the Meteorological Office experiment aboard Ariel III, partly because of the method adopted to collect data from altitudes below the satellite (i.e. at sounding rocket height as shown above), and also because the detectors used had a very short life in space (a half-life in orbit of 20 days),[47] and their design had been tested before hand on Skylark flights (for instance SL406 in March 1967).

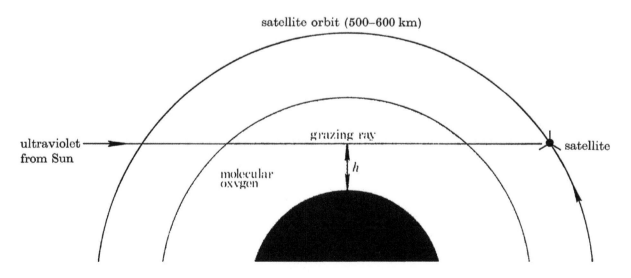

Figure 10.15 The principle of the Meteorological Office molecular oxygen experiment on Ariel III.

(Stewart and Wildman (1969), figure 1) [46]

---

[43] Reproduced courtesy Royal Society London.

[44] As Desmond King-Hele expressed it, "Most spacecraft chatter continuously, sending back to the ground stations so much data that storage can be quite a problem." (King-Hele (1992), *A tapestry of orbits*, p.ix, © Cambridge University Press, reproduced with permission.).

[45] Ladd and Smith (1969), 'An introduction to the Ariel III Satellite Project', p.487.

[46] Reproduced courtesy Royal Society London.

[47] Stewart and Wildman (1969), 'Preliminary results of molecular oxygen observations from the Ariel III satellite', p.592.

There were no Skylark launches from Woomera in May, but there were two launches in Europe. The first was S11/2, whose predecessor S11/1 had crashed after launch in November 1966. On that occasion, the second stage Raven motor failed to ignite, so the launch of **S11/2** had been postponed

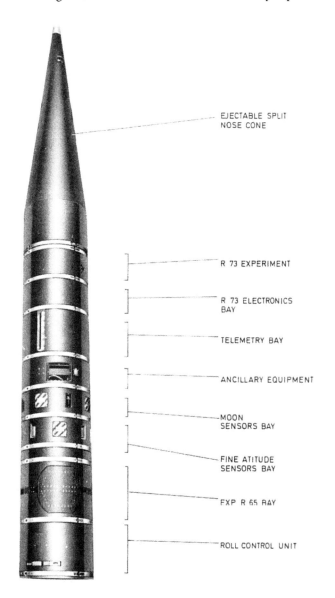

for investigations, and the payload was returned to BAC for modifications. These and flight clearance tests at ESTEC were completed by April 1967, and on the 25th the payload was returned to the range at Sardinia. Range preparation commenced on the 30th, and on the 16th May, the payload was placed in the tower for telemetry tests. Unfortunately, problems continued, during the night there was heavy rain, and the following day the payload had to be stripped down and checked for water damage.[48]

After various minor problems had been sorted, launch preparations took place on the 20th, but the launch was cancelled because of a heavy ground mist and a leak in the roll-control unit. Finally, launch took place in the very early hours of the 22nd May at 01:11 local time:

This time all was successful, the payload reaching an altitude of 194 km (121 miles). Both experiments worked well, the only problem being the loss of some attitude information because the Moon sensors and one of the three magnetometers failed. This meant the experimenters had to spent considerable time on attitude re-constitution.

S05/2 had had a similar history to S11/2, in that its predecessor S05/1 had also failed. The problem that time had not been rocket failure, but lack of any scientific results partly because an instrument cover failed to eject, and partly because very little attitude information had been returned. The second payload had therefore been returned to ESTEC for a complete redesign. This had taken nearly two years (the payload was returned a second time for redesign of the Moon

Figure 10.16 A general view of payload S11/2.
(ESRO (1973), report SP-78, p.29, figure 2)

Seq. Nos	Launch date	Ref. (sponsor) launch site	Config-uration	Apogee km (miles)	Experi-menters	Experiments	Result
164 (7)	22 May 1967	S11/2 (ESRO) Sardinia	Un, Rav.6 +C	194 (121)	PIB	Ionosphere/Astronomy – study of low energy (X-ray) proton component of cosmic X-rays (experiment R73)	S
					ROE	Astronomy – night sky random stellar UV survey (experiment R65)	S

Table 10.6 A summary of S11/2.

48   ESRO (1973), report SP-78, p.26.

sensors), so apart from the experiments this second flight unit was regarded as a completely new payload.[49] In addition, at the request of the experimenters, a roll-control unit[50] to optimise the spin rate was included, a first for ESRO.

Both experiments were from the Royal Observatory Edinburgh, and, as with S11/2, involved ultraviolet observations of stars, although this time spectral analysis was included. The launch conditions were quite stringent, requiring a night launch between three hours after sunset and three hours before sunrise, within three days of full Moon, and with a clear sky and preferably dry conditions. Bad weather in Sardinia on the 24th May forced the countdown to be abandoned after five hours, when the ballistic wind was such that the theoretical impact point of the rocket was on land. However, the following night things were better and the launch took place just after midnight local time. See Table 10.7.

This time the instrument covers ejected successfully, the attitude sensing devices worked, the new roll control unit reduced the spin to 28° per second as required, and the experiments were a success.

Figures 10.17 and 10.18 Schematic and general views of payload S05/2.

(ESRO (1973), report SP-78, p.12 & 14, figures 2 & 3)

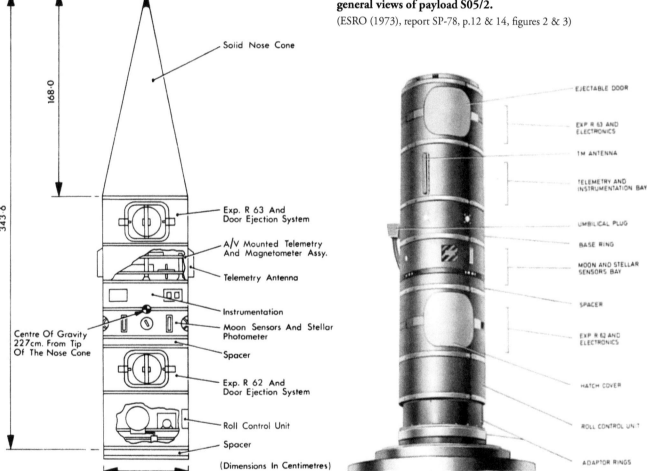

Seq. Nos	Launch date	Ref. (sponsor) launch site	Config- uration	Apogee km (miles)	Experi- menters	Experiments	Result
165 (8)	26 May 1967	S05/2 (ESRO) Sardinia	Un, Rav.6 +C	239 (149)	ROE	Astronomy - stellar UV emission (photometer) (experiment R62)	S
					ROE	Astronomy - stellar UV emission (spectrophotometer) (experiment R63)	S

Table 10.7 A summary of S05/2.

---

[49] ESRO (1973), report SP-78, p.7.

[50] The single axis roll control unit was made by Space General Corporation (Campbell (1970b), p.133), and used a gas jet system rather than the electric motor driven unit previously used by the RAE. (See Chapter 6, Figure 6.34 onwards).

The background to the mission was that since 1962, the Space Research Division of the Royal Observatory Edinburgh had been planning and launching rocket experiments aimed mainly at observing in the absolute UV brightness of particular types of stars.[51] Flights in 1965 and 1966 had been unsuccessful (S05/1 and S11/1), but the ROE persisted, and were rewarded by these successes in 1967.

The R62 photometer instrument was mounted with its optical axis at right angles to the roll axis of the rocket, and observed the sky through a 25 x 23 cm (10" x 9") rectangular port in the side of the payload. This was covered by a tight fitting door, which was pneumatically ejected at an altitude of 80 km (50 miles). Each of the primary mirrors had a collecting area of 120 sq.cm, and at the focus were photomultipliers, which required a voltage of 1.4 kV. Approximately five minutes of observing time was obtained above 90km (56 miles), the data was telemetered to the ground, and as no recovery system was employed, at the

end of the flight, the spent rocket and payload disappeared into the Mediterranean.

The R63 instrument was similar, but used a diffraction gating to produce a first-order spectrum.[52] Despite the complexity, this time all went well, and the attitude sensors allowed the stars observed to be identified. As a result of the S05/2 and S11/2 experiments, pioneering European observations of some 30 stars were published.[53] Similar experiments were flown the following year (S47/1 and S27/1), as described later in this chapter.

August 1967   SL305, SL581B, SL521, SL522

There were no Skylark launches in June or July, but August was another busy month at Woomera, and on the 8th, the launch of the second of 1967's three stabilised flights took place. See Table 10.8.

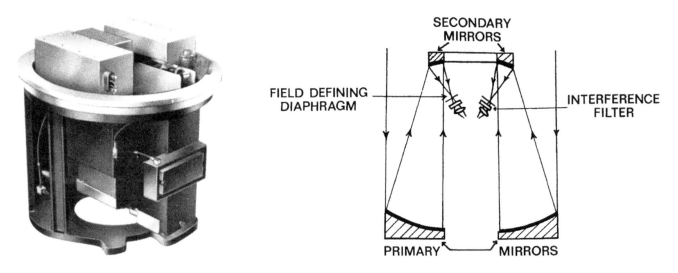

Figures 10.19 and 10.20 A general view and optical arrangement of ROE experiment R 62.
(Left: ESRO (1973), report SP-78, p.13, figure 2. Right: Campbell (1970b), figure 2)

Seq. Nos	Launch date	Ref. (sponsor) launch site	Config- uration	Apogee km (miles)	Experi- menters	Experiments	Result
166 (9)	08 Aug. 1967	SL305 (UK) Woomera	Sun, Rav.6 +C	182 (113)	MSSL	Solar physics – X-ray spatial resolution (8-18Å) (scanning spectroheliograph)	S
					MSSL	Solar physics - Lyman-α (ionisation chamber)	?
					Lei	Solar physics - soft X-ray high res. (counter crystal spectrometer)	S

Table 10.8 A summary of SL305.

[51] Campbell (1970a), 'Absolute Stellar Photometry in the Region 1200 Å – 3000 Å', p.135.
[52] ESRO (1973), report SP-78, p.7.
[53] Campbell (1970b), 'Absolute Stellar Photometry in the Region 1900Å - 3000Å'.

Two of the three instruments flown were similar to those on SL304 in May the previous year. The Leicester experiment for instance comprised two slitless Bragg crystal spectrometers,[54] improved to provide higher spectral resolution than had been obtained before, so providing more detailed information on the physics and the elements within the Sun.[55]

In addition the same scanning X-ray spectroheliograph was flown as part of a joint UCL/Leicester research programme, again it successfully produced an 'image' by using the Skylark Attitude Control Unit (ACU) to scan the Sun, see figure 10.21

The third instrument on SL305 was the MSSL Lyman-α telescope, which used the same type of grazing incidence mirror, but the detector was an ionisation chamber. This was used to produce a contour map of that particular ultraviolet emission from the Sun.

SL581B was an RAE proving round; a repeat of SL581A launched the previous December. Originally, the mission was to have been performed by SL583A, but SL581A was soft-landed in such good condition that it was re-used instead.[57]

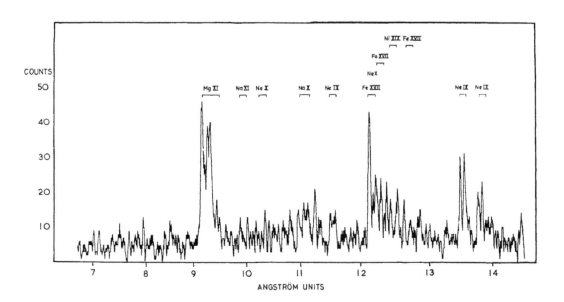

Figure 10.21 SL305 – the University of Leicester high-resolution solar X-ray experiment – spectrum observed with beryl crystal from 7.5Å to 15Å, (0.75 – 1.5 nm).

(Batstone, Evans, Parkinson & Pounds (1970), figure 2)

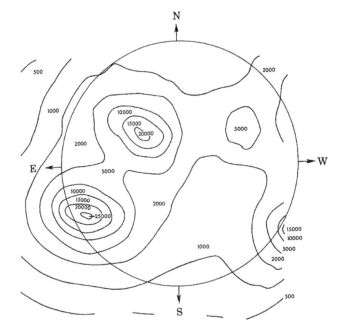

Figure 10.22 SL305 - X-ray map of the Sun on 8th August 1967.

(Negus, Glencross & Pounds (1970), figure 7) [56]

---

[54] Observing X-rays was not easy, and space scientists had to devise many types of sophisticated instruments and techniques for the purpose, see for instance Boyd (1964), 'Techniques for the Measurement of Extra-Terrestrial Soft X-Radiation' (1964), (over 50 pages long!).

[55] Batstone, Evans, Parkinson & Pounds (1970), 'Further X-Ray Spectra of Solar Active Regions'.

[56] Reproduced courtesy Royal Society London.

[57] Telex from WRE to RAE 1st Feb.1967. (WRE SL581B Trials Preparation file J5555/2/581B). SL583A was instead used in February 1968 to test the new Goldfinch boost motor.

It carried two main and half a dozen subsidiary experiments. The first main experiment was to flight test the components of the improved standard Raven ignition system, a repeat of the test carried out by SL581A.[58] The second was to check the feasibility of reducing impact dispersion by spinning the vehicle using spin-up motors as well as canted fins. The idea was that a much greater reduction of dispersion might be achieved if the spin was induced as soon as possible after leaving the launcher, rather than waiting until aerodynamic forces had taken effect via the canted fins.[59] Thus, SL581B was fitted with six IMP VI spin motors (see page 310) at the interface between the Raven fins and the Cuckoo adaptor, as well as canting both the Raven and Cuckoo fins.

The subsidiary experiments included a revised Raven ignition system that was expected to be more reliable and easily

adjusted and tested. It was monitored for performance, but in this case not actually used for Raven ignition. Several experiments tested aspects of the new ACU (Attitude Control Unit); including one to measure how the amount of sunlight reflected from the Earth or clouds (the albedo) might affect the pointing accuracy of the ACU when operating in space. A new electronic programmer developed by the WRE was also flown for the first time, and tested by operating some aspects of the other subsidiary experiments.

SL581B was ready for launch on August the 10th, but the weather was unsuitable,[60] and after nearly a week of waiting it was not until the 16th that firing took place. The Imp spin motors added an extra 15 minutes to the arming time,[61] and were ignited by trip switches as the vehicle cleared the launch tower:

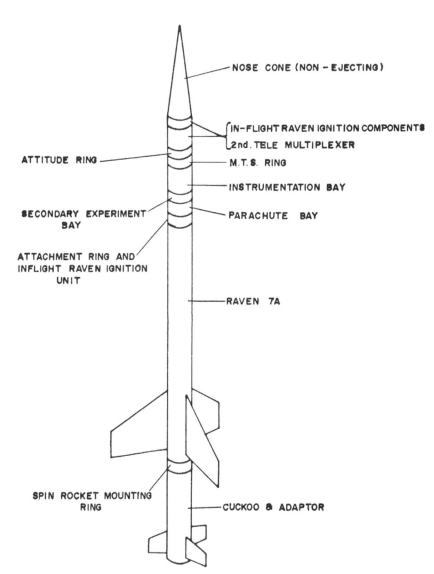

Figure 10.23 The configuration of SL581B, including the new spin rocket mounting ring.
(WRE (1967), SL581B Trials Preparation file, Trials Instruction No.BS143, p.8)

NOSE CONE (NON – EJECTING)

IN–FLIGHT RAVEN IGNITION COMPONENTS
2nd. TELE MULTIPLEXER

ATTITUDE RING

M.T.S. RING

INSTRUMENTATION BAY

SECONDARY EXPERIMENT BAY

PARACHUTE BAY

ATTACHMENT RING AND INFLIGHT RAVEN IGNITION UNIT

RAVEN 7A

SPIN ROCKET MOUNTING RING

CUCKOO & ADAPTOR

---

58   "Advance information on Skylark SL581B", WRE (1967) SL581B Trials Preparation file J5555/2/581B, also minutes of Fourth Skylark Policy Meeting, 28/2/1967, p.7, para.3.4.1.

59   "Advance information on Skylark SL581B", para.2.2. (WRE (1967) SL581B Trials Preparation file J5555/2/581B).

60   One of the subsidiary experiments required a preferred 4/8 cloud cover made up of large belts rather than patches!

61   WRE Trials Instruction No. BS143, p.8. (WRE (1967) SL581B Trials Preparation file J5555/2/581B).

	0 sec	Cuckoo ignition
Approx.	1 sec	Spin rocket ignition
	6 sec	Raven ignition & Cuckoo separation

As this was the first time the technique had been tried, high speed long focal length cameras were used to record the performance of the spin rockets, the spin rate and Cuckoo separation.[62] Initially all went well, and after three and a half minutes SL581B successfully reached 152 km (94 miles), after which head separation duly took place.

Unfortunately, on the return leg the parachute recovery system failed yet again. Although the WRE 'Preparation' file for the SL581B trial (J5555/2/581B) has survived in the Australian Defence Archives (Edinburgh), for unknown reasons the corresponding 'Results' file has been destroyed,[63] although the recovery photographs have survived, apparently having been removed beforehand. Thus, it is only possible to deduce the results of the flight. Head separation is known to have taken place, as the motor landed separately, see Figure 10.1.

The various SL581 trials appear to have been successful in reducing impact dispersion, because by November 1967 the spinning using canted fins was considered flight proven, and released to BAC as a build option.[64] However, it was a year or two before the use of Imp motors was approved.

'Imp' motors

These were a family of very small solid propellant motors that had been developed over the years by RPE. During that time there had been about 15 different versions and in March 1968 11 types were still in production.[65] They were available with burning times from 0.1 to 2 seconds, and thrusts from 80 to 1130 lbf (355N – 2.2kN), and were used on Black Knight and Blue Streak, as well as many smaller projects.

The type first used on Skylark was the Mark VI,[66] which was just 5.8 inches (147 mm) long, and had a nominal thrust of 110 lbf (520 N) for just half a second. Six were used on SL581B.

Figures 10.24 and 10.25 Unusually, because of the use of the spin-up motors, the spent SL581B Cuckoo boost was photographed. On the left, it can be seen that its fin assembly has broken away on impact; on the right, two used Imp motors have broken free.

(WRE (1967), SL581B Trials Preparation (sic) file)

[62] "Advance information on Skylark SL581B", para.7. (WRE (1967) SL581B Trials Preparation file J5555/2/581B).
[63] Roger Henwood, personal correspondence, February 2011.
[64] *Skylark Policy and Programme – Second Review*, document ref. DS/55/01 06/11/1967, p.3. para. 3.1.2.1. (TNA: PRO document file AVIA 92/144).
[65] RPE Westcott (1968), *Index to Solid Propellant Motors*, p.4.
[66] WRE (1967), *Trials Instruction No. BS143*, p.65. (WRE SL581B Trials Preparation file J5555/2/581B).

Figures 10.26 and 10.27 SL581B came to earth some 75 miles (121km) down range.[67]
Clearly, this third flight was its last!
(WRE (1967), SL581B Trials Preparation (sic) file)

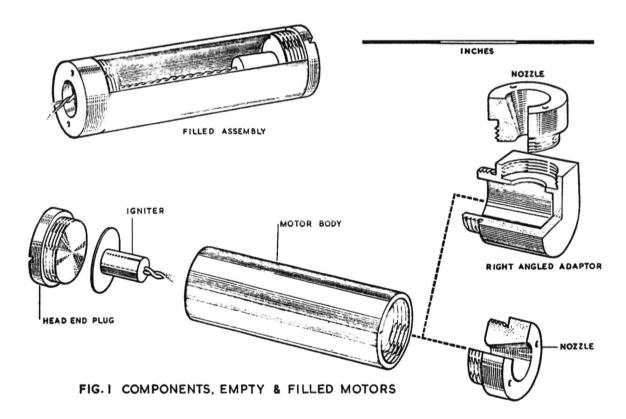

FIG.I COMPONENTS, EMPTY & FILLED MOTORS

Figure 10.28 The construction of the IMP Mk I, II & III series A motors.
(RPE Westcott Solid Motor Data Sheet, March 1961)

[67] 'Skylark Impact Points 1964 – 1969', WRE Drawing No. T 2414, Issue 1 (via R.Henwood).

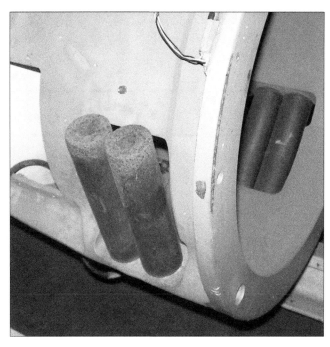

Figures 10.29 and 10.30 New and used Imp spin-up motors.
(Left: Sounding Rocket Services. Right: Bristol Aero Collection, ex Kemble Airfield, author 100_1867)

The University of Oxford's first Skylark Experiment

Just over a week later, the first Skylark mission for Oxford University was launched, with experiments from their Astrophysics Department. The main purpose of **SL521** was to measure the surface brightness of the night sky at two particular wavelengths simultaneously, in order to help resolve the debate on the source of night-time Lyman-α and Hα emissions (in effect ultraviolet versions of the airglow).[68] This source of intense radiation had been discovered in 1955, but the question of its origin had not been satisfactorily settled.[69] One possibility was that ultraviolet emissions from the Sun were being scattered in some way when they reached the Earth, but if so, the mechanism was far from understood.[70]

The night sky brightness instruments used relatively simple detectors,[71] which did not produce an image of the Sun, but instead measured the radiation arriving at the Earth. Hence, they have been classified by the author as aeronomy rather than solar physics instruments. A second experiment using a similar detector was designed to measure attitude with respect to the horizon, using a prism looking at 90° to the axis of the vehicle.[72]

A practical problem was that the detectors used in the experiments contained a source of Cerenkov radiation,[73] used for in-flight calibration.[74] This source was activated by 30 millicuries of Strontium 90, a radioactive isotope used in medicine and industry. Its use in Skylark, (which might break up on impact), had to be cleared with the Australian authorities,[75] a process which had been started in January 1965, and was finally granted with conditions towards the end of that year.

The launch was scheduled for a moonless period from 23rd August until 6th September 1967, and **SL521** was fired promptly on the 24th. Unfortunately, although the flight appears to have been successful, no usable experimental results were obtained.[76]

---

[68] Lyman-α is a spectral line of hydrogen at 121.6 nm (1216 Å) in the far ultraviolet part of the electromagnetic spectrum. UCL had flown several Lyman-α instruments since the first on SL12 in 1959, but these had been directed at the Sun's disc rather than the Earth's upper atmosphere.
[69] See for instance Friedman (1960), 'Recent Experiments from Rockets and Satellites', p.267.
[70] Ingham (1969), 'Sources of the Lyman-α emission in the night sky', p.401.
[71] Ingham (1969), p.401.
[72] BAC (1967), *Round Specification for Skylark Nos. SL521 and 522.* (WRE SL521 Trials Preparation file, J5555/2/521).
[73] Visible or UV light generated by high-energy particles.
[74] *Advanced Information for Skylarks SL521 & 522* & many other documents in WRE (1967), SL521 Trials Preparation file J5555/2/521.
[75] Including the Atomic Weapons Tests Safety Committee!
[76] Ingham (1969), 'Sources of the Lyman-α emission in the night sky', p.401.

Seq. Nos	Launch date	Ref. (sponsor) launch site	Config- uration	Apogee km (miles)	Experi- menters	Experiments	Result
168 (11)	24 Aug. 1967	SL521 (UK) Woomera	Un, Rav.7 +C	178 (111)	Oxford	Aeronomy - Lyman-α & Hα night sky brightness, and attitude with respect to the horizon via airglow	F
169 (12)	29 Aug. 1967	SL522 (UK) Woomera	Un, Rav.7 +C	124 (77)	Oxford	Aeronomy - Lyman-α & Hα night sky brightness, and attitude with respect to the horizon via airglow	Ps

Table 10.9 A summary of SL521 and SL522.

An identical **SL522** followed five days later. However, soon after launch, SL522 developed spin-yaw resonance,[77] and the apogee was only 124km (77 miles), compared to 178 km (111 miles) for SL521. Ironically, this time the experiment was partly successful, although only for the Lyman-α part of it. Parachutes were not fitted, and the results were returned by telemetry only. From the attitude information obtained, it was concluded there were probably both terrestrial and galactic sources for the emissions measured.

September & October 1967	S26/1, S19/1, S26/2, S19/2

It had originally been intended to launch **S26/1** and **S26/2** back in May, but because of a decision to postpone the associated campaigns of ESRO sounding rocket launches D30

and D34 from Andøya in Norway, the payloads were initially placed into store.[79] Launch preparations eventually started at Sardinia in September, and were carried out at the same time as those for Skylark S19. (At this time Sardinia still had to be used, because although the facilities at the new Esrange centre in Sweden were almost complete, the new Skylark launch tower being built there was not yet ready).

S26/1 and S26/2 were identical combined ionosphere and aeronomy missions, carrying experiments from two British universities. Those from Birmingham were designed to measure the electron temperature and density in the ionosphere. Unusually the measurement probes were carried on one-metre booms deployed either side of the payload at altitude. (The actual probes were similar to those flown on SL38 in 1959, Figure 6.27).

Figures 10.31 and 10.32 The motor from SL522 landed only about 45 miles (72 km) downrange,[78] and the casing appears to have been mostly destroyed after impact on hard ground.
WRE (1967), SL522 Trials Results file J/5555/3/522)

---

[77] The spin-yaw resonance problem with Skylark is described in Chapter 6.
[78] "Skylark Impact Points 1964 – 1969", WRE Drg. No. T 2414, Issue 1 (via R.Henwood).
[79] ESRO (1973), report SP-78, p.76, para. 3.2.2.

The other three experiments were from the RSRS (Radio and Space Research Station), formerly the RRS.[80] Two were designed to investigate the formation of the D-region of the ionosphere, by measuring UV and X-rays from the Sun by means of on-board detectors deployed at 65 km. The other experiment enabled the electron density of the D-layer of the ionosphere to be deduced by means of radio waves transmitted from the ground.

Flight unit integration and testing had been carried out in April/May 1967 by BAC's GW Division at their Filton factory in Bristol:

Figures 10.33, 10.34 and 10.35 Assembly of an S26 flight unit payload.[81]

Top left: The Sun sensor and magnetometer based attitude determination bay being added to the 'housekeeping' instrumentation section. Top right: The Birmingham experiment bay came next, and was followed by the RSRS experiment bays. Left: Finally, the glass fibre nosecone was added to complete the payload.

[80] As noted in Appendix 3, in 1965 the Radio Research Station (RRS) had been renamed the Radio and Space Research Station (RSRS), and transferred from the DSIR to the new Science Research Council (SRC). So despite the name change, the Skylark experiments originated from the same organisation. For more information on the RRS and Ditton Park archive visit *www.ukssdc.ac.uk/ditton_park_archive/history.html* . (Last accessed August 2014).

[81] These photographs are stills from the film "Skylark: Sounding Space" taken by the BAC film unit. For details, see section 5 of the list of references at the end of this book. At the time of writing, the film was available online via an ESA website, see *http://spaceinvideos.esa.int/Videos/Undated/Skylark_Sounding_Space* (last accessed August 2014).

Figures 10.36 and 10.37 Integration and vibration testing in the Filton environmental laboratories. On the left one of the booms is being tested in the lab, on the right testing included use of a 'Pye Ling model 335 15,000 lb thrust vibration system'.[82]

Figures 10.38, 10.39 and 10.40 Skylark S26 being readied for launch from Sardinia in late September 1967. This sequence shows the Cuckoo and Raven motors being installed in the launch tower.

[82]   The "Pye Ling" information is from the back of a BAC black and white photo of S26 being vibration tested. (Via J.A.Hill). See also *www.pamphonic. co.uk/html/pye___ling.html* (last accessed August 2014).

Figures 10.41, 10.42 and 10.43 The payload is added, and S26/1 is successfully launched at 14:32 local time.

Seq. Nos	Launch date	Ref. (sponsor) launch site	Config-uration	Apogee km (miles)	Experi-menters	Experiments	Result
170 (13)	27 Sept. 1967	S26/1 (ESRO) Sardinia	Un, Rav.7 +C	183 (114)	Bir	Ionosphere - electron density (rf probe) (expt. R105)	S
					"	Ionosphere - electron temperature (double Langmuir probe) (experiment R106)	S
					RSRS	Aeronomy – Lyman-α flux (detector) (expt.R123)	S
					"	Aeronomy – solar X-rays (detector) (experiment R131)	S
					"	Ionosphere – D-region electron density (lf propagation/Faraday rotation) (experiment R132)	S

Table 10.10 A summary of S26/1. S26/2 (launched ten days later) was similar.

Figures 10.44 and 10.45 S19 payload preparations in the heat at Sardinia. Presumably smoking in the preparation area would be frowned on these days!

(John Raymont / MSSL)

S19/1

The purpose of the S19 Skylarks was to study the properties of the mesosphere (50-85 km), the intermediate region for which sounding rockets are the best tool to investigate. The plan was to carry out a study simultaneously at different latitudes, with each S19 flight corresponding with the launch from Andøya in Norway of a D34 [83] payload carrying an identical principal experiment (a neutral mass spectrometer).[84]

Figures 10.46 and 10.47 Rocket away! – Skylark S19 ignition and early flight.

(John Raymont \ MSSL)

---

[83] The ESRO 'Dxx' designation referred to flights made by the French 'Dragon' sounding rocket, a medium sized vehicle capable of taking a payload of about 75 kg to about 440 km. (HSR-38).

[84] ESRO (1973), report SP-78, p.41.

Seq. Nos	Launch date	Ref. (sponsor) launch site	Config-uration	Apogee km (miles)	Experi-menters	Experiments	Result
171 (14)	04 Oct. 1967	S19/1 (ESRO) Sardinia	Un, Rav.7 +C	207 (129)	Breisach	Ionosphere – electron density profile (inverse Seddon expt., 3-channel radio receiver) (experiment R20)	F
					MSSL	Ionosphere – electron temperature (Langmuir probe) (experiment R44)	S
					Bonn	Aeronomy – densities neutral atmosphere components (Two neutral mass spectrometers) (experiment R79)	S
					IAP	Aeronomy – atmospheric pressure & density (gauges) (experiment R104)	S

Table 10.11 A summary of S19/1.

As well as the principal experiment, each S19 payload contained another aeronomy and two ionosphere experiments, one of the latter being from the UK's MSSL laboratory. As noted above, the two S19 Skylarks were being prepared for launch at Sardinia at the same time as the S26 Skylarks, and it was in September that John Raymont from MSSL (who in 1965 had accompanied SL48's payload to Australia) visited there, and later recalled:

> My next launch campaign was to Sardinia (Sept. '67), which was ESRO's main launch site during its early programme. This was for [the] Skylark S19 payload. The payload team from ESTeC remained my good friends for several years. The launch site was in the Sardinian mountains at Perdasdefogu, a village which was also an army, air force and naval base. Not much air force or navy work in the mountains! [85]

Unlike at Woomera, personal cameras were allowed at Sardinia, so John Raymont was able take some photographs of the preparations and launch. (Figures 10.44 to 10.47.)

S19/1 was placed in the launch tower on October 2nd. The countdown started at 10:10 on the 4th, but was held at -4 minutes awaiting confirmation of the successful launch of D34/1 from Andøya. At -30 seconds there was a brief hold because of an unsuccessful umbilical extraction, but a few minutes later S19/1 was successfully launched only eleven minutes after that at Andøya. (See figures 10.46 and 10.47.)

S19/1 was fitted with a radar transponder, and was successfully tracked over almost the whole of its 9.5-minute flight, until after it splashed down some 86 km (53 miles) down-

range. This was the first time a payload assembled by ESTEC required separation from the rocket,[86] which was successfully accomplished by their newly designed explosive actuator at +65 seconds. (Necessary because the antenna for experiment R20 was mounted on the underside of the lowest bulkhead). Three of the four experiments worked well, unfortunately the fourth (R20) was unsuccessful because an inadequate signal was received from the ground transmitter.[87]

S26/2 - Following the interruption caused by the launch of S19/1 on the 4th October, **S26/2** was launched on the 7th. It was ESRO's 50th sounding rocket launch.[88] Both S26 missions worked perfectly in spite of the complexity of the payload – large 'lazy-tong' booms, deployment of four Lyman-α counters, two X-ray tubes and reception of three ground frequencies.[89]

S19/2 - After the launch of S26/2, the countdown for **S19/2** started during the morning of the 10th. At -30 minutes, a hold was introduced to meet the Andøya countdown schedule. The launch of D34/2 from Andøya finally occurred at 15:01 local time but was a failure. Despite this, it was decided to proceed with the launch of S19/2, which was duly fired at 15:33 local time. This was successful, the results being slightly better than for S19/1, as all the experiments produced useful scientific data. However, because of the failure of the D34 launch, the principal scientific objective of the overall mission was not achieved.[90]

Another event of October 1967 worth noting was the launch of the NASA OSO 4 (Orbiting Solar Observatory 4) satellite on the 18th, as two of the nine experiments on board were solar physics instruments from the UK.[91] These were

---

[85] John Raymont "Memories of early trips", visit *www.ucl.ac.uk/mssl/about-mssl/heritage/archive-documents* , click on "John's Memoirs" and scroll down. (Last accessed August 2014).

[86] ESRO (1973), report SP-78, p.42.

[87] ESRO (1973), p.45.

[88] FLIGHT International, 2 November 1967, p.740, mentions this, but the report is a little muddled.

[89] ESRO (1973), report SP-78, p.78.

[90] ESRO (1973), p.45.

[91] See for instance Massey & Robins (1986), *History of British Space Science*, pp.342 & 442, and the NASA master catalogue at *http://nssdc.gsfc.nasa.gov/* by searching using "OSO 4", (last accessed August 2014).

Seq. Nos	Launch date	Ref. (sponsor) launch site	Config-uration	Apogee km (miles)	Experi-menters	Experiments	Result
174 (17)	01 Nov. 1967	SL407 (UK) Woomera	Sun, Rav.6 +C	206 (128)	Cul	Solar physics – UV spectrum 500-1540Å (normal incidence spectrograph)	S
					"	Solar physics - XUV spectrum 12-400Å (grazing incidence spectrograph)	F
					Lei	Solar physics - solar disc X-ray spectrum	S
					MO	Aeronomy – solar radiation flux (Ariel III sensor)	S
					"	" - molecular oxygen concentration	S

Table 10.12 A summary of SL407.

from MSSL and the University of Leicester, and had been developed from those flown on Skylark and Ariel I. OSO 4 operated successfully for over two years, providing many hundreds of broadband X-ray spectra, "providing quantitative data of unsurpassed quality on the solar X-ray spectrum during a wide range of activity".[92]

November 1967   SL407, SL423, SL424

SL407 was the fourth stabilised flight of 1967. Launched from Woomera, it carried five experiments, and was similar to SL406 launched at the beginning of the year.

The Culham solar physics UV and XUV spectrum experiments continued from those successfully flown on SL303 in 1965 and SL406 earlier in 1967. Their purpose on this flight was to extend the original solar limb spectrum observations to shorter wavelengths.[93] A technical problem and conditions on the Sun near the limb meant that accurate measurements

below 750Å (75 nm) were not possible,[94] but results above this wavelength were successfully obtained. Similar instruments used were flown later on SL408 in 1968, see below.

The Leicester and Meteorological Office experiments were repeats of those flown on SL406 in March.

SL423 was launched just under two weeks later, and was a 'standard' unstabilised scientific round. The ionosphere experiment from Imperial College was their first on Skylark for two years, a repeat of the magnetometer experiment flown on SL129 and SL128 in March 1964. The deployment was particularly complicated, as after separation the sensor had to be extended behind the head on an inflatable telescopic tube to a distance of six metres (20 feet),[95] which had to be maintained by gas pressure from compressed nitrogen bottles. The experiments from the RSRS continued their studies of the ionosphere and associated phenomena. (Table 10.13.)

All three experiments were successful, as were those on the similar SL424, a repeat flight launched only three days later.

Seq. Nos	Launch date	Ref. (sponsor) launch site	Config-uration	Apogee km (miles)	Experi-menters	Experiments	Result
175 (18)	14 Nov. 1967	SL423 (UK) Woomera	Un, Rav.7 +C	178 (111)	IC	Ionosphere - E-region current (rubidium magnetometer)	S
					RSRS	" - small electron density variation	S
					"	Aeronomy - absorption of solar Lyman-α	S
176 (19)	17 Nov. 1967	SL424 (UK) Woomera	Un, Rav.7 +C	181 (112)	IC	Ionosphere – as SL423	S
					RSRS	" "	S
					"	Aeronomy - "	S

Table 10.13 A summary of SL423 and SL424.

[92] Pounds (1986), 'British X-ray Astronomy', p.438.
[93] Burton and Ridgeley (1970), 'The solar limb Emission Spectrum between 300Å and 2803Å', (a much cited paper that included the results from SL303 (1965), SL407 (1967), SL408 (1968) and SL606 (1969).
[94] Ibid p.4.
[95] Round Specification for Skylark Nos. SL423 and SL424, March 1967. (WRE SL423 Trials Results file J5555/3/423).

This time the deployment of the Imperial College magnetometer experiment was monitored in flight by a WRECISS miniature wide-angle camera,[96] the results of which would be most interesting to see, but have not been found by the author.

WRESAT

An event of note in November 1967 was the launch of the first satellite from Woomera, Australia's WRESAT (**W**eapons **R**esearch **E**stablishment **Sat**ellite, 1967-118A). This project comprised the development and launch from Woomera of a small scientific satellite, successfully fired into a near polar orbit on the 29th, making Australia only the fourth country to launch its own satellite from its own territory, after the USSR, USA and France. (The UK's Ariel satellites had been launched from the USA).

It was a project of opportunity, which used a spare US Redstone rocket left over at the end of the multinational 'Sparta' re-entry study (see the start of this chapter). The satellite

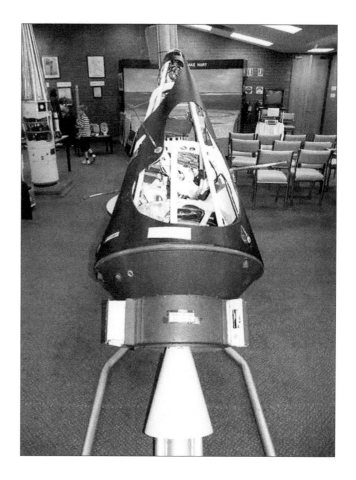

Figure 10.48 A model of WRESAT at the Woomera Heritage Centre c.2003. (A Skylark payload can be seen in the background.)

(Stuart Jackson)[97]

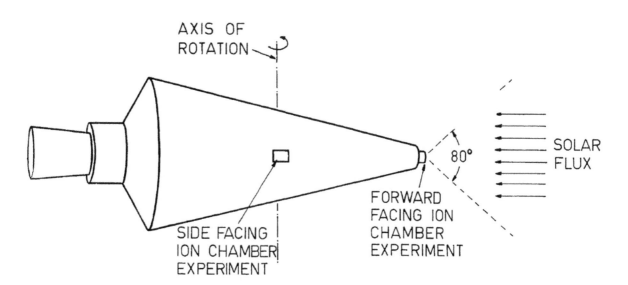

Figure 10.49 The arrangement of ion chamber detectors on the WRESAT satellite.

(Carver *et al.* (1972), figure 2)

---

[96] The WRECISS (Weapons Research Establishment Camera Single Shot) had been developed by WRE and was made by the Fairey Aviation Co of Australasia Pty Ltd at Salisbury. It used Ilford film in the form of 0.93 inch discs punched from 35 mm strip. Its main use was in missile testing.

[97] For this and similar photographs, see *www.nachohat.org/gallery/travel_woomera* (last accessed August 2014).

Seq. Nos	Launch date	Ref. (sponsor) launch site	Config- uration	Apogee km (miles)	Experi- menters	Experiments	Result
177 (20)	01 Dec. 1967	SL422A (UK) Woomera	Un, Rav.7 +C	181 (112)	RAE	Test (Skylark technology) - no Cuckoo fins	S
					UAT	Astronomy - celestial X-ray scan (proportional counters)	Ps

Table 10.14 A summary of SL422A.

itself was developed by the WRE and the University of Adelaide, and the project (despite being considered by many to be too ambitious) took less than a year from concept to launch. The USA donated the modified Redstone launch vehicle and the services of the TRW vehicle preparation team, NASA supplied global tracking and data services, and the Woomera Joint Project supported the launch activities.[98] WRESAT had a mass of approximately 45 kg (99 lbs) and was in the form of a cone, which went into orbit attached to the third stage of the launch vehicle. It transmitted data for its first 73 orbits (like Sputnik 1, it had no solar panels and was powered only by batteries[99]), and having completed 642 revolutions, re-entered over the Atlantic Ocean on 10 January 1968.

The purpose of WRESAT was to extend the range of scientific data relating to the upper atmosphere, to assist the US in its research programmes, to develop techniques relevant to ELDO and the British satellite programme, and to demonstrate Australian capability and low-cost launching facilities at Woomera.

Its scientific aims followed on from the Australian programme of sounding rocket launches, and included ion chambers to measure ultraviolet radiation from the Sun.[100]

December 1967   SL422A

There was only one Skylark launch in December. **SL422A** was launched on the 1st, and was mainly an RAE proving flight. The letter 'A' suffix meant that the payload had been rebuilt in

Australia from the original SL422 (launched 31 May 1966), and launched with a new motor shipped from the UK.

SL422A carried the third experiment from the Universities of Adelaide and Tasmania (UAT), an X-ray astronomy experiment known as UAT 'Flight III', similar to those flown on SL426 and 425 earlier in the year. Although technically only partially successful (only two of the four X-ray detectors worked satisfactorily), the observations provided evidence for a significant new X-ray source designated 'Cet XR-1', which had the distinction of being the third discovered off the plane of the galactic disc.[101] The payload was probably recovered successfully by parachute, as the instrument package was used again on UAT 'Flight IV' (SL781, January 1969).[102]

SKYLARK LAUNCHES AND SCIENCE IN 1968

During 1968, there were 17 Skylark launches, slightly down on the total of 20 the year before, but many were of particular significance. Also during the year, the UK introduced two smaller sounding rockets for more routine scientific purposes. These were the Petrel and Skua, as described below.

Later during the year at Woomera, the first all stages live flight of the ELDO Europa Blue Streak based rocket took place in November, but failed when the third stage exploded.

Within Europe, the ESRO sounding rocket programme continued to expand, and its 15 different payloads on 20 flights during the year achieved a higher success rate than previously. Two advances in the technology used by ESRO took place, the successful launch of their first stabilised

Jan.	Feb.	March	April	May	June	July	Aug.	Sept.	Oct.	Nov.	Dec.
	SL583A	SL408		SL761	SL723	SL403	SL524		S47/1	S41	S27/1
		S16/1		SL762		SL523	SL501		SL791R	S43/1	SL601
											SL725

Table 10.15 The 17 Skylark launches in 1968. (For full details see Appendix 3)

(Key: black = test launches, blue = UK national programme (unstabilised), plum = UK (stabilised), pink = ESRO programme)

---

[98]   See for instance the website *www.honeysucklecreek.net/supply/WRESAT/index.html* , *(last accessed August 2014).*

[99]   "The short time available to build WRESAT meant that solar cells could not be obtained in time". (McCracken (2008), p.215).

[100]   Carver *et al.* (1972), 'Ultraviolet Ion Chamber measurements of the Solar Minimum Brightness Temperature'.

[101]   Barnden and Francey (1969), 'A New X-ray object at High Galactic Latitude'.

[102]   Barnden (1972), *Studies of X-rays and Cosmic Rays of Galactic Origin*, p.iii.

Skylark payload (S41), and the first launches of Skylark from Esrange in Sweden.[103]

Skylark manufacture and development in 1968

By 1968, the Mk.I build standard of Skylark had been superseded for manufacturing purposes by the improved Mk.II version, already in use for stabilised rounds.[104]

BAC manufacture at Filton in Bristol continued, based on a future SRC requirement of six unstabilised and six stabilised rounds per year. Unstabilised rounds were already being built at Filton,[105] and from January 1968, it was also planned to build the SRC Stage 1 stabilised vehicles there. ESRO requirements were increasing, and estimated as an additional 15 rounds, ten to be launched from Kiruna and five from Sardinia. Production at RAE Farnborough would be as required for prototype stabilised rounds of about two per year, plus as needed for space technology requirements. Under a new agreement, additional system proving assembly work would start at WRE in Australia.

The standard motors for the British national programme Skylarks were the Raven Mk.VIA sustainer with the Cuckoo Mk.IA boost. Flight clearance for the Raven VIA for unboosted/unstabilised service was under way.

By now, the design of the original Stage 1 (Sun-pointing) attitude control system had been released, with production of about six units per year for the SRC and up to another two per year for the RAE's space technology experiments. The Stage 3 (Sun and Moon) system was still in development with the first proving (solar) flight scheduled for May 1968, and the first lunar pointing flight about the spring of 1969. However, Stage 3 as such was no longer required operationally by the SRC, a modification to Stage 1 meeting all solar needs, and the lunar version now being only used as the basis for the Stage 5 (star-pointing) system just commencing its project definition phase.

The main development effort at RAE still involved the attitude control units; in particular the Stage 3 flight prototypes and Stage 5 planning. In addition, 'housekeeping' work on Skylark design continued with improvements to such items as the Raven motor ignition circuit, explosive type piston actuators, telemetry and ground equipment. Studies on improvements to operational capability, such as higher performance and payload recovery, were also in progress.

In Australia, the WRE's primary responsibility continued to be the preparation and launching of rounds built in the UK for the national programme, although for many proving flights, vehicles continued to be refurbished in Australia from

Figure 10.50 Skylark payload assembly and testing at BAC, Filton, Bristol. The test equipment with the many dials is the 'priming unit', see Figure 3.27 for a modern photograph.
(BAC Sounding Rocket Services brochure SIG2, August 1968)

[103] ESRO (1974), report SP-79, p.1.

[104] The information in this section is based on the *Skylark Policy and Programme – Second Review*, document ref. DS/55/01 (6 November 1967 version), paragraph 2.3 onwards. Written by 'Space 1(c) (Ministry of Aviation)', and distributed for the fifth Skylark Policy meeting November 1967. (TNA: PRO AVIA 92/144).

[105] At one time BAC had some 200 people working on the Skylark Project. (Ellis (1992), 'Skylark Sounding Rockets – Past and Present', p.179).

recovered parts,[106] with new items supplied as required from the BAC stocks at Filton. The WRE was also assisting the RAE by undertaking some experimental and design work on the more important Skylark improvement projects.

Smaller sounding rockets for scientific purposes

As noted above, in 1968 the UK introduced two new small sounding rockets. The first of these had started as the 'Skua', a simple meteorological rocket developed by Bristol Aerojet[107] for the Meteorological Office. It used a solid propellant motor developed by the Rocket Propulsion Establishment at Westcott, had a diameter of 5 inches (13 cm), and could carry a payload of some 13lb (6 kg) to an altitude of about 65 km (40 miles). At apogee it released a partially metallised parachute that could be tracked by radar to allow the winds at altitude to be computed. Its use began in 1964 from an

Army firing range on the island of South Uist, situated in the Outer Hebrides off the west coat of Scotland. By July 1967, eighty of the original version had been launched.[108]

The first Skua design was not fitted with telemetry equipment, so for scientific purposes a modified version named Skua 2 was developed. This included a 465 MHz telemetry transmitter made by EMI Ltd., and with an improved rocket motor, altitudes of 100 km (62 miles) could be achieved. The first two launches of 'Skua 2' with scientific experiments on board appear to have taken place from the South Uist range in July 1967; these were followed by a programme of 11 launches in 1968.[112]

Back in 1964, development of a similar but larger rocket called Petrel had also been approved,[113] the intention being to produce a rocket capable of useful space science for under

Date	Ref.	Apogee km(miles)	Experimenters	Experiment	Result
3 Feb 1968	P 5H	140 (87)	RSRS	Ionosphere - electron density variations (probe)	S
			"	Ionosphere - electron flux & density (Geiger counters)	S
29 Feb 1968	P 6H	150 km (93)	RSRS	Ionosphere - as P 5H	Sf
			"	" " "	Sf
6 Mar 1968	P 7H	155 km (96)	Bir	Ionosphere - electron temp. in C, D & E regions	Ps
			Sth	Ionosphere - fluxes of charged particles (scintillation counter)	Ef
25 Mar 1968	P 8H	135 (84)	Bir	Ionosphere - as P 7H	S
			Sth	" " "	S

Table 10.16 Details of the first four Petrel flights to include scientific payloads.

(Data compiled from Massey & Robins (1986), *History of British Space Science*, p.414, and *www.rocketservices.co.uk/spacelists.php*, last accessed December 2010.)

Rocket	Diameter	Length	Gross payload	Typical apogees
Skua 2	13 cm (5 in)	2.4 m (8ft)	6 kg	75-100 km
Petrel 1	19 cm (7.5 in)	3.3 m (11 ft)	18 kg	115-143 km
Fulmar[109]	25 cm (9.8 in)	7.5 m (24.5 ft)	50 kg	250-260 km
Skylark + Cuckoo	44 cm (17.4 in)	9.4 m (30.8 ft)[110]	100-300 kg[111]	175-250 km

Table 10.17 A comparison of British sounding rockets c.1968.

(Data from Massey & Robins (1986), Chapter 8 & pp. 425 & 426)

[106] SL581 underwent this process several times, having flown as SL581 on 17th March 1966, SL581A on 14th December 1966 and SL581B on 16th August 1967.
[107] Bristol Aerojet also manufactured the motor cases for Skylark's Raven motors, see Chapter 3.
[108] Massey & Robins (1986), *History of British Space Science*, p.185.
[109] Fulmar was a short-lived British sounding rocket first launched in 1976, included here for completeness. It was abandoned after only six launches.
[110] Dorling (1959), *The First Six Skylark Firings*, (GW530), figure 48.
[111] Thomas (1969), 'Suborbital probes', figure 3. (Raven VI with Cuckoo).
[112] I.e. this compares to about £8000 for Skylark at the time, see Chapter 6.
[113] MSSL (1967), *Work of the Laboratory*, p.3.

£1000 (at 1960s prices!),[114] about one eighth of the cost of Skylark.[115] Like Skua, Petrel was developed by Bristol Aerojet and the RPE, with the co-ordinating research and development authority being the Atomic Weapons Research Establishment (AWRE).

During the opening of the new MSSL laboratories in May 1967, this new rocket was welcomed:

> The Petrel, in particular, will make a significant contribution to British space research. It is a budget price vehicle costing many times less than the Skylark and with a much simpler launching system. It will be used extensively from the new British range at South Uist in the Hebrides which will reduce costs of experiments by big savings in travel expenses.[116]

The first two proving launches took place from South Uist in June 1967, with the last of the eight development flights in March 1968, the final four of which included scientific payloads, see table 10.16.

As shown in the table, the Petrel flight on the 3rd February achieved an altitude of 140 km; it appears that the first proving flights in June the previous year had reached a similar altitude,[117] so Petrel appears to have the distinction of being the first rocket launched from the UK to reach space.

Petrel carried a payload of 18 kg (40 lbs) to an altitude of about 143 km, or alternatively 25 kg to 115 km. It was a two-stage 'booster–sustainer' design, the launch normally boosted by a cluster of three 'Chick' motors which burnt for about 0.2 seconds before separating from the main vehicle and descending by parachute to be reused. The main sustainer motor, the Lapwing 1, burnt for about 31 seconds. Stabilisation was by six fins at the rear. The launcher was a 10-metre long tube,[119] the same as that used for Skua, sufficiently wide to take the boost carriage that was fitted with wheels.

However the boost system and convenient launcher did have a downside. Experimenters had to be aware that Skua 2 and Petrel had the disadvantage of very high acceleration levels of about 60g, whereas the maximum acceleration of Skylark at launch was only 12g.[120]

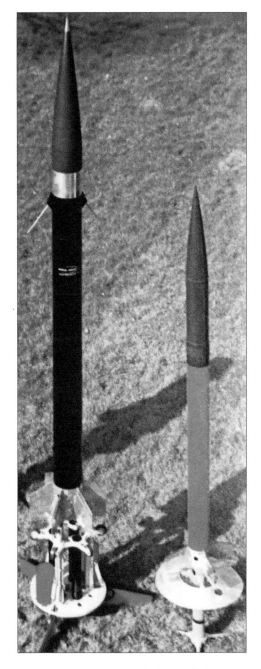

Figure 10.51 Petrel on the left and Skua on the right.[118]

---

[114] Massey & Robins (1986), p.426.

[115] Massey & Robins (1986), p.187. The approval and funding process was very complicated. In this case, the scientific case and recommendation were made in 1964 by the BNCSR, which in turn was approved by the 'Steering Group on Space Research'. This appears to have released funds from the Scientific Space Research budget of the UK National Space Programme. For those brave enough to delve further, Godwin (2007), *The Skylark Rocket*, Chapter 10 'Space Policy 1965-72', provides a thought-provoking account of the administration of the time.

[116] Where £1,000 in 1960 was worth from £18K to £58K by 2011. (2011 figure derived using the "Historic Opportunity" and "Economic Cost" measures for a large project, from Lawrence H. Officer and Samuel H. Williamson, "Five Ways to Compute the Relative Value of a UK Pound Amount, 1270 to Present," MeasuringWorth, 2013, *www.measuringworth.com/ukcompare/* , last accessed August 2014).

[117] See for instance Jonathan McDowell's sub-orbital launch vehicle database, via *http://planet4589.org/space/lvdb/list.html* , and clicking on 'Petrel'. (Last accessed August 2014).

[118] This photograph is from the UK Industrial Space Committee brochure *Britain in Space*, but it is acknowledged that the original image may be from the manufacturers, BAJ. (Bristol Aerojet).

[119] An example of the launching tube may be seen at the Royal Gunpowder Mills Heritage Museum in Essex, see Appendix 6 for location details.

[120] Seibert (2006), *The History of Sounding Rockets and Their Contribution to European Space Research*, p.43.

Seq. Nos	Launch date	Ref. (sponsor) launch site	Config- uration	Apogee km (miles)	Experi- menters	Experiments	Result
178 (1)	08 Feb. 1968	SL583A (UK) Woomera	Un, Rav.6 +G	300 (186)	RAE	Test (Skylark technology) - first proving flight for Goldfinch II booster	S

Table 10.18 A summary of Skylark SL583A.

A later version, the Petrel 2, could reach 175 km (109 miles). Both Petrel and Skua were to become very successful, many hundreds being used around the world in locations from Greenland to India.[121] The Petrel also had the unusual distinction that military versions [122] were developed from the civilian original, in the rocket world it was usually the other way around! Indeed, although the Petrel sounding rocket programme ceased in 1982, the military version appears to have remained in production for another 20 years.[123]

February 1968   SL583A

The first Skylark of 1968 was **SL583A**, an RAE proving round the main purpose of which was to test the new 'Goldfinch' booster motor.

The flight of SL583A was a great success, reaching an apogee of 300 km, a new record for Skylark.[124] The only problem was the short burning time for the Raven VIA sustainer motor, 23

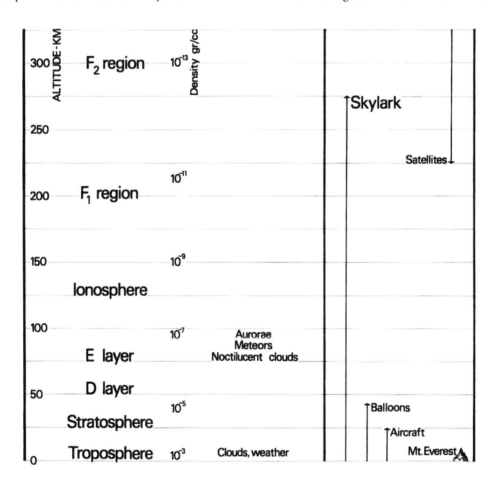

Figure 10.52 This scale diagram illustrates how Skylark was now capable of reaching the F region of the ionosphere, above the altitude of low orbiting satellites.
(BAC booklet (c.1966), *skylark upper atmosphere research vehicle*, p.4)

---

[121] See Massey & Robins (1986), *History of British Space Science*, Chapter 8, for a good description of the scientific background and use of these smaller sounding rockets.

[122] Fisher (1975), 'The Use of Sounding Rocket as Targets'. The Sea Petrel supersonic target was a variant with Radar augmentation modifications to make it suitable for Royal Navy use. See also Morton (1989), pp.354-355, for a description of testing at Woomera.

[123] It apparently featured on the Meggitt Aerospace stand as late as Farnborough 2000, although production appears to have ceased in 2002. (*www. royalgunpowdermills.com/must-see-attractions/rocket-vault/*), last accessed August 2014).

[124] SL67 had reached 247 km in November 1960, S04/1 an estimate d 250 km in September 1965.

Code Name	Time of burning (sec)	Nominal Thrust	Impulse						Overall length (inc.nozzle)		Propellant Formulation
			Total		Specific						
		lb	N	lb sec	N sec	Lb sec/lb	Ns/ Kg		In	Cm	
Cuckoo I	4.1	18200	80600	81000	360000	204	2000		51.7	131	RD 2409
Goldfinch IIA	3.6	41000	182000	158000	701000	235	2200		87.6	223	RD 2418

Table 10.19 A comparison of the Cuckoo and Goldfinch II boost motors used on Skylark.

(Data from RPE Westcott (1968), Index to Solid Propellant Motors, Tables 1, 2 and 3)

seconds instead of the expected 30 seconds, an effect it was thought depended on the ambient temperature at launch.[125]

Although capable of powering Skylark to greater altitudes, the Goldfinch boost motor was being introduced primarily to provide extra power and accuracy to counteract the increased weight of the stabilised rounds and improve dispersion.[126] The new requirements had been quantified by the SRC's requirement to send 600 lb (272 kg) gross payload / 90 lb (41 kg) net scientific payload, to 210 km.[127] Replacing the Cuckoo booster with the more powerful Goldfinch II motor had been selected as the main way to do this.

The original Goldfinch I motor had been designed and statically fired for an early anti-ballistic missile project called

Sprint, but that project had been cancelled.[129] Instead, the motor was developed into the slightly slower burning Goldfinch II, for use both as the Skylark first stage, and on another RAE project, the Jaguar hypersonic research vehicle.[130]

The table above shows that although the Goldfinch II motor burnt for a slightly shorter time than the Cuckoo, it had over twice the thrust and twice the total impulse. It achieved this by using a more efficient, faster burning propellant and being larger - at over two metres in length (but still the same diameter) it was 70% longer overall than the Cuckoo.

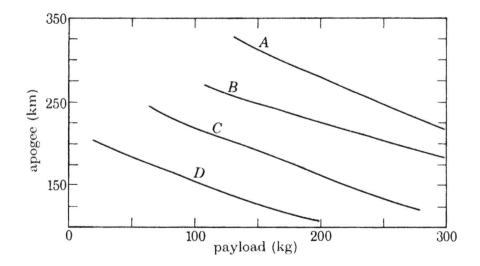

Figure 10.53 This diagram of Skylark apogee against gross payload for various motor combinations shows the improvement expected using the Goldfinch booster.
A = Raven VI + Goldfinch (Skylark 6)
B = Raven VI + Cuckoo
C = Raven VIII + Cuckoo
D = Raven VIII
(Thomas (1969), figure 3) [128]

---

[125] Minutes of the Sixth Policy Meeting on the Skylark Rocket, March 1968, p.4, para.3.3.3. (TNA: PRO AVIA 92/144).
[126] For instance, see the minutes of the Second Policy Meeting on the Skylark Rocket, August 1966, p.5, para.3.3.4. (TNA: PRO AVIA 92/144).
[127] *Skylark Policy and Programme – Second Review*, document ref. DS/55/01 06/11/1967, p.4, para.3.3.2. (TNA: PRO AVIA 92/144).
[128] Reproduced courtesy Royal Society London.
[129] Harlow (1998), 'Sustainer propulsion for the UK air defence weapons – The early history', p.8. As noted in Chapter 3, the proven nozzle design of Goldfinch was used on the original Raven motor.
[130] The RAE Jaguar (later named Jabiru) was a three-stage Hypersonic Research Vehicle (HRV) used to test components for re-entry vehicles and analyse the effects of kinetic heating.

The first purely scientific flight of 1968 was that of **SL408** in March. This had a stabilised payload similar to SL406 and SL407 the previous year, and included a similar set of experiments:

As with SL406, three experiments were from the Culham laboratory. These had improved instruments and the main objective of this flight was to extend the previous observations of the solar limb emission spectrum within the 2000-3000Å (200-300 nm) region. Several improvements were made to the optical system in order to improve performance.[131] Good limb spectra were recorded on photographic film, despite the

Seq. Nos	Launch date	Ref. (sponsor) launch site	Config- uration	Apogee km (miles)	Experi- menters	Experiments	Result
179 (2)	20 Mar. 1968	SL408 (UK) Woomera	Sun, Rav.6 +C	217 (135)	Cul	Solar physics – X-ray & XUV spectrums 12-70Å & 140-500Å (2 grazing incidence spectrographs)	S
					Cul	Solar physics - spectrum 1100Å to 2810Å (normal incidence spectrograph)	S
					Cul	Solar physics - UV image (pin-hole camera)	F
					Lei	" " - X-ray image (pin-hole camera)	S
					MO	Aeronomy - solar radiation flux (detector)	S
					MO	" - molecular oxygen concentration (attenuation of radiation)	S

Table 10.20 A summary of SL408.

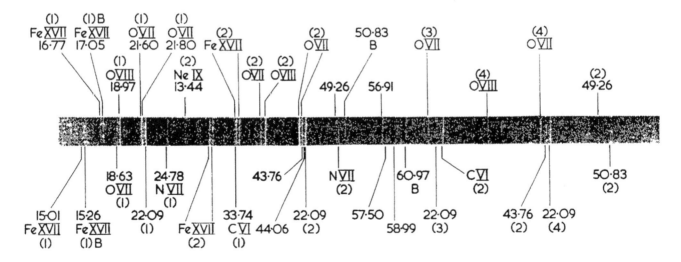

Figure 10.54 Solar soft X-ray spectrum, recorded by Skylark SL408. Exposure time 200 sec., Kodak SC-7 emulsion.

(Freeman and Jones (1970), figure 4)

[131] Burton and Ridgeley (1970), 'The Solar Limb Emission Spectrum between 300 Å and 2803 Å, p.4.

fact that "recovery of the payload was delayed for six days and during this time the condition of the films deteriorated, so reducing the accuracy of photometric measurements from this flight."[132] No explanation for this little misadventure is given! (However at least the parachute worked on SL408, as the instruments were recovered intact allowing post flight checks on them to be made.[133])

In the event SL408 produced the first resolved photographic spectrum of the Sun between 14Å and 25Å.[134] The results from this and the other flights in the series identified hundreds of solar emission lines, and as the spectra were of the best quality available at the time,[135] the information extended our knowledge of the physics of the Sun.

The other three experiments on board, those from the University of Leicester and the Meteorological Office, were similar to those flown on SL406 and SL407 the previous year, but the actual results are not known.

Esrange and Kiruna – a new rocket range for Skylark

A week after SL408 was launched at Woomera; the third Skylark mission of the year was launched from a new and very different launch site. ESRO flight **S16/1** on the 27th March was the first of many Skylarks to be launched from 'ESRANGE' (**E**uropean **S**pace and Sounding Rocket **Range**)[136] near Kiruna in Sweden. ESRO's report for 1968 stated:

> The other significant event of 1968 was the launch of the first Skylark rocket from ESRANGE. This gave the capability of lifting larger payloads to greater altitudes than had been possible with Centaure rockets, and specifically, opened the way for the use of large mass spectrometers at ESRANGE.[137]

Except for its remote location, Esrange was in many ways the opposite of Woomera. Situated inside the Arctic Circle, the area was typified by snow and reindeer rather than semi-desert and kangaroos. (The nearby town of Kiruna owed its origins to the valuable iron ore deposits mined there).

Figure 10.55 The location of Esrange north of the Arctic Circle.[138]

[132] Ibid, p.6.
[133] Freeman and Jones (1970), 'Grazing Incidence Spectra of the Sun', p.294.
[134] Ibid, p.305.
[135] Massey & Robins (1986), *History of British Space Science*, p.343.
[136] Original documents tend to spell the acronym in upper case 'ESRANGE', but except when quoting such original text the author has adopted the more modern usage 'Esrange', which 'shouts' less!
[137] ESRO (1974), report SP-79, p.1.
[138] Source: *www.daviddarling.info/encyclopedia/E/Esrange.html* , (last accessed August 2014). Reproduced with permission.

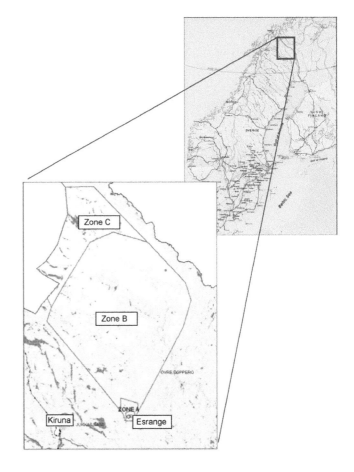

Figure 10.56 Detailed location of Esrange. The 'rangehead' itself was and is 43 km (27 miles) east of the town of Kiruna. Zone A is the impact area for boosters, zones B & C for second and third stages as well as payloads.
(Ceglia (2005), figure 5-9)

The Kiruna locality had been chosen for Esrange during the formation of ESRO in 1964. As well as extending into an uninhabited area, it had the advantage of being situated where the aurora borealis (northern lights) occur, into which sounding rockets could be directly launched. Sir Robert Boyd later recalled:

> I chaired the committee or subcommittee that was concerned with ionospheric work to start with and pressed very strongly to get a range set up at Kiruna, so that we could continue studies of the aurorae from polar regions...I remember going to Kiruna and we hired a helicopter and flew down range to see where it would be suitable to put a downrange station and so on.[139]

Although a very different environment from Woomera, some of the practical issues and solutions were remarkably close to those dealt with in Australia some 15 years earlier:

> One concern was the reindeer herding and the possibility of a reindeer being hit by a rocket or a burnt-out rocket stage. The Lapps got, and still have, a yearly compensation for this eventuality. Also, special impact-

proof shelters supplied with food and dry fire wood had to be built for those who happened to be in the impact area, and the Lapps received a battery-powered radio for them to listen to the countdown of each rocket launch. These measures became quite popular and the shelters are still used as fishing and hunting huts by the local people and, so far, not a single reindeer has been hurt.[140]

As described previously, the first Skylark launches in Europe were in 1964, and took place from Sardinia using an existing Italian military facility. Sardinia had been used because ESRO's purpose built range at Kiruna in Sweden did not start operations until the end of 1966, when in November that year it was inaugurated by the launch of a French Centaure rocket.

For launching Skylark, ESRO were originally offered the free loan of the spare launcher from Aberporth, an offer that remained on the table in 1966.[141] However, BAC's tender to re-erect it at Kiruna was not accepted; instead, tenders were invited for the provision of a new launcher to be ready by the summer of 1967. In 1965/66 a contract was given to

---

[139] Boyd in 2001, CCBH (2005), *Skylark Sounding Rockets1957-1972*, p.56, & *Prospero* No.2.p.121.
[140] Fredga (2008), 'A life in Space', ESA Bulletin 136, p.10.
[141] Briefing document ref.DS/55/01 28 March 1966, para. 11.3, circulated before the first Skylark Policy meeting April 1966. (TNA: PRO AVIA 92/144).

Figure 10.57 A general view of the Esrange rangehead (c.2006), showing the main building and the Skylark launch facility in the middle distance.

(Swedish Space Corporation)

the Spanish SENER Corporation, for a Skylark tower that was commissioned in early 1968.[142] (First used by S16/1 in March 1968 as described below).

It is quite possible that the spare Aberporth launch tower was not considered suitable for use in Arctic conditions. The Esrange facility is 145 km (90 miles) north of the Arctic Circle, and in nearby Kiruna the average temperature rises above freezing on only seven months of the year. In addition, ten years of being exposed to the salt laden elements on the headland at Aberporth had taken their toll, and in February 1967 it was reported that many of the launcher parts were in far from sound condition, being wafer thin through corrosion, although the basic structure "was quite sound".[143]

The Skylark launch tower constructed at Esrange was therefore enclosed to provide a weatherproof working environment. The associated assembly hall had a direct connection

with the launch tower enclosure through an indoor corridor, a convenient facility in adverse conditions. The temperature in the launcher building was controlled, and the building constructed so that the rocket could be elevated and positioned in azimuth before it was opened. Just before launch, the roof and blast doors were opened, and in the event of a hold after the opening of the building, could be closed and the temperature rapidly brought back to normal.[144]

John Raymont later recalled:

> And in Kiruna they also built, at huge expense, one of the most beautiful Skylark towers. I love the Skylark tower at Woomera, but the one in Kiruna, because of the climatic conditions, is beautiful. The one in Kiruna was air conditioned and heated; the whole thing was built inside galvanised cladding.[145]

[142] Dorado, Bautista and Sanz-Aránguez, *Spain in Space*, ESA report HSR-26, pp. 13 and 35.
[143] Minutes of the Fourth Skylark Policy Meeting, 28th February 1967, para. 3.13.3. (TNA: PRO AVIA 92/144).
[144] Swedish Space Corporation (2011), *User's Handbook – Sounding Rockets & Balloons*, p.8.
[145] John Raymont in 2001, CCBH (2005), *Skylark Sounding Rockets 1957-1972*, p.82, & *Prospero* No.2. p.144.

Figure 10.58 Left: a closer view of the Esrange sounding rocket launch area. It shows the access corridor between the assembly building and the Skylark launch enclosure.

(Swedish Space Corporation)

Figure 10.59 Right: The Skylark launch tower as photographed by John Raymont in the winter of 1970/71.

(John Raymont)

The UK scientific community had made good use of previous ESRO sounding rocket flights, and with three British experiments, the first Skylark launch from Kiruna (S16/1) was no exception.

In fact, the S16 payload had been approved for the ESRO programme back in November 1964, but because the Sky-

lark launch tower had not been built, the first payload meeting was not held until May 1966, with design starting that September. Flight acceptance tests duly took place in February 1968, ready for when the tower became available in March.[146]

Seq. Nos	Launch date	Ref. (sponsor) launch site	Config-uration	Apogee km (miles)	Experi-menters	Experiments	Result
180 (3)	27 Mar. 1968	S16/1 (ESRO) Kiruna	Un, Rav.8	172 (107)	MSSL	Ionosphere - electron temperature (Langmuir probe) (experiment R44)	S
					MSSL	Ionosphere - auroral ionisation structure (positive ion probes) (experiment R45)	S
					IC	Aurora – magnetic fields in aurora (proton magnetometer) (experiment R49)	Ps

Table 10.21 A summary of Skylark S16/1.

146 ESRO (1974), report SP-79, p.13.

Figure 10.60 The launch of S16/1, the first Skylark fired from Esrange.[147]

(Swedish Space Corporation / P.G.Lönn)

[147] The particular Skylark is not identified by the SSC website, although it does identify the photograph as being from the late 1960s or very early 1970s. The same photograph also appears in a BAC brochure (SIG 2) dated August 1968, hence S16/1 is the only candidate. (The second Skylark launched from Esrange was S43/1 in November 1968). (The SSC website title for this photograph includes the words "pissing scientist", which rather detracts from the drama of the event!).

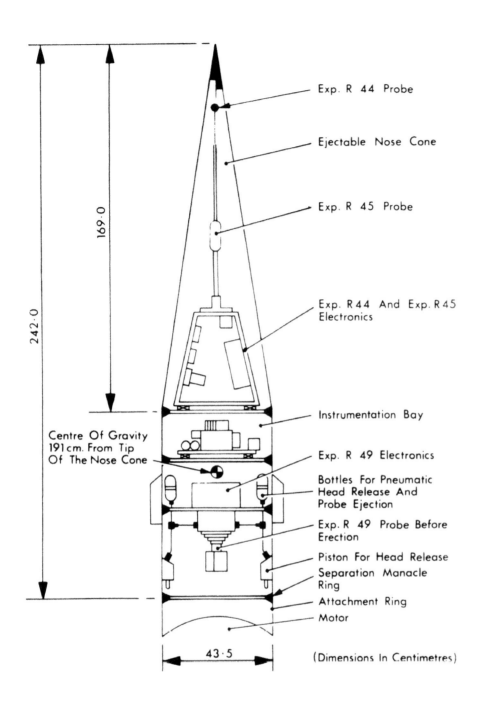

169.0

242.0

Centre Of Gravity
191cm. From Tip
Of The Nose Cone

43.5

Exp. R 44 Probe

Ejectable Nose Cone

Exp. R 45 Probe

Exp. R 44 And Exp. R 45
Electronics

Instrumentation Bay

Exp. R 49 Electronics

Bottles For Pneumatic
Head Release And
Probe Ejection

Exp. R 49 Probe Before
Erection

Piston For Head Release

Separation Manacle
Ring

Attachment Ring

Motor

(Dimensions In Centimetres)

Figure 10.61 A diagram of the payload for S16/1.

(ESRO SP-79, p.18, figure 1)

The main experiment was that from Imperial College, which used a very sensitive "proton magnetometer", designed to investigate the relationship between auroral events and the polar electrojet. Thus, the payload needed to be launched at night and during an auroral display, in the winter period with a clear sky.[148] At Kiruna, testing of the magnetometer experiment was complicated by the virtual impossibility of carrying it out in a magnetically stable environment (away from power lines etc), and only one of the flight models was considered satisfactory by the experimenter. Despite this difficulty and the fact that the tower was being used for the first time, the payload was completed and loaded into the

launcher on schedule on the 24th March. However, the countdown the following night was abandoned at 02:26 because of the lack of suitable auroral conditions.[149]

The launch finally took place the night after, despite a countdown pause at -1 minute because of a technical problem. The flight went well, with nose cone ejection taking place at +69 seconds and pneumatic separation of the payload at +72 seconds.

The Imperial College R49 magnetometer experiment was similar to that flown from Woomera on SL423 and SL424 the previous November. The deployment was particularly

---

[148] ESRO (1974), report SP-79, p.13.
[149] ESRO (1974), report SP-79, p.15.

complicated, as after separation the sensor had to be extended on an inflatable telescopic tube to a distance of six metres (20 feet) behind the payload, and had to be maintained there by gas pressure from compressed nitrogen bottles. This was successfully accomplished at +76 seconds; the payload reached an apogee of 172 km (107 miles), and after some ten minutes impacted 80 km (50 miles) downrange.

The launch was of particular importance, being the first of a Skylark from the new Esrange complex near Kiruna, and technically and ballistically it was a complete success.[150] The two MSSL experiments, R44 and R45, worked well and valuable results were obtained. Disappointingly, no results were obtained from R49, because the high-gain amplifier was saturated with noise, probably pick-up from the telemetry aerials. Launch of the second flight unit was therefore postponed so this problem could be cured, and it was not until March 1971, three years later, that the launch of S16/2 took place. (See Chapter 12).

The range area available at Esrange was relatively small compared to that at Woomera or the sea range at Sardinia. This resulted in the following interesting comment about the early years of operation:

> Some of the rockets strayed outside the designated safety zone. Some even fell in Finland and Norway. This caused a great deal of worry among Swedish authorities - a concern that was not always shared by their European colleagues. One is reminded of the time when a Skylark rocket was launched in an inhabited area of South America, and the responsible general reassured a visitor from Esrange: "No important people live there." In time, impact dispersion at Esrange was much reduced through the introduction of improved guidance and tracking systems.[151]

May 1968	SL761, SL762

There were no Skylark launches in April, but at the end of May at Woomera, a double Skylark launching took place on the morning and evening of the 31st. (See table 10.22)

This was a joint UK – Australian project in which a series of coordinated measurements were taken of the neutral atmosphere between 90 and 250 km altitude, which involved the release of contaminants and grenades at height to provide information on wind velocity, turbulent structure, temperature and density.[152]

The resulting contaminant trails could even be seen from Adelaide, 430 km (270 miles) away, and for scientific purposes were observed by several specialised ground based instruments. Photographs were taken by a satellite tracking Baker Nunn camera from the extraordinary distance of 160 km (100 miles) away, which produced the following intriguing images. (See figure 10.62 on the next page.)

The results contributed to knowledge of the diurnal behaviour of the Earth's atmosphere, the turbopause (below which turbulent mixing dominates), and standard models of the atmosphere, including the Global Reference Atmospheric Model developed for the design phase of the Space Shuttle.[153]

Seq. Nos	Launch date	Ref. (sponsor) launch site	Config- uration	Apogee km (miles)	Experi- menters	Experiments	Result
181 (4)	31 May 1968	SL761 (UK) Woomera	Un, Rav.7 +C	238 (148)	UCL	Neutral atmosphere - wind velocity & atmospheric density (grenades & TMA dispenser)	S
182 (5)	"	SL762 "	"	242 (150)	"	"	S

Table 10.22 A summary of SL761 and SL762.

[150] ESRO (1974), report SP-79, p.17.
[151] See the excellent website *www.zenker.se/Space/Jubilee/jubilee-a.shtml* - Part 1, under "ESRO and Esrange". (Last accessed August 2014). Reproduced with permission.
[152] Rees, Roper, Lloyd and Low (1972), 'Determination of the structure of the atmosphere between 90 and 250 km by means of contaminant releases at Woomera'.
[153] Roper & Edwards (1980), *Theoretical and Experimental Investigations of Upper Atmosphere Dynamics*, p.11.

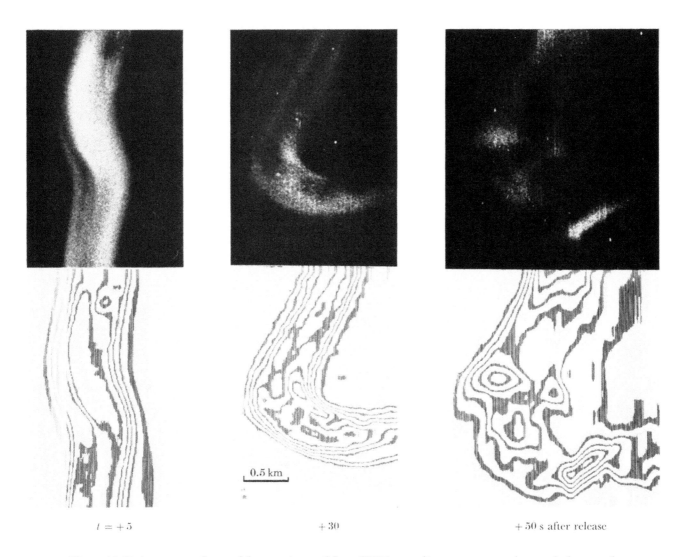

$t = +5$ $+30$ $+50$ s after release

Figure 10.62 A montage of part of the morning trail from SL761, revealing upper atmosphere turbulence and flow at +5, + 30 and + 50 seconds after release. The kink is at an altitude of 103 km (64 miles), where the sudden change in atmospheric properties is known as the turbopause.

(Rees *et al.* (1972), figure 4) [155]

June 1968   SL723

SL723 was a follow up to the successful SL118 of 1967. Launched from Woomera on June 12th, it was an unstabilised rocket, dedicated to an improved cosmic X-ray astronomy experiment from the University of Leicester.[154] Each X-ray detector was of 1385 square cm (four square feet) effective area, totalling the largest flown up to that time.[156]

They provided more sensitivity and a wider range of X-ray energy detection than the 295 square cm effective area detector flown on SL118 and SL119 the previous year. The detectors were mounted back to back under the nose cone, and covered a range of 1.4 to 18 keV compared to 2 to 5 keV previously.

---

[154] Adams, Cooke, Evans & Pounds (1970), 'Rocket Observations of Virgo XR-1'.
[155] Reproduced courtesy Royal Society London.
[156] Massey & Robins (1986), *History of British Space Science,* p.371, and Pounds (1986), 'British X-ray astronomy', p.440.

Figure 10.63 The payload of SL723 undergoing final checks at the Bristol works of the Space and Instrumentation Group of BAC Guided Weapons Division. Half of the split nosecone has been removed, revealing one side of the X-ray detector.

(BAC \ Roger Cooper)

SL723 was launched from Woomera after dark at 20:00 local time,[157] and the mission was completely successful. The observations were received by radio telemetry, attitude information was provided by on-board Moon sensors and magnetometers, and in addition, the payload (including the star-camera) was recovered by parachute.

Seq. Nos	Launch date	Ref. (sponsor) launch site	Config- uration	Apogee km (miles)	Experi- menters	Experiments	Result
183 (6)	12 June 1968	SL723 (UK) Woomera	Un, Rav.5A[158] +C	184 (114)	Lei	Astronomy - cosmic X-ray survey (proportional counters)	S

Table 10.23 A summary of SL723.

---

[157] Cooke, Griffiths & Pounds (1970), 'Evidence for a Galactic Component of the Diffuse X-ray Background', p.280.

[158] A Raven 5A was used because by this time the Raven 5 motors and igniters at Woomera were considered unserviceable. (Minutes of 7th Skylark Policy Meeting 10 June 1968, para.3.3.1) (TNA: PRO AVIA 92/144).

Figure 10.64 Despite apparently landing by parachute, the SL723 instrument looks in a sorry state.

(WRE \ Cooper)

Being unstabilised, the natural spinning motion of SL723 (75° per second) combined with the precession of the spin axis, allowed the experiment to scan 80% of the visible sky. On 25 consecutive scans, the 'Vir XR-1' X-ray source was viewed, providing significant data, and evidence for the view that part of the diffuse X-ray background could originate from outside our own galaxy.[159]

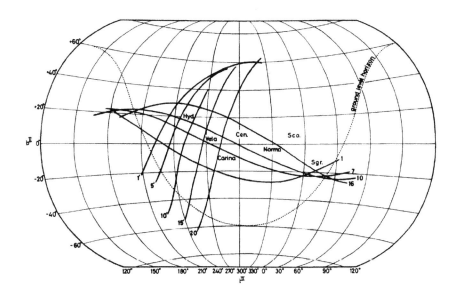

Figure 10.65 A sky map of the region of the galactic equator surveyed by SL723.

(Cooke, Griffiths & Pounds (1970), figure 1)

Seq. Nos	Launch date	Ref. (sponsor) launch site	Config- uration	Apogee km (miles)	Experi- menters	Experiments	Result
184 (7)	8 July 1968	SL403 (UK) Woomera	Moon, Rav.6 +C	177 (110)	RAE	Test (Skylark technology) – 1st flight Stage 3 Attitude Control Unit	S
					Lei	Astronomy – cosmic X-ray emission (proportional counters scanning M-87 galaxy)	S
					Lei	Astronomy – cosmic X-ray image (pin-hole camera stabilised on M-87 galaxy)	S

Table 10.24 A summary of SL403.

---

[159] Cooper (2006), p.4.

July 1968   SL403, SL523

A few weeks later, the University of Leicester also had exclusive use of the first Stage 3 stabilised Skylark rocket for a continuation of the SL723 mission. **SL403** was launched on the 8th July, and the new Stage 3 attitude controlled unit (ACU) payload worked first time, (an important milestone on the way to the development of the forthcoming Stage 5 version).

As described at the start of this chapter, the Stage 3 ACU had been developed by Elliott Bros in conjunction with the RAE, and had a greatly improved accuracy over the previous Stage 1 units. Where the earlier units had accuracies of 20 arc min in respect of Sun pointing, and roll stabilisation to five degrees, the new unit could use either the Sun or Moon as a reference, and had a pointing accuracy of 30 arc sec and stability in roll of one degree.[160]

Although generally known as the 'Moon pointing' version, curiously for an astronomy mission, this first flight of the Stage 3 ACU was actually used in Sun-pointing mode. Thus, it was launched during daylight, at 15:35 local time. The scientific payload had two small X-ray proportional counters, each of 25 square cm effective area, aligned at 76° to the sun-pointed payload axis, allowing them to scan the region of sky containing the source Vir XR-1 during the four minutes of stabilised flight. Correct pointing was later verified by an on-board star camera,[161] so the payload must have been successfully landed by parachute. It was the first stabilised flight to use this technique, i.e. the first to look away from the Sun to a celestial X-ray source.[162]

Optical identification of X-ray sources remains a classic problem of modern astronomy, because only together with optical studies can an understanding be reached of what have proven to be enigmatic galactic and extra-galactic objects. The SL403 results contributed to the then speculation that Vir XR-1 could be identified with the galaxy M87, one of the largest known, a source of intense optical and radio emissions with a curious jet of material emanating from its centre. By 1969, Vir XR-1 was regarded as the only convincing case of an extragalactic X-ray source.[163]

SL523 and **SL524** were launched a couple of weeks apart, and continued the series of flights carrying UCW experiments to measure the properties of the ionosphere. (See table 10.25 below)

The previous such experiments had been flown on SL426 and SL425 in April 1967, which were themselves successors to earlier flights including SL121 and SL120 in 1964. The radio sounding method used to measure electron density is described under 'SL120' in Chapter 8.

Seq. Nos	Launch date	Ref. (sponsor) launch site	Config-uration	Apogee km (miles)	Experi-menters	Experiments	Result
185 (8)	23 July 1968	SL523 (UK) Woomera	Un, Rav.5A +C	258 (160)	UCW	Ionosphere - electron density profile & layer heights (cw & pulse propagation)	Ps
186 (9)	05 Aug. 1968	SL524 (UK) Woomera	Un, Rav.5A +C	235 (146)	"	"	S

Table 10.25 A summary of Skylarks SL523 and SL524.

160 Flight International magazine 18th July 1968, p.111.
161 Adams, Cooke, Evans and Pounds (1970), 'Rocket Observation of Virgo XR-1', p. 83.
162 Reed (1974), *An Historical Review of Stabilisation Systems for the Skylark Rocket*, p.5.
163 Gratton (1969), 'Ground based observations of X-ray sources – a short review'.

Seq. Nos	Launch date	Ref. (sponsor) launch site	Config-uration	Apogee km (miles)	Experi-menters	Experiments	Result
187 (10)	29 Aug. 1968	SL501 (UK) Woomera	Sun, Rav.6 +C	210 (131)	MSSL	Solar physics – intensity of solar emission lines (scanning spectrophotometer)	Ps
					MSSL	Solar physics – extreme UV solar spectrum (grazing incidence spectrograph)	Ps
					MSSL	Ionosphere - electron temperature (probe)	Ps
					MSSL	" - positive ion density (probe)	Ps
					Bir	Ionosphere - electron density (probe)	Ps

Table 10.26 A summary of SL501.

August 1968   SL524, SL501

SL524 has been described just above. **SL501** followed at the end of August with a Sun-pointing stabilised payload.

SL501 included the first stabilised payload with MSSL experiments since SL305 the previous year. For reasons not known, all the experiments were only partially successful. However the payload was repeated on SL502 the following April, when all went well.

October 1968   S47/1, SL791R

Despite the inauguration of Kiruna in Sweden by Skylark, ESRO continued to use the sea range at Sardinia. From October to December another four Skylark launches took place there, three of which included experiments from British institutions.

Some interesting figures on the British use of ESRO sounding rockets have been published by ESA.[164] They show that over the period 1961-1968, the number of UK sounding rocket experiments exceeded 400, of which about 20% were on ESRO sponsored rocket flights:

UK national programme: 127 launches, 333 experiments
ESRO sponsored: 45 launches, 75 experiments

The rockets used for the 127 UK national launches were:

- 103 Skylarks from Woomera
- 11 Petrel and 13 Skua II from South Uist.

An analysis of the types of sounding rockets by ESRO about this time is also revealing, Skylark and the French Centaure were the most used:

Rocket type	Country of origin	No. of launches
Skylark	United Kingdom	83
Centaure	France	64
Skua	United Kingdom	15
Arcas	USA	14
Dragon	France	4
Belier	France	2
Petrel	United Kingdom	1
Zenit	Switzerland/Germany	1

Table 10.27 Sounding rockets used by ESRO from 1964-74.[165]

The Royal Observatory at Edinburgh (ROE) in particular tended to use ESRO sounding rockets, and Skylarks S47/1 (7th October) and S27/1 (3rd December, see below), both included ROE experiments:

Seq. Nos	Launch date	Ref. (sponsor) launch site	Config-uration	Apogee km (miles)	Experi-menters	Experiments	Result
188 (11)	07 Oct. 1968	S47/1 (ESRO) Sardinia	Un, Rav.6 +C	208 (129)	ROE	Astronomy – UV sky brightness (photomultiplier) (experiment R120)	S
					ROE	Astronomy – absolute stellar UV emission (twin-channel photometer) (experiment R121A)	F
					ROE	Astronomy – stellar UV emission (Cassegrain telescope photometer) (experiment R121B)	F

Table 10.28 A summary of S47/1.

164 Seibert (2006), *The History of Sounding Rockets and Their Contribution to European Space Research*, p.43.
165 Seibert (2006), table 5-1.

These experiments continued the ROE stellar UV observational programme that had been running since 1962.[166] As described at the start of this chapter, the first successes had been achieved with S11/2 and S05/2 early in 1967, and these two 1968 flights extended the programme by including observations at a shorter wavelength.[167] (At the time, there was very little data for observations below the wavelength of 2000Å (200nm), and practically none from Europe.[168])

The R120 experiment was successful, despite the complete failure of the vehicle roll control unit. Eleven sky scans were achieved during 400 seconds of flight above a height of 110 km, and these provided UV sky background observations in the range 1300 to 5000 Å (130-500 nm).[169] Unfortunately, neither version of the photometry experiment (R121) was successful,[170] but a very similar experiment flown on S27/1 in December did work, and is described below.

The month concluded with the curiously numbered **SL791R**. This was an RAE test flight launched from Woomera on the 9th October to the relatively low height of 106 km, but its purpose is unknown.

November 1968   S41, S43/1

S41 introduced a new and important phase in the ESRO sounding rocket programme, as it was the first stabilised payload prepared and launched by them.[171] It used an ESTEC version of the Elliott attitude control unit (ACU), which differed from the standard British version,[172] and its introduction meant ESRO had to bring in new procedures to prepare and launch a Sun-stabilised payload.

It was also originally intended to recover the payload from the sea, and although this requirement was subsequently dropped because it proved too complicated to implement in the time available,[173] it still had a significant impact on the development of the project, which took some two and a half years from approval until launch.

During payload preparation, the complete payload was mounted on a new single-axis air bearing and tested using a solar simulator in order to perform balance and ACU tests:

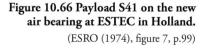

Figure 10.66 Payload S41 on the new air bearing at ESTEC in Holland.
(ESRO (1974), figure 7, p.99)

---

[166] The first ROE experiment had been flown on SL140 in March 1965.

[167] Campbell (1971a), 'Stellar Photometry in the region 1300Å -2000Å. Part I', p.417.

[168] Campbell (1971b), 'Stellar Photometry in the region 1300Å -2000Å. Part II', p.189.

[169] Campbell (1970a), 'Absolute Stellar Photometry in the Region 1200 Å – 3000 Å', p.136.

[170] ESRO (1974), report SP-79, p.138.

[171] ESRO (1974), p.85.

[172] It included rate gyros and magnetometers that in the British Skylark were provided in the instrumentation bay. (SP-79, p.88).

[173] However, with the future in mind, a contract was still placed with industry for a new recovery system for Skylark payloads, suitable for use over either land or sea. The concept combined a standard parachute system with a flotation torus surrounding the payload to sustain it after impact. (ESRO (1974), SP-79, p.2).

Seq. Nos	Launch date	Ref. (sponsor) launch site	Config- uration	Apogee km (miles)	Experi- menters	Experiments	Result
190 (13)	22 Nov. 1968	S41 (ESRO) Sardinia	Sun, Rav.6 +C	210 (131)	UTR	Solar physics - X-ray spectrometry (experiment R7)	Ps
					Lei	Solar physics – crystal X-ray spectrometry (Bragg crystal spectrometer) (experiment R56)	S

Table 10.29 A summary of S41.

Range preparation at Sardinia started on the 28th October, and because of preparation and alignment delays, was launched on the 22nd November without a practise countdown.

The launch went well and the payload was a complete success, although acquisition of stability took 11 seconds longer than the 25 anticipated because the new ESTEC designed nose cone caused significant payload movement when ejected. However, 290 seconds of stabilised Sun-pointing flight was achieved, the experiments worked well, and impact into the sea occurred 196 km (122 miles) downrange. Leicester experiment R56 produced good results, but although R7 functioned well, the results were inconclusive.[174] For the first time in ESRO's Skylark programme, there was no second flight planned, probably because S41 was primarily a technology proving flight, with the scientific experiments as additions.

Meanwhile, the second Skylark to be launched from Sweden was being prepared. The purpose of S43/1 was to take auroral measurements at the same time as the satellite ESRO 1

was passing overhead. ESRO 1 had been launched by NASA on behalf of ESRO the previous month, and carried experiments primarily to study the polar ionosphere. The main input for its experiments had been from UK scientists,[175] using their experience on the British national Skylark programme and Ariel I.[176] These included two experiments from MSSL, and John Raymont later recalled:

ESRO 1 was the first satellite for me to work on. I guess this gives it a special place in my mind. Basically I assisted with the tests at MSSL / AWRE / ESTeC. The instrument was then integrated in Paris at the Laboratoire Central de Telecommunications (LCT). Spacecraft integrated tests, i.e. vibration and Thermal Vacuum testing, were done at *ESTeC*, the facilities were large enough for spacecraft of those days. Sometimes a couple of us would go to ESTeC and I found myself working on a sounding rocket during the weekdays and then working on ESRO 1 at night-times and weekends, during a Thermal Vacuum test.[177]

S43/1 carried similar experiments to ESRO 1:

Seq. Nos	Launch date	Ref. (sponsor) launch site	Config- uration	Apogee km (miles)	Experi- menters	Experiments	Result
191 (14)	25 Nov. 1968	S43/1 (ESRO) Kiruna	Un, Rav.8 +C	212 (132)	Breisach	Aurora - electron density (experiment R21)	S
					Liège	" - UV spectrum (experiment R81)	Ps
					Kiruna	" – auroral particles (experiment R86)	Ps
					Bir	" - electron density (experiment R105)	S
					"	" - electron temperature (experiment R106)	S

Table 10.30 A summary of Skylark S43/1.

[174] ESRO (1979), report SP-79, p.91.
[175] From MSSL, RSRS and Belfast.
[176] See for instance Massey & Robin (1986), *History of British Space Science,* p.145.
[177] John Raymont's memoirs, visit *www.ucl.ac.uk/mssl/about-mssl/heritage/archive-documents* , and click on "John's Memoirs" (Last accessed August 2014).

The launch conditions specified for S43/1 were stringent. As originally scheduled, launch required a night in a new moon period with a visible aurora in the zenith and with the ESRO-1 satellite passing overhead. This was the first boosted Skylark to be launched from Esrange, and so there were also tight wind restrictions to reduce dispersion. To help reduce dispersion and to ensure the payload booms were deployed, canted fins were fitted to produce a defined roll rate.

During range preparation, it was found that the telemetry radio frequencies being used were subject to severe interference by a new Finnish television station! This added yet another launch restriction, because firing had to take place outside the television station broadcasting hours.[178] This final straw meant that the correlation with the ESRO 1 satellite had to be abandoned, after calculations showed that the restrictions now gave a probability of only one launch possibility every four years.

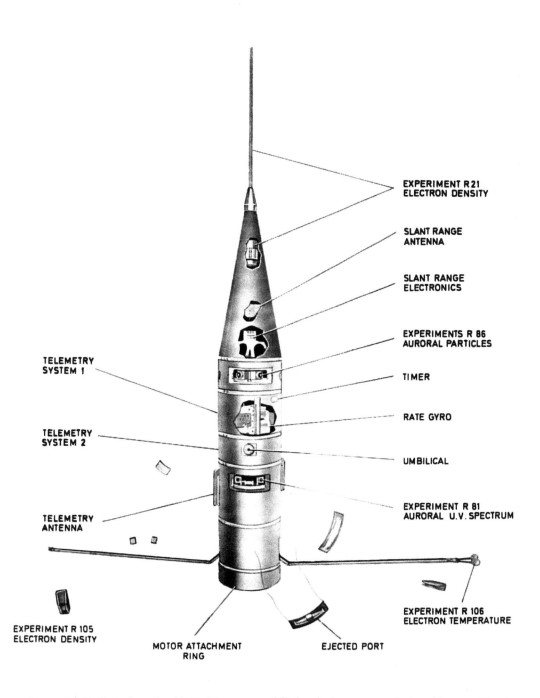

EXPERIMENT R 21
ELECTRON DENSITY

SLANT RANGE
ANTENNA

SLANT RANGE
ELECTRONICS

EXPERIMENTS R 86
AURORAL PARTICLES

TIMER

RATE GYRO

UMBILICAL

EXPERIMENT R 81
AURORAL U.V. SPECTRUM

EXPERIMENT R 106
ELECTRON TEMPERATURE

TELEMETRY
SYSTEM 1

TELEMETRY
SYSTEM 2

TELEMETRY
ANTENNA

EXPERIMENT R 105
ELECTRON DENSITY

MOTOR ATTACHMENT
RING

EJECTED PORT

Figure 10.67 Skylark payload S43. After powered flight, the booms were deployed by centrifugal force, using an oil-damped piston to ensure a balanced steady motion.

(SP-79, figure 1, p.120)

[178] ESRO (1974), report SP-79, p.118.

Seq. Nos	Launch date	Ref. (sponsor) launch site	Config-uration	Apogee km (miles)	Experi-menters	Experiments	Result
192 (15)	03 Dec. 1968	S27/1 (ESRO) Sardinia	Un, Rav.6 +C	198 (123)	ROE	Astronomy - integrated night sky spectroscopy (Cassegrain telescope) (experiment R65)	S
					ROE	Astronomy – stellar UV emission (photometer) (experiment R100)	S

Table 10.31 A summary of S27/1.

S43/1 was finally launched on 25th November and the experiments were generally successful. The apogee of 212 km (132 miles) was close to that expected, however the impact range was 102 km rather than the 81 km expected, and SL43/1 landed on the Norwegian border outside the range safety area. It was therefore decided to delay the launch of the second unit (S43/2) to permit further consideration of the launch criteria and change the frequencies of the telemetry channels to escape interference from the Finnish television station.

December 1968   S27/1, SL601, SL725

The fifth and final ESRO Skylark launch of 1968 was that of **S27/1**. It was an astronomy mission similar to S47/1 in October, and again had on board two ROE experiments, see table 10.31 above.

As with S47/1, the mission was designed to observe stars at shorter UV wavelengths than had been achieved before, although the combination of spectroscopy and photometer experiments was closer to that flown on S05/2 the previous year.

Experiment R65 was designed to measure the ultraviolet spectrum of the Galaxy, and experiment R100 to measure the stellar radiation from as many stars as possible.[179] The instruments included a number of stellar photometers, each of which included a 23 cm (9 inch) Cassegrain telescope optical system feeding a photomultiplier detector and associated electronics, and which viewed the sky through ports in the

side of the vehicle. As an unstabilised payload was used, data rate collection was optimised by using a roll control unit to maintain roll at 18 degrees per second.

The successful launch took place during the early evening of the 3rd December. A total of five minutes was spent above 90km (56 miles), during which time over 92 stars were detected. Good data was received via radio telemetry throughout the duration of the flight - which was just as well, as "No recovery system was included in the payload, and the equipment fell into the Mediterranean Sea."[180] The disadvantage of a sea range!

Unlike S47/1, the photometer experiment results were completely successful, and detailed measurements of the 92 stars observed at the shorter wavelength of 1450Å (145 nm) were published.[181] These were the first such European observations at that wavelength, and for 80 of the stars, were the first ever such observations.[182]

High accuracy solar UV measurements

Three days later **SL601** was launched from Woomera, the last stabilised flight of 1968. It carried two joint Queen's University Belfast and Culham solar physics UV experiments, see table 10.32 below.

This flight appears to have been the first of a Stage 1 ACU with the 'Fine Eyes Forward' modification to improve pointing accuracy.[183] Because the original fine Sun sensors were originally mounted on the skin of the ACU bay at the rear of the

Seq. Nos	Launch date	Ref. (sponsor) launch site	Config-uration	Apogee km (miles)	Experi-menters	Experiments	Result
193 (16)	04 Dec. 1968	SL601 (UK) Woomera	Sun, Rav.6 +C	182 (113)	Cul/Bel	Solar physics - Mg II doublet profile (Fabry- Perot interferometer)	S
					Cul/Bel	Solar physics - image (imaging camera)	S

Table 10.32 A summary of Skylark SL601.

[179] ESRO (1979), report SP-79, p.29.
[180] Campbell (1971a), 'Stellar Photometry in the region 1300Å -2000Å. Part I', p.418.
[181] Campbell (1971a), Table 1, p.420.
[182] Campbell (1971b), 'Stellar Photometry in the region 1300Å -2000Å. Part II', p.201.
[183] BAe (1990), *Record of Skylark Launches 1957-1990*.

payload, there had been some concern that payload bowing during flight might cause pointing errors to the experimental apparatus at the front. Hence, the Sun sensors were removed from the ACU and fitted at the front of the vehicle adjacent to the experiments; this both eliminated possible problems from bowing and made alignment much simpler.[184]

The interferometer instrument on SL601 seems to have been selected to take advantage of this improvement. It was designed to produce measurements of the Mg II line[185] at 2800Å (280 nm) as emitted from different regions of the solar disk and limb, in particular to provide high spectral resolution (0.03Å) measurements combined with a high pointing accuracy (6 arc seconds) along a solar diameter.[186] The apparatus was sophisticated, and comprised a Fabry-Pérot interferometer[187] (being flown for the first time), internally mounted in an echelle spectrograph. (Details of the improved version as

flown on SL603 the following November are given in the next chapter).

Both the launch and payload operation were successful. Forty-five interferograms were recorded producing 500 useful spectral profiles at fifteen positions on the solar disk,[188] showing how accurately it had become possible to point the payload with the Skylark attitude control unit. The payload also included a pinhole camera assembly to record monochromatic solar images at different wavelengths, including the extreme ultraviolet.

The final flight of 1968 was SL725, the first of two identical payloads launched from Woomera to study the ionosphere.

Its companion was SL726, launched in January after the Christmas break, see the next chapter.

Seq. Nos	Launch date	Ref. (sponsor) launch site	Config- uration	Apogee km (miles)	Experi- menters	Experiments	Result
194 (17)	06 Dec. 1968	SL725 (UK) Woomera	Un, Rav.7 +C	146 (91)	MSSL	Ionosphere - positive ion density in Es layer (probes)	S
					RSRS	Ionosphere – magnetic field in Es layer (Rb magnetometer)	S
					Bir	Ionosphere - electron density (probe)	S

Table 10.33 A summary of Skylark SL725.

---

184 Reed (1974), *An Historical Review of Stabilisation Systems for the Skylark Rocket*, p.2.
185 Because of the high cosmic abundance of magnesium, these lines are particularly important in ultraviolet astronomy.
186 Bates *et al.* (1970), 'Fabry-Pérot Interferograms of the Solar Mg II resonance lines'.
187 Interferometry is a technique where electromagnetic waves are superimposed in order to extract scientific information.
188 Bates *et al.* (1970), 'Fabry-Pérot Interferograms of the Solar Mg II resonance lines', p.274.

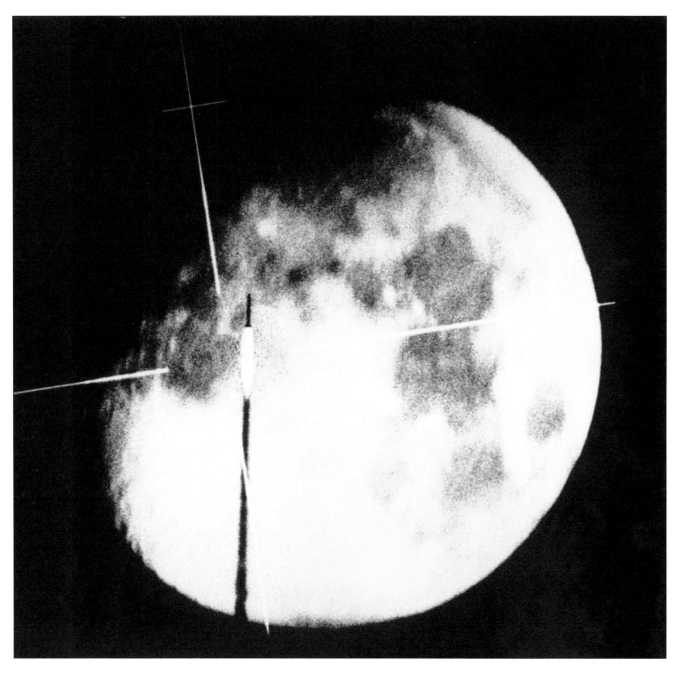

**Figure 11.1 A Skylark captured passing in front of the Moon after launch from
the Salto di Quirra range in Sardinia.**

(Seibert (2006), page vi)

CHAPTER 11

(1969-70)

THE YEARS OF ACHIEVEMENT

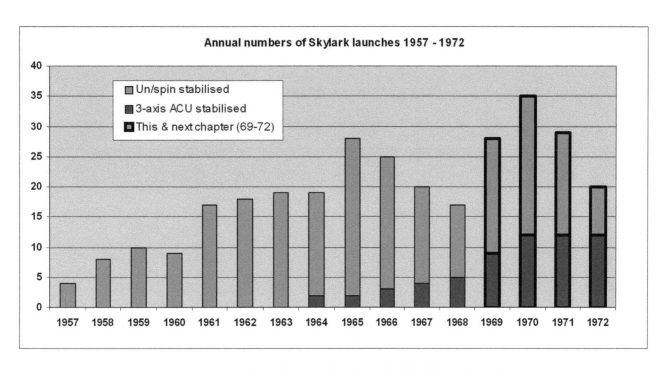

Figure 11.2 This chart shows the annual numbers of Skylark launches until 1972, i.e. up to the end of the next chapter. It illustrates how activity peaked in 1970, and how the proportion of stabilised flights steadily increased.

The two years covered by this chapter were some of the busiest ever for Skylark, and in 1970, the annual total of 35 launches was an all time record.

The increasing proportion of stabilised payloads indicates that during this time a greater number of astronomy experiments were being flown. Originally, experiments on stabilised Skylarks were exclusively concerned with direct observation of the Sun. However in July 1968 the first stabilised experiment had been flown that looked instead to the stars (on SL403), opening up another aspect of astronomy that was set to grow.

1969 at Woomera also saw the first launch of Black Arrow, followed a month later by the launch of Europa 1/Blue Streak F8, that project's second orbital attempt. In 1970, the second and third Black Arrow launches took place, as did the final Blue Streak launch from Woomera. Meanwhile, on the greater stage, in July 1969 Armstrong and Aldrin became the first men to land on the Moon.

FURTHER ENHANCEMENTS

The star-pointing Attitude Control Unit

As explained in previous chapters, the Attitude Control Unit (ACU) was an important enhancement for Skylark. The first prototypes had been flight tested in 1964, and as shown above the number of 'stabilised' flights using the original Stage 1 ACU had steadily increased.

In 1967, Elliott Bros Ltd had submitted a proposal to implement an upgrade, and the company was awarded a contract for what became known as the 'Starling' system to meet the specification for a star-pointing (Stage 5) ACU. The solution adopted was to make the Stage 5 unit an extension of the Moon-pointing Stage 3 system, then in an advanced stage of development. In 1969, it was decided to concentrate resources on the star-pointing Stage 5 rather than continue an extensive Stage 3 programme.

For the Stage 5 ACU, it was required to be able to select target stars down to visual magnitude +5,[1] and a star sensor capable of doing so was designed.[2] In turn, this requirement led to even more development work, as explained by Grant Privett:

> As part of that project, a starlight simulator was entirely designed and built by the RAE Instrumentation and Elec-

tronic Engineering department. Construction took some time to achieve as it ambitiously attempted to simulate the colour characteristics of a star, atmospheric seeing effects, the influence of other stars in the field of view and the brightness and 'temperature' of the background sky.[3]

Figure 11.3 A general view of the star simulator developed by the RAE – the projector like arrangement on the left generated the images (see next figure), on the right is the 12" collimator mirror mounted on a concrete plinth.

(RAE \ Grant Privett)

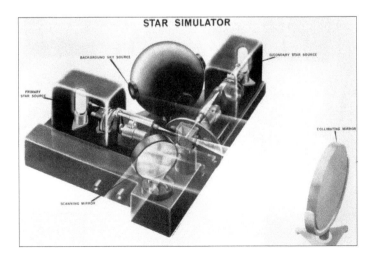

Figure 11.4 A close-up diagram of the star simulator optical system. This shows the primary and secondary simulated star sources and background sky source, with the collimating mirror on the right and scanning mirror in the centre.[4]

(RAE \ Grant Privett)

---

1. The larger the number, the fainter the star. The unaided human eye can detect down to about +6.
2. Abbott (1971), *A Star-pointing Attitude Control System for Skylark*, p.3.
3. Privett (2001), 'The dome on Ball Hill – the RAE observatory', p.317. Reproduced courtesy Journal of the British Astronomical Association.
4. For details, see Gleave (1970), *The alignment and photometric calibration of a star and skylight simulator*.

This level of complexity was, at that time, unprecedented and it was felt essential to compare real-time stellar images obtained with the simulator with those from real stars. So it became necessary to be able to view stars during working hours – weather permitting.[5]

So whilst the star simulator was being built and tested, a sophisticated six-inch refracting telescope with a Coudé configuration mount [6] was ordered from the Zeiss company. It was placed in a purpose built aluminium and steel observatory next door to the simulator laboratory:

At this time valve (vacuum tube) based technology was approaching its peak and quite sophisticated photo-multiplier tube devices were available, but transistors were only quite recent inventions. Yet despite this the star simulator was quite compact, could mimic a wide range of star types and was able to simulate stars from 2nd to 7th magnitude.

Eventually, after much effort, the actual star sensors for the ACU were successfully designed and tested. Testing included strapping the sensor to the side of the telescope aligned with its axis, and recording the sensor's performance as the telescope automatically tracked the stars. The sensor could then be conveniently moved next door for further tests using the range of simulated conditions.

The star sensor package allowed light collected by a compact 75 mm (3 inch) Cassegrain telescope to fall onto a high voltage photo-multiplier tube. The signals from this allowed the control electronics to determine when the star was centrally placed in the field of view. All this was

Figure 11.5 The simulator laboratory and RAE observatory ('The Dome') on Ball Hill in the late 1960s.
(RAE \ Grant Privett)

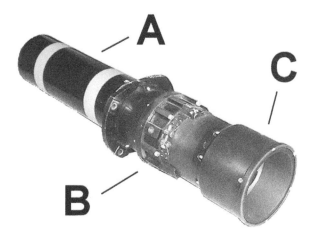

Figure 11.6 An example of the Skylark ACU star sensor developed at Ball Hill, now in the Science Museum, London.[7]
A = photo-multiplier assembly,
B = shutter system and focal plane,
C = optical assembly.
(Privett (2001), figure 3)

5   Privett (2001), 'The dome on Ball Hill – the RAE observatory', p.317. Reproduced courtesy Journal of the British Astronomical Association.
6   This type of mount allows a telescope to point in different directions without the focus (eyepiece) moving – very useful when testing cumbersome equipment.
7   Probably Science Museum object number 1979-39.

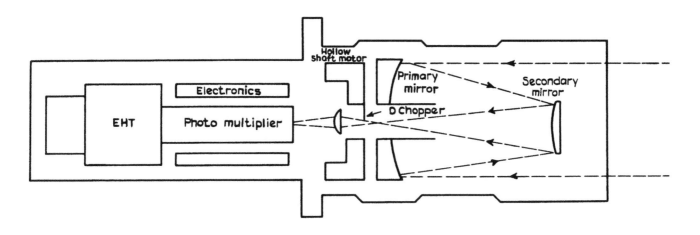

Figure 11.7 A block diagram of the star sensor operation.
(After Abbott (1971), figure 6)

achieved in a telescope/shutter/photo-multiplier package roughly 460 mm (18 inches) long and 100mm (4 inches) wide.

The star sensor instrument was first used on SL811 in July 1970, see later in this Chapter.

Restoration of one of the few surviving operational Skylark installations [8]

"Eventually, after much work and with the concept proven, some of the development work was moved away from RAE. The last logged observation from the dome is for 1972 when the pointing accuracy was again checked.[9] It was then closed down and subsequently used as a storeroom for 24 years until the arrival of Hale-Bopp[10] when the founder of CAS (Cody Astronomical Society), Phil Alner, obtained the permission of DERA management to undertake the restoration of the facility. Happily, on entering the dome he discovered that someone had thoughtfully left an electric bar fire on when the building was closed. This had kept the worst of the damp (over the years the dome had sprung a few leaks) from

damaging the equipment. The asbestos insulated power cable/flex to the fire was at the end of its life but the heating element still worked - sadly the name of the manufacturer is not recorded." [11]

Figure 11.8 The observatory restored - Phil Alner, chairman of the Cody Astronomical Society, and David Mayhead, who designed the dome from scratch back in 1966, when working for the Technical Facilities Department of the RAE.
(Phil Alner)

[8]　Another is the Skylark launch tower at Esrange, even though it has now been adapted for another rocket.
[9]　Although sensor testing was still taking place there in 1973. (John Hargreaves, personal correspondence, February 2014.)
[10]　Hale-Bopp was the brightest comet seen for many decades, passing closest to the Sun in April 1997.
[11]　Privett (2001), 'The dome on Ball Hill – the RAE observatory', p.320. Reproduced courtesy Journal of the British Astronomical Association.

Restoration has now been completed and the observatory is used by the Cody Astronomical Society for visual, CCD and photographic observations of the planets, Moon Sun and deep-sky objects.[12] Thus the observatory is one of the few RAE buildings to survive, and may well hold the honour of being the only installation and equipment from the UK Skylark programme to still be in use.

The cost of Skylark

The Stage 5 ACU was relatively expensive to develop; the contract with the Elliott Bros company at this time (1969-72) was running at an average of £142,000 a year.[13] (Worth some £1.5M to £3.7M in 2011 terms.[14])

As can be seen from the chart below, this was about one eighth (14%) of the total 'extramural' budget for Skylark.

(I.e. that spent on external contractors rather than within the RAE or UK government departments).

The chart indicates that Skylark was a very economical and modest programme for a government space project, even allowing for the fact that many of the indirect running costs are not included.[16] This may have allowed the programme to survive whilst others (such as Black Arrow in 1971) were cancelled, but it was recognised at the time that it was being run on a shoestring, with a comment on the 'pinchpenny' tactics appearing in the minutes of the Skylark policy meetings.[17] As shown in figure 11.10 on the next page, this spending on Skylark was about one third of the UK's Space Science budget, but only about one fifteenth (6.6%) of the UK's spending on its National Space Programme activities at the time.

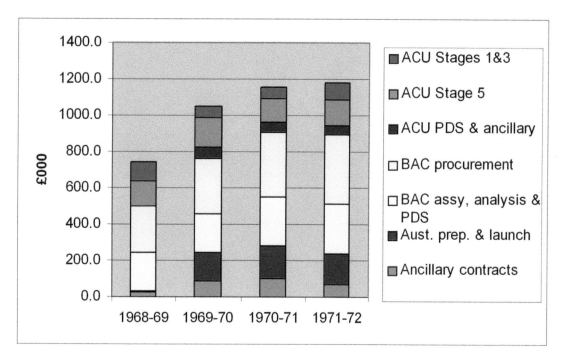

Figure 11.9 'Extramural' expenditure on Skylark, 1968-72.[15] As shown, the annual spend on the development and procurement of Skylark in this manner had reached £1.2M by 1972. (Worth about £11.8M in 2011).

[12] For details of the Cody Astronomical Society visit *www.codyastrosoc.co.uk* (last accessed August 2014).

[13] Figures from the appendices of the minutes of the Skylark Policy Meetings 1969-72 (TNA: PRO document file AVIA 92/145).

[14] 2011 figures based on the "Historic Opportunity" and "Economic Cost" measures for a large project, from Lawrence H. Officer and Samuel H. Williamson, "Five Ways to Compute the Relative Value of a UK Pound Amount, 1270 to Present," MeasuringWorth, 2014, *www.measuringworth.com/ ukcompare/* , (last accessed August 2014).

[15] Extramural actual expenditure figures taken from the appendices of the minutes of the Skylark Policy Meetings 1969-72.

[16] For instance, the cost of the Ball Hill star simulator and observatory appear to have come from the RAE running costs.

[17] For instance, in paragraph 3.2 of the minutes of the 12th policy meeting (4/12/1969) "RAE raised the whole question of the "pinchpenny" tactics being adopted for Skylark and said this could well be uneconomic in the long run if rounds were lost."

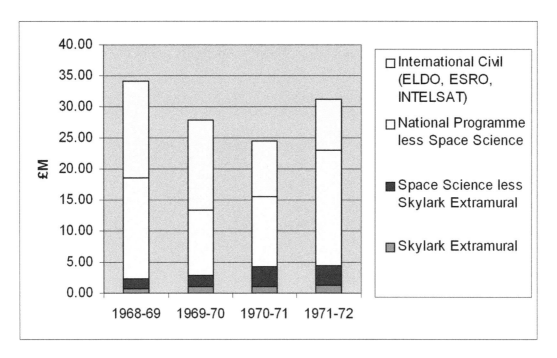

Figure 11.10 The cost of Skylark and the space science programme within the overall UK expenditure on space activities, 1968-72.[18]

SKYLARK LAUNCHES AND SCIENCE IN 1969

As can be seen from the chart at the start of this chapter, the notable feature of 1969 was the increase in the annual number of Skylark launches, up to 28 compared to 17 in 1968. In particular, the number of stabilised flights increased from five to nine.

On the scientific research side, financial pressures on the UKAEA resulted in the transfer of their Astrophysics Research Unit to the relatively new SRC. The staff and their work on solar spectroscopy using stabilised Skylarks remained at Culham, but from April 1969 were financed by the SRC as part of their 'in-house' research effort.[19]

BAC as launch authority

The role of BAC since 1965, that of prime contractor for the Skylark Mk.I build, has been described in previous chapters. At the end of 1968, the company achieved a significant new role, when a contract for the preparation and actual launching

Jan.	Feb.	March	April	May	June	July	Aug.	Sept.	Oct.	Nov.	Dec.
SL781		S43/2	SL724	SL404		S38/1	SL605		S29/1	S46/1	
SL726			SL502			S64/1			SL861	SL602	
			SL606			S38/2			SL862	SL801	
			SL604			S64/2			S29/2	SL603	
						SL722			SL586		
						SL729			SL821		
						SL721			S68/1		
						SL730					

Table 11.1 The 28 Skylark launches in 1969. (For full details, see Appendix 3)
(Key: black = test launches, blue = UK national programme (unstabilised), plum = UK (stabilised), pink = ESRO programme)

---

[18] The overall figures are from an HMSO report 1971, as tabled in Godwin (2007), *The Skylark Rocket*, p.291. (The 1971-72 figures were estimates.) See also Acton (1974), p.345, for some useful notes on the costs of Skylark with respect to the SRC budget.

[19] Massey & Robins (1986), *History of British Space Science*, p.221.

of Skylarks at Woomera was awarded to the company's Australian division. Thus, in early 1969, they took over those activities from the Research Vehicles Group of the Australian Weapons Research Establishment (WRE), who had previously launched all the Skylarks from Woomera.[20]

| January 1969 | SL781, SL726 |

A brief training period for BAC took place. As part of this, the company's first 'Officer in Scientific Charge' (OISC), Ted Chambers,[21] was invited to join WRE in the launch bunker to witness procedures and a launch, that of proving flight **SL781**. He later described this rather unfortunate experience as follows:

> I witnessed the operations of the "wind monitor", whose duty it was to receive wind data from the met. people and plot these on a special chart, thus to obtain the correct launcher training angles, and so ensure the rocket went somewhere near its required impact point. I watched the operations of the "priming monitor" whose task it was to sit at a control console with many switches and dials, to carry out switching functions at the request of final preparation staff on the launcher, then when the launcher was cleared for action, to oversee the semi-automatic twenty minute sequence, ensuring that all the required switching events took place at the right time.
>
> I shared the excitement of the experimenters, whose experiment sat on the nose of the rocket, upon which one of them may have a potential PhD hanging, and as the seconds ticked by noting the air of expectancy slowly rising in temperature.
>
> I noted the WRE OISC checking the wind monitor's progress, and passing and receiving information

from "CON1", the Range Authority's man in overall control of the launch.

> I heard the great roar as the zero time arrived, and the boost motor lit up and the mass of the rocket zoomed upwards, all faces in the launch bunker intent on their instruments.
>
> We all heard CON1 say, "all personnel to remain under cover! The rocket has broken up overhead, and pieces are falling on the launcher area. Stay under cover until we advise you".[22]

Thus, Ted Chambers was observing the launch of SL781 on the 21 January 1969. This was the second proving round for the Goldfinch booster, during which the head separated from the sustainer prematurely after 4.8 seconds:[23]

Further details of this sorry mishap have emerged, revealing why the head separated from the sustainer motor. Dr Ian Tuohy:

> … Skylark SL781 [was] launched on 21 January 1969. It was the second launch of the Goldfinch booster with a Raven motor, and was carrying a large X-ray Astronomy payload built by the Universities of Adelaide and Tasmania. Unfortunately the WRE launch crew didn't lock the manacle ring connecting the payload to the Raven motor. As a result, the payload separated during the Goldfinch burn and in tipping off, fouled the igniters of the Raven motor which continued upwards and then impacted not far down-range, exploding violently. It was not a good way to start my rocket career as a young PhD student - I still have vivid memories of a flashing piece of metal (a nosecone half) being ripped off not long after the vehicle cleared the tower while the Goldfinch was burning.[24]

Seq. Nos	Launch date	Ref. (sponsor) launch site	Config-uration	Apogee km (miles)	Experi-menters	Experiments	Result
195 (1)	21 Jan. 1969	SL781 (UK) Woomera	Un, Rav.6 +G	~3 (1.8)	RAE	Test (Skylark technology) – 2nd proving flight for Goldfinch booster (Head separated from the sustainer prematurely at 4.8 seconds)	Vf
					UAT	Astronomy – X-ray survey of the southern sky	Vf

Table 11.2 A summary of SL781.

20 See Godwin (2007), p.206, for some of the political ramifications of this change.
21 The BAE (Australia) team was led by Ted Chambers, "an inspiring and likeable aeronautical engineer with a touch of well meant piracy about him." (Cruise (2008), *Skylark Ascending, online* article p.14, and *Prospero* number 5, Spring 2008, p.48.
22 Chambers (2000), *Woomera, Its human face*, p.54.
23 J.F.Hazell, minutes of ninth Skylark Policy Meeting January 1969, para. 3.3.1, p.5. (However, the Goldfinch motor itself appeared to have operated correctly and there was no indication it was responsible.) (TNA: PRO AVIA 92/144).
24 Ian Tuohy, personal communication, September 2009.

Ian Tuohy later added:

> This was my first Skylark launch as a student experimenter, and I witnessed (with horror) the break-up from ~1km away outside Test Shop 1. Also the dramatic explosion when the un-ignited Raven motor impacted a few hundred metres downrange (instead of the expected 150-200km downrange!). I can still recall the shock wave rattling the Test Shop doors.[25]

This must have been particularly frustrating for the Australian scientists, as this 'Flight IV' experiment was unique in the UAT series, being their only payload to be flown as a primary experiment on Skylark. This status had permitted the construction of a very large and versatile detection system, and had allowed UAT to choose the optimum launch time.[26]

The principal objective of the flight had been to conduct a high sensitivity survey of the southern sky, with particular

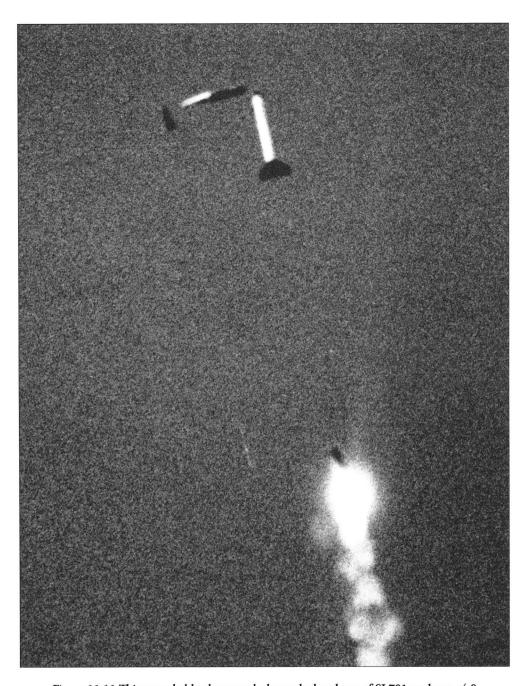

Figure 11.11 This remarkable photograph shows the break-up of SL781 at about +4.8 seconds, just after the Goldfinch boost motor had been jettisoned. The small dark shape at the top left is the nose cone half, as referred to above.

(WRE \ Tuohy (1972), plate 2b)

[25] Ian Tuohy, personal communication, July 2014.
[26] Tuohy (1972), 'Celestial X-ray Surveys from the Southern Hemisphere', p.24.

interest in the galactic centre and the constellation Cetus where an earlier UAT flight (SL422A, December 1967) had produced evidence for a new X-ray source. However as SL781's experiment was destroyed at launch no results were obtained, although hardware elements were reproduced for later flights. (SL728 and SL727 in 1970).

Those in this (1968/69) photograph are (from left to right): Ian Tuohy (PhD student), Les Doherty (technician), Roger Francey (PhD student) and Leighton Barnden (PhD student). The vacuum chamber was situated in the University Physics Department, and had originally been built for thermal/vacuum testing of the WRESAT spacecraft a year or so before.

Figure 11.12 SL781 payload preparation - the X-ray astronomy equipment being loaded into a vacuum chamber at the University of Adelaide.

(National Archives of Australia: A1200, L79561)

Figure 11.13 The UAT SL781 payload assembly less nose
cone, showing the three tier nose-cone detector system,
the electronics bay, and the base-ring experiment.
The keen eyed may be able to make out the two small
Australian flags on top!

(Tuohy (1972), plate 2a)

SL781 was followed two days later by the last Skylark launch carried out by the WRE. **SL726** was launched on 23 January, and was the 171st they had launched during the twelve years since February 1957. The success of Skylark had meant that by 1963 the Research Vehicles Group of WRE had been fielding four teams, so that several Skylarks could be prepared at once.[27]

However, from now on, most Skylark launches at Woomera were to be handled by BAC (Australia), although the range itself was still run by the WRE. As mentioned in an earlier chapter, the launch arrangement for Skylark had been unusual, being a continuation of that arranged by the RAE for the early RTV1 and CTV5 series of firings. Most range users had supplied their own teams for the purpose, and the new arrangement for Skylark conformed to that pattern.

SL726 carried the same ionosphere experiments as SL725 flown the month before, and fortunately, this last WRE prepared launch was completely successful.

Seq. Nos	Launch date	Ref. (sponsor) launch site	Config- uration	Apogee km (miles)	Experi- menters	Experiments	Result
196 (2)	23 Jan. 1969	SL726 (UK) Woomera	Un, Rav.7 +C	149 (93)	MSSL	Ionosphere - positive ion density in Es layer (probes)	S
					RSRS	Ionosphere - magnetic field in Es layer (Rb magnetometer)	S
					Bir	Ionosphere - electron temperature (probe)	S

Table 11.3 A summary of SL726.

---

[27] Morton (1989), *Fire across the Desert*, p.399.

Spring flights for the Petrel

A Petrel sounding rocket launcher had been installed at Esrange in Sweden, and on 3 February 1969, the first UK Spring campaign from there started with the launch of a Petrel to 157 km. By the end of March, a total of eight Petrels had been launched with a wide variety UK ionosphere experiments.[28] Despite their size, these small rockets were spacecraft in their own right, albeit briefly, but capable of spending a few minutes above the atmosphere. As with Skylark, their value included the ability to take measurements on the way up and back down through the atmosphere (a "vertical profile"). For instance, on the 18th March, Petrel P11K reached the respectable altitude of 170 km (106 miles), in order to take measurements of the E-layer of the ionosphere. [29]

| March 1969 | S43/2 |

There were no Skylark flights in February, but on 15th March, the third to be fired from Esrange in Sweden was launched. This was S43/2, and was the second flight of an ESRO S43 payload. It was the successor to S43/1, launched from Esrange the previous November, and like S43/1, the original aim had been to carry out auroral studies intended for correlation with results from the satellite ESRO 1 when it passed overhead at the same time.

However, following the launch of S43/1, a number of changes had been made to S43/2, including the adoption of different frequencies for the telemetry in order to avoid interference from a newly opened Finnish television station.[30] Even though the ESRO 1 satellite correlation exercise had been abandoned, these changes, together with the difficulty in meeting the remaining launch criteria (night, aurora in zenith, new-moon period) when the wind was low, led to this very delayed launch of S43/2. Range preparations at Esrange had started in January, and over a three-month period, the payload was counted down to standby on every evening during the two week new-moon period of each month. In total, about 35 countdowns were performed before launch finally took place! [31]

Despite the months of delay, the flight of S43/2 and the experiments on board were mostly successful. The apogee was 210 km (131 miles), although the impact was only 42 km down range compared to the 76 km predicted. Despite the

short distance impact was again outside the range safety zone and relatively close to a populated area, and as a result of this and the impact of S43/1, the Swedish authorities imposed a ban on the use of boosted Skylark rockets until the impact dispersion had been reduced.

Dispersion and the spinning of Skylarks

Dispersion is the variation of a sounding rocket impact point from that predicted. Skylark was the most powerful of the rockets then being launched from Esrange, and care had to be taken to keep the impact within the safety zone. However, as noted above, this had not been achieved when the Cuckoo booster had been used on S43/1 and S43/2. Thus, in January 1969, it was reported that the use of Skylark by ESRO had been vetoed because of dispersion, which leant weight to the argument to spin at launch by the firing of spin-up motors to spin the vehicle on exit from the launcher.[32]

In particular, at the January Skylark policy meeting that year, Frank Hazell had clarified the effects and purpose of spinning Skylark at launch. He explained that spin motors produced an initial spin rate of one revolution per second, which would be quickly damped out unless canted fins were also fitted. The purpose of spin motors was primarily to reduce dispersion, whereas the slower to act but faster spin produced by canted fins was mainly to provide a scanning facility for experimenters, although there would also be a secondary effect on dispersion.[33]

He further proposed that all rounds should be spun at launch by spin-up motors, and in addition, selected rounds should be fitted with canted fins, but added that this did not necessarily mean that Skylark would be acceptable at Esrange. There would be side effects if canted fins were fitted to all rounds, and these were under investigation. (The ACU could not cope with the spin rates involved, and there was a problem that jettisoned nose cones would not fly clear but collide with the experiments).

He therefore also warned that whilst the problem of the jettisoned nose cone was under investigation the SRC were going ahead with spun rounds at their own risk. However, it appears that this warning was not heeded, as when SL821 was subsequently launched in October 1969 (see below) that very problem occurred, ruining the instrument, and no data was obtained.[34]

[28] Massey & Robins (1986), *History of British Space Science*, p.415.
[29] Massey & Robins (1986), p.415.
[30] ESRO (1974), report SP-79, p.59.
[31] ESRO (1974), report SP-79, p.60.
[32] Minutes of the Ninth Skylark Policy Meeting January 1969, p.2, para. 3.1.1. (TNA: PRO AVIA 92/144).
[33] Ibid.
[34] See for instance Mike Cruise's description of the failure. (Cruise (2008), *Skylark Ascending*, online article p.23, and *Prospero* number 5, Spring 2008, p.57).

The BAC launches start

The first BAC conducted launch at Woomera was that of SL724 on 1st April 1969, and from then onwards Skylark launches were concentrated into a series of 'campaigns' instead of taking place evenly throughout the year:

> From 1968 to its last firing at Woomera in about 1978, a campaign system for launches was adopted, whereby three or four teams per year would spend some two months or so preparing about four rockets for launch. This system encouraged competition between the participants of the teams and generally proved to be cost effective in getting rockets away on time." [35]

Talking of getting away on time, Ted Chambers also recalled:

> Many rockets carried more than one experiment, and getting each experimenter to be ready at the same time was never easy. One had the impression that the ability to have all ready on time seemed to be indirectly proportional to the square of the number of experiments, i.e. a payload with two independent experiments seemed to be four times as difficult as a payload with just one experiment. However meeting one's commitment regarding launch date became something of a matter of honour for experimenters, and there were always twenty-four hours in a day to catch up if necessary.[36]

SL724 was the first of a sequence of five Skylarks to be launched from Woomera, four in April (BAC Campaign 1) and one in May. It carried a cosmic X-ray astronomy survey experiment from the University of Leicester, the instrument of which was similar to that used on SL723, as described in the previous chapter. The flight was successful, and provided intensities and spectra of several X-ray sources in the constellations of Norma and Centaurus, including a new source, Cen-5.[37] As before, the observations were returned to the ground by radio telemetry - which was just as well, as this time payload recovery was not so successful – it was lost for about 18 months until a passing recovery Land Rover came across it in the desert! It was recovered and displayed in the London Science Museum as found, complete with Australian desert dust and all![38]

Figure 11.14 This Leicester X-ray detector is stored at the London Science Museum large objects store at Wroughton, and is probably the one launched into space by SL724. (Compare with Figure 10.63 and Figure 10.64)

(Science museum object 1976-255, author 100_4986) [39]

---

[35] Chambers (2000), *Woomera, Its Human Face*, p.57.

[36] Ibid.

[37] Pounds and Cooke (1971), 'Rocket Observations of galactic X-ray sources in Norma and Centaurus'.

[38] Cooper (2006), *Rocket Man*, p.4.

[39] Image taken at the London Science Museum (Wroughton), permission granted by Science & Society Picture Library.

Seq. Nos	Launch date	Ref. (sponsor) launch site	Config-uration	Apogee km (miles)	Experi-menters	Experiments	Result
199 (5)	03 April 1969	SL502 (UK) Woomera	Sun, Rav.6 +G	273 (170)	MSSL	Solar physics - intensity of solar emission lines (scanning spectrophotometer)	S
					MSSL	Solar physics – extreme UV spectrum (grazing incidence spectrograph)	S
					MSSL	Ionosphere - electron temperature (probe)	S
					MSSL	" - positive ion density (probe)	S
					Bir	Ionosphere - electron density (probe)	S

Table 11.4 A summary of SL502.

Four stabilised flights in a row

SL502 followed on the 3rd April.

SL502 was fired using the more powerful Goldfinch II booster, which as described in the previous chapter, had been designed to cope with the heavier stabilised payloads. It was only the third such launch, and the first with an all-scientific payload. However, it was very successful, reaching a record altitude for a Skylark with a stabilised payload - the apogee of 273 km being well above the 230 km achieved by the similar but Cuckoo boosted SL501 the previous August. The only drawback was that "..a Goldfinch entailed more recti-fication of the launcher than was the case with Cuckoo but the damage was largely superficial".[40]

SL606 was launched two weeks later on the 17th April, and included three experiments from the Astrophysics Research Unit at the Culham Laboratory, and one from the Mete-orological Office. It had the distinction of being the 200th Skylark launch, celebrated in the UK by the presentation of a silver plaque, see figure 11.16 overleaf.

By now, the Astrophysics Research Unit at the UK Atomic Energy Authority's Culham Laboratory had become one of the largest users of Skylark. Their experiments were aimed at the detailed understanding of thermonuclear fusion, the controlled use of which then, (as now), promised the pros-pect of an almost inexhaustible source of energy for human-ity. Fusion is the process that takes place in the Sun and stars, during which matter is converted to energy. There, massive gravitational forces create the right conditions for this con-version, but on Earth, such conditions are extremely difficult and expensive to achieve. Hence observing the Sun from sta-bilised Skylark flights offered a way of extending laboratory observations to naturally occurring plasmas,[41] and by 1968 Culham was launching four different types of solar observa-tion instruments.

Figure 11.15 This 'First Day Cover' celebrated the start of BAC's first launch campaign.
(Author's collection)

[40] Minutes of the 10th Skylark Policy Meeting April.1969, p.8, para. 8.1 (TNA: PRO AVIA 92/144).
[41] An activity still continued by the UK's AWE, see *www.awe.co.uk/* (last accessed August 2014).

Figure 11.16 The 200th launch of Skylark was commemorated by this silver plaque, presented by Mr D.Rowley, executive director of BAC Electronic and Space Systems, to Mr J.H.Twinn, head of Space Department, RAE, Farnborough.

(Flight International magazine, 22 May 1969, page 845)

The four types of Solar Physics spectrographs used by the Culham Laboratory

The first series of instruments observed 'standard' solar UV emissions. These instruments were the 'normal incidence' spectrographs, as described before, and launched on SL303 in 1965, SL407 in 1967, SL 408 in 1968 and also SL606. They used the accurate pointing ability of the Skylark ACU to compare observations of the solar disc and limb, in an ingenious series of experiments to investigate a significant temperature gradient at the surface of the sun. The improved instrument on SL606 allowed mathematical models of this chromosphere-corona[42] transition to be derived,[43] an exercise that would be continued with the subsequent flight of SL902 in 1971.

Seq. Nos	Launch date	Ref. (sponsor) launch site	Config-uration	Apogee km (miles)	Experi-menters	Experiments	Result
200 (6)	17 April 1969	SL606 (UK) Woomera	Sun, Rav.6 +C	202 (126)	Cul	Solar physics – UV spectrum (normal incidence spectrograph)	Sf
					Cul	Solar physics - UV spectra (grazing incidence spectrographs	Sf
					Cul	Solar physics - extreme UV image (normal & grating pin-hole camera)	Sf
					MO	Aeronomy - molecular oxygen concentration (ionisation chambers)	S

Table 11.5 A summary of SL606.

[42] The corona is the plasma 'atmosphere' of the Sun, it is very much hotter (by a factor of several hundred) than the visible surface (the photosphere), from which it is separated by the relatively shallow chromosphere. The mechanisms that heat the corona (the coronal heating problem) are still being investigated and debated 40 years later – i.e. this is still (in 2014) an unsolved problem in physics.
[43] Burton *et al.* (1971), 'The structure of the chromosphere-corona transition region from limb and disk intensities'.

The second series of instruments were designed to investigate higher temperature regions of the Sun, requiring the study of relatively short wavelengths (soft X-rays and XUV), hence the use of grazing incidence techniques.[44] The instruments flown on SL407 in 1967 and SL408 in 1968 were examples of these, and that on SL606 was a further variation of those on SL408.

The third series of instruments comprised a Fabry-Perot interferometer mounted within an échelle spectrograph, the first of which was flown on SL601 in December 1968. As described in the previous chapter, this joint Culham / Queen's University Belfast instrument was designed to provide high spectral resolution (0.03Å) measurements combined with a high pointing accuracy (6 arc seconds). It was flown on SL601 in 1968, and again on SL603 in November 1969, as described later in this chapter.

The fourth series of experiments used a version of the series 3 instrument, an "all reflecting échelle grating spectrograph", which produced a high-resolution solar ultraviolet spectrum over a broad spectral range of UV wavelengths, (1000Å /100 nm). The first of these was launched on SL604 in April, as described below.

Results from SL606

The designers of the grazing incidence spectrograph instrument were well aware of the unreliability of Skylark's payload recovery system, because the film cassette was constructed "sufficiently robust to withstand a severe landing impact and allow a good possibility of data retrieval in the

event of a failure of the recovery parachute." [45] This was a wise precaution, because, (in a masterpiece of understatement), a scientific paper on the SL606 results states "...the conditions were not ideal for maintaining the laboratory calibrations." It goes on to explain:

> The experiments on SL606 were marred by the failure of the payload parachute recovery system which resulted in severe damage to the spectrograph on landing. Further, the vehicle landed in difficult country in the Woomera desert and was not located for seven days during which time the photographic film was subjected to an unfavourable environment. When the payload was returned to the field laboratory it was found that the instrument had been impact-welded into an almost solid mass and it was therefore despatched back to the Astrophysics Research Unit at Culham for the extraction of the film.[46]

Some emulsion fogging due to pressure damage and small light leaks in the cassette was evident, but a spectrum of 120 lines was recorded despite the photographic processing having taken place two weeks after the flight. (See figure 11.17 below).

One reason it had taken so long for the payload to be recovered was that the radar tracking had not been successful. As a result, it was agreed that the RAE and SRC would look into the requirement for an active location device, and the RAE would discuss the overall recovery system at Woomera with WRE.[47] Subsequently, in September, a proposal was put forward to use a coloured parachute, and "... no further action was contemplated until the success rate had been es-

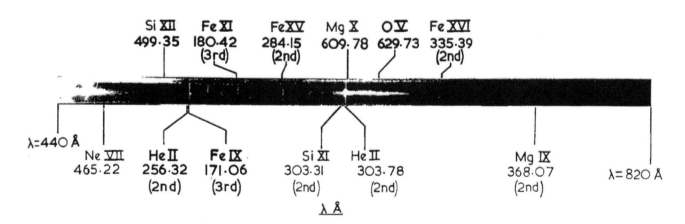

Figure 11.17 The Solar XUV spectrum recorded by SL606. Exposure time 200 sec. Kodak 101-01 emulsion. The damage incurred during recovery can be seen on the emulsion.

(Freeman and Jones (1970), figure 6)

[44] See for instance Massey & Robins, *History of British Space Science*, p.343.
[45] Freeman and Jones (1970), 'Grazing incidence spectra of the sun', p.289.
[46] Freeman and Jones (1970), p.294.
[47] Minutes of the 10th Skylark Policy Meeting April 1969, p.3, para. 3.1.2. (TNA: PRO AVIA 92/144).

tablished." [48] The reluctance to use a 'proper' location device seems most extraordinary. The need must have been quite clear, because as described in Chapter 9, the WRE had unsuccessfully tried their own radio recovery aid four years previously. It was certainly apparent to ESRO, who offered their own device free for use on an SRC round, although curiously this was (at least initially) declined.[49]

What appears to have been the fourth and final Skylark launch in this first 'campaign' by BAC was **SL604** on the 22nd.

During launch, the collector mirror was accidently contaminated, which reduced its efficiency below 2000Å.[50] However, during the flight four exposures of 10, 25, 100

Seq. Nos	Launch date	Ref. (sponsor) launch site	Config-uration	Apogee km (miles)	Experi-menters	Experiment	Result
201 (7)	22 April 1969	SL604 (UK) Woomera	Sun, Rav.6 +C	180 (112)	Cul	Solar physics - UV spectrum (échelle grating spectrograph)	S

Table 11.6 A summary of SL604.

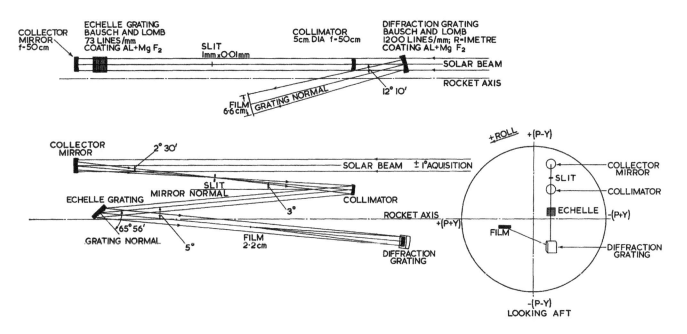

Figure 11.18 Plan and elevation views of the complicated optical layout of the "rocket-mounted Echelle-Diffraction Grating Spectrograph" as flown on SL604.

(Boland, Jones & Engstom. (1971), figure 1)

---

[48] Minutes of the 11th Skylark Policy Meeting September 1969, p.3, para. 6.1. (TNA: PRO AVIA 92/144).
[49] Minutes of the 12th Skylark Policy Meeting December 1969, p.2, para. 4.1. (TNA: PRO AVIA 92/144).
[50] Boland, Jones & Engstrom, (1971), 'An echelle spectrograph for high resolution studies...', p.351.

and 50 seconds were successfully made on film, which was recovered after the flight, and so scientists in Sweden and Italy were able to help with the analysis. This revealed the first high-resolution Fraunhofer spectrum in the range 200nm – 220nm (2000 - 2200Å).[51] The resulting wavelength list gave 663 absorption lines[52] and identifications were proposed for nearly 90% of them.[53]

SL604 appears to have completed the first non-WRE launch campaign; the four Skylarks concerned had been successfully fired over a period of three weeks. "BAC/Elliott were congratulated on the successful launch of the three stabilised and one unstabilised rounds comprising the first campaign well within the planned period although this had been marred by the late recovery of SL606." [54]

May 1969	SL404

Three weeks later **SL404** was launched on the 14th May, and appears to have been a 'stray' fired outside the first campaign. It had the second Stage 3 (Sun and Moon pointing) ACU as a payload, but a vehicle failure (the nose cone failed to jettison[55]) meant disappointment for the Culham laboratory and Leicester University experimenters.

The reason for the failure may have been investigated by the RAE at Farnborough, as the Science Museum in London now has an ex-Farnborough item from SL404, an "Equipment bulkhead no 8 from skylark rocket, SL404. Probably stabilisation platform." [56]

The payload included a grazing incidence spectrograph from Culham, but the vehicle failure meant no results were obtained. Hence this group of scientists must have felt jinxed, as following the problems on SL606 and this failure on SL404, the next launch of their instrument (SL801 on 20th November) suffered from further vehicle failures, as described at the end of this chapter.

Black Arrow

Skylark was only one of the many rockets and weapons launched during this busy year at Woomera.

On the 28th June, the first launch took place of Black Arrow (see figure 11.19 overleaf), the first all British satellite launch vehicle and successor to the earlier Black Knight rocket.[57] The vehicle was designated R0, and comprised live first and second stages and a dummy third stage. Unfortunately, the flight was unsuccessful, as a fault in the first stage engine control system resulted in the vehicle tumbling out of control after 64 seconds, and it only reached 9000 feet (1.7 miles / 2.7 km), before being destroyed by ground command.[58]

July 1969	S38/1, S64/1, S38/2, S64/2, SL722, SL729, SL721, SL730

There were no Skylark launches in June, but July with eight launches was one of the busiest months to date.[59] During the first two weeks, four ESRO Skylarks were launched from Sardinia. The first was **S38/1**, the scientific aim of which was to gain information on the photochemistry of possible cometary parent molecules by permitting a study of the behaviour of a propylene cloud at high altitude. Two technological tests were also carried out, one being the first use of Imp spin up motors on an ESRO flight, the other being the test of an improved Raven ignition unit.[60]

The scientific experiment comprised a single large container filled at the experimenter's laboratory, plus a pyrotechnic device on top to be exploded after nose cone ejection, thus releasing the propylene to create the cloud. This combination was considered so dangerous that dummy experiments were used for the prototype, integration and flight acceptance tests, the actual experiment only being fitted at the range in Sardinia.

Range preparation for the pair of S38 payloads started on the 21st June in parallel with S64 (see below), and S38/1 was duly launched during evening twilight on the 5th, after a three day wait for inclement weather to clear. The flight was successful, although the ground radar did not acquire and so the exact apogee was not obtained, but was approximately as expected (220 km).[61]

[51] Around this time the nanometre (nm) started to replace the Ångström (Å) as a unit of spectroscopic measurement, the nanometre is ten times larger than the Ångström.
[52] Absorption (Fraunhofer) lines – these 'dark' lines in the solar spectrum are caused by chemical elements in the upper layers of the Sun, and are used to identify those elements.
[53] Boland *et al.* (1971), 'A high resolution solar ultraviolet spectrum between 200 and 220 nm', p.29.
[54] Minutes of the 10th Skylark Policy Meeting April.1969, p.8, para. 8.1. (TNA: PRO AVIA 92/144).
[55] BAe (1990), *Record of Skylark Launches 1957-1990.*
[56] Science Museum London, Inv. No. 1993-2384.
[57] For a good description of the origins of Black Arrow, see Hill (2001), *A Vertical Empire,* Chapter 10.
[58] See Hill (2001), p.198, for further details.
[59] As noted in Chapter 9, April 1965 had been the busiest ever month for Skylark launches, with nine launches taking place, albeit seven were on one night.
[60] ESRO (1974), report SP-80, p.28.
[61] Ibid, p.29.

Figure 11.19 Black Arrow R0 lifts off into a clear Woomera sky. As can be seen, the vehicle had a very clean exhaust, the clouds on the right were steam produced by the engine's heat vaporising thousands of litres of exhaust-duct cooling water. (See the Black Knight launcher test - Figure 6.14.)

(WRE)

Seq. Nos	Launch date	Ref. (sponsor) launch site	Config-uration	Apogee km (miles)	Experi-menters	Experiments	Result
203 (9)	05 July 1969	S38/1 (ESRO) Sardinia	Spin, Rav.7 +C	c.220 (137)	Liège	Aeronomy – photochemistry of possible cometary parent molecules (propylene release) (experiment R85)	S
					BAC/ESRO	Test (Skylark technology) – Imp motor spin-up trial & Raven ignition improvement tests	S
204 (10)	06 July 1969	S64/1 (ESRO) Sardinia	Un, Rav.6 +C	275 (171)	IASB	Aeronomy – atmospheric temperature & chemical kinetics (methane & oxygen release & burn at 150 & 275 km), (experiment R149)	S
					BAC/ESRO	Test (Skylark technology) – Imp motor spin-up	S

Table 11.7 A summary of S38/1 and S64/1. S38/2 and S64/2 were respectively the same.

S64/1 was then launched on the 6th, followed by S38/2 on the 11th. The scientific experiments on both the S38 flights worked well, and in addition, the new ignition system worked and was subsequently cleared for use by ESRO. S64/2 followed on the 13th, a repeat of S64/1 shown in the table above. An unusual feature was that the forward part of the payload had to be separated from the remainder at 100 km, to allow gas release at 150 and 275 km. Both flights were successful.

On all four flights the Imp spin-up system ignited correctly and imparted an initial spin; however the dispersion of both impacts was still much greater than hoped for. Analysis revealed that once the Imp motors stopped burning, all rotation had stopped and the vehicles effectively became non-spinning. Post-flight investigation revealed that the damping effect of having straight rather than canted fins had been considerably underestimated, but that canted fins would allow the spin-up system to work correctly.[62] On

this basis, boosted Skylarks were once more accepted for use at Esrange.[63]

Meanwhile, at Woomera, BAC had started their second launch campaign, and another four Skylarks were launched during the second fortnight in July, followed by a "stray" on the 15th August. SL722 and SL729 were launched on the 15th and 17th July respectively. They were followed by SL721 (a repeat of SL722) and SL730 (a repeat of SL729) on the 25th and 30th.

SL721's ionosphere payload reached 213 km (132 miles) and all the experiments were successful. However, recovery was a problem, and the recovery officer wrote these cryptic comments in his log:

- The Motor is in two pieces of equal length and without fins.
- No sign of head and OISC has withdrawn requirement.
- Total man hours spent on recovery, 35, total aircraft hours 7.7.[64]

Seq. Nos	Launch date	Ref. (sponsor) launch site	Config-uration	Apogee km (miles)	Experi-menters	Experiments	Result
207 (13)	15 July 1969	SL722 (UK) Woomera	Un, Rav.5A +C	216 (134)	Shf	Ionosphere - electron density (lf impedance probe)	S
					UCW	Ionosphere - electron density profile & layer heights (pulse propagation)	Ps
					UCW	Ionosphere - electron density profile (cw propagation)	Ps

Table 11.8 A summary of SL722.

---

[62] Thus supporting and augmenting Frank Hazell's previous analysis, see earlier in this chapter (under March).
[63] ESRO (1974), report SP-80, pp.30 & 126.
[64] Roger Henwood, personal correspondence, October 2010.

**Figure 11.20 Boosted by its Cuckoo motor,
SL721 clears the tower at 13:40 local time on 25 July 1969.**

(WRE)

Thus, the ground crew spent one and a half days searching for the payload without success.

July was certainly a busy time at Woomera; Skylark **SL730** was launched on the 30th July, and on the following day the second 'all stages live' launch took place of Europa 1/Blue Streak F8, and the second orbital attempt. Sadly, this ended in failure, the first two stages operated as designed, but soon after third stage ignition, it exploded.[65]

Meanwhile, in the outside world

Apollo 11 was launched on July 16, 1969; it carried Mission Commander Neil Armstrong, Command Module Pilot Michael Collins and Lunar Module Pilot Edwin Eugene 'Buzz' Aldrin, Jr. On July 20, Armstrong and Aldrin became the first men to land on the Moon, while Collins orbited above, and they all returned safely to Earth on July 24th. Although Woomera was not directly involved, most of Neil Armstrong's first moonwalk was relayed to the world via the Parkes Radio Telescope in New South Wales.[66] However, because of technology limitations at the time, relatively low quality images were forwarded, and amazingly, it appears that all the original superior quality recordings have been lost.[67]

August 1969	SL605

August saw the launch of the fifth stabilised Skylark of the year, that of **SL605** on the 21st. This comprised two University of Leicester solar X-ray experiments. The first, a high-resolution crystal spectrometer failed in this instance (because of a faulty connector[68]), but appears to have flown successfully aboard SL804 in November 1970. (See the next chapter.) The second, a pinhole camera, successfully produced X-ray images of the Sun.

October 1969	S29/1, SL861, SL862, S29/2, SL586, SL821, S68/1

A busy October

September brought another pause in Skylark launches, but October was nearly as busy as July, with seven Skylarks launched from three different launch sites in just under three weeks. In addition, the prototype 'Falstaff' rocket vehicle was launched from Woomera on the first of the month.[69] (Falstaff was a larger military cousin of Skylark, see the chapter after next).

The first Skylark launch of October was **S29/1** from Kiruna in Sweden on the 5th, with an all-British set of experiments, see table 11.9 overleaf.

The Birmingham experiments were repeats of those flown on S43/2 in March, however this time the booms were positioned under the nose cone rather than being strapped to the outside of the payload. Indeed, S29 presented a particular

Figure 11.21 The launch of the first 'Falstaff' rocket.
(WRE / BAC)

---

[65] Launch of F8 – see for instance Hill (2001), *A Vertical Empire*, p.150.

[66] See for instance, *www.parkes.atnf.csiro.au/news_events/apollo11/tv_broadcasts.html* , last accessed August 2014.

[67] The so-called "Apollo 11 Lost Tapes" - *http://en.wikipedia.org/wiki/Apollo_11_missing_tapes* , last accessed August 2014.

[68] SRC (1972), *Space Research Report 1969-70*, p.27.

[69] Harlow (2000), 'The Larger Solid Propellant Rocket Motors of the United Kingdom', p.10.

Seq. Nos	Launch date	Ref. (sponsor) Launch site	Config- uration	Apogee km (miles)	Experi- menters	Experiments	Result
212 (18)	05 Oct. 1969	S29/1 (ESRO) Kiruna	Un, Rav.8 +C	225 (140)	Bel	Neutral atmosphere – winds, temperature, diffusion by ground tracking (TMA release) (experiment R37)	S
					RSRS	Aurora – particle energy (channel multiplier detector) (experiment R52)	S
					Bir	Ionosphere – electron density (RF probe) (expt. R105)	S
					Bir	" - electron temp. (Langmuir probe) (expt. R106)	S

Table 11.9 A summary of S29/1.

challenge to the mechanical designer as most of the scientific experiments needed to be located under the nose cone, and a protective framework was integrated into the structure to prevent the danger of the nose cone halves damaging them when it was ejected.[70]

After nose-cone ejection, the two arms of the boom were designed to deploy umbrella fashion until they locked into place. Also mounted under the cone and looking through the protective framework was the sensor system of experiment R52. The other experiment, R37, was contained in

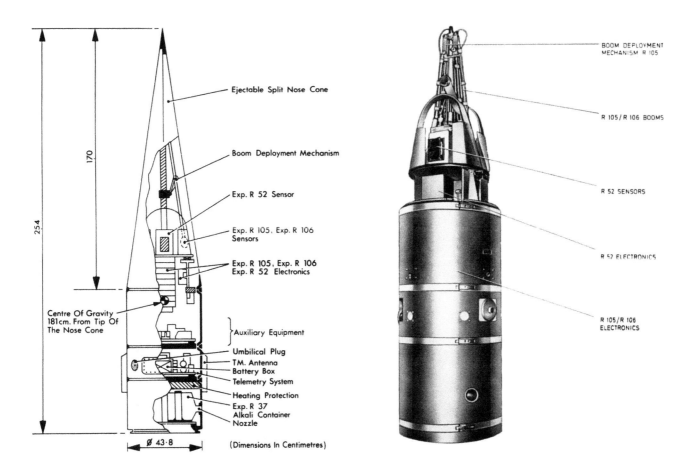

Figures 11.22 and 11.23 Schematic and general views of payload S29.
(ESRO SP-80, p.13 figure 1 and p.15 figure 3)

70 ESRO (1974), report SP-80, p.10.

Figure 11.24 A commemorative envelope for SL861.
(J.A.Hill collection)

a bay at the rear of the payload and the two containers of TMA were secured to a 10 cm (4 inch) pad of thermal insulation to protect the rest of the payload from the heat generated during the vapour-release operation.

The launch criteria for S29 were quite strict – a clear sky during winter, twilight with no full moon, visible aurora with absorption, launch window 8 pm – 4 am, and a launch hold at – 3 minutes to await optimum conditions. Nevertheless, S29/1 was successfully launched at the first attempt on the 5th, and the Imp spin-rocket system, used for the first time at Esrange, worked well, keeping the impact range close to that predicted. S29/2 was ready for launch on the 7th, but wind conditions were excessive until it was launched on the 17th. This flight too was completely successful:

> In many ways the performance of S29 was almost exemplary. No major problems were encountered in design, integration or testing. The launch campaign was short considering the type of auroral payload, visual sighting and tight wind restrictions for Skylark at Esrange. The low impact dispersions which coincided with the first use of spin rockets on Skylark at Esrange were particularly encouraging for the future.[71]

Meanwhile on the other side of the world at Woomera, in very different temperatures, BAC's third Woomera launch campaign was running in parallel. **SL861** and **SL862** were launched on the 16th and 17th October respectively, both reached the same record Skylark altitude of 319 km (198 miles). The UCL grenade and TMA (Trimethyl Aluminium) release experiments aboard were similar to those of

SL761 and SL762 in May 1968, and in conjunction, the University of Adelaide conducted ground-based experiments on the upper atmosphere using radio meteor and spaced receiver drift methods.[72]

Most unusually, it appears that the scientific results from one of the SL861/SL862 experiments were used again 25 years later, because in 1994 a paper was written using the TMA trail results once more re the "Turbulence and Scale of gravity waves".[73] This must be some sort of record!

These two launches were closely followed by that of **SL586**[74] three days later. This was a Stage 1 Sun-stabilised Skylark, with a variety of instruments designed and built by the RAE as part of the development of future spacecraft systems. The main objective was to test the horizon sensor developed and manufactured at Farnborough, as part of the Establishment's contribution to the X3 satellite, which in due course was launched by a Black Arrow rocket in 1971.[75] In this flight test, the sensor was mounted on a motor driven platform that scanned the sensor field of view back forth over the horizon, the sensor accuracy being determined by comparing the results with other independent instruments on board.[76]

The other five instruments shown (figure 11.25 overleaf) were included to provide both the attitude information required, and fundamental information for the development of attitude sensors for both Skylark and future British spacecraft. They were (i) an albedo radiometer, (ii) a conical scan horizon detector, (iii) a scanning Moon sensor, (iv) a star photometer and (v) a two-axis sun sensor developed under contract by Elliott Brothers Ltd to an RAE requirement.

71 ESRO (1974), report SP-80, p.12.
72 Lloyd *et al.* (1971), 'Thermospheric Observations combining chemical seeding and ground based techniques......'.
73 Roper (1995), 'Rocket vapour trail releases revisited...'.
74 The SL58x numbering sequence was used only for proving/test flights.
75 RAE News, November 1969.
76 Barnes & Kenward (1972), *Sensor Trials on Skylark 586*, p.3.

Conical scan horizon sensor

2 - Axis sun sensor
(behind)

Albedo radiometer
(centre)

X3 Horizon
sensor

Star
photometer

Moon
sensor

THE RAE SKYLARK PAYLOAD

Figure 11.25 The payload of SL586 with the doors open and the X3 horizon sensor and the star photometer deployed.
(RAE News)

were contained in the aircraft's freight hold under their feet. The decisive moment came when they arrived at Adelaide to find that the equipment was not with them. In the meantime, staff at Farnborough were making frantic efforts to get the equipment from Luton to London Airport and put it onto a BOAC aircraft arriving in Australia shortly after the charter flight. Again, fortune stepped in, and although the crates were moved to London Airport two were misplaced, and when Derek and Chris opened the boxes in Australia they found, to their dismay, spare parts that had nothing to do with Skylark!

Urgent signals went backwards and forwards between Adelaide and Farnborough until finally the right boxes were found and despatched. By the time all the equipment had reached its proper destination the preparation schedule was two weeks late. However, the time was made up and the rocket reached the launch tower on Sunday the 19th.

Talking about their experience to *RAE News*[77] after their return to England, Derek and Chris said they had little time to think of anything that might go wrong with the experiments. The tension came when they had completed their work one and half hours before the launch, which was due at 16:40 on the 20th when the Sun was 20 degrees above the horizon. It was then they realised that the moment had come to test the results of more than eighteen months work by a great number of people. "Would it all work?" This question and many others went through their minds as the final 20 minutes countdown started.

The test schedule carried out during the countdown went well until one of the last measurements, that of the star photometer calibration, was due at -9 minutes. No calibration appeared. The countdown was stopped and the Cuckoo boost motor disarmed. An immediate check on the Skylark itself was made and it was found that the umbilicals were satisfactory. After fifteen minutes, the fault was found in the control console, satisfactorily corrected, and the countdown continued.

The best laid plans...

The right conditions for the launch of SL586 were on the 20th or 21st October, when a 50 minute period was available when the Sun, Moon and Earth were in the right position. If either of these dates were missed, it would mean a four week wait until conditions were again suitable. Two of the scientists from the RAE Space Department who were closely connected with the experimental payload, Derek Kenward and Chris Farr, accompanied the equipment together with BAC and Elliott Bros. Ltd teams on a chartered aircraft that left Luton Airport for Australia on the 19th September.

The two RAE representatives departed on schedule, with the firm conviction that the payload and their test equipment

Finally, SL586 was launched completely successfully and all its systems worked well. The launch took place at half moon to allow the attitude of the payload to be measured using the standard Stage 1 Sun sensors which were fitted to the payload, and by the special scanning Moon detector developed by Stan Craig. Additional attitude data was derived from Chris Farr's star photometer. The main purpose of this photometer, the most complex instrument in the payload, was to measure the brightness of the sunlit sky above the Earth's atmosphere and to assess techniques developed in the Space Department to assist in the detection of stars in daylight.[78]

SL586 was followed only two days later by **SL821**, carrying three X-ray astronomy experiments from MSSL. The payload was accompanied by Mike Cruise, then a young PhD student:

> My first visit to Australia was with this large area detector payload. This, too, was launched on a spin stabilised Skylark with canted fins, but the large area detector occupied almost all the room under the nose cone…The payload also contained some booms which deployed after nosecone release with electron density probes attached.[79]

Disastrous communication problems

Mike Cruise later had to recount the failure of the mission:

> Unfortunately the dynamics of releasing a split nosecone from a fast spinning vehicle had not been thought through by the design authorities at RAE Farnborough, or at BAE. Once released, the nosecone halves began to rotate about their longitudinal axes, unable to dispose quickly of their angular momentum. The following edge of each half nosecone chopped through the detectors before the heavy nosecones drifted away from the vehicle and no data was obtained.[81]

In fact, nine months before this failure, at the January 1969 Skylark Policy meeting, a costed proposal had been received from BAC for the study of this very problem, and chief designer Frank Hazell had warned that in the meantime, the SRC were going ahead with spun rounds at their own risk.[82] Clearly, this had not been communicated to the experimenters, and unfortunately the damage to MSSL's instruments meant the scientific aspect of the mission was completely unsuccessful.[83]

Figure 11.26 The payload as flown on SL821, showing two of the MSSL astronomy experiments - the large area X-ray detector and the folded booms of the electron density probes.[80]
(Cruise (2008), figure 6)

[78] Stars down to +3.0 visual magnitude were observed within 45° of the Sun: Farr (1971) 'Broadband determination of Sky Brightness from a Skylark Sounding Rocket'.

[79] Cruise (2008), *Skylark Ascending*, online article p.23, and *Prospero* number 5, Spring 2008, p.57. Mike Cruise gained his PhD in 1973, became a lecturer at UCL, and Deputy Director of MSSL in 1985. He moved to the Rutherford Appleton Laboratory where he became Associate Director of Space Science in 1993. After moving to the University of Birmingham, he was appointed Professor of Astrophysics and Space Research in 1997.

[80] OK, this does appear to be attached to SL905, but the same instruments were flown on both, see SL905 later in this chapter.

[81] Cruise (2008), *Skylark Ascending*, online article p.23, and *Prospero* number 5, Spring 2008, p.57

[82] Minutes of the Ninth Skylark Policy Meeting January 1969, p.1, para. 3.1.1. (TNA: PRO AVIA 92/144).

[83] The problem was eventually solved by 'de-spinning' the payload; see for instance SL905 launched in November 1970.

Seq. Nos	Launch date	Ref. (sponsor) launch site	Config- uration	Apogee km (miles)	Experi- menters	Experiments	Result
218 (24)	24 Oct. 1969	S68/1 (ESRO) Sardinia	Un, Rav.7 +C	184 (114)	ESRO	Test (vehicle & range facility) – flight trial of the RESY sea recovery system	Ps
					PIB	Aeronomy – background primary cosmic X-ray measurements (scintillation counters) (expt.R73)	S
					SSD -ESTEC	Ionosphere – positive-ion density in D-layer, 80-40km (experiment E1)	S

Table 11.10 A summary of S68/1.

The final October launch was that of S68/1 from Sardinia on the 24th. The main objective was to provide the final flight, re-entry and flotation trial of the recovery system (RESY) developed for the ESRO Sounding Rocket programme. The opportunity was also taken to carry two scientific experiments – one to measure positive-ion density in the lower ionosphere and the other to measure primary cosmic X-rays.[84]

The background was ESRO's need to recover sounding rocket payloads launched to a greater altitude than was possible from Esrange, a need which led to a system being developed to permit recovery from the Mediterranean Sea after launch from Sardinia. Thus the year before, in 1968, Dornier System GmbH had been awarded a contract to develop a parachute recovery system for Skylark. It was designed to provide a cushioned landing for payloads weighing up to 100 kg (220 lb) from altitudes of up to 250 km (155 miles), both on water and on land, the flotation bags acting as impact attenuators for soft landing on the ground.[85] Multiple detection aids such as smoke rockets, flares, a radio beacon and a water colouring agent were specified for locating the payloads.[86]

The experiments required the launch to be immediately after sunrise under clear-sky conditions during the period 20th October to 30th November, with sea and weather conditions in the recovery area suitable for the use of a search boat and aircraft. After some three weeks of preparation at the Sardinian range, these conditions occurred, and launch took place at 06:44 local time on the 24th.

At first, all went well. Experiment E1 from the Space Science Division (SSD) at ESTEC was interesting and unusual, and consisted of a parachute-borne instrument package built into a standard Skylark body section from which it was ejected at very high altitude during ascent.

Ejection was successfully accomplished after 50 seconds of flight at an altitude of about 45 km (28 miles) and the instrument package continued upwards to approximately 80 km (50 miles) with the momentum gained from the main vehicle. It then floated back down by parachute for over 30 minutes, sending back data on the lower ionosphere via its own telemetry system.

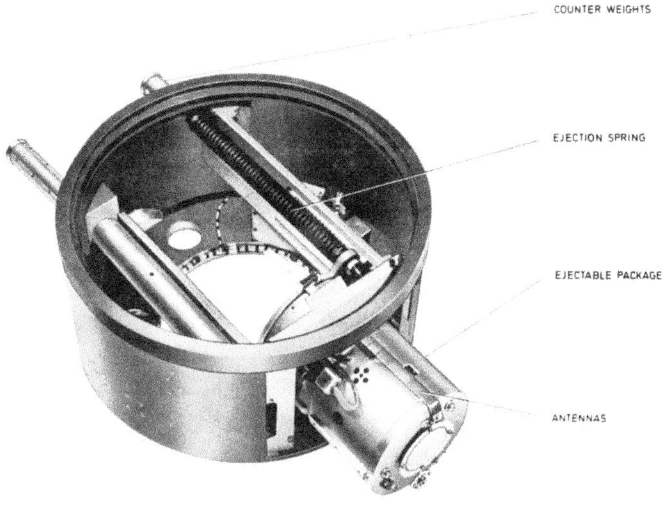

Figure 11.27 Experiment E1, showing how it would be ejected sideways from Skylark.
(ESRO (1974), report SP-80, p.140 figure 3)

---

[84] ESRO (1974), report SP-80, p.133.
[85] For technical details, see Häuser (1971), *The Parachute Recovery System RESY*.
[86] Flight International, 11 July 1968, p.70.

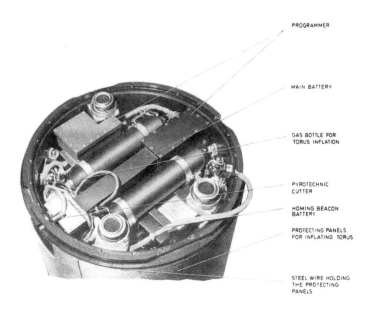

PROGRAMMER

MAIN BATTERY

GAS BOTTLE FOR
TORUS INFLATION

PYROTECHNIC
CUTTER

HOMING BEACON
BATTERY

PROTECTING PANELS
FOR INFLATING TORUS

STEEL WIRE HOLDING
THE PROTECTING
PANELS

**Figure 11.28 A general view of the top
of the S68/1 recovery bay.**
(ESRO (1974), report SP-80, p.141 figure 4)

Meanwhile, after nose cone jettison at 68 seconds, experiment R73 started to scan the sky as S68/1 continued to an apogee of 184 km (114 miles), returning data by telemetry in the normal way.

The payload recovery operation was the first conducted by ESRO from the sea, and involved a fair amount of effort, including three aircraft, a rescue boat, a minesweeper, two frogmen and a communications control centre.[87] The planes and boats were all equipped with homing devices actuated by the beacon in the Skylark recovery bay. The two boats were stationed on the edge of the estimated impact circle, one due north and one due south of the anticipated impact point, whilst two of the aircraft circled nearby.

The payload separated from the motor before re-entry and just over eight minutes into the flight at a height of six km (four miles), it successfully deployed its parachutes and the flotation torus was inflated. Six minutes later, it landed on the sea. By then the aircraft and boats had received the recovery beacon radio signal, but a minute after splashdown the beacon ceased transmitting. One aircraft conducted a visual search, and the pilot reported seeing the marker dye and a white object, but no sign of the yellow torus. The pilot directed the boats and the other aircraft to the spot, and the minesweeper stopped engines in the middle of the dye and carried out a tentative sonar search but with no result. It was decided the payload had sunk, and the frogmen were not used,[88] and the launch of S68/2 was postponed until the post-flight investigation had been completed.

An intensive investigation duly took place. It was concluded that aerodynamic heating during ascent and descent had

weakened the torus, which had then burst whilst being inflated. However, the payload had retained some buoyancy for a short period and the white object seen by the first pilot was the parachute in the process of sinking. The design of the torus was modified to try to avoid this occurring in the future.

This new feature raised the question of whether it was worth considering the firing of Skylark at the Hebrides range and so saving the time of going to Woomera. This however would probably have required reduced dispersion and a more accurate guidance system for launching.[89]

November 1969   S46/1, SL602, SL801, SL603

S68/1 was followed two weeks later by another ESRO launch, this time from Sweden. The aim of the payload on **S46/1** (the 100th ESRO launch[90]) was to study the effect of auroral activity on electrons in the D and E layers of the ionosphere.[91]

After various weather related and technical problems, S46/1 was launched at the tenth countdown, the 100th launch in the ESRO sounding rocket programme. All three experiments were completely successful, although the launch of the second flight payload, S46/2, was deferred so that a fourth experiment (R134), which had been withdrawn by the experimenter in September, could be included once more. (S46/2 was eventually launched in January 1971).

[87] ESRO (1974), report SP-80, p.136.
[88] ESRO (1974), report SP-80, p.137.
[89] Thomas (1968), 'Suborbital probes', p.249.
[90] ESRO (1974), p.143.
[91] ESRO (1974), p.67.

Seq. Nos	Launch date	Ref. (sponsor) launch site	Config-uration	Apogee km (miles)	Experi-menters	Experiments	Result
219 (25)	10 Nov. 1969	S46/1 (ESRO) Kiruna	Un, Rav.8 +C	214 (133)	Breisach	Ionosphere – electron density profile (inverse Seddon expt., 3-channel radio receiver) (expt.R20)	S
					CES	Ionosphere – distribution of low-energy electrons (experiment R110)	S
					Shf	Ionosphere – small scale structure of ionisation in the lower ionosphere (Langmuir probe) (expt. R125)	S

Table 11.11 A summary of S46/1.

The November Campaign at Woomera

SL602 was the first of three Sun-stabilised (Stage 1 ACU) Skylarks that comprised a short November launch campaign from Woomera. It had on board just one experiment, a new MSSL astronomy instrument, a Fresnel shadowgraph camera for viewing galactic X-ray sources. Unfortunately the ACU failed,[92] the first time it had done so, and no results were obtained.

SL801 was launched two days later on the 20th, and included four experiments, see table 11.22 below. The Culham solar physics experiments were a continuation of those previously flown on the ill-fated SL606 and SL404 missions nine months previously, and as noted before, this group of Culham scientists must have felt jinxed, because SL801 suffered not just one but two vehicle failures. Firstly premature deployment of the split nose cone resulted in severe heating of the experiment during the ascent through the upper atmosphere, degrading the final results. Secondly, the para-

chute recovery system failed once more, resulting in a 'hard landing'. However at least they were again able to recover their robustly constructed film cassette and obtain reasonable observations,[93] their fellow scientists from the Meteorological Office were not so fortunate, and their experiments appear to have produced no results.[94]

At an official level, the reaction in the UK to these disastrous and expensive recovery system failures seems to have been rather defensive and 'laid back'. For instance at the subsequent Skylark policy meeting in December it was acknowledged, "There had recently been an unfortunate series of parachute bay failures and BAC stated they now had a good idea of the causes. RAE accepted an action to have an overall look at the parachute bay design, bearing in mind it was now required to recover heavier payloads from greater heights." [95] However, in the background urgent action must have been taking place, because within a few months, modifications had been introduced into flight vehicles. (See March 1970 below).

Seq. Nos	Launch date	Ref. (sponsor) launch site	Config-uration	Apogee km (miles)	Experi-menters	Experiments	Result
221 (27)	20 Nov. 1969	SL801 (UK) Woomera	Sun, Rav.6 +C	274 (170)	Cul	Solar physics - UV spectrum (normal & grazing incidence spectrographs)	Ps
					MO	Solar physics - UV intensity (ionisation chambers)	Vf
					MO	Aeronomy - molecular oxygen concentration (ionisation chambers)	Vf
					Cul	Solar physics - extreme UV image (pin-hole cameras)	Vf
						(Vf = recovery system failed)	

Table 11.12 A summary of SL801.

[92] BAe (1990), *Record of Skylark Launches 1957-1990.*
[93] Freeman and Jones (1970), 'Grazing incidence spectra of the sun', p.302.
[94] Massey & Robins (1986), *History of British Space Science*, p.409.
[95] Minutes of the 12th Skylark Policy Meeting, December 1969, para. 4.3, p.3. (TNA: PRO AVIA 92/144).

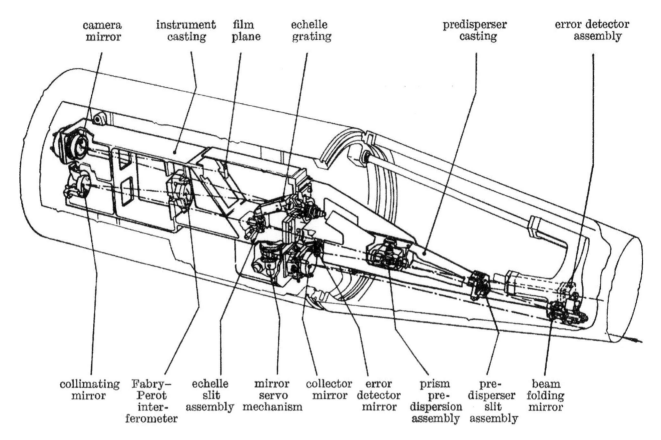

camera mirror   instrument casting   film plane   echelle grating   predisperser casting   error detector assembly

collimating mirror   Fabry–Perot interferometer   echelle slit assembly   mirror servo mechanism   collector mirror   error detector mirror   prism pre-dispersion assembly   pre-disperser slit assembly   beam folding mirror

Figure 11.29 Details of the Culham solar physics instrument flown on SL603.
(Bates *et al.* (1971), figure 1)

The final Skylark flight of 1969 was similar to the final flight of 1968. **SL603** was launched on the 27th November and contained an improved version of the joint Queen's University Belfast and Culham solar UV 'series 3' astronomy experiment previously flown on SL601.[96]

The diagram above indicates how sophisticated the instruments flown on Skylark had become. Once in space, the disk of the Sun was scanned producing a set of 30 solar image settings, each of which produced four exposures/UV interferogram recordings. The rocket payload also included a pinhole camera to record solar images in the extreme ultraviolet, this produced four separate images with an exposure time of 228 seconds during the 180 km apogee.

This time the Skylark recovery system worked as planned. On the descent, the ACU separated from the payload under pneumatic control, and the payload was successfully landed by parachute for recovery of the exposed film. Even post-flight calibration of the recovered instrument was possible, and showed that no changes to its performance had occurred during flight.

The scientific results provided many detailed observations, and showed how the parameters under study varied between limb and disk and quiet and active regions of the Sun's surface. The experiment produced the most detailed solar spectrum between 275 and 283 nm to date. Even a short sounding rocket flight such as this (some four minutes in space) produced a great deal of data, some of which remained to be analysed over a year later.

SKYLARK LAUNCHES AND SCIENCE IN 1970

Skylark's 1970 season was its busiest ever, with a record 35 launches, an average of one every 10.4 days.[97] This increase was a result of the record number of ESRO sponsored launches, 19 compared to 9 the year before. In comparison, the number of UK sponsored launches was down to 14 compared to 19 the year before, whilst a new customer, Germany,[98] emerged with two launches. Thus 1970 was the first year in which ESRO use of Skylark overtook that of the UK national programme.

[96]   Bates *et al.* (1971), 'High resolution interferometric studies of the solar magnesium II doublet spectral region'.
[97]   Allowing for the fact there were no launches during May, August or September, the average during the remaining months was one every 7.8 days, nearly one a week!
[98]   At this time West and East Germany had not been re-united, an event that did not occur until 1990, so until that year references in this book to 'Germany' refer to the Federal Republic of Germany (FRG/West Germany).

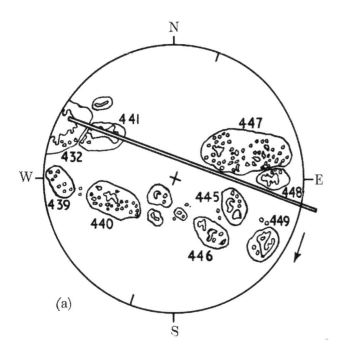

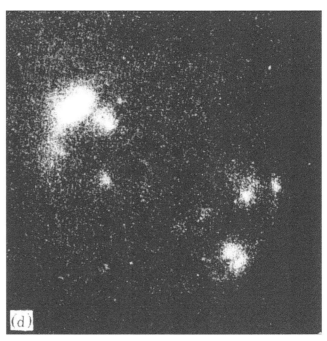

Figures 11.30 and 11.31 Left: A solar activity map showing the initial position/coverage of the SL603 spectrographic slit (from limb to disk) relative to the main regions of solar activity. Right: The corresponding SL603 pinhole camera extreme ultraviolet image. The map shows how extraordinarily accurate the Skylark ACU had now become.

(Bates *et al.* (1971), figures 2(a) and 2(d))

Many of the launches supported the emerging science of X-ray astronomy, and from 1970 to the conclusion of the UK Skylark programme in 1978, 27 such payloads were launched.[99]

Also at Woomera in 1970, the second and third Black Arrow test launches took place, as did the final Blue Streak launch from Australia.

The First ESRO Campaign

The year began with a series of seven ESRO launches, two from Sardinia, one from Woomera, and four from Kiruna. All included UK instruments. However, a difficulty arises in describing these flights. For the years from 1964 to 1969 ESRO produced a series of five excellent reports (SP-76 to SP-80), which document in detail every ESRO sounding

Jan.	Feb.	March	April	May	June	July	Aug.	Sept.	Oct.	Nov.	Dec.
S56A/1	S44/1	SL921	S66/1		S68/2	S63/1			SL972	SL905	S69
	S72	SL901	S28/1			S63/2			SN5/2	SL904	
	S66/2	SL401	SL803			SL727			SL1021	SL804	
	S70	SN5/1	SL728			SL971			S53		
	S61/1	SL802				SL811			S58		
	S61/2					S56A/2			S67/1		
						S65/2			S67/2		
						S65/1					

Table 11.13 The record number of 35 Skylark launches in 1970. (For full details, see Appendix 3)

(Key: black = UK test launches, blue = UK national programme (unstabilised), plum = UK (stabilised),

pink = ESRO programme, red = German national)

[99]   Massey & Robins (1986), *History of British Space Science*, p.370.

rocket mission during that time. Unfortunately, it appears that no more of these reports were published,[100] so from 1970 the details of ESRO Skylark missions have had to be pieced together from other sources.

January 1970	S56A/1

The first such launch, S56A/1, was fired from Sardinia on the 24th January. It included two experiments from the RSRS that were similar (possibly the same) as those on previous ESRO missions such as S26/1 and S26/2. These experiments were designed to investigate the formation of the unpredictable D-region of the ionosphere by measuring its electron density and at the same time the intensity of the ionising radiation (Lyman-α) from the Sun.[101] However there appears to have been a vehicle failure as the instrument covers did not deploy,[102] and only one of the experiments may have worked.[103]

February 1970	S44/1, S72, S66/2, S70, S61/1, S61/2

The next Skylark, S44/1, was a UV astronomy mission launched from Sardinia on the 6th February. This had the first Skylark payload with an attitude control unit (ACU) designed to point to a star rather than the Sun.[104] Although ESRO had successfully used a version of the Elliott/RAE Sun-pointing ACU on S41 in November 1968, this star-pointing ACU appears to have been a 'Space General' unit,[105] acquired from the Space Electronics Corporation of the USA,[106] possibly because the British equivalent was not yet ready.[107] Unfortunately, the ACU failed, and the mission was not a success.

The third Skylark launch of 1970 was S72, the first ESRO sponsored Skylark to be fired from Woomera, the launch procedure being carried out by BAC. This too had a non-British star-pointing ACU, which again failed.[108] However,

Figure 11.32 The first ESRO star-pointing payload undergoing flight-clearance testing.
(Seibert (2006), p.62)

---

[100] Seibert (2006), *The History of Sounding Rockets and Their Contribution to European Space Research*, ESA report HSR-38, p.65.

[101] ESRO (1973), report SP-78, p.75.

[102] The BAe (1990) *Record of Skylark Launches 1957-1990*, includes for S56A/1 the cryptic comment "Covers left on".

[103] The R132 type electron density experiment used radio aerials under a fibreglass nose cone so would not have been affected, but the R123 type Lyman-α detection chambers were designed to be uncovered and deployed at an altitude of 65 km.

[104] BAe (1990), *Record of Skylark Launches 1957-1990*.

[105] See for instance the minutes of the 17th Skylark policy meeting, March 1971, item 7, p.6. (TNA: PRO AVIA 92/144).

[106] Space Electronics Corporation had merged with the spacecraft division of Aerojet in 1961 to form the Space General Corporation.

[107] The first flight of the Stage 5 star-pointing ACU was a few months later on SL811 in July.

[108] BAe (1990), *Record of Skylark Launches 1957-1990*.

Figures 11.33 and 11.34 Left: A spent Cuckoo booster at Kiruna. Right: Recovery of a different type of booster,
– a far cry from conditions at Woomera!

(John Raymont)

the UV high-resolution stellar spectroscopy experiment from UCL appears to have been partially successful.[109] It probably also included an ESRO radiolocation aid,[110] but it is not known how well it worked.

The final four launches in February were by contrast launched in the winter snow in Sweden. **S66/2** fired on the 14th included an UCL/MSSL instrument, and this event may have been attended by John Raymont, who recalled:

> I think the coldest temperature I ever remember in Kiruna was ~-38 C. The humidity was so low you could not make snowballs!! The main hazards here were snow, ice and reindeer (large reindeer!!!).[111]

As with S66/1 that followed in April, several other instruments were also carried that simultaneously measured the electric field in the ionosphere.[112]

S70/1, S61/1 and S61/2 followed, and were all successful conventional (non-stabilised) launches, fired on three successive days (24th – 26th) from Kiruna, and each included British instruments. (See Appendix 3).

March 1970	SL921, SL901, SL401, SN5/1, SL802

Back at Woomera, the first Skylark launches of the year were preceded by the second flight test of Black Arrow, when vehicle R1 was fired on March 4th. This had two live stages, and this time was a success.

The First Woomera launch campaign of 1970

March and April saw six UK sponsored Skylark launches take place during BAC's fourth launch campaign from Woomera. The first and last were unstabilised vehicles, the others all attitude controlled. For this campaign, modifications were incorporated into the parachute recovery system to improve reliability "and there was no reason to believe an acceptable success rate should not be achieved".[113] From this time on, the parachute recovery system does indeed appear to have been more reliable.

The first launch of the six was **SL921** on the 12th. This had just one instrument on board, a new type of X-ray astronomy instrument from MSSL. This used a 'Rotating Modulation Collimator' (RMC) to replace the standard 'egg box' collimator in front of the X-ray detector, a modification capable of providing positional and spectrum measurements simultaneously, a significant advantage not previously possible.[114] It was a complicated piece of equipment, involving a spinning platform producing rotating patterns requiring later decoded by computer analysis to produce an image – very different from the valve (vacuum tube) technology of the first Skylark flights!

A similar RMC was being proposed for flight on the forthcoming UK-5 scientific satellite,[115] but had not been tried in practice. This Skylark flight was intended to test the instrument and gain more scientific information on the location of X-ray sources.

---

[109] Massey & Robins (1986), *History of British Space,* p.434.

[110] Minutes of the 11th Skylark Policy Meeting, September 1969, item 15, p.6. (TNA: PRO AVIA 92/144).

[111] His memoirs are unclear as to whether he is referring to 1970 or 1971.

[112] Fahleson *et al.*(1961), 'Simultaneous Electric Field Measurements Made in the Auroral Ionosphere by Using three Independent Techniques'.

[113] Minutes of the 13th Skylark Policy Meeting, March 1970, para. 6.2, p.3. (TNA: PRO AVIA 92/144).

[114] See for instance Brabban, Glencross & Herring (1971), 'Studies of the Solar X-ray Spectrum as a Function of position on the disk'.

[115] An RMC was indeed included on UK-5 (Ariel 5) which was subsequently launched in October 1974. Ariel 5 was one of the most successful British scientific satellites, and made many pioneering extra-galactic X-ray observations. (See for instance Massey & Robins (1986), *History of British Space Science,* p.382).

Figure 11.35 The RMC instrument in its Skylark bay.
(Cruise (2008), figure 3)

Unfortunately, the telemetry system on SL921 failed only 10 milliseconds after launch, and no data was returned, "… the experiment was launched and presumably worked but no data came back to Earth for me to analyse." [116] (However, a second attempt with an RMC was more successful, see SL971 in July). Thus Mike Cruise's second visit to Woomera ended with no data, although fortunately it was third time lucky for him, see SL905 in November.

The four attitude controlled flights of this Woomera campaign began with **SL901** a week later on the 19th. Although the 'Stage 5' star-pointing version of the ACU was not yet available (its first flight would be on SL811 in July), this earlier Sun-pointing payload achieved the same end by means of an additional University of Leicester X-ray sensor system. This successfully locked onto Scorpius X-1 (the brightest star-like X-ray source), and achieved a pointing accuracy in roll better than 10 minutes of arc (one sixth of a degree):

> A unique feature of this flight was the use of a pair of proportional counters to provide an error signal from which the rocket roll datum was locked onto the Sco X-1 source, the main rocket axis being pointed at the Sun. [117]

The background was that following the successful flights of the large area X-ray survey experiments on Skylarks in 1967, 68 and 69, the Leicester group changed the emphasis of its cosmic X-ray astronomy programme to detailed observations of specific sources using attitude-controlled vehicles. [118] To achieve this, they built a new type of instrument, a sophisticated 'Bragg Crystal Spectrometer' (BCS), to allow a high-resolution search for line emissions in the X-ray spectrum. [119]

The launch of SL901 was successful, and after stabilisation was achieved, the large LiF (Lithium Fluoride) crystal spectrometer was switched on to view Scorpius X-1 and search for the anticipated line emission of highly ionised iron. Three spectral scans were obtained in a total exposure of 240s, but a provisional analysis unfortunately revealed no evident emission line. [120] (An improved version was later flown on S55 in March 1971). It was the first such instrument ever used on a cosmic X-ray source, preceding a similar experiment flown later in the USA. Hence it was the precursor to similar instruments to be flown on satellites such as UK-5 and OSO-I. [121]

---

[116] Cruise (2008), *Skylark Ascending*, online article p.23, and *Prospero* number 5, Spring 2008, p.58. This article is also well worth reading as a personal account of how Skylark payloads were tested and launched.

[117] Pounds (1971), 'Measurement of the Polarisation, Spectra and Accurate Locations of Cosmic X-ray Sources', p.165.

[118] Pounds (1971), p.165.

[119] An instrument that uses a crystal to split X-rays according to energy, just as a prism splits visible light into the colours of the spectrum. Named after the British physicist William Henry Bragg (1862–1942), the device has the highest resolution of any X-ray spectrometer, but suffers from low efficiency and can operate only in a very narrow band.

[120] Pounds (1971), p.165, & Massey & Robins (1986), *History of British Space Science,* p.371.

[121] Griffiths (1971), 'A review of Cosmic X-ray astronomy', p.135.

Figure 11.36 The crystal spectrometer flown on SL901.
(Griffiths (1971), figure 5)[122]

The next launch of this busy campaign was **SL401** only 17 hours later, a little after midnight that evening. This time the ACU (Attitude Control Unit) used was the third of the four Stage 3 Sun/Moon-pointing units to be flown, although the first used to actually point at the Moon.[123]

The use of this type of ACU meant that it had to be a night-time firing within three days of full moon, so that the coarse Moon sensor would work.[124] In the event, launch took place at 01:18 local time on Friday the 20th. There were two astronomy experiments on board, both from the ROE (Royal Observatory, Edinburgh). These were an objective prism Schmidt ultraviolet camera and an associated scanning photometer, which allowed the ROE to photograph two adjacent areas of the night sky in ultraviolet light.[125] Spectra of some 70 stars down to about 1800Å (180nm) were successfully obtained in the region of Lupus/Centaurus:

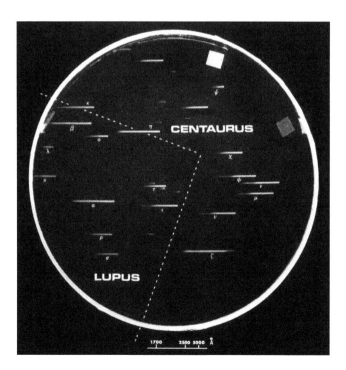

Figure 11.37 Objective prism ultraviolet spectra obtained from SL401 (exposure 35 seconds on Kodak SC5 emulsion).
(ROE \ SRC (1972), plate 7) [126]

[122] *Journal of the British Interplanetary Society*, Vol.24 no.3 (Mar.1971), p.136. Reproduced with permission.
[123] As explained at the start of this chapter, development of the Stage 3 ACU had been overtaken by that of Stage 5, and as a result only four Stage 3 ACU's were flown.
[124] Abbott (1971), *A Star-pointing Attitude Control System for Skylark*, p.3.
[125] Massey & Robins (1986), *History of British Space Science*, p.204.
[126] Reproduced courtesy Royal Observatory Edinburgh Archives.

The BAC launch team at Woomera must have been glad of the weekend break, but the following week it was back to work in the heat and flies. **SL802** was launched early on Wednesday the 25th at 07:30 local time, it was attitude controlled by a conventional Stage 1 Sun-pointing ACU and carried a University of Leicester X-ray astronomy survey experiment using three instruments. This included conventional and modulation collimated detectors intended to identify celestial X-ray sources with visible astronomical objects.[127] Unfortunately, the success of the Leicester experiment on SL901 the week before was not to be repeated, because of a vehicle system data failure,[128] and no results were returned from the detectors. However a Robot[129] star camera worked, presumably being recovered after landing.[130]

Back in Europe

Meanwhile, a new customer had appeared for Skylark. Since the early 1960s, in addition to cooperating in bilateral and ESRO programmes, West Germany had been conducting an extensive sounding rocket programme of its own. Indeed, German sponsored sounding rocket launches had increased from 1 in 1963 to 38 in 1968.[131]

The first Skylark launch attempt in the German programme was that of **SN5/1** on the 22nd March from Sardinia. Unfortunately, this was unsuccessful because of a motor failure, probably when the Raven second stage failed to ignite.[132] However, a repeat attempt in October did succeed – see later in this chapter.

April 1970	S66/1, S28/1, SL803, SL728

Soon afterwards, two ESRO sponsored launches took place from Kiruna. **S66/1** on the 2nd April was an Ionosphere mission that included an electron temperature probe from UCL/MSSL, similar to those flown on S66/2 in February,[133] and SL729 and SL730 in July 1969.[134] It was followed two days later by **S28/1**, designed for auroral and ionosphere investigation, and which included a sodium release experiment from Belfast, and electron density and temperature probes from the University of Birmingham.[135] All the British experiments were successful.

Back at Woomera, **SL803** was launched a few days later on the 7th. It carried a Culham[136] experiment that was a very successful repeat of the solar physics experiments flown on SL604 in April the year before. This time the 'échelle grating spectrograph' successfully extended the range of solar UV observations down to 1200Å (120nm). (See figure 11.38.) The payload was recovered in good condition and the instrument returned to Culham for checking. The purpose of the experiment was to investigate the hypothesis that the Sun's corona was heated by non-thermal energy, in particular mechanical energy from sound waves propagated from the photosphere below,[137] and the results provided the most definite available evidence in support of this idea.[138]

Also in April, the last Skylark of the current Woomera campaign was launched. **SL728** was a conventional unstabilised vehicle, with experiments from the UK Meteorological Office (molecular oxygen and ozone concentrations) and the Universities of Adelaide and Tasmania (UAT). UAT designated this as Flight V, the Flight V and VI vehicles being an almost identical pair of Skylark rockets (this and SL727 in July) on which UAT were allocated space for two ancillary experiments. The two experiments were the first in a series of flights intended to search for variability in known X-ray sources, and to survey the sky for undetected weak, or newborn X-ray sources. An important secondary objective was the testing of a newly developed, low background 'wall-less' proportional counter.[139]

---

[127] Adams, Janes & Whitford (1972), 'A variable Spacing Modulation Collimator for X-ray Astronomy', p.121.

[128] There was no data because of an EHT voltage loss in flight after pressurisation leakage (SRC (1972), *Space Research Report 1969-70*, p.27).

[129] 'Robot' in this sense is a proper noun, Robot was and is a German imaging company that produced clockwork driven sequence cameras taking 24 x 24 mm format images on standard 35mm film. Confusingly, one of the cameras they introduced in the 1950s was called the 'Star', so it is not clear if the camera referred to here was taking photographs of stars or not!

[130] SRC (1972), *Space Research Report 1969-70*, p.27.

[131] See for instance Seibert (2006), *The History of Sounding Rockets and Their Contribution to European Space Research*, table 4-1, and p.32.

[132] Minutes of the 16th Skylark Policy Meeting, December 1970, item 6, p.5. (TNA: PRO AVIA 92/144).

[133] For a paper on the S66/2 and S66/1 results, see Fahleson *et al.* (1971).

[134] MSSL (1972), *Report of the MSSL for the Period 1 January – 30 September 1972*, part A, p.3.

[135] Massey & Robins (1986), *History of British Space Science*, p.434.

[136] In 1969, funding for the Astrophysical Research Unit (ARU) of the UK Atomic Energy Authority's Culham Laboratory in Oxfordshire had been transferred to the SRC, although the staff remained at Culham.

[137] The Sun's corona (atmosphere) is much hotter (by a factor of about 200) than the visible surface, in places hotter than the core. The "coronal heating problem" in solar physics relates to the question of why this is so. Even today (2014), despite much study, the reason is not fully understood, thus the problem has puzzled researchers for more than six decades. Currently it is believed the effect is caused by the complex magnetic interactions that occur between the surface and the corona. (See for instance Cox (2010), p.49).

[138] Boland, Engstrom, Jones & Wilson (1973), 'The Heating of the Solar Corona', p.168.

[139] Tuohy (1972), 'Celestial X-ray Surveys from the Southern Hemisphere', p.29.

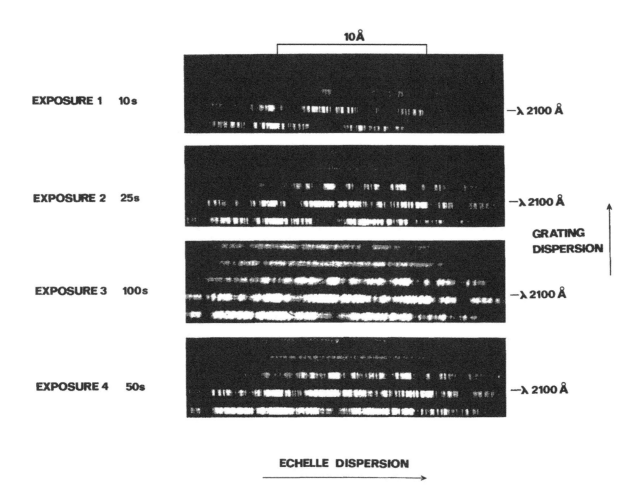

Figure 11.38 Although not a very clear image, this figure indicates the wealth of detail obtained by the SL803 spectrograph. Exposure 3 is blurred because of loss of resolution caused by frictional heating as the payload rose through the atmosphere.

(Boland, Engstrom, Jones & Wilson (1973), figure 1)

SL728 was completely successful; its natural spin provided the UAT instruments with good X-ray observations of the Lupus-Norma area of the sky,[140] which corresponded to subsequent NASA Uhuru satellite observations.[141] The upper part of the recovered payload is now on display at the Woomera Heritage Centre.[142]

June 1970   S68/2

Half way through 1970

After a pause in May, Skylark flights resumed in June with the launch of ESRO S68/2 from Sardinia, marking the 17th Skylark launch of 1970, the halfway point of a busy year. As described earlier in this chapter, S68/2 had been postponed after the failure in October to recover the payload of S68/1 from the sea.

Unfortunately, this launch faired even worse than the first attempt, when a second stage ignition failure occurred,[143] and the vehicle crashed back to Earth after reaching an altitude of about 3 km (2 miles). This was the second such failure of the year (the first probably being the German SN5/1 in March), and as a result, ESRO suspended all boosted launchings from Sardinia until completion of an investigation.[144]

Back at Woomera, a more serious failure occurred when Europa 1/ Blue Streak F9 was launched on the 12th June. This was its third orbital attempt, but a fairing failed to separate on the third stage and the satellite failed to reach orbit. It was the last such launch from Woomera, and the end of an era.

---

[140] Luyendyk *et al.* (1973), 'An X-ray Observation of the Norma-Lupus Region', p.3039.

[141] Uhuru was launched by NASA six months later, in December 1970, and carried out the first comprehensive X-ray survey of the sky.

[142] Ian Tuohy, personal correspondence, September 2009.

[143] BAe (1990), *Record of Skylark Launches 1957-1990*.

[144] Minutes of the 15th Skylark Policy Meeting, September 1970, item 6, p.3. (TNA: PRO AVIA 92/144).

Seq. Nos	Launch date	Ref. (sponsor) launch site	Config-uration	Apogee km (miles)	Experi-menters	Experiments	Result
242 (20)	10 July 1970	SL727 (UK) Woomera	Un, Rav.5A +C	203 (126)	RSRS	Ionosphere - ionospheric currents (rubidium magnetometer)	S
					MSSL	Ionosphere - wind profile (positive ion plate probes)	?
					MSSL	Ionosphere - ion concentration profile (wire probes)	?
					UAT	Astronomy - celestial X-ray sources spectra & intensities (gas-filled proportional counters)	Ps

Table 11.14 A summary of SL727.

July 1970	S63/1, S63/2, SL727, **SL971**, SL811, S56A/2, S65/2, S65/1

Skylark launches resumed at Sardinia with **S63/1** and **S63/2**, two unboosted rounds fired on July the 3rd and 8th. They were both successful ionosphere investigation missions, and each included a positive ion probe experiment from UCL.

July at Woomera

The month continued with BAC's sixth launch campaign from Woomera, starting with **SL727** on the 10th, see table 11.14 above.

The flight reached a respectable 203 km, i.e. into the F1 layer of the ionosphere, and was the last occasion on which a Raven

VA sustainer motor was used; this version having been super-seded by the Raven VI first tested in 1965. (See Table 9.2).

The mission was only a partial success, because in error, straight fins had been fitted to the vehicle instead of canted ones. This caused great consternation back in the UK, and steps were taken to prevent a similar mistake in the future.[145] This also caused problems for Ian Tuohy, one of the UAT experimenters, who recalls:

> I ended up basing my thesis on this flight and recall spending the first 3-4 months developing an attitude solution for the unexpected and complex motion that we experienced.[146]

UAT Flight	Designation	Date	Time	Apogee	Experiment	Comments
1	SL426	4 Apr 1967	0032 UT	219.9 km	X-ray astronomy payload (secondary experiment)	Successful
2	SL425	20 Apr 1967	2236 UT	218.6 km	X-ray astronomy payload (secondary experiment)	Successful Flaring of Cen X-2
3	SL422A	1 Dec 1967	0608 UT	181.5 km	X-ray astronomy payload (secondary experiment)	Experiment partially successful
4	SL781	21 Jan. 1969	0449 UT	~3 km	X-ray astronomy payload (dedicated to UAT)	Launch failure due to insecure manacle ring
5	SL728	16 April 1970	0907 UT	214 km	Aeronomy payload X-ray astronomy payload	Successful
6	SL727	10 July 1970	0030 UT	208 km	Ionospheric payload X-ray astronomy payload	Incorrect fins fitted to Raven motor
7	Aerobee 4.301 UG (Nike booster)	29 May 1970	1345 UT		X-ray astronomy payloads (University of Wisconsin and UAT)	UAT payload unsuccessful due to hatch separation

Table 11.15 A summary of the Universities of Adelaide and Tasmania (UAT) X-ray Astronomy Rocket Flights from Woomera. (I.Tuohy)

[145] Minutes of the 15th Skylark Policy Meeting, September 1970, item 2, p.1. (TNA: PRO AVIA 92/144).
[146] Ian Tuohy, personal communication, 2009.

Figures 11.39 and 11.40 Left: In later years, the canted fin assemblies were very clearly marked.
Right: A close-up of a recovered fin, showing paint blistering caused by friction with the air.
(Bristol Aero Collection, author 100_1853 and 100_1872)

The UAT experiment on SL727 measured the X-ray emissions of the 'Large Magellanic Cloud', an astronomical object only visible from the Southern Hemisphere, and the third closest galaxy to the Milky Way. The experiment resulted in the optical identification of a likely nebula in the cloud as the X-ray source.[147] This appears to have been the last Australian X-ray astronomy experiment to fly on Skylark.[148] (See table 11.15.)

Next from Woomera was **SL971**, launched four days later on the 14th July to an altitude of 223 km (139 miles). This was primarily an RAE proving flight, apparently part of the development of the Goldfinch booster, the fourth time it had been flight-tested. However, the payload did include one science experiment, which had 'hitched a lift'. This was an MSSL X-ray source astronomy experiment using the RMC (Rotating Modulation Collimator) instrument, and thus in part a repeat of that launched aboard the faulty SL921 in March.

This time the telemetry system did work, and the experiment was basically successful. It collected data from the constel-

lation of Vela, although unfortunately the attitude sensors did not observe the Sun throughout the flight. This problem generated ambiguities in the subsequent data analysis, but the flight did at least pave the way for more fruitful ones to come.[149] (SL1021 in October 1970 and SL973 in October 1971.) Analysis of the data depended critically upon knowing the attitude of the vehicle during flight, but it took 14 months for the data to arrive from BAC – and even then, it was not sufficiently accurate, and new solutions had to be calculated by MSSL! Subsequently it was estimated that analysis to produce a map would take in excess of 200 hours of CPU time on the IBM 360-65 mainframe computer at University College London.[150]

The first flight of the star-pointing Stage 5 ACU

The third and final launch of this short July campaign was that of **SL811** on the 16th. This was significant in being the first launch of the new Stage 5 star-pointing ACU (Attitude Control Unit). As described at the beginning of this chapter,

---

[147] Tuohy *et al.* (1972), 'An X-ray observation of the Large Magellanic Cloud'.
[148] Although other types of Australian experiments may have flown later, see for instance SL1022 in 1972.
[149] Cruise and Willmore (1975), 'The analysis of Data from Rotation Modulation Collimators', p.166.
[150] MSSL (1972), *Report of the MSSL 1 January – 30 September 1972*, part B, p.4.

it was designed to lock onto specified stars during flight. It used the Moon as the initial attitude reference, which meant that this ACU had to be launched at night,[151] but that was appropriate for a star-seeking mission.

This Stage 5 ACU was the first Phase 1 prototype, and it was only partially successful in that it failed to acquire the correct target stars because of faults in the magnetometer and Moon sensor areas. However, the star search and star lock sequences were correct and gave confidence in that part of the design.[152]

The scientific experiment on board SL811 was a joint one from ARU(Culham)/MSSL, it comprised high resolution objective grating spectrographs designed for UV stellar spectroscopy in the range 900 Å-2300 Å. However because of the fault described above these were pointed at the wrong target star.[153]

July at Sardinia

July also saw a short ESRO campaign of three launches from Sardinia, where all the payloads included significant UK participation. S56A/2 was launched on Thursday the 23rd, and was a repeat of the mostly unsuccessful S56A/1 launched in January, but with an additional Solar X-ray experiment from Leicester/RSRS. This time the covers were not left on, and the mission was completely successful!

Next day S65/2 was launched, the instruments included an RF impedance probe from Sheffield, and an experiment from RSRS to carry our solar Lyman-α measurements. On Monday 27th, its companion S65/1 was launched with a similar payload. Both missions were successful.

No summer holiday for UK space science

There were no Skylarks launched in August or September 1970, although at Woomera the third test flight test of Black Arrow took place, when vehicle R2 was fired on September 2nd. This was the first orbital attempt, but failed when the second stage shutdown prematurely.

However as described by John Raymont of MSSL, British space science launches of a more modest kind continued, this time from the UK:

> I went twice to South Uist for launches in the early 70s, once for a group of Petrel sounding rockets, all made at MSSL, and once for a special campaign with three Skua payloads. This was a special launch based on the collaboration between Peter Willmore (deputy director of MSSL) and a group (I don't remember Government or University) in India who agreed to launch rockets at approx. the same time of day (I believe they were called 'synoptic' launches). Keith Norman was in Thumba, India, and would communicate to MSSL whether the launch had taken place. I would then prepare the Skua for launch from South Uist.[154]

The Petrel sounding rocket launches must have been P30H, P32H & P32H, which took place on the 8th and 11th September 1970. P30H and P32H reached respectable apogees of 147 and 149 km respectively. All three carried ionosphere experiments that successfully measured electron and positive ion densities in the D and E regions.[155]

Figure 11.41 MSSL Petrel Payloads.
(MSSL \ J.Raymont)

---

[151] Although the most serious limitation of the two Phase 1 prototypes was that the coarse Moon sensor design limited firing to full moon ±3 days. (Abbot (1971), *A Star-pointing Attitude Control System for Skylark*, p.3).

[152] Reed (1974), *An Historical Review of Stabilisation Systems for the Skylark Rocket*, p.4.

[153] Massey & Robins (1986), *History of British Space Science*, p.206.

[154] John Raymont "Memories of early trips", visit *www.ucl.ac.uk/mssl/about-mssl/heritage/archive-documents* , click on "John's Memoirs" and scroll down. (Last accessed August 2014).

[155] Massey & Robins (1986), *History of British Space Science*, p.416.

The Skua payloads were probably those of Su 16H, 17H and 18H, launched earlier in 1970 on the 14th and 17th April. These successfully carried ion density-measuring payloads to a height of 92-95 km.[156] The corresponding launches from Thumba[157] in India would have been Su 15T/C and Su 14T/C on 15th and 16th April 1970.

John Raymont again:

> We flew from London to Glasgow and then Glasgow to Benbecula.[158] The main hazards here were wind, rain, cattle and sheep and the locals who apparently drank large amounts of whiskey [sic]. Another slight risk appeared to be the driving. We rented cars from a small island garage. I had one small SIMCA saloon on one visit and one of the locals told me it had been rebuilt three times. The launch platform was quite unique, an adapted Bedford lorry, the same size as the emergency fire engine ('Green Goddess') used today when we have fire brigade strikes.

The Petrel and Skua sounding rockets were fired from an Army Firing Range, currently (2014) run by QinetiQ on behalf of the UK Ministry of Defence. It is a sea range that faces the open Atlantic Ocean, and it is said that spent rocket parts used to be washed up on the local beaches!

October 1970	SL972, SN5/2, SL1021, S53, S58, S67/1, S67/2

A busy October

In contrast to August and September, October was a busy month for Skylark, with seven launches. First was **SL972** launched from Woomera on the 8th. This was similar to SL971 launched three months previously, in that it was primarily a RAE proving flight, apparently part of the continuing development of the Goldfinch II booster. This time the scientific experiment on board was from the University of Leicester, an astronomy instrument that made a large area sky survey of cosmic X-ray sources,[159] and used similar instruments to those flown in previous years on SL723 and SL724. In particular, it is said to have included a re-flight of detectors C1 and C2 from SL724,[160] which sounds remarkable, as after launch in April 1969 the payload of SL724 was lost in the desert for 18 months!

SL972 is also likely to have tested the new 'yo-yo' despin system designed to prevent jettisoned split nose cones from colliding with the payload on spinning vehicles. This solution had been recommended by the RAE, and was being tried out on Goldfinch development rounds.[161] It "...involves the release of a tightly wound holas-type arrangement of tied

Figure 11.42 This Bedford lorry looks an unlikely candidate for launching sounding rockets into space, but appears to have been an economical means of doing so.

(J.Raymont)

---

[156] Massey & Robins (1986), p.427.

[157] Situated close to the magnetic equator, the fishing village of Thumba was a good location to conduct atmospheric research. The Thumba Equatorial Rocket Launching Station (TERLS) was (and still is) used for many international and Indian sounding rocket launches. The Vikram Sarabhai Space Centre (VSSC) is now situated nearby, and is the lead centre for the development of Indian satellite launch vehicles and associated technologies.

[158] The Outer Hebridian Isle of Benbecula is connected by causeways to the Isles of South Uist.

[159] See for instance the Leicester list of launches at www2.le.ac.uk/departments/physics/research/xroa/astronomical-facilities-1/rocket-science-at-leicester/the-skylark-rocket , (last accessed August 2014).

[160] SRC (1972), *Space Research Report 1969-70*, p.27.

[161] Minutes of the 13th Skylark Policy Meeting, March 1970, para. 4.1, p.2. (TNA: PRO AVIA 92/144).

Figures 11.43, 11.44 and 11.45 Loading the Petrel launcher at South Uist.
(J.Raymont)

weights within the rocket, which gives a strong thrust in the opposite sense to the direction of spin. The heavy yo-yo as it is termed, then flies out under centrifugal force and descends to Earth with a hard impact, of no consequence in an unpopulated desert…" [162]

SL972 was followed by SN5/2 from Sardinia on the 13th, the second Skylark launch of the German national programme, and a repeat of the attempt with SN5/1 the previous March. This time the launch was successful, reaching an apogee of 288 km (179 miles). The first German Skylark launch (SN5/1) had failed because of an ignition fault, this time an RAE certificated ignition unit was used,[163] and all was well.

The experiment on board was from the University of Bonn.[164] It was designed to measure neutral gas in the upper atmosphere, and for the first time in a rocket payload used a mass spectrometer with an ion source cooled to low temperatures by supercritical helium.[165] Many similar experiments were to follow on Skylark.

This was closely followed on the 14th by the launch of SL1021, which had the distinction of being the 200th Skylark launched from Woomera. (Coincidently the 250th overall.)

SL1021 was an MSSL astronomy mission, designed to measure the position and energy spectra of cosmic X-ray sources. The instruments were a rotating modulation collimator (as flown on SL 971 in July) and proportional counters. The rocket was spin-stabilised at three rotations per second, and the instruments successfully surveyed the Sagittarius-Scorpius region of the sky.[166] The resulting data required considerable processing, as described in the next chapter under SL973, which a year later (October 1971) was launched with a similar instrument.

One participant recalls, "I well remember the party to celebrate the 200th Skylark – at least the first hour of it!"[167]

The day afterwards, on the 15th, the third October Skylark launch took place. S53 was an ESRO mission launched from Woomera. The payload was a Sun-pointing Stage 1 ACU with solar X-ray experiments from Utrecht, Tubingen and Culham. Although it reached 209 km (130 miles), unfortunately both the ACU and the Dornier recovery system failed.[168] This was the second ESRO sponsored launched at Woomera, events which don't appear to have gone very well, as S72 in February also had major payload problems. The failure of S53 led ESRO to make enquires about the UK land recovery system.

---

[162] Savigear *et al.* (1977), *The Appraisal of Photography from Skylark SL1081 over Woomera.*
[163] Minutes of the 16th Skylark Policy Meeting, December 1970, item 6, p.5. (TNA: PRO AVIA 92/144).
[164] Although this was Bonn University's first successful flight on a West German National Programme Skylark, they had previously flown instruments on ESRO Skylarks, starting with S19/1 in 1967.
[165] Offermann & Trinks (1971), 'A Rocket Borne Mass Spectrometer with Helium Cooled Ion Source'.
[166] Cruise and Willmore (1975), 'The analysis of Data from Rotation Modulation Collimators', p.166.
[167] This quotation had better be Anon!
[168] Minutes of the 16th Skylark Policy Meeting, December 1970, item 6, p.4. (TNA: PRO AVIA 92/144).

Figure 11.46 A dramatic photograph of the launch of SL972 from Woomera at 17:50 local time on 8 October 1970. The dark original has been digitally enhanced from what looked like a night launch, but must have been taken in daylight against the late afternoon sun low in the West. What looks like the Moon on the right is presumably a camera reflection caused by shooting into the sun.

(WRE \ J.A.Hill)

Figure 11.47 This 'First Day Cover' commemorates SL1021, the 200th Skylark to be launched from Woomera.

(J.A.Hill collection)

References to a possible Skylark "S58" launch are a mystery. Some secondary sources[169] list an ESRO S58 as being fired from Woomera on 19th October 1970, others[170] simply do not include it. However, a search of primary records about Woomera indicates that no such launch took place.[171] Hence, although S58 has been listed in the table of 1970 launches (above), and in some of the Appendices, this is only for the purposes of clarification.

However, there is no mystery about the next two ESRO launches. S67/1 and S67/2 were launched from Kiruna on the 28th and 29th October respectively. They were Aurora investigation missions, taking advantage of Kiruna's northerly location. Each included electrostatic analysers from the Radio and Space Research Station (RSRS), designed to measure electron densities over various energy ranges, in order to study the magnetosphere and its interaction with the ionosphere in the auroral zone.[172]

November 1970	SL905, SL904, SL804

1970 closed with the launch of four Cuckoo boosted Sun stabilised Skylarks, three in November from Woomera, and one in December from Sardinia.

The first was **SL905**, which carried another MSSL astronomy experiment to study X-ray sources:

MSSL flew two proportional counters of 1000 cm^2 collecting area on a stabilized Skylark rocket on 11 November 1970 in a successful survey of the centre of the galaxy, the large and small Magellanic Clouds and several pulsars for X-ray sources in the energy range, 0.5 to 12 keV. This flight was related to three unstabilized Skylark flights, two in 1970, one on 14 July [SL971] carrying a rotation collimator, the other on 14 October [SL1021] carrying a rotation collimator and proportional counters, and the third on 7 October 1971 [SL973, see next chapter] carrying a rotation collimator, so that a large area of sky could be surveyed with good space and wavelength resolution.[173]

To avoid the disastrous nose cone damage encountered on SL821 in October 1969, an ACU was used, and the payload de-spun[174] before the nose cone halves were jettisoned. The attitude was then ACU controlled as standard using the Sun as a reference, and slow scans in roll were carried out to survey the chosen parts of the sky. On this flight, the instruments carried did not include an RMC (Rotating Modulation Collimator); instead, a second large area detector as flown on SL821 was used.[175] After the failures of SL821 and SL921 this launch proved third time lucky for Mike Cruise, providing his first data, although not what his thesis was supposed to be about.[176]

[169] For instance Massey & Robins (1986), *History of British Space Science*, p.435.

[170] For instance BAe (1990), *Record of Skylark Launches 1957-1990*.

[171] Woomera's ESRO programme financial and administration files and the range recovery logs have no mention of an S58 being fired. (Roger Henwood, personal communication November 2011). The latest mention is in a Telex dated 17/8/70, where "S58" was said to be at the submission stage, with a possible launch on Feb.10 1971. This could well be a typographical error for S85, which was launched on Feb.22 1971.

[172] Massey & Robins (1986), *History of British Space Science*, p.305.

[173] Fox (c.1984), *From Lardner to Massey – A history of physics, space science and astronomy at University College London, 1826 to 1975,(Cosmic X-ray and Ultra Violet Astronomy)*.

[174] Presumably using the new 'yo-yo' despin mechanism.

[175] Cruise (2008), *Skylark Ascending*, online article p.24, and *Prospero* number 5, Spring 2008, p.58.

[176] Cruise (1973), Rocket studies of cosmic X-ray sources.

Seq. Nos	Launch date	Ref. (sponsor) launch site	Config- uration	Apogee km (miles)	Experi- menters	Experiments	Result
255 (33)	20 Nov. 1970	SL904 (UK) Woomera	Sun, Rav.6 +C	209 (130)	Lei	Astronomy - measurement of variation in X-ray background : origin of non X-ray pulses (collimated proportional detectors)	S
					RAE	Test (space tech.) - Mk.II X3 horizon sensor array	S

Table 11.16 A summary of SL904.

This was followed on the 20th by **SL904**. It too carried an X-ray astronomy experiment on board, the first of three in a row from the University of Leicester.

SL904's Leicester experiment carried out a study of cosmic X-ray sources and the cosmic X-ray background using two large proportional detectors mounted under the nose cone. Each detector was collimated by a honeycomb type arrange-ment to look sideways from the vehicle, and the ACU (At-titude Control Unit) was used to slowly roll the payload through 130° to scan regions of the sky in Virgo, Crater, Centaurus, Vela and Carina. Roughly 100,000 X-ray counts were recorded, processed on board electronically, and good data telemetered back to Earth.[177] Preliminary results con-firmed that the X-ray source Cen X-3 exhibited a most pe-culiar behaviour.[178]

In addition, the RAE included a complementary space tech-nology test that made use of the rolling motion of the pay-load, and which was a continuation of the work done on SL586 thirteen months previously. This time, a Mk.II ver-sion of the X3 horizon sensor was successfully flight-tested. This used nine sensors, compared to just one before.[179]

The final Woomera launch of 1970 was that of **SL804** on the 25th, which carried another Leicester experiment, this time

a solar physics instrument that obtained high-resolution X-ray spectra of the Sun. The instrument comprised two Bragg Crystal spectrometers which obtained an X-ray spectrum of the quiet corona between 5 and 14 Å, and which used a field collimator to improve spectral clarity:[180]

> This problem [spectral overlap] was removed by the spectrometers first flown on *Skylark SL804* …….The pointing accuracy of the Stage I *Skylark* allowed individ-ual active regions to be examined during flight. Unam-biguous coronal X-ray spectra of the highest resolution to that date were obtained in this way.[181]

December 1970   S69

A very similar solar physics experiment was flown on the last Skylark flight of the year. **S69** was launched from Sardinia by ESRO on 6th December. This time the Leicester instrument comprised four 6 sq.cm crystal spectrometers, and obtained an X-ray spectrum between 5 and 23 Å.[182] Similar experi-ments were to follow, for instance on SL1101 in November 1971, see the next chapter.

---

[177] Adams & Janes (1972), 'Preliminary Results from the X-ray experiment SL904'.

[178] As noted in later chapters, by 1974 Cen X-3 was being recognised as an X-ray source with an accretion wake trailing behind it during its passage through the stellar wind from its optical companion.

[179] Barnes & Kenward (1972), *Sensor Trials on Skylark 586*, pp.9 & 11.

[180] Parkinson, Evans and Pounds (1972), 'Recent High Resolution X-ray Spectra of the Sun'.

[181] Pounds (1986), 'British X-ray Astronomy', p.439.

[182] Parkinson, Evans and Pounds (1972), 'Recent High Resolution X-ray Spectra of the Sun', p.740.

Figure 12.1 This photograph of 'Trials staff Range E' reflects the size of the operation at Woomera. The date of the picture is said to be c.1969, although the presence on the left of (presumably) a model of Black Arrow, indicates it may be a year or so later. On the far right is a Skylark with Cuckoo boost motor.

(WRE)

CHAPTER 12

(1971-72)

ESRO AND PROSPERO

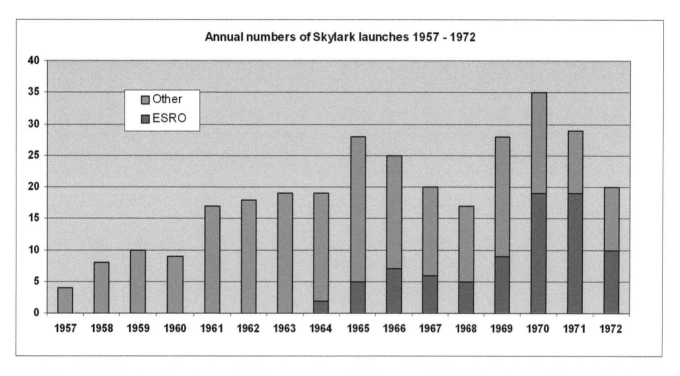

Figure 12.2 This chart shows how in 1971 the proportion of ESRO sponsored Skylark launches reached a record high.

In 1971, the total number of Skylark launches was 29, down from the record peak of 35 the year before, but still the second highest annual total. The number of ESRO sponsored launches remained at 19; still nearly double that of the UK's national programme.

However 1971 was also notable for the first (and at the time of writing, only) launch of a satellite by a British launch vehicle. Although not part of the Skylark project, it was masterminded by the RAE and launched from Woomera, so is described below. 1972 saw a new application for Skylark, when it became the world's first 'Earth Resources' rocket.

Competition from scientific satellites

In December 1970, NASA had launched the Uhuru satellite, which carried out the first comprehensive survey of the sky to be made in X-radiation. As previously discussed, the field of cosmic X-ray astronomy was still very new, at this time only eight years old.[1] Until Uhuru, the American Aerobee and British Skylark sounding rockets had made the largest contribution to X-ray astronomy by means of observations above the Earth's atmosphere, and by 1970, thirty-three cosmic X-ray sources were considered to have been established.[2]

---

[1] Although the discovery of the first cosmic X-ray source had been preceded by over ten years of observations of solar X-ray emissions from the Sun.

[2] Kellogg (1970), 'A Catalog of Soft X-ray Sources, 2nd Edition', as referenced by Griffiths (1971).

However, scientists in both countries had recognised that observations from instruments in orbit would vastly increase the available observation time. Indeed, back in 1961, undeterred by the absence of any evidence that observable cosmic X-ray sources existed, a UCL group under Boyd and Willmore had proceeded with the design of an instrument which could be included in a satellite to observe cosmic X-rays.[3] As described later, these plans came to fruition with the launch of the Copernicus satellite in 1972, and Ariel 5 in 1974. However, as revolutionary as the satellite era was, the sounding rocket's simplicity and flexibility meant it still had a valuable role to play.

The role of sounding rockets in the satellite age

In 1971, NASA published an interesting report on the history of their sounding rocket programme from 1958 to 1968.[4]

It included the following diagram illustrating their scientific fields of use, see figure 12.3.

The report clearly laid out the advantages and disadvantages of sounding rockets compared to satellites. The advantages were identified as vehicle and payload simplicity, low costs, payload recoverability, and geographic and temporal flexibility. The disadvantages were restricted time of observation, localised coverage, and payload limitations:

> Certainly satellites are superior in terms of staying power and geographical coverage - if that is what the experimenter wants. Often this is not what he wants; often he wishes to make measurements in regions of the atmosphere that are too thick and dense for satellites to orbit and yet too high for balloons to reach. Sometimes he does not wish to wait two or three years for the design, development, and launch of a scientific satellite.[5]

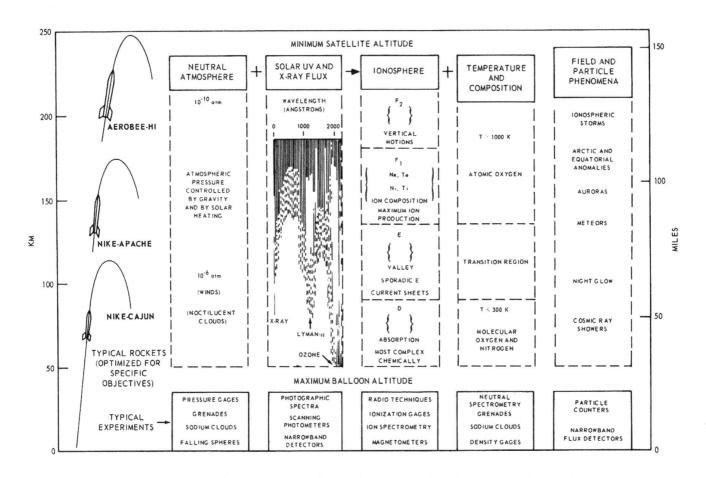

Figure 12.3 Some basic upper atmosphere and space research studies requiring the use of sounding rockets. Skylark could reach the same altitudes as the Aerobee-Hi shown on the left.

(Corliss (1971), p.2)

---

[3]   Massey & Robins (1986), *History of British Space Science*, p.367.
[4]   Corliss (1971), *NASA Sounding Rockets 1958-1968, A Historical Summary*.
[5]   Corliss (1971), p.1.

Jan.	Feb.	March	April	May	June	July	Aug.	Sept.	Oct.	Nov.	Dec.
LT.1	S80/1	SL922		SL812		S73	SL902	SL1002	SL973	S44/2	SL903
S46/2	S80/2	S55		S56B/2				S47/2	S81	S70/2	S82
SL1001	S80/3	S16/2							S89	SL1101	
	S85	S87/1							SL974		
	S54	S87/2									
		S56B/1									

Table 12.1 The 29 Skylark launches in 1971. (For full details see Appendix 3)

(Key: black = test launches, blue = UK national programme (unstabilised), plum = UK (stabilised), pink = ESRO)

SKYLARK LAUNCHES AND SCIENCE IN 1971

January 1971	LT.1, S46/2, SL1001

The first Skylark launch from the UK

1971 began with the first Skylark launch from the UK, an event that took place on 14th January from Aberporth in Wales.

As explained in Chapter 3, in 1957 a Skylark launch tower had been built at the RAE's Aberporth establishment on the Welsh coast. Unfortunately, this tower was destined never to be used, and this first firing from Wales was used to test Skylark compatibility with a mobile launcher built by Maschinenfabrik of Germany.[6]

During the early years of Skylark, the Aberporth launch ban appears to have resulted from an early failure at Woomera, when a fin came off causing a flight failure. Hence, it was deemed that the chance of a Skylark launched from Aberporth coming down on land was not remote enough.[7]

Later on, the range and dispersion of Skylark must have been considerations. Hence, for this proving flight no Raven sustainer motor was fitted, only a Goldfinch boost motor. This was sufficient to test the mobile launcher, but still allow Aberporth to be used - the altitude reached was only 21,000 feet (6.4 km / 4 miles).

The reason for testing a mobile launcher was to permit firing away from established launch sites, for instance in the event of a solar eclipse. Although the UK eventually used a cheaper home produced mobile launcher (see SL1183, July 1972), this trial must have been technically successful, as from 1973, the MAN launcher was used for several German Skylark launches from El Arenosillo in Spain, as part of the German national programme. (For photographs including the launcher, see SL1304 in the next chapter).

January also saw the launch of ESRO flight S46/2 in the freezing cold at Kiruna. This mission had been deferred after

Figure 12.4 The first launch of a Skylark from the UK.
(RAE / BAC / Bristol Aero collection)

the launch of S46/1 in November 1969, so that a fourth experiment (R134) which had been withdrawn by the experimenter, could be included again. One of the experiments, the auroral-particle study experiment (R110) was summarised as:

Twelve auroral electron detectors from 300 ev to 30 kev were launched on the ESRO S46/2 Skylark rocket from Kiruna, Sweden, on January 28, 1971, at 2120 MLT into an auroral westward-traveling surge.[8]

[6] Flight International magazine, 28 January 1971, p.137.
[7] Dorling in 2001, CCBH (2005), *Skylark Sounding Rockets 1957-1972*, p.77, & *Prospero* No.2. p.140.
[8] RèMe & Bosqued (1973), 'Rocket Observations of Electron Precipitation in a Westward-Travelling Surge'.

The following day, 29th January, saw the next Skylark launch take place, this time in the contrasting heat of mid-summer on the other side of the world. The payload of **SL1001** included a Sun-pointing Stage 1 ACU with two MSSL astronomy experiments on board. These measured fluctuations in the cosmic X-ray background,[9] and resulted in a study of the low energy diffuse background appearing in 'Nature' magazine.[10]

February 1971	S80/1, S80/2, S80/3, S85, S54

Three in one night

Saturday 6th February was a busy day at Salto di Quirra in Sardinia. The plan was to launch three Skylarks (**S80/1, S80/2 and S80/3**) that night [11] to investigate the ionosphere. ESRO and the UK representatives from the University of Birmingham and the Radio and Space Research Station at Slough must have had to work hard to prepare and check everything in time.

BAC had prepared and delivered the payloads, all three of which carried the same set of experiments. Instruments had been supplied by the University of Birmingham to measure electron density and temperature, and the RSRS to measure night-time Lyman-α radiation.

All three launches were successful, although it was early in the morning by the time S80/3 was fired.[12]

February 22nd

Three weeks later on the 22nd, the next Skylark launch was ESRO **S85** from Woomera. This appears to have been ESRO's third attempt with their own source of Star-pointing ACU, but like the previous two,[13] it failed. It was further reported that this round had been fitted with a 'Space General' star-pointing system,[14] but had suffered a failure of the experiment cover to open.[15] The payload included an MSSL

high-resolution stellar spectroscopy experiment, however this was flown again in December, see SL903 below.

February 26th

Four days later ESRO and MSSL suffered a second disappointment, this time in Sardinia. Although **S54** reached an apogee of 250 km (155 miles), its RAE Stage 1 ACU failed to stabilise the payload, and the X-ray spectroheliograph experiment came to nothing. The ACU failure may have been caused by a power supply problem and in March was under investigation.[16]

March 1971	SL922, S55, S16/2, S87/1, S87/2, S56B/1

March was another busy month, with six launches from three sites.

SL922 was launched from Woomera on the evening of the 2nd March through a stable and intense sporadic E-layer of the ionosphere. On board was a collaborative seven-instrument payload provided by four British institutions, designed to check possible shortcomings in the conventional 'Wind-Shear' theory of sporadic E-layer formation.[17] The instruments included barium and TMA[18] release canisters to measure the winds, a magnetometer for the magnetic fields, and several electric field and ion detection probes. The vehicle was launched at twilight so the glow trail from the TMA (trimethyl aluminium) could be photographed from the ground.[19]

Whilst confirming the theory in general terms, the results showed that the stabilising effect of the ambient electric field should be taken into account as well as neutral wind effects.[20] This was a very successful and significant mission, and the scientific paper that resulted was still being cited over twenty-five years later.[21]

---

[9]   MSSL (1972), *Report of the MSSL 1 January – 30 September 1972*, part B, p.5.
[10] Culhane & Fabian (1972), *Origin of the Low Energy Diffuse Cosmic X-ray Flux.*
[11] BAe (1990), *Record of Skylark Launches 1957-1990.*
[12] McDowell (2009), *List of Skylark Launches.*
[13] S44/1 and S72 in February 1970.
[14] Space Electronics Corporation had merged with the spacecraft division of Aerojet in 1961 to form the Space General Corporation.
[15] Minutes of the 17th Skylark Policy Meeting, March 1971, item 7. (TNA: PRO AVIA 92/144).
[16] Ibid.
[17] This theory had been proposed in 1961 by Whitehead in Australia, suggesting that horizontal winds moving in opposite directions at slightly different altitudes moved the ions across the Earth's magnetic field subjecting them to vertical forces resulting in their concentration as the E-layer.
[18] TMA produces a trail by means of a chemical reaction in the atmosphere. It was used for instance by SL761 & SL762 on 31 May 1968. For many purposes, it superseded the earlier methods of glow production.
[19] For a useful academic summary of SL922, see Dorling (1991), *Reminiscences of the Mullard Space Science Laboratory to 1991*, pp.67-68.
[20] Rees, Dorling, Lloyd & Low (1976), 'The Role of Neutral Winds and Ionospheric Electric Field in Forming Stable Sporadic *E*-layers.
[21] E.g. Weixing Wan *et al.*, *Journal of Atmospheric & Solar-Terrestrial Physics*, Volume 61, Issue 18, 1999.

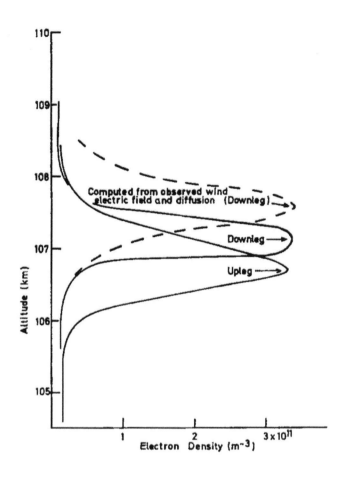

Figure 12.5 The sporadic E-layer altitude profiles were very precisely observed by SL922. The 0.5 km separation in the peak up leg and down leg values indicated the E-layer was inclined to the horizontal by approximately 0.5°.

(Rees, Dorling, Lloyd & Low (1976), figure 2)

S55 was launched from Sardinia on Thursday 11th March, two weeks after the unsuccessful S54. Like its predecessor, it had an ESRO designed sun-stabilised payload, but unlike S54 (and S53 before that), the ACU operation was successful, and so it appears to have been the first such ACU to work.

This was an X-ray astronomy mission, and included stellar X-ray spectra (crystal spectrometer improved from that on SL901) and interstellar absorption instruments from the University of Leicester. Although a Sun-pointing ACU, the payload achieved its stellar pointing capability by rotation of the payload using X-ray sensors,[22] which were the same pair of proportional counter instruments used for scientific measurements.[23]

The Leicester experiments were designed to measure X-radiation from the direction of the brightest astronomical (non-solar) source in the sky, the star-like Scorpius X-1, a task that they achieved successfully. Also on board was an experiment from Tübingen and MPE in Germany, probably a solar X-ray instrument.[24]

Three from Kiruna

ESRO activities continued with Skylark **S16/2** being launched the following day at Kiruna, the first of a series of three more conventional ionosphere missions. S16/2 was similar to S16/1, which in 1968 had been the first Skylark mission launched from Kiruna (see Chapter 10). It too included three UK experiments - electron temperature and positive ion density instruments (R44 and R45) from MSSL, and from the RSRS, a magnetometer instrument. This time the magnetometer experiment was successful, but appears to have originated from the RSRS rather than Imperial College, and measured ionospheric currents rather than magnetic fields.[25]

Also on that same Friday the 12th at Kiruna, the second UK 'spring campaign' of Petrel rocket launches began. The first carried an electron density probe from RSRS to an altitude of 150 km (93 miles). By the 2nd May, a total of 11 Petrel rockets had been launched with a wide variety of UK experiments on board.[26]

---

[22] BAe (1990), *Record of Skylark Launches 1957-1990*.

[23] As introduced by the Leicester group on SL901 in March 1970. (Griffiths (1972), 'A Further High-Resolution Search for Fe xxv Line emission from Scorpius X-1, p.97).

[24] McDowell (2009), *List of Skylark Launches*.

[25] Massey & Robins (1986), *History of British Space Science*, p.435.

[26] Massey & Robins (1986), *History of British Space Science*, p.417.

Meanwhile, Skylark launches at Kiruna continued successfully with Skylarks S87/1 and S87/2 being launched on the 16th and 24th March respectively. These two missions carried out ionospheric electric field measurements in a similar manner to S66/2 and S66/1,[27] although this time there were no UK experiments on board.

Back at Sardinia, on the 25th March **S56B/1** was launched with three UK experiments on board, but unfortunately telemetry and transponder failure meant that the mission was unsuccessful. However its successor, S56B/2 with the same experiments, succeeded in May two months later.

May 1971	SL812, S56B/2

In contrast to the hectic activity of February and March 1971, there were no launches in April, just two in May and none in June.

SL812 was launched on the 10th May from Woomera, propelled by a Raven VI and Goldfinch booster. Following proving tests in 1970 (on SL 971 and SL 972), the Goldfinch was now appearing in service, and would be used on another four launches later in the year. SL812 had been the subject of much pre-flight technical discussion on its aerodynamic stability, but the actual flight showed no indication of flutter.[28] The vehicle successfully propelled its heavy star-pointing ACU payload to an altitude of 219 km (136 miles), but ironically, the Stage 5 ACU then failed.

However, this was still a prototype ACU design, being the second of the two Phase 1 units, and companion to that which only partially worked on SL811 in July 1970. It also failed to acquire the correct target stars because of faults in the magnetometer and Moon sensors areas. This time it was a Leicester stellar X-ray experiment that bore the brunt.[29] The failure was made worse because yet again the parachute recovery system did not work.[30]

The end of the week brought better news from Sardinia, as on Friday the 14th May ESRO mission **S56B/2** fared better than its predecessor in March. On board were three UK experiments, repeats of those launched not only on S56B/1, but also on S56A/2 the previous July. These comprised a joint experiment from Leicester/RSRS to measure solar X-rays, one from the RSRS to measure electron properties, and another from the RSRS to measure solar Lyman-α radiation. A sea recovery of the payload was apparently successful.[31]

Figure 12.6 The Leicester variable spacing modulation collimator instrument built for a star-pointing Skylark, and probably flown on SL812.

(Adams, Janes & Whitford (1972a), figure 7)

[27] Fahleson, Fälthammar & Pedersen (1974), 'Ionospheric temperature and density measurements by means of spherical double probes'.
[28] Minutes of the 18th Skylark Policy Meeting, June 1971, p.4, item 4. (TNA: PRO AVIA 92/145).
[29] Details of the experiment are given in Pounds (1971), 'Measurement of the Polarisation, Spectra and Accurate Locations of Cosmic X-ray Sources, pp.165-166.
[30] Minutes of the 18th Skylark Policy Meeting, June 1971, p.5, item 7. (TNA: PRO AVIA 92/145).
[31] BAe (1990), *Record of Skylark Launches 1957-1990*.

July 1971   S73

There were no Skylark launches in June, and just one in July, when ESRO launch **S73** took place from Sardinia on the 2nd. It had a Sun-stabilised payload carrying a German experiment to study the inner zodiacal light,[32] using an array of five photometer telescopes. It was the first attempt to measure the zodiacal light in the daytime with the non-eclipsed Sun near zenith, and successfully provided coverage of the observational gap between the Earth-bound measurements of the inner zodiacal light and outer corona data.[33]

Launch took place near local noon, and to reduce background light reflected from the Earth, it was necessary to have low cloud coverage during flight in an area of about 1500 km (930 mile) radius. Similar studies were later made by Skylark mission 'Astro 7' in October 1975, see the next chapter.

There may also have been a solar X-ray experiment on board, but nothing further is known of this.

August 1971   SL902

SL902 was launched on the 12th August from Woomera, with a Sun-stabilised payload, which reached an altitude of 272 km (169 miles) aided by a Goldfinch booster. It was the first flight of an upgraded version of the ACU (the "twin pack ACU"), in which the pneumatic mechanism[34] was separated from the ACU bay, so the latter could be included in the recoverable portion of the payload for re-use.[35] However on this flight the change was in vain, because as noted below the parachute recovery system failed, and the payload smashed into the ground.

The Culham Laboratory astronomy experiment on board was a continuation of that flown on SL606 in April 1969. As before, it measured the solar limb ultraviolet spectrum by means of spectrographs, the purpose of this flight being to make measurements of increased accuracy. Alas, also as before, the parachute recovery system failed, and "the quality of the recorded spectra was unfortunately degraded by severe impact damage of the rocket payload". Surprisingly, much new data was still recovered, and several new spectral lines were identified and classified.[36]

September 1971   SL1002, S47/2

Spring at Woomera

In the Australian Spring, five Skylark launches took place during a four-week period starting at the end of September:

(i) BAC's ninth Woomera launch campaign began with Skylark **SL1002** on the 27th September.

The optical identification of cosmic X-ray sources was of particular importance at the time, since most were unidentified and remained rather enigmatic objects, somewhat removed from the mainstream of astronomy.[37] SL1002 was part of an ingenious and difficult astronomy collaboration by the University of Leicester and MSSL to try to identify the optical source of the X-ray object GX3+1.

The basis of the experiment was to use an X-ray detector to record the exact instant when the edge of the Moon passed in front of an X-ray source, temporarily cutting off its radiation. In order to observe this eclipse or occultation, the Skylark firing had to be precisely timed – no easy task as there was only a 'one minute' launch window, and it was said the opportunity would not occur again for 17 years![38]

As the Skylark star-pointing ACU was not yet available, a Sun-pointing ACU was used with auxiliary roll control. Thus, the payload carried two X-ray sensors; the smaller to lock onto Sco X-1 to control roll, the larger to observe GX3+1. (See figure 12.7 overleaf.)

In the event all went well, the flight observed the occultation, and led to the location of GX3+1 being determined within an arc only +0.4 arcsec wide.[39] A repeat experiment by MSSL was carried out by SL974 a month later on the next lunar orbit, which let to an accurate 'fix' being obtained, as described below.

(ii) **S47/2** was an ESRO mission launched from Woomera on the 30th September local date (29th GMT). The payload was built by SAAB for ESTEC, and reached an altitude of 210 km (131 miles). The ROE stellar photography experiment was a southern hemisphere version of those on S47/1 and S27/1 launched in October and December 1968 from Sardinia; but was only a partial success because of the failure of the recovery system.[40] The results were still undergoing analysis over a year later "...the final reduction having been

32 Zodiacal light is produced by sunlight reflecting off interplanetary dust which exists in a cloud centred on the Sun. It is very faint, but on Moonless nights may be seen after twilight or before dawn (when it causes the "false dawn" effect).
33 Leinert, Link & Pitz (1974), 'Rocket Photometry of the Inner Zodiacal Light'.
34 The pneumatic mechanism separated the Skylark head/payload from the spent motor section.
35 Dorling (1975), 'Early History of the Skylark Rocket', p.185.
36 Ridgeley & Burton (1972), 'Further Observations of the Solar-Limb Spectrum in the region 550-2000 Å', p.101.
37 Pounds (1986), 'British X-ray Astronomy', p.440.
38 Minutes of the 20th Skylark Policy Meeting, December 1971, p.6. (TNA: PRO AVIA 92/145).
39 Pounds (1986), 'British X-ray Astronomy', p.440.
40 Minutes of the 20th Skylark Policy Meeting, December 1971, p.3, item 8. (TNA: PRO AVIA 92/145).

subject to the usual delays in obtaining an accurate rocket altitude solution." By then a comparison between the data obtained from the Skylark experiment and that obtained from the OAO II orbiting observatory was under way.[41]

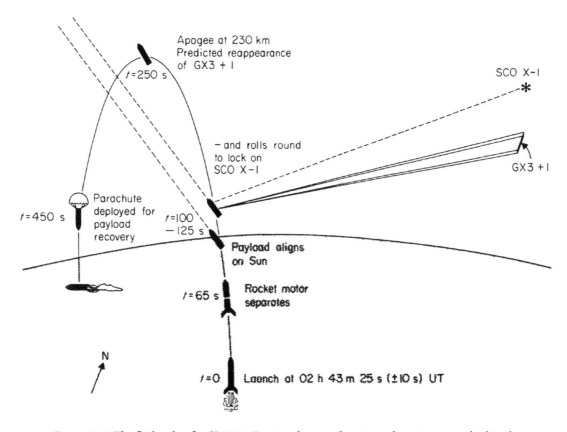

Figure 12.7 The flight plan for SL1002. Despite the complications, the mission resulted in the successful observation of the occultation of GX3+1.

(Pounds (1986), figure 3a)

Figure 12.8 This commemorative cover reveals that SL1002 was nicknamed Apollo 15½! (NASA's Apollo 15 Moon mission had taken place just over two months earlier, from 26th July to August 7th 1971.)

(Author's collection)

[41] Brück (1973), Royal Observatory, Edinburgh. 'Report for year ending 1973 March 31', p.43.

| October 1971 | SL973, S81, S89, SL974, |
| | Black Arrow R3 |

(iii) **SL973**, launched from Woomera on 7th October, carried the latest in a series of astronomical X-ray instruments from MSSL. (The two preceding being SL971 and SL1021 in 1970). The instrument was a 'Rotating Modulation Collimator' (RMC), a sophisticated type of X-ray telescope

designed to provide more accurate observations of galactic sources.

SL973's payload successfully reached an altitude of 230 km (143 miles) where it observed the Sagittarius-Scorpius region of the evening sky. It was spin-stabilised at three revolutions a second, and the attitude of the instruments was reconstructed using data from a magnetometer and a pair of crossed sun-slits.

Figure 12.9 This photograph is probably of SL973,[42] which was launched in the evening local time on Thursday 7th October 1971. The exhaust glow from the three pairs of Imp spin-up motors can be seen above the Goldfinch boost motor.

(WRE \ J.A.Hill)

[42] J.A.Hill, personal correspondence, September 2009.

Figures 12.10 and 12.11. The recovery of SL973.

(WRE \ Rapley)

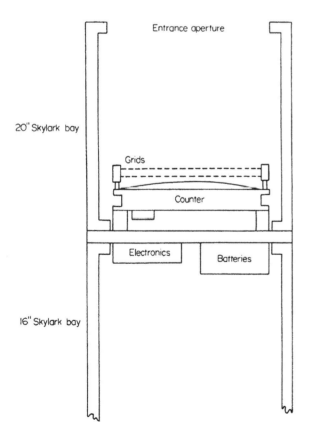

Figures 12.12 and 12.13 Left – A cross-sectional diagram of the rotation collimator payload (This corresponds to the photograph in Figure 11.35). Right – The "image" of the X-ray source 2U 1756-25 obtained from the instrument flown on SL973.

(Cruise and Willmore (1975), figures 1 and 5)

An RMC instrument was being prepared for flight on the forthcoming UK5 scientific satellite,[43] and this and the earlier RMC missions were partly undertaken to gain experience with such instruments. The RMC instrument did not provide images as such, and a considerable amount of data processing was required to interpret the results. The data from these Skylark test launches allowed different methods of analysis to be compared. In due course an algorithm was developed that would reduce the computer time required to map a source by a factor of about 30.[44] Analysis of these early results also revealed that the 'images' could be severely compromised if the payload had a small 'coning' motion:

> The main outcome of this analysis was that the RMC instrument proposed for the UK5 satellite might also suffer from this problem of smearing images over quite small circles. A simple additional control was hurriedly added to the UK5 instrument to limit this smearing to only half of the rotation cycle, dramatically reducing its adverse effect.[45]

(iv) Four days after SL973, on Tuesday 12th Oct, Skylark ESRO **S81** was launched from Woomera to an altitude of 210 km (131 miles). The payload had been built by ESTEC, and included an Italian experiment for surveying X-ray sources. The mission was a complete success, and recovery was achieved using the land version of the Dornier RESY system.[46]

(v) The 24th of October saw the launch of **SL974**, companion to SL1002 launched two weeks before. Its purpose was to carry out the second part of the experiment to identify the optical source of the X-ray object GX3+1. The payload on this occasion was provided by MSSL, and it too observed the occultation of GX3+1, this time on the next lunar orbit.[47] This yielded a second lunar arc, and together they provided a 'fix' for the location of GX3+1, the accuracy of ± 0.4 arcsec being for many years the most accurate determination of any X-ray source.[48]

The search for the optical counterpart of GX3+1

In 1970, a failed search for the optical counterpart of GX+3 had been reported, concluding that improved X-ray positions might well be required.[49] Presumably, it was this that

inspired these Skylark missions. Unfortunately, despite the excellent result obtained, for many years GX3+1 remained (and continues to remain?) optically unidentified, since heavy obscuration towards the Galactic centre means that no optical counterpart appears to have been found. For instance in 1983 a paper listing 96 optical identifications of X-ray sources presumed to be compact sources was published, but GX3+1 was still listed as "Bright Unidentified"[50] In 1991(20 years later!) another paper used the Skylark results again, but still with no plausible candidate.[51] By 2003, an optical counterpart had still not been identified, but using results from the BeppoSAX X-ray satellite it was concluded "GX 3+1 is a low-mass X-ray binary that is persistently bright since its discovery in 1964. It was found to be an X-ray burster twenty years ago proving that the compact object in this system is a neutron star."[52] In 2007 the search was continuing.[53] In 2012 the author was unable to determine the current status – this is left as an exercise for the reader!

Black Arrow, the launch of R3 and Prospero

To round off a busy October at Woomera, another significant launch took place on Thursday 28th. This was the launch of the satellite X3/Prospero by Black Arrow R3, the first (and to date only) launch of a satellite by a British rocket. Prospero was the first British technology satellite, (not to be confused with the Ariel series of scientific satellites, launched by US rockets).

Derek Mack had led the R3 Trials team at Highdown (Isle of Wight) from October 7th 1970 and taken the team to join the hardware at Woomera in early August 1971. For inter-contractor reasons, the UK team leader became Deputy Team Leader for the launch trial and was responsible for all the preparation tasks involving flight hardware. He had previously fulfilled the same role on the R0 trial, and had run the night-shift crews on the Rl and R2 trials.

Although not directly part of the Skylark story, his fascinating account[54] of the launch is of great interest and captures the atmosphere and emotion of the time:

"October 28th 1971 started as a typical late spring day in the Australian outback. It felt cool and fresh and the sky was clear. As we drove the 30 miles from the village to Range E, we could see light mist lying between the shallow hills.

[43] Cruise and Willmore (1975), 'The analysis of Data from Rotation Modulation Collimators', p.165. UK5 / Ariel 5 was launched in October 1975.
[44] MSSL (1973), *Report of the MSSL 1 October 1972 – 30 September 1973*, Part 3, p.10.
[45] Cruise (2008), *Skylark Ascending*, online article p.25, and *Prospero* number 5, Spring 2008, pp.59-60.
[46] Minutes of the 20th Skylark Policy Meeting, December 1971, p.3, item 8. (TNA: PRO AVIA 92/145).
[47] Janes *et al* (1972), 'Identification of GX3+1 from Lunar Occultations'.
[48] Pounds (1986), 'British X-ray Astronomy', p.440.
[49] Kunkel *et al* (1970), 'An Optical Search for the X-Ray Sources GX3+1, GX5-1, GX9+1, and GX17+2'.
[50] Bradt & McClintock (1983), 'The optical counterparts of compact galactic X-ray sources', p.17.
[51] Naylor, Charles & Longmore (1991), 'Infrared Observations of low-mass X-ray binaries…'.
[52] Hartog *et al* (2003), 'Burst-properties as a function of mass accretion rate in GX 3+1'.
[53] Zand, Jonker & Markwardt (2007), 'Six new candidate ultracompact X-ray binaries'.
[54] Derek Mack via BROHP Newsletter Spring 99 / Spufford / BBC? The author has enquired further without success.

The "minus 30" minute in the launch countdown (when all the personnel were required to be under cover or at a safe distance) was due at 1300 hours but the readying of R3 had begun the previous midnight when the overnight crew filled the HTP tanks and adjusted the kerosene tank levels to match the engine mixture ratios. These tasks, and the arming of the many pyrotechnic systems in each of the three stages, took most of the night to complete. During this phase, safety regulations limit each person to eight-hour stints, so I started shift at 0700 hours so as to have a few hours overlap before my opposite number had to stand down. He advised that the night work had run smoothly and activities were about thirty minutes ahead of plan.

By 1100 hours the service tower (or gantry) was rolled back and the launch pad evacuated for radio checks. This activity took about an hour and was done to confirm radio aerial performance between rocket and the associated ground stations. During this period the Attitude Reference Unit, which steers the rocket flight path, began to exhibit erratic velocity outputs. This behaviour caused some concern and consternation before it was realised that without protection from the gantry, the rocket structure was swaying slightly under the influence of a gentle breeze gusting from the west. The ARU was measuring these small displacements and expressing them correctly in equivalent rate changes - potential panic over!

By 1230 hours the flight destruction system had been armed and the release jack safety pin withdrawn to make it active. Now all the work at the launcher was finished and the area was fully evacuated. The Equipment Centre (EC5) lies about 700 metres from the launcher and accommodates the personnel and equipment dealing directly with the rocket systems up to launch. With the launcher crew, I retired to EC5 with a feeling of anticipation and waited on the Range Controller to start the final 30 minute count down. Between - 30 minutes and 2 minutes, all activities are manual actions and therefore have a degree of flexibility. However, at 2 minutes all events become automatic and proceed under the control of a central timer and interlock system.

Before triggering the automatic 2 minute sequence, the Range Controller progressively confirms the readiness status of each station involved. By - 10 minutes everyone except the apogee telemetry station at Charters Towers in North Queensland, had responded to his can. At - 5 minutes the Range authority called a ten minute hold to complete a cloud cover assessment. So far everything at the equipment had gone to plan, and rocket functions were looking good. The time count was resumed with still no apparent response from the North! As minus 2 minutes approached the tension became almost tangible - a possible abort was on the cards if they didn't call in. Suddenly, at about - 4 minutes [sic] a cheerful voice came on to say all was OK at Charters Towers and they were ready to go if we were! Mutterings and unprintable comments from all round.

The final two minutes ticked through without interruption and all visual indicators were nominal. At time zero, time seemed to hang still until the "Instant of Move" event was signalled at plus 4 seconds. As usual at this point, I turned around to view the rocket directly through the Equipment Centre windows and watched its clean, controlled and un-hurried climb upwards. Unfortunately, the windows only allow a view up to about 90 feet so I then turned my attention to the 1st and 2nd stage telemetry monitors to follow onboard events and listened to flight progress reports coming in from various external sources over the intercom net.

When the first stage burn ends, personnel may leave the cover of EC5, but there is only a dying condensation trail to see by this time, so I stayed inside with the telemetry and intercom data.

At plus 130 seconds first stage burn ended and the second stage engine sparked up on cue and burned for the required duration to plus 245 seconds. Before this, at plus 180 seconds on the dot, the payload fairings were discarded[55]. It was unbelievable, everywhere I focused my mind, systems were responding with copybook returns. At plus 510 seconds Charters Towers reported a successful apogee event- this was peaches and cream to me but was it in the right direction? Had it spun up? Did the satellite separate? - so many things yet to go wrong.

I returned to Test Shop 4 to make ready for the formal communiqué meeting scheduled to start at plus 1 hour. Here the satellite team were already over the top with excitement and lavished compliments on the launch team for the success. They had followed the satellite telemetry in detail from their own receivers, and as relayed from Charters Towers, and were convinced all was perfect. But the launch team had been here before only to find success turned to failure as the mature data came to hand. We tempered our joy, kept our powder dry and wondered if the Mess bar would witness a celebration or commiseration that night.

Finally, just after 1400 hours a message came over from Fairbanks (part of the global satellite tracking network) "we have an operational satellite on 137 MHz passing overhead". That was it, that's what we had been waiting for, and all hell let loose as pent-up emotions found their release. At last! We had shown everybody that it could be done, and that it could be done on a shoe string, and despite a lack of official will."

---

[55] For an excellent description of the ascent to orbit, see Millard (2001), *The Black Arrow Rocket,* pp.46-48.

Figure 12.14 Black Arrow R3 lifts off from Woomera, 28th October 1971.
(WRE)

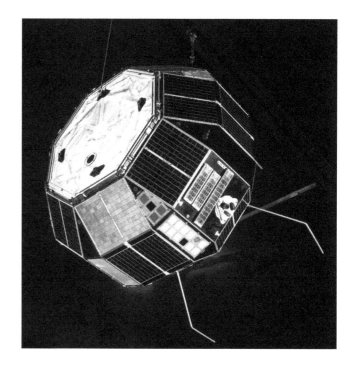

Figure 12.15 The X-3 / Prospero satellite as launched from Woomera by Black Arrow R3.
(Prospero flight spare, © Science Museum / Science & Society Picture Library, image 10321409)

"The essential tidy up actions were done double quick and a general exodus to the village began. After the formal communiqué meeting I also returned to the village, showered and joined what by now was a massive rave up at ELDO Mess. Clearly the word had gone ahead and the revelry was well established - everyone from taxi and bus drivers through to very senior members of both government services was enjoying the moment.

Efforts to prolong the celebrations next day dwindled as the knowledge penetrated that Black Arrow would never fly again and that many must look elsewhere for their employment.

Black Arrow was the last liquid fuelled rocket produced by the UK. With its demise, liquid fuel technology was erased from the UK's engineering repertoire and one of the most cost effective co-operations between civil service teams and multi-company teams was disbanded. To those involved, the success of the project was paramount and as a final reward to all the believers, Black Arrow has left behind a lasting witness of its successful existence that will endure for many years - Prospero."

The reference to those that had to look elsewhere for employment comes from the fact that in July 1971 the UK government had cancelled the Black Arrow project.[56] This, in the opinion of the author, is a good example of a the government

and civil service snatching defeat from the jaws of victory, and being happy to throw away taxpayer's money without ensuring a return on the investment. The British government and their civil service advisors appeared unable to recognise that technology continually moves forward and is not frozen in time.[57]

More bluntly:

> Naturally, in keeping with British tradition, the project was immediately cancelled once it was a success. Wikipedia comments: 'As of 2009, the UK is the only country to have successfully developed and then abandoned a satellite launch capability.'[58]

Thus the fifth Black Arrow launch vehicle R4, was never fired, and together with the flight spare of Prospero, may be seen in the Space Gallery of the Science Museum in London.

However, Prospero remains in orbit to this day, where it is expected to continue for another 150 years.[59] As with the UK's Ariel series of satellites launched by NASA, Prospero had an alphanumeric designation before launch (in this case X-3), and was only awarded its Shakespearean name[60] once successfully launched. The launch made Britain the sixth nation to place a satellite into orbit using a domestically developed launch vehicle (after the USSR, USA, France, Japan and China).

---

[56] For further analysis of this sorry tale, see for instance Hill (2008), 'The cancellation of Black Arrow'.
[57] See also *www.spaceuk.org/ba/blackarrowcancellation.htm*, last accessed July 2014.
[58] Hamilton-Paterson (2010), *Empire of the Clouds*, p.319.
[59] UKSA (2014), *UK Registry of Outer Space Objects*, p.5.
[60] Shakespeare's apparent allusion "I'll put a girdle round about the earth in forty minutes" (Puck, A Midsummer Night's Dream, Act 2 Scene 1) was substantially quicker than Black Arrow's satellite's 82 minutes - perhaps Shakespeare thought the Earth's diameter was much smaller than it really is!

Prospero orbit details	Predicted	Achieved
Orbital inclination	82.06	82.06
Orbital period (minutes)	106	106.5
Minimum (perigee) altitude (km)	556	547
Maximum (apogee) altitude (km)	1570	1582

Table 12.2 Details of Prospero's Orbit.[61]

Details of Prospero

Prospero was placed in a low Earth orbit very close to that predicted, see table 12.2 just above.

Prospero has been assigned the designation S005580 1971-093A,[62] and the third stage Waxwing motor (still in orbit as 'space junk') is S005581 1971-093B. Even the aerial that broke off when the Waxwing motor collided with Prospero after release went into orbit and was designated S005582 1971-093C. However the orbit of that decayed, and it burnt up in the Earth's atmosphere on 16th December 1979, some eight years later.

Prospero was mainly a technology satellite, with three technology and one university experiment on board:

1. Solar cells - several different types were evaluated for possible future use.
2. Hybrid electronic assemblies – the investigation of new lightweight electronic circuitry.
3. Thermal control surfaces – this tested different surface coatings.
4. Micrometeoroid detector – a University of Birmingham experiment to investigate micrometeoroids by means of the latest method - an impact ionisation detector, three orders more sensitive than any flown before.[63]

A tape recorder was also on board, which lasted 730 plays but failed on 24 May 1973. However in 2006, radio trans-

missions from Prospero could still be heard on 137.560 MHz, despite the fact that it had officially been switched off ten years earlier, when the UK's Defence Research Establishment decommissioned their satellite tracking station at Lasham, Hampshire.

In October 2011, attempts were made to receive radio signals from Prospero, forty years after it was launched. However, at the time of writing, the effort appears to have been unsuccessful.[64]

The Prospero Launch facilities

The Black Arrow rockets had re-used the Black Knight launch pad area (LA5). As mentioned above, the Prospero satellite was prepared for launch in Test Shop 4, situated about 5 km (3.1 miles) away at the rangehead.[65]

Part of Test Shop 4 had been converted by WRE into an operational clean room incorporating test and assembly bays, and the author has a manual describing the construction and operation of this facility. The construction must have been a feat in itself, and with its air conditioning and dust count monitoring, provided an environment very different from that found in the gibber desert by the first surveyors in 1947!

Sadly, all this investment went to waste when the UK government cancelled the Black Arrow programme.

W. R. E. MANUAL FOR THE OPERATION OF THE SATELLITE CLEAN ROOM AND SATELLITE TEST AND ASSEMBLY BAY IN TEST SHOP NUMBER 4, BUILDING 206, RANGE 'E', WOOMERA, SOUTH AUSTRALIA

Figure 12.16 The building plan for this facility is shown in Appendix 5.
(WRE \ author's collection)

---

[61] Figures from Millard (2001), *The Black Arrow Rocket*, p.46.
[62] UKSA (2014), *UK Registry of Outer Space Objects*, p.5.
[63] Bedford & Bryan (1974), 'The Micrometeoroid Detector Aboard the Satellite Prospero', and Massey & Robins (1986), *History of British Space Science*, pp.293 & 430.
[64] *www.ucl.ac.uk/mssl/news/mssl-news/news-sep-2011/prospero*, last accessed August 2014.
[65] As noted at the start of this book, in the 1970's ground distances began to be metricated in the UK and Australia, hence from about this Chapter onwards metric distance measurements have been placed first!
[66] Morton (1989), *Fire across the Desert*, opposite p.428. Reproduced courtesy Australian DSTO.

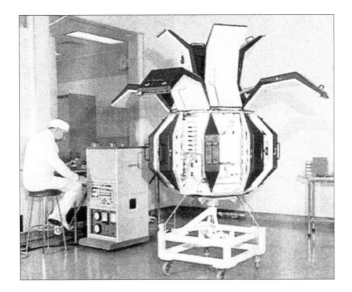

Figure 12.17 The X-3 / Prospero satellite being prepared in the clean room at Woomera Test Shop 4. (For a plan of the clean room see Appendix 5, Figure A5.1)
(WRE \ Morton) [66]

Failures at Sardinia

Meanwhile, back in Europe, ESRO Sun-stabilised Skylark **S89** was launched on 20th October from Sardinia. It was a solar X-ray astronomy mission, and included a Leicester crystal spectrometer instrument. It successfully reached an altitude of 210 km (131 miles), but unfortunately on the way down the payload suffered a "DFVLR parachute failure".[67] This meant that the mission as a whole appears to have failed,[68] presumably, the experiment was due to provide its results in photographic form rather than by telemetry, and the parachute failure meant the film simply disappeared into the Mediterranean.

November 1971   S44/2, S70/2, SL1101

November 16th saw further disappointment at Sardinia. Skylark **S44/2** was a UV astronomy mission with an ESRO star-pointing payload, but appears to have suffered a motor failure at launch, reaching only "0km".[69]

However **S70/2**, launched on the 25th from Kiruna, fared better. It carried ionospheric experiments from Denmark, RSRS Slough and Birmingham, and was a total success.[70]

Last two of 1971 from Woomera

Early rocket observations of the Sun had confirmed that its corona was a source of X-rays, and that the emissions were concentrated above active (sunspot) regions. Some instruments (such as that flown on Ariel I) had recorded that the

total intensity increased when a solar flare occurred, but could not localise the event.

Following Ariel I (launched in 1962 as described in Chapter 7), the UCL and Leicester research groups, anticipating the availability of Sun-stabilised Skylark rockets, planned an extensive programme to study the distribution of X-ray sources over the Sun.[71]

Many of the resulting X-ray instruments flown on stabilised Skylarks have been described in previous chapters, and the end of 1971 saw two flights, which continued this programme. The payloads carried improved instruments, which further narrowed down the field of view in order to improve the accuracy of the results.

The first was **SL1101**, fired from Woomera on 30th November. This carried three instruments from the University of Leicester group, one for solar X-ray photography, one for solar white light photography, and a high-resolution X-ray crystal spectrometer. The mission was successful, and the crystal spectrometer provided details of 98 X-ray emissions lines between 9 and 22.5 Å from a single non-flaring active region on the Sun's disk, and a mathematical model of the emitting plasma was constructed.[72]

December 1971   SL903, S82

The last 1971 Woomera Skylark was **SL903,** launched the following week from Woomera at 14:30 local time on 10th December. It carried a similar solar X-ray astronomy experiment to that of SL1101, this time from MSSL, and as described

---

[67] BAe (1990), *Record of Skylark Launches 1957-1990*.

[68] Massey & Robins (1986), *History of British Space Science*, p.435.

[69] McDowell (2009), *List of Skylark Launches*.

[70] Minutes of the 20th Skylark Policy Meeting, December 1971, p.3, item 8. (TNA: PRO AVIA 92/145).

[71] See for instance Massey & Robins, *History of British Space Science,* p.340.

[72] Parkinson (1975), 'The analysis of a high-resolution X-ray spectrum of a solar active region'. See also Hutcheon, Pye & Evans (1976),' The spectrum of Fe XVII in the solar corona'.

10th DECEMBER, 1971

Payload
SL903

Experimenter: Mullard Space Science Laboratory. **Purpose of the experiment:** To study the line spectrum of the x-ray region 10-25A. This rocket was launched at 14.30 hours local time. It weighed 243.65kg and its apogee was 198km.

AUSTRALIAN - EUROPEAN PROJECT

Left: Figure 12.18 This 'First day cover' marked the launch of SL903.
(Author's collection)

below it had the ability to point to different regions on the Sun's disk.

The main instrument comprised a pair of "collimated Bragg crystal spectrometers" prepared by MSSL to study solar X-rays between 1.0 and 2.2 nm (10 – 22 Å).[73] (It appears to be the same type of instrument flown on the failed S85 in February).

The field of view of the spectrometer was limited (9 arc min square)[74] to allow individual regions on the Sun's disk to be studied. The attitude control unit successfully pointed the payload initially to the centre of the Sun, and then at regions of interest.

This spectrometer is a good example of how sophisticated the scientific instruments flown on Skylark had become. Before use, it had to be extremely carefully aligned and calibrated, and whilst in flight the crystals (which reflected the X-rays) were rotated by stepper motors to scan the small area of interest, before signalling the ACU to point to the next area on the Sun's disk. To reduce poisoning of the detectors through their thin plastic windows, gas was flowed through the detectors whilst the experiment was in the launch tower. Then, two minutes before launch, electrically operated valves were closed sealing the counters for the duration of the flight.

The active regions of the Sun viewed were seen to be sources of X-rays, and the spectra and hence temperature variations

of several of these 'plages' (bright regions near sunspots) were obtained, allowing mathematical models of the operation of these parts of the Sun to be derived. In each case, these suggested a hot, dense central core.[76]

Right: Figure 12.19 The crystal spectrometer instrument as flown on SL903.
(Brabban and Glencross (1973), figure 1.3) [75]

[73] Brabban and Glencross (1973), 'Crystal spectrometry of active regions on the sun'.
[74] I.e. just under one tenth of a degree.
[75] Reproduced courtesy Royal Society London.
[76] MSSL (1973), *Report of the MSSL 1 October 1972 – 30 September 1973*, Part 3: Astrophysics, p.2, and Brabban (1974), 'A Comparison of three Solar Active Regions based on their Soft X-ray Line Spectra'.

Finally

The 29th and last Skylark launch of 1971 was that of **S82,** launched from Sardinia at 12:11 GMT on 14th December during the maximum of the Geminid meteor shower. It included a Swiss mass spectrometer for measuring positive ion composition in the ionosphere,[77] but the reason for launching during a meteor shower was that the payload also included a set of microphone detectors to measure micrometeorite properties.

SKYLARK LAUNCHES AND SCIENCE IN 1972

The 1972 total of twenty launches was well down on the figure of 29 for 1971, a sign of things to come. It could be argued that the economical Black Arrow satellite launcher should have been the natural successor to Skylark, but that was not to be.

The Skylark parachute problem solved?

At least by December 1971 the basic cause of Skylark's parachute problem had at last been identified:

Mr Hazell reported on progress with the solution to the problem of the parachute being prematurely ejected and damaged due to the violent behaviour of the rocket which could occur on re-entry. An urgent modification had been introduced to fit retaining cables to hold in the parachute and cutter to sever the cables when necessary to release. There had been a subsequent flight, but whilst the retaining and release system had worked, there had been no indication of the possible preceding violent behaviour to really prove the system.

It was necessary to emphasise that the basic cause of the trouble (the flat spin) had not been eliminated, and there had been no upgrading of the rest of the components of the rockets, for these high loadings.[78]

Proving tests must have continued during 1972, as by June 1973 it was the opinion of Frank Hazell "that (supported by actual flight results) the existing parachute system for recovery of payloads had achieved a reliable standard." [79]

Copernicus

Another sign of the times in space science was the launch by NASA in 1972 of the "Orbiting Astronomical Observatory 3" (OAO-C) satellite[80], later named 'Copernicus' by President Nixon. It included an important British X-ray instrument, similar to those developed for Skylark. The event was described by MSSL in their annual report for 1972:

There is no doubt, however, that the highlight of the nine months period is the successful launching of OAO-C with its triple X-ray prime focus telescopes conceived in 1961 before any cosmic sources had been discovered. This project has been much more demanding especially in manpower and travel than could have been foreseen when the invitation to participate came in 1963. However to have a real observatory in orbit with direct control of pointing and instrument characteristics – especially field of view – is an ample reward for the long wait, involving the employment of three successive project scientists.[81]

As noted previously, the background was that back in 1961, before any cosmic X-ray sources had been detected, a UCL group under Boyd and Willmore had proceeded with a design for an instrument using grazing incidence parabolic reflectors with proportional counters at the foci, which could be included in a satellite to observe cosmic X-rays. They had also considered the design of detectors that could be used in Stage 3 stabilised Skylarks. Following the discovery in 1962 of the first (and astonishingly powerful) cosmic X-ray source by Giacconi, they had proposed their system for inclusion in the payload of the third US astronomical satellite 'OAO 3', as an auxiliary

Jan.	Feb.	March	April	May	June	July	Aug.	Sept.	Oct.	Nov.	Dec.
	S84	S77/1			S91	SL1191		S94	S105	S95	SL1202
	S90	SL1023				SL1183		S77/2	SL1022		SL1005
		SL1009							SL402		
		S75/1							SL1003		
		SL1081									
		S75/2									

Table 12.3 The 20 Skylark launches in 1972. (For full details see Appendix 3.)

(Key: black = test launches, blue = UK national programme (unstabilised), plum = UK (stabilised), pink = ESRO programme)

---

[77] Zbinden *et al.* (1975), 'Mass spectrometer measurements of the positive ion composition in the D and E regions of the ionosphere'.
[78] Minutes of the 20th Skylark Policy Meeting, December 1971, p.4, item 4. (TNA: PRO AVIA 92/145).
[79] Minutes of the 26th Skylark Policy Meeting, June 1973, p.3, item 4. (TNA: PRO AVIA 92/145).
[80] For a good description of Copernicus, see *http://heasarc.gsfc.nasa.gov/docs/copernicus/copernicus.html* . (Last accessed August 2014).
[81] MSSL (1972), *Report of the MSSL 1 January 1972 - 30 September 1972*, Part B, p.1.

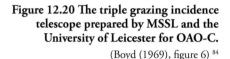

Figure 12.20 The triple grazing incidence telescope prepared by MSSL and the University of Leicester for OAO-C.
(Boyd (1969), figure 6) [84]

experiment to the main ultraviolet observing system to be carried. Their proposal had been accepted in 1963, but the satellite was not launched until 1972 - although in the event this delay proved a benefit.[82] The MSSL report continues:

> The eventual launch precisely on time on 21 August this year, a decade later, nevertheless marks the first occasion on which satellite borne reflectors have been orbited for the study of non-solar sources of X-rays. It is particularly gratifying that this long gestation should have resulted in a genuine observatory situation in which the instrument may be fully controlled from the ground as regards aperture, pointing, observing time and so on. The intervening ten years has served only to enhance the value of the work by providing Sky catalogues of source positions and by posing far more questions for study than can possibly be answered in the 10% of satellite time available to us.[83]

The original discovery by Giacconi had been made by sounding rocket and despite the launch of OAO-C and similar scientific satellites, cosmic X-ray observations from sounding rockets would continue, including many launched on Skylark.

The ESRO sounding rocket programme draws to a close

Towards the end of 1971, it was reported:

> For ESRO Sounding Rockets, unless there is a last minute reprieve, the future is all too clear. During the last months of this year and during 1972 we will launch the 24 payloads at present in progress and then our work will be complete. We leave behind a very different picture in Europe from that when we launched our first Skylark in April 1964. At that time sounding rocket activity was somewhat restricted whereas now Britain, France, Germany, Spain and Sweden have flourishing programmes and other member states have collaborative programmes with them and NASA.[85]

To greater things – except for Britain!

Also on the European scene, in April 1972 at an ELDO council meeting, a proposal was put forward for a £200m development programme for a 'Europa III' launch vehicle (Blue Streak F11 had been 'Europa II'), capable of putting 750 kg (1650 lb) into geostationary orbit. This proposal was finally agreed at a European Space Conference in December, the funding to be mainly provided by France and Germany.[86] This was the culmination of a process whereby the UK government had left ELDO and voluntarily abandoned its hard earned lead in European space launcher capability, allowing the vast tax-payers investment go to waste, and bestowing a lucrative industry to its European rivals. The December meeting also agreed to combine ELDO and ESRO into a new European Space Agency (ESA).

The rest, as they say, is history, and from this time onwards, Skylark gained the sorry distinction of being the largest remaining British space rocket![87]

[82] Massey & Robins (1986), *History of British Space Science*, p.367.
[83] MSSL (1972), *Report of the MSSL 1 January 1972 - 30 September 1972*, Part B, p.5.
[84] Reproduced courtesy Royal Society London.
[85] Eaton (1972), 'A Survey of the ESRO Sounding Rockets Programme 1964-1971', p.199.
[86] See for instance Flight Magazine, 27 April 1972, p.599.
[87] The only others being Skua and Petrel, both much smaller than Skylark.

February 1972	S84, S90

Skylark's 1972 season began with two launches on the same day from Sardinia. These took place early in the day on February 28th, with **S84** being launched some four hours before **S90**. They carried aeronomy experiments to carry out simultaneous upper air composition measurements at an altitude range of 115 – 220 km.[88] This included the measurement of solar ultraviolet radiation reaching the Earth, a matter of fundamental importance in upper atmosphere physics.

March 1972	S77/1, SL1023, SL1009, S75/1, SL1081, S75/2

March 1971 had been the busiest month that year for Skylark launches, and the same was true in March 1972, with a total of six launches.

The month started with **S77/1** being launched from Kiruna on the 2nd. This used a Goldfinch booster, the first used there.

SL77/1 was launched into a pulsating aurora, and was the first Skylark to have a separating payload. One of the difficulties in studying variable phenomena from a sounding rocket is to determine whether the changes being observed are spatial or temporal, i.e. are caused by the distance the vehicle has moved between readings, or are actually changing with time. On this rocket, part of the payload was ejected forward at 20 metres/second so that the incoming streams of auroral particles were sampled at the same time from two separate points.[89]

As described below, on S77/1 most changes were observed simultaneously on the main and ejected payloads, showing they were temporal in nature, and helping explain how the aurora was formed. The experiment was reported at a MIST[90] meeting at Exeter in 1975.[91]

> Pulses in electron intensity, occurring during the expansion phase of an auroral substorm,[92] were studied using a *Skylark* sounding rocket launched from Kiruna, Sweden at 2226:50 UT on 1972 March 2. The pulses were typically of 5 s duration and occurred sporadically

Figure 12.21 The Northern Lights (Aurora Borealis) as encountered by Skylark S77/1.

(© jamenpercy – Fotolia.com)

---

[88] Ackerman *et al.* (1974), 'Simultaneous Upper Air Composition Measurements…'.

[89] Massey & Robins (1986), *History of British Space Science*, p.324.

[90] MIST is still (2014) an active organisation, for details visit *www.mist.ac.uk* (last accessed August 2014).

[91] Royal Astronomical Society (1975), 'MIST Meeting at Exeter' (March 1975).

[92] An auroral substorm is a brief (a few hours) disturbance in the Earth's magnetosphere that causes energy to be released into the high latitude ionosphere. They are distinct from geomagnetic storms that take place over a period of several days.

with a mean interval of 15 s. The rocket carried main and ejected payloads, and the pulses, occurring simultaneously at both, are found to be temporal rather than spatial in origin.[93]

BAC Launch Campaign 10

Campaign 10 opened at Woomera when a further study of the ionospheric "Sq" current system was initiated on the 16th March with the launch of a combined payload of experiments on the spin-stabilised Skylark **SL1023**. The payload included the Birmingham electron density and electric field probes, the MSSL positive ion plate probes, the UCL rubidium magnetometer and the UCL lithium/sodium burner for daytime neutral wind measurements.

Launch took place at 11:30 hours local time, and apogee was reached just after four minutes:[94]

+4 min. 27 sec.   Apogee.

+6 min. 14 sec.   Lithium Grenade Experiment Commenced.

+7 min. 04 sec.   Lithium Grenade Experiment Ceased.

+8 min. 32 sec.   Head Released.

+8 min. 25 sec.   Impact.

The MSSL plate probes provided good data over a large part of the ascent but the almost explosive burning of the lithium/sodium mixture ended their useful life prematurely; and the trial yielded wind data over only 40 km of the planned 160 km. It had been hoped that the data analysis would improve on that obtained from SL922 (March 1971) but the probes' accident limited the use to which the data could be put.[95]

SL1009

On the following day (Friday 17th March), SL1009 was launched from Woomera:

The Stage 1 ACU pointed an RSRS solar astronomy instrument at the Sun, but unfortunately, this mission was only partially successful, probably because the recovery system failed yet again, and only some observations were obtained.

This failure was doubly unfortunate. Firstly, because it involved implications of shortcomings in design approval and clearance of the very modifications that were being urgently introduced to eliminate the pattern of previous parachute failures. Secondly, the failure had affected an experimenter who had suffered previous setbacks because of parachute failure, and apologies had to be made.[96]

The reason for the failure appears to have been investigated by the RAE at back at Farnborough, and the Science Museum in London now has an ex-Farnborough item from SL1009, a card with sample of rope showing damage to a drogue rigging line.[97]

S75/1 and S75/2

These two Skylark launches were the fourth and sixth to take place in March, this time from Sardinia. Both were similar ionospheric research missions launched after midnight local time, carrying for the first time a mass spectrometer with a cryogenically cooled ion source. The thermospheric densities of several gasses were determined, including for the first time carbon dioxide between 120 and 140 km.[98]

SL1081 and a new role for Skylark

Meanwhile at Woomera, on 27th March the final launch of Campaign 10 took place. This was an RAE proving flight with a difference, one with an Earth Surveying payload where the cameras pointed downwards instead of upwards.

SL1081 was the world's first "Earth Resources" rocket, and it also preceded the first Earth Resources satellite, ERTS-1, a technology proving venture launched by NASA four months

Seq. Nos	Launch date	Ref. (sponsor) Launch site	Config- uration	Apogee km (miles)	Experi- menters	Experiment(s)	Result
291 (5)	17 Mar. 1972	SL1009 (UK) Woomera	Sun, Rav.6 +G	237 (147)	RSRS	Solar physics - line profiles in range 100-210 nm (échelle diffraction grating spectrograph). Parachute failed	Ps

Table 12.4 A summary of SL1009.

[93]   Smith and Bryant (1975), 'Evidence for stretching of geomagnetic field-lines'.

[94]   The SL1023 timing information has been taken from a 'First Day Cover'. (J.A.Hill & author's collection).

[95]   MSSL (1972), *Report of the MSSL 1 January 1972 - 30 September 1972*, part A, p.2.

[96]   Minutes of the 22nd Skylark Policy Meeting, June 1972, item 4. (TNA: PRO AVIA 92/145).

[97]   Science Museum London, Inventory No. 1993-2341.

[98]   Offermann and Grossmann (1973), 'Thermospheric Density and Composition as Determined by a Mass Spectrometer with Cryo Ion Source'.

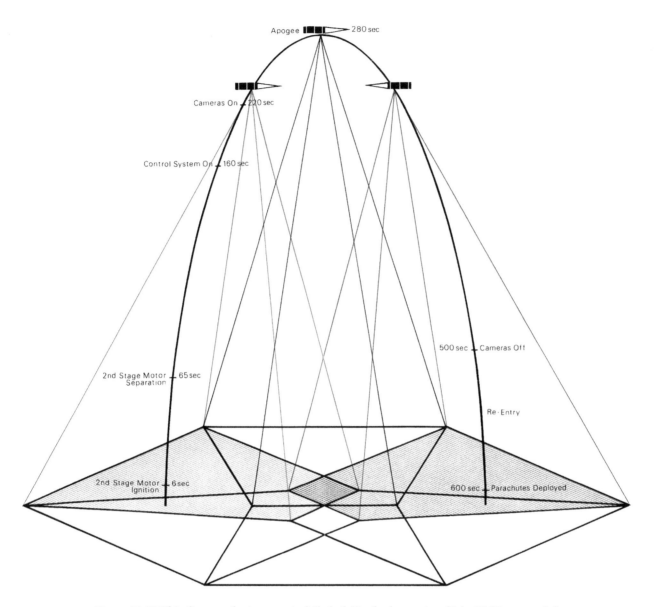

Figure 12.22 This diagram depicts a typical Skylark Earth observation flight.[101] (Not to scale.)
(BAC / University of Reading)

later.[99] SL1081 carried a 375 lb (170 kg) three axis-stabilised payload of cameras to a height of 184 miles (287 km). During the 4 min 40 seconds of filming, the payload was rotated in six 60° steps about its vertical axis, providing coverage of an area about the size of the United Kingdom.[100]

This was a radical departure for Skylark, and one that needed several new technical developments. These included a zenith (horizon) pointing attitude control system to point the cameras earthwards; a new transportable launcher, so that it could be launched from anywhere in the world; and the introduction of the new Raven X motor which provided faster initial acceleration, allowing the use of a short launcher rather than

a tower. For safety reasons, the nose cone was not jettisoned, allowing the attitude control system to be built into it.

The new Earth-pointing attitude control system did not need same high-performance stability as the previous astronomical ACUs (the photographic exposure times being of the order of a thousand times shorter[102]) and was developed in-house by the RAE. It used Earth albedo horizon-sensors in the roll and pitch axes to provide positional information that controlled a compressed nitrogen gas-jet system operating through nozzles recessed into the skin of the payload head. This contrasted with the arrangements employed in the Sun, Moon and star-pointing control systems, in which

[99] NASA's ERTS-1 (Earth Resources Technology Satellite 1) (Later named Landsat 1) was launched on 23rd July 1972.
[100] Flight International magazine, 27 April 1972, p.599.
[101] Savigear, et al. (1974), 'Rocket Photography for Earth Resource Surveys', figure 2, also BAC The Earth Resource Rocket brochure.
[102] With photographic exposure times of 10ms rather than 10s of seconds (Jude (1974), p.273).

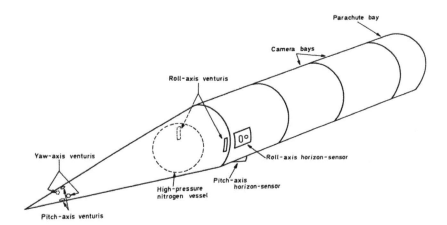

Parachute bay
Camera bays
Roll-axis venturis
Yaw-axis venturis
0°
Roll-axis horizon-sensor
High-pressure nitrogen vessel
Pitch-axis horizon-sensor
Pitch-axis venturis

Figure 12.23 The positions of the attitude control system components on the head of SL1081.

(Jude (1977), figure 4)[103]

the control system was mounted in between the parachute bay and the remainder of the head. Interestingly, at a nominal altitude of 250 km, the Earth's horizon would be 15° below the horizontal, and the optical axis of the horizon sensors had to be inclined appropriately.

This first proving flight was just to test the new ACU and camera payload, and used the existing launcher and facilities at Woomera. The new mobile launcher would be tested at Aberporth the following July, as described below, and the development of the new motor is described at the start of the next chapter. However, even for this first test, a great deal of work had to be done in the form of preliminary ground surveys. These were carried out under contract by the UK's University of Reading:

"For weeks before the two launches, parties skilled in geology and soils and flora ventured into the districts intended for photographic investigation carrying out 'ground truth' tests so that deductions made from the photographs from the rocket could be evaluated for accuracy against the true ground data."[104]

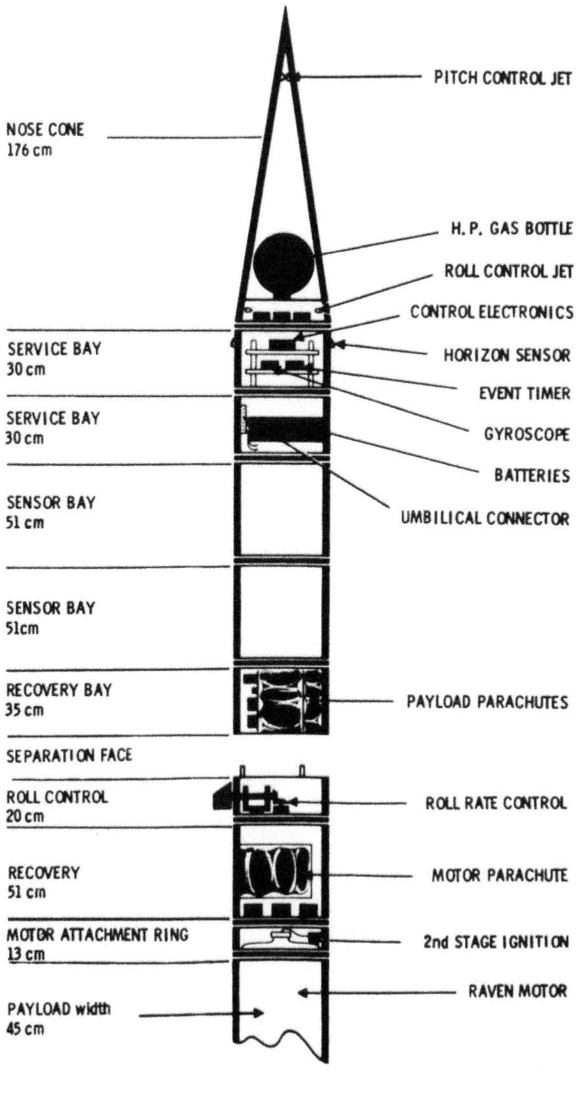

PITCH CONTROL JET
NOSE CONE 176 cm
H. P. GAS BOTTLE
ROLL CONTROL JET
CONTROL ELECTRONICS
SERVICE BAY 30 cm
HORIZON SENSOR
EVENT TIMER
SERVICE BAY 30 cm
GYROSCOPE
BATTERIES
SENSOR BAY 51 cm
UMBILICAL CONNECTOR
SENSOR BAY 51cm
RECOVERY BAY 35 cm
PAYLOAD PARACHUTES
SEPARATION FACE
ROLL CONTROL 20 cm
ROLL RATE CONTROL
RECOVERY 51 cm
MOTOR PARACHUTE
MOTOR ATTACHMENT RING 13 cm
2nd STAGE IGNITION
PAYLOAD width 45 cm
RAVEN MOTOR

Figure 12.24 The SL1081 payload configuration.
(BIS 'Spaceflight', magazine, Vol.14 No.8 August 1972, p.284, reproduced with permission.)

[103] Journal of the British Interplanetary Society, Vol.30 no.7 (Jul.1974), p.274. Reproduced with permission.
[104] Chambers (2000), *Woomera, Its human face*, p.102.

**Figure 12.25 The payload of SL1081 being prepared in Woomera Test
Shop 1 by personnel from BAC and the RAE.**

(WRE \ University of Reading)

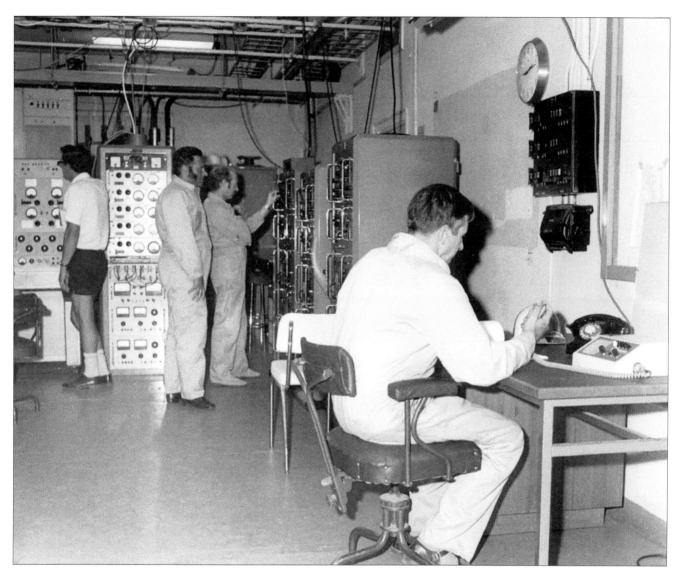

Figure 12.26 This rare view shows the Equipment Control room (EC2), during preparations for the launch of SL1081. The room was situated beneath the edge of the launch apron, and was of heavily reinforced construction. (See Figure 9.26 for an exterior view). The equipment on the left with the dials and knobs is the remote priming unit, the racks being observed in the centre are three telemetry receiving sets.[106]

(WRE \ University of Reading)

"Test Shop 1 was a large building with a green painted concrete floor. The main preparation area ran from one set of huge sliding doors to the other. On the left were the offices of the BAC staff and on the right were the labs for the attitude control staff from Marconi together with the preparation area for the canted fins and other vehicle items." [105]

The launch took place at 9.00 am local time on the 27th March. The mass of the head was 172 kg (379 lb) and it reached an apogee of 279 km (185 miles).

---

[105] Cruise (2008), *Skylark Ascending*, online article p.16, and *Prospero* number 5, Spring 2008, p.50.
[106] See Chapter 3 for further details of the test equipment.

Figure 12.27 The launch of SL1081.
(WRE \ Savigear et al. (1974), plate 4.2)

Figures 12.28 and 12.29 SL1081 some five seconds after launch, at a height of several km.
Left – the Goldfinch boost motor separates. Right – the Raven VI sustainer takes over.
(WRE \ University of Reading)

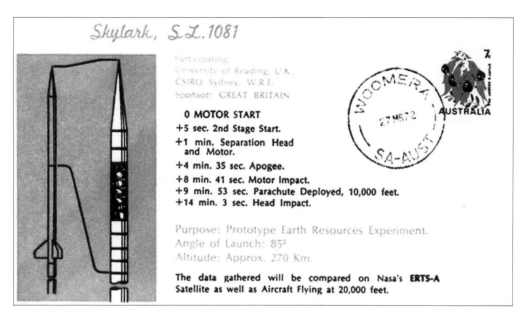

Figure 12.30 A summary of the flight of SL1081.

(Author's collection)

The flight was completely successful, and the payload head remained stabilised for just over 4.5 minutes. During this time, 135 frames of good quality photographic imagery were taken, and the payload with its precious film was successfully recovered by parachute:

Figure 12.31 The advance recovery team locate the SL1081 payload.[107] (The helicopter is an 'Alouette' – French for 'Skylark'!)

(WRE \ University of Reading)

[107] University of Reading, photo SL1081-27-03-72_12, originally in Geography department collection, now archived as MS 5492 in the Special Collections, the index may be accessed at *www.reading.ac.uk/adlib/search/advanced*, by setting the drop-down menu to 'Archives – Special Collections' and entering 'MS 5492' in the 'Reference' field , (or 'Skylark' in the 'title/description' field). (Last accessed August 2014).

Figure 12.32 SL1081 - The payload in virtually mint condition – just a slightly bent nose! [108]
(WRE \ University of Reading)

Figure 12.33 SL1081 – the ground team arrives.[109]
(WRE \ University of Reading)

---

[108] University of Reading, photo SL1081-27-03-72_16, originally in Geography department collection, now archived as MS 5492 in the Special Collections, the index may be accessed at *www.reading.ac.uk/adlib/search/advanced*, by setting the drop-down menu to 'Archives – Special Collections' and entering 'MS 5492' in the 'Reference' field. (Last accessed August 2014).

[109] University of Reading, photo SL1081-27-03-72_10, originally in Geography department collection.

Figure 12.34 The exposed F24 camera film being recovered from the payload of SL1081.
(WRE \ University of Reading, photo SL1081-27-03-72_8)

Figure 12.35 The spent SL1081 motor impacted the ground – the new motor parachute system apparently fitted appears not to have worked. The charred area indicates why during the Australian summer (November to April), the possibility of Skylark causing bush fires had to be taken into account.
(WRE \ University of Reading)

Afterwards, Mr Michael Heseltine, then UK minister for Aerospace, said, "Skylark will provide an inexpensive alternative to aircraft and satellites for those countries that seek to know more about the potentialities of their own territory." [110] It was stated that at a cost per launch of £75,000 to £100,000, [worth £756K to £2335K by 2011], [111] the Skylark system would provide coverage at about £0.1/km², compared with £1-£2 for an aircraft survey, i.e. 1/10 to 1/20th of the cost.

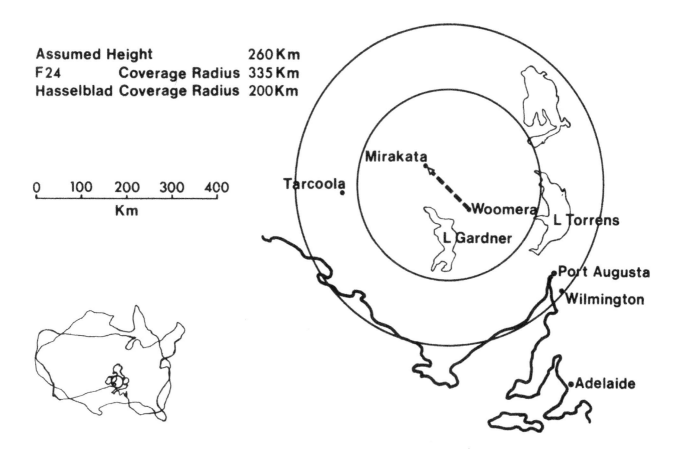

Assumed Height   260 Km
F24   Coverage Radius 335 Km
Hasselblad Coverage Radius 200 Km

Figure 12.36 The photographic coverage achieved by SL1081 around Woomera. The smaller circle represents the limited range of the single Hasselblad camera.
(Beattie (1974), figure 2)[112]

---

[110] Quoted by FLIGHT International, 27 April 1972, p.599. To put this in context, a few years before, in 1958, it was said that no less than 84% of the whole world's land surface was unmapped except at scales smaller than 1:75,000, and some 35% had no maps at all. (Brown, R. (1958), 'Progress of World Mapping', *The Times Atlas,* Vol.1, 1958).

[111] 2011 figures based on the "Historic Opportunity" and "Economic Cost" measures for a large project, from Lawrence H. Officer and Samuel H. Williamson, "Five Ways to Compute the Relative Value of a UK Pound Amount, 1270 to Present," MeasuringWorth, 2014, *www.measuringworth.com/ukcompare/* , last accessed August 2014.

[112] Journal of the British Interplanetary Society, Vol.27 no.1 (Jan.1974), p.15. Reproduced with permission.

The detailed purpose and description of the project is
neatly summarised by the following document:

DETAILS OF UNITED KINGDOM SOUNDING ROCKET MISSIONS FOR REMOTE SENSING OF EARTH
RESOURCES

1   <u>Test firing to prove the system in March 1972</u>

   <u>Location</u>

     South Australia. Firing from the permanent launch site at Woomera.

   Objectives

     Land survey and terrain mapping.

     Distribution of soil moisture in river basins.

     Spectral reflectance measurements for CSIRO, Mineral Research

     Laboratories, Australia.

   Payload (Photographic)

     Approximately 170 kg. incorporating two cameras.

     (i) Camera - F24 with Ross EMI F/4 lens, focal length 125 mm.

        Film - Kodak plus Aerographic type 648

        Spectral Bands - 0.5 to 0.7 μm, 0.47 to 0.6 μm, 0.59 to 0.70 μm.

        Ground Coverage - 88,000 sq.km., 80 frames

        Resolution - 100 m.

     (ii)Camera - Hasselblad 500 EL/70m with Zeiss F/2.8 lens, focal

        length 80 mm.

        Film - Kodak Aerochrome infra-red type 2443 false colour

        reversal.

        Spectral Band - 0.35 to 0.90 μm.

        Ground Coverage - 40,000 sq.km., 50 frames.

        Resolution - 150 m.

  Ground Truth Observations

    Soil samples, surface micro-morphology and vegetation. Aerial survey carried out

    by helicopter using the same film and multi-spectral camera (SDC).

Figure 12.37 This document provides details of the SL1081 mission.[113]

[113] *Details of UK Sounding Rocket Missions for Remote Sensing of Earth Resources* – two-sided document accompanying a letter from E.J.Lindsay of the DTI, dated 9 August 1973, in the "Remote Sensing from Rockets" document file of the Directorate of Overseas Surveys. (TNA: PRO OD 6/1604).

Seq. Nos	Launch date	Ref. (sponsor) Launch site	Config- uration	Apogee km (miles)	Experi- menters	Experiment(s)	Result
293 (7)	27 Mar. 1972	SL1081 (UK) Woomera (BS201)	Earth, Rav.6 +G	297 (185)	RAE	Test (Skylark technology) - remote sensing - proving of zenith pointing attitude control system & Earth resources photographic equipment	S

Table 12.5 A summary of SL1081.

Figure 12.38 An annotated view from space of the region surrounding Woomera. It was taken by SL1081 from a height of about 250 km (155 miles), and covers an area of around 300 x 300 km (186 x 186 miles). The 'lakes' are in fact salt pans. An F24 camera ("position 1"[115]) panchromatic photograph exposed through a yellow Wratten filter No.12. (500-700 nm).

(Savigear *et al.* (1977), Vol.II, plate 6.3)

---

[114] See Savigear *et al.* (1977), Vol.1, figure 4.11, for a diagram showing the F24 camera coverage positions.

Ted Chambers later commented:

>...[It] produced brilliant photographs of the area around Woomera and even extending as far as the town of Ceduna to the south. The detail was outstanding, showing roads, the differing vegetation, salt lakes and geographical features of great interest to the likes of the South Australian Mines Department. These photographs were freely distributed at the time, and a real first for Skylark...

Before the demise of the Woomera range as a trials venue, one could purchase locally such pictures for something like ten dollars each, which showed in some detail the layout of the range and the Woomera village and its surrounding countryside.

This was somewhat amusing because right up to the bitter end, all itinerants flying from Adelaide to Woomera by civil aircraft were warned by the friendly air hostesses that "Passengers are advised that the use of cameras in the Woomera area is prohibited".[114]

The camera installation was originally chosen without any particular performance or installation in mind, because of the limited objectives of the trial. The filter/emulsion combinations

Figure 12.39 This F24 camera view to the north east of Woomera ("position 3") was also taken by SL1081 from a height of about 250 km (155 miles). It shows Lake Eyre at the top, and in the mid-distance clouds with their shadows. As with the previous figure, it covers an area some 300 km square, as indicated on the topographical map overleaf.
(RAE / University of Reading, Photo BS201-7 No16)

---

[115] Chambers (2000), *Woomera, Its human face*, p.102.

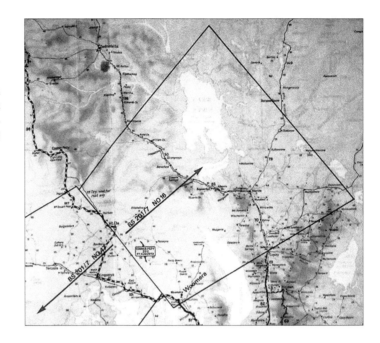

Figure 12.40 A map of the Woomera area in South Australia showing the extent of the photograph figure 12.39 on the previous page.
(BAC press release April 1972)

were simply selected to be broadly similar to those used in the Apollo 9 multiband photography experiment[116] – imagery that was well known and much assessed by users in the USA, and approximate to those used in ERTS.[117]

As noted above, fieldwork was carried out from Woomera around the time of the launch so that the usefulness of the rocket photography could be evaluated. Measurements and samples were taken of ground features to help determine just what the rocket photographs were capable of detecting. To aid this, some standard aerial photography was also carried out. These operations were carried out by members of the Department of Geography of the UK's University of Reading, and the Mineral Physics Section of the Australian Commonwealth Scientific and Industrial Research Organisation (CSIRO).

The geographers were interested in the ability to detect known surface rock, soil, landform and vegetation patterns, the physicists in the general evaluation of multispectral remote sensing techniques and their use in minerals search. The aerial photography was taken from an Alouette helicopter adapted with three aerial survey cameras, and used up to the 6000-metre ceiling of its flying height.

Panchromatic (black and white) prints were available three days after the rocket flight, and the quality of the images was

as good as expected, with resolution of the order of 100-150 metres, although narrower linear features such as fifteen-metre wide roads could be distinguished clearly. The broad scale terrain patterns, sand ridge belts and major geological structures stood out distinctly, and individual paddocks at Ceduna (near the coast) were well defined by their straight boundaries and individual tones. However, the multispectral techniques used were immediately recognised as being of limited value, the band-pass properties of the filters used in front of the camera being too coarse to allow for the differentiation of separate ground attributes.

The preliminary conclusion was that the rocket photographs came up to expectations in revealing atlas map scale ground features more boldly than had ever been seen before, but fell short of the standard that would be required for more detailed mapping of natural resources.[118] This pioneering work resulted in many articles and papers being written, culminating in a four hundred page two volume report from the University of Reading Department of Geography.[119]

Following the success of this prototype trial, a full-scale user trial was undertaken twelve months later with two Skylark launches from Argentina in March 1973. This is described in the next chapter.

---

[116] During their final four days in low-earth orbit in March 1969, the Apollo 9 crew took hundreds of colour photos of the Earth, using single, handheld cameras. They also conducted the SO65 experiment that employed an array of four Hasselblad cameras with different filters, mounted against a spacecraft window - a precursor to the ERTS programme. (NASA's ERTS-1 (Earth Resources Technology Satellite) (Later named Landsat 1) was launched on July 23, 1972.

[117] Simmons (1974), 'Rockets for Earth Environment Monitoring', p.5.

[118] Ridgeway and Hardy (1973), *Skylark over Woomera*, p.296.

[119] Savigear *et al.* (1977), *The Appraisal of Photography from Skylark SL1081 over Woomera…*

Skylark on movie film

Back in 1966, the UK's Central Office of Information (COI)[120] had considering making a film of Skylark for showing at the 1967 Montreal Exhibition (The Expo 67 World Fair).[121] They appear to have gone ahead with this, although the author has been unable to locate a copy. At the same time the SRC (Science Research Council) were also considering making a 20-minute colour film of Skylark,[122] but it is not clear if this proposal came to anything.

However, what did come to fruition in 1972, was a 16mm colour documentary film that included a feature about the Earth-sensing use of Skylark. This was one of a series made by the COI called 'Tomorrow Today', a magazine style film similar to the 'Tomorrow's World' programme then appearing on BBC television. The first six minutes of 'Tomorrow Today' number 117 explained the development of Skylark's Earth resources programme, with shots of the payload being tested, launches taking place and a simple animation showing how photographs would be taken from space. It included presenter Howard Williams interviewing Robert Ridgway of Reading University, who explained some of the results, including how the photographs of Lake Eyre (taken over South Australia by SL1081) had allowed scientists to recognise for the first time the significance of a second drainage channel coming in from the north. It is not clear when or how the film was shown to the public (perhaps it was a 'schools' programme), but the original script is now in the UK National Archives,[123] and the film itself has been archived by the British Film Institute in London, where it may be viewed by appointment on payment of a small fee.[124]

June 1972   S91

There were no Skylark launches in April or May, but the 25th June saw the launch of **S91** from Sardinia. This was an ESRO astronomy mission, with a Sun-stabilised payload that carried an MSSL experiment to measure the cosmic X-ray diffuse background. The measuring instrument used collimated X-ray detectors, and extended to the northern hemisphere similar observations carried out using SL1001 launched from Woomera in January 1971.

The S91 experiment worked well, observing both the X-ray background and discrete objects. However a sentence in the MSSL annual report for 1972 reveals frustration caused by political problems in the background – "The run down of ESRO staff on data handling has both delayed the receipt of results and greatly reduced the work the organisation would normally have undertaken on the basic information".[125]

Another problem was that the recovery parachute failed,[126] and the attempted sea recovery was unsuccessful, and the attitude camera was not recovered. However, unlike S89 the previous October, observations were obtained, as a significant amount of data was returned by telemetry.[127]

The cause of the cosmic X-ray background was one of the big astronomical questions of the day, and indeed would be investigated by astronomers for decades to come. MSSL's next venture in this field would be SL402 in October.

July 1972   SL1191, SL1183

Next was a rare military use of Skylark, the first of the 'DAWD' rounds,[128] a series of military trials that would test various design aspects of the 'Chevaline' upgrade to Britain's Polaris nuclear weapon delivery system.

SL1191 was launched on 5th July from Woomera. It was designated test 'S1', and was:

> ...a test of the platform from which the decoys were to be launched: it was a partial failure. The lessons learned from S1 were successfully incorporated in S2 when the platform operated well.[129]

S2 was SL1291, launched a year later in July 1973. (See the next chapter for details of this and Chevaline).

Two of the problems with SL1191 are known - there was a tailing off in the burning of the Raven VI motor, and the ACU took longer than usual to acquire.[130] The motor problem was undesirable as it affected the clean separation of the motor and the payload, but further firings indicated it was an isolated fault.[131]

---

[120] Established in 1946 after the demise of the wartime Ministry of Information, the COI was active for 66 years until 2012. During that time, it was responsible for producing hundreds of public information films, many of which can be viewed online at *www.nationalarchives.gov.uk/films/* (Last accessed August 2014).

[121] Minutes of the 3rd Skylark Policy Meeting, November 1966, p.10, item 4.1. (TNA: PRO AVIA 92/144).

[122] Minutes of the 4th Skylark Policy Meeting, February 1967, p.16, item 3.16. (TNA: PRO AVIA 92/144).

[123] TNA document INF 6/1549.

[124] 'Tomorrow Today and Living Tomorrow' No 117, see *www.bfi.org.uk* for contact and archive viewing details. (Last accessed August 2014).

[125] MSSL (1972), *Report of the MSSL 1 January 1972 - 30 September 1972*, part B, p.5.

[126] BAe (1990), *Record of Skylark Launches 1957-1990*.

[127] Fabian (1974), 'Galactic Contributions to the Isotropy of the Cosmic X-ray Background'.

[128] Minutes of the 24th Skylark Policy Meeting, December 1972, item 4. (TNA: PRO AVIA 92/145).

[129] McDowell re TNA-PRO DEFE documents, personal communication, April 2010.

[130] Minutes of the 23rd Skylark Policy Meeting, September 1972, item 4. (TNA: PRO AVIA 92/145).

[131] Minutes of the 24th Skylark Policy Meeting, December 1972, para. 5.1. (TNA: PRO AVIA 92/145).

SL1183

Later that month, on 20th July, the second and final UK launch of a Skylark took place from Aberporth on the Welsh coast.

This proving launch tested a new simple single rail transportable launcher designed by BAC and constructed by RAE Farnborough. It was designed for use in the new Skylark Earth observation programme, in particular the forthcoming Argentine exercise.[132] It was cheaper than the general-purpose transportable launcher developed by MAN of Germany, which had been tested by the previous Aberporth launch in January 1971. (The MAN launcher cost about £200K in total, made up of £50K for the mechanical hardware, £100K for the electronics and £50K for the shelter.[133])

As for its predecessor (Skylark LT.1), in order to limit its range, SL1183 was powered only by a Goldfinch boost motor, and the dummy payload was of concrete.

The new launcher was exhibited by BAC at the Farnborough Air Show that summer.

September 1972	S94, S77/2

There were no Skylark launches in August, but apparently, on September 20th **S94** was launched from Sardinia with a Sun-stabilised astronomy payload, designed to make X-ray studies of the Crab Nebula.[134] Information on S94 is scarce, and some sources say it was launched on November 20th.[135]

Figure 12.41 The second and final Skylark launch from the UK.
(RAE/BAC/MSSL)

Figure 12.42 M1, the Crab Nebula, a composite image taken by the Hubble Space Telescope.[136]
(NASA/ESA - J. Hester and A. Loll (Arizona State University) - STScI-PRC2005-37)

---

[132] Flight International magazine, 10 August 1972, p.218.
[133] Minutes of the 18th Skylark Policy Meeting, June 1971, item 2. (TNA: PRO AVIA 92/145).
[134] BAe (1990), *Record of Skylark Launches 1957-1990.*
[135] For instance McDowell (2009), *List of Skylark Launches.*
[136] This Crab Nebula image was assembled from 24 individual Wide Field and Planetary Camera 2 exposures taken in October 1999, January 2000, and December 2000. (NASA press release STScI-PRC2005-37).

The Crab Nebula is a supernova remnant in the constellation of Taurus. At X-ray and gamma ray energies above 30 KeV, it is generally the strongest persistent source in the sky.

With the run-down of the ESRO sounding rocket programme, S94 was the 56th [137] and last Skylark to be launched from Sardinia, the first launch having taken place eight years earlier, in July 1964. (A reunion took place at the base of the tower in 1994, see Figure 16.20).

S77/2 was launched from Kiruna on 24th September, and carried a similar RSRS experiment to S77/1 launched in March. It too had a separating payload and was launched into an auroral feature; although this time, the changes in intensity were not observed simultaneously, showing they were spatial in character.[138]

| October 1972 | S105, SL1022, SL402, SL1003 |

S105 – the 300th Skylark Launch

In October two MSSL payloads were launched from Scandinavia to study suprathermal electrons[139] in aurorae. The first was on a Petrel rocket launched from Andøya in Norway, but unfortunately, this provided no results because of a rocket system failure. However the second, on ESRO Skylark S105 launched from Kiruna in Sweden, was successfully fired into the recovery phase of an exceptionally bright aurora. The payload comprised two electrostatic analysers from MSSL to measure the energy spectrum of electrons, two retarding potential analysers to measure ion density, a magnetometer gauge and photometers.[140]

Figures 12.43 and 12.44 SL1022 is launched into a clear dawn sky, two views taken a very short time apart. The unusual viewpoint shows other launchers used at LA2, on the left is the beam launcher used for Falstaff,[141] at the centre right the Australian 'Long Tom' launcher.

(WRE \ Hazell)

[137] 54 sponsored by ESRO, plus two for the German programme.

[138] Massey & Robins (1986), *History of British Space Science,* p.325. See also Bryant (1981), 'Rocket studies of particle structure associated with auroral arcs'.

[139] Electrons with an energy greater than that possible by thermal means, typically arriving as particles from the Sun and being involved in the creation of aurorae. Apollo 12 took a suprathermal ion detector to the Moon in 1969.

[140] MSSL (1972), *Report of the MSSL 1 January 1972 - 30 September 1972,* part 2, p.3.

[141] See Figure 14.44 for a close-up view.

Skylark Serial No.
S.L. 1022

Spin stabilised vehicle with separation of the payload into two sections, launched at 05.09 hours, 19th October, 1972 at Woomera, South Australia.

TIME
    0 Sec.   Ignition
+   6 Sec.   2nd Stage fires.
+ 70 Sec.   Nose cone jettison.
+ 71 Sec.   Sheffield & Tasmanian Universities experiments start working.
+ 73 Sec.   Forward section jettison.
+ 77 Sec.   Start of calibration pulses.
+ 205 Sec.   Apogee at 502 kft (150 KM).
+ 372 Sec.   Head Separation.

After nose cone jettison No. 1 Experiment separates from No. 2 and moves forward to allow No. 2 to look forward. At 71 Sec. Experiments 2 and 3 switch on and doors covering No. 3 field of view open to allow No. 3 to look out sideways. Payload 222 Kgrams, 4 metres long.

Figure 12.45 This commemorative envelope for SL1022 was postmarked at Woomera on the day of the flight.

(Author's collection)

Seq. Nos	Launch date	Ref. (sponsor) Launch site	Config- uration	Apogee km (miles)	Experi- menters	Experiment(s)	Result
301 (15)	19 Oct. 1972	SL1022 (UK) Woomera (BS205)	Un, Rav.8 +C	143 (89)	Bel	Aeronomy - resonance scattering of sunlight by upper atmosphere (photometers)	S
					Shf	Ionosphere - ion composition (cryogenic mass spectrometer)	F
					Tas	Astronomy - X-ray observations?	?

Table 12.6 A summary of SL1022.

Analysis of the data was very seriously held up because of delays by ESRO in digitising the telemetry tape data, but results were eventually obtained. These helped explain how aurorae are formed, by obtaining energy spectra of very low energy electrons with better resolution than previous experiments, thus throwing light on the loss processes between electrons arriving from the Sun and atmospheric nitrogen and oxygen.[142]

By September, campaigns 11 and 12 of the SRC (UK National) Programme had been combined into one campaign of five rounds at Woomera, to be completed by the end of the year.[143] The first to be launched was SL1022 on 19th October, in which the payload was designed to separate in two after launch.[144] This unusual technique was used so that two forward-looking experiments could be flown on the same rocket.

Unexpectedly, the commemorative envelope above provides a useful contemporary summary of the flight of SL1022.

The Belfast experiment listed above was an 'Airglow' study, and it successfully observed the resonant scattering of the early-morning sunlight. Evidence for the existence of metallic atoms and ions at an altitude near 100km was found.[145]

Unfortunately, as indicated in the table, the Sheffield experiment was a failure, although it is not known why. However, it was repeated more successfully on SL1005 in December. Nothing is known of the 'Tasmanian' experiment, the only evidence for which is the commemorative envelope (Figure 12.45), although it may have been an X-ray astronomy experiment similar to those launched on SL728 and SL727 in 1970.

[142] MSSL (1974), *Report of the MSSL 1 October 1973 – 30 September 1974*, part 2, p.3, and Byrne & Marsden (1975).

[143] Minutes of the 23rd Skylark Policy Meeting, September 1972, item 8. (TNA: PRO AVIA 92/145).

[144] BAe (1990), *Record of Skylark Launches 1957-1990*.

[145] Byrne & Marsden (1975), 'Concentration of metallic neutrals and ions by resonance fluorescence scattering', also Massey & Robins (1986), *History of British Space Science*, p.291.

SL402 was the fourth and last Skylark to be flown with a Stage 3 Attitude Control Unit, although only the second to use Moon pointing as such.[146]

The first experiment was from MSSL, and designed to help determine whether the cosmic diffuse X-ray background was universal in origin, or came from particular sources. The method used was to search for a possible absorption of low energy diffuse X-rays in the Small Magellanic Cloud.

The second SL402 experiment was from the UK's Meteorological Office, and was designed to measure the lunar UV albedo and the Earth's night-time ozone concentration.

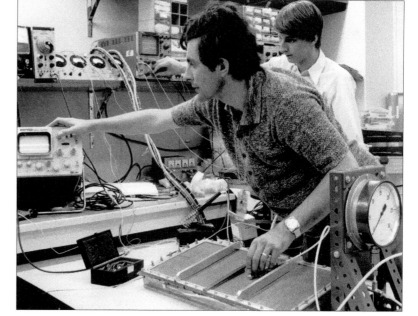

Figure 12.46 The MSSL X-ray detector instrument during payload integration of SL402 at BAC Filton, Bristol, UK.
(BAC \ Rapley)

Figure 12.47 Not long to go! SL402's MSSL experiment being prepared at Woomera on 22 September 1972 by Chris Rapley, aided by Barry Lee.
(WRE \ Rapley)

[146] Skylarks SL401 to 404 flew the Stage 3 ACUs, SL401 (March 1970) was the other to point at the Moon.

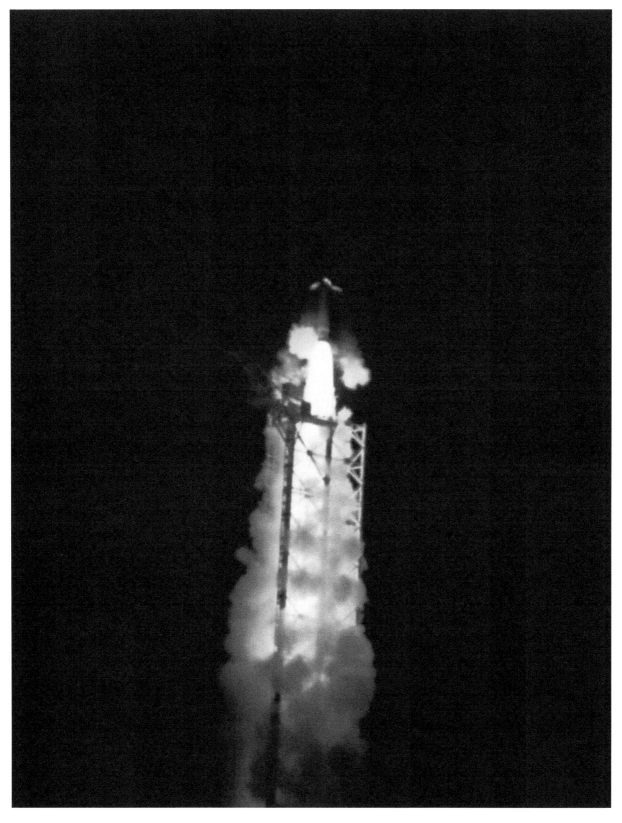

Figure 12.48 SL402 clears the Woomera launch tower at 22:21 hours local time Monday 23rd October, heading for space with two astronomy experiments on board. The exhaust glow from the three pairs of small Imp spin-up motors can be seen at the top.

(WRE \ Rapley)

Figure 12.49 This commemorative cover provides further details of SL402's flight.

(Author's collection)

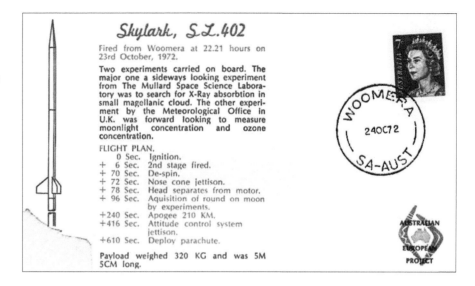

The launch went as scheduled; the nose cone jettisoned successfully, and the ACU correctly pointed at the Moon. The Meteorological Office experiment successfully measured the lunar UV albedo and the night-time ozone concentration, but unfortunately, the MSSL experiment failed after 20 seconds because of gas loss from the proportional counter supply system. However the parachute recovery system worked, and tests on the recovered payload revealed an intermittent fault in a gas valve, the design of which was improved for future use.[147]

Figures 12.50 and 12.51 Back to Earth – SL402's payload and motor remains located.

(WRE \ Rapley)

[147] MSSL (1973), *Report of the MSSL 1 October 1972 – 30 September 1973*, part 3, p.9.

There is an interesting personal story behind the MSSL experiment failure on SL402:

> After Chris Rapley had joined MSSL, the Laboratory Director, Robert Boyd, became a key mentor. His attitude was simple: 'if you're not making mistakes, you're not working at the edge… if you're not working at the edge, you shouldn't be here'.
>
> Boyd's philosophy was thoroughly tested a year or so later when Chris' first rocket payload [that on SL402] failed. Chris went to see him, in abject misery. Boyd lived by his word, and asked. 'Has the world ended?'. Chris felt it had, but had to observe, as a scientist, that it did, indeed, still exist. 'I wanted you to push the limits, and that means taking risks. I'll find you more money to keep studying… But go sit on a hill, and ask yourself… 'Is there anything I could have done that would have prevented this?'.
>
> This was a crucial lesson for Chris. On that hill, he realised that he had had some concerns about features of the payload. But 'experts' had assured him it was OK, and that he need not trouble himself. He realised then that he should never again allow himself to be browbeaten by anyone, and that he should always listen to that small, quiet inner voice that sometimes niggles you, and says you need to attend to something which may be going wrong.[148]

Thus, despite its failure to achieve the experimental objectives, the experience gained on SL402 was successfully utilised on SL1203, then being planned for launch in February 1974 with a similar but more ambitious experiment.

26 Oct 1972	SL1003

By September 1972, another MSSL payload had reached Woomera, and on 26th October 1972 was launched on

SL1003. This was an ACU stabilised solar X-ray astronomy mission, the two identical instruments combining rotation modulation collimator techniques used on SL973 (October 1971) with the modified Bragg crystal spectrometer as used on SL903 (December 1971). This provided spatial as well as spectral information, allowing several active areas on the solar disc to be observed at once.[149] The payload included a pinhole camera, to correlate the results.

The text of the associated commemorative envelope reads: "Purpose of the experiments: To study the line spectrum emitted by the sun in the wave length 10.5A and to compare the emission from the plage regions and background simultaneously using a modulation collimator and crystal spectrometer. To obtain solar x-ray photographs using a pinhole camera."

The mission was a success, and by September 1973, data analysis was complete and a thesis prepared.[150] The flight showed that the instrument technique worked, and was able to compare active and less active regions on the Sun's disc. It also revealed that the instrument would be particularly suitable for use on a satellite for observing long-term changes, but that it was also possible to make interesting observations during a short rocket flight.

November 1972	S95

On Thursday 2nd November 1972 the 82nd [151] and last ESRO sponsored Skylark was launched, a Sun-pointing solar physics and astronomy mission fired from Woomera. It carried a solar X-ray imaging experiment from the Space Research Laboratory at Utrecht in Belgium, and an astronomy instrument from CEN (Centre d'Etude Nucleaire) in France to study X-rays from Pulsars.

Seq. Nos	Launch date	Ref. (sponsor) Launch site	Config-uration	Apogee km (miles)	Experi-menters	Experiments	Result
303 (17)	26 Oct. 1972	SL1003 (UK) Woomera	Sun, Rav.6 +C	194 (121)	MSSL	Solar physics - X-rays (crystal spectrometer & rotating collimator)	S
					MSSL	Solar physics - X-ray photography (pinhole camera)	S

Table 12.7 A summary of SL1003.

[148] University of Bristol, from the webpage *www.bristol.ac.uk/pace/graduation/honorary-degrees/hondeg09/rapley.html* , last accessed August 2014. Chris Rapley went on to become Associate Director of MSSL, and later, Director of the Science Museum in London!
[149] Brabban, Glencross and Rosenberg (1975), 'Crystal spectrometer studies of the sun employing a rotation modulation collimator', p.355.
[150] MSSL (1973), *Report of the MSSL 1 October 1972 – 30 September 1973*, part 1, p.4.
[151] Some sources say 83rd – but this is only true if the 'phantom' S58 on 19/10/70 is counted!

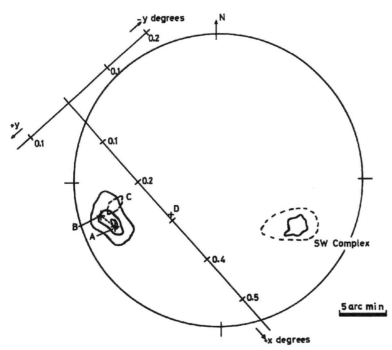

Figure 12.52 This drawing shows the path tracked across the Sun by the SL1003 MSSL pinhole camera. The capability of the main instrument allowed both spectral and spatial X-ray observations of areas A–D.

(Brabban, Glencross and Rosenberg (1975), figure 4)

Figure 12.53 This commemorative envelope provides details of ESRO's last Skylark mission.

(Author's collection)

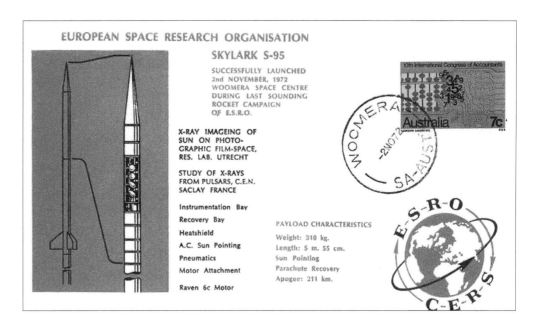

The ESRO decision to withdraw from sounding rocket activities meant that ESTEC[152] had sounding rocket equipment to dispose of, and in cases where ESRO would not be completing scheduled rounds themselves, kits of parts would be issued to appropriate members of the organisation.[153] There was also an outstanding Stage 5 ACU round which BAC would be launching under an ESTEC contract.[154] During the year, a new agreement on the use of the ESRANGE (Andøya/Kiruna) sounding rocket range had been signed by Germany, France, Belgium, Switzerland, Sweden and the UK, making the range available for use by direct negotiation from these ESRO member states.[155]

---

[152] ESTEC = European Space Research and Technology Centre. Located in the Netherlands, it is now the largest ESA site.
[153] Minutes of the 21st Skylark Policy Meeting, March 1972, item 9. (TNA: PRO AVIA 92/145).
[154] Minutes of the 24th Skylark Policy Meeting, December 1972, item 9. (TNA: PRO AVIA 92/145).
[155] Minutes of the 22nd Skylark Policy Meeting, June 1972, item 9. (TNA: PRO AVIA 92/145).

| December 1972 | SL1202, SL1005 |

SL1202 was an astronomy mission launched from Woomera on 7th December. The payload was a Leicester experiment designed to very accurately measure the position of the X-ray source GX5-1, using the lunar occultation method successfully employed on SL1002 in October the previous year. Unfortunately, a vehicle system failure meant that the experiment failed. The problem was a 'despin-failure'. As can be seen from the launch sequence below, the 'Yo-Yo' despin device was supposed to operate one minute three seconds into the flight, its purpose being to cancel out the spin of the rocket before the payload was released. Subsequent investigation revealed:

> It was almost certain that what had happened was that duplication of a system to ensure reliability had resulted in the opposite effect. Two explosive choppers were fitted in each system to cut the YOYO wire. Both had functioned but the inner one had operated fractionally before the outer one so that the latter had attempted to cut a moving wire, which had consequently jammed in the mechanism.[156]

The design was modified, but this was scant consolation for the Leicester experimenters, because the next occasion on which such an occultation would be visible from Woomera would be in ten years time! The commemorative envelope for SL1202[157] provided this planned sequence:

Minutes	Secs	
	0	Goldfinch Boost Ignition
	6	Raven Motor Ignition
1	3	Yo-Yo Despin
1	5	Nose Cone Jettison
1	7	Head/Motor Separation
1	7	ACU Eyelid Release
1	9	ACU Gas On
4	21	Apogee (831 ft.)[sic] 253 km.
7	30	ACU/Head Separation
10	0	Parachute Deployment
8	17	Motor Impact
14	10	Head and Parachute Impact

SL1005

The UK's Woomera campaign 11/12 ended with the launch of **SL1005** on Monday 11th December. This carried the fifth successive stabilised Skylark payload into space, powered by a Raven VI motor and the first Cuckoo III boost motor.

The Cuckoo III[158] was a fast burning version of the Cuckoo IA boost motor used on Skylark, and had been under development for several years with low priority and limited funding. The SRC required the Cuckoo III for a particular round, but were not prepared to finance the completion of its development. Hence, it was decided to provide an economical flight test by using one to replace a standard Cuckoo boost motor on a scheduled launch,[159] and this took place on SL1005.

The launch was a success. The payload included several experiments, those from Belfast and Sheffield were the same as flown on SL1022 in October, and were partially successful. That from the UK Meteorological Office was designed to measure molecular oxygen concentration using ionisation chamber, and may have been carried out in conjunction with the Adelaide Meteorological Office. This was the same as flown on the ill-fated SL801 in November 1969, but this time success was achieved. There appears also to have been an ancillary experiment from the University of Adelaide, but of that, nothing is known.

---

[156] Frank Hazell, minutes of the 20th Skylark Policy Meeting, December 1972, para. 4.2. (TNA: PRO AVIA 92/145).
[157] Author's collection.
[158] Designated Cuckoo III as Cuckoo II was an enhanced version of Cuckoo IB used on Black Knight. (See Harlow (1990), 'Black Knight Upper Stages', Table 1).
[159] Minutes of the 22nd Skylark Policy meeting, June 1972, p.4, item 5. (TNA: PRO AVIA 92/145).

Seq. Nos	Launch date	Ref. (sponsor) Launch site	Config- uration	Apogee km (miles)	Experi- menters	Experiments	Result
306 (20)	11 Dec. 1972	SL1005 (UK) Woomera	Sun, Rav.6 +C(III)	195 (121)	Bel	Aeronomy - resonance scattering (photomultipliers)	Ps
					Shf	Ionosphere - ion composition of lower ionosphere (cryogenic mass spectrometer)	Ps
					MO	Aeronomy - molecular oxygen concentration (ionisation chambers)	S
					Adel	?	?
					RAE	Test (Skylark technology) – 1st flight of Cuckoo III	S

Table 12.8 A summary of SL1005.

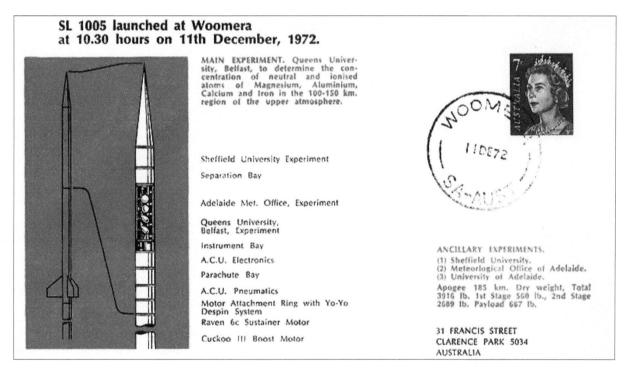

Figure 12.54 This commemorative envelope provides details of SL1005.

(Author's collection)

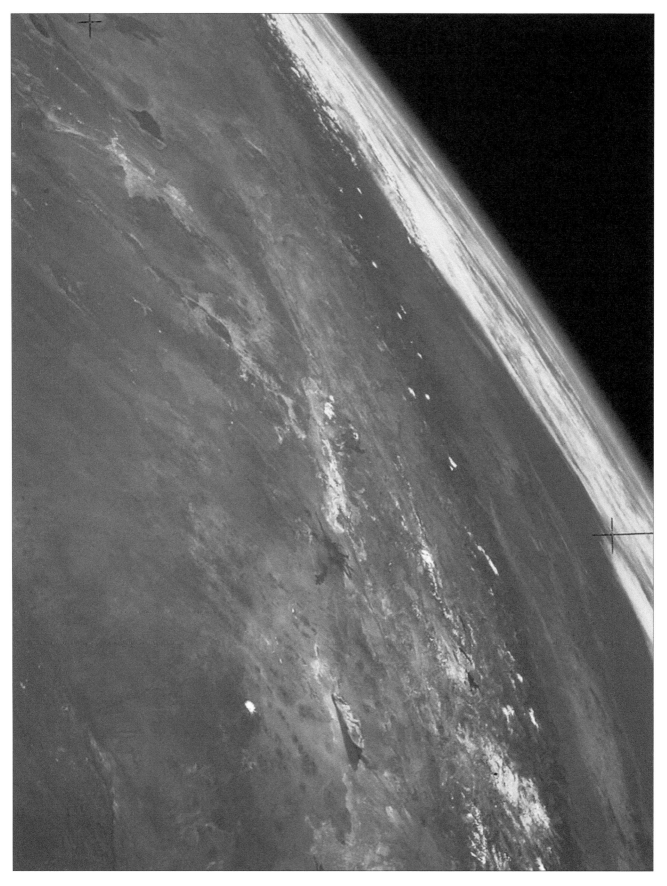

Figure 13.1 The snow-capped peaks of the Andes with the Pacific Ocean beyond, as photographed in March 1973 by SL1182 looking west from an altitude of about 200 km (125 miles) above central Argentina. (F24 large format air-survey camera with 127 mm lens and Kodak Aerochrome 2443 false-colour infrared film).

(RAE \ University of Reading)

CHAPTER 13

(1973)

ARGENTINA AND SCANDINAVIA

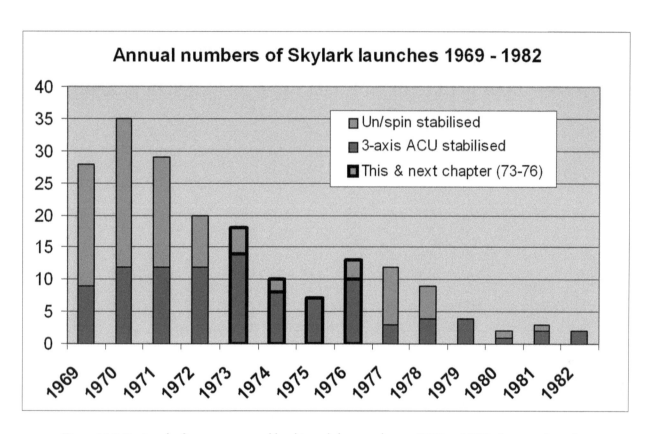

Figure 13.2 During the four years covered by this and the next chapter (1973 to 1976), the annual number of Skylark launches continued to decline from the peak of 35 in 1970. The total number during this four-year period was only 48, compared to 112 in the preceding four years.

The demise of the ESRO sounding rocket programme in 1972 marked the beginning of the decline in the fortunes of Skylark. In 1973, the annual number of launches reduced again, although in contrast some of the payloads became very sophisticated.

Despite this fall in the number of launches, the following chapters are some of the most detailed in this book, partly because the payloads were more complex, and partly because more recent records and recollections are available.

THE CHALLENGES FACING SKYLARK FROM 1973

From the scientific user point of view, satellites were taking over space science work, particularly for astronomical observations - "the era of the scientific satellite had arrived".

This trend was reflected in the MSSL annual reports. In the eight pages of the 1972-73 publically available report,[1] some 67% was devoted to satellite experiments, and 31% to sounding rocket work (mostly Skylark). By 1978,[2] the proportions were 71% and 11%.

---

[1] UCL (1974), 'MSSL report for 1972 – 1973' as published by the Royal Astronomical Society. Explanatory note: these early MSSL annual reports appeared in two forms (i) a shorter 'UCL' version that appeared in the *Quarterly Journal of the Royal Astronomical Society*, and (ii) a fuller 'in-house' 'MSSL' version that the author has viewed at MSSL, Holmbury House. From now on, these footnote references follow that pattern.

[2] UCL (1979), 'MSSL report for 1977-1978' as published by the Royal Astronomical Society.

Figure 13.3 A Skylark (with Goldfinch boost motor) and attendants outside building Q65 at the RAE Farnborough open day in 1973.
(RAE \ FAST)

At this time, satellite experiments included those on British scientific satellites. Ariel 4 had been launched in 1971, and although it was switched off in May 1973, it was reactivated later in the year to provide additional data for use in conjunction with sounding rocket observations.[3] In 1974, the very successful Ariel 5 would be launched, as described in the next chapter. These events provide a good illustration of the evolution of space technology, as some of the scientific instruments on board had evolved from those used on Skylark.

Despite the move to satellite experiments, towards the end of 1973 Professor R.L.F.Boyd, head of MSSL wrote:

> I foresee an important role for sounding rockets for several years yet, especially in the study of rapid variations of cosmic X-ray sources.[4]

Moreover, in 1971, a NASA document had reported:

> With the coming of scientific satellites, sounding rockets temporarily seemed obsolete for space research. But their intrinsic simplicity and low cost, their short lead times, and the informality of sounding rocket research have effectively erased that stigma.[5]

Skylark Exhibited

The RAE continued to hold its annual Farnborough air show and open days, and in 1973 Skylark was exhibited as shown on the left.

Managing Skylark

In 1973, the Procurement Executive of the UK Ministry of Defence was still managing the Skylark Project by means of the quarterly Policy Meetings that had begun in 1966. Each meeting brought together about twenty people from government and industry, representing government organisations such as the DTI (Department of Trade and Industry)[6], various civil service administrative departments, agencies such as RSRS at Slough, RAE Space Department, RPE Westcott, and the industrial contractors BAC at Filton, and MSDS/ Elliott[7] from Frimley.

The meeting in March 1973 (the 25th) was concerned with a typical range of matters. These included promoting commercial exploitation (in particular the Earth Resources use) and details of Skylark's manufacture and procurement. On the technical side, there were PDS[8] problems to solve, such

---

[3] Massey and Robins (1986), *History of British Space Science*, p.103.

[4] MSSL (1973), *Report of the MSSL 1st October 1972 – 30 September 1973*, Part 1, Introduction.

[5] Corliss (1971), *NASA Sounding Rockets 1958-1968, A Historical Summary*, Chapter 12.

[6] A change of UK Government in 1970 (Edward Heath had become Prime Minister) had resulted in departmental changes, there was a new Ministry of Aviation Supply, which subsequently merged with the Board of Trade to form the Department of Trade and Industry, and also a new Procurement Executive of the Ministry of Defence which took over supply of Skylarks. See for instance Godwin (2007), p.253.

[7] Elliott Bros at Frimley (ACU development) had become part of Marconi Space and Defence Systems as a result of a complex series of company takeovers and mergers in the late 1960s.

[8] The PDS (Post Design Services) function is to address the many technical problems that arise after any product has been released for manufacture.

as parachute recovery and ignition unit redesign, and technical improvements such as more powerful motors and an inertial version of the ACU.

The meeting also monitored the success or otherwise of Skylark in the current campaigns such as that at Woomera, and looked at the long term planning requirements. In particular, the 'SRC Facilities Working Group' had expressed an interest in using one Skylark 7 and three Skylark 12s for their future geophysics programme, and the introduction of Skylark 8 to replace Skylark 7 rounds from 1975 onwards. (See below).

Another important aspect was monitoring costs and applying for new funding, the former being the responsibility of 'SPC' (Space Projects Costs), and for new funding, approval had to be obtained from the 'SPGC' (Space Policy & Grants Committee). Regarding funding, the lack of a national space agency becomes apparent - Skylark was the responsibility of no single government body,[9] and appears to have proceeded on a 'grace and favour' basis, as the civil service[10] and Treasury saw fit. (For many years, the Treasury had occupied a position of great importance in relation to science, and it had in essence been the *de facto* science policymaking body).[11]

Stabilised Skylarks

From August 1964 until March 1968, all experiments flown on stabilised Skylarks had been concerned with direct observation of the Sun. However from July 1968, when the first Skylark experiment was flown which looked away from the Sun to a celestial source, cosmic observations had become more and more common, and in 1974 accounted for all but one of the seven[12] stabilised scientific missions. This trend was accompanied by the steady growth of experimental equipment in terms of size, weight and complexity, which in turn imposed demands for more powerful propulsion and better stabilisation facilities.[13]

Towards the end of 1972, Professor Boyd of MSSL had also been looking forward to the availability of the star-pointing (Stage 5) ACU:

> The next three year grant period is one in which the capital invested in the stage V Skylark ACU could be increasingly realised and it is with some concern that I learn that the supply may not be adequate for the programme I propose.[14]

	Stage 1	Stage 3	Stage 5	Magnetic pointing
1964	2			
1965	2			
1966	3			
1967	3			
1968	3	1		
1969	8	1		
1970	6	1	1	
1971	5		1	
1972	5	1		
1973	5		2	
1974	3		2	1
Totals	45	4	6	1

Table 13.1 Stabilised Skylark launches to the end of 1974 showing the Stage 5 ACU coming into use. (UK civilian sponsored launches only.)

(Based on Reed (1974), table 2)

Figure 13.4 The Rook IV test vehicle (Ranger 32) ready for launching at Aberporth in 1967.

(Harmer (1972), figure 2)

---

[9]   See for instance Acton (1974), 'Some Aspects of the Management of the Science Research Council's Space Activities'.

[10]   In June 1972, it was said that "all research work was now funded by the DTI", but this appears to have been separate from the running costs for the "Skylark project". (Minutes of the 22nd Policy Meeting June 1972, p.4).

[11]   Godwin (2007), *The Skylark Rocket*, p.161.

[12]   The apparent disagreement with Table 13.1 is because there was one German as well as six British missions, see Appendix 3.

[13]   Reed J.W. (1974), *An Historical Review of Stabilisation Systems for the Skylark Rocket*, p.5.

[14]   MSSL (1972), *Report of the MSSL 1st January 1972 – 30 September 1973*, Part B, Introduction.

Motor	Time of burning (s)	Nominal Thrust		Total Impulse	
		Lb	N	Lb s	N s
Rook III	5.5	73300	326 000	442 000	1 960 000
Rook IV	6.65	66700	296 000	478 000	2 120 000
Raven VI	30	15000	66 500	410 000	1 820 000
Raven VIII	30	10000	44 500	340 000	1 510 000
Raven X	16.8	28000	124 000	493 000	2 190 000

Table 13.2 The performance of Rook and Raven motors current in 1972.[17]

VEHICLE ENHANCEMENTS - a new motor for Skylark

By 1973, there were two variations of Raven sustainer motors being used on Skylark. These were the Raven VIII (nominal thrust 10,000 lbf / 44.5kN) and the more powerful Raven VI (50% more nominal thrust at 15,000 lbf / 66.5kN).[15]

However, in the background, the RPE (Rocket Propulsion Establishment) at Westcott had continued to develop new motors. For instance, a few years earlier, it had developed the Rook IV, a more powerful version of the 17-inch solid propellant motor used by the RAE Aerodynamics Department to launch single and multi-stage free-flight test vehicles. This motor had been successfully flight tested from Aberporth in 1967.[16]

The RPE went on to develop the Raven X, with a burning time midway between the Rook (6 seconds) and Raven (30 seconds) motors, and this was successfully test fired in January 1970.

The Raven X used an improved high-energy propellant, coupled with a high-loading density, to provide not only a shorter burning time, but also increased performance compared with the Raven VI then in use on Skylark.

It had been developed by RPE solely for possible use in free-flight tests, filling a gap in the range of motors available, (perhaps numbered as Raven 'X' rather than 'IX' on a 'Project X' basis). However as early as 1967 there had been mention of an improved Raven, the Raven XI, as a possible means of meeting the SRC's longer term requirement of 600 lb (272 kg) gross payload (90 lb (41 kg) net scientific payload) to 250 km.[18] (This compares with the 600 lb to 210 km the Goldfinch/Raven VI combination was designed for).

Development without a budget – a case study

The development of the Raven XI for Skylark was a slow and laborious process, aggravated by the lack of funding, as the following account shows. Readers with a weak disposition are advised to skip the rest of this section!

The Raven XI was based on the Raven X, but with the burning time restored to 30 seconds, and with a total impulse of about 20% greater than the most powerful version then in use on Skylark, the Raven VI.[19] However, R&D work proceeded slowly, and in April 1969, propellant difficulties were reported.[20] Then in June that year a discussion document was produced on the technical possibility of an alternative 21 inch motor, which would lift 600 lb to over 400 km.[21] By September difficulty was being experienced with the pressing of the Raven XI charge, and it was agreed to cost the R&D required for the 21 inch motor.[22] By December the Raven XI had been ground fired but the motor casing had failed, and "it was no longer considered as a possibility for Skylark".[23]

Against this background, in September 1970 the Skylark Policy Meeting considered five alternative proposals for a more powerful Skylark motor.[24] These were:

[15] RPE Westcott (1968), *Index to Solid Propellant Motors*, p.15.

[16] Harmer (1972), *Flight-test results for two new versions of the Rook/Raven solid propellant rocket motor.*

[17] Harmer (1972), *Flight-test results for two new versions of the Rook/Raven solid propellant rocket motor*, Table 1.

[18] *Skylark Policy and Programme – Second Review*, document Ref. DS/55/01 (6th November 1967), item 3.3.2, written by 'Space 1(c)' (Ministry of Aviation), distributed before the fifth Skylark Policy meeting on 28th November 1967. (TNA: PRO AVIA 92/144).

[19] RPE Westcott (1968), *Index to Solid Propellant Motors*, p.15.

[20] Minutes of the 10th Skylark Policy meeting, April 1969, para. 3.3.6. (TNA: PRO AVIA 92/144).

[21] Hazell, J.F. (June 1969), *Higher Performance Sounding Rocket,* distributed with the agenda for the 11th Policy meeting September 1969. (TNA: PRO AVIA 92/144).

[22] Minutes of the 11th Skylark Policy meeting, September 1969, items 9.1 and 10. (TNA: PRO AVIA 92/144).

[23] Minutes of the 12th Skylark Policy meeting, December 1969, item 7.3. (TNA: PRO AVIA 92/144).

[24] Minutes of the 15th Skylark Policy meeting, September 1970, item 3. (TNA: PRO AVIA 92/144).

- The Raven Mark XI
- IMI[25] propellant in a Raven case
- CTPB[26] propellant in a Raven case
- A 21 inch motor - this was attractive to Culham and UCL – but not to the extent of funding any development!
- Adoption of the Black Brant Mark 5 motor

At the December 1970 meeting a feasibility report narrowed this down to three possibilities – the Raven XI, a Raven filled with CTPB propellant, or the new 21 inch motor (which would require a major redesign of the rocket).

However by March 1971 "possible new developments had been overtaken by the cold financial climate[27] and that because of this, there was one candidate only, the Raven XI." [28] As noted above, a firing had already taken place, and whilst the motor case lining had been faulty, it was anticipated that the proving of the new motor could be established substantially in a year. By December further ground firings had been satisfactory.

Unfortunately, in March 1972 it was reported that the total impulse was likely to be rather lower than originally hoped for, and concern was expressed that "whilst we were hoping to achieve a motor up to Black Brant performance we now appeared to be falling short of this." In response, it was commented that this motor was being developed on a shoestring budget with no SRC financial backing, which gave very little scope for R&D work.[29]

In June 1972 the nozzle design was being changed, and the performance data was still not available. By September, some addition funding had been obtained, but Frank Hazell commented that during the recent visit of the Argentineans, it had been revealed that they were actively looking at the possibility of using the Black Brant motor. This would do the ER [Earth Resources] Skylark job without the need for a boost motor and so remove the risks attendant upon a boost motor hitting the ground.[30] In December 1972, a representative from BAC stressed the need for an all out effort to produce Raven XIs. "Its performance will be inferior to that of the Black Brant VB but we must have something better than Raven VI."

As described later, in the end the first flight test for the Raven X1 did not occur until that on SL1301 in February 1975!

VEHICLE ENHANCEMENTS – a possible new recovery system

In March 1973 a feasibility study for an unlikely sounding "hot air balloon snatch recovery system" for Skylark was initiated. The concept would allow the recovery of payloads over impossible terrain and water, and could result in less damage to more sophisticated payloads such as star-pointing rounds.[31]

By this time, there were three existing Skylark payload recovery systems. The most commonly used was the parachute recovery system as used at Woomera and described in Chapter 7. The second had been developed by ESRO for recovery

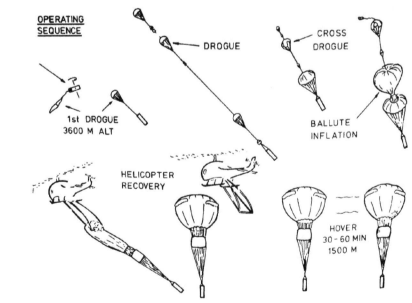

Figure 13.5 The proposed 'Ballute' deployment sequence.

(Salway (1975), figure 4)[35]

25 Presumably Imperial Metal Industries Ltd, as in "IMI Summerfield", see Nicolson (2009), *Summerfield*.
26 The RPE had said that the proposed CTPB (Carboxy-Terminated PolyButadiene) propellant would give improved reproducibility and a flatter thrust curve. (Minutes of 15th Skylark Policy meeting, September 1970, item 3. (TNA: PRO AVIA 92/144).
27 The 1970s began with high inflation, low growth, unemployment, and fluctuating exchange rates.
28 Minutes of the 17th Skylark Policy meeting, March 1971, item 4b. (TNA: PRO AVIA 92/144).
29 Minutes of the 21st Skylark Policy meeting, March 1972, item 5. (TNA: PRO AVIA 92/145).
30 Minutes of the 23rd Skylark Policy meeting, September 1972, item 5. (TNA: PRO AVIA 92/145).
31 Minutes of the 25th Skylark Policy meeting, March 1973, p.3, item 4.1. (TNA: PRO AVIA 92/145).

from the sea, and involved considerable support in terms of search aircraft and a recovery ship. It comprised a two stage parachute system and a torus (inflated before impact) to support the partly submerged payload. A third system had been produced by the DFVLR and was based on the Sandia system[32], which used a ram air inflated bag to support the submerged payload. (These latter two systems both required waterproofing of the experimental data).

The study [33] concluded that an air-snatch system based on an existing Goodyear P.A.R.D.[34] system was feasible. This used a parachute system to deploy a 12.8 metre (42 foot) diameter 'ballute' (balloon + chute = ballute!) that could be recovered by helicopter whilst still airborne, see figure 13.5 on the previous page.

However, by June 1973 it was concluded that the existing parachute system for recovery of payloads had achieved a reliable standard,[36] and further investigations into the ballute recovery system could be put on hold.[37] (Although of course, this did not provide the same benefits.)

This would not have been the first time helicopter recovery had been used:

> An interesting feature of the dropsonde trials was the air-borne recovery method. An Allouette helicopter flew over the dropsonde as it fell slowly, and caught it up with a hook suspended on a cable about 10 metres below the helicopter. Dropsondes were recovered in this fashion for some years, until, during a practice [sic] session at Woomera, the steel cable wrapped around the drive shaft to the tail rotor and sheared it. The helicopter landed safely, but the technique was abandoned afterwards as unsafe.[38]

VEHICLE ENHANCEMENTS – a range of possible new Skylarks

The impending arrival of the Raven XI motor either gave rise to or coincided with a new numbering system for Skylark rockets. The first of these, 'Skylark 8', featured in a paper presented at a British Interplanetary Society Symposium in September 1971,[39] and was mentioned in the March 1972 Skylark Policy Meeting ,[40] where it was revealed that it had been the subject of a BAC proposal in January 1972. At the March 1973 Policy Meeting the Skylark 7 and Skylark 12 versions were also being discussed.

The use of this numbering system appears to have its origin in the commonly used Goldfinch booster and Raven VI sustainer combination. Since 1968 this had provided the most powerful version of Skylark, and presumably set a convenient baseline, and by custom came to be known simply as 'Skylark 6'.[42] Hence, the variation where the Raven XI replaced the Raven VI would naturally be called the 'Skylark 7', and so on.

This numbering method has been used 'in reverse' by various online sources, to assign the numbers Skylark 1 through to Skylark 7 to various motor combinations. However, this unofficial numbering can lead to ambiguities. For instance, some documents and online lists use 'Skylark 7' to refer to a Skylark with the earlier Raven VII and no booster. However British Aerospace literature clearly uses the 'Skylark 7' designation to refer to a build standard comprising a Goldfinch booster and Raven XI sustainer, (as shown in the table below), and so only such 'official' designations have been used in this book.

Skylark Type	Booster	Sustainer	Possible 3rd stage	1st flight
6	Goldfinch II	Raven VI	-	1968
7	Goldfinch II	Raven XI	-	1975
8	Stonechat	Waxwing	-	n/a
9	Stonechat	-	-	(1969)[41]
12	Goldfinch II	Raven XI	Cuckoo IV	1976

Table 13.3 The Skylark numbering system used from about 1971.

---

32 Salway (1975), 'Recovery of Skylark Payloads using an Air Snatch System', p.257. The Sandia National Laboratories comprise two major United States Department of Energy research and development National Laboratories.

33 Salway (1975), 'Recovery of Skylark Payloads using an Air Snatch System', p.257.

34 The Goodyear Pilot Airborne Recovery Device (PARD) originally combined a parachute and hot air balloon to allow a pilot who had ejected to float above enemy territory and alert rescuers. Development ceased after the end of the Vietnam War in 1975.

35 Journal of the British Interplanetary Society, Vol.28 no.4 (April 1975), p.260. Reproduced with permission.

36 The cable retaining system with cutters, a solution designed to stop premature parachute ejection when the payload went into a flat spin, had been introduced by December 1971. (Minutes of the 20th Policy Meeting, December 1971, p.4, item 4.) (TNA: PRO AVIA 92/145).

37 Minutes of the 26th Skylark Policy meeting, June 1973, p.3, item 4.1 (TNA: PRO AVIA 92/145).

38 Morton (1989), *Fire across the Desert*, p.403.

39 Furst (1972), 'Design for High Performance Sounding Rockets'.

40 Minutes of the 21st Skylark Policy meeting, March 1972, p.5, item 5. (TNA: PRO AVIA 92/145).

41 Skylark 9 was only ever launched in the form of the 'Falstaff' military rocket.

42 See for instance its use by Brown (1976), 'Recent additions to the Skylark family of Sounding Rockets', p.439.

The proposed Skylark 8

The requirements for longer observation times for astrophysical experiments and higher altitudes for geophysical experiments resulted in a BAC proposal for a new high altitude sounding rocket designated Skylark 8. This was an entirely new design, although based on existing motors, and would have been a relatively powerful vehicle. The proposed Stonechat booster was a 36 inch diameter motor (i.e. twice the diameter of the existing Skylark), and was the UK's largest ever solid propellant motor, with a total impulse of over three times that of the Raven XI.[43]

Even without a Waxwing sustainer, it would have been capable of lifting a tonne in excess of 100 km, as indeed it did later in the form of the 'Falstaff' military rocket,[45] (see the next chapter). Used together with the Waxwing motor[46] (used as the third stage of Black Arrow to launch Prospero into orbit) it would have made a formidable sounding rocket. It could have lifted 260 kg to 1000 km,[47] or provided zero g conditions three times as long for a given payload than even the later Skylark 12.

Skylark 8 appears to have been a particularly well designed vehicle, incorporating lessons learnt from the pioneering Skylark days, and from experience with the Black Arrow launcher. For instance, by this time the solutions to flight stability problems were understood, and the fin cant angle was designed to avoid the problems of roll-yaw resonance.[48] The split nose cone was designed with a high velocity pneumatic separation system to allow ejection at the vehicle spin rate without causing damage to experiments mounted inside.[49] Positive second stage separation (to avoid separation collisions) was to be achieved with 32 compressed short-stroke springs, designed using Black Arrow experience to avoid possible damage to the Waxwing nozzle, and excessive tip-off rates and dispersion. Both static and dynamic balancing would have been carried out on the payload section and Waxwing motor, and a transponder fitted to assist with radar tracking and payload recovery.

Skylark 8 would have provided a relatively low cost high performance vehicle using existing motor and payload hard-

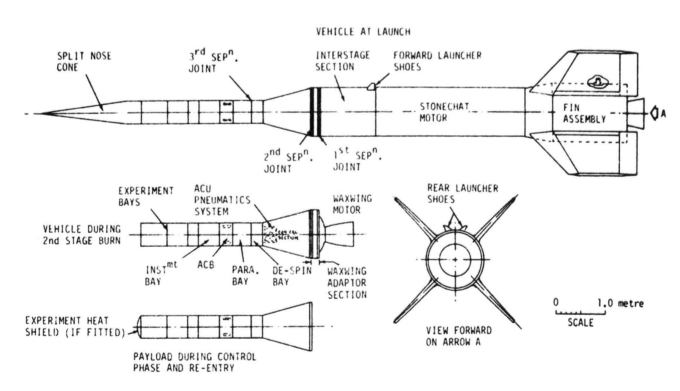

Figure 13.6 The proposed Skylark 8, phase 1 version.
(This phase 1 version made use of the existing Skylark 44 cm (17") diameter payload sections.)
(Furst & Brown (1974), figure 1) [44]

[43] RPE Westcott (1968), *Index to Solid Propellant Motors*.

[44] Journal of the British Interplanetary Society, Vol.27 no.7 (July 1974), p.486. Reproduced with permission.

[45] The Falstaff prototype was launched (apparently in great secrecy) in October 1969, after which the concept of the Skylark 8 publically surfaced in 1971. The Falstaff 'production models' were launched starting in 1975, see Chapter 14.

[46] As described in the previous chapter, in 1971 the Waxwing motor had boosted the Prospero satellite into orbit, the Waxwing itself remaining in orbit to this day. (2014). It was a most versatile motor.

[47] Furst & Brown (1974), 'Skylark 8 – High Altitude Sounding Rocket', p.489.

[48] Furst & Brown (1974), 'Skylark 8 – High Altitude Sounding Rocket', p.491.

[49] Ibid, p.494.

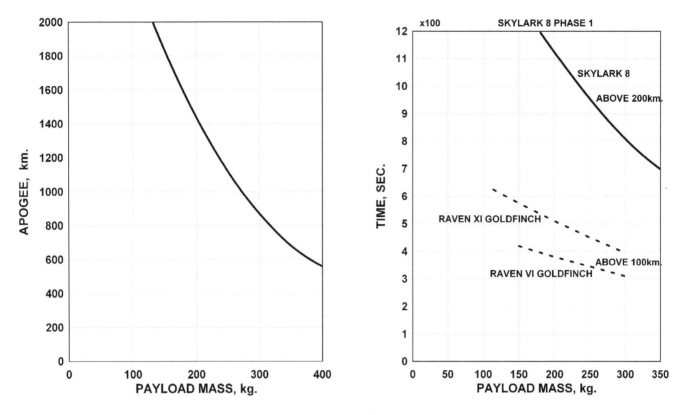

Figures 13.7 and 13.8
Left: Skylark 8 projected apogee. It would have been able to reach five or six times the altitude of Skylark 6 for a given gross payload.[50] Right: Skylark 8 zero g/available observation time v. payload, showing how it would have been able to increase the times to as long as 20 minutes (1,200 seconds), more than double that for Skylarks 6 or 12.[51]

(After Furst & Brown (1974), figures 4 & 5) [52]

ware, and provided a much higher performance than any of the then current Skylark variants.

The main use envisaged was with the existing Skylark star-pointing ACU for which it would have been ideal. The existing Skylark provided about five minutes (300 seconds) in space,[53] of which one and half was required for the star-pointing ACU to point in the correct direction,[54] leaving only three and a half minutes pointing at the target. Under similar conditions Skylark 8 would have extended the ACU time to thirteen minutes (800 seconds) (see the fig-

ure above), leaving a potential eleven and a half minutes for pointing at the target or acquiring new stars. Thus, it would have provided a much better return on the heavy investment that had been made on the Stage 5 ACU.

Another benefit was that despite being too large for the existing Skylark launcher at Woomera, it could have used the existing Falstaff launcher already in place next to it. (Visible in the photographs of the launch of SL1022 towards the end of the previous chapter, see figures 12.43 and 12.44).

---

[50] For instance, 1400 km compared to 250 km for a 200 kg, payload - see Figure 10.53 curve A.

[51] The Skylark 8 curve is labelled "above 200 km" rather than 100 km because second stage burnout would not have occurred until that altitude.

[52] Journal of the British Interplanetary Society, Vol.27 no.7 (Jul.1974), p.488 & p.489. Reproduced with permission.

[53] Between about +100 seconds and +400 seconds, see for instance Farr (1975), *Flight Performance of the Skylark SL1011 Star-pointing Attitude 14.Control System*, pp 7-9.

[54] Abbott (1971), *A Star-pointing Attitude Control System for Skylark.*

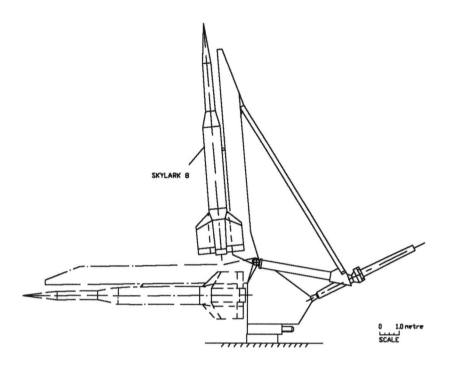

SKYLARK 8

0   1.0 metre
SCALE

Figure 13.9 The proposed method of deployment of Skylark 8 on the existing 'Falstaff' launcher at Woomera. (See Figure 14.44 in the next chapter for a close-up of the launcher with the Falstaff rocket being prepared.)
(After Furst & Brown (1974), figure 12) [55]

The demise of Skylark 8

The March 1972 minutes of the Skylark Policy committee reveal that an SRC panel on future propulsion requirements had been set up. Its brief included deliberations on the Skylark 8 proposal, for which the findings were expected by the end of the year. In March 1973 it was reported that they had expressed scientific interest in using improved performance vehicles (Skylark 7 and 12's); and also the introduction of Skylark 8 on the astrophysics programme on the basis of replacing some of the Skylark 7 rounds at the rate of two in 1975, four in 1976 and six in 1977.[56]

At this point, all seemed set for the Skylark 8, and Frank Hazell was asked to organise a small planning mission to WRE to obtain formal approval on the safety aspects. On the technical side both BAC and the RAE agreed that the general design and specification of the motors was suitable for the purpose envisaged but needed bringing to production standard.

By June 1973 it was reported that the Skylark 8 cost estimates were in draft form, but that the Skylark 8 proposal "because of its significant cost, would require very careful consideration."[57] By September the Germans (DFVLR) were

also taking an interest in Skylark 8 for their next five year programme, and the Skylark 8 and Skylark 12 proposals had been submitted to the SPGC.[58] "Unfortunately the submissions were caught up in the problem of the overall [cost] escalations and had gone into the melting pot. It could be twelve months before a full decision is made on Skylark 8."[59]

At this point, the quarterly policy meeting records lodged at the UK National Archives unfortunately cease; presumably, because in April 1974, the SRC took over the Skylark management function from the MOD Procurement Executive,[60] and the author has been unable to locate any equivalent SRC records. However it appears from subsequent events that Skylark 12 was approved by the SRC, but Skylark 8 was not, as Skylark 12 was first launched three years later (in November 1976), but there was no further sign of Skylark 8 in connection with the British National programme.

However, proposals for Skylark 8 did emerge much later, in 1987, when what had become BAe proposed it as a vehicle capable of providing 15+ minutes duration of microgravity. Clearly little development had occurred in the intervening decade, as it was stated "… [it]…could be developed from existing qualified motors and Skylark subsystems." [61]

[55] Journal of the British Interplanetary Society, Vol.27 no.7 (Jul.1974), p.497. Reproduced with permission.

[56] Minutes of the 25th Skylark Policy meeting, March 1973, p.6, item 9.2. (TNA: PRO AVIA 92/144).

[57] Minutes of the 26th Skylark Policy meeting, June 1973, p.4, item 5. (TNA: PRO AVIA 92/144).

[58] It appears that none of the parties managing Skylark had control over their own spending; it all had to be approved by yet another government entity, the Space Policy & Grants Committee or "SPGC". (Acton (1974), p.345). The commercial equivalent might be a company where the bookkeepers in accounts had the last say, rather than the board of directors!

[59] Minutes of the 27th Skylark Policy meeting, Sept. 1973, p.3, item 5. (TNA: PRO AVIA 92/145).

[60] Minutes of the 26th Skylark Policy meeting, June 1973, p.3. (TNA: PRO AVIA 92/145).

[61] Ellis (1987), 'Skylark Sounding Rocket Development – Skylark 8' p.440.

Jan.	Feb.	March	April	May	June	July	Aug.	Sept.	Oct.	Nov.	Dec.
SL1205		SL1010	SL1011		SL1111	SL1291	SL1081A		S93	SL1123	SL1124
		SL1004							S92	SL1206	
		SL1102							SL1121	S74	
		SL1182							SL1122		
		SL1181									

Table 13.4 The 18 Skylark Launches in 1973. (For full details see Appendix 3.)

(Key: blue = UK national programme (unstabilised), plum = UK (stabilised), red = German national)

SKYLARK LAUNCHES AND SCIENCE IN 1973

Despite the decline in the annual number of Skylark launches, 1973 was a year full of interest with progress on many fronts. The scientific instruments flown became ever more sophisticated, the Stage 5 star-pointing ACU had its first two fully successful flights, the Earth resources user trial produced good results in Argentina, and the high latitude campaign from Norway at the end of the year played to the sounding rockets' strengths. A new long-term customer (Germany's DFVLR) sponsored three launches, and two new firing ranges (in Norway and Spain) were used for the first time.

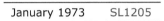

January 1973   SL1205

During 1972, the Mullard Space Science Laboratory (MSSL) had been preparing an experiment to observe from Woomera the lunar occultation of X-ray source GX 2+5. This rare astronomical event meant the launch had to take place at a particular time on 30 January 1973. The main purpose was to increase the accuracy of the known position of the X-ray source by a factor of 60 (from approximately one arc minute to one arc second), thus greatly enhancing the probability of finding its optical or radio counterpart. It was also hoped to obtain a good spectrum of the source and to carry out a search for pulsar activity. The mechanics of the experiment were arranged so that a Stage 1 Sun-seeking ACU could be used, rather than the Stage 5 star-seeker then still under development.[62]

Figures 13.10 and 13.11 The large multi-wire X-ray detector installed in the SL1205 nose bay, showing how the detector would be deployed at an angle in flight, so the X-ray source could be targeted.

(MSSL \ Coker)

62   MSSL (1972), *Report of the MSSL 1st January – 30 September 1972*, Part B, p.7.

The payload was duly launched on **SL1205**, the first of that year's Campaign 13 at Woomera. Unfortunately, the flight did not go as planned, and at the regular policy meeting in the UK two weeks later it was reported, "… the occultation had not taken place as expected. The reason for this was being investigated by the experimenter." [63] Frank Hazell also mentioned a second problem, "SL1205 had come to earth outside, but near the range boundary, which may lead to a requirement to spin Cuckoo boosted rounds to reduce dispersion."

The subsequent MSSL annual report throws a little more light on the matter, "Due to violent weather conditions at the tightly determined time of launch however, the rocket was blown substantially off course and prevented the occultation from being observed. Nevertheless, the payload performed very well and considerable data was acquired on two other X-ray sources." [64]

These two rather short accounts hint at an interesting story, revealed many years later by Mike Cruise:

> Lunar eclipses repeat every 18 years or so and the timing of the launch had to be accurate to about two seconds making them very tricky launches indeed. On this occasion the wind at ground level was close to the permitted limit and the wind monitor, a member of the attitude control team, was concerned about the size of the gusts although things were better at higher altitudes. At mi-

nus two minutes, I had frankly given the launch away in my mind, but the wind monitor had a theory that the gusts around the launcher were somehow periodic, and when the time came for stop actions to be called out he remained silent and the vehicle was launched. He believed that the wind would drop in the last few seconds. It didn't. Cine film of the launch showed that the vehicle took a huge gust immediately on leaving the launcher and veered wildly off track. In fact it landed just outside of the Woomera territory and close to the North-South railway.

> We missed the eclipse - the detectors were never in the right place to observe it due to the unexpected trajectory. The team of experimenters drove at some speed down to Woomera village to hear the evening news since the arrival of the train from Alice Springs was normally reported on the local radio. Luckily there was no disaster such as the train being hit by a descending Skylark but we knew soon afterwards that the wind monitor, who was trying his best to help, had received a good deal of trouble from the range authorities. [65]

A ground impact outside the range was a cardinal sin at Woomera (see for instance SL02 in Chapter 5), and rumour has it that when the recovery helicopter found SL1205 it picked it up and dropped it back down again just inside the range boundary!

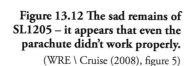

Figure 13.12 The sad remains of SL1205 – it appears that even the parachute didn't work properly.
(WRE \ Cruise (2008), figure 5)

[63] Frank Hazell, minutes of the 25th Policy Meeting on the Skylark Rocket, March 1973, p.5, item 7. (TNA: PRO AVIA 92/145).
[64] MSSL (1973), *Report of the MSSL 1st October 1972 – 30 September 1973*, Part 3, p.9.
[65] Cruise (2008), *Skylark Ascending*, online article p.19, and *Prospero* number 5, Spring 2008, p.53.

March 1973	SL1010, SL1004, SL1102, SL1182, SL1181

There were no Skylark launches in February, but five took place in March - the last month in the history of Skylark when that many launches occurred.

At Woomera, preparations had continued during February, culminating in the launch of **SL1010** in the early morning of 1st March local time. This had on board an X-ray astronomy experiment from the University of Leicester that carried out a low energy survey at low galactic latitudes, using a parabolic reflector telescope and proportional counters mounted in a Sun-stabilised ACU. Unusually there was also a 'Robot' camera on board.[66] This had been included to investigate a problem in which motor casings collided with the payload after separation. Photographs from the camera showed the expended motor overtaking the payload. This observation was said to be "cause for concern but not alarm" as the introduction of increased separation velocity was already in hand.[67]

Figure 13.13 This remarkable picture shows a spent Raven motor, photographed in space from its payload just after separation. The author has not been able to locate the original photographs from 1973 mentioned above, but this image (probably taken much later, between 1999 and 2005[68]), indicates what it must have looked like.

(SSC \ Sounding Rocket Services)

---

[66] Robot was and is a German imaging company that produced clockwork driven sequence cameras taking 24 x 24 mm format images on standard 35mm film.

[67] Minutes of the 25th Skylark Policy Meeting, March 1973, p.5 item 7. (TNA: PRO AVIA 92/145).

[68] As it originally appeared on the Sounding Rocket Services Ltd website, a company that was only involved with Skylark during those years.

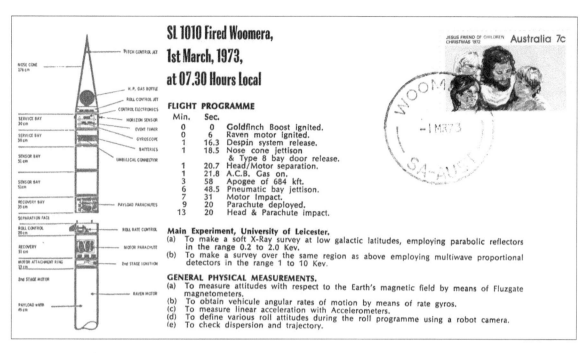

Figure 13.14 This 'First Day Cover' provides comprehensive details of SL1010.

(Author's collection)

Two weeks later, SL1010 was followed by the launch of **SL1004**, which carried a solar physics experiment from Culham.[69] This was a brave continuation of the experiments flown on board SL606 and SL902 in 1969 and 1971, both

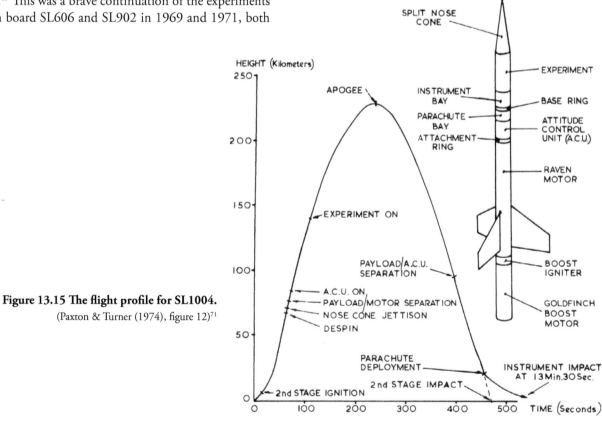

Figure 13.15 The flight profile for SL1004.

(Paxton & Turner (1974), figure 12)[71]

---

[69] The Astrophysics Research Division was part of the UK Atomic Energy Authority's Culham Laboratory, which was carrying out significant work on nuclear fusion.

[70] Firth *et al.* (1974), 'Observations of the Solar Spectrum in the Region 150Å to 870Å emitted from the disk and above the limb', p.543.

[71] Journal of the British Interplanetary Society, Vol.27 no.11 (November 1974), p.858. Reproduced with permission.

of which had suffered from parachute failure. The main purpose this time was to extend the measurement of solar limb/disc intensity ratios to shorter (XUV) wavelengths, and thereby to the hotter zones of the solar atmosphere.[70]

The SL1004 payload instrument consisted of three grazing-incidence spectrographs (two for the disk, one for the limb), each preceded by a grazing-incidence telescope mirror that imaged the solar disk onto the entrance slit, the spectra being recorded on photographic film. In-flight information on image position and stability was obtained by using small cine cameras operating at one frame per second.[72] This all resulted in what must have been the most complex instrument to date flown on a Skylark rocket. See Figure 13.16.

Not only was the instrument was very complicated, but it also had to be designed to maintain its pointing stability during the arduous environmental conditions imposed by its flight into space. The pointing requirement was ten times finer than that provided by the standard Skylark attitude control unit, so it included an additional system of stabilisation for the internal mirror.

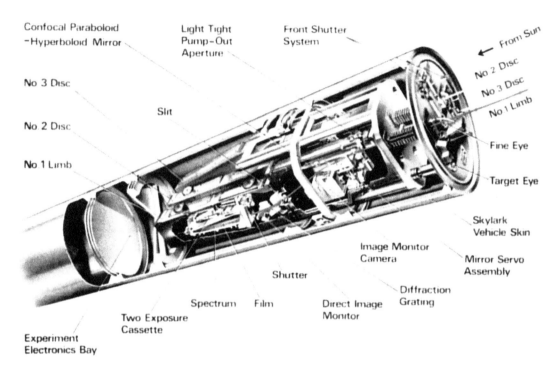

Figure 13.16 The solar physics instrument flown on SL1004.

(Paxton & Turner (1974), figure 1) [73]

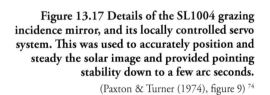

Figure 13.17 Details of the SL1004 grazing incidence mirror, and its locally controlled servo system. This was used to accurately position and steady the solar image and provided pointing stability down to a few arc seconds.

(Paxton & Turner (1974), figure 9) [74]

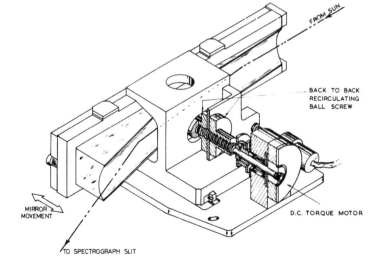

---

[72] Firth *et al.* (1974), 'Observations of the Solar Spectrum in the Region 150Å to 870Å emitted from the disk and above the limb', p.544.

[73] Journal of the British Interplanetary Society, Vol.27 no.11 (November 1974), p.850. Reproduced with permission.

[74] Journal of the British Interplanetary Society, Vol.27 no.11 (November 1974), p.855. Reproduced with permission.

Another requirement was that temperature variations had to be kept within 2°C during the several minutes of photographic film exposure. Previous flights had shown that the inner surfaces of the Skylark body skin rose to about 100°C during launch because of kinetic heating as it passed through the atmosphere, and so the SL1004 payload had to be specially mounted within the rocket to avoid excessive conducted and radiated heating effects. To ensure maximum mechanical stability, the metal for the payload castings was specially treated, the castings were acid reduced, rough machined, stress relieved and then final machined.[75]

This time the flight was completely successful, even the parachute recovery system worked, and the payload was returned to the preparation laboratory at Woomera within three hours of landing. A large amount of UV spectral information was obtained, and used to provide new information on the Sun's temperature, structure and energy transfer mechanism.[76]

Two years later, the experiment was flown again on the more powerful SL1301, see the next chapter.

SL1102 was the fourth Skylark launch of Woomera Campaign 13. This took place on the 20th March, and carried another type of solar physics experiment from the ARD (Astrophysics Research Division) at Culham. The instrument flown was an improved version of the echelle spectrograph previously flown on SL803 in April 1970, and provided a high-resolution ultraviolet spectra from 1400-2200Å (140-220nm), i.e. at longer wavelengths than those observed by SL1004 the week before. The information provided by the corresponding 'First Day Cover' in the author's collection summarises this as follows:

> Experiment – To measure line profiles in the UV spectrum in the range 1150A [sic] to 2200A from the quiet regions of the sun using a high spectral resolution

Echelle Diffraction Grating Spectrograph

Time of Flight – 12m 5 secs (nom).

Apogee – 225 Km

The flight was successful (although only two of the four planned exposures were made because of loss of pointing control), the instrument was recovered in good condition (the payload films were processed less than five hours after launch), and was used back in the UK to assist the analysis of the flight data.[77] Improvements in the instrument's reflective coatings and better thermal stability resulted in an increase in both number and quality of profiles recorded, and resulted in an updated model of how the Sun operated.

The Skylark work carried out by Culham is usefully put into context by the following:

> This UV research was led by [Sir] Robert Wilson …. as Director of the Astrophysics Research Unit, he led a programme of UV solar-plasma observations with rocket-borne instruments, including the first flights of stabilized Skylark rockets, obtaining the first ultraviolet spectra of the solar limb. These pioneering efforts produced the first identifications of many intersystem lines, crucial to the determination of electron densities in astrophysical plasmas….With later rocket flights, he went on to obtain some of the first high-resolution ultraviolet spectra of stellar sources. This work established the foundations of the continuing tradition of UK involvement in ultraviolet astrophysics.
>
> With this background, it was inevitable that Wilson should lead British participation in the European Space Research Organisation's first astronomy satellite, and its most ambitious project to that time, the TD-1 mission…. The satellite included an outstandingly successful Anglo-

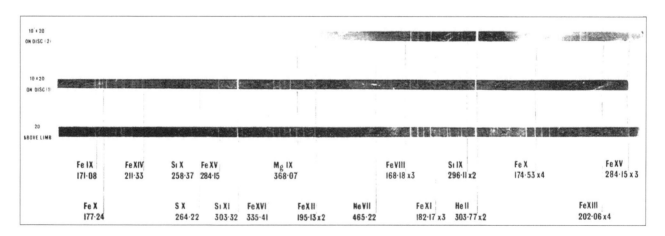

Figure 13.18 The solar UV spectra recorded by SL1004.
(Firth *et al.* (1974), plate III)

[75] Paxton & Turner (1974), 'An Engineering Profile of a Sounding Rocket Payload for Observation of the Sun', p.853.
[76] Firth *et al.* (1974), 'Observations of the Solar Spectrum in the Region 150Å to 870Å emitted from the disk and above the limb'.
[77] Boland *et al.* (1975), 'Further Measurements of Emission Line Profiles in the Solar Ultraviolet Spectrum'.

Belgian experiment....named S2/68 which, starting in 1972, conducted the first survey of the entire sky in UV; as one of the first all-sky surveys it predated current trends in wide field astronomy by a quarter of a century.[78]

SL1182 and SL1181 - the First Earth Observation User Trials

The concept of using sounding rockets for remote Earth sensing had been attributed to Commodore Tasso of the Argentina Space Research Committee, who in 1969 first propounded the idea.[79] Thus, it was in Argentina in South America that the first user trial for Skylark Earth monitoring took place. This tested both technical and user aspects; on the technical side it exercised the ability to conduct operations away from a normal firing range, and for the user it assessed the agricultural value of the photography as an operational tool for corn crop differentiation and total crop measurement.[80]

Two rounds were flown, very similar to the prototype (SL1081) launched from Woomera the year before, except that three Hasselblad cameras were installed in place of one. Again, the necessary ground truth investigations were conducted in parallel.

The operational aspects of the trial were not easy, this being the first occasion on which heavy sounding rockets had been fired outside an established rocket range. Work on making the two rounds for Argentina had proceeded satisfactorily, although the schedule had been tight and power cuts had not helped.[81] The Argentineans had wanted to see some results by November 1972,[82] but it was only by December 1972 that an agreement had been signed, and equipment was in transit.[83]

There had also been technical problems with the screw-jack mechanism of the new transportable launcher, but alternative hydraulic components had been procured, and it was successfully set up on hard standing at the Argentina Air Force base at Villa Mercedes near the centre of the country:

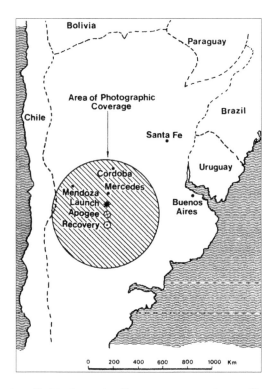

Figures 13.19 and 13.20 Left: The transportable Skylark launcher installed in Argentina.[84] (Simmons (1974), figure 3) [85]
Right: The location and extent of the 1973 Skylark trial in Argentina. The coverage spanned the foothills of the Andes in the West to the wheat growing pampas in the East.
(Beattie (1974), figure 3) [86]

[78] Howarth & Willis (2003), *Sir Robert Wilson*, p.134.
[79] Beattie (1974), 'The Earth Resource Skylark – A Progress Report'.
[80] Simmons (1974), 'Rockets for Earth Environment Monitoring', p.5.
[81] Minutes of the 21st Skylark Policy Meeting, March 1972, p.1 (TNA: PRO AVIA 92/144). The comment on power cuts refers to the UK coal miners' strike of January to February 1972, during which electricity was turned off across the country on a rota basis, and factories and businesses were forced to work a 'three day week'.
[82] Minutes of the 18th Skylark Policy Meeting, June 1971, p.2. (TNA: PRO AVIA 92/144).
[83] Minutes of the 24th Skylark Policy Meeting, December 1972, p.2. (TNA: PRO AVIA 92/145).
[84] The Science Museum depository in London (Blythe House) holds several 1/10th scale models of this launcher (ref. 1993-2297).
[85] Journal of the British Interplanetary Society, Vol.27 no.1 (Jan.1974), p.5. Reproduced with permission.
[86] Journal of the British Interplanetary Society, Vol.27 no.1 (Jan.1974), p.16. Reproduced with permission.

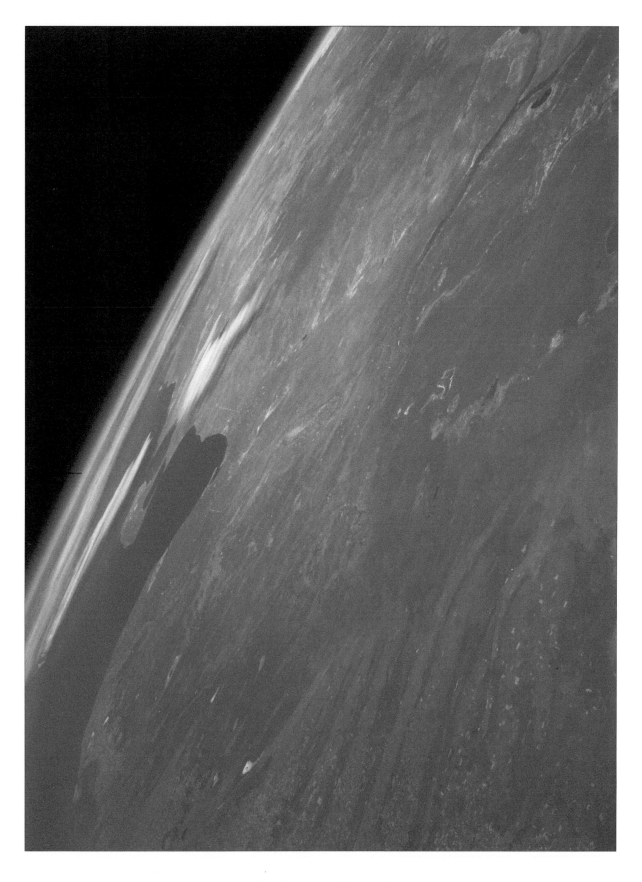

Figure 13.21 One of the many spectacular views taken by SL1182 from an altitude of about 200 km (125 miles) above central Argentina. In this photograph, the horizon is due south and the Atlantic coast is visible about 800 km (500 miles) away. The darker blue bay on the left is the 'Golfo San Mateas' into which juts the 'Peninsula Valdes' just before the cloud. (F24 large format air-survey camera with 127 mm lens and Kodak Aerochrome 2443 false-colour infrared film).

(RAE / University of Reading)

**Figure 13.22 Skylark SL1181
ready for launch in Argentina.**
(Savigear *et al.* (1977), Vol.I, plate 4.4)

After many anxious moments caused by technical and administrative problems,[87] SL1182 was launched on Thursday 22nd March at 13:43 local time after waiting for a brief period of clear weather in an untypically poor Argentinean Autumn.[88]

Unfortunately it suffered a partial malfunction of the attitude control unit[89] and it was anticipated that the results from the cameras would be somewhat downgraded,[90] although in the event about 100 good photographs were obtained. Ironically, because the camera platform was not properly stabilised, the angle at which the cameras pointed produced the most spectacular photographs ever taken by Skylark. Although of little use for mapping purposes they were probably the highest resolution pictures to date obtained from space, at least in the civilian sphere.[91]

The fault on SL1182 was recognised during the actual flight and the standby round brought to readiness immediately.

This second round, SL1181 was launched on 28th March at 13:51 local time, and was completely successful, although the new parachute system to recover the empty motor cases proved ineffective.

---

[87] Minutes of the 26th Skylark Policy Meeting, June 1973, item 2. (TNA: PRO AVIA 92/145).
[88] Jude (1977), 'An Attitude-Control System for an Earth-Pointing Skylark Rocket', p.279. The ER Skylarks were apparently launched on the "only two cloud-free days during March 1973". (Ellis (1992), 'Skylark Sounding Rockets – Past and Present', p.180).
[89] After 57 seconds the attitude control electronics ceased to function because of a short-circuit in the +15V power supply rail (Jude (1977), p.279).
[90] Beattie (1974), 'The Earth Resource Skylark – A Progress Report', p.15.
[91] Until 1973, NASA astronauts had used only medium-format Hasselblad cameras with 70 mm film producing 55 mm square images, whereas the large-format F24 aerial survey camera on SL1182 used 140 mm film producing 127 mm (5 inch) square images. It appears to have been some months later before NASA launched their first large format camera into orbit on board Skylab. This "Earth Terrain Camera" (S190B) consisted of a single high-resolution camera that used five-inch film and an 18-inch focal length lens. Even so, it only pointed straight down and not at the horizon.

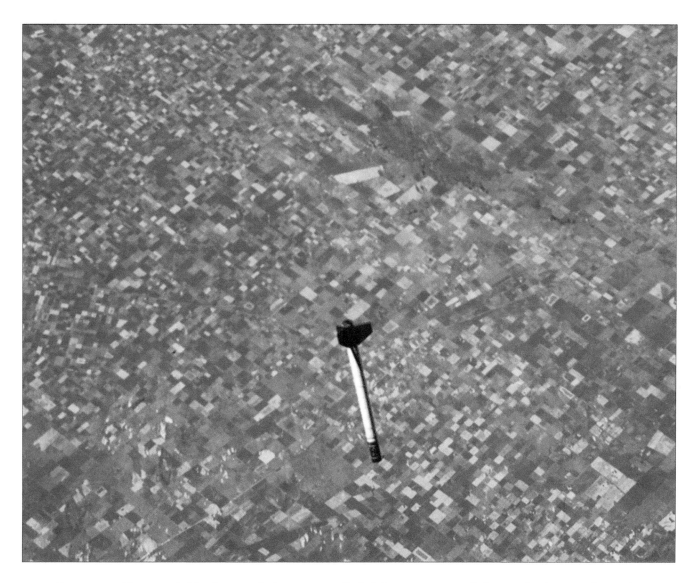

Figure 13.23 This remarkable photograph shows a spent Skylark Raven motor caught by a payload camera during the Argentine Earth survey exercise. The spent motor separated at about 75 km, but would have followed the payload up, and was photographed from an altitude of about 210 km, when the payload started to operate. The view below depicts an area approximately 60 km (37 miles) across at the centre of the image.[92]
(Kodak 2443 false colour infrared film with a 150mm lens from Skylark SL1181)
(RAE / University of Reading)

The special arrangements for tracking and recovery of the payloads were particularly successful, and both payloads were recovered virtually undamaged. The cameras used for the Argentine trial differed from those used in Australia the previous year, in that the large-format F24 air-survey camera was loaded with false-colour infrared rather than panchromatic (black and white) film, and rather than just one Hasselblad medium–format camera, three were used, two with true colour film and one with false-colour infrared film.

SL1181 provided 100 frames of photography from the F24 camera, and 270 frames from the three Hasselblad cameras.

The total area of Argentina photographed was 330,000 square km., and the resolution varied from 45 m to 15 m.[93]

The area surveyed was extremely interesting from an Earth Resources point of view. A great variety of topographical and land use features were included in the coverage which encompassed an area from the foothills of the Andes in the West to the great wheat growing areas of the Argentina pampas to the East. As in South Australia, Reading University carried out ground truth observations.

[92] Townshend (ed.) (1981), *Terrain Analysis and Remote Sensing*, p.120.
[93] Jude (1977), 'An Attitude-Control System for an Earth-Pointing Skylark Rocket', p.279.

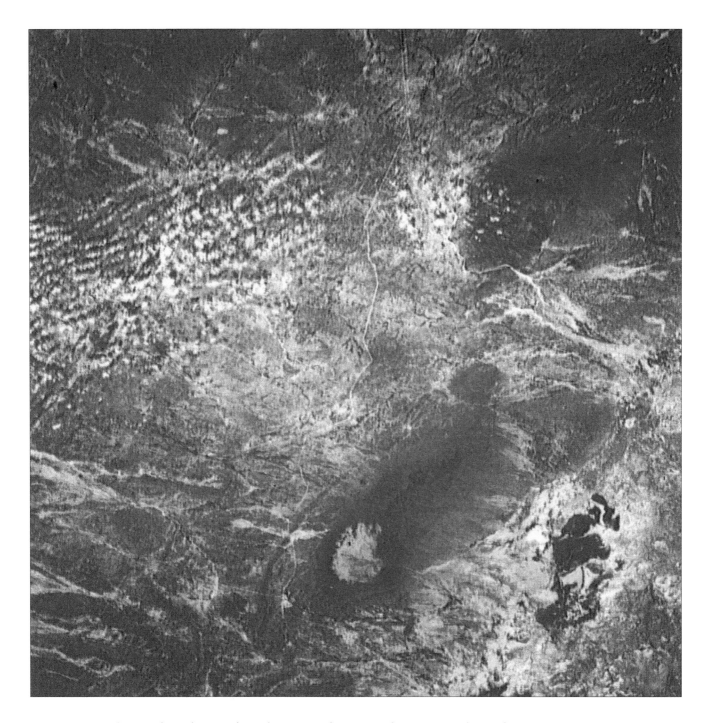

Figure 13.24 True colour photography with a 250 mm lens camera from SL1181 of part of San Luis Province, Argentina.
(RAE \ Townshend et al. (1974), plate 1)

It was concluded that the main lesson from an operations point of view for a campaign of this nature was expecting too much from the existing ground facilities, in particular, the communication network. On any future campaigns, away from the known ranges, there would be a need for a careful preliminary survey of facilities.

Following this success, the future for Skylark sounding rocket surveys looked good, and the results in general had delighted the Argentineans. Despite photographic processing difficulties, they had been provided with copies of some of the photographs before the UK team left the country, and at the Embassy cocktail party after the launch, it had been mentioned that there was the possibility of an agricultural survey, probably in 1976.[94]

[94] Minutes of the 26th Skylark Policy Meeting, June 1973, item 2, p.2. (TNA: PRO AVIA 92/145).

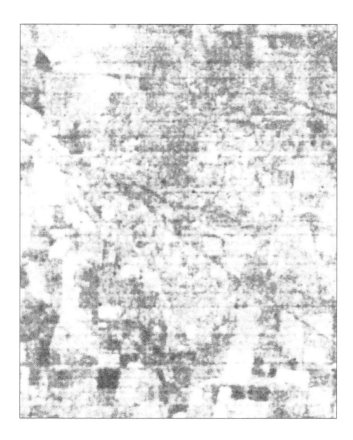 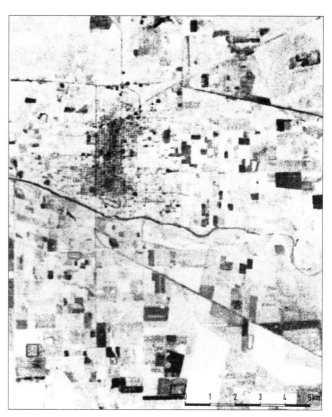

Figures 13.25 and 13.26 These two views of Mercedes Town, San Luis Province, compare images from the NASA ERTS-1 satellite channel 5 (left) and a Skylark true colour 150 mm lens camera (right). In this case, the better resolution available from Skylark shows the urban area more clearly, although the same did not always apply in open terrain.

(Left: NASA, Right: RAE \ Townshend *et al.*[95])

Ground truth measurements

As in Australia, work was carried out to interpret and evaluate the photography obtained from Skylark. There were two elements, one the evaluation of the potential of Skylark type photography as a tool in general, the other more immediate, to produce land use/crop inventory statistics from the cultivated part of the area photographed. (It was said that the Argentine authorities employed six men to visit farmers and ask how much wheat they were growing, in order to work out how many ships had to be booked for export purposes, thus they were keen to improve on this method!)

A team from the University of Reading had first visited Argentina in September 1972, followed by a second visit in November and December. In March and April 1973, a field programme of crop surveys, aircraft and helicopter photography was carried out. There were many difficulties and problems to be overcome before the results could finally be presented, not least that the sponsors never specified the detailed requirements for the work.[96] However, a first estimate of crop statistics[97] was produced within ten days of the complete photography reaching the University of Reading, in time for a visit by Comodoro J.J.Tasso of the Argentine CNIE.

A wide range of studies was carried out. Crop inventories for a sample of 24,000 km² were produced, with semi-automated digital methods[98] being investigated by Bedford College, University of London. Specimen topographical maps were produced and compared with existing counterparts, and maps of solid and superficial geology were produced at various scales.

[95] Townshend, Savigear, Justice, Hardy, Drennan & Bray (1974), *A Comparison of the Capabilities of ERTS-1 and the Skylark Earth-Resources Rocket for Resources Surveying in Central Argentina,* figures 3 (a) and (b).

[96] Hardy and Townshend (1975), *Anglo-Argentinean Geoscopy Experiment Report,* Section 1, p.1.1.

[97] Hardy (1973), *First estimation of crop area statistics for the area of Argentina photographed by Skylark SL1181, using ground truth data.*

[98] See also (re Woomera) Owen-Jones, Custance (1974), 'Digitised Analysis of Skylark Rocket Imagery', and (re Argentina) Owen-Jones & Chandler (1977), 'The Use of Photographic Imagery in Earth Resources Studies'.

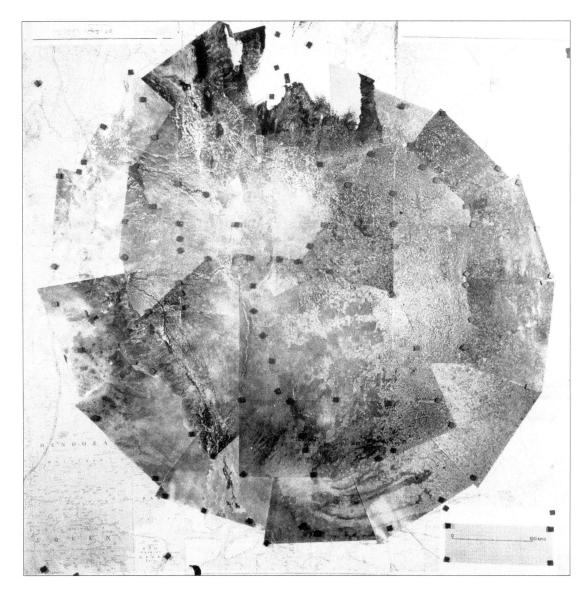

Figure 13.27 A photo mosaic of the whole area photographed by SL1181. Scale of original = 1:500,000 (2 mm = 1 km).[99]
The small black squares are the weights used to hold the original photographic prints in place!
(Hardy (1975), figure 7.14)

Over two dozen articles and papers followed the survey.[100] For instance, in December 1973 three papers on the project were presented by the University of Reading's Professor Savigear at a United Nations conference in on the peaceful uses of outer space at Buenos Aires. The Skylark survey was also referred to in a later textbook on 'Terrain Analysis and Remote Sensing'.[101]

In addition, a cost benefit analysis was carried out by the Economist Intelligence Unit. The University of Reading also prepared for a post-firing field programme, but this was postponed then cancelled by the Argentineans. The final report from the University of Reading was extremely comprehensive, running to nine sections/volumes,[102] the final ones not being produced until December 1975.

It had soon became apparent that there was the potential for a large amount of work to be done, and with hindsight it can be seen that this pioneering project (with probably the first such comprehensive crop inventory ever carried out[103]) was in at the start of an entire new field of scientific endeavour. This has since become a major subject in its own right, and Skylark's ad-hoc financial and administrative arrangements were barely able to cope, and certainly not exploit.

[99] For a simplified but annotated version of this image, see Townshend (ed.) (1981), *Terrain Analysis and Remote Sensing*, p.41.
[100] Listed in Appendix 1.3 of Hardy and Townshend (1975), *Anglo-Argentinian Geoscopy Experiment Report,* Section 1.
[101] Townshend (ed.) (1981), *Terrain Analysis and Remote Sensing*, p.41.
[102] Savigear, Hardy, Townshend *et al.* (1975), *Anglo-Argentinian Geoscopy Experiment Report – December 1975.*
[103] Hardy and Townshend (1975), *Anglo-Argentinian Geoscopy Experiment Report*, Section 1, p.1.3.

April 1973   SL1011

On April 18th at Woomera **SL1011** was launched with the first Stage 5 Phase 2 star-pointing ACU payload. It carried a Leicester astronomy experiment that was the first British experiment to study low-energy X-ray sources (below 1 keV). A parabolic mirror array determined precise positions of sources in the Centaurus and Circinus regions.[104] This Phase 2 engineering prototype of the Stage 5 ACU had a modified design for Moon acquisition,[105] and was successful in finding and locking onto the target stars. It must have been a relief when it worked successfully, as its development programme had continued to slip[106] since the unsuccessful Phase 1 launch in May 1971 (SL812) nearly two years before.

The Stage 5 ACU star acquisition sequence

The Stage 5 star-pointing ACU used the magnetometer based Moon-pointing system from the Stage 3 ACU, modified by the addition of a relatively inexpensive 'strap-down gyro system'[107], which further controlled the cold gas jets to point to the required star.

The figure below shows the Stage 5 ACU star acquisition sequence, as used for this 'Phase 2' version. (This version extended the launch window from full moon ±3 days to ±7 days). After the payload had separated from the rocket motor case, operation was in three main phases:

1. Moon acquisition
2. Pointing to the vicinity of the target star by a twist then a slew manoeuvre
3. Scanning a small area of sky, and pointing to the brightest star scanned

After a delay, similar manoeuvres could be initiated to transfer lock to up to four additional stars.

All this would have been implemented by what in today's terms would be very basic electronic circuitry, made using discrete components and possibly early integrated circuits.

Typical times for each of the sequence of operations were:

Achieve Moon lock	45 seconds
Twist	10 seconds
Slew	15 seconds
Search	15 seconds
Return	5 seconds

Thus, the acquisition time totalled 90 seconds, a significant proportion of the possible 300 seconds of useful time available on a Skylark flight. Indeed, it was considered by some that "a

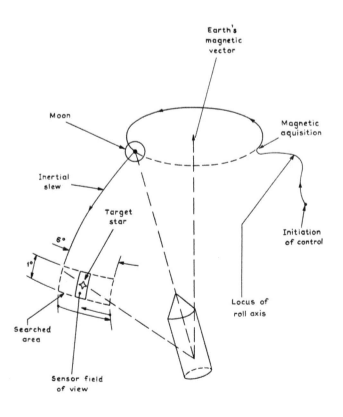

Figure 13.28 The three part Stage 5 ACU star acquisition sequence.

(Abbott (1971), figure 1)

---

[104] Massey & Robins (1986), *History of British Space Science*, p.208.
[105] Lunar acquisition was by coning round the local magnetic vector rather than using the optical coarse moon sensor of the Stage 1 ACU.
[106] Minutes of the 20th Skylark Policy Meeting, December 1971, p.5, item 6. (TNA: PRO AVIA 92/145).
[107] So called because their sensors are strapped to the vehicle, making them simpler and cheaper than otherwise.

typical Skylark may well have reached apogee before acquisition had been completed and measurements begun."[108] (Although see the flight profile of SL1004 earlier in this chapter for accurate flight timings.) There were other limitations such as limited available launch times and constraints in the position of the target stars in the sky. Other disadvantages included complexity and weight. These problems were recognised at the time,[109] and improvements using inertial navigation techniques were initiated to address them, as described later in this chapter.

Flight performance of SL1011

Two pre-selected target starts of visual magnitude +1.5 and +3.5 were successfully acquired by the control system during the flight, permitting measurements to be carried out in two closely defined areas of the sky by the Leicester University X-ray telescope, the principal experiment in the payload.[111]

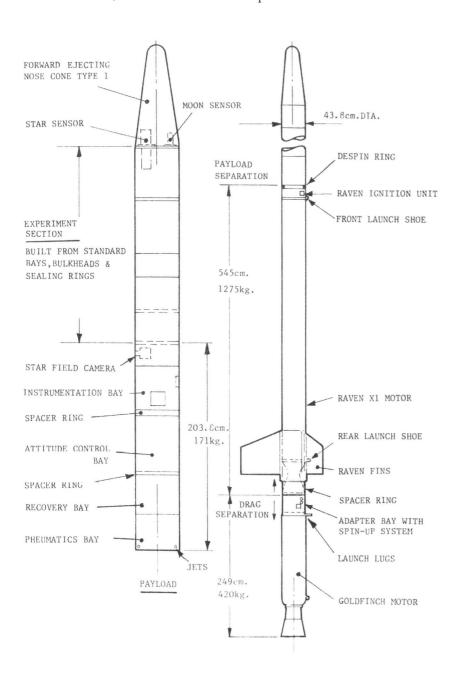

Figure 13.29 A typical star-pointing vehicle configuration for Skylark.
(Massey & Robins (1986), p.207) [110]

[108] Dorling (1975), 'Early History of the Skylark Rocket', p.186.

[109] Abbott (1971), *A Star-pointing Attitude Control System for Skylark*, sections 5 and 7.

[110] Massey & Robins (1986), *History of British Space Science,* © Science and Engineering Research Council 1986, published by Cambridge University Press, diagram reproduced with permission.

[111] Farr (1975), *Flight Performance of the Skylark SL1011 Star-pointing Attitude Control System*, p.3.

Scientific Results

It was recognised that there was a very clear link between the scientific usefulness of Skylark, and its advanced attitude control systems. However, on this flight an anomaly arose on one of the observations that was only explained later:

> The rocket, SL1011, flown in 1973, worked perfectly, as did the star-pointing system and the X-ray equipment. However nothing was seen – Cen X-3 was apparently not there! (Only later, with the flight of the *Uhuru* satellite did the reason emerge: Cen X-3 is an eclipsing binary, with a 1 in 4 chance of being 'off' at any time.)[112]

The RAE bows out

"The completion of the development of the Stage 5 Skylark stabilisation system marked the culmination of the long association of the RAE with the scientific Skylark programme. Responsibility for the procurement of Skylark rockets for Science Research Council purposes was formally transferred from the Ministry of Defence, Procurement Executive, to the Appleton Laboratory (previously the Radio and Space Research Station) of SRC in April 1974. Space Department of RAE provided an advisory service until April 1976." [113]

June 1973	SL1111

There were no Skylark launches in May, but in June at Woomera a short (two launch) Campaign 14 opened with the flight of the second Stage 5 Phase 2 star-pointing ACU.

This was launched on board **SL1111** on June 16th, which reached an altitude of 227 km (141 miles), providing about three minutes of stabilised observation time above 120 km before the payload was recovered by parachute. The astronomy experiment instrumentation from the Culham laboratory comprised a package of three Wadsworth-mounted objective grating spectrographs,[114] each of which recorded spectra on Kodak 101-01 photographic film.[115]

The new star-pointing ACU again worked successfully, and far UV spectra of the bright southern hemisphere stars γ^2 Velorum and ζ (zeta) Puppis were recorded. Two exposures were obtained for each star, 78 and 24 s for γ^2 Vel; 40 and 22 s for ζ Pup.

These two stars had been chosen as suitable background stars for an investigation of the interstellar medium in the direction of the Gum nebula.[116] This is an area associated with a supernova remnant of great interest to astronomers. Analysis of the spectra provided information about the physical and chemical properties of the interstellar medium in the line of sight, and useful data on the stellar atmospheres.[117]

As short as the observation time was, it still provided scientists with work for several years afterwards, as a further paper was published on the results three years later.[118]

---

[112] Pounds (1986), 'British X-ray Astronomy', p.442.

[113] Massey & Robins (1986), *History of British Space Science*, p.208. © Science and Engineering Research Council 1986, published by Cambridge University Press, reproduced with permission.

[114] As flown on SL811 in July 1970, the first flight of the star-pointing ACU, that was only partially successful.

[115] Burton, Evans & Griffin (1975), 'Skylark Rocket Observations of ultraviolet spectra of γ^2 Velorum and ζ Puppis'.

[116] Named after its discoverer, the Australian astronomer Colin Stanley Gum (1924-1960).

[117] Burton, Evans & Griffin (1974), 'The interstellar medium in the direction of the Gum nebula'.

[118] Burton, Evans & Griffin (1976), 'The absolute spectral flux distribution from γ^2 Vel'.

Figure 13.30 The Vela Supernova Remnant and part of the Gum nebula, in the area of the sky targeted by SL1111.

(© Australian Astronomical Observatory, photograph by David Malin from UKST plates, ref. UKS 2a).[119]

---

17 July 1973   SL1291

SL1291 was the second (S2) of nine Skylarks fired as part of a UK military programme, the 'Chevaline' project, where it appears to have been part of the project definition work.

The Chevaline project had its origins in British Polaris missile nuclear deterrent improvement studies undertaken in 1967-70. Project definition work continued until 1975/76, when it was finally decided to proceed with the project as the UK strategic nuclear weapon system with the ability to penetrate possible Soviet ABM defences.[120] The improvements were based on the concept of replacing the single Polaris RV (Re-entry Vehicle) with a Penetration Aid Carrier (PAC) that would include decoys to confuse an ABM system.[121]

The RAE became involved in aerodynamic issues and design. "Decoy ejection was an issue because the length of the threat cloud in the engagement zone needed to be as long as practical … The eject motors, the tubes, the static and dynamic balance of the decoys, the mountings, the clearances, and the

PAC motion, all posed problems only solvable iteratively."[122] After tests in vacuum chambers (during which most of the UK capacity was used), the RAE conceived a trial requirement to fire submissiles (as they referred to them) to establish the performance above the atmosphere. They decided that Skylark was by then a well-proven rocket, and placed an order on Frank Hazell's department (RAE Farnborough Space Dept.) for eight vehicles to be fired at Woomera.[123]

The main objectives of the Skylark programme were to photograph the submissiles as they left the payload, and to track them with radars installed specifically for the purpose. (One or more of the radars was subsequently dismantled and ended up at Jodrell Bank). The idea was that they would also be able to physically recover the submissiles (as Woomera was a land range), and observe any mistakes that were made during the progress of the experiments.

This S2 mission was designed to test decoy (submissile) ejection and erection. The six decoys ejected satisfactorily but all failed to erect; only one decoy showed any signs of erection.[124]

---

[119] See the website *www.davidmalin.com/* for similar fascinating images. (Last accessed August 2014).
[120] Panton (2004), 'The Unveiling of Chevaline', p.91.
[121] Dommett (2008), 'Engineering the Chevaline Delivery System', p.101.
[122] Ibid, p.109.
[123] John Ray in 2001, CCBH (2005), *Skylark Sounding Rockets 1957-1972*, p.74, & *Prospero* No.2, p.137.
[124] McDowell re TNA: PRO DEFE documents, personal communication, April 2010.

Overall, the trials were designated 'CQ941' for Australian purposes, but were of Chevaline origin. The Skylark part of the programme continued until 1979, when the series of nine launches was completed with SL1299. The Skylark vehicle itself, as was hoped, was extremely reliable, all the launches and recovery aspects were successful. The cameras were recovered and the actual performance of the submissiles was accurately recorded.[125]

> It was very successful from the Chevaline project point of view. We obtained the required data on the performance of the devices we were ejecting and it was extremely successful. We were able to pick up our bits, and also we were able to, as a result of the results from the Skylark, to influence the design of the system that was required. So from a Chevaline/CQ941 point of view the Skylark was an extremely successful programme...[126]

The CQ941 designation was also used for the operational Falstaff rocket firings from the Skylark launch pad at Woomera; these launches were numbered F1 to F5 and took place during a relatively concentrated campaign from May 1978 to April 1979,[127] thus overlapping the last three Skylark launches of the project. (See Chapters 14 and 15).

August 1973 SL1081A

The **SL1081A** Earth Survey mission in Sweden began with high hopes. It was a re-flight of parts of the recovered SL1081 payload, originally flown at Woomera in March 1972. There had been interest in Skylark survey flights from several parts of the world, including Indonesia and Thailand,[128] and in June 1972, the Skylark Earth observation platform had been exhibited during the RAE open days at Farnborough.[129]

As before, the Department of Trade and Industry sponsored the UK share, with BAC as main contractor and the RAE providing assistance. However, in this case a tripartite agreement between the UK, West Germany and Sweden allocated responsibility for the sensor package to the DFVLR,[130] and for the range facilities, ground truth survey and analysis to the Swedish Space Corporation.

The main interest from the survey point of view was the extent of the reindeer feeding grounds in Lapland, although studies of forestry and geomorphology were also planned. The launch took place from the ex-ESRO site at Kiruna in Northern Sweden, with intended coverage as shown by the map below:

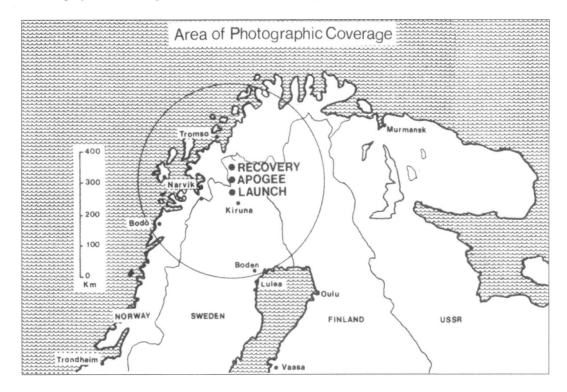

Figure 13.31 The anticipated coverage of SL1081A in Sweden.
(Beattie (1974), figure 4)

[125] John Ray in 2001, CCBH (2005), *Skylark Sounding Rockets 1957-1972*, p.74, & *Prospero* No.2, p.138.
[126] Ibid (CCBH), p.76, & *Prospero* No.2, p.140.
[127] BAe (1990), *Record of Skylark Launches 1957-1990*.
[128] Minutes of 24th Skylark Policy Meeting, December 1972, p.2 item 2. (TNA: PRO AVIA 92/145).
[129] The RAE open days took place from June 6-9 1973, and the platform was Exhibit 68. (TNA: PRO file OD 6/1604).
[130] DFVLR – the initials of this translate to '*German Test and Research Institute for Aviation and Space Flight*', then the equivalent the UK's RAE. It was formed in 1969 from several earlier institutions.

Disaster Strikes

Unfortunately, the Australian and Argentine successes were not to be repeated. At the subsequent Skylark policy meeting, a report on the launch of SL1081A explained:

> It was launched at Kiruna on 4 August 1973 but unfortunately, it had been a failure. The boost motor had operated correctly and there was evidence that the ignition unit and igniter of the main motor had operated but the motor had failed to light up. As a result, the payload crashed and was destroyed.
>
> RPE Westcott would be publishing a report on this failure. It was believed to be due to deterioration of the propellant surface. The motor, a RAVEN VIII, a type not normally used by SRC, was a seven year old ex ESRO stock and had been opened up a number of times for inspection.[131]

With this failure, the whole Skylark Earth-resources programme started to unravel. The lack of any imagery from the Swedish firing perhaps emphasising and revealing the apparent lack of a commercial market. Even before the Kiruna trial the DTI (Department of Trade and Industry) were reported as saying:

> DTI have supported the trial firings (and subsequent follow-up studies) at Woomera and in Argentina and will also support the Kiruna trials. They feel however that from then on the Skylark resources Rocket should pay for itself and that it will be a British Aircraft Corporation responsibility to find paying customers.[132]

Another comment regarding the meeting was "There seems no one responsible for integrating the programme and ensuring commercial benefit,"[133] a further sign that there was no single agency responsible for Skylark, and indeed that the 'Policy' committee had no executive or management staff responsible to it for implementing the decisions it made.

The DTI may not itself have been prepared to fund any more Skylark Earth resources launches, but it was prepared to help find paying customers from within other government departments. The files show that in 1974 and 1975 they pushed quite hard for Skylark to be used to provide an Earth resources survey of Sierra Leone, a Commonwealth country on the west coast of Africa about the size of Ireland.

It was estimated that the entire country could be covered by one flight.

However rather than grasp the opportunity, other government departments charged with carrying out such overseas surveys and mapping (for instance the Directorate of Overseas Surveys of the Ministry of Overseas Development [134]), were very reluctant to cooperate. They threw up many valid and non-valid arguments against using Skylark, on the basis that all real or imagined objections would have to be overcome by someone else before they could even consider offering financial support.[135]

However, it has to be said that in the debate by civil service memo and letter, several valid points did emerge. One was that in order to achieve the economies of scale a sounding rocket survey was capable of, most of a large geographical area would have to be clear of cloud or haze. In some parts of the world this would not only be an unusual event, but also difficult to monitor and communicate back to a firing base. Another problem was that the final report by Reading University of the Argentina user trials took years to appear (the trial was in March 1973, and by December 1974 the report was still not available[136]), thus the possible benefits of the Skylark user trial results remained undocumented.

Another major factor in the demise of the Skylark Earth resources survey project must have the fact as far as costs were concerned,[137] the playing field was far from level, and that although the ERTS-1 satellite launched in 1973 was much more expensive than any sounding rocket, the US government funded NASA was able to hide the true cost. Even before ERTS-1, at an international meeting in 1973 it was noted, "...at present, satellite imagery is available at no cost, at least for the purposes of scientific and technological cooperation with NASA." [138]

As for Argentina, it was reported in June 1973 [139] that, "the USA was applying pressure for that country to set up an Earth receiving station for reception of signals from ER satellites", and "the Argentineans were highlighting the need to establish the validity of the present results before further plans could materialise," and the report from Reading University was awaited. In the end, no business was forthcoming, and it became clear to the FCO (Foreign and Commonwealth Office) that 'Argentina is in a financial mess', and we seem to have picked the wrong country'.[140]

[131] Minutes of the 27th Skylark Policy Meeting, September 1973, p.2 item 2. (TNA: PRO AVIA 92/145).

[132] Handwritten note dated 19/7/73 of a visit to Mr C.I.M.O'Brian (Directorate of Overseas Surveys) by Miss E.J. Lindsay of DTI (TNA: PRO OD 6/1604).

[133] K.Doble, 19 June 1973, informal notes on 26th Skylark Policy Meeting, doc. ref.ZF167/01/PartB. (TNA: PRO AVIA 92/145).

[134] Successor to the Directorate of Colonial Surveys set up after the war to map the Colonial Empire.

[135] See the many letters and notes dated November and December 1974 in TNA: PRO document file OD 6/1604.

[136] Letter from D.Clark to M.Brunt dated 5 December 1974, TNA: PRO document file OD 6/1604.

[137] A proposal to use the smaller and cheaper Skua and Petrel sounding rockets (Pooley (1976)) for ER purposes appears to have come to nothing.

[138] Simmons (1974), 'Rockets for Earth Environment Monitoring', p.9.

[139] Minutes of the 26th Skylark Policy Meeting, June 1973, p.2. (TNA: PRO AVIA 92/145).

[140] See Godwin (2007), *The Skylark Rocket,* pp. 213 to 217 for a useful analysis of the politics behind the Argentine exercise.

Thus the true advantages (at the time) of rocket imagery over satellite imagery (better resolution, private ownership of data), did not prevail.

The Skylark remote sensing programme may have ended in 1973, but the Indonesian interest remained, and a few years later an Indonesian proposal surfaced for taking photographs over Java, using a payload powered by a Japanese 'Kappa' sounding rocket.[141] It is not known if this scheme came to anything.

In conclusion

A useful summary of these early remote sensing developments is provided by Dr John Townshend, at the time with the University of Reading, who carried out much work on the first two Skylark Earth resource projects:

> There were significant early remote sensing activities going on in the US stimulated largely by astronauts in [the] Gemini series taking pictures from space and the US made considerable investments in the intelligence Corona missions (photographic capsules being sent down to Earth and captured by aircraft when descending under a parachute)[142] and more relevantly Landsat [ERTS-1] whose images first became available to us during the Argentinean experiments. The latter in fact rang the death knell for Skylark as an Earth observing system. The resolution of the images was better than Landsat but the advantages of a polar orbit with repeat capability and global coverage were overwhelming: later the fact that the images were digital also became very important. So did Skylark matter. I think the answer is in the affirmative. It led to the first large scale terrestrial remote sensing activity based in the UK - both in terms of geographic coverage and in terms of the size of the

activity. It was crucial in getting the UK geared up to participate in and take advantage of remote sensing. It also provided the initial funding for many of those UK scientists who subsequently played major roles in the UK and elsewhere in the world.[143]

September 1973　　-

SL1271 - a Skylark that never was?

There were no Skylark launches in September; instead, one proposed Skylark flight around this time was cancelled. Concern had been expressed at RAE technical meetings that the longer and heavier payloads being flown on Skylark could compromise its stability; the remedy might require the use of ballasting, and in the longer term a change in the fin design. However, at the September Policy meeting it was reported that:

> The instrumentation on the two ER [Earth Resources] rounds fired in the Argentine had provided high quality information on round stability and the proposed stability investigation round, SL1271, could be put on ice and the money it would have cost could well be used to finance the new fin design.[144]

However, there is some evidence that the 'SL1271' designation may have been used by some parties as an alternative for SL1211, launched in May 1976, see the next chapter.

October 1973　　S93, S92, SL1121, SL1122

In October, four launches took place from two launch sites new to Skylark.

Figure 13.32 The location of the El Arenosillo launch site on the south-west coast of Spain.

(© OpenStreetMap contributors)

---

[141] Salatun (1979), 'An Earth Survey System Design using the Kappa-8 Rocket'.

[142] The reference to photographic capsules being returned from space is a reminder that in the early days of space satellites, it was not possible to return high-resolution images to Earth by radio telemetry, but as the technology improved, that situation rapidly changed. The plot behind Alistair MacLean's 1963 novel "Ice Station Zebra" concerned the recovery of such a film capsule.

[143] Dr John Townshend, personal communication, August 2009. Reproduced with permission.

[144] Minutes of the 27th Skylark Policy Meeting, September 1973, p.4, item 4. (TNA: PRO AVIA 92/145).

First were the **S93** and **S92** astronomy missions launched from the 'El Arenosillo' site in Spain. This sounding rocket range had been established in 1966, and was located on the Atlantic coast between Portugal and Gibraltar.

Over the years, many hundreds of sounding rockets have been fired out over the Atlantic from El Arensillo, as part of various international cooperative programmes. Many of these were British made Skua sounding rockets, and BAJ Aerojet (manufacturers of the Skylark rocket case) had helped the Spanish agency INTA equip the site, and later on develop the INTA 255 and INTA 300 sounding rockets. (The INTA 300 also being produced in the UK as the Fulmar.)[145]

S93 and S92 were launched on the 2nd and 6th of October, and were sponsored by the German DFVLR[146] institute, who may have taken them over after the demise of the ESRO sounding rocket programme. S93 had a test UV astronomy and astrophysics payload, with what appears to have been the successful operation of Skylark's first inertially stabilised Attitude Control Unit.[147] This was followed four days later by S92, an optical and UV astronomy mission utilising a star-pointing ACU.

The deployment of an inertial ACU on S93 poses an interesting question – why did the UK National and ESRO Skylark programmes develop such expensive hardware separately rather than pooling their R & D efforts?

Inertial ACU considerations

In fact, back in 1967, only three years after ESRO had started using Skylark, meetings exploring the possibility of a joint R&D programme for the Stage 5 ACU had taken place.[148] However, nothing transpired; the difficulties of coping with the additional logistics and management of a programme that already involved a wide variety of UK parties appear to have been just too much. Again, it seems that the lack of any single authority in charge of Skylark (such as a British Space Agency) was taking its toll.[149] The surprising thing is how well the Skylark programme ran, considering how many departments were involved.

The following extract in the next column illustrates the point:[150]

Skylark – Technical Authorities	
Policy Authority	- D/Space
Co-ordinating R&D Authority	- R.A.E/Space
Co-ordinating Design Authority (for the approved design)	- B.A.C Ltd

Specialist R&D and Design Authorities:

	R&D	Design
Vehicle Structure	RAE/Space	RAE/Space
Attitude Control System	RAE/Space	Elliott Bros. Ltd.
Propulsion	R.P.E.	R.P.E.
Motor Ignition	RAE/Space	RAE/Space
Telemetry	RAE/I&R	E.M.I. Ltd.

Standard Instrumentation:

Doppler and M.T.S.	RAE/I&R	Ether Engineering
Magnetometers	RAE/I&R	Dynamco Systems Ltd
Remainder of Instrumentation	RAE/Space	RAE/Space
Ground and Test Equipment	RAE/Space	RAE/Space
Trials	RAE/Space	W.R.E./A.D. (Range User)
Packaging (non-explosives)	RAE/Space	RAE/Space
Packaging (explosives)	AD/GW (P&W)	AD/GW (P&W)
Inspection Authority (non-explosives) -	D.A.I. (or his nominated Representative)	
Inspection Authority (explosives) -	D.A.I. (or his nominated Representative)	

Concerns expressed several years earlier at the Fifth Skylark Policy Meeting reveal some of the issues:

> …ESRO [had] waited so long for a satisfactory payload recovery system that they had now gone out to tender for it. For this and similar reasons there was a distinct danger that in about a year's time ESRO's version of the Skylark would be substantially different from the UK design. It already had different telemetry and gyros, it did not use Doppler tracking and it was unpressurised.

[145] Dorado, Bautista and Sanz-Aránguez, *Spain in Space,* ESA report HSR-26, p.21.

[146] DFVLR – the '*German Test and Research Institute for Aviation and Space Flight*'.

[147] BAe (1990), *Record of Skylark Launches 1957-1990.*

[148] See for instance the minutes of the 4th Skylark Policy Meeting, February 1967, p.17, item 4.5. (TNA: PRO AVIA 92/144).

[149] That this was a management rather than technical problem is illustrated by the fact that the in 1979 the Astro-Hel Skylark successfully used a German inertial guidance control system linked to a British Stage-1 pneumatic platform. (Weber & Henkel (1980), p.160).

[150] Appendix 1 of Skylark *Policy and Programme – Second Review*, briefing document Ref.DS/55/01, as attached to agenda for 5th Skylark Policy Meeting. (TNA: PRO AVIA 92/144).

ESRO were now looking into the use of tubing rather than castings, long term. Thus, only the Raven motor would remain a common item.[151]

The concern in this instance appeared to be that it was all very well for BAC to sell third parties a standard Skylark to a 'frozen' design, but once customers started changing things, who would pick up the pieces when things went wrong? (In fact, exactly this happened when ignition failures started to occur and the RAE had to step in and certify the ignition units[152]). In general, BAC's response was that they either did what the customer wanted, or turned down the business.

Regarding the possibility of an inertially controlled ACU, even as the UK Stage 5 ACU was being developed and flight-tested, it was realised that great strides were being made in the development of gyroscopically stabilised inertial platforms for other purposes such as aircraft navigation systems. It had always been appreciated that this developing technology might lead to a simpler and cheaper system for Skylark. For instance when discussing future developments, an RAE report issued in December 1971 had stated:

> The most likely means of meeting these objectives … would be the development of a system using a precision inertial platform, which would maintain orientation through launch and take the vehicle directly to star orientation. This possibility was rejected during the study phase [1968] of the present [Stage 5] development on grounds of cost. However the wider use of such platforms has reduced their relative cost.[153]

The Ferranti company for instance had developed an inertial navigation system for use on the TSR2 aircraft, and although the TSR2 was cancelled in 1965, the Ferranti effort was not all wasted, but had gone on to be used for as the basis of the Attitude Control Unit of the Black Arrow rocket, as first flown from Woomera in 1969.

By June 1971, ESRO had gone their own way regarding inertial guidance, and ordered a system called CASSIOPE to meet part of their need.[154] Following the demise of the ESRO sounding rocket programme at the end of 1972, it was presumably CASSIOPE that had been tested on S93 by the DFVLR.

In the UK, the development of Phase 2 of the Stage 5 star-pointing ACU had continued to slip[155] since the unsuccessful Phase 1 launch in May 1971 (SL812). Despite representations at director level, it was nearly two years before the Phase 2 version was successfully tested (SL1011 in April 1973). During this time, the Skylark Policy Meeting had been through the tortuous procedure[156] necessary to obtain funding approval for even a design study of an inertial platform ACU, but at last, in January 1973 a contract was placed with Ferranti Ltd. The hope was that an inertial based ACU could overcome the operational limitations of the Stage 5 system,[157] and provide freedom from launch restraints (for instance it could be used in daylight); and also provide detailed trajectory information, and supply output for thrust vector control if that became a requirement.[158]

The resulting report was considered in December 1973. By then, (as described above), S93 had successfully flown a similar ACU apparently developed by ESRO. However, this did not stop the parallel development in the UK, the results of the study were favourable and in due course development of a flight unit was put in hand for installation on SL1611.[159] (See the chapter after next, under the '1978' heading).

The 1973 High Latitude Campaign

The other two Skylarks launched in October were **SL1121** and **SL1122**, which initiated the 1973 'British National High Latitude Campaign'. They were the first Skylarks to be launched from Andøya in Norway, a site described below. They carried geophysical payloads to study the ionosphere at northern latitudes, in particular they were "a concentrated effort to gain a better understanding of the mechanism of the auroral substorm" (sudden changes in the brightness and motion of the aurorae).[160] This 1973 high latitude campaign was a continuation of studies begun with the ESRO rocket programme (e.g. Skylark S105 in October 1972), previous UK Petrel launchings at high latitudes, the Scandinavian rocket programme and experiments on satellites such as ESRO 1. The campaign extended from October to December 1973, and included four Skylark and nine Petrel rockets, typical apogees being 250 km and 140 km respectively. The other Skylarks were SL1123 (launched 16th November) and SL1124 (5th December).

[151] Minutes of the 5th Skylark Policy Meeting, November 1967, p.10, item 4. (TNA: PRO AVIA 92/144).
[152] In 1970 RAE certificated ignition units were being used. (Minutes of 16th Policy Meeting December 1970, p.5, item 6. (TNA: PRO AVIA 92/144).
[153] Abbott (1971), *A Star-pointing Attitude Control System for Skylark*, p.15
[154] Minutes of the 18th Skylark Policy Meeting, June 1971, p.5, item 6(b). (TNA: PRO AVIA 92/144).
[155] Minutes of the 20th Skylark Policy Meeting, December 1971, p.5, item 6. (TNA: PRO AVIA 92/145).
[156] Management by Civil Service committee! - the SRC had to be asked to investigate the possibility of supporting the development, and in turn an SRC working group had to convince the 'SPGC' to approve the funding (Minutes of the 20th Skylark Policy Meeting, December 1971, p.5, item 6. (TNA: PRO AVIA 92/145).
[157] Its complexity, weight and long acquisition time to the first target star resulted in lengthy preparation, short flights and erosion of useful observing time. (Reed (1974), *An Historical Review of Stabilisation Systems for the Skylark Rocket*, p.5).
[158] Minutes of the 25th Skylark Policy Meeting, March 1973, p.5, item 6.2. (TNA: PRO AVIA 92/145).
[159] Massey & Robins (1986), *History of British Space Science*, p.209.
[160] MSSL (1972), *Report of the MSSL 1st January – 30 September 1972*, part A, p.4.

The Skylarks must have sat on the launchers for many days, with the BAC launch team on standby whilst the experimenters scanned the skies for auroral activity. SL1121 was launched on 14th October, followed by SL1122 two weeks later on the 30th, which was launched into a multiple auroral-arc structure.

The instruments were supplied by several British Institutions (Appleton Laboratory, MSSL, the Universities of Birmingham, Southampton, Sheffield and Sussex), and included electron analysers, particle detectors, electric field probes, plasma wave probes and the like.[161]

The flights were very successful. On SL1121, SL1122 (and subsequently on SL1123) the aurora was observed during the expansion, growth and recovery substorm phases respectively.[162] The many instruments provided a wealth of data for the experimenters, information that kept them busy for several years. One MSSL paper was, for example, published three years later in 1976,[163] and in 1981 the results were still being reported.[164]

SL1121 was distinguished by having a modern 'PCM' electronic telemetry system fitted,[165] very different from the rotating mechanical switches of earlier years. This improved the time resolution of the telemetry data by a factor of ten compared to the other flights.[166] The Sussex University experiment on board SL1122 was unusual in that it used two high impedance probes deployed three metres apart on booms perpendicular to the rocket spin axis to detect electric fields.[167]

As noted above, these 1973 High Latitude Campaign Skylarks were launched from yet another new launch site. Andøya was a Norwegian national sounding rocket launch facility, established in 1962 on an island off its North Atlantic/Arctic Sea coast, well located for sounding-rocket launches in the auroral belt. It was a useful alternative to Kiruna in Sweden, and although land recovery was not possible, it offered splashdown recovery in an almost unlimited area of the Arctic Ocean. It therefore suited higher flying sounding rockets, particularly those with less accurate guidance systems than required for Kiruna.

Andøya had come into more general use after ESRO had terminated their sounding rocket programme in 1972. After the termination, the Esrange Special Project (ESP) was established and ESRO transferred its ownership of the Esrange launch base near Kiruna to Sweden. At the same time, the Norwegian Andøya launch base was also included in the Special Project, allowing coordinated European sounding-rocket research at high latitudes to be continued after ESRO's activities had ceased.[168]

The Andøya range was not as well equipped as that at Kiruna, and Skylark firings had to rely on the general-purpose transportable launcher developed by MAN of Germany.[169] (As tested at Aberporth in January 1971.) Today (2014) the site is still active, and known as the Andøya Space Center.[170]

The UK's smaller Petrel sounding rocket could also be launched from Andøya, where two launchers for it had been installed. Both could be loaded but only one was elevated at a time. These allowed successive firings, one as an event came up and another as it decayed. Thus, as well as the two Skylark launches, six Petrel launches also took place from Andøya in October, carrying similar instruments from the same British institutions.[171]

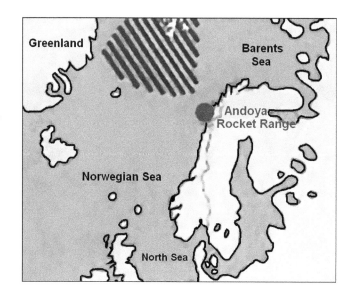

Figure 13.33 The location and impact area of the Norwegian Andøya rocket launch site (69°N, 16°E), situated 100 km southwest of Tromso.

(Andøya Space Center)

[161] Royal Astronomical Society (1976), 'MIST Meeting at Aberystwyth' (April 1976).

[162] Sojka & Raitt (1976), 'Secondary electron production in the upper atmosphere during auroral activity'.

[163] Basto, Raitt & Sojka (1976), 'A high resolution, low energy electrostatic analyser for rocket payloads'.

[164] Bryant (1981), figure 5 – republished again as part of an eBook in 2013!

[165] PCM stands for Pulse Code Modulation, in this context the digital sampling and combination of analogue signals for sending by radio telemetry.

[166] MSSL (1974), *Report of the MSSL 1st October 1973 – 30 September 1974*, part 2, p.3.

[167] Christiansen *et al.* (1976), 'Detection of high-frequency electrostatic signals in the auroral atmosphere'.

[168] Seibert (2006), *The History of Sounding Rockets and their contribution to European Space Research*, p.29.

[169] Minutes of the 20th Skylark Policy Meeting December 1971, p.3, item 8. (TNA: PRO AVIA 92/145).

[170] See *www.rocketrange.no/* for details. (Last accessed August 2014).

[171] Massey & Robins (1986), *History of British Space Science*, p.421.

Figure 13.34 A (summer!) sounding rocket launch from the scenic Andøya launch site on the Norwegian coast. This is not Skylark, but a much later firing of a student 'CanNoRoc' vehicle, c.2009.

(Andøya Space Center, Norway)

November 1973   SL1123, SL1206, S74

The high-latitude campaign continued through November, and a whole series of rockets were successfully flown from Andøya during a complex auroral substorm on the night of November 16-17. The first, Skylark **SL1123** (22:46 UT), carried instruments to measure neutral winds, electric and magnetic fields, plasma density and temperature, and a range of energetic particles from 10 eV to 26 keV. Petrels P145 (23:45 UT) and P146 (01:01 UT) carried neutral wind experiments, whilst P148 (01:22 UT) made plasma density and temperature measurements.[172]

Meanwhile, back at Woomera, **SL1206** was being prepared. It had been hoped to use the first Raven XI on this mission,[173] but that was not to be, and SL1206 was eventually launched on the 26th November with a standard Raven VI motor. The payload was dedicated to Leicester solar physics experiments using a Sun-pointing ACU and carrying out X-ray and white light photography. Interestingly, SL1206 was designed to coordinate with X-ray observations being carried out at the same time during the third (manned) operational period of NASA's SKYLAB mission. For this, the Leicester group used their Mk 3 Bragg spectrometer on SL1206, and an American group used the S-054 X-ray telescope on the SKYLAB ATM (Apollo Telescope Mount).[174]

Figure 13.35 The Leicester Mk 3 Bragg X-ray spectrometer as flown on SL1206.

(Roger Cooper)

---

[172] Rees *et al.* (1976), 'Structure of the auroral upper atmosphere and its response to substorm activity', p.463.
[173] Minutes of the 27th Skylark Policy Meeting, November 1973. (TNA: PRO AVIA 92/145).
[174] Pye *et al.* (1978), 'The Structure of the X-ray Bright Corona above Active Region McMath 12628 …' p.125.

Although the flight and experiment were successful, there were difficulties to be overcome along the way. During preparations for launch at Woomera early in November, the 'GIMIC' (Ground Instrumentation, Missile Instrumentation, Check) [175] was interrupted by a violent cyclone followed by torrential and continuous rain. The launch bunker was blacked out, the Range area became swampland, and for several days afterwards, Range personnel found themselves in the unlikely situation of having to ford streams to travel from the range head to Woomera Village and vice-versa, with water at times over the floorboards. Ted Chambers recalled:

> The inundation brought some interesting effects in its wake. The filling of Lake Koolymilka, normally a large white saltpan, introduced wild life of great variation to the scene...the lake and all the resulting ponds and puddles of water soon began to show signs of marine life. Strange water creatures, tiny bivalves and shrimp-like things swam or wriggled beneath the surface...

> ...The rains continued and one day, looking out of the Test Shop windows, it was puzzling to witness small dark objects bounding up and down about six inches from the ground. It proved to the first act of the great Frog invasion. Before long there were frogs everywhere, much to the delight of the seagulls. The frogs invaded the Test Shop in such numbers that careful foot placement was the order of the day...

> The rains and water left and then began the mice plague. Mice in their millions. They got everywhere. Into cable ducts, into electrical equipment, where they feasted on cable insulation and caused unlikely little puffs of smoke...[177]

Whilst on the subject, there were other fauna problems that beset Skylark:

> Flocks of raucous cockatoos were a never ending annoyance. For some reason these noisy creatures took a great delight in devouring the plastic covering used on the launcher air-conditioning system.[178] It was found that firing rockets managed to account for a few of them, like finding on post firing checks of the launcher that only the legs remained of the bird tenants, the claws still firmly holding on, while the bodies had gone with the wind. Since each rocket took only about one second to clear the tower, the birds had little notice of impending doom. Thought was given to providing the launcher with a pre-firing hooter, as a warning device, but that could have hazarded the rockets with a near sky full of cockatoos, so the cockatoo war was continued. The problem was never solved, other than maintaining a good supply of plastic.

> Then there were always the flies. Flies by the ton. Heaven knows what they found to eat in the sterile environment, apart from trials people. A pat on the back of a colleague at any time would guarantee to make him lighter and dispose of some fifty flies in the process. Outside, mouths were only opened if words were really necessary.

Figure 13.36 Lake Koolymilka, awash again in 2007 (34 years after SL1206!), following many years as a dry inland lake.[176]
('Gibber Gabber', 23/2/07, reproduced with permission)

---

[175] Described as "...a rehearsal for launch, a complete sequence rundown without lighting the blue touch paper." (Chambers (2000), *Woomera, Its Human Face*, p.79).

[176] The Royal Navy sailed (and capsized) a dinghy here in the winter of 1974! (Morton (1989), p.355).

[177] Chambers (2000), *Woomera, Its Human Face*, p.80-81.

[178] Introduced to stop the rocket motor filling 'slumping' in the heat.

One conclusion seemed to be that their only obvious food supply was other flies. A sort of perpetual motion.[179]

Meanwhile, back in the world of astronomy, the SL1206 experiment was a great success. SKYLAB carried excellent equipment for broadband X-ray imagery, but no high-resolution X-ray spectrometer; this was the feature that the Skylark instrument provided. The combined results, together with ground-based observations, were used to produce a partial model of the solar atmosphere above an active region of the Sun. (McMath 12628). It was possible to point the Leicester instrument very accurately (better than one arc minute, i.e. 1/60th of a degree),[180] as indicated on the figure below.

The launch was reported in the Australian press:

> A British Skylark research rocket was launched successfully at Woomera on Monday in a joint experiment between London's University College [sic] and the Nasa Skylab Space Station.
>
> The experiment is aimed at increasing knowledge of the Sun. The exact moment of the launching was coordinated with Skylab's minute-by-minute movements. After the rocket cleared the Earth's atmosphere equipment on board took X-ray pictures of the Sun. Information in the X-ray spectrum was radioed back to Earth. The Skylab instruments simultaneously made observations of the Sun with solar telescopes.

The information from the two sources will be combined and compared by computer.

> Scientists are hoping for new knowledge about the temperature of the solar Corona, the hot gasses around the Sun.[182]

The third and final launch of November was that of S74, another DFVLR astronomy mission launched from El Arenosillo in Spain. This appears to have been similar to S92 launched from the same site in October; it too carried an optical and UV astronomy experiment using a star-pointing ACU.

December 1973   SL1124

SL1124 was the fourth and last Skylark round of the 1973 High-Latitude Campaign. It had been hoped to have a fifth launch, but this had been added to the campaign a little late,[183] and it did not meet the deadline. (See SL1221 in the next chapter).

The data from these and other rocket flights during the 1973 campaign were used to model the observed structural changes of the neutral atmosphere and ionosphere behaviour during the substorms, one advantage of the campaign concept being that scientists from many different institutions could meet and compare results. For instance, a large part of the MIST (Magnetosphere, Ionosphere & Solar-Terrestrial Environment) meeting held at UCW Aberystwyth in April 1976 was devoted to discussions of the 1973 High Latitude Rocket Campaign, and was attended by about 100 people.[184]

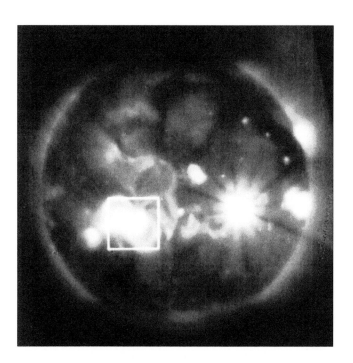

Figure 13.37 A 16-second X-ray exposure of the Sun on 26th November 1973, taken by the SKYLAB instrument, marked to show where the Leicester instrument on Skylark was pointed.
(Pye *et al.* (1978), figure 3a) [181]

[179] Chambers (2000), *Woomera, Its Human Face*, p.82.
[180] Pye *et al.* (1978), 'The Structure of the X-ray Bright Corona above Active Region McMath 12628 ...' p.124. See also Hutcheon, Pye & Evans (1976), 'The spectrum of Fe XVII in the solar corona'.
[181] Astronomy and Astrophysics, vol.65, p.123, 1978, reproduced with permission © ESO.
[182] The [Melbourne] Age, Tuesday 27th November 1973. Reproduced with permission.
[183] Minutes of 25th Skylark Policy Meeting, March 1973, p.5. (TNA:PRO AVIA 92/145).
[184] Introduction to the meeting report, the Quarterly Journal of the Royal Astronomical Society, Vol.17, p.457.

Figure 14.1 An unusual view of SL1304 at Arenosillo, October 1974.
(Giles (2010a), figure 14)

CHAPTER 14

(1974-76)

WINDING DOWN

Jan.	Feb.	March	April	May	June	July	Aug.	Sept.	Oct.	Nov.	Dec.
HRC1	SL1203		SL1207		SL1104	SL1292			SL1012	SL1221	
									SL1304	SL911	
									SL1471		

Table 14.1 The 10 Skylark launches in 1974. (For full details see Appendix 3)

(Key: red = German national, plum & black = UK (stabilised), blue = UK (unstabilised))

SKYLARK LAUNCHES AND SCIENCE IN 1974

In 1974 the number of Skylark launches was nearly half that of the previous year, down to ten compared with eighteen, although as in the previous chapter, an increasing amount of information has survived for these launches. Absent were the Earth observation and solar physics missions of earlier years. However, the number of astronomy payloads using attitude control units held up, contributing to six of the eight scientific flights. With the absence of solar physics experiments, all the astronomy missions were for cosmic/stellar purposes, i.e. observations outside the solar system. The only geophysics (Earth related) launches were SL1207 from Woomera in April and SL1221 from Norway in November.

Of the five UK sponsored cosmic astronomy missions, only two (SL1012 and SL911) used the Stage 5 star-pointing ACU, perhaps reflecting Professor Boyd's concern at the possible lack of availability.[1]

Behind the scenes, in November 1973 the RSRS (Radio and Space Research Station) had been renamed the Appleton Laboratory.[2] In April 1974, it took over from the UK's MOD procurement executive,[3] and become responsible for Skylark procurement, accountancy and contracts.[4] Its Sounding Rockets Division also took over the role of range user at Woomera in place of the Royal Aircraft Establishment's Space Department, thus trials in Australia became jointly planned by the Appleton Laboratory and the Australian WRE Trials Wing.[5] However as

before, British national programme Skylark payloads were assembled and integrated at BAC Filton, and then accompanied to Woomera by the payload engineers and experimenters. The experimenter's equipment was handled in the same way:

> …for all our test equipment and spares to be sent to Filton where it was professionally packed to the very highest standards. Every item left in the pile of equipment was packed into specially made boxes of 2 cm thick multilayered cardboard which had a sort of tar paper in the middle to protect against moist atmospheres. These boxes were beautifully constructed on site by the packers and were worth more than some of the equipment they contained. Unpacking the boxes in Australia held some surprises. On one occasion a cylindrical tube 4 cms long and 2 cm in diameter cased in antifungal packing paper was found at the centre of such a box. No one could think what it was until we opened it to find half a tube of polos left by one of us on our equipment pile in Filton, and dutifully packed to military standards for us to enjoy in Woomera.[6]

On the satellite front, on the 9th March 1974, the second British technology satellite to go into orbit was launched, although the cancellation of Black Arrow in 1971 meant that a US rocket had to be used. This 'X4' satellite, named 'Miranda' once in orbit, used an innovative propane cold gas thruster system for attitude control.[7] Skylark had been used to help develop this system, starting with SL20 in 1964. (See Figure 8.48.)

---

[1] See the start of the previous chapter.

[2] See Appendix 3.

[3] Minutes of the 26th Skylark Policy meeting, June 1973, p.3. (TNA: PRO AVIA 92/145).

[4] For details of the SRC's activities in this sphere, see Acton (1974), 'Some Aspects of the Management of the Science Research Council's Space Activities'.

[5] Dorling (1975), 'Early History of the Skylark Rocket', p.187.

[6] Cruise (2008), *Skylark Ascending*, online article p.10, and *Prospero* number 5, Spring 2008, p.44.

[7] For a useful outline description of the propane propulsion system used in orbit, see Fearn (2005), pp.5&6.

The Skylark **HRC1** mission was the fourth in the DFVLR (German) sponsored X-ray astronomy flights. Like the others, it was launched from El Arenosillo in Spain, and it reached the respectable height of 246 km (153 miles), the payload using an inertially controlled ACU for stabilisation. Unfortunately, the experiment appears to have failed, the only clue the author has found being the cryptic comment "Exp. door failure".[8] It may have had a German MPE payload with UV spectrometer to study comet Kohoutek.[9]

---
5 February 1974   SL1203

Unlike the previous HRC1 mission, the next Skylark was well documented, and so is described fully in the next few pages. **SL1203** carried the second MSSL soft X-ray payload, an astronomy experiment similar to, but more ambitious than, that which had failed aboard SL402 in October 1972. It was designed to carry out an X-ray search of the southern skies, in particular for low-energy (soft) diffuse emissions from two

large radio emitting structures known as "Loop I" and "Loop IV".[10] It was anticipated that the detection of soft X-rays[11] from such objects would be significant, and call for revision of the then current supernova theory.[12] The instruments consisted of three thin window multiwire proportional counters each fitted with a simple slat collimator and tilted to observe adjacent strips of sky. One detector was situated on the top bulkhead beneath a standard type 3 split nose cone, while the other two were housed in a recoverable bay of MSSL design. Such observations were technically difficult, and the systems developed were in many cases entirely new and of considerable sophistication.[13] They brought together significant MSSL experimental, mechanical and electronic design activity, and included a highly sophisticated control system that maintained gas density in the detector within a range of ± 0.15%.[14]

Designing the payload

One of the mechanical designers who worked on this in 1973 was John Coker (still working at MSSL 41 years later in 2014!) He recalls:

Figure 14.2 The special Skylark bay designed at MSSL for SL1203, showing X-ray detectors 2 and 3. The doors were designed to open and close in space to protect the detectors and permit performance to be monitored in flight. After launch, a restraining cable was cut by a pyrotechnic cutter, allowing the doors to be operated by winch motors.

(WRE \ Rapley)

[8]   BAe (1990), *Record of Skylark Launches 1957-1990*.
[9]   *www.rocketservices.co.uk/spacelists/sounding_rockets/decades/1970-1974.htm* (last accessed February 2013) (sic).
[10] At this time, four very large, shell-shaped astronomical features were known from surveys (c.1960-70) of radio emissions from the Galaxy. Ranging in angular diameter from 40° (Loop IV) to 116° (Loop I, the North Polar Spur), they had been identified as polarized, non-thermal radio sources that appeared to be associated with faint optical emission nebulae.
[11] X-rays from about 0.12 to 12 keV (10 to 0.10 nm wavelength) are classified as "soft" X-rays, and those at shorter wavelengths from about 12 to 120 keV (0.10 to 0.01 nm wavelength) as "hard" X-rays, because of their penetrating abilities.
[12] MSSL (1972), *Report of the MSSL 1st January 1972 – 30 September 1972*, Part B, p.8.
[13] Rapley (1974), *A Report on the Design and Performance of SL1203*, p.1.
[14] Massey & Robins (1986), *History of British Space Science*, p.373.

Figure 14.3 The SL1203 Gas Density Control Bay also designed and built by MSSL. As shown in the next figure, this was the first bay under the nose cone.
(MSSL \ Coker)

In addition to the detector under the nose cone we housed two more detectors in a special bay designed at MSSL by our engineer Peter Sheather and cast specially for us. This bay had two very large cut outs fitted with opening doors and so required a central stiffening rib to replace the lost strength/stiffness.

We also developed a highly sensitive gas density control system using very basic parts to regulate the detector fill density.[15]

> ...the gas density system shown in the picture represents very well the approach to payloads in the Skylark days. I don't mean to say that they were poorly done, but we did use a lot of ingenuity to put common parts into use and keep costs down. That was made possible because mass was generally not critical on Skylarks, so there was no need to go to expensive [parts] to produce very lightweight designs as we now have to for satellite instruments. Also, because the overall cost of the missions were a fraction of a satellite mission we were able to use everyday items selected by careful testing instead of the very expensive and usually specifically produced certified parts that we have to use nowadays to reduce risk of loosing a very expensive mission. For example the entire gas system in the picture was designed here [MSSL] and used standard Schrader valves opened by off the shelf solenoids from rotary sequence switches, the parts were brought to-

gether by a simple in house part and mounted with a bracket from alloy angle. All the tubing and fittings were standard Enots parts most commonly used for pneumatic control systems on machine tools etc. and the gas bottles were simply aluminium alloy tubing cut to length with in house end caps sealed with "O" rings and held together with studding tie rods.[16]

A second experiment was also included, an MSSL collaboration with the University of California at Berkeley. This was designed to search for XUV (Extreme Ultraviolet) objects. By launching the experiment from Woomera, it was possible to search a part of the southern Sky invisible from the White Sands range in the USA. The UCB telescope was a one-dimensional system consisting of gold plated mirrors focussing a line image onto five small thin window proportional counters, all housed in a special self-contained bay.

Difficulties at Woomera

By September 1973, the experiments were awaiting shipping to Woomera, and "in due course were launched on 5th February." However, this simple statement hides the fact that achieving success took tenacity and perseverance against surprising odds. This was no doubt true of many Skylark missions, but for SL1203 many of the original records and reports have been preserved by Chris Rapley, and provide an insight into the difficulties met and overcome.

[15] John Coker, personal correspondence, May 2009.
[16] John Coker, personal correspondence, April 2010.

Final preparation began at Woomera on Monday 26th November 1973, when the nose cone and instrument sections were unpacked.[17] The process continued, with only relatively minor problems including two missing test boxes, requiring phones calls and telexes to the UK. By the start of the following week, the complete payload was assembled, and experiment integration tests were carried out. However on Tuesday 11th December the cryptic comment appears in the Post Firing Report "Head due to be put on air bearing, however this was not done due to very high ambient temperature in the main test shop".[18] Investigation reveals the temperature that day reached 36ºC (97ºF) at nearby Woomera aerodrome,[19] so with the sun beating down all day on the test shop roof,[20] conditions inside must have been unbearable. However at least that day a photograph of progress so far was taken:

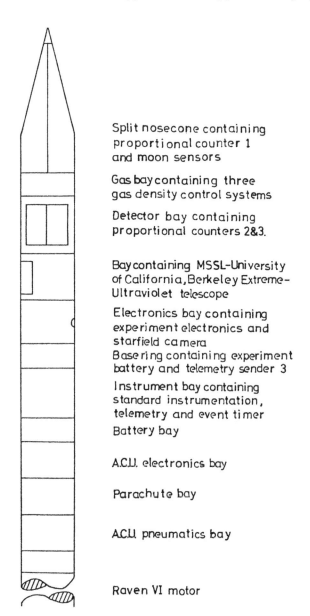

Split nosecone containing proportional counter 1 and moon sensors

Gas bay containing three gas density control systems

Detector bay containing proportional counters 2&3.

Bay containing MSSL-University of California, Berkeley Extreme-Ultraviolet telescope

Electronics bay containing experiment electronics and starfield camera
Base ring containing experiment battery and telemetry sender 3

Instrument bay containing standard instrumentation, telemetry and event timer

Battery bay

A.C.U. electronics bay

Parachute bay

A.C.U. pneumatics bay

Raven VI motor

Figures 14.4 and 14.5
Left: The SL1203 configuration as originally designed.

(Rapley (1976), figure 6-1)

Right: The corresponding payload head for SL1203 during final preparation at Woomera on Tuesday 11th December 1973. The cables are attached to the battery bay.

(WRE \ Rapley)

[17]   Chambers (1974), *SL1203 Post Firing Report*, p.11.
[18]   Ibid.
[19]   *www.tutiempo.net/en/Climate/Woomera_Aerodrome/12-1973/946590.htm*, (last accessed August 2014).
[20]   Test Shop 1 was a basic non-insulated structure, see the photographs of SL1081 being prepared in Figure 12.25.

Progress continued, but not for long. On Thursday 13th December, a rare heavy rainstorm caused all electrical power to the range to be lost when the power lines from Port Augusta to Woomera were struck by lightning. On Friday, there was still no power in Test Shop 1, so the round was secured for the Christmas stand down, and the team members returned to Adelaide.

As described in the previous chapter, the unusual weather was a feature that Woomera summer, this had affected preparations for the launch of SL1206 the month before, and the problems had continued into December. Chris Rapley, Principal Investigator on SL1203, recalls:

> The storms and floods of late 1973 were extraordinary.[21] I was amazed on our first drive up to the range from the village after our arrival to be confronted by a huge bright blue lake - Koolymilka - which in living memory had only ever been a dried out salt pan - although in the "restaurant" that operated outside the rangehead security fence there was a faded b&w picture over the bar of an old timber sailing boat supposedly on Lake Koolymilka[22] - which none of us had previously believed.[23] The rainfall resulted in the desert blooming (beautiful) followed by a plague of tiny frogs (which we had to drive over), a plague of grasshoppers (with disgusting effect on the car windscreen), dark clouds of budgerigars, after which a plague of mice (which urinated in the electrical

control gear and caused all sorts of problems) and in turn a problem with snakes - including a (tiger?) snake in Test Shop 1 which Mike Reynolds and I chose to leave to its own ends when we discovered it late one evening. We were also trapped by a flash flood when returning late one evening to the village, and had to sleep in the (Holden) car on a high spot and wait till the waters receded, which was not until breakfast time.[24]

After the stand down, the UK based members of the team were able to return home for a week or two, although even that had its moments. Chris Rapley again:

> We made it home over Christmas, but not without event as the Bristol Britannia had nose wheel steering problems which concluded with a major drama at Luton. We returned in the New Year by a British Airways scheduled "headshrinker" 747 flight.

Activity on SL1203 resumed on Monday 7 January, with tests concentrating on the Attitude Control Unit. This would be the first flight of a new variation of the Stage 1 ACU, modified to align itself with the Earth's magnetic field,[25] fortunately it turned out that preparation was simpler than for a standard Sun-pointing ACU. Two weeks later, the experimenter from UCB (University of California at Berkeley) arrived, although the long flights, the time differences and the heat had taken its toll:

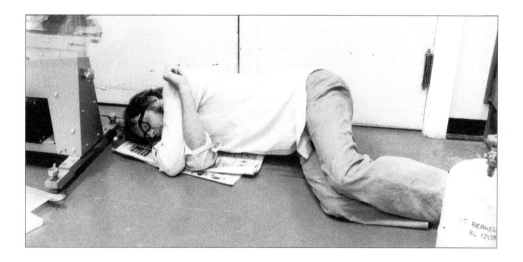

Figure 14.6 'Stu' Bowyer, University of California, Berkeley,[26] catching up on the 21st January,[27] following the three-day MoD charter flight from London. An official WRE photograph!

(WRE \ Rapley)

---

[21] For a further description of the storms and floods, see Chambers (2000), *Woomera, Its Human Face,* pp.80-83.
[22] Ted Chambers also mentions "The Kooly Yacht Club", in *Woomera, Its Human Face,* p.29. See also Figure 13.36 of this book!
[23] See Figure 13.36!
[24] Chris Rapley, personal correspondence, 2010. Reproduced with permission.
[25] The ACU consisted of a recovered Stage 1 electronics package with the solar "coarse eyes" replaced by magnetometers. (Rapley (1974), *A Report on the Design and Performance of SL1203,* p.3).
[26] Professor Stuart Bowyer is generally given credit for starting the field of extreme ultraviolet astronomy.
[27] Date deduced from Chambers (1974), *SL1203 Post Firing Report,* p.13.

On the 25th, the head was weighed and recorded, an operation that had to be done in two halves because of its length. The result was 335 kg (739 lbs), and at one third of a tonne, this was the heaviest Skylark payload fired from Woomera to date.[28] Next, during final telemetry checks on Thursday the 31st a serious fault developed, when one of the three SL1203 telemetry senders failed.[29] Local attempts to repair it were to no avail, and with no spare in Australia, a spare circuit board was ordered by Telex from the UK, and all work stopped to await it.[30] The flight had to be launched within five days of full moon, and there were some anxious moments when doubts arose as to whether the spare had caught its flight. However, on Sunday 3rd February it was discovered it had been off loaded in Perth, Western Australia. At 09.15 on

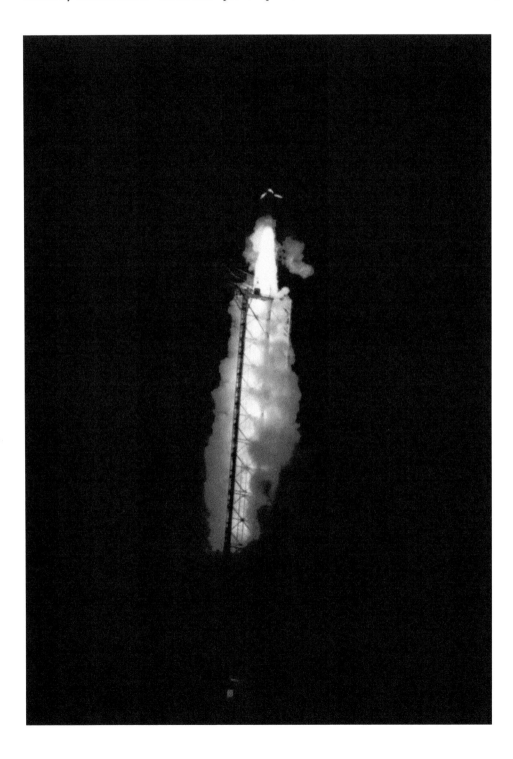

Figure 14.7 After all the hard work and preparation, SL1203 was successfully launched at 01:10 hours local time on Tuesday 5 January 1974. (The exhaust from the three pairs of small Imp motors can be seen at the top.

(WRE \ Rapley)

---

[28] The figures are from Chambers (1974), *SL1203 Post Firing Report*, p.16.

[29] The telemetry was a vital part of the experiments, as all the measurements were to be sent by radio link. To cope with the large volume of data, two newly developed RAE solid-state senders were used.

[30] Chambers (1974), *SL1203 Post Firing Report*, p.13.

Monday the 4th it arrived at Test Shop 1, was fitted and all was well. Final checks on the head were carried out during the day and it was transported to the launcher at 16.00 hours. Here it was fitted on top of the motor, and after further checks, SL1203 was launched that night, at 01:10 hours local summer time.[31]

The ten-minute flight plan went to schedule, SL1203 reaching space after one and a half minutes:[32]

Goldfinch ignition:		0 secs	
Raven ignition		6 secs	1.4 km
Despin	1 min	17 secs	85 km
Nose cone jettison	1 min	20 secs	95 km
Head release	1 min	22 secs	98 km
ACU gas on	1 min	26 secs	103 km
Apogee	3 min	49 secs	197 km
Pneumatic bay jettison	6 min	19 secs	93 km
Parachute bay deployment	9 min	30 secs	3.5 km

The flight itself started well, the new form of ACU (Attitude Control Unit) worked, aligning itself with the Earth's magnetic field in only nine seconds,[33] and then carrying out four controlled rolls at about 1° per second, so the experiments scanned the chosen area of the sky. However, at +17 seconds MSSL detector 1 started to leak gas, and after 86 seconds the supply ran out and it stopped working.[34] In addition, the detector 3 door failed to open, and the star- field camera film jammed because of a fault in the construction of the armoured take-up cassette.

Finally, on landing, the parachute system did not deploy correctly, the payload was badly damaged and the parachute torn. (At the design stage it had been realised that as SL1203 had the longest and heaviest payload of its time, and its weight was almost twice that the standard parachute system was designed to cope with.[35] However, it had been hoped that the star-field camera film and the X-ray calibration sources could be recovered, as well as much flight hardware for future use.)

In addition, the dispersion of SL1203 was much greater than expected; the aiming point was 152 km (94 miles) down range, but the payload landed 49 km (30 miles) further away. This caused concern because it exceeded the warning circle radius, an investigation determined this was because the wind had changed between wind sampling and applying the launcher correction.[37]

Figures 14.8 and 14.9 After searching for half an hour, the badly damaged payload of SL1203 was located by helicopter. The head had landed in soft mud.[36]

(WRE / Rapley)

[31] Astronomical X-ray experiments were usually launched at night to avoid effects from solar X-rays. (Charles & Seward (1995), p.33).
[32] Chambers (1974), *SL1203 Post Firing Report*, p.6.
[33] This was much faster than the nominal 30 seconds for a standard Stage 1 Sun-pointing ACU, because SL1203 flew relatively steadily and the pointing accuracy required was less.
[34] Rapley (1976), 'New techniques and observations in Soft X-ray astronomy', p.157.
[35] Rapley (1974), *A Report on the Design and Performance of SL1203*, p.3.
[36] Chambers (1974), *SL1203 Post Firing Report*, p.6.
[37] Ibid p.7.

Scientific Results

At first, it was thought that technically the flight had been 75% successful, loss of data from the star-field camera being the major problem,[38] reducing the accuracy to which the direction of pointing could be determined. However, because of the flight problems described above, in the end only one of the three MSSL detectors gave useful results.[39] Fortunately, the NASA EUV telescope operated successfully.

Overall, the flight was extremely successful, despite the complicated experiments and new technology being used. At least two scientific papers resulted,[40] and Chris Rapley was able to write his PhD thesis based on the result.[41] However for MSSL it was a narrow escape, if the third detector had failed for any reason, then there would have been no scientific result after three years of difficult and expensive work.

As it was, the MSSL experiment produced state of the art X-ray astronomy results. It discovered an enhancement associated with Radio Loop IV and confirmed the existence of soft X-ray emission from Loop I. In addition, soft X-ray absorption by a dense ridge of neutral hydrogen lying approximately 200 parsec (61 light years) away in Hydra was observed. This latter result was of great importance since it provided the first positive evidence for the existence of strong soft X-ray emission from beyond the bulk of the galactic absorbing gas.[42]

The NASA/Berkeley EUV experiment also produced good results, and discovered a new stellar EUV source near the South Equatorial Pole, only the fifth such source to be found,[44] although the first by a systematic search rather than the observation of known soft X-ray sources.[45] It also appears to have been the first discovered in the southern hemisphere.

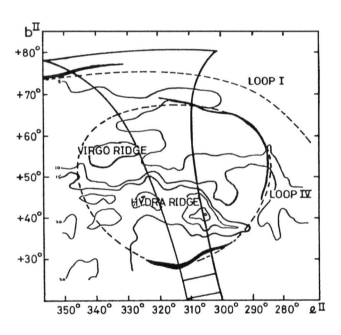

Figure 14.10 The SL1203 detector 2 scan path, superimposed on the astronomical features of interest.
(Rapley (1976), figure 8-1, and Rapley, Burnell[43] & Culhane (1976), figure 1)

---

[38] Chambers (1974), *SL1203 Post Firing Report*, p.8.
[39] Rapley (1976), 'New techniques and observations in Soft X-ray astronomy', p.164.
[40] Rapley, Bell Burnell & Culhane (1976), 'Observations of the Soft X-ray Diffuse Background', also Henry, Bowyer, Rapley & Culhane (1976), 'Direction of an Extreme-Ultraviolet Source in the Southern Sky'.
[41] He has also retained the nose cone tips from the two rounds he was involved in, SL402 and SL1203!
[42] MSSL (1975), *Report of the MSSL 1st October 1974 to 30th September 1975*, Part 3, p.7.
[43] Jocelyn Bell Burnell was a British astrophysicist who, as a postgraduate student, discovered the first four pulsars. Credit for her discovery was given to Antony Hewish, her thesis supervisor; Hewish was awarded the Nobel Prize without the inclusion of Burnell as a co recipient. Burnell's understanding of rapid set pulses occurring at regular intervals and position of unusual radio sources with respect to the stars was considered the greatest astronomical discovery of the twentieth century. (Melanie Sandoval (2009), ADS).
[44] The first is reported (Lampton 1976) to have been discovered with a grazing-incidence telescope during the Apollo-Soyuz mission in July 1975, a year later than SL1203!
[45] Henry, Bowyer, Rapley & Culhane (1976), 'Direction of an Extreme-Ultraviolet Source in the Southern Sky', p.L29.

There were no Skylark launches in March, but on 23rd April, **SL1207** was launched from Woomera. This carried five geophysics experiments from University College London and the UAR (Upper Atmosphere Rocket) group WRE, University of Adelaide. The experiments were designed to measure various daytime properties of the atmosphere and ionosphere. See Figure 14.11.

Although this envelope may seem a dubious source, the information provided by these 'first day covers' is surprisingly accurate, and may have been derived directly from the 'Tri-als Instruction' documents for the missions concerned. The generic illustration of Skylark on the envelope is however inaccurate, not least because SL1207 appears to have been the first fitted with a 'round tip nose cone'. [47]

The UAR/WRE experiment was one of nine flown on various rockets between 1973 and 1976. These released lithium vapour between 80 and 200 km in altitude, after which the drift of the resulting vapour trails was observed by a special scanning detector.[48] The SL1207 observations were generally in agreement with the theory of winds (the 'solar semidiurnal tide') at these very high altitudes.[49] The experiment was repeated two years later on SL1271 at the same time and season.

Figure 14.11 This commemorative envelope is one of the main sources of information the author has found for SL1207.[46]

(Author's collection)

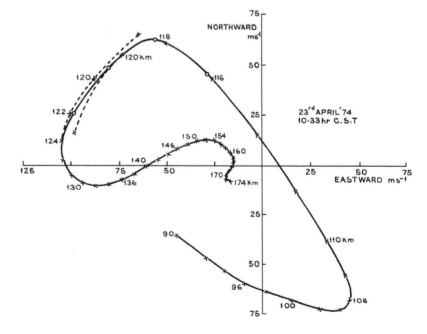

Figure 14.12 The UAR wind hodograph[50] **for Skylark SL1207, showing the characteristic anti-clockwise shape caused by atmospheric tides.**[51]

(Lloyd, Low & Hind (1977), figure 13)

[46]   See also Giovanni Bibbo (1977), *Rocket Studies of the Lower Thermosphere.*

[47]   BAe (1990), *Record of Skylark Launches 1957-1990.*

[48]   Lloyd, Low & Hind (1977), *Daytime Observations of Lower Thermospheric Wind Profiles at Woomera.* A photograph of the detector appears in Lloyd (1978), figure 16.

[49]   Ibid, p.5.

[50]   A hodograph is a diagram that gives a vectorial visual representation of the movement of a body or a fluid.

[51]   Lloyd (1978), *Upper Atmosphere Research at WRE – a Review*, pp.7-8.

June 1974   SL1104

SL1104 carried an astronomy experiment from MSSL designed to study the pulsating binary X-ray source Centaurus X-3, an object then under scrutiny by astronomers.[52] In particular, the experiment was designed to monitor very short variations in time. (Skylark rockets, with their high data rate had an advantage over satellites in a study of this kind) [53], and included a "random access MOSFET memory of 1K capacity" allowing time resolution down to 20 microseconds[54] – a far cry from the valve (vacuum tube) technology used on Skylark payloads some fifteen years previously! A simultaneous search for possible radio emission was due to be made by the Parkes Radio Observatory in Australia.

SL1104 was duly launched on June 18th, but unfortunately, the experiment was damaged by a collision with the rocket nose cone when it was released. This severely curtailed the extent and quality of the observations.[55]

22nd July 1974   SL1292

SL1292 was the third of the military Skylarks (SL1191, 1291-93 & 95-99), used to develop the decoys for the Chevaline re-entry vehicle,[56] an upgrade for the UK's submarine launched Polaris nuclear missile system. Although they were all basically successful, for this launch, the cryptic comment "Radar problem S.3" appears in the BAe Skylark launch list.[57]

October 1974   SL1012, SL1304, **SL1471**

SL1012 carried an astronomy experiment from MSSL, the original aim of which was to conduct a soft X-ray spectral analysis of the remnants of two supernova explosions.[58] At the time, no such X-ray spectral lines had been detected from any celestial object other than the Sun, and it was hoped that that the observations would be of paramount importance to the understanding of the physical processes in supernova remnants.[59] The particular supernova remnants were known to astronomers as Puppis A and the Cygnus Loop, although in the end only the former was viewed. To be able to target them, Skylark's new Stage 5 star-pointing ACU had to be used, this being only the third payload to use the Mk.II version.

Work on designing the experiment had been underway at the MSSL laboratories by 1972, the basis of the design being a Bragg crystal spectrometer as used in several earlier MSSL experiments.

Figure 14.13 The SL1012 electronics bay with instrument control and readout electronics.
(MSSL\ Coker)

---

[52]   Some two dozen scientific papers on Cen X-3 were published in 1974 alone. It was coming to be recognised as an X-ray source with an accretion wake trailing behind it during its passage through the stellar wind from its optical companion.

[53]   MSSL (1972), *Report of the MSSL 1st January - 30th September 1972*, Part B, p.8.

[54]   MSSL (1973), *Report of the MSSL 1st October 1972 - 30th September 1973*, Part 3, p.10.

[55]   MSSL (1975), *Report of the MSSL 1st October 1974 - 30th September 1975*, Part 3, p.7.

[56]   For an informed explanation of the complex engineering and management aspects of the Chevaline project, see Dommett (2008), 'Engineering the Chevaline Delivery System'.

[57]   BAe (1990), *Record of Skylark Launches 1957-1990*.

[58]   MSSL (1972), Part B, p.9.

[59]   MSSL (1974), *Report of the MSSL 1st October 1973 - 30th September 1974*, Part 3, p.12.

By September 1973, the experiment was awaiting shipping to Woomera, where it arrived in about February 1974. It was followed by two integration and testing visits by MSSL personnel. As described by John Zarnecki:

> So there we were at Woomera, a bunch of young scientists. Between us we had precisely zero years of space experience. Luckily there were a couple of very experienced engineers on the project. I think they had been working for all of five years in space research. They were the veterans. Between us we got the instrument and the rocket to the launch pad.[60]

SL1012 trials instruction document

Compared with earlier days, Woomera was now more formally organised, and each launch (or trial) was carefully documented by the Australian Weapons Research Establishment (WRE). This took the form of a 'Trials Instruction' document, which informed the Range 'front line' operations staff about a particular trial and specified all the actions required.

This was important, because a trial was complex logistical exercise involving many dozens of people. For instance observation posts were scattered all over the range, with operators having to travel many miles by Land Rover, light plane or helicopter in order to staff them. Woomera was a busy place, with many trials taking place other than Skylark, and each had to fit into a weekly schedule of activities. Should there be technical or other problems causing the delay or postponement of a Skylark launch, then another trial might be scheduled instead, involving complicated re-deployment of staff.

In the case of SL1012, the Trials Instruction document [61] ran for over 100 pages, demonstrating that the launch into space of even a relatively simple sounding rocket was a complex affair. The twelve sections of the document included vehicle specification and assembly, telemetry channel allocation, firing instructions, safety rules, range tracking instrumentation, countdown details, recovery instructions, the many different types of records required, and so on.

The firing instructions included the constraints on when the launch could take place, one of which was full moon ±7 days. A night launch between the end of April and the middle of June 1974 was anticipated, although serious problems must have occurred, because the launch was delayed for several months.

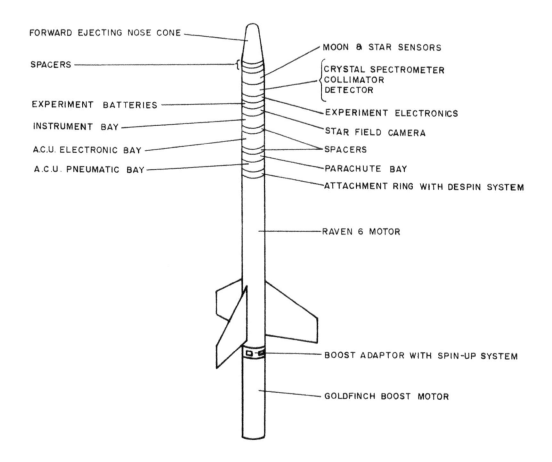

Figure 14.14 SL1012, as specified in Section 2 of its trials instruction document.
(WRE (1974), p.7A)

---

[60]   Zarnecki in *www.open2.net/oulecture2007/five_minutes.html* , (last accessed August 2014).
[61]   WRE (1974), *Trials Instruction No. BS217 (SL1012)*.

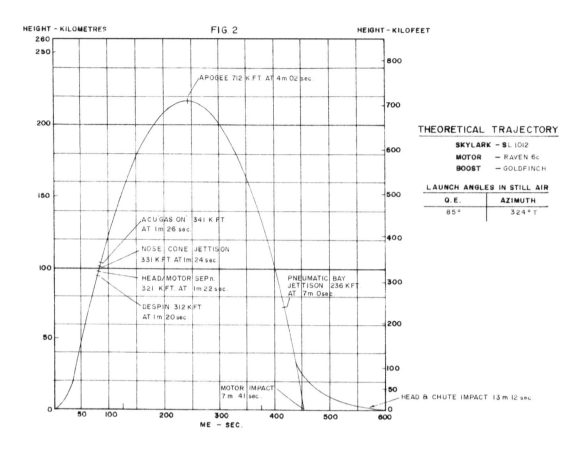

Figure 14.15 The anticipated trajectory for SL1012, as shown in Section 3 of the trials instruction document. In the event, the actual apogee was 10% lower than predicted.

(WRE (1974), p.17A)

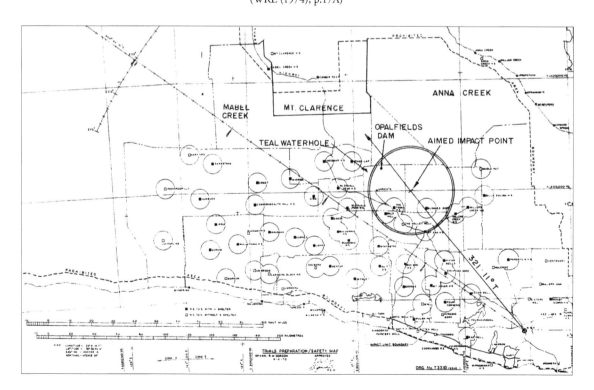

Figure 14.16 Part of the 'Warning Area' map for SL1012. The 'Aimed Impact Point' was 152 km (95 miles) downrange, the large circle being the associated 35 km (22 mile) radius 'Warning Circle'. The small circles mark homesteads that had to be warned and avoided.

(WRE (1974), p.17B)

SL1012 was finally launched on 5th October 1974 local time (4th October in UK), an event that has the very rare distinction for Skylark of a surviving audio recording of the countdown.[62] At the time of writing (2014), the background to this (and the actual recording) could be accessed on-line[63] as part of a fascinating lecture for the general public given in 2007 by John Zarnecki, by then a professor at the UK's Open University.

In the event the mission was successful, although at 144 seconds final acquisition took longer than expected, giving only 123 seconds of useful observation.[64] All payload instrumentation and experiments performed as expected, the experiment pointing to the correct source in the sky to an accuracy of about one hundredth of a degree. However, as described by John Zarnecki:

> … the data was sent by radio link back down to the ground, to the receiving station. And that was lucky because our luck ran out on the way down. The para-

chute should have opened so that our payload gently floated down. We could have used it again then on subsequent flights. Well, the parachute never opened. The payload hit the ground at about a hundred and twenty miles an hour. It was a mangled pile of metal.[65]

The experiment included photographic observations for both the main experiment and an associated one to measure the vehicle attitude from photographs of the star background. Unfortunately, the parachute failure meant that these were destroyed. However thanks to the telemetry, the basic aim was successful, and evidence of oxygen in the supernova remnant was obtained, the first time an element had been detected beyond the Sun by means of X-rays.[66]

The observations would be extended on SL1212 in 1976, see later in this chapter.

SEQUENCE/COUNTDOWN				
TIME RELATIVE TO ZERO	SERIAL NO.	ACTION/EVENT	PERSON/POST RESPONSIBLE	REMARKS
MIN. SEC.				
-15		'Minus 15 seconds' Call	TCO	
-13		U_1-C_1 and U_1-C_2 to high speed	MSU	
-10		Long Peep	MSU	
		20 pps Contraves FL & SH pulses start	MSU	
- 6		Contraves Start Recording	Operator	
- 6		Vintens Start	Operator	
- 5		Short Peep	MSU	
- 4		Short Peep	MSU	
- 3		Short Peep	MSU	
- 2		Short Peep _ F95 Camera Start	MSU	
- 1		Short Peep	MSU	
		CTD to TIM 100 Code	MSU	
		CTD to R1 or R2 - LR155 or LR100	MSU	
Zero		Goldfinch Ignited	MSU	
		Check Operations of Gates	RTC	
		ITD to TIM 100 Code	MSU	
		Tele ITD - LR 105	MSU	
+ 1		1 second Counts to +10 seconds	MISCO	
		U_1C_1 and U_1C_2 to Low Seed	MSU	
+ 2		F95 Camera Stop	MSU	
+20		'Plus 20 seconds' Call and then every 10 seconds to +15 mins.	MISCO	
+1		M40 T1 or T2 Stop	MSU	
+1 26		Chronos to 'High Speed' and OFF	MSU	
+2		Contraves Pulses OFF	MSU	
+7 41		Motor Impact	MISCO	
+13 12		Head and Parachute impact	MISCO	
		MSU OFF after Tele Signals Cease and Tele Recorders OFF	MSU	

Figure 14.17 The final 15 seconds of the countdown for SL1012. The countdown was governed by an automatic sequencer started two minutes before launch, which issued the actual firing pulse to the detonator in the boost motor, although several people had 'Stop Action' buttons that could abort the launch up to two seconds before firing. ('TCO' stood for 'Trials Control Officer' in overall control; 'Contraves' referred to the kinetheodolite posts down range, and 'Vintens' to the high-speed cine cameras.)

(Table after WRE (1974), p.80B)

[62] The only similar audio recording the author is aware of is that for SL1306 in 1976, see later in this chapter.

[63] *www.open2.net/oulecture2007/five_minutes.html*, (last accessed August 2014).

[64] MSSL (1975), *Report of the MSSL 1st October 1974 - 30th September 1975*, Part 3, p.7.

[65] Zarnecki in *www.open2.net/oulecture2007/five_minutes.html*, (last accessed August 2014).

[66] Zarnecki in *www.open2.net/oulecture2007/five_minutes.html*. See also Zarnecki & Culhane (1977), 'Detection of O VIII line emission in the X-ray spectrum of Puppis A'.

SL1304

From October to December 1974, a series of lunar occultations of the Crab Nebula[67] gave astronomers a rare opportunity to study the size and position of the Crab's X-ray emission. The October 7th occultation was visible only over the North Atlantic and Europe, thus it was from the Spanish test range at El Arensillo that a joint British-German Skylark astronomy experiment on **SL1304** was launched, the fifth Skylark to be fired from there.

As Roger Cooper from the University of Leicester explained:

> An experiment to establish the exact location of the x-ray source in the Crab Nebula was derived whereby the instrument was placed in space by Skylark, at precisely the time when the moon occulted the source, thereby acting as a camera shutter. By sophisticated timing measurements the location of the x-ray source could be resolved to much greater accuracy than previously measured….The window of firing was within six minutes on a particular day in October 1974, the next opportunity being in eleven years time![68]

More detailed enquiry reveals that the launch window was in fact only ±10 seconds – in effect no margin at all! This was because it was the occultation of the pulsar within the Crab nebula that had to be observed, and that in the centre of a four minute window of usable observing time above 100 km.[69] As well as positional information, such occultations also provide a unique opportunity to study the surface brightness of the source, making it possible to obtain a very detailed (even though only in one dimension) scan across the surface.[70]

There were two separate X-ray detector systems on SL1304. The Leicester one was a dual layer, large area, gas proportional counter that sat under the nose cone. The German experiment was mounted inside the payload and looked out sideways through an ejecting door aperture. It consisted of an array of four high-energy X-ray crystal/PMT detectors provided by the University of Tübingen and the Max Planck Institute for Extraterrestrial Physics.[71]

The conceptual side of the Leicester payload had formed part of a presentation to the UK Science Research Council. Following mission approval by the SRC, engineers were assigned to the project and many hours of talks and sketches on the backs of envelopes and other media ensued to translate the ideas of the scientists into practical hardware that could be built. The data expected from the instrument when observing the target dictated the multiplexing of the telemetry systems and careful design of the data marshalling was necessary.[72]

SL1304 had become very much a multi-national project.[73] The launch site at El Arenosillo was operated by the Spanish Air Force; BAC provided the Skylark, the universities from Britain and Germany the experiments. The rocket was launched by the German mobile rocket launching team of DFVLR-MoRaBa, which transported 125 tonnes of equipment to Spain.[74] The team that came together on site for this particular launch comprised over two dozen people, the integration and preparation taking about six weeks.

Figure 14.18 The 'Campaign Patch' for SL1304, which includes the Moon in front of a crab! (Huelva is the province in which the El Arenosillo range is located.)
(Giles (2010a), figure 1)

[67] The Crab Nebula is the remnant of the supernova observed by the Chinese in AD 1054, see Figure 12.42.
[68] Cooper (2006), *Rocket Man,* p.5.
[69] Barry Giles, personal correspondence, February 2013.
[70] Janes (1975), 'Rocket X-ray studies of supernova remnants', p.781.
[71] Giles (2010a), *A Skylark in Spain (SL-1304),* p.1.
[72] Cooper (2006), *Rocket Man,* p.5.
[73] SL1304 was originally a purely British mission due to be launched from Woomera, but became a joint project rescheduled to be launched sooner from Spain in order to obtain scientific data in advance of other groups. (Klein (1975), p.250).
[74] Klein (1975), 'Equipment and Programme of the Mobile Raketenbasis', p.250. Two "INTA-300" rockets were launched after SL1304.

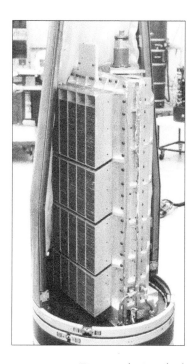
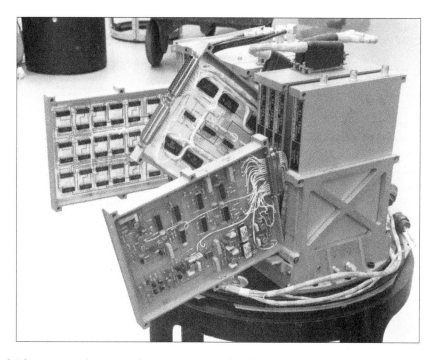

**Figures 14.19 and 14.20 Left: The Leicester large area detector positioned under half a nose cone.
Right: The module used for signal processing and telemetry, with some of the electronics boards pulled out - basic by today's (2014) standards, but a huge advance over the valve (vacuum tube) based technology used when Skylark began.**

(Roger Cooper)

Unlike at Woomera, there were no restrictions on photography at El Arenosillo; so many informal aspects of this launch were well covered.

**Figure 14.21 The University of Leicester Crab Nebula Occultation Science team.
(Barry Giles – post graduate PhD student, Roger Cooper – engineer, Roy Daldorph – technician, Dr Jeff Hoffman – astrophysicist). Roger Cooper's Land Rover had been brought over from the UK by ferry and road to provide local transport.**

(Roger Cooper collection)

Figure 14.22 The launch site at El Arenosillo, with SL1304 set up on its portable launcher.

(Giles (2010a), figure 12)

Figures 14.23 and 14.24 Above: The famous coloured sandstone cliffs right by the range – "the beach was a great spot for a swim after lunch if we were not too busy". Right "Leicester XRA, SL-1304" was mysteriously carved, in large letters; half way up the cliff on the right, by ? – surely a unique distinction for Skylark!

(Giles (2010a), figure 10)

Figures 14.25 and 14.26 SL1304 assembly by BAC and Leicester personnel.
(Giles (2010a), figures 7 and 8)

Figure 14.27 Possibly incorrect handling procedure! – the Leicester team again - "Jeff,[75] Coops, Roy and Bazza".
(Giles (2010a), figure 11)

[75] For Jeff Hoffman, this was a sign of things to come! Four years later he joined NASA, and in April 1985 made his first actual space flight, as a mission specialist on Space Shuttle Discovery mission *STS 51-D*. He took several mementos from Leicester into orbit. These included a pennant from the Lord Mayor's Rolls Royce, a beer mat from the Wheel Inn in Oadby and two Union Jack flags. (University of Leicester (2010), *Fifty years of Space Science at Leicester*, p.9). He made a total of five flights as a space shuttle astronaut, including the first mission to repair the Hubble Space Telescope in 1993, when the orbiting telescope's flawed optical system was corrected. On his fifth flight he became the first astronaut to log 1000 hours aboard the Space Shuttle.

Figure 14.28 SL1304 mounted on the launcher, seen here in the semi-lowered position.
(Giles (2010a), figure 16)

**Figure 14.29 Roger Cooper and Jeff
Hoffman gassing the detector.**
(Giles (2010a), figure 5)

Figure 14.30 SL1304 in the launch position. (A great contrast to the climatic conditions of Figure 15.1!)
(Giles (2010a), figure 17)

Because of the exacting launch timing requirement, there were two full practise countdowns, one during the day, and a second during the night to simulate the real thing.[76]

As described above, SL1304 carried both proportional and scintillation[77] X-ray counter experiments, but shortly before the actual launch, the Leicester proportional counter power supply failed, leaving only the German scintillation counter operational.[78] This was a very difficult moment for the Leicester experimenters, because the time of launch was critical, so despite having spent months or years preparing the instrument, there was no time to fix it.

The launch duly took place at 06.33 UTC (07:33 local time) the 7th October 1974, and was otherwise successful.

SL1304 successfully reached an altitude of 190 km (118 miles), and provided four minutes of observing time above 100 km. Although launched before sunrise at ground level, the Sun-seeking ACU was able to operate because at altitude, the Sun had just risen.[79] The payload altitude was measured to an accuracy of ± 500m in flight using radar transponder data, allowing the position of the lunar limb as seen from the rocket to be calculated very accurately (±1 arc sec).

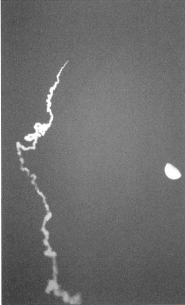

**Figures 14.31, 14.32, 14.33 and 14.34.
SL1304's dawn launch at 07:33 local time.**
(Giles (2010a), figures 23-26)

---

[76] Giles (2010a), *A Skylark in Spain (SL-1304)*, p.2.

[77] A scintillation counter consists of a transparent crystal that fluoresces when struck by ionising radiation. These detectors were originally used for X-rays with energies above 20 KeV, and could be used at balloon height.

[78] Staubert *et al.* (1975), 'The Crab Nebula: High Energy X-ray Observation of a Lunar Occultation', p.L15.

[79] Giles (2010a), *A Skylark in Spain (SL-1304)*, p.2.

All data was returned by radio telemetry, there was no recovery, because the payload and spent motor landed in the Atlantic.

Roger Cooper recalls:

> … SL1304 was only partially successful as the +12 volt rail for the detector processing electronics failed about 5 hours before launch. Not sure why as we were unable to dismantle the vehicle to try and fix it. I do recall thinking it was a sticking relay and we drilled a hole in the bay to tap the power relay with a rod in hope to free it but it probably wasn't the cause. We had to launch as is and let the other experiment take the credit for success, so all was not lost. Yes, the stress of a time sensitive firing along with all the rest that goes with it can be quite harrowing. However we survived. With over 14 Skylarks to my credit, SL1304 and SL119 were the only part failures. My last round was cancelled after the government pulled the plug on Woomera leaving the Aussies in the lurch.[80]

The published result showed that hard X-rays in the energy range 15-150 keV were successfully observed.[81] The measurement of both the size of the diffuse nebula and its offset from the optical pulsar was achieved, which along with other data gave information on the energy transfer process in the Crab. In addition, measurements of a point source close to the pulsar were made.[82]

The Crab Nebula[83] was (and is) of great interest to astronomers, and this measurement of the size and position of the X-ray source in the Nebula was only one of many similar experiments. Between 1964 and 1974 nine rocket, balloon and satellite based experiments took place, conducted by American, British and continental European groups.[84] Indeed, on 7th October, the same occultation was also observed by MSSL using their X-ray detector on board the Copernicus satellite, and that too provided further information on the size and the position of the X-ray emission from the Crab Nebula.[85]

Figure 14.35 SL1304's impressive telemetry reception complex. The antennas had to physically track the vehicle as it climbed.

(Giles (2010a), figure 19)

[80] Roger Cooper, personal communication, September 2010.
[81] Staubert *et al.* (1975), 'The Crab Nebula: High Energy X-ray Observation of a Lunar Occultation'.
[82] Janes (1975), 'Rocket X-ray studies of supernova remnants'.
[83] A supernova remnant (SNR). See Figure 12.42.
[84] Staubert *et al.* (1975), 'The Crab Nebula: High Energy X-ray Observation of a Lunar Occultation', table 2.
[85] Davison and Culhane (1975), 'Measured offset between the Crab pulsar and Tau X-1'.

SL1471 – the first and only Skylark 10A

SL1471 was one of the few major variants of Skylark that was actually launched (10 Oct 1974), although this appears to have been its one and only flight. In contrast to the proposed Skylark 8, Skylark 10A (also known as the Meadowlark) was a smaller version of the existing Skylark rocket.

Skylark 10A was designed to carry a smaller and lighter payload than the soon to be introduced Skylark 7, although to a similar altitude. This perceived market requirement arose from the autumn 1973 'High Latitude' campaign at Andøya in Norway.[86]

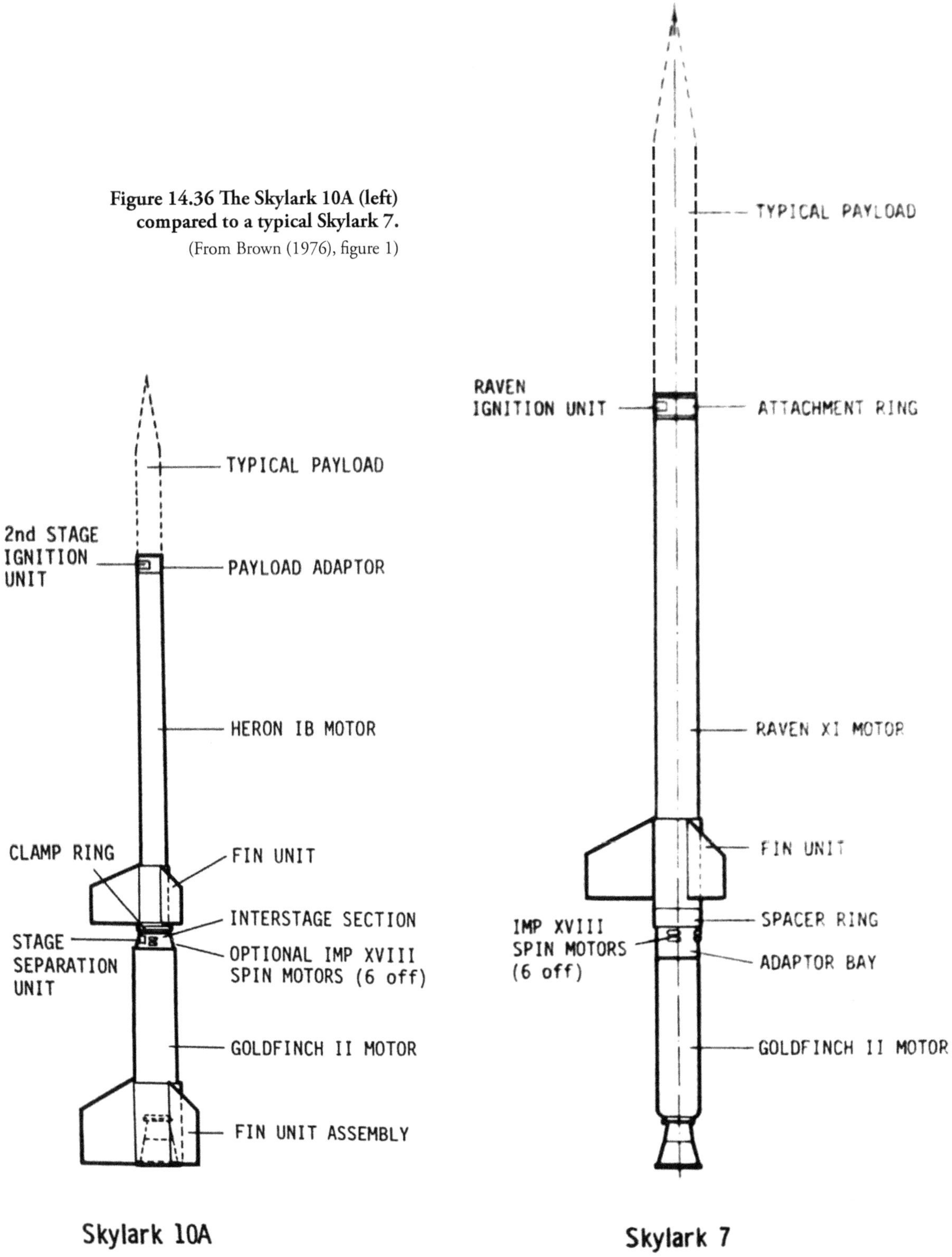

Figure 14.36 The Skylark 10A (left) compared to a typical Skylark 7.

(From Brown (1976), figure 1)

---

[86] Brown and Crosse (1975), 'The Development of the Skylark 10A Sounding Rocket'.

As shown in the graph below, Skylark 10A could carry a gross payload of 30 to 100 kg mass to altitudes from 450 to 250 km. SL1471 was the prototype flight model and was fitted with an instrumented payload of 51 kg prepared by the Space Department of RAE Farnborough. The trial was very successful and reached an altitude of 270 km (169 miles).

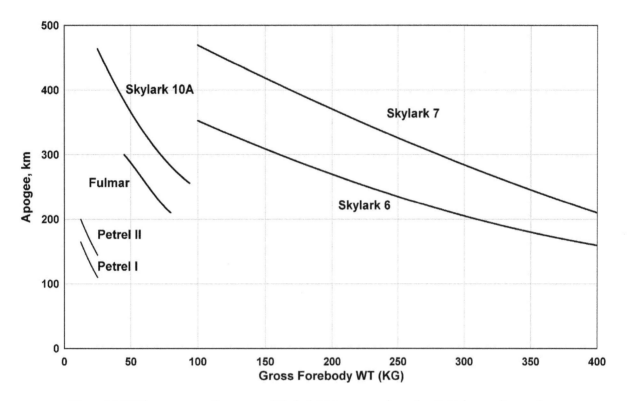

Figure 14.37 The apogee performance of Skylark 10A compared to other British sounding rockets
(After Delury (1983), figure 1, and Brown & Crosse (1975), figure 3)

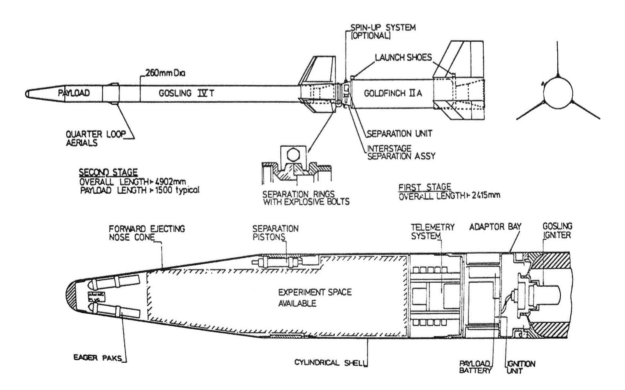

Figure 14.38 Details of the Skylark 10A vehicle.
(Brown & Crosse (1975), figure 1)

Type	Booster	Sustainer	3rd stage	1st flight
6	Goldfinch II	Raven VI	-	1968
7	Goldfinch II	Raven XI	-	1975
8	Stonechat	Waxwing	-	-
9	Stonechat	-	-	(1969)[90]
10	Raven XI	Gosling IV	-	-
10A	**Goldfinch II**	**Gosling IV**[91]	**-**	**1974**
11	Goldfinch II	Raven VI	Cuckoo IV	-
12	Goldfinch II	Raven XI	Cuckoo IV	1976

Table 14.2 The Skylark 10A as part of the expanding family of Skylark rockets.

Unlike the original Skylark designed by the RAE, this version was designed by BAC as a private venture. For economy and reliability, it used existing proven motors and Skylark components, including the Goldfinch booster.

Following earlier work,[87] BAC had carried out a design study in January 1974, after which this launch took place remarkably quickly. At the time, Skylark 10A was stated to be available for flights from 1976,[88] but this early confidence does not seem to have resulted in any orders. As far as the author knows, SL1471 was the only flight, although it was considered as a possible substitute for the Fulmar rocket for the UK's high latitude campaign from Andøya in late 1976/early 1977.[89]

Ariel 5 – the UK's X-ray satellite

October 1974 was a busy month for British space science, for as well as the three Skylark firings; the fifth British scientific satellite (UK-5 / Ariel 5) was placed in orbit. It was successfully launched on the 15th by an American rocket from the San Marco platform off the coast of Kenya, and after launch became known as Ariel 5.

As explained in the last few chapters, the new and rapidly expanding field of X-ray astronomy relied upon observations carried out from above the Earth's atmosphere, and in the early years, these observations were carried out by instruments mounted on sounding rockets. Indeed, in 1974, five of the eight Skylark scientific missions were for this purpose.

Meanwhile, back in December 1970 the UHURU satellite had been launched by NASA, which provided the first comprehensive survey of the sky to be made in X-radiation. (UHURU carried only simple sounding rocket-like instrumentation but being spin-stabilised was able to scan the sky every 12 minutes.[92]) However, the observations were of limited accuracy, and it became clear that more accurate measurements would extremely valuable to astronomers. As described in Chapter 12, in 1972 the OAO3 (Orbiting Astronomical Observatory 3) satellite had been launched (becoming known as Copernicus), and this had carried into orbit an important British X-ray instrument, similar to those developed for Skylark.

However even earlier, in 1968, British astronomers had made proposals for a cosmic X-ray scientific payload in the Ariel series of satellites. The idea was accepted, and UK-5 (in due course Ariel 5) became the first British scientific satellite in which the instruments all looked away from the Earth. It was built by Marconi Space and Defence Systems and carried five British and one American X-ray experiments, most of the British experiments coming from groups who had provided instruments for Skylark.

In particular, the 'Instrument A' experiment from MSSL, designed to measure X-ray source positions, relied heavily on Skylark work. Much of the work on the rotation modulation collimator Skylarks (SL's 921, 971, 973, 1021 & 1003) was relevant to this instrument and the interpretation of its data.[93] In particular, the experience gained from the prototype instrument and data from SL1003 (October 1972), had led to the development of processing programmes that greatly enhanced the ability to produce results.[94] This was particularly important given the astonishingly limited computing facilities available at the time:

---

87 An RAE study in 1962 and BAC work in 1972.
88 Brown and Crosse (1975), 'The Development of the Skylark 10A Sounding Rocket', p.234.
89 Thomas & Bryant (1975), 'Proposed UK high latitude rocket campaign in late 1976/early 1977'.
90 Only launched in the form of the 'Falstaff' military rocket.
91 An earlier source says Gosling, a later one Heron.
92 Charles & Seward (1995), *Exploring the X-ray Universe*, p.35.
93 MSSL (1972), *Report of the MSSL 1 January 1972 – 30 September 1972*, part B, p.11.
94 MSSL (1974), *Report of the MSSL 1 October 1973 – 30 September 1974*, part 3, p.9.

The volume of computing increased markedly during the year with the launching of ARIEL 5, and we have recently been taking up the whole of the 60 minutes per week granted in our 1975/76 application for computing facilities, and whatever additional time can be spared. It is now clear that the need for time throughout the remainder of 1975/76 is around 90 minutes per week and we shall be seeking a supplement of the award. The quality of the service we have received from the ATLAS laboratory[95] has been high, and we are very indebted to the staff there and at the RHEL [Rutherford High Energy Laboratory].[96]

For the first time UK responsibilities included control of the operation of the spacecraft when in orbit, carried out by a specially designed control centre at the Appleton laboratory (formerly known as the RSRS) of the SRC, connected to NASA ground stations at Quito and Ascension Island. Further processing and data links to each experimenter gave each one a close monitoring facility almost equivalent to having his cosmic X-ray telescope in his own laboratory.[98]

All the experiments worked well for five years until the satellite re-entered the atmosphere on 14 March 1980. During much of this time, the facilities available to UK X-ray astronomers were unsurpassed in the world and full advantage of this strong position was taken to make many new discoveries.[99]

November 1974   SL1221, SL911

SL1221 was a 'leftover' from the previous year's Autumn High Latitude Campaign launched from Norway. In March 1973 the SRC had accepted that this chances of launching this fifth round (that had been added later) at the end of 1973 were marginal,[100] and in the end it was only launched from Norway on 1st November 1974.

It was fired into the end of a growth phase of an isolated auroral substorm, and carried a separating payload to simultaneously measure electrons at two points. [101] This produced a comprehensive set of data on the electron intensity and electric fields to help explain the physics of the aurora.[102]

The last Skylark of 1974 was **SL911** launched from Woomera on 28th November. It carried a UV stellar astronomy experiment from the Appleton Laboratory and UCL, incorporating a high-resolution echelle spectrograph instrument with the fourth series II Stage 5 star-pointing ACU. Although the rocket reached 203 km (126 miles), the mission was a failure, possibly because of an ACU problem.

Figure 14.39 The rotation modulation collimator X-ray detector instrument as flown on Ariel 5 ('Instrument A'). It was designed by P. Willmore and colleagues of MSSL. Both the collimator and proportional counters presented considerable technical problems during building and environmental testing.
(Science Museum object 1986-1433, author 100_2248) [97]

---

[95] There were some six Ferranti Atlas mainframe computers in the UK. That used by MSSL must have been at Chilton in Berkshire on a site adjacent to the Rutherford High Energy Laboratory of the Science Research Council and to the Atomic Energy Research Establishment (Harwell) of the United Kingdom Atomic Energy Authority. For details see *www.chilton-computing.org.uk/acl/home.htm* , (last accessed August 2014).

[96] MSSL (1975), *Report of the MSSL 1 October 1974 – 30 September 1975*, part 1, p.2.

[97] Image taken at the London Science Museum, permission granted by Science & Society Picture Library.

[98] Massey & Robins (1986), *History of British Space Science*, p.105.

[99] For a good summary of the results, see Massey & Robins (1986), pp.380 to 387.

[100] Minutes of the 25th Skylark Policy Meeting, March 1973, p.5, item 7. (TNA: PRO AVIA 92/145).

[101] Edwards *et al* (1975), 'Electric fields and energetic particle precipitation in an auroral arc'.

[102] Edwards, Bryant & Smith (1976), 'Electron intensities and electric fields in a quiet auroral arc'.

Jan.	Feb.	March	April	May	June	July	August	Sept.	Oct.	Nov.	Dec.
	SL1301	S98			SL1105	SL1295			S103	SL1112	
	SL1293										

Table 14.3 The seven Skylark Launches in 1975. (For full details see Appendix 3)

(Key: red = German national, plum = UK (stabilised))

SKYLARK LAUNCHES AND SCIENCE IN 1975

1975 saw the lowest number of Skylark launches for 18 years. Only in 1957, Skylark's first year of operation, had there been fewer. In addition, of the seven launches that did take place, only five were for scientific purposes, the other two being military proving flights.

However, in December it was reported that BAC at Bristol had received orders for 11 more Skylarks from the German organisation DFVLR. The intention was to launch one from Woomera, two from Arenosillo in Spain and eight from Andøya in Norway, the latter as part of the International Magnetospheric Study 1976-1978. Four of the orders were for the latest version, Skylark 12.[103]

February 1975   SL1301, SL1293

As can be seen from the table above, there were no launches in January, but there were two from Woomera in February.

SL1301 was launched on 25th, and had the distinction of being powered by the first flight test of the long awaited Raven XI motor. The slow and tortuous development of this motor has been described at the start of the previous chapter, and it had been hoped to flight test it on SL1206 in November 1973.[104] Clearly, there had been further development problems - it was now five years since the go-ahead had been given in 1970!

However once it had arrived, the Raven XI performed well, and produced 20% more total impulse than the Raven VI, by means of increased propellant mass and burning rate. This was achieved within the same case size by changing from a star shaped conduit to a slot in the propellant, which increased the mass of propellant without affecting the burning time. A twin fuze igniter was used for added reliability, which operated at +12 seconds to provide an extended coast period (approximately six seconds) following completion of Goldfinch burning. This restricted aerodynamic heating to an acceptable level.[105]

As SL1301 used the Goldfinch II booster, the combination comprised the first Skylark 7 to be launched. The extra power raised SL1301 to a record altitude of 282 km (175 miles) for a Skylark with an ACU.[107] Skylark 7 was suitable for payloads from 100 kg to 400 kg, and provided an increase of around 25% in apogee performance over the Skylark 6, (see Figure 14.37). This was important to experimenters because it could compensate for the extra weight of the attitude control units (ACUs) that were now often used.

As far as the payload was concerned, SL1301 provided a repeat flight for Culham's sophisticated solar physics telescope/spectrometer previously flown on SL1004 in March 1973. The 282 km it reached compared with 226 km for SL1004, an increase of 25%, and the experiment was again successful.

Main variations		Minor structural changes		Propellant change
Raven II (1958)	►	Raven VII (1962)	►	Raven VIII (1966)
▼				
Raven V (1961)				
▼				
Raven VA (1962)	►	**Raven VIA/VI (1964)**		
▼				
Raven XI (1975)				

Table 14.4 The continuing evolution of Skylark's Raven sustainer motor.

(**BOLD** = more powerful variants)

---

[103] Journal of the British Interplanetary Society, Vol.8 No.12 (December 1975), p.820.

[104] Minutes of the 28th Skylark Policy Meeting, November 1973, p.6, item 9. (TNA: PRO AVIA 92/145).

[105] Brown (1976), 'Recent additions to the Skylark family of Sounding Rockets', p.444.

[106] This document was issued in 1968, so it is assumed the Raven XI duly met its design specification!

[107] The previous highest with an ACU being SL801 which reached 274 km in November 1969.

Motor	Nominal Thrust		Total Impulse		First used on
	Lbf	kN	Lb s	kN s	
Raven VI	15,000	66.5	410,000	1,820	SL87A (1964)
Raven VIII	10,000	44.5	340,000	1,510	SL582 (1966)
Raven XI	**18,000**	**79.9**	**500,000**	**2,220**	**SL1301 (1975)**

Table 14.5 The Raven XI performance compared to the other two Raven motors in use when it was introduced.

(Data from RPE Westcott (1968), *Index to Solid Propellant Motors,*[106] Table 1 Part 3)

SL1293 was launched three days later on the 28th, and was the fourth of the nine military Skylarks (SL1191, SL1291-93 & 95-99), used to develop decoys for the Chevaline re-entry vehicle.

March 1975   S98

S98 was a German (DFVLR) mission launched on 14th March, their first to be launched from Woomera. As the designation suggests, this was an ex-ESRO project, and was launched from Woomera rather than Natal in Brazil because a new water recovery system would not be ready in time.[108] Recovery of the primary experimental cameras was essential because only housekeeping data would be sent by telemetry. It appears to have been a solar X-ray mission, but was only a partial success, as the Dornier 'RESY' recovery system failed.[109]

Figure 14.40 The DFVLR's first launch from Woomera. S98 clears the tower at 14:22 hours local time on 14th March 1975.
(WRE)

[108] Klein (1975), 'Equipment and Programme of the Mobile Raketenbasis', p.254.
[109] BAe (1990), *Record of Skylark Launches 1957-1990,* and Joneleit (1976), 'The German Scientific Balloon and Sounding-Rocket Programme', p.28.

Falstaff

There were no Skylark launches in April or May 1975, but on the 9th May the launch took place of a military rocket, the 'Falstaff'. Although it was exclusively for military purposes, it was very similar to the proposed Skylarks 8 & 9 (neither of which saw the light of day), so is worth describing here. This was the start of the main programme of Falstaff launches, the prototype of which had been fired back in October 1969. (See Figure 11.21.)

Falstaff was an unguided fin-stabilised solid fuel rocket used as a test-bed for the UK Polaris missile improvement programme (Chevaline). It was developed as an economical means of proving control systems in a space environment, and designed to lift a 1000 kg payload in excess of 100 km, and allow it to freefall for at least 120 seconds. Visually, its distinctive features were a bulbous nose[110] and large fins.

The design used the Stonechat 36 inch diameter solid fuel motor that had been developed by RPE.[111] In this respect, it was similar to the Skylarks 8 & 9 proposed as additions to the Skylark family by BAC. However Falstaff was designed, developed and produced under a UK Ministry of Defence contract by the Saunders-Roe division of Westland,[112] the company that had produced the Black Knight and Black Arrow rockets.

As noted in the previous chapter, the Stonechat was the largest solid fuel motor ever produced in the UK. The main motor

Figure 14.41 The launch of a Falstaff rocket from Woomera. (WRE)

body was 4.42 m (14' 6") long and 0.92 m (3' 0") in diameter.[113] A Mark II version was used for Falstaff, but even the earlier Mark 1 version[114] produced a total impulse of 1,810,000 lb-sec (8MN-sec) in 53 seconds, compared to 500,000 lb-sec

Figure 14.42 This photograph of a Falstaff rocket being prepared for launch shows the relatively large scale of this vehicle. (Tagg & Wheeler (1989), p.231)

---

[110] Sir John Falstaff was a portly character who appears in three plays by William Shakespeare – so perhaps using this name extended the British tradition of naming space satellites after Shakespearean characters!

[111] Stonechat had been started as an experimental development in the 1960s; see Harlow, J. (2000), 'The Larger Solid Propellant Rocket Motors of the United Kingdom', p.9, and Moore (1992), 'Stonechat', p.145.

[112] Saunders-Roe, based on the Isle of Wight, were taken over by Westland Aircraft in 1959, in turn renamed Westland Aerospace in 1985.

[113] Moore (1992), 'Stonechat', p.148.

[114] Used to power the 'original' Falstaff launched on 1st October 1969.

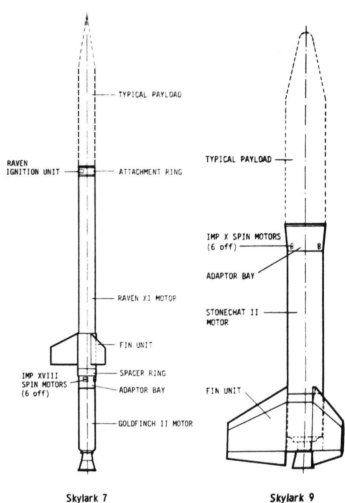

Figures 14.43 and 14.44 A comparison to scale of the existing Skylark 7 and the proposed Skylark 9.[117] Falstaff was very similar to BACs proposed Skylark 9.

(From Brown (1976), figure 1)

(2.2MN-sec) in 30 seconds for the latest Raven XI used on Skylark.[115] The Falstaff payload was protected from kinetic heating in the atmosphere by deployable fairing technology already developed for Black Arrow and Diamant B.[116]

Falstaff was rail launched, and used ten Imp spin rockets to improve stability and keep dispersion within tolerable limits.[118] These were fired at launch, producing the distinctive effect that can be seen in the photo on the previous page.

Anticipating a test programme of ten flights, twelve Falstaff vehicles were built,[119] although their successful operation meant that only six were fired. The launches were all from Woomera, and took place between 1975 and 1979, although as noted in a previous chapter, an early prototype had been tested on the 1st October 1969.

June 1975   SL1105

SL1105 was launched from Woomera on the 24th June. It carried an astronomy experiment from the University of Leicester designed to measure the X-ray emission from the supernova remnant Vela-Puppis. The instrument was a special telescope consisting of reflecting mirrors for focusing X-rays onto a position sensitive detector, the arrangement producing a one-dimensional scan of the area of interest. The mirror had an effective forward-looking area of about 40 cm², and the detector was quite complicated, comprising a set of resistance wires in an argon-methane gas mixture. An X-ray photon landing on a certain position along one of the wires produced a current pulse, the position of which was detected by associated electronics.

To avoid scattered X-ray photons from the Sun, the rocket was flown at night when the Sun was at least 45º below the horizon. Because of this, the Moon and the magnetic field of the Earth had to be used to control the Stage 1 ACU.[120] The launch accordingly took place at 20:48 local time, the payload reached an altitude of 180 km (112 miles), and the experiment was successful.

[115] RPE Westcott (1968), *Index to Solid Propellant Motors*, p.11.

[116] Tagg and Wheeler (1989), *From Sea to Air*, p.101.

[117] Brown (1976), 'Recent additions to the Skylark family of Sounding Rockets', p.442.

[118] Furst & Brown (1974), 'Skylark 8 – High Altitude Sounding Rocket", p.490.

[119] Tagg and Wheeler (1989), *From Sea to Air*, p.230.

[120] Janes (1975), 'Rocket X-ray studies of supernova remnants'.

3rd July 1975   SL1295

SL1295 was the fifth of the nine military Skylarks (SL1191, 1291-93 & 95-99), used to develop decoys for the Chevaline re-entry vehicle. For some reason no 'SL1294' was ever fired. The UK's AWE (Atomic Weapons Establishment) has a Skylark rocket in their Educational Collection[121] but they will reveal nothing except it was important in a project that ran 30-40 years ago (i.e. 1969-1979).[122] It can be speculated that this might be the 'missing' SL1294, or a payload returned from Woomera after use.

October 1975   S103

S103 (**Astro 7**) was another German (DFVLR) astronomy mission, launched at 04.49 GMT on October the 9th, this time from El Arenosillo in Spain rather than Woomera. It carried an ultraviolet observation experiment (Astro 7), using the third inertially stabilised platform to be flown on Skylark, (the first being on S93 in October 1973).

As with the other German launches, Astro 7 was part of an astronomical sounding rocket programme initiated by West Germany after the end of the ESRO sounding rocket pro-gramme. The Astro 7 experiment was designed to measure the ultraviolet part of the zodiacal light (brightness of the sky) in the early morning, in a manner that complemented the two Helios space probes.[123] The mission was successful and it determined that airglow and galactic background radiation were important constituents of the observed sky brightness.[124]

November 1975   SL1112

SL1112 carried a joint University of Leicester and Saclay[126] astronomical experiment, designed to make X-ray observations of the soft X-ray spectrum of the Crab nebula in order to search for interstellar oxygen. (This technique used the X-ray emissions from the Crab nebula as a diagnostic tool to investigate the properties of the interstellar medium in that direction.)

The launch took place at Woomera just after midnight local time on the night of 24/25th November, and the payload comprised an instrument consisting of a mirror and cooled Si (Li) detector/titanium gas detector,[127] mounted in a Stage 5 (star-pointing) ACU. This reached an altitude of 251 km (156 miles) by means of a Skylark using only the second Raven XI deployed to date. The mission was successful.

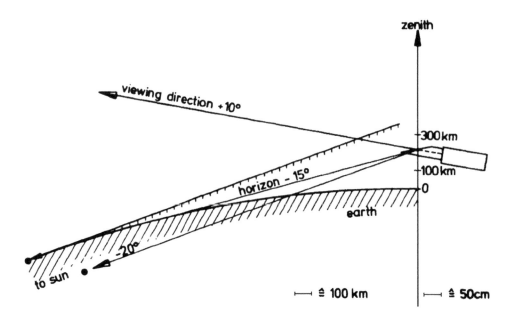

Figure 14.45 This diagram shows how the Astro 7 payload observed the early morning sky from above the atmosphere, whilst the Sun was still below the payload's horizon.

(Pitz *et al.* (1978), figure 2) [125]

---

[121] Not open to the public but used for the induction of new AWE staff.

[122] AWE, personal correspondence, 2009.

[123] The Helios I and Helios II space probes were launched into orbit around the Sun by NASA in 1974 and 1976 respectively. They were a joint venture between the Federal Republic of Germany (West Germany) and NASA.

[124] Pitz, Leinert, Schulz & Link (1978), 'Ultraviolet Zodiacal Light Observed by the Astro 7 Rocket Experiment'.

[125] Astronomy & Astrophysics, vol.69, p.297, 1978, reproduced with permission © ESO.

[126] Saclay - the Institut de Physique Théorique (IPhT) (France).

[127] Massey & Robins (1986), *History of British Space Science*, p.412.

Jan.	Feb.	March	April	May	June	July	August	Sept.	Oct.	Nov.	Dec.
B-II-1				SL1115	SL1212	SL1402				SL1306	SL1114
B-II-2				SL1211	SL1501					SL1422	SL1425
PL029											
SL1302											

Table 14.6 The 13 Skylark launches in 1976. (For full details see Appendix 3)

(Key: red = German national, plum = UK (stabilised), blue = UK (unstabilised))

SKYLARK LAUNCHES AND SCIENCE IN 1976

1976 saw a resurgence in the number of Skylark launches, up to thirteen from seven in 1975. These included a run of six successive Skylark 7s. Unfortunately, about half of the year's launches had major failures, but the two Skylark 12s introduced in November and December were very successful.

In April the RAE R&D (Research and Development) support duties for Skylark ceased, thus ending a very successful twenty-year association with the vehicle. During this time, 345 Skylarks had been launched, making it one of the world's most successful sounding rockets.

Also in 1976, Frank Hazell retired after 28 years working for the RAE. The 'RAE News' reported this as sown below, see figure 14.46.

January 1976   B-II-1, B-II-2, PL029, SL1302

B-II-1 and **B-II-2** were launched from El Arensillo in Spain on the 4th and 22nd January respectively. Each included the same geophysics experiment, a 'Retarding Potential Analyzer' instrument to measure electron density and profiles from 90 to 120 km.[128] They were part of the German contribution to the 'Western European Winter Anomaly Campaign', an integrated campaign of ground-based, balloon and rocket-borne measurements that was performed in Western Europe during winter 1975-76.[129]

During the campaign, several techniques were used to observe the large-scale dynamics of the mesosphere.[130] Meteor radar observations at Garchy, France and Sheffield, UK revealed a typical winter regime for tidal and prevailing wind components. Successive afternoon launches of meteorological rockets and foil cloud experiments from El Arenosillo in Spain provided wind profiles from 20 to 60 and 80 to 95 km. Continuous additional observations were also made in Spain, Austria, and Germany.[131] (The meteorological rockets included some two dozen Skuas and Petrels).

Skylark **PL029** was launched from El Arenosillo a week later, on the 28th. It was a space technology proving flight, carrying a 'Heatpipe I', but this time disaster struck. The rocket reached an altitude of only 2 km (1.2 miles), so presumably the Raven VIII sustainer failed to ignite, and the Skylark crashed into the sea. (A 'Heatpipe II'[132] was successfully launched on board a Black Brant V on 10th June 1977).

Figure 14.46 The retirement of Frank Hazell, as reported in the RAE News. (The last sentence should have read "new solid propellant rocket motor"!)

(RAE News January 1978)

A founder member of Space Department, Mr. J.F. Hazell, has retired after 28 years at RAE. The most important part of his career began in 1954 when he was promoted PSO and became responsible for the design, manufacture and launching of the upper atmosphere research vehicle 'Skylark'. In addition to the design of the vehicle it was also necessary to design and manufacture a 100ft long launcher and a new rocket motor which at that time was the largest in the world.

---

[128] Spenner *et al.* (1977), 'Plasma measurements during the Western European Winter Anomaly Campaign'.

[129] Offermann (1980), 'A Winter Anomaly Campaign in Western Europe'.

[130] The mesosphere is the atmospheric layer above the stratosphere, at about 50 to 120 km. It lies above the maximum altitude for aircraft and below the minimum altitude for orbital spacecraft, thus has only been accessed through the use of sounding rockets. As a result, it is the most poorly understood part of the atmosphere. (See also Figure 15.17).

[131] Bernard *et al.* (1977), 'Large scale dynamics observed during the Western Europe Winter Anomaly Campaign 1975/76 from wind, temperature and absorption'.

[132] Heat pipes are very efficient heat transfer devices; this was part of an international "Heat Pipe Experiment" (McIntosh, Ollendorf, Harwell (1976)).

SL1302

SL1302 was a solar physics mission with an MSSL experiment intended to make X-ray observations of several features on the Sun's disk. The rocket was a Skylark 7, comprising a Goldfinch boost and Raven XI motor, with a Stage 1 ACU for the payload. It was successfully launched from Woomera on 30th January, and reached an altitude of 278 km (173 miles) in just under five minutes.

Instrumentation

The payload was built in collaboration with the Lockheed Palo Alto Research Laboratory in California. Preparation had started back in 1972/73, and the main instrument comprised three collimated Bragg crystal spectrometers designed to investigate the temperature and emission distributions in quiet coronal structures at solar minimum. The construction of the multi-grid collimator, designed to give a very narrow field of view of two arc minutes, posed many problems. It was built up from eleven grids arranged in geometrical progression along the optical axis, was made by MSSL, and successfully tested by Lockheed in California.[133]

Post Firing Report

The SL1302 payload had arrived at the Woomera range on 3rd November 1975, after many delays at Filton[134] and in transit. Experiment preparation proceeded smoothly, but the following account provides a revealing view of other problems encountered: [135]

> The launch of SL1302 was intended to be early in December 1975. An unusually large number of defects associated with the vehicle delayed the preparation .... The first time the vehicle was loaded into the launcher on 7th December 1975 there were two [vehicle] faults that necessitated the removing of the payload from the

Figure 14.47 This view shows the X-ray instrument collimator mounted in the lower part of the SL1302 nose cone. The geometrical progression of the collimator grid mounting positions can be clearly seen.
(Author, 100_3002)

---

[133] MSSL (1976), *Report of the MSSL 1st October 1975 – 30 September 1976*, part 2, p.10.

[134] The payloads underwent final test and assembly at BAC Filton in Bristol.

[135] BAC (Australia) Post Firing Report for SL1302, as affixed to the recovered vehicle at MSSL.

launcher. These were a gyro/demodulator fault and a PCM failure. Additionally an experiment gas valve required replacing.

The payload was reloaded into the launcher on 8th December 1975 but during check out for a launch on 9th December 1975 a large drift was noted on the gyro demodulator and the trial was cancelled. No further launch attempt was made until 30 January 1976 as a replacement gyro bulkhead was required and the WRE range staff were on holiday from 12 December 1975 until 19 January 1976.

Warm conditions at Woomera[136] again presented problems during the check out of the vehicle in the launcher. It is felt necessary to restate that that the local launcher air conditioner will maintain the air in the working areas to plus or minus 10°C of ambient. Additional cooling can be obtained by operating an aircraft Ground Services Unit at the base of the launcher, but because of the noise made by this unit it is difficult to have any communication at the launcher when the unit is operating. The local birds (Galahs) also upset the air-conditioning during nesting because of their liking of the ducting material for nest lining.

On the day of the launch, the trial was delayed from 1130 hours to 1337 hours (local time) because of faults or apparent faults in the vehicle power supplies and in the Cuckoo IV bay. These indications delayed the start of final arming.

The recovery bay suffered more than usual re-entry heating but the operation of the parachute provided a soft landing of the payload that was recovered in very good condition.

The payload also included a special camera, to take images of the Sun to confirm pointing accuracy. The camera did work, but when the film was processed only confirmed that the payload motion when pointing close to the Sun was complex and difficult to interpret.

Figure 14.48 Part of the recovered payload from SL1302, conveniently located for viewing in the stairwell at MSSL's Holmbury House! This cutaway view shows the bay under the nose cone, in which the spectrometers were mounted.

(Author, 100_3000)

(For more details of SL1302 at this location, see the MSSL entry in Appendix 6)

---

[136] The long-term average daily maximum temperature at Woomera in January is 34°C (93°F)! This is in the shade, of which the metal framework of the Skylark launcher offered very little. On Friday 30th January 1976, the temperature reached 33°C at nearby Woomera Aerodrome. (*www.tutiempo.net/en/Climate/Woomera_Aerodrome/02-1976/946590.htm*). (Last accessed August 2014).

Scientific results

Hence, although the actual MSSL experiment performed perfectly, the ACU had failed to achieve fine stabilisation, so after years of work no useful data was obtained. Ironically, the payload recovery was excellent, the experiment being returned to the test shop in just over four hours with minimal damage.[137] One of the purposes of the trial had been to test the new PCM telemetry system for the SRC, but the post firing report[138] concluded that although this functioned throughout the flight, because of an interface problem, the PCM system had created the fault that caused the ACU failure to achieve fine lock.[139]

The recovered payload could have been used again, but at the end of the year the MSSL annual report recorded:

> It is a matter for regret that financial stringency prevents the reflight of the successfully recovered payload at present. [140]

The reflight was not to be, the recovered payload was returned to the UK and now (2014) forms part of a Skylark exhibit at the MSSL HQ near Dorking. (See Appendix 6).

May 1976   SL1115, SL1211

After SL1302, there were no Skylark launches for three months, but on 12th May, **SL1115** heralded a burst of activity when it became the 250th Skylark to be launched from Woomera. It was a Skylark 7 with a Stage 5 star-pointing ACU; and carried an astronomical experiment that was a collaborative project between MSSL, the University of Birmingham and the Marshall Space Flight Center in the USA. The experiment was designed to obtain a high-resolution X-ray map of the Puppis A supernova remnant, and the instrument had far higher sensitivity than any previously used for such observations.[141] MSSL regarded it as a particularly important venture, and work had been proceeding for some time, (in November 1973 the X-ray mirror and MSSL counters had been tested and calibrated in the USA[142]), and towards the end of 1975, the following comment appeared in their annual report:

> A particularly interesting payload, SL1115, ... is now at Woomera. It uses the same large imaging X-ray reflector that gave such remarkable solar X-ray photographs from the Apollo Telescope Mount,[143] and the first of our position-sensitive detectors. We are hopeful that a successful flight will not only provide a unique observation of a supernova remnant but will promote the payload as a possible Shuttle experiment.[144]

The SL1115 mission was reported as follows by 'Gibber Gabber', the Woomera local newspaper:

An X-ray telescope from Marshall Space Flight Centre forms a major part of a joint Mullard Space Science Laboratory/NASA payload for a Skylark rocket which has been prepared for flight by British Aircraft Corporation, Electronic and Space Systems at Bristol.

The payload (SL1115) measures 17 ft. (5 metres) in length and when connected to rocket motors at the Woomera, Australia range, the completed Skylark will measure 42 ft. 6 in. (13 metres), the longest Skylark rocket ever launched.

Due for launch this month SL1115 will be flown to a height of some 162 miles (260 kms) well clear of the earth's atmosphere.

Its purpose will be to produce an energy level map of X-radiation emitted by the Puppis-A supernova remnant which astronomers think may have at its centre a neutron star or pulsar.

Figure 14.49 The Woomera local newspaper reported on SL1115.
('Gibber Gabber', 1st April 1976, reproduced with permission)

[137] SL1302 Experimenter's Report, as affixed to the recovered vehicle at MSSL.
[138] BAC (Australia) Post Firing Report for SL1302, also as affixed to the recovered vehicle at MSSL.
[139] This sounds like an early (and expensive) EMC (Electromagnetic Compatibility) effect. EMC problems began when electronic equipment started to use higher frequencies, these days even consumer equipment has to meet stringent EMC standards, but in the 1970s, the problem was only beginning to emerge.
[140] MSSL (1976), *Report of the MSSL 1st October 1975 – 30 September 1976*, part 2, p.10.
[141] MSSL (1974), *Report of the MSSL 1st October 1973 – 30 September 1974*, part 3, p.13.
[142] Froechtenigt (1973), *Study of X-ray Optics*, NASA contract report.
[143] The Apollo Telescope Mount, or ATM, was the name of a solar observatory that was attached to Skylab, the first US space station. The ATM was at the centre of the large windmill like array of solar panels, and exposed film had to be recovered during astronauts' spacewalks. (Skylab was crewed a total of three times during 1973 & 1974).
[144] MSSL (1975), *Report of the MSSL 1st October 1974 – 30 September 1975*, Introduction.

Figure 14.50 SL1115's 5-metre payload being prepared in the range Test Shop at the end of March 1976.
(WRE)

Figures 14.51 and Figure 14.52 Preparations for the firing of SL1115, in EC2 under the Skylark Launcher Apron.
(WRE)

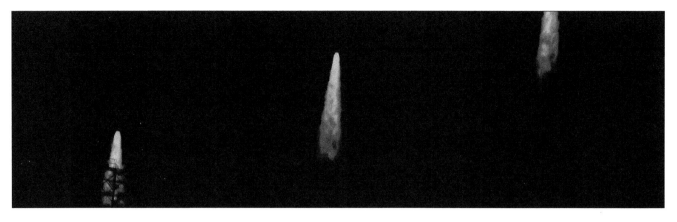

Figure 14.53 SL1115 is finally launched, three successive photographic frames of the night launch.[145]
(WRE)

After a month's delay at Woomera caused by problems with the experiment, SL1115 was finally launched at 21:20 local time on the evening of Wednesday 12th May.

Sadly, the high hopes for the mission were dashed because of a defect in the rocket motor, so the rocket head remained out of control during the entire flight and no observations were possible. (The motor suffered a casing burn through.[146])

However the payload did reach an altitude of 231 km (144 miles), and, as with the preceding SL1302, the instrument performed well and was recovered in good condition.

Despite the overall failure, useful information was obtained on the performance of the MSSL position sensitive detector, and the design of the position-sensitive counter for EXOSAT[147] benefited greatly from experience with SL1115.[148]

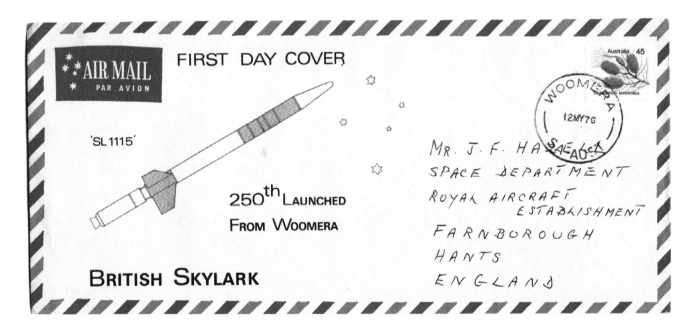

Figure 14.54 This rather nice first day cover was addressed to Frank Hazell, Skylark designer and project leader. He must have been very proud of the success of Skylark. The envelope was probably used to send him the press cutting about SL1115 shown in Figure 14.49.
(C.Hazell)

---

[145] The Vinten F95 high speed camera that covered the launch was typically required to take 8 frames per second from -2 secs to +2 secs, see Figure 14.17 and WRE (1974), *Trials Instruction No. BS217 (SL1012)*, p.43. The Vinten company still exists today, see *www.vinten.com/en/timeline* , (last accessed August 2014).

[146] BAe (1990), *Record of Skylark Launches 1957-1990.*

[147] ESA's cosmic X-ray satellite EXOSAT (originally ESRO's Highly Eccentric Lunar Occultation Satellite – Helos) was eventually launched by NASA in May 1983.

[148] MSSL (1976), *Report of the MSSL 1st October 1975 – 30 September 1976*, part 3, p.8.

Two weeks later, on 27th May, **SL1211** was launched from Woomera. This was a Skylark 7 (Raven XI and Goldfinch) proving flight with an unstabilised payload, that reached an altitude of 254 km (158 miles). The flight was a proving test, which included a UCL/WRE lithium vapour-release wind measuring experiment that appears to have 'hitched a ride'. A paper describing this series of experiments[149] lists this launch as SL1271 rather than SL1211, which appears to be explained by the fact that, as noted in the previous chapter (under "September 1973"), proving mission SL1271 had been 'deleted' from the flight programme:

> The instrumentation on the two ER [Earth Resources] rounds fired in the Argentine had provided high quality information on round stability and the proposed stability investigation round, SL1271, could be put on ice and the money it would have cost could well be used to finance the new fin design.[150]

Hence, the original designation may have lived on in some quarters. In addition, as this proving flight used the new Raven XI motor, it can be speculated that as the previous flight using the Raven XI suffered a disastrous motor casing burn through, this test may also have been used to improve confidence in the new motor design.

| June 1976 | SL1212, SL1501 |

SL1212 was a night launch from Woomera during the early hours of 11th June 1976. It carried an MSSL astronomy experiment, and after the failures of the previous two Skylarks with MSSL payloads, the experimenters must have been very relieved when it behaved perfectly:

The vehicle was a Skylark 7 complete with star-pointing Stage 5 ACU, and the mission was to study the X-ray line emissions from a supernova remnant. It was similar to SL1012 launched in 1974, although this time the experiment was aimed to observe the Cygnus Loop. The instrument used was a similar Bragg crystal spectrometer; however, the use of the new Raven XI motor and an improved version of the instrument led to an anticipated increase in experimental sensitivity by a factor of six.[151]

As hoped, the new more powerful Raven XI performed well, and the payload reached an altitude of 281 km, 40% higher than the 196 km of SL1012. The Stage 5 ACU operated correctly and locked onto the target after 197 seconds, and a total of 233 seconds of useful on-source data was obtained.[152] A star-field camera monitored the attitude of the payload.

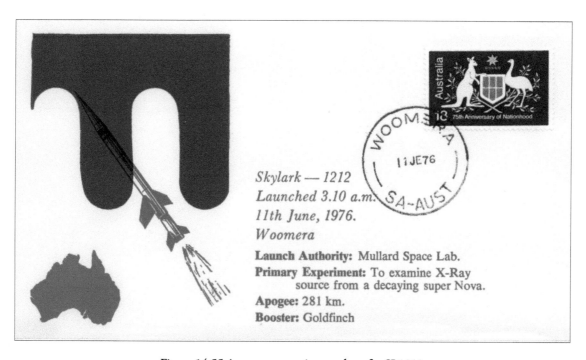

Figure 14.55 A commemorative envelope for SL1212.

(Author's collection)

[149] Lloyd, Low & Hind (1977), *Daytime Observations of Lower Thermospheric Wind Profiles at Woomera*.
[150] Minutes of the 27th Skylark Policy Meeting, September 1973, p.4, item 4. (TNA: PRO AVIA 92/145).
[151] MSSL (1975), *Report of the MSSL 1st October 1974 – 30 September 1975*, part 3, p.8.
[152] MSSL (1976), *Report of the MSSL 1st October 1975 – 30 September 1976*, part 3, p.7.

Unlike SL1012, where the recovery system failed, the experiment was recovered in good condition, with only slight mechanical damage to the sensitive crystals. The X-ray emission lines searched for were not detected despite the sensitivity of the instrument, a result that nevertheless allowed a great deal to be deduced about the physics of the Cygnus supernova remnant.[153]

SL1501

SL1212 was followed less than a week later by the launch of **SL1501** on the 17th. Again, the rocket was a Skylark 7, although this time with a Stage 1 ACU. It carried a University of Birmingham astronomy experiment with a new type of X-ray instrument (a coded mask telescope) to study the region within about 2º of the galactic centre, and marked the University's move from studying the ionosphere to the broader field of astrophysics. Observing the centre of our galaxy was a problem for astronomers:

> It is ironical that we can see the nuclei of other galaxies better than that of our own. With a conventional telescope directed towards the galactic centre, only foreground stars can be seen, the nuclear regions being obscured by vast clouds of dust and gas that lie in the galactic plane.
>
> The same is not true at all wavelengths. Radio and infrared radiation penetrates the clouds and it is through observations at wavelengths greater than a few metres that most of our knowledge of this important region has been obtained....For X-ray wavelengths less than about 5 Å we are again permitted a view into the nuclear regions.[154]

SL1501 was a pioneering mission, the flight being the first successful use in astronomy of a 'coded mask' telescope for imaging cosmic X-ray sources.[155]

The SL1501 flight was a complete success, and although the observations lasted for less than six minutes (compared to several years for the Ariel 5 satellite), the newer design of the instrument on board SL1501 was capable of finer resolution, thus complementing Ariel 5 and other X-ray satellite observations. The results from SL1501 were combined with those from Ariel 5 to produce the best map to date of X-ray sources at the galactic centre, revealing new detail and several new sources, see figure 14.57. [156]

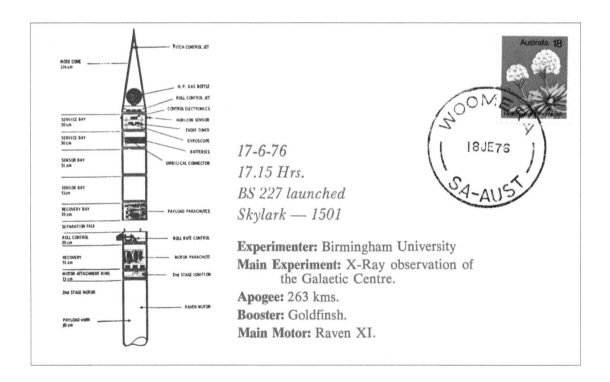

Figure 14.56 A commemorative envelope summarising SL1501's mission.
(Author's collection)

[153] Stark and Culhane (1978), 'A search for X-ray line emission in the spectrum of the Cygnus loop'.
[154] Skinner (1979), 'The galactic centre', p.345.
[155] Skinner (1979), 'The galactic centre'.
[156] See Skinner (1979), and Proctor, Skinner and Willmore (1978), 'X-ray emission from the region of the Galactic Centre'.

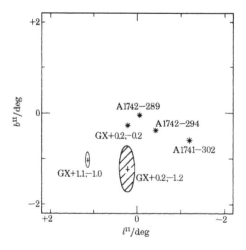

Figure 14.57 The galactic centre X-ray sources as observed
by SL1501 and the Ariel 5 satellite RMC ('Instrument
A'). Most of these sources were new discoveries.

(Skinner (1979), figure 3) [157]

Thus the experiment was a notable success, producing the
first X-ray image of the centre of the galaxy, and as described
below, it led to an award of a free launch by NASA on the
Spacelab 2 Shuttle mission for a large telescope operating on
the same principle.[158]

The Science Museum description in figure 14.58 confirms
that the success of the instrument as flown on Skylark led
to a place on the Spacelab 2 Shuttle mission. It explains that
Dr Peter Willmore of the University of Birmingham had a
dual X-ray telescope on board Space Shuttle mission STS51-
F/Spacelab 2, launched in July 1985.[160] (Spacelab was an

assembly of science instruments flown and operated in a
NASA Space Shuttle payload bay, not to be confused with
the Skylab space station of 1973-79).[161] This X-ray telescope
(XRT) was the first orbiting instrument able to make images
directly at high energies.[162]

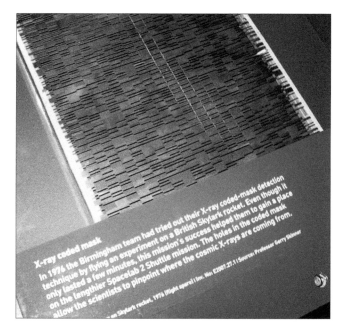

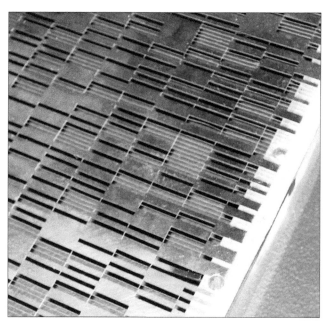

Figures 14.58 and 14.59 The flight spare of the coded mask for the X-ray telescope used
on Skylark SL1501, as displayed in 2009 at the Science Museum in London.

(Science Museum object E2007-27-1, author 100_2275 & 100_2278) [159]

---

[157] Reproduced courtesy Royal Society London.

[158] Willmore (1987), 'Thirty Years of Space Research', p.147.

[159] Images taken at the London Science Museum, permission granted by Science & Society Picture Library.

[160] See for instance webpage *http://science.ksc.nasa.gov/shuttle/missions/51-f/51-f-press-kit.txt* , (last accessed August 2014).

[161] Spacelab was developed by the European Space Agency (ESA) in the 1970s and early 1980s as its entry into manned space flight. After exploring several
options, NASA and ESA agreed upon a modular research laboratory that would fit inside the Shuttle's payload bay. The two basic sets of hardware
allowed scientists to conduct experiments inside - protected in a pressurized module - or outside - with instruments mounted on pallets exposed to
space. As well as Birmingham's XRT, Spacelab 2 included the CHASE (Solar UV spectroscopy) experiment from the Rutherford Appleton Laboratory.

[162] See for instance *https://heasarc.gsfc.nasa.gov/docs/heasarc/missions/spacelab2.html* (last accessed August 2014) or *www.sr.bham.ac.uk/instrument/* (last
accessed August 2014).

Figure 14.60 The University of Birmingham's Spacelab 2 X-ray Telescope (XRT), seen during its 1985 Space Shuttle flight. (STS 51F, Challenger's 8th journey into space.)
(NASA)
(Coincidentally, the Spacelab external pallet, (on which the XRT was mounted), was built by British Aerospace, the company into which BAC (responsible for Skylark) was subsumed in 1977).

July 1976   SL1402

SL1402 was launched from El Arenosillo in Spain on 17th July, carrying an astrophysics experiment. This was a collaborative effort between MSSL in the UK, and the University of Tübingen and the Max Planck Institute, both of Germany.[163] It was designed to measure X-ray emissions from source Cas-A, in particular the line strengths of sulphur and iron, in order to find out about the character (temperature, density, elemental abundances) of the X-ray emitting medium within Cas-A.[164]

The instrument comprised a large area proportional counter and three Bragg crystal spectrometers that used a new technique whereby the crystals did not move but were bent in the plane of dispersion.

The engineering design and construction were completed in the autumn of 1975, and integration with the payload instrumentation took place at BAC Filton in the spring of 1976. In May, the payload was shipped to El Arenosillo where the mobile rocket launching team of DFVLR provided launch support. For MSSL, the Principal Investigator was

Figure 14.61 The MSSL SL1402 X-ray detector. The two rotary solenoids operated arms that swung out of the housings (with the radio active warning symbols on them) and positioned radioactive sources over the detector window for calibration. The small cube nearest the camera was an HV [High Voltage] unit and the other long boxes probably front-end detector electronics. The tall bracket at the back carried connectors and valves for the detector gas-density control system.
(MSSL \ Coker)

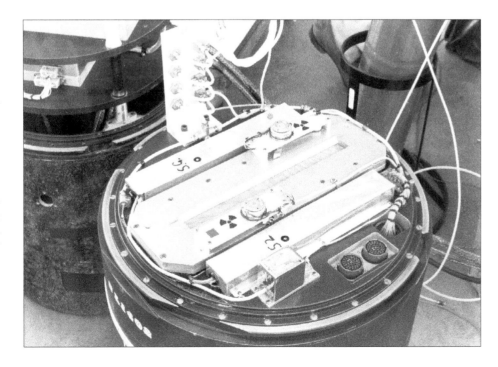

[163] The same two German institutes who had collaborated with the University of Leicester on SL1304 in 1974.
[164] MSSL (1975), *Report of the MSSL 1st October 1974 – 30 September 1975*, part 3, p.9.

Richard Berthelsdorf, and also working on it was a PhD student, Rick Mitchell. Phil Guttridge of MSSL also took part:

> That campaign was quite an adventure for me. We took a rented estate car on the ferry to Santander then drove down across Spain. Living in the village of Mazagon (near the range) was an interesting experience - very primitive. The DFVLR (mobile rocket launching team) brought everything bar the kitchen sink - a container full of bicycles (to get around at the range) and a container full of refrigerators (for their beer). It was a night time launch and they set up a PA system broadcasting music typical of a German beer cellar during the early hours of the count down. Our experiment preparation building was also primitive. Several pieces of test gear literally went up in smoke and upon investigation, we found our mains electricity was coming from a truck mounted diesel gen set that had been wired in wrongly. There was 230V between live & neutral but another 230 between neutral and Earth, causing power filters to explode! [165]

After a relatively uneventful final preparation, SL1402 was duly launched on the 17th.[166]

Then things started to go wrong. Phil Guttridge again:

> I remember the boost motor landed a few metres away from the launch tower (which was a mobile single rail structure) and set fire to some undergrowth. From my recollections, a hole burned through the [sustainer] rocket motor casing, causing a spurious jet of thrust to spin the vehicle to a higher rate than the AOCS [Attitude and Orbit Control System] could cope with. I remember during the flight the BAC crew watching the telemetry stream saying, I think the AOCS has locked, and I said back, I'm afraid it hasn't (because I could see the cyclic change in downlink signal strength due to the spin).

The payload reached an altitude of 256 km (159 miles) over the Atlantic, but unfortunately the Stage 1 ACU did indeed fail to acquire the target, no observational results were obtained, and the payload duly landed downrange in the ocean.

> As far as I know there was no attempt at a recovery of SL1402. In fact this gave rise to another (light hearted?) incident. The hardware for the launch campaign was all brought in overland and the rocket was declared to have a value of some large amount (£M ballpark) at Spanish customs, so when the trucks returned to Germany, apparently they had a hard time at the Spain/France border with customs, who refused to believe that the thing that cost £M had been left on the seabed!

Despite the failure it was hoped that the experience gained in making the instrument would be useful in the design of a large area crystal array proposed for the ESA Spacelab payload.

Figure 14.62 The launch of SL1402 at El Arenosillo on 17 July 1976.

(MSSL \ Coker)

---

[165] Phil Guttridge, personal communication, September 2009.
[166] MSSL (1976), *Report of the MSSL 1st October 1975 – 30 September 1976*, part 3, p.8.

Following SL1402 in July, there was a four-month gap until the next Skylark launch. **SL1306** was powered by a Skylark 6 with Goldfinch booster, thus bringing to an end a run of six successive Skylark 7s using the new Raven XI motor. It was launched from Woomera on 4th November with one experiment, an X-ray astronomy instrument from the University of Leicester designed to carry out a large area high time

resolution study of the source Cygnus X-1. It would turn out to be their last instrument flown on Skylark.

The SL1306 project had started life back in 1973. It was originally intended to study the X-ray source Circinus X-1; and planned to have a similar detecting area to previous large area detectors developed at Leicester, about 1500 square cm. However, the target "was soon changed to Cygnus X-1, the early and famous stellar mass black hole candidate, after the

Seq. Nos	Launch date	Ref. (sponsor) launch site	Config-uration	Apogee km (miles)	Experi-menters	Experiment(s)	Result
351 (10)	04 Nov. 1976	SL1306 (UK) Woomera (BS229)	Sun, Rav.6 +G	191 (119)	Lei	Astronomy – high time resolution study of Cygnus X-1 (large area proportional counter)	Ps (Vf)

Table 14.7 A summary of SL1306.

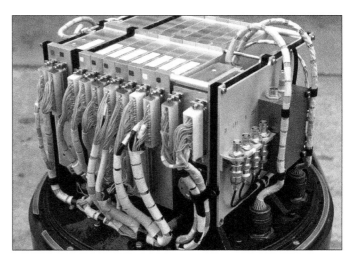

Figures 14.63, 14.64 and 14.65. (Giles (2010b), figures 3, 6 & 7)
Left: The SL1306 detector in the laboratory prior to shipment to Bristol, showing partially deployed panels. Top right: A close up of the deployment mechanism. The shocks, chain and sprockets were an unusual use for motor cycle parts! Bottom right: The main electronics assembly consisted of many integrated circuit cards; a world away from the electronic valves (vacuum tubes) used nearly 20 years previously on the original Skylark payloads!

dramatic announcement of the discovery of millisecond X-ray burst from this source by the NASA/GSFC team of Rothschild *et al.* in 1973/74."[167] In addition, the performance of the planned design was greatly improved in both its detection area and its electronic data processing capability, the area being increased to about 4000 square cm by using folding panels that opened out after the ACU had obtained target lock.

Equally important was the development of a novel two-stage nose cone by BAC engineers. This gave a far greater volume/area than the standard split nose cone, and might have become a standard option, although as far as is known this didn't happen.[168] Basically a standard 20-inch bay was sawn in half, strengthened, and fitted with the same set of gas piston actuators as the standard nose cone. These two bay halves were jettisoned a short interval after the main nose cone, thus exposing the remainder of the large area detector.

Figure 14.66 The SL1306 payload head in Woomera Range E Test Shop 1.
(BAC/ Giles (2010b) fig. 14)
From the left: Dave Gallery (BAC(A)), M.Cross (BAC), Dave Watson (Leicester), Mike Tayler (BAC(A)), Barry Giles (Leicester), Tony Emmett (BAC)

Before SL1306 was shipped to Australia, there was yet another target change, after an interesting 'rapid burster' X-ray source was identified by satellite.[169]

SL1306 arrived on site at Woomera on 5 August 1976, "It travelled up from Adelaide by truck which was a vibration test of sorts…"[170] Experiment preparations were carried out in a small air-conditioned mobile hut positioned just outside Test Shop 1. Barry Giles recalls:

> Eventually all the preparations and test were complete. One of the most interesting tests was the nose cone jettison test. Due to the novel 2-stage nose cone [see above], the whole sequence was filmed which might still exist somewhere at BAe. It was quite a dramatic moment, and a lot of preparation was required to get everyone ready with ropes attached to the four pieces so folks could stop them falling on the TS1 [Test Shop 1] floor or swinging back into the round.[171]

The head was loaded onto the motor in the launch tower on Monday 13th September 1976, and a trial countdown (GIMIC), conducted the next day.[172] However a message soon came through that the 'burster' target was no longer active, and so it was back to plan B and a return to Cygnus X-1.

Activities resumed a month later, when the whole round and experiment were checked out again. Another GIMIC was performed on 1st November - although interrupted at 3 pm so the commentary for the Melbourne Cup horse race could be piped live around the range intercom network![173] The following day, the first launch attempt was scrubbed because of high winds and cloud, the same happened on the 3rd. Finally, Barry Giles recalls:

> The next day, 4 November (shame it was not the 5th!) we finally launched at 18:15 local time into a sky that was still very cloudy. During these critical few minutes of a trial the range head goes 'radio-quiet' and all traffic stops to absolutely minimise any possible RF [Radio Frequency] interference. These brief moments have an air of dreamlike unreality about them. A weird kind of

---

[167] Giles (2010b), *A Skylark in Oz (SL1306)*, p.1

[168] Barry Giles, personal correspondence, March 2013.

[169] Giles (2010b), *A Skylark in Oz (SL1306)*, p.3.

[170] Giles (2010b), *A Skylark in Oz (SL1306)*, p.4. Large parts of the road from Adelaide were still unsealed, i.e. no tarmac, only a gravel surface.

[171] Giles (2010b), *A Skylark in Oz (SL1306)*, p.5.

[172] Giles (2010b), p.6.

[173] A similar interruption had occurred in 1973, apparently during the preparations for SL1206, which also had a Leicester payload, (Chambers (2000), *Woomera, Its human face*, p.79).

excitement – once experienced, never forgotten. In fact a bit like experienced during a total solar eclipse.[174] During the final countdown Watto [Dave Watson] and I were in the underground bunker at the side of the launch area. This blockhouse had a door, facing away from the actual launch location, which was left slightly ajar. The round leaves the launch tower rather quickly, like a firework

rocket, so at the instant of zero it's clear that ignition has occurred and the potential 'bomb' has left the immediate area. Then it's a quick rush for the door and a rapid turn round to see the Goldfinch burn-out (burn duration only six seconds) and the following Raven ignition. Then it's straight back into the blockhouse to monitor the unfolding events for the next few minutes.[175]

Figure 14.67 SL1306 finally gets away into a cloudy Woomera sky at 18:15 local time, Thursday 4th November 1976.
(WRE \ Hazell)

[174] Barry Giles had experienced a total eclipse of the Sun in South Australia less than two weeks previously.
[175] Giles (2010b), *A Skylark in Oz (SL-1306)*, p.7.

All the deployment aspects worked well, and the three experiment detectors were good. Unfortunately, after initially locking onto the target the ACU system failed to hold the experiment on target for the whole flight and a rather shortened data set was obtained.

SL1306 is one of the rare instances where an audio recording of the launch has survived.[176] This came about because although no personal recording devices were allowed at Woomera, the Leicester experimenters had an FM instrumentation tape recorder to log flight PCM data.[177] This had an audio channel with a microphone that was used to pick up the range intercom so the tape would contain useful time

marker information. The audio recoding was preserved for posterity by Leicester scientist Barry Giles, and although never of high quality, it captures the moment.[178]

The launch was rather late in the day, so recovery took place the following morning. Barry Giles recalls:

> I went out to the Woomera township airfield not long after sunrise on the following day. There we had a short preflight briefing and then it was off down range at 2000 ft in an Alouette helicopter. This was exciting. There were three of us in the chopper – the pilot, an experienced range recovery officer and me. A ground

Table 1: SL-1306 Flight Event Sequence

Min	Sec	EVENTS Skylark System	EVENTS Experimental Action
0	0	Goldfinch ignition	
0	6	Raven ignition	
0	57		Detector EHT's on
1	14	Despin	
1	16	Nose cone jettison	
1	18	20* bay jettison	
1	20	Head/motor separation	
1	21		Calibration source on
1	22	ACU gas on	
1	38	ACU roll acquired	
1	41		Detector deploy
1	44		X-rays from Cyg X-1
1	48	Roll acquire recovery	
1	55		Cal. off
3	46	Apogee (191 km alt.)	
5	58		Cal. on
6	8	Pneumatic bay separation	
6	18		Cal. off
9	15	Parachute deploy	
8	15	Motor impact	
11	15	Head and chute impact (~ 130 km down range)	

Figure 14.68 The flight sequence for SL1306, based on the BAC (A) Post Firing Report dated 30/11/76.

(Giles (2010b), table 1)

Figure 14.69 SL1306 real-time audio recording comments list.

(Giles (2010b), table 2)

Table 2: SL-1306 real time audio recording – comments list

Min	Sec	Person	COMMENTS Transcript
		Range	Time call at intervals plus 1 second beeps
-1	-12	Watto	'SL-1306 test recording'
	-10	Range	Single long beep
	-5	Range	Five short beeps down to launch
	0		Distant noise of launch roar
	+58	Watto	'EHT on'
1	13	Bazza	'HT on'
2	32	Bazza	'Terribly low rate'
4	11	Bazza	'sig back on'
11	10	Watto	'That's your lot Barry'

[176] The only similar audio recording the author is aware of is that for SL1012 in 1974; see earlier in this chapter, although the launch of SL01 appears on the soundtrack of two film extracts. (Details in Appendix 6, section 5.2).

[177] SL1306 used the then relatively advanced PCM (Pulse-Code Modulation) digital encoding technique on the telemetry data.

[178] At the time of writing (2014), the audio recording (barry-hiss96) was available for download from *http://space50.star.le.ac.uk/2010/10/15/unique-sound-recording-of-sl-1306-launch/index.html* , (last accessed August 2014).

crew truck had gone out overnight to the vicinity of the estimated impact site but had not located the payload by the time we arrived some 130 km [81 miles] down range. The pilot then commenced a low-level zigzag search pattern. My brain thought this was great but my stomach was not so keen. After a while we had to land to refuel. The aviation fuel was transferred to the machine from several 44-gallon drums on the truck using a rotary hand pump.

Spotting the remains from the air is not easy, apart from perhaps the parachute if it is well laid out. Eventually we found the Raven …and then the head with the two outer panels torn off by aerodynamic forces during re-entry. The Raven and head were separated by several kilometres, mainly due to parachute drift…The experiment part of the head was detached and was just within the size and weight limit to travel back to Woomera on the back seat of the chopper. The main prize on recovery trips was to get the small screw-on nose cone tip, usually spirited away, and I never even saw the cone split halves. Later, the experiment was carefully packaged up and eventually returned to Leicester.[179]

The post flight briefing was carried out a few days later in Test Shop 1. The main issue was that the ACU had failed to stay on target for the whole flight,[180] and it was stated this was the first failure of this type of Sun-pointing ACU for 33 flights.[181] However, as noted above, this failure meant that the amount of data returned was considerably reduced.

Before leaving Woomera, the SL1306 team observed a possibly unique event, the launch of a Canadian Black Brant rocket from the Skylark launcher. Barry Giles recalls, "The Black Brandt [sic] diameter was so similar to that of Skylark[182] that the BAC (A) engineers only had to fix new shoes to enable it to run up the rails inside the launch tower. We managed to see a spectacular night launch just before we finally left for Adelaide".[183] The ability of Black Brant to fit the Skylark tower was of course no coincidence, because as explained in Chapter 7, it had a common ancestry with Skylark.

During the development of the SL1306 payload, there had been various proposals to fly versions of the experiment by other means, including the Space Shuttle, but these went nowhere. After the actual flight, another proposal was made to launch again on Skylark in March 1979, but by this time,

Figures 14.70 and Figure 14.71
(BAC \ Giles)
Left: The SL1306 motor after impact, with one fin on the ground. The search helicopter can just be seen behind the surviving fins. Right: The experiment successfully soft-landed.
(Barry Giles in the background.)

---

[179] Giles (2010b), *A Skylark in Oz (SL-1306)*, p.9.

[180] Telemetry records showed that one of the attitude control jets had failed to work correctly. (Giles (1981), 'Observations of sub-millisecond bursts from Cygnus X-1', p.721).

[181] BAe (1990), *Record of Skylark Launches 1957-1990*, records "ACU jet failure".

[182] Both were 44 cm (17.4 inches).

[183] This cosmic X-ray astronomy mission was launched at 23:02 local time on 9th November, using a Black Brant 5B (VB APD-VB-42) that reached 215 km (133 miles). It was sponsored by the NRCC (National Research Council Canada), and appears to have been their only launch from Woomera.

Figure 14 72 Not an emu, but a kangaroo, apparently being pursued by the Woomera helicopter.
(National Archives of Australia: A1200, L20773)

the UK was winding up its sounding rocket programme, and this too came to nothing. SL1306 was therefore the last Skylark to fly a University of Leicester experiment, so bringing a near 20-year tradition to an end.[184] The large detectors used for the experiment were displayed at the City of Liverpool Museum for many years.

Barry Giles was not the only one to experience Woomera helicopter 'rides', Ted Chambers also recalled:

> Travelling downrange by helicopter was like a magic carpet. The author recalls one such flight, just above tree level, where the pilot demonstrated the machine's manoeuvrability by hounding a poor innocent emu through the stunted scrubland...[185]

The UK SRC 1976/77 High Latitude Campaign

In November 1976, three years after the successful 1973/74 campaign, the second major UK high-latitude rocket campaign began. Approval had been obtained and payload space allocated in 1973/74 soon after the end of the previous campaign[186]. The objectives were similar to before, and a comprehensive set of measurements of high-latitude auroral phenomena were carried out, requiring the co-ordinated launchings of high-altitude (740 to 950 km) and smaller medium-altitude (320 to 370 km) rockets.[187]

The high-latitude rockets comprised five Skylarks;[188] the smaller medium-altitude vehicles used were three of the new short-lived Fulmar rockets.[189] At the same time as the UK campaign, similar co-ordinated European scientific activity was taking place, which from 1977 also used the Skylark, as described at the start of the next chapter.

SL1422 was not only the first Skylark of the campaign, but also the first flight of a Skylark 12 (see below). It was launched through a quiet auroral arc on 21 November 1976 from Andøya in Norway. The payload reached an amazing record altitude of 715 km (444 miles), well over twice the 318 km altitude of the previous highest Skylarks.[190] (To put this in perspective, the International Space Station orbits between 300 and 400 km.)

The payload included experiments from the Universities of Sussex and Southampton,[191] the Appleton Laboratory[192] and from MSSL. The latter prompted the following passage from

---

[184] The University remains very active in space science, see *http://www2.le.ac.uk/departments/physics/research/xroa* . (Last accessed August 2014).
[185] Chambers (2000), *Woomera – Its human face*, p.101.
[186] MSSL (1974), *Report of the MSSL 1st October 1973 - 30th September 1974*, Part 2, p.5.
[187] Thomas & Bryant (1975), 'Proposed UK high-latitude rocket campaign in late 1976/early 1977'.
[188] Two (SL1423 & SL1421) were launched in late 1977, and one (SL1424) in November 1978.
[189] The Fulmar rocket project was terminated after six launches. See Massey & Robins (1986), *History of British Space Science*, pp.190-191.
[190] SL861 & 862 had reached 318 km / 198 miles in October 1969.
[191] Christiansen & Collin (1979), MIST meeting at Southampton, 1978.
[192] The Radio and Space Research Station (RSRS) had been renamed The Appleton Laboratory in 1973.

Professor R.L.F. Boyd in MSSL's subsequent annual report:

> The very successful flight of Skylark 1422 through an auroral arc could lead to new discoveries in magnetospheric physics. While this is no place to write an ode to the Skylark, which in any case would, regrettably, be more of a swan song, it does seem fitting to recall Shelley's lines "Higher still and higher, from the earth thou springest" when contemplating the remarkable flight of the first 3-stage Skylark 12 to a height of 715 km. It is even more fitting that this flight should at last have realised, so well, the original suggestion made by Sydney Chapman in 1953,[193] at the conference in Oxford which marked the beginnings of scientific space research in the United Kingdom.[194]

Further to Sydney Chapman's suggestion, the Appleton Laboratory (formerly RSRS) experiment included for example electrostatic analysers to study particle streams and plasma waves associated with the auroral arc.[195]

Figure 14.73 A Skylark 12 in the winter darkness on the launcher at Andøya in Norway.
(Jan Olav Anderson / British Aerospace)

---

[193] Chapman had suggested that during a magnetic storm a rocket could be fired obliquely through an auroral arc to determine the thickness and intensity of the current flowing along it. (Chapman (1954), 'Rockets and the Magnetic Exploration of the Ionosphere').

[194] MSSL (1977), *Report of the MSSL 1st October 1976 - 30th September 1977*, Part 1, Introduction.

[195] Massey & Robins (1986), *History of British Space Science*, p.305.

The design of the 3-stage Skylark 12

Skylark 12 represented a big step forward for Skylark, the first time a third stage had been added. See Table 14.8.

The Skylark 12 vehicle consisted of a Skylark 7 plus a third stage (or apogee) motor, a Cuckoo IV. The vehicle was stabilised by spin (from the Raven fins) until the third stage burn in vacuum, after which spin stabilisation using the existing rotation was used.

The system used for separating the third stage and initiating its ignition was housed in a new 'Interstage Adaptor', attached to the forward end of the Raven XI motor. After the nose cone was ejected at 70 km and the manacle ring released, eight springs were used to provide an even thrust on the aft end of the third stage until there was a gap of about 60 mm, when a firing pulse was delivered to the Cuckoo IV igniter.[198]

In turn, the payload adaptor at the forward end of the Cuckoo IV could accommodate a pneumatic separation system capable of separating the payload at a nominal 3m/sec, and if required a despin system that could reduce the payload spin to a preferred value.[199]

Type	Booster	Sustainer	3rd stage	1st flight
5	-	Raven XI	-	-
6	Goldfinch II	Raven VI	-	1968
7	Goldfinch II	Raven XI	-	1975
8	Stonechat	Waxwing	-	-
9	Stonechat	-	-	(1969)[196]
10	Raven XI	Gosling IV	-	-
10A	Goldfinch II	Gosling IV[197]	-	1974
11	Goldfinch II	Raven VI	Cuckoo IV	-
12	**Goldfinch II**	**Raven XI**	**Cuckoo IV**	**1976**

Table 14.8 The Skylark 12 as part of the Skylark family of rockets.

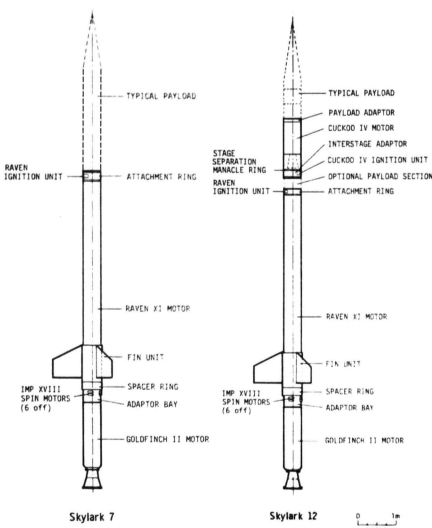

Figure 14.74 A comparison to scale of the existing Skylark 7 and the new Skylark 12, showing how the stage 3 Cuckoo motor was added in place of part of the original payload.

(From Brown (1976), figure 1)

---

[196] Only launched in the form of the 'Falstaff' military rocket.
[197] An earlier source says Gosling, a later one Heron.
[198] Brown (1976), 'Recent additions to the Skylark family of Sounding Rockets', p.445.
[199] Brown (1978), 'Recent Advances in Skylark Vehicle Technology', p.412.

Figures 14.75 and 14.76
Left: Skylark 12 third stage payload despin & separation system.
Right: A flown Skylark 12 third stage payload pneumatic separation ring.

(Sounding Rocket Services)

Mark	First Flight	Details
1A	12.04.60 (SL 51)	Developed as a booster motor to be fitted beneath the Raven motor for improved Skylark performance
1B	21.06.60	Identical to 1A but with an interface change for Black Knight use
II	11.03.64	Developed to increase the velocity change delivered to re-entry payloads for Black Knight
III	11.12.72 (SL1005)	Developed as an improved performance booster to the Raven motor for uprating Skylark performance
IV	21.11.76 (SL1422)	Developed for use as a third stage on Skylark 12

Table 14.9 The Cuckoo motor build standard configurations.

(After Harlow (1990), table 1)

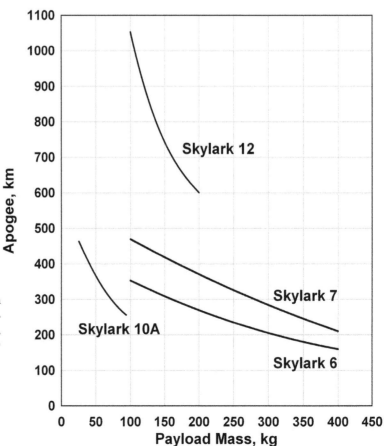

Figure 14.77 This chart shows the great increase in apogee that could be achieved by Skylark 12.

(After Brown (1976), figure 3, Delury (1983), figure 1, and Brown & Crosse (1975), figure 3)

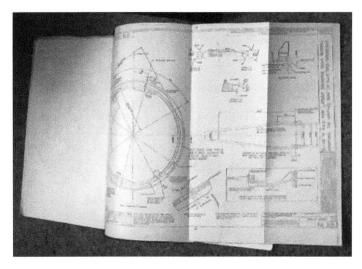

Figure 14.78 A page from the Skylark 12 User's Handbook.
(Author's collection)

The Cuckoo IV motor had been developed especially for Skylark 12 and together with its previous use in space by Black Knight, resulted in the statement "..Cuckoo, in its various forms, has perhaps the unique distinction of being used in space, in atmosphere and underwater."[200]

Skylark 12 was designed by BAC/BAe rather than the RAE, and the British Aerospace press release information on the back of the photograph for Figure 14.73 claimed:

> Skylark 12's unique weight lifting and altitude performance is unequalled by any other presently available research rocket, the new 3 stage version represents the most significant single advance since the first Skylark was launched in 1957.

December 1976   SL1114, SL1425

SL1114 was launched from Woomera on the night of 2nd/3rd December. It was a Skylark 7 with a star-pointing ACU carrying an ARD Culham astronomy experiment (high-resolution UV stellar spectroscopy using a Cassegrain telescope & echelle spectrograph).[201] It successfully reached 263 km (163 miles) but unfortunately the experiment failed, and no imagery was produced.[202]

SL1425 was the second Skylark of the 1976/77 High Latitude campaign, launched from Andøya in Norway on 11th December, some three weeks after SL1422. It was the second Skylark 12 launched, and reached an altitude of 695 km (432 miles), just slightly less than SL1422. A multinational payload included instruments from three UK institutions, the Norwegian Defence Research Establishment and the Goddard Space Flight Center in the USA. The mission was a great success and provided measurements of the structure of an aurora during strong geomagnetic disturbance.

As far as Skylark was concerned, the 1976/77 High Latitude Campaign took place in two phases, because as described in the following chapter, the final two Skylarks in the series (SL1423 and SL1421) were not launched until the end of 1977.

---

[200] Harlow (2000), 'The Larger Solid Propellant Rocket Motors of the United Kingdom', p.5.
[201] Massey & Robins (1986), *History of British Space Science*, p.413.
[202] BAe (1990), *Record of Skylark Launches 1957-1990*.

Figure 15.1 A 3-stage Skylark 12 ready to launch at Andøya on the Norwegian coast.
(Compare the weather with that of the Andøya launch site shown in Figure 13.34!)

(BAC)

CHAPTER 15

(1977-87)

MICROGRAVITY

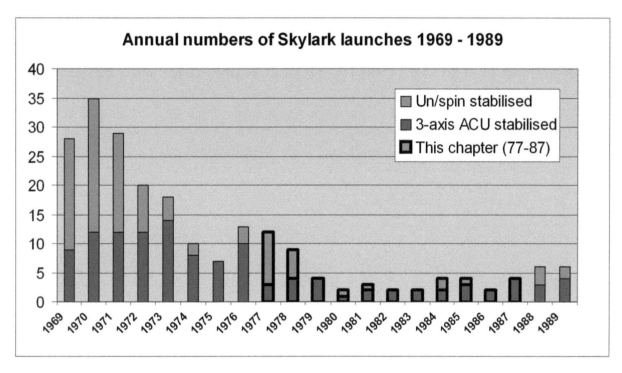

Figure 15.2 During the eleven years covered by this chapter, (1977 to 1987, marked in bold outline), the total number of Skylark launches was only 48, the same as for the preceding four years.

The previous two chapters have shown how the fortunes of Skylark declined following the end of the ESRO sounding rocket campaign in 1972. This chapter reveals how in 1979 the UK national programme also ended, leaving only the German programme and the occasional Swedish launch. However, in 1977 the first Skylark microgravity mission would be launched, an application that would become the mainstay of Skylark during its last 25 years of use.

The general situation at this time for Skylark (and for British space science in general) is revealed by the following passage from Professor R.L.F.Boyd,[1] which appeared in the MSSL annual report towards the end of 1976:[2]

As might be expected in a period of rapid inflation (in instrumentation much higher than the Retail Prices Index[3]) and falling opportunities, no new spaceflight project has been introduced into the programme of the laboratory during the year. On the contrary the total elimination in my most recent grant award of any flexibility in the programme, one already committed at the time of my last report, has resulted in the discontinuance of work on SL1401,[4] though it remains a most significant proposal, and a delay to the collaborative Aries project,[5] though it too remains important both scientifically and as a prototype for the Shuttle. An aspect of the same situation is the

---

[1] Robert Boyd was founding director of MSSL from 1965 to 1983, and was knighted in 1983.

[2] MSSL (1976), *Report of the MSSL 1st October 1975 – 30 September 1976*, Part 1, Introduction.

[3] During 1975, inflation resulted in the UK Retail Prices Index increasing by a staggering 25%, before falling back to 'only' 15% during 1976!

[4] The SL1401 mission was cancelled to make way for the re-flight of SL1115.

[5] 'Aries' was a proposed collaborative X-ray astronomy sounding rocket project with Lockheed in the USA, which finally gained NASA approval in 1975/76.

Jan.	Feb.	March	April	May	June	July	August	Sept.	Oct.	Nov.	Dec.
PHA2	S22	PHA4	SL1115A		SL1298				IMS1	IMS2	TEXUS 1
	PHA1								SL1423	SL1421	
	PHA3										

Table 15.1 The 12 Skylark launches in 1977. (For full details see Appendix 3)

(Key: red = German national, light blue = Swedish, plum = UK (stabilised))

virtual end of the National Skylark programme after over twenty years. This is probably right in the current economic context. It is good, looking back to my discussions at RAE in 1954, to recognise that this rocket has served us well, despite three most unfortunate failures in it or its systems which have been a severe blow this year, not least to my colleagues who devoted their time and hopes to SL1302,[6] SL1115[7] and SL1402.[8] Without Skylark our present strong position in satellite payloads would never have come about, nor our ability to look ahead to Shuttle and Spacelab with a confidence only challenged by financial pressure and conscious external decisions of policy.

SKYLARK LAUNCHES AND SCIENCE IN 1977

1977 marked 20 years of Skylark use, as it was back in April 1957 that SL01 had been launched. The Skylark vehicle had evolved considerably since then.

Despite the problems described above, 1977 was a relatively busy year for Skylark, with a dozen launches. However, it was a sign of the times that only four were UK sponsored, and one of those was for military purposes:

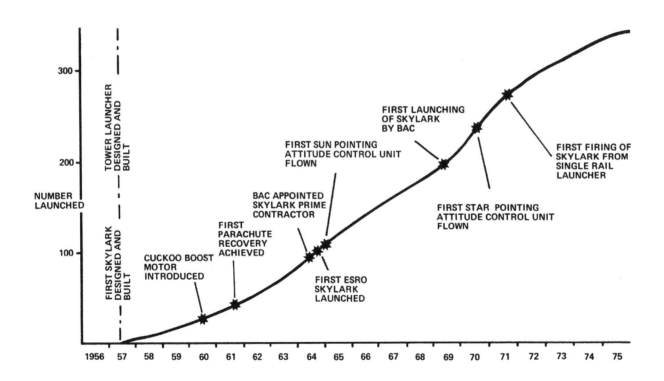

Figure 15.3 This timeline for Skylark neatly summarises the first two decades of Skylark development.

(After Hilton (1977), figure 6)[9]

---

[6]   SL1302 had been launched at the end of January 1976, but the ACU had failed. As described in the previous chapter, the payload is now on display at MSSL's HQ near Dorking. (See also Appendix 6).

[7]   SL1115 had been launched in May 1976, but because of a motor problem, the rocket head remained out of control during the entire flight and no observations were possible.

[8]   SL1401 had been launched from El Arenosillo in Spain in July 1976, but the ACU had failed to lock, and the vehicle disappeared into the Atlantic Ocean with no observations returned.

[9]   Journal of the British Interplanetary Society, Vol.30 No.10 (October 1977), p.380. Reproduced with permission.

The **PHA** (**P**olar **H**igh **A**tmosphere) series of four launches was carried out by the German DFVLR from January 22nd to March 16th. All were Skylark 7s (Raven XI with a Goldfinch booster) launched from Andøya in Norway. The PHA launches were part of the longer term "International Magnetospheric Study" that included both British and German sounding rocket campaigns carried out in conjunction with satellite measurements.[10] The scientific purpose of the PHA series was to measure the response of the high atmosphere during the arrival of an auroral substorm,[11] events which carried a large amount of energy into the auroral and polar high atmosphere.

The payloads carried similar sets of eight instruments,[12] and the launches were timed to coincide with different phases of typical auroral substorms. All were successful, except for PHA3 on February 20th, which was only partly successful because of a "Dornier nose cone failure",[13] when the nose cone failed to separate, and two of the instruments produced no results.[14]

Also launched during this time was **S22**, the first Swedish sponsored Skylark. This took place in the early evening of February 8th from Esrange in Sweden, and was an 'Auroral Arc Mission' that included a Swedish Space Corporation (SSC) UV spectrometer, apparently produced in partnership with the University of Liège in Belgium.[15] The German **PHA1** Skylark was also launched on the same day, (although from Andøya rather than Esrange) just four hours later, but the author does not know if they were deliberately co-ordinated.

Although there were no UK sponsored Skylark launches during this quarter, in February several UK sounding rockets experiments were launched into space, although from South Uist using Petrel rockets rather than Skylark.[16]

The original SL1115 had been launched from Woomera in May 1976, but because of a motor problem, the rocket head had remained out of control during the entire flight, and no useful observations had been possible. However the imaging X-ray telescope had performed well, was recovered in good condition, and a re-flight approved by the SRC. As noted in the previous chapter, this re-flight meant that SL1401, originally planned for this launch slot, had to be abandoned.

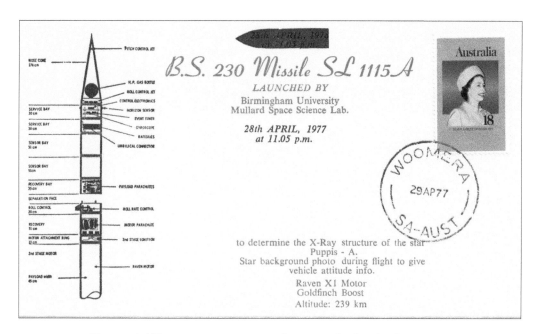

Figure 15.4 This commemorative envelope provides details of SL1115A.

(Author's collection)

[10] Theile (1976), 'Support of satellite missions by high-latitude rocket campaigns'.
[11] Auroral substorms are a brief (a few hours) disturbance in the Earth's magnetosphere that causes energy to be released into the high latitude ionosphere. They are distinct from geomagnetic storms that take place over a period of several days.
[12] Theile (1978), 'Initial Results of the Sounding Rocket Campaign "Polar High Atmosphere", p.115.
[13] BAe (1990), *Record of Skylark Launches 1957-1990*.
[14] Theile (1978), p.116.
[15] Jamar *et al.* (1976) 'The E1 experiment aboard S22 payload: Capabilities of the prototype model'.
[16] Petrel launches – see for instance Massey & Robins, *History of British Space Science*, Appendix B, p.424.

Figure 15.5 The SL1115A payload ready in the Woomera test shop. Mike Taylor 2nd from left, Ron Jeffery 3rd, John Ison 1st on right, Bob Beatttie 2nd, Ted Chambers 4th, Dave Gallery 5th, Vic Mankelow 6th.[17]

(WRE)

The instrument was duly re-launched as the payload of SL1115A[18] on 28 April 1977, the last Skylark to be launched from Woomera by BAC.[19] Most unfortunately, although this time the rocket motor worked perfectly, the Stage 5 star-pointing ACU failed. What this meant to those involved is brought home by this passage in the subsequent MSSL annual report:

> The loss, for a second time, of any astrophysical data from the SL1115 project, due to an incomprehensible failure of the attitude control system that by now should have been totally reliable, robbed us again of a great expectation – the first ever two-dimensional picture of an

extended cosmic X-ray source. We had our new position-sensitive proportional counter working well at the focus of the MSFC's[20] very large ATM X-ray reflector; the results would have been unique and of great value as a demonstration of an important technique for the future. I am particularly sorry for and grateful to Dr Richard Berthelsdorf, the project scientist, who spent many weary weeks at Woomera for both attempts, with no scientific yield to the credit of his name.[21]

The Stage 5 ACU from SL1115A was presumably that recovered with the SL1115 payload, the previous year. It was returned to the UK, probably for investigation, and was

[17]   The names are from Chambers (2000), *Woomera, Its human face*, p.71.
[18]   Some sources refer to these two flights as SL1115A and SL1115B, but the convention that the flight of a 'refurbished' Skylark be given the suffix 'A' is retained here.
[19]   BAe (1990), *Record of Skylark Launches 1957-1990*.
[20]   MSFC = Marshall Space Flight Center, Alabama, USA.
[21]   MSSL (1977), *Report of the MSSL 1st October 1976 – 30 September 1977*, part 1, p.3.

Figures 15.6 and 15.7 The unreliable Stage 5 ACB (ACU inside Bay) used on SL1115 and SL1115A photographed over 30 years after use, having been recovered from its second flight into space and returned to the UK. (A small section on the right of the left-hand image has been enhanced to try and show the designation "SL1115".)

(Science Museum object 1994-158, author 100_5000 & 100_4999) [23]

viewed by the author in 2010, when held in store by the London Science Museum, see the figures just above.[22]

___

May – September 1977   SL1298

___

There was only one Skylark launch during the five months from May to September. **SL1298** (8th June) was the sixth of the nine military Skylarks (SL1191, SL1291-93 & 95-99), used to develop decoys for the Chevaline re-entry vehicle.

___

October 1977   IMS1, SL1423

___

The 'IMS' series of four Skylark launches were part of the continuing West German contribution to the "International

Magnetospheric Study", which had started at the beginning of 1977 with the 'PHA' series. They were designed to study auroral substorm phenomena, and were part of the scientific programme that included SL1423 described below.

IMS1 was launched from Andøya on 13th October, on the same day and only half an hour before SL1423 described below. The two launches were carefully co-ordinated, steps were taken to use different telemetry frequencies, and the Germans provided a second launcher.[24] The altitude reached by IMS1 (536 km / 333miles) reflects the fact that it was the first Skylark 12 to be launched by the DFVLR. There must have been a few anxious moments before and during the launch, as the window of opportunity was very short and unpredictable, and in the event, IMS1 was launched only

Seq. Nos	Launch date	Ref. (sponsor) launch site	Config-uration	Apogee km (miles)	Experi-menters	Experiment	Result
362 (8)	13 Oct. 1977	IMS1 (DFVLR) Andøya	Spin, Rav.XI +G+C	536 (333)	Tüb/ Freib	Aurora – (International Magnetospheric Study), observations of auroral substorm	S

Table 15.2 A summary of Skylark IMS1.

22 Science Museum object number 1994-158, "Stage 5 ACB from Skylark Rocket. Flown on SL1115. (Found at Hayes store during move, February 1994)". When viewed by the author in 2010, it was held at the Science Museum large object storage facility at Wroughton near Swindon, UK.
23 Photographs taken at the London Science Museum (Wroughton), permission granted by Science & Society Picture Library.
24 MSSL (1974), *Report of the MSSL 1st October 1973 – 30 September 1974*, Part 2, p.5.

Seq. Nos	Launch date	Ref. (sponsor) launch site	Config- uration	Apogee km (miles)	Experi- menters	Experiment(s)	Result
363 (9)	13 Oct. 1977	SL1423 (UK) Andøya	Spin, Rav. XI +G+C	788 (490)	AL/ MSSL/ Shf/UCL	Aurora - 1976/77 high latitude campaign continued – study of VLF waves, suprathermal electrons, electron & neutral ions, neutral winds	S

Table 15.3 A summary of SL1423.

four minutes after the auroral substorm started, and the substorm lasted only eight minutes altogether! All experiments and sub-systems worked perfectly, providing a wealth of data when the payload encountered at least two current sheets at the northern boundary of the auroral activity region.[25]

Following IMS1, the launch of SL1423 marked the resumption of the series of the UK Skylark 12 launches of the previous year, now termed the 1977/78 High Latitude campaign. Just before the campaign resumed, Professor RLF Boyd of MSSL had written:

> Magnetospheric research has become a highly complex subject, a difficult research area and opportunities, at least in the UK, are few and far between. Yet the UK groups have achieved one series of experiments from Andøya, and are now about to commence a second, making a comprehensive and well-planned attack on outstanding problems connected with aurorae.[26]

SL1423 was the particular responsibility of MSSL, and the original intention had been that:

> SL1423 will be launched into widespread, diffuse aurora in the morning in an attempt to make comparisons with observations made by the GEOS satellite which is expected to be in position, conjugate with Northern Scandinavia, at that time.[27]

In the event, SL1423 was launched into a diffuse aurora in the evening rather than the morning, just half an hour after the German IMS1 Skylark launch described above. The altitude reached of 788 km (490 miles) was a new record for Skylark, exceeded only by that of SL1424 the following year,

and higher than all except two of the larger Black Knight rockets previously launched from Woomera.[28]

The MSSL instrumentation on SL1423 comprised two GEOS-type[29] suprathermal particle detectors, and that from the AL (Appleton Laboratory, formerly RSRS) included electron and proton energy measuring equipment.[30] The Sheffield experiment measured very low frequency (VLF) radio waves characterised by chorus, hiss and noise associated with magnetospheric propagation.[31]

The analysis of the data from complex payloads such as this could take some time, for instance two years later in 1979 it was reported:

> The most significant result obtained in the last year has come from a comparison of the MSSL suprathermal electron data with the University of Sheffield VLF [Very Low Frequency radio] wave data from Skylark rocket SL1423.[32]

These results were then compared with those from a University of Texas experiment on the ISIS satellite, leading in turn to a more significant understanding of the processes that produced stable auroral arcs.[33]

The collaborative use of rockets large and small, and other experiments, was a feature of these high latitude campaigns. For instance three days later, on 16th October, a British Fulmar rocket was launched from Andøya. This Fulmar, (F3), was fired into a bright active aurora, and carried experiments from the Appleton Laboratory and UCL to an altitude of some 260 km.[34]

---

[25] Wilhelm *et al.* (1980), 'Sounding Rocket Observations of Field-Aligned Current Sheets', p.279.

[26] MSSL (1977), *Report of the MSSL 1st October 1976 – 30 September 1977*, Part 1, p.3.

[27] MSSL (1974), *Report of the MSSL 1st October 1973 – 30 September 1974*, Part 2 p.5.

[28] See for instance Gordon & Parkin (1964), *A Summary of "Black Knight" Flight Data from 1958 to 1962*, or *www.spaceuk.org/bk/bk2/bk_flights.htm* (last accessed August 2014).

[29] The ESA Magnetospheric Observatory satellite GEOS-1 had been launched into a 12-hour orbit by NASA in April 1977, and included MSSL suprathermal plasma analysers.

[30] Massey & Robins (1986), *History of British Space Science*, p.325.

[31] Gibbons *et al.* (1981), 'Magnetospheric waves measured on high altitude skylark rockets SL 1423 and SL 1424'.

[32] UCL (1980), 'MSSL report for 1978 – 1979' as published by the Royal Astronomical Society, p.77.

[33] Ibid.

[34] Massey & Robins (1986), *History of British Space Science,* p.325 and p.425.

Figure 15.8 A fine time-lapse photograph of the launch of Petrel P207A from Andøya.

(J.O.Andersen \ SRC)

Petrel 2

To improve the performance of the smaller Petrel sounding rocket, a Petrel 2 variant was brought into service in 1977. It used four (rather than three) Chick boosters at takeoff and a lengthened Lapwing motor that burned for 40 seconds, and could send 18 kg to 175 km altitude.[35] One of the first of

these (P207A) was fired from Andøya, also on 16th October. It reached a respectable 207 km (127 miles) and carried an AL/UCL experiment to measure neutral winds by laser tracking the emission from a sodium thermite canister.[36]

**Figures 15.9 and 15.10 Left: Assembly of a German Skylark 12 in the main assembly hall at Andøya.
Right: Two German Skylark 12 payloads in the checkout room at Andøya.**

(Bjurstrøm & Gundersen (1978), figures 3 and 4)

[35] Massey & Robins (1986), p.190.
[36] Massey & Robins (1986), *History of British Space Science*, p.425.

Seq. Nos	Launch date	Ref. (sponsor) launch site	Config-uration	Apogee km (miles)	Experi-menters	Experiment(s)	Result
365 (11)	17 Nov. 1977	SL1421 (UK) Andøya	Spin, Rav.XI +G+C	718 (446)	AL/GSFC/ MSSL/Sx	Aurora – 1976/77 high latitude campaign continued – study of supra-thermal electrons & ions, electrons & positive ions	S

Table 15.4 A summary of SL1421.

November 1977	IMS2, SL1421

Two weeks later, on 2nd November, the German **IMS2** Skylark was also launched from Andøya. It was the second of the IMS Skylark 12s designed for auroral substorm observations, and successfully reached 541 km.

This in turn was followed another two weeks later by **SL1421**, the fourth Skylark launch of the UK's high latitude campaign from Andøya:

SL1421 was launched at the moment of breakup of an auroral curtain or arc, and nearly simultaneously a Fulmar rocket (F1) was fired into the same aurora, the results providing the basis for several scientific papers on the physics of auroras.[37]

> At one stage both rockets were engulfed at different altitudes in the same moving form. The combined results from all experiments on these rockets and at the ground provide what is probably the most detailed and comprehensive set of measurements yet made in any form of aurora.[38]

At this stage in the High Latitude Campaign, MSSL also reported:

> ...we now have data sets of suprathermal electron distributions from eight sounding rockets collected since 1973 over a wide altitude range in a variety of auroral conditions. The studies underway use the data from several of the rockets at a time to contrast and compare the plasma processes occurring...[39]

December 1977	TEXUS 1

The launch of the DFVLR **TEXUS 1**[40] Skylark from Esrange on 13th December was the first European use of a sounding rocket for multiple microgravity experiments.[41] The project was originally started to gain expertise and allow scientific microgravity experiments to be carried out before the Shuttle 'Spacelab' facility was available,[42] but took on a life of its own, and became an application that was to become the mainstay of Skylark for the next two decades:

> The TEXUS program was originally intended as a space shuttle payloads preexperiment project, but its advantages of quick preparation and reduced safety requirements[43] made it a self reliant program.[44]

This first flight was used only for materials science experiments, a field of space science in its infancy, where the early experiments on Apollo and Skylab had showed great promise. The Shuttle borne Spacelab was still five years in the future, and so at this time the only way to provide flight opportunities was to use sounding rockets.[45]

To meet this emerging requirement, BAC had proposed a version of Skylark that, except for a simplified attitude control unit, used only standard 'building blocks', see figure 15.11.

The attitude control unit was based on that developed by the RAE for the Earth resources Skylark, but with the horizon sensors removed. The control jets were switched on at an altitude of 90 km (56 miles), and used to reduce the angular spinning velocity about each of the three axes to a

---

[37] Royal Astronomical Society (1979), 'MIST Meeting at Southampton' (April 1978).

[38] SRC (Appleton Laboratory) (c.1980), *Radio and Space Research 1977-1979*, p.50.

[39] UCL (1979), 'MSSL report for 1977 – 1978' as published by the Royal Astronomical Society, p.77.

[40] The acronym 'TEXUS' was derived from the German *"Technologische Experimente unter Schwerelosigkeit"* (Technological Experiments in Weightlessness).

[41] The ESA EEA database sounding rocket index lists 15 sounding rocket flights with weightlessness experiments during the 16 years before TEXUS. 1, although none carried more than one such experiment. They were mostly life science studies, and included the flights of rats, a goldfish, a salamander, cats, monkeys and leeches!

[42] Construction of the European made Spacelab had been started in 1974, and in due course Spacelab components would be flown on some two dozen Shuttle missions between 1983 and 1998. An example is shown as Figure 14.60.

[43] The reduced safety requirements refer to the fact that Skylark instruments did not have to be 'man rated' (as for the Space Shuttle), thus were much cheaper.

[44] Ahlborn (1983), 'The future of materials science on sounding rocket flights'.

[45] At this time, returning samples to Earth was only practical for sounding rockets or manned spaceflights.

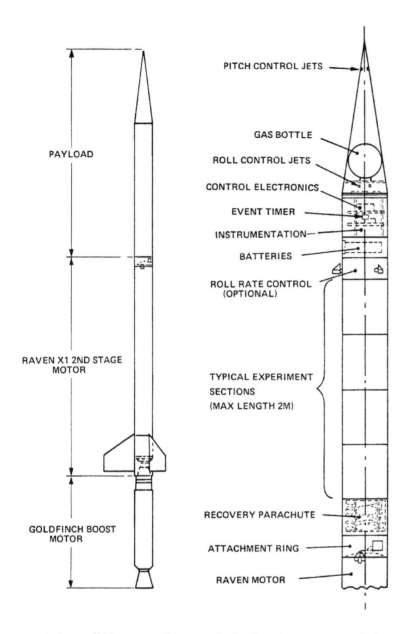

PITCH CONTROL JETS

GAS BOTTLE

ROLL CONTROL JETS

CONTROL ELECTRONICS

EVENT TIMER

INSTRUMENTATION

BATTERIES

ROLL RATE CONTROL
(OPTIONAL)

TYPICAL EXPERIMENT
SECTIONS
(MAX LENGTH 2M)

RECOVERY PARACHUTE

ATTACHMENT RING

RAVEN MOTOR

PAYLOAD

RAVEN X1 2ND STAGE
MOTOR

GOLDFINCH BOOST
MOTOR

Figure 15.11 BAC's original layout for a space processing Skylark.

(Hilton (1977), figure 1)

nominal zero.[46] They were then switched off so the gas jets did not cause disturbing accelerations, and the payload left to free fly through space. Once in this mode the acceleration from residual atmospheric drag was calculated to be down to 10^{-4} g by 112 km and 10^{-6} g by 170 km. Thus with a 300 kg gross payload, Skylark 6 (Raven VI with Goldfinch) was calculated to provide five minutes of micro-gravity, and the more powerful Skylark 7 (Raven XI with Goldfinch) about two minutes longer.[47]

TEXUS 1 used the Skylark 7 option, and the launch took place from Esrange at Kiruna in Sweden. In the event, the

flight was able to provide about six minutes of microgravity. The Germans developed a 40 kg reusable materials science experiment module for the payload, this incorporated several rapid heating and cooling furnaces. Altogether, thirteen experiments were flown on this first flight, mostly from Germany but with two from Sweden.[48] Most involved the study of metals, (for instance examining how they formed alloys under microgravity conditions[49]), one studied fluid physics, one hydrogen bubble generation on a cathode surface, one the electro deposition of metal from an electrolyte, and another examined diffusion phenomena within a glass melt.[50]

---

[46] This became known as the 'Zero Rate Control' version ('ZR' in Appendix 3).

[47] Hilton (1977), 'Skylark Sounding Rocket for Space Processing Experiments', p.379.

[48] ESA EEA and NASA MICREX databases, TEXUS 1. For details of Swedish involvement, see *www.zenker.se/Space/Jubilee/jubilee-b. shtml#Microgravity%20research%20-%20the%20sounding%20rocket* . (Last accessed August 2014).

[49] Grahn and Stenmark (1980), 'Swedish Materials Science Experiment in the TEXUS 1 and 2 Rockets'.

[50] Frischat *et al.* (1983), 'Reactions in Glass Melts'.

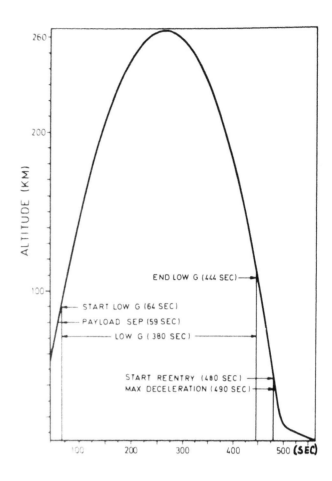

Figures 15.12 and 15.13 Left: Payload preparation for the first TEXUS flight. (Seibert (2006), p.33)
Right: TEXUS 1 flight profile showing the start and end of the low G phases. (Schmidt et al. (1978), figure 1)

Some of the experiments used cine cameras to record the results under weightless conditions.

In stark contrast to the UK's SRC, which by now had abandoned the development of Skylark, the Germans embraced its use. They extended its adaptable modular concept, and introduced decentralised instrumentation, where each experiment carried its own power supply, sequencer and data acquisition system. This provided both redundancy, and design experience for the forthcoming Spacelab payloads. The new system worked well right from its first use on TEXUS 1.[51]

Success was achieved because "Successful recovery of the payload was a mandatory feature of the TEXUS-1 mission."[52] The Germans were clearly aware of Skylark's payload recovery problems. Their requirement led to theoretical

work concerning the simulation of the re-entry phase involving factors such as tumbling motion, drag deceleration etc. This was compared with NASA results on the same "re-entry flat spin" phenomena, and they were able to identify different factors above and below Mach 1[53] during Skylark payload re-entry. These showed that if the centre of gravity of the returning payload was within 5% of the centre of the payload, oscillation and dynamic forces were kept within bounds. Telemetry results during TEXUS 1 re-entry confirmed drogue parachute deployment at the point where oscillations stopped and the payload turned over from a flat spin to a vertical attitude.[54]

Hence accurately balancing the payload in this manner appears to have finally solved the Skylark payload recovery problem.

---

[51] Geisel and Franke (1979), 'Experiment modules and facilities in TEXUS 1 and 2'.
[52] Schmidt *et al.* (1978), 'The Space Processing Mission of TEXUS-1 with respect to Micro-G Environment and Recovery', p.475.
[53] I.e. the supersonic and subsonic phases.
[54] Schmidt *et al.* (1978), p.479 and figure 10.

A summary of the UK scientific experiments flown on Skylark up to the end of 1977

As described in the next section, the UK national scientific programme using the Skylark rocket ended in 1978. Hence the following table, covering up to the end of 1977, conveniently summarises almost all the scientific experiments flown on UK national programme Skylarks. (It excludes British experiments flown on ESRO sponsored Skylarks.) The table was produced for a presentation to an ESA sounding rocket symposium in June 1978,[55] although the title is a little misleading, as by the time the SRC was created in 1965, Skylark had been launching experiments for nearly ten years.

Table 1 SRC Skylark Programme – Experiments						
INSTITUTION	1957-61	1962-66	1967-71	1972-76	1977	TOTALS
BIRMINGHAM UNIVERSITY	9	10	5	6	1	31
GEC	-	8	-	-	-	8
IMPERIAL COLLEGE, LONDON	15	20	2	-	-	37
JODRELL BANK	2	2	-	-	-	4
LEICESTER UNIVERSITY	8	28	18	8	-	62
MPE, GARCHING	-	-	-	2	-	2
METEOROLOGICAL OFFICE	1	6	6	2	-	15
MULLARD SPACE SCIENCE LABORATORY	-	-	18	16	1	35
QUEENS UNIVERSITY, BELFAST	8	9	6	2	-	25
ROYAL AIRCRAFT ESTABLISHMENT	34	54	8	4	-	100
SRC, APPLETON LABORATORY	-	8	6	7	1	22
SRC, ASTROPHYSICS RESEARCH DIVISION	-	4	13	7	-	24
SHEFFIELD UNIVERSITY	-	6	3	3	1	13
SOUTHAMPTON UNIVERSITY	-	2	-	4	-	6
SUSSEX UNIVERSITY	-	-	-	3	1	4
UNIVS. ADELAIDE & TASMANIA	-	-	4	3	-	7
UCB (BIRKBECK COLLEGE)	3	6	-	-	-	9
UNIVERSITY COLLEGE LONDON	29	52	8	5	1	95
UNIVERSITY COLLEGE OF WALES	-	2	11	-	-	13
WEAPONS RESEARCH ESTABLISHMENT	3	8	-	-	-	11
OTHERS	2	6	4	8	-	20
EXPERIMENT ANNUAL *TOTALS	114	231	112	80	6	543
SKYLARK ROCKET - *TOTALS	49	95	68	40	3	255

* Many Skylark rockets contain more than one experiment

Table 15.5 A summary of the more than 500 UK scientific experiments flown on UK National Programme Skylarks from 1957 to 1977. (After Delury (1978), Table 1)

Jan.	Feb.	Mar.	Apr.	May	June	July	Aug.	Sept.	Oct.	Nov.	Dec.
IMS3				SL1305		S26A	S26B			SL1424	SL1297
IMS4										SL1296	
										TEXUS 2	

Table 15.6 The nine Skylark Launches in 1978. (For full details see Appendix 3)

(Key: red = German national, plum = UK (stabilised), light blue = Swedish, blue = UK (unstabilised), black = UK military proving)

55 Delury (1978), 'Review of the British Scientific Sounding Rocket and Balloon Programmes', pp.45-49.

SKYLARK LAUNCHES AND SCIENCE IN 1978

April 1978 was the 21st anniversary of Skylark's first launch. This was not as auspicious as it might have been, because during the year the number of Skylark launches declined to nine compared to twelve in 1977. Despite this, the Skylark launch area at Woomera was still relatively busy, with the launch of three Falstaff rockets, (F1,[56] F2 and F3), in May, September and December respectively. Despite the low number of Skylark launches, there was a wide variety of missions; they included aeronomy (aurora and ionosphere), astronomy (solar physics), microgravity and military proving rounds. All were successful, although there was still one parachute failure (SL1305).

However, for reasons discussed below, Skylark's UK sponsored science programme was drawing to a close. The table below shows the very thin SRC approved programme for 1978.

In the event, only two of these three were launched, SL1305 in May and SL1424 in November. SL1611 in October was to have flown the first flight unit of a new improved design of attitude control unit, based on a Ferranti aircraft navigation inertial (gyroscopically controlled) reference control system.[57] Unfortunately, the design of the software proved more difficult than expected, and this led to delays and the abandonment of the launch.[58]

January 1978	IMS3, IMS4

1978 opened with the launch of the final two German IMS (International Magnetospheric Study) missions. **IMS3** and **IMS4** were fired within half an hour of each other during the evening of 30th January, and both were successful.

April 1978	-

There were no Skylark launches in April, but a 'postcard' produced by BAe marked the 21st anniversary. Information on the back summarised the first 21 years:

The original Skylark research rocket was developed by the Royal Aircraft Establishment to carry a payload of 45 Kg. (100lb.) to an altitude of 160 Km. (100ml.). Since those successful first flights the Skylark series has been progressively developed and its performance continuously improved to meet the changing requirements of its many users, embracing Sun, Moon and star-pointing variants, applications for science and space processing experiments.

Skylark 12, the latest high performance 3-stage version - of which seven have been flown this winter - will typically carry a payload of 135 Kg. (300 lb.) to an altitude of 800 Km. (500 ml.) – a fifteen fold increase in payload/altitude performance over Skylark 1.

Table 2 1978 Skylark Programme

Experimenter Group	No. and type of rocket	Payload Designation	Launch Conditions	Launch Period	Frequency	Remarks/ Science
University of Leicester	1-Skylark 7	SL 1611 Astrophysics (1st inertial a.c.u.)	Quiet ionosphere Crab Nebula to be visible	Woomera Oct. 1978	227.2 MHz) PCM 258.5 MHz)	Study of interstellar matter by X-ray scattering from grains
Appleton Laboratory (ARD)	1-Skylark 7	SL 1305 Astrophysics (Stage 1 a.c.u.)	Sun altitude to be as high as possible	Woomera April/ May 1978	434 MHz) FM 449 MHz)	Relative abundance of helium in solar corona
Sheffield/ UCL/ AL	1-Skylark 12	SL 1424 Geophysics (Spin stabilised)	Auroral chorus in conjunction with Fulmar F6	Andøya -	400.85 MHz (FM) 258.5 MHz(PCM)	Study of VLF chorus

Table 15.7 The SRC's very limited Skylark programme for 1978.

(Delury (1978), Table 2)

---

[56] Although F1 was a catastrophic failure, see Harlow (2000), 'The Larger Solid Propellant Rocket Motors of the United Kingdom', p.11.
[57] As discussed previously, this was designed to overcome the operational limitations of the star-pointing Stage 5 ACU.
[58] Massey & Robins (1986), *History of British Space Science*, p.209. (Although Ferranti gyros went on to be used on Ariane and ESA satellites).

Figure 15.14 This BAe 'postcard' marked the 21st anniversary of Skylark's first launch in April 1957. On the left is SL03 with the original fin design,[59] on the right a colour version of the Skylark 12 image shown in Figure 15.1.

(BAe \ author's collection)

May 1978	SL1305

Design studies for **SL1305** had started back in 1973/74, a collaborative venture between the then ARD at Culham, and MSSL. It was a solar physics experiment comprising a grazing incidence spectrograph designed to observe UV emission lines from the solar corona, the main objective of which was to determine accurately the relative abundance of hydrogen to helium,[60] this quantity being an important verification of models of the birth of the universe.

It had been hoped to launch in 1977, but SL1305 was finally fired from Woomera on 12 May 1978. Not only was it the last Woomera launched Skylark with which MSSL and ARD Culham were associated, but also the last UK sponsored 'scientific' Skylark to be launched from Australia. The recovery problem haunted things to the end, as the parachute failed during the final part of the flight, but fortunately, the essential data were recorded by telemetry.[61]

Good data was returned, and led to a similar instrument from ARD/MSSL being accepted by NASA for inclusion in the *Spacelab 2* payload, for a nine-day flight during the latter part of 1981.[62] In the event, this CHASE (Coronal Helium Abundance Spacelab Experiment) was launched on the Space Shuttle *Challenger* (STS-51F) on July 29, 1985.[63] The Spacelab 2 mission was dedicated to astronomy, solar observation and biology, and the CHASE experiment was one of four solar observation instruments, the only one not from the USA:

> The Coronal Helium Abundance Spacelab Experiment (CHASE) obtained one of the most accurate measurements of the abundance of solar helium relative to solar hydrogen. By recording ultraviolet emissions from hydrogen and ionized helium, both on the solar disk and in the corona above the limb, an abundance ratio of helium to hydrogen of 10% ± 2% was measured. Understanding several important astrophysical processes depends on an accurate accounting of helium in the universe. Since all the helium in the surface layers of the sun is thought to be primitive in origin, data collected on the Spacelab 2 mission are of great importance to cosmologists as well as solar physicists.[64]

---

[59] See this book Figure 5.21.
[60] MSSL (1975), *Report of the MSSL October 1974 – September 1975*, Part 2, p.10.
[61] Massey & Robins (1986), *History of British Space Science*, p.345.
[62] UCL (1979), 'MSSL report for 1977 – 1978', as published by the Royal Astronomical Society.
[63] See for instance *http://solarscience.msfc.nasa.gov/SpaceLab2.shtml* and *www.stfc.ac.uk/RALSpace/11216.aspx* (last accessed August 2014).
[64] *http://history.nasa.gov/NP-119/ch4.htm* , (last accessed August 2014).

Figures 15.15 and 15.16 Left: the Spacelab 2 Instrument Pointing System (supplied by ESA), a sophisticated mechanism for aiming telescopes and detectors. Right: Crewmembers used controls in a Shuttle workstation to point telescopes at specific areas of the Sun – a far cry from the Skylark Sun-pointing ACU!

(NASA) [65]

(As described in the previous chapter, Shuttle ST51-F also carried another Skylark derived instrument, the X-ray telescope (XRT) from the University of Birmingham.)

July & August 1978   S26A, S26B

S26A and **S26B** (also known as S26/1 and S26/2[66]) were two Skylarks launched from Esrange and sponsored by the SSC (Swedish Space Corporation). They were part of a multinational rocket campaign to investigate the mesosphere and lower ionosphere in the presence of noctilucent[67] clouds (NLC), and on ascent used mass spectrometers to take measurements.[68] The campaign contributed significantly to the understanding of noctilucent clouds.

S26A and S26B were amongst the last Skylark rockets to use the older Raven VIII motors,[69] and reached altitudes of 114 and 127 km respectively. Although though not as high as

most later Skylark flights, this was ideal for the study of these clouds,[70] as the diagram opposite shows.

November 1978   SL1424, **SL1296**, TEXUS 2

SL1424 was fired from Andøya, and not only was it the final Skylark launch of the UK's High Latitude Campaign, it also had the dubious honour of being the last UK sponsored scientific Skylark. It did however "go out with a bang", as the altitude reached (796 km / 495 miles) was another record for Skylark, and higher than most of the larger Black Knight rockets previously launched from Woomera.[71]

It carried instruments from no less than four UK institutions and the NRDE (Norwegian Defence Research Establishment); including some that designed to detect VLF (Very Low Frequency) radio waves. It was launched in the very early morning of 10th November when an ELF/VLF chorus

---

[65]   http://history.nasa.gov/NP-119/ch4.htm , (last accessed August 2014).
[66]   Not to be confused with ESRO S26/1 & S26/2 launched in 1967.
[67]   Literally, 'night shining'.
[68]   Kopp *et al.* (1985), 'Positive ion composition of the high-latitude summer D-region with noctilucent clouds'.
[69]   The very last were the four ROSE missions in 1988/89.
[70]   Noctilucent clouds are a unique feature of the summer night sky at higher latitudes. They exist only in the mesopause region at altitudes of about 80 to 86 km, and are composed of small particles, which because of their high altitude, are sunlit long after sunset at ground level.
[71]   See for instance Gordon & Parkin (1964), *A Summary of "Black Knight" Flight Data from 1958 to 1962*, or www.spaceuk.org/bk/bk2/bk_flights.htm (last accessed August 2014).

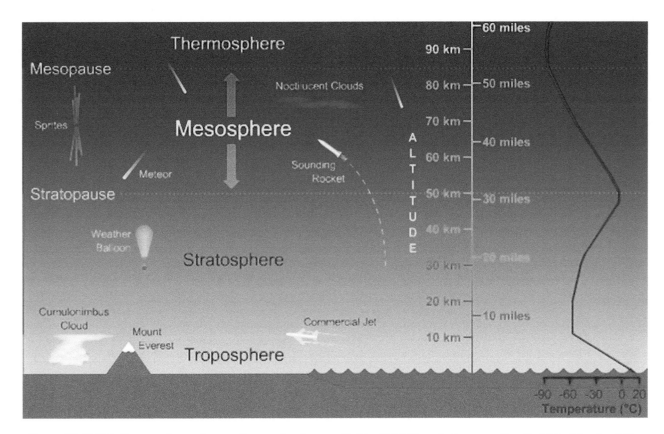

Figure 15.17 This diagram shows the noctilucent clouds as studied by S26A/B, at their extraordinarily high altitude within the mesosphere on the edge of space. (The ionosphere is not shown as such, because it is formed of layers from 85 km upwards within the mesosphere, thermosphere and above.)

(Image based on content from *Windows to the Universe*® (*http://windows2universe.org*) © 2010, *National Earth Science Teachers Association*.) [72]

event [73] was observed by the GEOS 2 satellite and ground-based receivers. The satellite above the equator, the rocket in the ionosphere and the ground-based receivers were all approximately in magnetic conjugacy, and good observations were obtained.[74]

This was the last Skylark to be used by MSSL:

> It was after we had finished using Skylark and one of our electronics engineers, who happened to be a keen gardener, spotted an old Skylark body module that was never going to be used and decided it would make a good garden incinerator. Not a good idea of course as they were made of magnesium alloy! I think he actually got away with it a couple of times until one day he got to the critical temperature and the magnesium ignited and lit up the area rather well. The fire brigade were called, but as it was luckily away from anything valuable

and by then burning very fiercely they decided the safest thing to do was to stand back and enjoy the show until it burnt out.[75]

SL1296 (15th November), was the seventh of the nine military Skylarks (SL1191, SL1291-93 & 95-99), used to develop decoys for the Chevaline re-entry vehicle.

This was closely followed on the 16th by the launch of the DFVLR's **TEXUS 2**. Like TEXUS 1 before it, this microgravity mission used a two-stage Skylark 7 launched from Esrange at Kiruna in Sweden. It carried a repeat of the TEXUS 1 materials science payload, with between 11 and 17 experiments (some had multiple parts).[76] The experiments were mostly a continuation of those flown before, with some new ones such as the evaluation of the effects of low-gravity on the vacuum brazing cycle,[77] and the first of a series to study the dynamics of liquid motion in capillary tubes.[78]

---

[72] This image is from the web page *www.windows2universe.org/earth/Atmosphere/mesosphere.html* , (last accessed August 2014), and used under a "*Creative Commons Attribution-ShareAlike 3.0 Unported License*", see *http://creativecommons.org/licenses/by-sa/3.0/* (last accessed August 2014).

[73] A VLF chorus is a naturally occurring electromagnetic wave phenomenon, which with the appropriate (Very Low Frequency) radio equipment can be heard as a series of random chirps, whistles, and quasi-musical sounds.

[74] Cannon *et al.* (1980), 'ELF/VLF wavefield measurements made at the time of launch of Skylark SL1424'.

[75] John Coker, personal correspondence, February 2013.

[76] ESA EEA and NASA MICREX databases, TEXUS 2.

[77] NASA MICREX database - TEXUS 2, 'Capillary Brazing', (Bathke & Schlecker).

[78] NASA MICREX database - TEXUS 2, 'Wetting Kinetics/Capillarity, (Sell & Reznow).

---

13 December 1978   SL1297

SL1297 was launched just a month after the similar SL1296, and was the eighth of the nine military Skylarks used to develop decoys for the Chevaline re-entry vehicle.

The end of the UK's scientific use of Skylark

As noted above, the launch of SL1424 in November 1978 was a significant milestone in the story of Skylark, because it marked the end of UK funded scientific use of the rocket.

This demise was spelt out at an ESA sounding rocket symposium held a couple of years later at Bournemouth in 1980:

> Over the last 5 years there has been a considerable reduction in the UK rocket programme with the average Petrel launchings reducing from 26 per annum down to 10 and the ongoing UK Science Research Council Skylark programme, which involved annual launchings of up to 10 rockets per annum, being halted in 1979. It is currently planned that future launchings of Skylark type rockets will only be considered by the UK Science Research Council for approval on a scientific project basis and not as part of an ongoing rocket programme.[79]

It was perhaps ironic that this demise took place under the auspices of the SRC, because, as explained in Chapter 9, one of the reasons why the SRC had been formed in the first place was to administer British Scientific Space Research.[80]

The extract above gives no hint as to why there should be such a sudden reduction and halt in the UK programme, a phenomena in contrast to the expanding use of sounding rockets by Germany and ESA, albeit mostly in the new field of microgravity. The author has been unable to locate any specific documentation on the decision, but for a more thorough commentary on the lead up to this event, the reader is referred to the conclusion of Mathew Godwin's book on Skylark,[81] and for the general British attitude described in C.N.Hill's final chapter of "A Vertical Empire".[82]

However, some of the factors determining the end of the UK's use of Skylark are apparent:

Technical aspects

Space science was a fast moving field, and in some ways, Skylark was an example of sounding rockets becoming the victim of their own success. The engineering and scientific skills it helped create (and the experiments it flew) were used to build the first British scientific Earth satellites, a technology that in turn became a more promising research tool. By the early 1970s, it was becoming apparent that for space-based astronomy at least, scientific satellites were the way forward. "… I think the writing was on the wall for Skylark as a scientific research vehicle from the early 1970's"[83] Indeed, one reason that ESRO had terminated their sounding rocket programme in 1972 was to allocate more resources to other activities such as satellites:

> Initially, the sounding-rocket programme was four times larger in annual budget terms than the satellite programme. This situation was reversed, however, in the early 1970s, when the ESRO Council decided on 14 July 1971 to terminate its sounding-rocket activities in 1972 and to extend the scope of the European (i.e. ESRO) space programme from 1973 onwards with the start-up of new application satellites (telecommunications, Earth observation) programmes, the development of the Ariane launcher, and the construction of the Spacelab laboratory…[84]

Another factor was the vast improvement in electronics. Telemetry was capable of a great deal more than previously, and once images could be returned from space, the sub-orbital sounding rocket's inherent ability to return exposed photographic film to Earth became much less important. Another aspect was the impending arrival of the NASA Space Shuttle, which began operational flights in 1982. It was originally perceived that this would significantly reduce the cost of having experiments launched into space, although it was soon realised that such experiments would have to be qualified for manned space flight, greatly adding to their cost.

Budgetary matters

Skylark payloads had become very much more sophisticated and expensive compared with the early days. The perception was that scientists could have an Ariel satellite for about the cost of ten Skylarks, and get much more science out of it.[85] "Why spend three years building rocket borne equipment to gather five minutes of data when you could spend five years building satellite borne equipment that would deliver three years of data?"[86] and "We have reached a stage by the mid 70's at which the opportunities open to British space scientists to make observations from satellites are sufficiently fre-

---

[79]   Delury (1980), 'The UK Sounding Rocket and Balloon Programme'.
[80]   Godwin argues that British Space Research was central to the Trend Enquiry. (Godwin (2007), Chapter 8).
[81]   Godwin (2007), *The Skylark Racket*, p.257.
[82]   Hill (2001), *A Vertical Empire*, p.223.
[83]   Ken Pounds in 2001, CCBH (2005), *Skylark Sounding Rockets 1957-1972*, p.49 & *Prospero* No.2, p.114.
[84]   Seibert (2006), *The History of Sounding Rockets and Their Contribution to European Space Research*, p.47.
[85]   Ken Pounds in 2001, CCBH (2005), *Skylark Sounding Rockets 1957-1972*, p.48 & *Prospero* No.2, p.113.
[86]   Cruise (2008), *Skylark Ascending*, online article p.26, and *Prospero* number 5, Spring 2008, p.61.

quent to make us reassess the role of the sounding rocket".[87] This of course was the point of view of those providing only the payload, as the Skylark launches were funded separately by the British National programme. The argument also relied on an 'Uncle Sam' in the form of NASA to provide a free satellite launches!

Lack of purpose and coherence

In fact, it appears that the UK's Skylark programme was doomed from the moment management was transferred to the SRC. There, despite its outstanding success, it became part of the "…story of wasted opportunities brought about by lack of purpose and the absence of any coherent organisation."[88]

Despite being the most modest of space programmes, it appears that for financial reasons the ongoing Skylark programme was simply was too much for the SRC to bear.[89] As made clear in the Bournemouth statement quoted above, the SRC did not have (or chose not to have) the resources to run a rocket programme as such, only to contribute to the scientific aspects of such a programme. In practice the overheads of the Skylark programme had always been shared with military budgets, and once the whole responsibility devolved on the SRC in a time of economic constraints, it appears to have been simply too much.

That said, the Skylark programme was still only a small part of the UK's space expenditure. As shown in Chapter 11, at the start of the 1970s, the few million a year spent on Skylark was about one third of the UK's Space Science budget, but only about one fifteenth (6.6%) of the UK's spending on its National Space Programme activities at the time.[90]

In its turn, the National Programme itself was only a small part of overall UK space expenditure, which as the graph below shows, was running at about £55M per year in 1978-79.

However, these figures do not take into account UK monetary inflation. This peaked at an annual rate of 24% in 1975, and even by 1979 was still running at 13% per annum. Thus by 1979 the Pound Sterling had halved in value since 1974.[91] Clearly, the pressure was on.

The author has been unable to find out how much of this UK space expenditure funding was transferred to the SRC along with its new responsibility for managing the ongoing Skylark programme; however, the SRC/SERC[92] had only a fixed 'pot of money' from which to finance the competing scientific research claims on its funds. By 1980 it was spending almost two-thirds less on space science than it had been just six years earlier.[93]

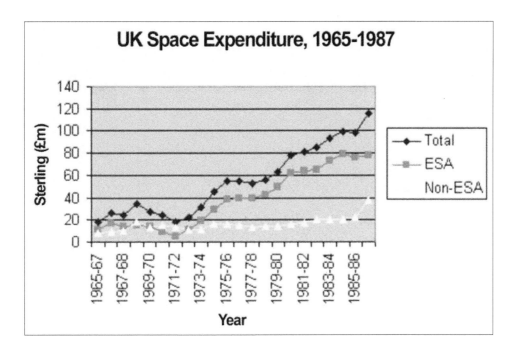

Figure 15.18 Summary of UK Space Expenditure 1965-1987.

(Millard (2005), p.24)

[87] Cruise (1974), 'Some Future Research Tasks For Stabilised Skylarks'.

[88] House of Commons Estimates Committee of 1967, as referenced by Millard (2005), *An Overview of UK Space Activity*, p.5.

[89] Although it would appear than even in 1973, only 10% (£6M) of the SRC's overall budget (£60M) was spent on space science. (Acton (1974), p.345).

[90] See this book Figure 11.9 and Figure 11.10.

[91] House of Commons research paper 99/20, *Inflation: the Value of the Pound 1750-1998*, Table 1, *www.parliament.uk/documents/commons/lib/research/rp99/rp99-020.pdf*. (Last accessed August 2014).

[92] The UK's SRC was renamed the SERC (Science and Engineering Research Council) in 1981.

[93] Millard (2005), *An Overview of UK Space Activity*, p.6.

In addition, as explained previously, the SRC now 'had two hats on'; they were no longer just a customer for Skylark, but also responsible for the administration and procurement of the ongoing sounding rocket programme.[94] Even if there was no new development required, one can surmise that the extras such as funding the inevitable post design engineering changes that any such project requires could have come as a nasty shock to a scientific organisation unused to the world of aerospace R&D; especially as the MOD funded RAE had ceased Skylark R&D support duties from April 1976.[95]

Conclusion

The author has concluded that the SRC sacrificed the UK sounding rocket programme for financial reasons, probably to protect its own budget against inflation. (It must be significant that the programme was not just reduced to account for inflation, but halted altogether).

The fundamental problem seems to be that the SRC was not a space agency, nor being funded as one, and was unable cope with this example of 'big science'. It had no remit to deal with the longer term benefits of such a programme, or to ensure that the country received a return on its investment in Skylark and its facilities. It simply had to balance the books at the end of each year.[96] It may well have used the perceived view that the day of the sounding rocket was over as an excuse, although in 1979 even the last British scientific satellite was launched.

Massey and Robins provide a useful summary of what happened in the UK. When writing about SL1611 and its inertial stabilisation unit they concluded:

> This development was in effect overtaken by events, in particular the rundown of the scientific Skylark programme as part of the overall policy under financial pressure of the Science Research Council, and the transfer of scientific interest in X-ray and ultraviolet astronomy to the even more powerful and comprehensive facilities for observations offered by scientific satellites such as Ariel 5 and the International Ultra Violet Explorer (IEU). So ended a long and successful chapter for UK space scientists.[97]

However, in other countries this was not the view, and even in the UK, many thought this policy was misguided.[98] Indeed,

by 1978-79 Skylark was less than half way though its operational life! – the mantle was passed to BAC/BAe, who promoted Skylark quite strongly.

To emphasise the point, ten years later in 1987, the following appeared in a paper delivered at ESA:[99]

> Originally, sounding rocket experiments were conceived as low-cost precursor experiments for long duration experiments like Spacelab etc. At the same time however, an increasing number of experiments with their own scientific justification have been developed.
>
> What makes sounding rockets such an attractive experiment platform for scientists is above all the relatively short lead time of only one or two years between experiment approval and flight, and the availability of experiment modules for a broad spectrum of scientific investigations.
>
> In addition, the experiment design for a sounding rocket mission is not constrained by the safety requirements which have to be satisfied on manned missions. This also results in much less cumbersome paperwork for the investigators.
>
> A further advantage is the rather high degree of flexibility with respect to late changes during the development of sounding rocket hardware.

Why didn't Skylark evolve into a satellite launcher?

The natural progression from Skylark would have been for the UK to have developed a small satellite launcher suitable for placing scientific satellites in orbit. Indeed, in one form that was exactly what happened with the development of Black Arrow, which (as described in previous chapters) had successfully launched Prospero in 1971. Foolishly (in the opinion of the author), the British Government cancelled this modest and economically run project in the same year.

Another way forward would have been the development of a solid-propellant motor based satellite launcher. Various proposals to do just this were put forward, these could have orbited satellites of 80-120 kg, and this concept is described later in this chapter under the '1987' heading.

---

94   Skylark programme management had passed from the MOD (PE) to the SRC in April 1974.
95   Minutes of the 26th Policy Meeting on the Skylark Rocket, June 1973, item 2, p. 3. (TNA: PRO AVIA 92/145).
96   What may be called "The Beeching fallacy"!
97   Massey & Robins (1986), *History of British Space Science*, p.209. © Science and Engineering Research Council 1986, published by Cambridge University Press, reproduced with permission.
98   See for instance the discussions in the CCBH Witness Seminar (2005), *Skylark Sounding Rockets 1957-1972*, & *Prospero* No.2, p.91 onwards.
99   Seibert & Herfs (1997), 'Microgravity Science from ESA's Microgravity Sounding Rocket Projects (Life and Physical Sciences', p.66.

Jan.	Feb.	March	April	May	June	July	Aug.	Sept.	Oct.	Nov.	Dec.
	Astro-4/2	SL1299							Astro-		
		Astro-4/1							Hel		

Table 15.8 The four Skylark Launches in 1979. (For full details see Appendix 3)

(Key: red = German national, black = UK military)

SKYLARK LAUNCHES AND SCIENCE IN 1979

In 1979 the number of Skylark launches fell to only four, well down compared to the already low total of nine the year before. This was the same number of launches as in 1957, the first year of operation, over two decades earlier. However, Skylark was still only halfway though its operational lifespan in terms of years, although 85% through its life in numbers of launches. From now onwards the pattern would be the same, the number of launches per year being less than that of some individual months during the busy years.

However, the Skylark launch area at Woomera remained active for the first few months of 1979, as the first two German 'Astro' Skylarks were launched from there, and the military Falstaff flights F4 and F5 took place in January and April respectively. However the end was in sight, and it would be eight years before another Skylark would be launched from Woomera.[100]

Also in 1979, the UK's Appleton Laboratory (formerly the RSRS) merged with the Rutherford Laboratory at Chilton in Oxfordshire, thus creating the Rutherford Appleton Laboratory.[101] This at least brought some stability to those who had supplied Skylark payloads, as the RAL has since thrived and remains under the same name today. The work of the original Appleton Laboratory has been continued within the Space Science and Technology Department of RAL, and has expanded to remain at the forefront of UK space research.[102]

In addition, in 1979, on 2nd June, the British scientific satellite UK6/Ariel 6 was launched by NASA. It included both cosmic ray and X-ray instruments,[103] but was the last in the Ariel series, as the SRC stopped supporting all-British designed spacecraft.

1979 also saw the last sounding rocket launched into space from the UK, when Petrel P211H was fired from Uist in July, reaching 145 km. However, the UK use of Petrel did outlast the UK use of Skylark a little longer, the last one being launched from Kiruna in 1981.[104] (Although as noted in an earlier chapter, the Petrel rocket lasted much longer in its military variants.[105])

February 1979   Astro 4/2

However, German use of Skylark continued for astronomical purposes as well as microgravity, and the two 'Astro 4' Skylarks were part of the German Astronomy Sounding Rocket Programme.[106]

Astro 4/2 investigated the cosmic X-ray sources Puppis A and the Crab Nebula by means of a Wolter telescope [107] using a position sensitive proportional counter detector. The location of these sources in the southern sky resulted in the Skylark being launched from Woomera, the first such German mission to be launched from there since S98 in 1975. Launch took place during the night of 22nd/23rd February, with the payload stabilised by a German star-pointing ACU.

The Astro 4/2 payload was the longest yet flown on Skylark. At 4.45 metres (14.6 feet), it was longer than the Raven VI sustainer motor on which it was mounted, and additional strength tests were undertaken by the motor manufacturer.[108] The all-new German payload modules were a completely new design, all updated compared with the aging UK versions. Scientific data was sent by telemetry directly to a ground-based TV screen so it could be monitored during flight (See below). Attitude control was by an inertially based system that was a further development of the German TIRACS (Telecommanded Inertially Referenced At-

---

[100] The German 'SN1987A' mission in August 1987.

[101] For details, see for instance *www.ukssdc.ac.uk/ditton_park_archive/history.html* , (last accessed August 2014).

[102] See *www.stfc.ac.uk/ralspace*, (last accessed August 2014).

[103] For details of Ariel 6, see Massey & Robins (1986), *History of British Space Science*, p.106.

[104] Massey & Robins (1986), p.426.

[105] The Sea Petrel supersonic target was a variant with Radar augmentation modifications to make it suitable for Royal Navy use. The original development is described by Fisher (1975), 'The Use of Sounding Rockets as Targets'. It apparently featured on the Meggitt Aerospace stand as late as Farnborough 2000, although production appears to have ceased in 2002. An example was displayed in the UK at the Bristol Aero Collection, Kemble, (now (2014) in storage), but apparently there is still an example at the Woomera Missile Park in Australia.

[106] Henkel & Pechstein (1980), 'Astro 4 – A Sounding Rocket Programme of the X-ray Astronomy', p.147.

[107] A Wolter telescope gathers X-rays using grazing incidence optics. The basic principle had been used on Skylark X-ray spectrographs for a several years, but only on SL1115 (May 1976) and SL1115A (April 1977) had an attempt been made to obtain 2-dimensional X-ray images using a Wolter telescope arrangement. Both had failed because of Skylark vehicle problems, not instrument faults.

[108] Henkel & Pechstein (1980), 'Astro 4 – A Sounding Rocket Programme of the X-ray Astronomy', p.152.

Figure 15.19 The Astro 4/2 X-ray mirror system, which had an aperture of 32 cm (12.6").
(MPE) [109]

titude Control System) as flown on Astro 7. It included a star sensor for fine lateral pointing, digital programming of manoeuvres, and a TV camera allowing the payload to be positioned around its roll axis by remote control during the mission.[110]

After launch, Astro 4/2 reached an altitude of 192 km, and during the flight was aligned for 70 seconds on Puppis A and for 140 seconds on the Crab Nebula. The parachute system worked, and the payload was recovered in good condition. [111]

"The inclusion of our first Wolter telescope with an opening [aperture] of 32 cm onboard a Skylark rocket in 1979 was a great success. The image of the supernova *Puppis A* was the first X-ray exposure of the sky ever taken with a spectral resolving imaging detector, a position sensitive proportional counter [PSPC] developed at the MPE.[112]."

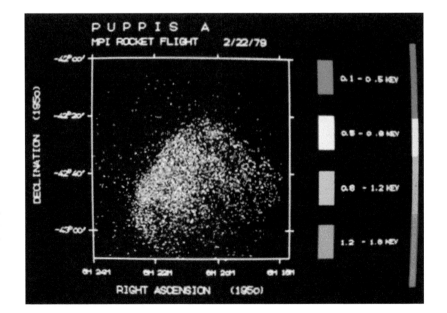

Figure 15.20 A false colour two-dimensional X-ray image of Puppis A from Astro 4/2.
(MPE) [113]

[109] Max-Planck-Institut für extraterrestrische Physik, (*www.mpe.mpg.de*), in particular, page *www.mpe.mpg.de/xray/wave/other_projects/astro4/index.php*, (last accessed August 2014).
[110] Henkel & Pechstein (1980), p.153.
[111] Remarkably, it was flown again eight years later; see 'Supernova' in 1987.
[112] MPE website, *www.mpe.mpg.de/xray/research/profile.php?lang=en* (last accessed August 2014).

This success must have been particularly galling for MSSL, especially as Skylark had by now been abandoned by the SRC. MSSL's similar payloads on SL1115 and SL1115A (1976 and 1977) had been designed to produce the first such two dimensional X-ray images, but produced no results because of Skylark vehicle failures, whereas this Astro 4/2 mission in 1979 had worked first time.

The Position Sensitive Proportional Counter (PSPC)[114] used with the Astro 4/2 telescope to detect the X-rays, is a good example how hardware for space use could be relatively cheaply proven on Skylark. The Astro 4/2 PSPC was a precursor of that used on the ROSAT[115] satellite, which was launched in 1990 and successfully operated in space for nine years:

> The ROSAT project is the continuation of a longstanding and successful programme for the development of instrumentation for soft X-ray astronomy at MPI. High resolution telescopes of 32 cm aperture have been built with the Carl Zeiss Co. Imaging proportional counters have been successfully manufactured by our group. The combination of both instruments has been successfully flown on a Skylark rocket and has obtained spectrally and spatially resolved pictures of Puppis A.[116]

March 1979   SL1299, Astro 4/1

SL1299 was successfully launched from Woomera on 1st March. Not only was it the last of the nine military Skylarks (SL1191, SL1291-93 & 95-99), but also the last ever UK sponsored Skylark. Thus, British use of Skylark at Woomera ended after 22 years, although German use at several locations continued for many years to come.

Astro 4/1 was the third German Skylark launched from Woomera; in contrast to Astro 4/1 it carried out X-ray studies of the Sun rather than examining cosmic sources.

The Skylark 7 powered vehicle was launched on 13th March, and the Sun-pointing stabilised payload successfully carried out spectroscopic observations and imaging of active regions of the solar corona. The main instrument was a four-channel KAP crystal[117] spectrometer, but there were nine experiments in all, including zone plate cameras and a Rowland spectrograph. The flight was completely successful, the apogee of 258 km being very close to the 260 km required. This time a Marconi Stage 1 ACU, modified for greater accuracy, was used rather than the German inertial system, and this provided a pointing accuracy of 10 arcsec. (0.003 of a degree), and an experiment measuring time of over five and a half minutes. A NASA-DFVLR-Sandia parachute system was included which successfully recovered the payload 172 km downrange, allowing the X-ray films to be removed immediately and developed with good results.[118]

The end of the Skylark launch tower at Woomera

Now that the British use of Skylark at Woomera had ended, the launch tower was demolished:

> … but sadly in 1979 at the completion of our trial programme – the *Chevaline* programme – the joint project between ourselves and the Australian government was no longer in being and therefore we had to pursue their clean range policy, as they called it, and this led to my having to get the launcher demolished. It is rather sad, but it *was* demolished by ourselves and taken away.[119]

This event was also noted by Ted Chambers:

> When the time came for the trials to cease, the launcher was declared redundant, its three legged support suffered one of its legs to be cut through by oxy torch at ground level, and it fell like a majestic forest giant.[120]

October 1979   Astro-Hel

It was a sign of the times that there was a seven-month gap until the next Skylark launch. **Astro-Hel** (Astro Helium) was another German solar physics mission, this time launched from a new location for Skylark – the province of Natal in Brazil. Here on the Atlantic coast the 'Barreira do Inferno' (literally, 'Barrier of Hell'[121]) Launch Centre (Centro de Lançamento da Barreira do Inferno [CLBI]), had been established in 1964, and used by the German DFVLR since 1967 for various non-Skylark sounding rocket missions.

The Astro-Hel payload was designed to observe different types of helium in the Sun's corona.[122] The instrument was an EUV (Extreme Ultra Violet) photometer, and comprised four measuring cells with a baffle system to help screen out

113 Max-Planck-Institut für extraterrestrische Physik, (*www.mpe.mpg.de*) in particular page *www.mpe.mpg.de/xray/wave/other_projects/astro4/index.php*, (last accessed August 2014).
114 Henkel and Pechstein (1980), 'Astro 4: A sounding rocket progress of the X-ray astronomy'.
115 The Roentgensatellit (ROSAT) was a very successful joint German, US and British X-ray astrophysics satellite launched in 1990. See for instance *http://ledas-www.star.le.ac.uk/rosat-goc/* (last accessed August 2014).
116 Aschenbach *et al.* (1981), 'The ROSAT mission', p.572.
117 KAP (potassium acid phthalate) crystals were used extensively in solar X-ray studies.
118 Henkel and Pechstein (1980), 'Astro 4: A sounding rocket progress of the X-ray astronomy', pp.147-153.
119 John Ray in 2001, CCBH (2005), *Skylark Sounding Rockets 1957-1972*, p.74, & *Prospero* No.2, p.138.
120 Chambers (2000), *Woomera, Its human face*, p.109.
121 Since the sunlight hits the red cliff at sunrise and local fishermen thought it looked as if the area were in flames.
122 I.e. similar to the last UK scientific Skylark SL1305, launched 18 months earlier.

background radiation.[123] The payload concept was based on experience from the Astro-6 rocket mission that had used a Black Brant sounding rocket launched from El Arenosillo in June 1976.

The instrument could only work at altitudes above 300 km, so the vehicle chosen for Astro-Hel was a three-stage Skylark 12. The requirement was for 12 minutes of observing time and an apogee of at least 800 km. A sophisticated payload comprising both instrument and ACU was designed and built between January 1978 and July 1979 by Dornier Systems under contact to the DFVLR. As the third stage of the Skylark 12 already included the Cuckoo IV apogee boost motor, the scientific payload had to be designed for low weight and volume, and was probably the first Skylark 12 payload with its own ACU. The payload included a special lightweight nose cone designed for minimum disturbance when jettisoned. The ACU comprised a roll-stabilised inertial platform and a two-axis sun sensor controlling a Marconi Stage 1 pneumatics and 3-axis nozzle system.[124]

The launch took place from Brazil at 11:09 local time, and was a great success:

> Beyond all expectations, it attained an apogee of 828 km [and] an experiment measuring time of 13 minutes and 37 seconds. The impact was 560 km off the coast of Natal in the Atlantic Ocean. The performance of the complete payload was as expected.[125]

This was a record altitude for Skylark, and the use of Brazil brought the number of different launch sites used over the years to eight.

Range	Sponsor						
	NASA	UK	ESRO	W.GERMANY	UK/ARGENTINA	SWEDEN	TOTALS
Andøya		10		8			18
Arenosillo		2		6			8
Kiruna		1	22	3		3	29
Argentina					2		2
Woomera	4	249	6	4			263
Sardinia			54	2			56
Aberporth		2					2
Brazil				1			1
TOTALS	4	264	82	24	2	3	379

Table 15.9 – Skylark launches by site and sponsor to the end of 1979.

(Updated from Hilton (1977), figure 7)[126]

1980	1981	1982	1983	1984
TEXUS 3A (Apr)	TEXUS 3B (Apr)	TEXUS 5 (Apr)	TEXUS 7 (May)	CAESAR1 (Jan)
EB1 (Nov)	TEXUS 4 (May)	TEXUS 6 (May)	TEXUS 8 (May)	MAP/WINE1 (Feb)
	EB2 (Dec)			TEXUS 9 (May)
				TEXUS 10 (May)

Table 15.10 The total of 13 Skylark launches from 1980 to 1984 was an average of only 2.6 per year, and the overall total for these five years was only the same as for the single year 1976!

(Key: red = German national)

---

[123] Fahr and Lay (1979), 'ASTRO-HEL: A new payload for high resolution EUV radiation analysis'.

[124] Weber & Henkel (1980), 'Astro-Hel – a Sounding Rocket project for High-resolution analysis of Helium EUV radiations', p.156.

[125] Weber & Henkel (1980), 'Astro-Hel – a Sounding Rocket project for High-resolution analysis of Helium EUV radiations', p.160.

[126] Journal of the British Interplanetary Society, Vol.30 No.10 (October 1977), p.380. Reproduced with permission.

SKYLARK LAUNCHES AND SCIENCE 1980 - 1984

The 1980's started quietly for Skylark, in 1980 itself there were only two launches, the lowest annual total to date.

A feature of this decade was that except for one BAe test flight (in 1988); all the launches were part of the German national programme, of which about three quarters were TEXUS microgravity missions. As part of the implementation, in December 1980 it was announced that the DFVLR had ordered five more Skylark sounding rockets from British Aerospace Dynamics (Bristol) in a deal worth £450,000, for launching from Esrange at Kiruna in Sweden. They were for the Texus materials science programme, with delivery between 1981 and 1983.[127]

Europe becomes involved in sounding rocket flights once more

As discussed previously, in 1972 the ESRO sounding rocket campaign had been closed down. Then, in 1975, ESRO was merged with ELDO to become ESA (European Space Agency). In January 1982, the ESA member states agreed to a small Spacelab precursor microgravity programme, which allowed it to participate in the German 'Texus' sounding rocket programme.[128] This ESA initiative provided microgravity flight opportunities for scientists in all its member states, so in ten years the wheel had turned full circle, and pan-European use of Skylark resumed.

---

28 April 1980   TEXUS 3A

The TEXUS 3 was the third in the series of German microgravity missions. Unfortunately, because of a rocket de-spin problem, the payload did not achieve the desired gravity level because of a "...residual spin of the rocket (1 Hz) and centrifugal acceleration of 0.19g resulting there from",[129] and although some results were obtained, the mission was basically a failure. However it was re-flown a year later as TEXUS 3B, see below.

---

16 November 1980   EB1

On 5th November 1980, an international sounding rocket campaign began at Kiruna in Sweden to investigate the Earth's atmosphere. This aeronomy project involved the launch of up to 57 rockets in six salvoes. Called 'Energy Budget', it was claimed to be the largest sounding rocket campaign ever mounted.[130]

Some 50 rockets and 14 balloons were launched and an extended network of 56 ground stations was operated in widely spread parts of Europe. Atmospheric behaviour during both geomagnetically disturbed and quiet conditions was investigated.[131] In particular, different energy production and loss processes in the mesosphere and lower thermosphere were studied. The sounding rockets and balloons investigated the behaviour of charged particles from altitudes of 30 km up to 240 km; the parameters measured included electron density and precipitation, ion composition and infrared emissions.

Although originally a German project, countries taking part included Austria, Norway, Sweden, America, Russia and the UK. The German Agency DFVLR launched two Skylark 7s; each carried a 325 kg payload to just over 230 km (143 miles). Other rockets in the campaign included three Petrels and eight Skuas sponsored by the UK.

The first of these Skylarks was EB1 (Energy Budget 1) launched from Kiruna in the very early morning of 16th November. There were five instruments on board what was termed "A Heavy 'Clean' Payload". One reason for the name was that during operation dust particles had to be avoided within range of the sensors of one of the instruments, a wide-angle (nearly 180º) infrared spectrometer. These dust particles could have been emitted by the payload surface, the inner payload during depressurisation or the rocket motor after separation. Hence, both the vehicle and its handling processes had to be as clean as possible. Special dust tight sealing was fitted, and venting ports designed in. A high-speed attachment ring was used to ensure the motor separated from the payload at greater than one metre/second.

Another important design criterion was reuse of the payload. This required a novel 'flip-over' manoeuvre to turn the payload over during parachute descent, to avoid damage to the infrared sensor, which was mounted on the front, see figure 15.21 overleaf.

Skylark EB1 reached an altitude of 231 km, and (perhaps surprisingly) recovery by parachute was successful and allowed the payload to be used again.[132]

Although by now the UK's SRC had abandoned the use of Skylark, as part of the same 'Energy Budget' campaign, three of the smaller Petrel sounding rockets were flown from Kiruna on the 11th, 15th and 30th November. These had on board experiments from the Rutherford Appleton Laboratory (RAL) and UCW to investigate Atomic Oxygen by means of resonance, fluorescence and absorption.[133]

---

[127] Flight Magazine, 6th December 1980, p.2126.
[128] Seibert (2001), *A World without Gravity*, p.29.
[129] NASA MICREX database - TEXUS 3, 'Stability of compound mixtures', (Walter & Ziegler).
[130] See for example "Flight International" magazine, 15 November 1980, p.1863.
[131] Offermann (1985), 'The energy budget campaign 1980 - Introductory review'.
[132] Hummeltenberg (1983), 'E2: A heavy clean payload of the Energy Budget Campaign', p.114.
[133] Massey & Robins (1986), *History of British Space Science*, p.426.

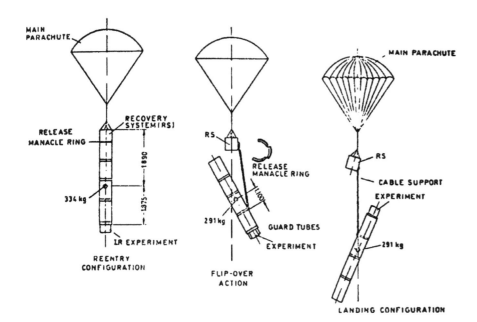

Figure 15.21 The EB1 payload landing 'flip-over' sequence.

(Hummeltenberg (1983), figure 3)

---

30 April 1981   TEXUS 3B

The **TEXUS 3B** mission was a repeat of the unsuccessful TEXUS 3A. This time the rocket flight was successful, reaching the same altitude of 253 km (157 miles), but without the despin problem. The set of microgravity experiments on board were the same as flown before, eleven or twelve from Germany and one from Sweden.[134]

These included metal alloy experiments similar to those flown on TEXUS 1 and 2; for instance a Swedish experiment to study low-gravity solidification phenomena,[135] in particular the processing of immiscible[136] alloys. However compared to TEXUS 1 and 2, on TEXUS 3B the proportion of fluid physics experiments increased to about one third of the total. One example consisted of a reservoir equipped with five stand pipes, into which glass capillary tubes of various shapes were lowered. It was discovered that under very low gravity conditions, the capillary force was reduced and the liquid rise time longer than observed on Earth, an observation that agreed well with theoretical predictions.[137] The first organic chemistry experiment also took place, the first of a series to investigate the growth of protein crystals.[138]

8 May 1981   TEXUS 4

The TEXUS 3B and **TEXUS 4** vehicles had been prepared in parallel, and only a week after TEXUS 3B, TEXUS 4 was successfully launched from Esrange to an altitude of 258 km (160 miles).

The payload module was similar to that used on TEXUS 1, and included a set of eight or nine materials science experiments,[139] most if not all from Germany. These were wide ranging in their scope, from fluid physics to the formation of metallic alloys. A new experiment involved the directional solidification of germanium semiconductor crystals.[140]

9 December 1981   EB2

Skylark EB2 (Energy Budget 2) was launched from Esrange during the evening of 9th December, and was similar to EB1 launched in November 1980. It reached an altitude of 237 km, and it too included a wide viewing angle infrared spectrometer for atmospheric observations. Both flight and recovery were again successful.[141]

---

[134] ESA EEA and NASA MICREX databases, TEXUS 3/3b.

[135] ESA EEA database - TEXUS 3, 'The Coalescence Process in Immiscible Alloys' (Fredriksson).

[136] Immiscible liquids, such as oil and water, will not mix with each other. Similarly, immiscible molten metals are normally unable to form alloys, a mixture may be possible when molten, but upon cooling, the metals separate into layers.

[137] Sell, Maisch and Siekmann (1991), 'Liquid motion in capillary tubes (TEXUS 3)'.

[138] NASA MICREX database - TEXUS 3, 'Diffusion and Growing of Protein Beta Galactosidase Crystals', (Littke).

[139] ESA EEA and NASA MICREX databases, TEXUS 4.

[140] ESA EEA and NASA MICREX databases, TEXUS 4, 'Directional Solidification of Doped Semiconductors' (Walter).

[141] Hummeltenberg (1983), 'E2: A heavy clean payload of the Energy Budget Campaign', p.114.

29 April 1982   TEXUS 5

TEXUS 5 was very similar to TEXUS 4 launched a year earlier, the Skylark 7 successfully propelling the payload to a virtually identical altitude of 245 km (159 miles). This time there were some twelve or thirteen materials science microgravity experiments on board,[142] three from Sweden and the rest from Germany. Most involved metals and alloys, three studied fluids or capillary action, one studied bubble formation and one protein crystal growth. All but one were repeats or extensions of experiments flown on earlier Texus flights, the sole new experiment studied the production of metallic foams under low-gravity conditions.[143]

8 May 1982   TEXUS 6

As noted above, in 1982 ESA started to participate in the German TEXUS microgravity programme, TEXUS 6 being the first involved. ESA activity expanded in due course to include the Swedish 'MASER' sounding rocket, (with predominantly ESA payloads). This ESA Phase-1 programme also covered the development of a first set of multi-user experiment facilities for Spacelab missions, for which the sounding rockets flights would fly precursor experiments.[144]

The original materials and fluid sciences microgravity experiments were soon extended to include the field of biology. The TEXUS experiments proved that sounding rockets were a powerful and a cost-effective means for preparing and developing the more complex and expensive experiments performed in orbit, and ESA found that the TEXUS payload concept provided a high degree of flexibility, as well as easy testing and maintenance/refurbishment of modules for reuse at moderate cost.[145]

TEXUS 6 was successfully launched from Esrange just over a week after TEXUS 5, although on the day before launch, the initial count down had to be cancelled five minutes before lift-off for meteorological reasons.[146] There were nine experiments,[147] of which seven were funded or co-funded by ESA.[148] Most were from Germany, but there were one each from Belgium, France and the Netherlands. This time there was a wider variety of materials science experiments, with only two involving metal alloys. All except two were continuations of earlier series.

The new one from the Netherlands studied the low-gravity solidification of cast iron, a sample of which had to be heated to 1000ºC just before launch.[149] That from Belgium studied the low-gravity melting and solidification of metallic composite materials. Although new to Skylark, it was the second of a series, the first having been flown nine years before on Skylab mission SL-3, launched in July 1973. An experiment from Germany achieved the remarkable feat of growing several centimetres of gallium doped germanium semiconductor crystal during the rocket flight,[150] a task that must have been made most difficult by the postponement from the day before! During the flight, solidifying samples were exposed to acceleration levels ranging from 20 g to 0.0001 g. (See figure 15.22 overleaf)

The end of Britain's last space rocket programme

In August 1982, the programme of UK sponsored Petrel sounding rocket launches ended,[151] thus outlasting the country's scientific use of Skylark by just four years. Petrel had been a very successful rocket design, and some 234 had been launched since it was introduced in 1968. About two-thirds of these firings were from South Uist in the Scottish Outer Hebrides, others were from Kiruna, Andøya, Thumba (India), Sonmiani (Pakistan) and Greenland.[152]

Thus, the UK's SRC had the dubious distinction of closing down the last UK sponsored space rocket programme, extremely modest as it was. This could hardly be a greater contrast to the actions of other European and Commonwealth countries with similar or lesser resources. For instance, in continental Europe, ESA was busy developing the Ariane 1 satellite launcher, a French sponsored design that had taken over from the Blue Streak based ELDO launcher that had been abandoned by the UK government in the late 1960s. By the beginning of 1982, Ariane had made three successful and one failed satellite launch attempts, and in coming years would develop into one of the world's most successful satellite launch vehicles.

---

[142] ESA EEA and NASA MICREX databases, TEXUS 5.
[143] ESA EEA and NASA MICREX databases, TEXUS 5, 'Metallic Foams' (Schäfer).
[144] Seibert et al. (2001), *A World without Gravity*, p.29.
[145] Seibert (2006), *The History of Sounding Rockets and Their Contribution to European Space Research*, p.55.
[146] ESA EEA and NASA MICREX databases, TEXUS 6, 'Directional Solidification of Eutectics' (Favier).
[147] NASA MICREX database - TEXUS 6.
[148] ESA EEA database - TEXUS 6.
[149] NASA MICREX database, 'Metallic Particle Composites - Dispersion Alloys' (Deruyttere & Froyen).
[150] ESA EEA database - TEXUS 6, 'Striations in Germanium' (Walter).
[151] P214K (a Petrel 1) was launched at 23.30 on the 11th August 1982 from Kiruna, and reached an altitude of 129 km. It was part of the 'Energy Budget' investigations. (For a list of Esrange launches go to *www.sscspace.com/Products-Services/rocket-balloon-services/launch-services-esc/esrange-space-center*, scroll down and click on "List of all rocket launches". P214K is number 273). (Last accessed August 2014).
[152] Massey & Robins (1986), *History of British Space Science*, p.190.

Arrow indicates growth direction. Base of arrow corresponds to the beginning of the coasting phase of the rocket ($10^{-4} g_0$)

Figure 15.22 A section of the directionally solidified germanium crystal doped with gallium grown on TEXUS 6. (The upper stripes were artificially created every four seconds to act as timing markers.)

(ESA EEA database - TEXUS 6, 'Striations in Germanium' (Walter), figure 1)

---

5 May 1983   TEXUS 7

In contrast to the demise above, in January 1983 it was announced that British Aerospace Dynamics[153] was to supply the "West German space agency DFVLR" with five more Skylark 7 sounding rockets, under a half-million pound contract. These were to be launched from Kiruna in Sweden as part of the continuing TEXUS programme.[154]

Meanwhile, the existing programme continued, with TEXUS 7 being successfully launched on 5th May. There appear to have been thirteen main experiments,[155] this time all except one were concerned with metals and alloys, the exception being a study of fluid physics. They originated from five different countries, and although the majority were from Germany, there were others from Sweden, Belgium and France, and a first from the UK.

The British experiment was concerned with the effect of gravity on immiscible alloys;[156] in particular, it studied the stability of a metallic dispersion of lead in liquid aluminium, an alloy composition of commercial interest as an improved plain bearing material. It was the precursor to a similar experiment flown later that year on the NASA Space Shuttle Spacelab 1 mission, launched in November 1983.[157] Unusually, it was originated by a private research company rather than an academic institution - Fulmer Research Institute Ltd.,[158] of Stoke Poges near Slough.

---

[153] BAC had been nationalised into British Aerospace in 1977.

[154] Flight International magazine, 29 January 1983, p.255.

[155] NASA MICREX database - TEXUS 7.

[156] ESA EEA database - TEXUS 7, 'Immiscible alloy system Al-Pb', (Caton and Hopkins).

[157] NASA MICREX database, Principal Investigator Index (Caton). STS-9, (launched November 1983 & also known as STS-41A), was the 6th mission of the Space Shuttle Columbia, its main payload was the ESA Spacelab 1.

[158] The Fulmer Research Institute was established in 1947 to provide confidential research facilities for industry, it specialised in metallurgical problems. It was bought out by the British Non-Ferrous Metals Research Association in 1991.

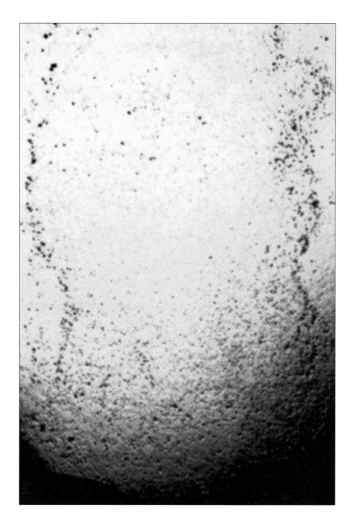 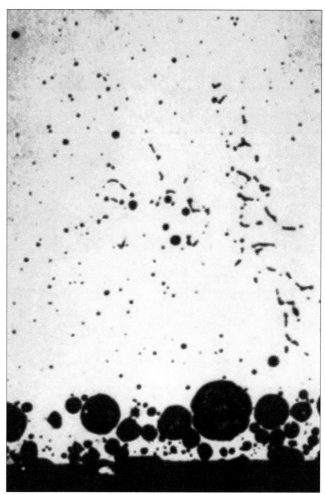

Figures 15.23 and 15.24 Results from the British experiment performed on TEXUS 7.
Left: Lead droplets relatively evenly dispersed in aluminium under microgravity conditions.
Right: Lead sedimentation in aluminium when the same experiment was performed on Earth.
(ESA EEA database - TEXUS 7, '*Immiscible alloy system Al-Pb*', (Caton and Hopkins), figure 1)

---

13 May 1983	TEXUS 8

Just nine days after TEXUS 7, **TEXUS 8** was successfully launched from Kiruna. There appear to have been only nine experiments, comprising seven from Germany and one each from Belgium and Italy. This time there were only two experiments concerning metals and alloys and three directly concerned with fluid physics; the others investigated the diffusion of liquid salts, bubble formation, and the study of a fluid-gas interface.[159]

---

27 January 1984	CAESAR 1

1984 saw a modest resurgence in the use of Skylarks, with a total of four being launched, twice that of the previous year.

The first of these was **CAESAR 1**, a three stage Skylark 12 launched from Andøya in Norway. This was part of the "Coordinated Auroral Experiment using Scatter And Rocket investigations", carried out by combining high-resolution in-situ measurements using rocket-borne instrumentation and ground-based observations with EISCAT.[160]

Two identical payloads were built, designed to investigate auroral magnetic substorm phenomena. They carried six experiments from Germany, one from the UK[161] and one from Japan. To avoid sensitivity loss from the magnetic sensors, non-magnetic materials and electromagnetic shielding were used, and the experiments were mounted on no less than nine booms that opened out for the measurement phase. The Skylark 12 third motor stage remained attached to the payload during the measurements, in order to avoid disturbance

---

[159] NASA MICREX database - TEXUS 8.

[160] EISCAT (the European Incoherent Scatter) Scientific Association, formed in 1975, still operates several incoherent scatter radar systems, used to study the interaction between the Sun and the Earth as revealed by disturbances in the ionosphere and magnetosphere. (For further information see *www.eiscat.se/about/whatiseiscat_new* (Last accessed August 2014).

[161] A "wave particle interaction" experiment from the University of Sussex.

during deployment of the booms. The combined mass was sufficient to hold the payload relatively steady during the measurements, and no attitude control unit was needed.[162]

The launch window was from 24th January to the end of March, and in the event, CAESAR 1 was launched during the early evening of January 27th. It successfully reached an altitude of 700 km (435 miles), but unfortunately the telemetry system appears to have failed ten seconds into flight,[163] and the mission was a failure. (The spent rocket and payload would have disappeared into the Norwegian Sea).

Fortunately, a repeat payload launched in January 1985 was successful, see below.

| 10 February 1984   MAP/WINE 1 |

The next Skylark to be launched was part of the MAP/WINE project. The Middle Atmosphere Programme (MAP) comprised a number of international scientific studies, one of which was the "Winter in Northern Europe" project, (WINE). This was a multinational study of the structure, dynamics and composition of the middle atmosphere (10-100km altitude) in winter at high latitudes. Coordinated field measurements were performed during the winter 1983 to 1984 by a large number of ground-based, air-borne, rocket-borne and satellite-borne instruments.[164]

A Skylark 6 (Raven VI & Goldfinch) was used, and had a German payload equipped with three experiments, attitude control and a land recovery system. It was launched from Esrange, and successfully reached an altitude of 180 km (112 miles). The experiments measured infrared radiation in order to determine the influence of various gases on the energy balance between 70 and 180 km.[165]

The MAP/WINE project stimulated a number of follow-on projects that studied the middle atmosphere at high and polar latitudes.[166]

| May 1984   TEXUS 9, TEXUS 10 |

TEXUS 9 was successfully launched on 3rd May, the ten microgravity experiments comprising seven from Germany, two from Belgium and one from Italy. All but one were continuations of earlier studies, indeed a German experiment was the eleventh of a series.[167] The only new experiment investigated the container-less solidification of a metal alloy.[168] Part of the Italian fluid dynamics experiment was illuminated by a laser beam and observed with a cine camera. A 30-second video clip of this is available online via the internet, and shows fluid convection under weightless conditions as the Skylark payload flew through space.[169]

TEXUS 10 followed twelve days later on the 15th, with at least ten experiments.[170] These were a slightly more cosmopolitan mix, with four from Germany, three from Sweden, two from the UK and one from Spain.

One of the UK experiments was part of a series designed to study the stability of a metallic dispersion, and a continuation of those performed on TEXUS 7 and Spacelab 1. Unfortunately it failed, as "...the furnaces malfunctioned and none of the specimens were processed correctly." However the experiment was successfully reflown on TEXUS 12 a year later.[171]

The second UK experiment was the first in a series of experiments designed by D.J.Turner of the Central Electricity Research Laboratories (C.E.R.L.), Leatherhead, to study ionic solutions near the critical point of water under low-gravity conditions. Such phenomena had potential importance in, for example, power station boilers.[172]

That from Sweden studied the growth of crystals of the semiconductor germanium, on the clear basis that "The ultimate goal of studies on the growth of electronic materials in space is to find a technique for the production of homogeneous and defect free crystals."[173]

[162] Schrieder and Henkel (1983), 'Coordinated Auroral Experiment using Scatter and Rockets (CAESAR): A sounding rocket project to study the ionosphere'.
[163] BAe (1990), *Record of Skylark Launches 1957-1990*.
[164] Vonzahn (1989), 'The project Winter in Northern Europe (MAP/WINE): Introduction and outlook'.
[165] Auchter, Demharter & Waldmann (1984), 'Sounding rocket program Aeronomie. The payload M-1 in the project MAP-WINE'.
[166] Vonzahn (1989), 'The project Winter in Northern Europe (MAP/WINE): Introduction and outlook'.
[167] NASA MICREX database - TEXUS 9, 'Metal-Metal Suspension' (Neuschütz and Pötschke).
[168] NASA MICREX database - TEXUS 9, 'Containerless Solid Solidification of a PdCuSi Sample' (Herlach).
[169] ESA EEA database - TEXUS 9, experiment 10, 'Thermal Marangoni convection in a floating zone' (Monti). Scroll down to "Attachments" and click on "Video 1", (last accessed August 2014).
[170] NASA MICREX database - TEXUS 10.
[171] NASA MICREX database - TEXUS 10.
[172] ESA EEA database - TEXUS 10, experiment 8, 'Ionic Solutions near the Critical Point of Water' (Turner).
[173] ESA EEA database - TEXUS 10, 'Floating zone crystal growth of GA-doped Germanium' (Carlberg).

1985	1986	1987
CAESAR 2 (Jan)	TEXUS 13 (Apr)	TEXUS 14B(May)
INTERZODIAK (Mar)	TEXUS 14 (May)	TEXUS 15 (May)
TEXUS 11 (Apr)		SUPER NOVA (Aug)
TEXUS 12 (May)		TEXUS 16 (Nov)

Table 15.11 Skylark launches from 1985 to 1987. The average rate of 3.3 per year was slightly up on the 2.6 of the preceding five years.

(Key: red = German national)

SKYLARK LAUNCHES AND SCIENCE 1985 – 1987

---
30 January 1985   CAESAR 2

CAESAR 2 was a repeat launch of the failed CAESAR 1 mission, launched twelve months earlier to investigate auroral magnetic substorm phenomena. As before, a three stage Skylark 12 was launched from Andøya in Norway. It reached a similar altitude (703 km, 437 miles), fortunately this time the mission was successful.

---
3 March 1985   INTER-ZODIAK

The **INTER-ZODIAK** (DLR N-GRC-137) mission was a German solar physics project. It was an extension of the study done by the earlier Astro 6 and Astro-Hel (Astro Helium) experiments, the latter launched by a Skylark 12 to a record altitude from Brazil in October 1979. The instrument on board was an improved version of the EUV (Extreme Ultra Violet) photometer used on Astro-Hel, and was designed for high-resolution spectral analysis of solar Helium and Hydrogen radiation during a circular scan round the Sun's disc.[174] The experiment was also designed to provide information on the interplanetary dust near the Sun.

Work on the concept was underway by 1980,[175] and a great deal of work had been carried out by the time it was all assembled to be launched in Brazil in 1985. Thus, it must have been particularly bitter blow for those involved when the Skylark 12 launch failed when the Cuckoo IV third stage motor ignited prematurely[176] (the vehicle appears have gained no altitude[177]). Fortunately, the similar INTERZODIAK II mission three years later was successful, see the next chapter.

---
27 April 1985   TEXUS 11

There was better luck with the next Skylark launch, when the following month **TEXUS 11** successfully reached 266 km (165 miles) above Kiruna. On board this time were seven microgravity experiments. Five were variations on previous German experiments, this time that on the low-gravity solidification of metallic composites was the twelfth of a series.

An experiment on fluid physics was the first of its type from France, but the final one from Germany was significant in being the first of the life sciences experiments flown by the TEXUS programme. It investigated and photographed through a microscope how yeast cells acted under microgravity; in particular, it studied the "electrofusion of yeast protoplasts". [178] (Electrofusion being a process employed to produce cell hybrids in biotechnological, medical, and agricultural sciences). A two-fold increase of hybrid yield over electrofusion experiments performed on Earth was observed.

---
6 May 1985   TEXUS 12

Just over a week later **TEXUS 12** was also successfully launched from Kiruna, with some eleven experiments on board.[179] These included a wide range of materials science experiments from all over Europe: five from Germany, two each from the UK and Sweden, and one each from France and Spain. Judging from previous comments about the difficulty of a Skylark launch being proportional to the square of the number of experiments,[180] the hours before launch must have been difficult indeed![181]

---

[174] Neuman, Boison & Henkel (1983), 'INTER-ZODIAC: A sounding rocket project for high resolution of EUV radiations'.
[175] Fahr, Ripken & Lay (1980), 'INTER-ZODIAK: A High-Apogee Rocket Experiment for the Observation of Dust-Generated Neutrals in the Solar Vicinity'.
[176] BAe (1990), *Record of Skylark Launches 1957-1990*.
[177] The INTER-ZODIAK Skylark may have crashed before any significant altitude was gained, see McDowell (2009), *List of Skylark Launches*.
[178] NASA MICREX database - TEXUS 11, 'Electrofusion of Yeast Protoplasts' (Zimmermann).
[179] NASA MICREX database - TEXUS 12.
[180] Chambers (2000), *Woomera, Its Human Face*, p.57.
[181] The experiments required very specific conditions to be set up during the hours before launch, for instance metals being heated to melting point.

Both the British experiments were continuations of those flown on TEXUS 10 the year before. That from D.J.Turner of C.E.R.L. continued the study of ionic solutions near the critical point of water under low-gravity conditions. Results indicated that:

> …destratification of the solution takes considerably longer than the 6 minutes of low gravity available during the rocket flight…To provide data suitable for thoroughly testing theories of compressible solutions, studies in orbiting craft will be required.[182]

The other was a repeat of that also flown on TEXUS 10 to directionally solidify an aluminium melt containing a fine dispersion of insoluble particles, unfortunately despite thorough ground testing it failed again:

> Although Extensive ground tests were undertaken, both at Surrey on a model test and at the Swedish Space Corporation (SSC/ACR), and many specimens were processed without incident, the cartridges all leaked during the actual flight and again none were processed correctly. Therefore no results were gained…. [183]

An experiment of particular interest was that from Spain, for which the main objectives were to establish a liquid bridge in a minimum amount of time and observe its properties. A secondary objective was to test experimental concepts to be used during future STS Spacelab mission experiments. This experiment had first been flown on TEXUS 10, but had failed because of a mechanical problem. This time it was successful, and it was found possible to form a liquid column up to 30 mm (1.2 inches) in diameter by 80 mm (3.2 inches) long, in less than a minute of weightlessness. It was concluded that this left 90% of the available time for potential experiments using the column, even in sounding rocket flights such as this, where the duration available was only about six minutes.[184]

The scientists conducting the experiment acknowledged the problem in gaining access to the microgravity environment; their comments throw interesting light on the issues:

> By far the best approach is to have the liquid bridge floating free in a drop tower, on a parabolic aircraft flight, on a sounding rocket, or in Spacelab, the choice depending on the duration of the microgravity period needed (typically 3s, 25s, 6 min and open-ended respectively.

The Spacelab option is obviously preferable, but the flight opportunities are limited and call for some five years of preparation. Consequently, until permanent Space Stations can offer a turnaround time of less than a year, sounding rockets are best suited to provide the microgravity environment, giving up to 6 min of research per flight. They are also of great help for testing new apparatus and procedures for Spacelab/Space Station. Consequently it is not surprising that microgravity research aboard sounding rockets has proliferated during recent years.[185]

The experiment was filmed using a 16 mm cine camera, and produced some striking images, as shown opposite.

SKYLARK LAUNCHES AND SCIENCE IN 1986

1986 was a quiet year for Skylark, with only two launches, although BAe received an order for the manufacture of eleven more Skylark vehicles.[186] As it turned out, '13' was a lucky number for the TEXUS programme, out of the two launches, TEXUS 13 was the successful one, see opposite.

30 April 1986	TEXUS 13

There appear to have been only six materials science and two life science experiments on board **TEXUS 13**, comprising five from Germany, one each from France and Belgium, and a first from Japan, on the fabrication of superconducting materials.[187]

12 May 1986	TEXUS 14

The launch of **TEXUS 14** followed two weeks later. The payload comprised nine experiments, four from Germany, two from Sweden, and one each from Belgium, Italy and the UK. Eight were materials science experiments, the other a life science experiment.

Unfortunately, although the payload reached an altitude of 250 km (155 miles) above Kiruna, an unexpected 'wobbling motion' took place, producing uncontrollable accelerations. Thus the desired microgravity level was not attained, and none of the experiments could be successfully carried out.[188] This resulted in a similar payload being flown again the following year as TEXUS 14B, when the mission was successful.

---

[182] NASA MICREX database - TEXUS 12. Turner, D. J.: Electrolyte Solutions near the Critical Point of Water. See also 6th European Symposium on Material Sciences Under Microgravity Conditions, Bordeaux, France, December 2-5 1986, ESA SP-256, pp. 125-129.

[183] NASA MICREX database - TEXUS 12. Goodhew, P. J. and Clyne, D.: 'Retention of a Fine Precipitate Dispersion'. In BMFT/DFVLR Texus 11/12 Abschlussbericht, 1985, p.55, (post-flight).

[184] Martínez and Sanz (1985), 'Long Liquid Bridges Aboard Sounding Rockets'.

[185] Martínez and Sanz (1985), p.324.

[186] Flight International magazine, 12 September 1987, p.35.

[187] ESA EEA and NASA MICREX databases, TEXUS 13.

[188] NASA MICREX database - TEXUS 14a, see for instance Carlberg 'Floating Zone Experiments with Germanium Crystals'.

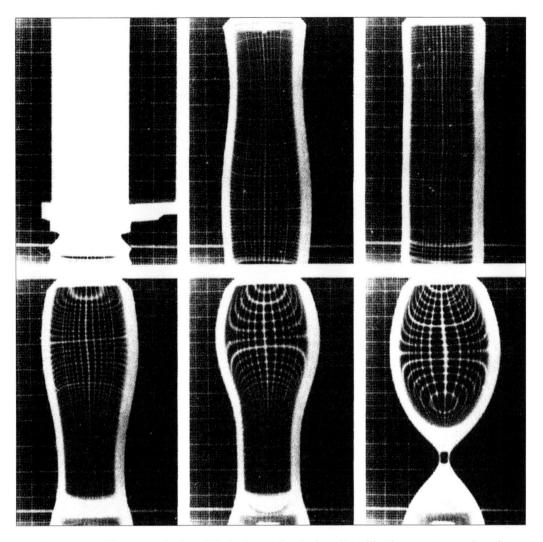

Figure 15.25 Negatives of selected flight frames for the long liquid bridge experiment aboard TEXUS-12. These show the formation of the initially cylindrical column then its destabilisation after two minutes of weightlessness by an inertial wave.

(Martínez and Sanz (1985), figure 4)

SKYLARK LAUNCHES AND SCIENCE IN 1987

1987 was a little busier, with four launches, but a bad year for Skylark, as two of the four missions failed.

Also in 1987, the management of the TEXUS programme changed, when the DFVLR transferred the management to ERNO (today part of EADS), which offered Texus flights to paying customers on a commercial basis.[189]

In a separate move, in 1987 the Swedish National Space Board offered to fly ESA microgravity experiments under the Swedish Maser (Materials Science Experiment Rocket) programme, managed by the Swedish Space Corporation

(SSC). Maser had practically the same technical capabilities as Texus, but instead of the Skylark 7 it had originally used a Canadian Black Brant rocket. However from Maser 6 onwards (April 1992), this programme also used Skylark 7 rocket motors.[190]

3 May 1987	TEXUS 14B

As noted above, **TEXUS 14B** was a re-flight of the failed TEXUS 14 payload, although on this flight there was one additional life science experiment added. This time all went well, and the studies were carried out as expected.[191] The results from

[189] Seibert (2006), *The History of Sounding Rockets and Their Contribution to European Space Research*, p.56.
[190] Seibert (2006), p.55.
[191] ESA EEA database - TEXUS 14b.

the Italian fluid dynamics experiment are interesting, because two short video clips of it are (2014) available online via the ESA EEA database, and show fluid convection under weightless conditions as the Skylark payload flew through space.[192] The experiment was achieved using an improved version of the module already used for a similar experiment previously flown on TEXUS 9. The advances in electronics and communications technology during the decades that Skylark was in use are illustrated by the fact that the cine camera previously used was replaced by a CCD camera to allow observation in real time of the fluid motion during the experiment, using a live video link from Skylark in space to the Earth below!

---

9 May 1987   TEXUS 15

Six days later **TEXUS 15** was launched from Kiruna. The payload carried at least seven experiments, five from Germany and one each from Belgium and Holland.

Unfortunately shortly after the successful launch of the rocket, data and television transmitters experienced a partial failure. It was later discovered that a lateral burn through of the second stage of the rocket had occurred and the stage, in turn, had collided with the prematurely separated payload. The upper part of the payload parachuted to the Earth undamaged, but some of the experimental modules (presumably in the lower part of the payload) were damaged in the collision.[193]

The lateral burn through on the Raven XI motor was revealed by subsequent investigations into the problem,[194] and modifications and a special test flight were then carried out. (See the next chapter). The failure was a particularly untimely setback, as celebrations should have been in order; not only was this the 400th launch of Skylark, but also the 10th anniversary of the start of the TEXUS project and the 30th anniversary of the first Skylark launch:

> The 400th Skylark was memorable. The Kiruna launch site was filled with journalists, the champagne was on ice and the vehicle was ready. Unfortunately the Raven motor burnt through its hypalon insulation and the mission was a complete failure. It turned out that a "minor" change had been made to the hypalon liner such that it failed in flight. The problem was fixed, and the Skylark went on to a further 41 successful launches.[195]

---

24 August 1987   SUPERNOVA

In February 1987, supernova 1987A appeared in the night sky in the Large Magellanic Cloud (LMC). It was located in the outskirts of the Tarantula Nebula, approximately 51.4 kiloparsecs (167,648 light-years) from Earth, and despite this vast distance, at its brightest was visible to the naked eye. It was the closest supernova observed since the year 1604, and offered the possibility of studying the evolution of a relatively nearby supernova remnant from its earliest beginnings over the entire electromagnetic spectrum with unprecedented sensitivity:[196]

> The discovery of supernova 1987A on the 23rd of February '87 marked the beginning of considerable activity by scientists around the world, to gather first hand data on the development of this phenomena, and presented the sounding rocket community with a unique opportunity to demonstrate that even for astronomy, sounding rockets still have a part to play. The current lack of spacecraft with telescopes for EUV and X-ray detection meant that the only possibility for exoatmospheric research with high resolution, position resolving detectors, during the most interesting first few months of the development of the supernova, was to refurbish, modify and launch existing sounding rocket hardware.[197]

Thus, August 1987 saw the first Skylark deep space astronomy mission for eight years, specifically designed to study the 1987A supernova. As the Large Magellanic Cloud is in the southern skies, the launch was carried out from Woomera, becoming the last Skylark launch to take place from there.

A German team refurbished the Astro 4/2 payload, which had been launched and recovered from Woomera back in February 1979. As technology had advanced considerably in the meantime, a new inertially controlled ACS (Attitude Control System) was designed, despite the extremely short preparation time from the start in early April until launch at the end of August. Similarly, the Astro 4/2 on-board TV camera was replaced by two CCD cameras, where the physical dimensions and power consumption of each were less than 10% of the original.[198] The manpower and resources were made available by delaying the attitude control system development of another sounding rocket and a balloon gondola by six months. In most cases, long lead items were borrowed from INTERZODIAK II, TEXUS and other programmes.

---

[192] ESA EEA database - TEXUS 14b, experiment 5: 'Experimental results on microgravitational fluid dynamics' (Monti & Fortezza). Scroll down to "Attachments" and click on "Video 1" or "Video 2", (last accessed August 2014).

[193] NASA MICREX database - TEXUS 15.

[194] BAe (1990), *Record of Skylark Launches 1957-1990*.

[195] Harlow (2012), 'Why Composites? The History & Technology of Composite Rocket Propellants', pp.32-33. (Hypalon is a trademark for a type of synthetic rubber noted for its resistance to chemicals and temperature extremes).

[196] Aschenbach *et al.* (1987), 'A search for soft X-rays from supernova 1987A'.

[197] Turner (1989), 'The Supernova 1987A Attitude Control System', p.117.

[198] The original vidicon tube based TV camera had a mass of 8 kg and took 40 watts of power! (Turner (1989), p.118).

Figure 15.26 An aerial view of launch apron LA2 at Woomera in August 1987, with the German 'SUPERNOVA' and NASA teams setting up. The Skylark launch tower had been demolished eight years previously, but this foreshortened aerial view shows the original instrumentation building still there in the background, and the EC2 blockhouse in the right foreground. (Compare with the earlier views in Figure 7.19 and Figure 9.26)

(DSTO \ Henderson)

Figure 15.27 A close-up, taken from the left of the general view above. In the centre is the German single rail Skylark launcher, and behind it emerging from the white covering one of the two NASA launchers. This and the previous photograph were taken from a helicopter by the Range Safety Officer, Bruce Henderson.

(DSTO \ Henderson)

Negotiations for the reactivation of the Woomera rocket range were concluded in early May, halfway through the payload development period, although the final agreement was signed only two days before the first launch attempt in August. Heavy equipment was despatched by sea transport in early June, but acceptance of the ACS was achieved only on the day before the departure of the Hercules transport aircraft, which delivered the payload and checkout equipment directly to the range.[199]

Flight Performance

Bad weather aborted the first three launch attempts, but fortuitously the actual launch took place on 25th August, previously selected as the ideal day regarding the position in the sky of the Sun, Moon and target supernova.

The launch took place during the night at 02:00 local time, and as with Astro 4/2, the TV cameras onboard were designed to help the payload be positioned via 'telecommand' during the mission. This time the ground system control console included five joysticks for manual correction of attitude if required. However after launch:

> Because of a problem in the autotracking system of the ground telemetry station antenna control, no satisfactory television reception was obtained until +1 min 50 secs. Fortunately, no manual operations were foreseen during this period, and the only detrimental effect of the absence of TV star images until this time were an excessive production of adrenalin and strong language by the ACS and telemetry operators. A traumatic nervous shock was suffered by the by the payload team, who misinterpreted the intercom report to the telemetry station, of extremely bad TV signals, as indicating that the nose cone had failed to release.[200]

Once in space the telescope successfully pointed at the first target, a known X-ray source used for calibration purposes. After some two minutes it was pointed to the supernova, but the star tracker used to help position the payload then stopped working, and the telescope had be kept aligned manually, by keeping the supernova in the centre of the TV image being received on the ground. This rescued the mission, and allowed some four minutes of X-ray measurements of the supernova to be made.

Hence overall, the project was successful, the payload reaching an altitude of some 265 km (165 miles). Unexpectedly, no positive signal was detected from the supernova during the 220 second observation time, although an upper limit for the X-ray luminosity between 0.2 -2.1 keV was established.[201] Hence the scientific purpose of the experiment and the performance of the payload were considered a success, as the lack of measurable soft X-ray radiation indicated an unexpected process in the development of the supernova.

It was not until over ten years later, after the more powerful ROSAT orbiting X-ray telescope had been launched, and the level of soft X-ray emissions increased, that observations were finally made.[202] The PSPC (Position Sensitive Proportional Counter) X-ray detector flown on Skylark was the precursor to that flown on ROSAT,[203] an example of how Skylark was used to help design and prove orbiting satellite instruments.

For this Skylark mission it was concluded that:

> The refurbishment of the payload and development of the ACS was a typical case of sounding rocket ad hoc solutions to obtain maximum performance from available components within extremely tight time scale and cost restraints. … At a time when the use of sounding rockets for astronomy research in Europe had almost come to an end, the supernova provide a rare opportunity to demonstrate the unique advantages of this technology over other forms of space vehicles for quick, effective and cheap solutions.[204]

NASA follows on

In response to the opportunity afforded by the supernova, NASA organised a complete sounding rocket campaign to South Australia to support both soft X-ray and UV observations of SN 1987A. Thus, the following month, on November 14th, their campaign of six Black Brant IX sounding rocket launches from Woomera opened with the launch (flight 36.030) of a similar payload to that of the 'SUPERNOVA' Skylark. The NASA results supported those from the Skylark experiment, as they too were only able to set an upper level for the soft X-rays received from SN1987A.[205]

---

[199] The Germans were able to mobilise relatively quickly, because they maintained a mobile sounding rocket launching facility (MORABA – Mobile Rocket Base), as used for SL1304 in Spain in 1974. MORABA was presumably created because there was no suitable rocket launching site on German soil, and the mobile facility is still in use today (2014).

[200] Turner (1989), 'The Supernova 1987A Attitude Control System', p.121.

[201] Aschenbach *et al.* (1987), 'A search for soft X-rays from supernova 1987A'.

[202] The soft X-rays postulated to originate from the interaction of the explosion blast wave with circumstellar matter were not observed until 1991, when they were discovered for the first time by ROSAT. See *www.mpe.mpg.de/xray/wave/rosat/publications/highlights/sn_1987a.php* , (last accessed August 2014).

[203] See *www.mpe.mpg.de/xray/wave/other_projects/astro4/index.php* (last accessed August 2014).

[204] Turner (1989), 'The Supernova 1987A Attitude Control System', p.122.

[205] Burrows *et al.* (1987), 'Search for soft X-ray emission from SN 1987A with a CCD X-ray imaging spectrometer', p.1114.

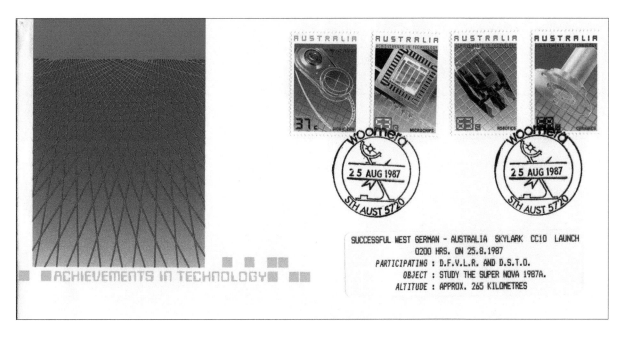

Figure 15.28 This 'First Day Cover' commemorates the last launch of Skylark from Woomera, just over 30 years after the first launch in February 1957.

(Henderson collection)

---

23 November 1987   TEXUS 16

TEXUS 16 carried ten materials science microgravity experiments, seven from Germany, two from Belgium and one from Sweden.[206] Four were repeats from the failed TEXUS 15 mission six months before.

Most unfortunately, this mission also failed because of a Skylark fault. Shortly after the initially successful launch, the Raven XI second stage did not ignite. After the apogee was reached (at only about 7 km[207]) and the rocket began to fall, the yo-yo despin system deployed as programmed. However because of the unexpected excess rocket mass, there was an incomplete reduction of rocket spin. Subsequently the payload separated from the second stage, but the parachute was not released. The 'unbraked' impact of the payload resulted in the destruction of all of the experiment modules.[208]

This was the second Skylark failure in six months. BAe and Royal Ordnance conducted exhaustive investigations into these failures and demonstrated two unrelated causes. Appropriate modifications to the Raven XI second stage motor were introduced, and a proving flight was carried out in May 1988,[209] see the next chapter.

---

[206] NASA MICREX database - TEXUS 16, (last accessed March 2013).
[207] This was the altitude reached by SL1081A, which suffered a similar failure in 1973.
[208] NASA MICREX database - TEXUS 16, (last accessed March 2013).
[209] Ellis (1989), 'The Skylark Sounding Rocket Programme and Future Launcher Developments', p.269. *ESA document SP-291.*

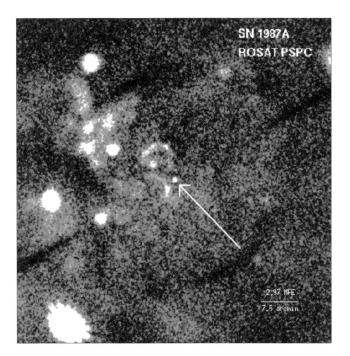 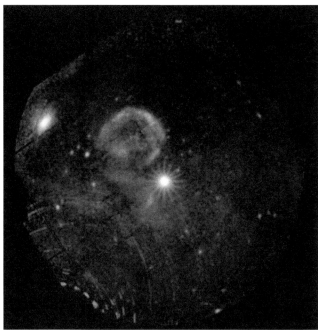

Figures 15.29 and 15.30 X-ray imaging technology developed from that used on Skylark. On the left is an original ROSAT satellite image of supernova 1987A (arrowed centre), dated 1997, on the right (almost 20 years after SN1987A's discovery) the XMM-Newton satellite observed the stellar remnant in X-rays on 17 January 2007. Continuously brightening since the first detection in X-rays by ROSAT in 1992, it now outshines all other X-ray sources in its immediate neighbourhood.
Left: MPE (Max-Planck Institute) / *www.mpe.mpg.de/xray/wave/rosat/publications/highlights/sn_1987a.php* , (last accessed July 2014).[210]
Right: ESA / *http://spaceinimages.esa.int/Images/2007/02/XMM-Newton_view_of_supernova SN 1987A* , (last accessed July2014).

---

[210] Max-Planck-Institut für extraterrestrische Physik, (*www.mpe.mpg.de*), (last accessed August 2014).

Figure 16.1 Preparing for the last ever Skylark launch – the MASER 10 payload being loaded into the Skylark launch tower at Esrange in May 2005. The bright red Skylark 7 motor assembly can be seen already in place.

(Swedish Space Corporation)

CHAPTER 16

(1988-2005)

ENDGAME

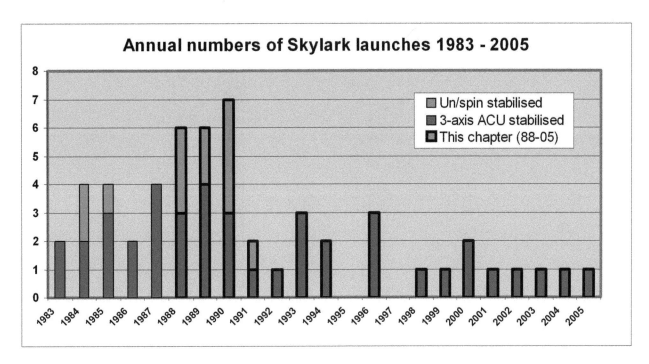

Figure 16.2 From 1988 until the last launch in 2005, the annual numbers of Skylark launches remained very low. However, there was a peak of seven in 1990, the highest annual number of launches since 1978. The number launched during these last 18 years was 39, an average of just over two per year.

THE LAST 18 YEARS

In 2005, Skylark came to the end of its career after 441 launches. All the later missions as described in this chapter took place outside Australia, as the last launch from Woomera was in 1987.

The advent of a BAe test flight in 1988 is a reminder that, despite the fact that the SRC had abandoned the UK's scientific programme for Skylark, other British organisations were still busy promoting it and similar ventures.

Skylark 17

In about 1987, ESA had started looking at the possibility of using a new larger sounding rocket to provide up to 15 minutes of microgravity.[1] In the press it was announced:

> A German-Swedish long duration sounding rocket, based on the US Castor IVA booster used on Delta, is being studied by the Esa microgravity programme committee. Castor could carry 718kg on a 15 min flight. Esa is also studying British Skylark 8 and 17 proposals, along with multistage sounding rockets based on the Canadian Black Brant.[2]

---

[1] For a history of ESA microgravity initiatives including Spacelab and other methods, see pages 29-33 of Seibert (2001), *A World without Gravity*, ESA document SP-1251.

[2] Flight International Magazine, 6th February 1988, p.34.

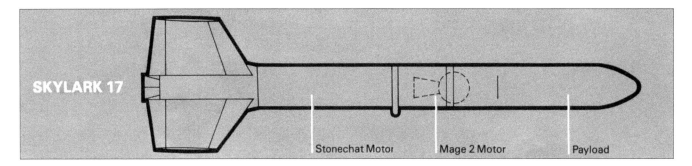

Figure 16.3 An outline of the Skylark 17 design.
(BAe (Space Systems) Ltd \ Hazell)

Skylark 8 was a Stonechat motor based design, originally proposed by BAC in the UK in 1973/74, as described in Chapter 13. At that time it came to nothing, but in 1987 it emerged again as a BAe proposal, a paper on it appearing in an ESA symposium in May that year.[3]

Skylark 17 was a similar design, based on the same Stonechat first stage motor, but with a 'Mage 2'[4] second stage, rather than the Waxwing proposed for Skylark 8. BAe promoted Skylark 17 quite strongly, and it appeared alongside Skylarks 5, 7 and 12 in a BAe sales brochure of the time, see figure 16.3 above.

The BAe sales brochure also included an 'artist's impression' of Skylark 17, although this was in fact a photograph of the similar prototype 'Falstaff' rocket vehicle, launched from Woomera in October 1969 (see Figure 11.21).

Unfortunately, the Skylark proposals were unsuccessful, and ESA ended up as the sole customer for an ERNO/SSC vehicle based on the Castor IV A motor – as used by the US Thiokol Corporation as a strap-on booster to the US launch vehicle Delta.[5]

> Unfortunately the internal pricing policy prevalent in RO [Royal Ordnance] at the time meant that commercially, it [Skylark 17] was no match for the Castor ...It is perhaps pertinent to mention here that the internal pricing policies reflected the poor price competitiveness of plastic propellant motors and this spelt the death knell for what remained of the plastic propellant capability in the UK.[6]

The resulting 'MAXUS' sounding rocket programme was based on experience with the Texus and Maser projects, indeed the name was derived from MAser-teXUS. Although in due course successful (the first flight in 1991 malfunc-

tioned), and continuing until the time of writing (2014) the number of MAXUS missions has dwindled, averaging only one every three or four years.[7]

As part of the development, in November 1990 a Skylark 12 was used to test MAXUS guidance, control and safety systems. See under 'MAXUS TEST' in November 1990, later in this chapter.

Satellite Launcher Proposals – Skylark 13, Spacelark and Small Orbiter

For many years, scientists and engineers at Westcott had been carrying out calculations on the solid propellant rocket motors (SPRMs) developed there, regarding their potential for use in small launch vehicles, both for test and orbital work. The table below shows how such potential might have been be realised for launching space satellites into Low Earth Orbit (LEO):

Name	Stage	Motor	LEO mass (kg)
Skylark 13	1	Stonechat*	80
	2	Stonechat II	
	3	Waxwing	
Spacelark	0	4 x Rook	100
	1	Stonechat II	
	2	Raven	
	3	Waxwing II	
Small Orbiter	1	4 x Rook (?)	120
	2	Stonechat*	
	3	Stonechat II	
		Waxwing II	

Table 16.1 Small Launch Vehicle Possibilities.[8]
(Harlow (2000), p.10. * = short burn Stonechat)

---

[3] Ellis (1987), 'Skylark Sounding Rocket Development – Skylark 8', pp. 437-40.

[4] The Mage 2 was an apogee boost motor similar to Waxwing. The Mage family of motors was developed under an ESA contract with three European companies; development of Mage 2 was completed in 1983.

[5] Seibert (2006, *The History of Sounding Rockets and Their Contribution to European Space Research*, p.57.

[6] Harlow (2000), 'The Larger Solid Propellant Rocket Motors of the United Kingdom', p.13.

[7] MAXUS 7 was launched 2nd May 2006, MAXUS 8 on 26th March 2010, and at the time of writing MAXUS 9 is due to be launched "in 2014".

[8] Harlow (2000), table 8.

Unfortunately, the Skylark 13 / Spacelark / Small Orbiter proposals were another technical possibility that came to nothing:

> I can only refer you to Dr John Furst, who was the prime mover behind *Spacelark, or Skylark 13*. I had taken him into S10, which is the empty hardware store at Westcott, many times and he was like a kid with a penny in a sweetshop. He looked around at all the empty hardware, and he thought 'I could put one of those on top of one those and I could do this with it'. He had got it all into his head, exactly what he wanted to do and what he could do. I am not sure he was a very good businessman, in the sense of understanding what BAe's or even BAC's business objectives were, he was an engineer. And capabilities to an engineer are not capabilities to a businessman. We have to look at it in the round, not just as simple engineers.[9]

Skylarks 14, 15 and 16

Also around this time, several enhancements to the existing Skylark sub-orbital vehicles were proposed, none of which came to fruition. Skylark 14[10] was a version where the standard Goldfinch booster was replaced by the more powerful

Rook IIIA, which was approximately three times more powerful. Skylark 15[11] was a similarly modified version of Skylark 12, and with a payload of 100 kg, it could have reached an apogee of 1400 km, compared with 1000 km for Skylark 12.[12]

The author has been unable to find any official references to Skylark 16, but it might have referred to an undesignated Raven XI / Snipe combination that appeared in a paper that included Skylark 14.[13]

Satellite Launcher Proposals - LittLEO

LittLEO was a small launcher initiative proposed by a consortium led by General Technology Systems Ltd.,[16] a project in which BAe was heavily involved, and which included Royal Ordnance. It was a European answer to a worldwide market need perceived for a cost effective vehicle capable of lifting 500 – 1000 kg into Low Earth Orbit. This was considerably more than the Skylark variants listed above, a requirement that resulted in a move away from using existing British solid propellant motors. The concept included a recoverable capsule for microgravity experiments, and was linked to the use of Andøya in Norway as the initial launch site for polar orbits.[17]

Type	Booster	Sustainer	3rd stage	1st flight
5	-	Raven XI	-	-
6	Goldfinch II	Raven VI	-	1968
7	Goldfinch II	Raven XI	-	1975
8	Stonechat	Waxwing	-	-
9	Stonechat	-	-	(1969)[14]
10	Raven XI	Gosling IV	-	-
10A	Goldfinch II	Gosling IV[15]	-	1974
11	Goldfinch II	Raven VI	Cuckoo IV	-
12	Goldfinch II	Raven XI	Cuckoo IV	1976
13	**Stonechat**	**Stonechat II**	**Waxwing**	-
14	**Rook IIIA**	**Raven XI**	-	-
15	**Rook IIIA**	**Raven XI**	**Cuckoo V**	-
16	**?**			-
17	**Stonechat**	**Mage 2**	-	-

Table 16.2 This table shows the proposed Skylarks 13 to 17 added to the Skylark family of rockets.
(Spacelark was similar to Skylark 13 but with the addition of four Rook boosters).

[9] John Harlow in 2001, CCBH (2005), *Skylark Sounding Rockets 1957-1972*, p.62, & *Prospero* No.2, p.126.
[10] The Skylark 14 configuration appears in several papers, e.g. Harlow (1992b), 'On the many guises of the Rook', p.142, and Brown (1978), 'Recent Advances in Skylark Vehicle Technology', p.412 (ESA SP-135), and also in an undated BAe sales brochure.
[11] The Skylark 15 configuration appears in Harlow (1992b), 'On the many guises of the Rook', p.142, and also in the same undated BAe sales brochure as Skylark 14.
[12] BAe Dynamics Group sales brochure c.1978.
[13] Brown (1978), 'Recent Advances in Skylark Vehicle Technology', p.412.
[14] Only launched in the form of the 'Falstaff' military rocket.
[15] An earlier source says Gosling, a later one Heron.
[16] GTS Ltd. was originally founded in 1973 by Geoffrey Pardoe and Bill Stephens, both of whom had worked on Blue Streak.
[17] Ellis (1989), 'The Skylark Sounding Rocket Programme and Future Launcher Developments by British Aerospace (Space Systems) Ltd.', p.270. *ESA document SP-291.*

Configuration	
STAGE	**MOTORS**
1	4 x CASTOR IVB
2	1 x CASTOR IVB
3	CASTOR IVB (Shortened version)
4	STAR-48

Figures 16.4 and 16.5
Left: Schematic and configuration of the LittLEO design.
(Ellis (1989), figure 1)
Right: An artist's impression of the vehicle in operation.
(Flight International 28 May 1988, p.19)

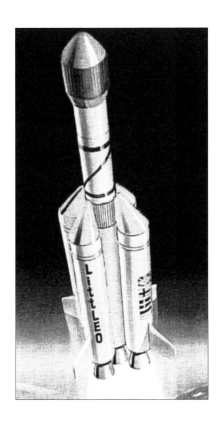

A three-year plan for the development of LittLEO was drawn up, with the intention of leading to an initial test flight in late 1991.[18] This project very nearly made it, but despite the promising start and British Aerospace's confidence that it would prove a commercially viable project, no more was heard.

A new Australian satellite launch site?

Woomera had not been located with satellites in mind, and was only suitable for launching into polar orbits. In 1986 and 1987 the Queensland Government had commissioned feasibility studies for a launch site on Cape York, the peninsula forming the north-eastern tip of Australia. The advantages of Cape York as a possible spaceport site included its proximity to the equator, and its weather and geographical situation which are similar to Cape Canaveral in Florida. The Cape York Space Agency became the first commercial organization involved, as the following indicated:

> Cape York Space Agency has won the competition between six companies to conduct a feasibility study into the proposed A$l-5 billion Queensland, Australia, launch site. The company consists of 64 partners, in-

cluding Price Waterhouse and TNT. West Germany's MBB, meanwhile, has requested permission to launch a Skylark sounding rocket from the site in September.[19]

However, the Agency ran out of money in 1989 and the Essington Group took over. The Essington Group also ran into financial difficulties and in 1992 Space Transportation Systems (STS) were granted the rights. At the end of 1992 Space Transportation Systems ceased its investigations of Cape York and instead began looking at the island of Emira in Papua New Guinea.[20]

In the end, the Cape York launch site initiative foundered because little political interest was shown by the Australian federal government, and it would have needed considerable tax payer funds to set up the local infrastructure. There was also local opposition, and from an operational point of view access to polar orbits was difficult.

In 2001 another Australian move, to establish the world's first fully commercial space launch facility on Christmas Island, also came to nothing, and to date (2014) a reduced area Woomera range remains the only significant launch site in Australia.

---

[18] Ellis (1989), p.271. See also the article on p.19 of Flight International 28 May 1988.
[19] Flight International Magazine, 19 Mar 1988, p.33.
[20] *http://members.optusnet.com.au/virgothomas/space/spaceport.html*, last accessed August 2014.

Jan.	Feb.	March	April	May	June	July	Aug.	Sept.	Oct.	Nov.	Dec.
				BAe				INTER-		ROSE 1	TEXUS 20
				TEST				ZODIAK		TEXUS	ROSE 2
								II		19	

Table 16.3 The six Skylark launches in 1988. (For full details see Appendix 3)

(Key: black = proving test, red = German national)

SKYLARK LAUNCHES AND SCIENCE IN 1988

Meanwhile, Skylark launches continued. Compared with 1987, when two out of four missions failed, 1988 was a much better year. After a successful BAe proving flight in May, there were five successful flights towards the end of the year.

24 May 1988   BAe Test Flight

This launch took place from Esrange, to test motor modifications designed to improve reliability of the Raven XI, after the failures on TEXUS 15 & 16.

The flight was successful, and there were no more Skylark motor failures. This also appears to have been the first ever launch into space by a UK commercial company!

3 September 1988   INTERZODIAK II

INTERZODIAK II was a German solar physics mission, a repeat of the failed INTERZODIAK launch attempt in March 1985, when the Skylark 12 Cuckoo IV third stage motor ignited prematurely. That had resulted in more than three years of extra work to repeat the launch.

As before, this took place from the CLBI range (Centro de Lançamento da Barreira do Inferno) near Natal, Brazil. Fingers must have been crossed as the rocket took off, but this

time all went well, and the payload reached a new all time record altitude for Skylark of 857 km (533 miles), exceeding that of Astro-Hel in 1979 by 28 km (17 miles).

A total of 13 different celestial targets near the Sun were successfully observed during the 16-minute flight.[21]

November 1988   ROSE I, TEXUS 19

The ROSE campaign of winter 1988/1989 comprised "**Ro**cket and **S**catter **E**xperiments", ionosphere experiments investigating the dynamics and the structure of the auroral E-region. The distinguishing feature was that measurement from the ground stations (the scatter experiments) would take place at the same time as the measurements made by sounding rocket. The campaign involved four Skylark launches, two from Andøya in Norway (ROSE I and ROSE II) in late 1988, and two from Kiruna in Sweden (ROSE III and ROSE IV) in early 1989. Each rocket contained nine different experiments and a star sensor,[22] and all were successful.

The first, **ROSE I**, was launched from Andøya on the 26th November. The Sporadic E-layer lies at a height of 100-120 km, so the experiments did not require a particularly high altitude, and the rocket used for all the ROSE launches was the relatively low powered combination of a Raven VIII and Cuckoo booster.[23] ROSE I attained a correspondingly low apogee of 120 km (75 miles).

Seq. Nos	Launch date	Ref. (sponsor) launch site	Config- uration	Apogee km (miles)	Experi- menters	Experiment	Result
403 (1)	09 May 1988	BAe Test (BAe) Kiruna	Spin?, Rav.XI +G	262 (163)	BAe	Proving flight – to test Raven XI modifications introduced after TEXUS 15 & 16 failures	S

Table 16.4 A summary of the BAe Skylark 7 test flight.

---

[21] Lay, Fahr & Nass (1989), 'Interzodiak 2: Observation of EUV-resonance radiation' (*ESA SP-291*). See also Neuman, Boison & Henkel (1983),'Interzodiak – A Sounding rocket Project for High-Resolution of EUV Radiations'.

[22] Rose (1989), 'Preliminary Results of the Rocket and Scatter Experiments "Rose" ', p.141. It was surely not a coincidence that the principal investigator's name coincided with the name of the project!

[23] It was over ten years since the Raven VIII had last been used, so they may have been made as a special order.

Skylark microgravity missions resume

As described at the end of the last chapter, the previous microgravity mission launched by Skylark was TEXUS 16. However the TEXUS 17 (2nd May 1988) and TEXUS 18 (6th May 1988) payloads were not launched by Skylark, but by Nike-Black Brant 5B rockets.[24] This may have been because of doubts on the reliability of the Raven XI, or simply because of a motor shortage, possibly caused by the use of a Skylark 7 on an unexpected 'target of opportunity' mission, launched from Woomera in August 1987 to observe the supernova, 1987A.

After the failures of TEXUS 15 and 16 in 1987 there must have been sighs of relief all round when on the 28th November the TEXUS 19 launch by a Skylark 7 (Goldfinch II and Raven XI) was completely successful.

The payload reached an altitude of 244 km (152 miles) above Kiruna; it contained ten experiments, six from Germany, two from Japan and one each from Sweden and Belgium. Eight were materials science experiments, the other two studied life sciences.[25]

December 1988   TEXUS 20, ROSE II

On the 2nd December, just a week after TEXUS 19, TEXUS 20 was successfully launched from Kiruna. It carried seven microgravity experiments, five from Germany, and one each from Belgium and Japan. Six were materials science experiments, and one a life science experiment.[26]

ROSE II was launched from Andøya in Norway on the 5th December, just over a week after the launch of ROSE I from the same site. As the name suggests, it carried a continuation of the 'ROSE' series of auroral E-region geophysics experiments, see ROSE I above.

Figure 16.6 Left: 'First Day Covers' were not limited to Australia; this example posted in Sweden marks the launches of TEXUS 19 & 20. Even the postage stamp includes Skylark!

(Author's collection)

Figure 16.7 Right: The Swedish postage stamp on the First Day Cover above shows Skylark leaving its tower at Esrange, with the Aurora Borealis in the background.

(© Posten Frimärken)

---

[24] For a list of launches from Esrange, go to *www.sscspace.com/Products-Services/rocket-balloon-services/launch-services-esc/esrange-space-center* , and click on "List of all rocket launches". (Last accessed August 2014).

[25] ESA EEA database - TEXUS 19, (last accessed August 2014).

[26] ESA EEA database - TEXUS 20, (last accessed August 2014).

Jan.	Feb.	March	April	May	June	July	Aug.	Sept.	Oct.	Nov.	Dec.
	ROSE III		TEXUS	TEXUS						TEXUS	TEXUS
	ROSE IV		21	22						23	24

Table 16.5 The six Skylark Launches in 1989. (For full details see Appendix 3)

(Key: red = German national)

SKYLARK LAUNCHES AND SCIENCE IN 1989

1989 was a relatively busy year for Skylark, with six successful scientific flights, although it was a quiet year at Esrange, with only four launches other than Skylark.[27] During the year, the TEXUS programme was taken over from the German Federal Ministry of Research and Technology by DASA-RI, Bremen, so it could be continued on a commercial basis. It was anticipated that this would result in increased third party use, but by 1997 the main customers remained DARA[28] (the German Space Agency) and ESA.[29]

February 1989   ROSE III, ROSE IV

ROSE III and **ROSE IV** were launched from Kiruna on the 7th and 9th of February respectively, and brought the ROSE campaign to a successful conclusion.

---
30 April 1989   TEXUS 21

The first of the four TEXUS flights in 1989 was that of **TEXUS 21**, which carried at least five experiments. Four of these were from Germany and one from Belgium. Three were life science studies on plant material, and two were materials science studies in the field of fluid physics.[30]

Those taking part appear to have become quite involved, even to the extent of creating a logo for the TEXUS 21 flight, see figure 16.8 below.

One of the life science experiments was from the University of Bonn, in the field of plant biology and physiology. It sought to "gain insight into the dynamics of the cytoplasma streaming of the green alga Chara under conditions where gravity has no interference effect."[33]

Figure 16.8 The logo created for TEXUS 21 and 22. The space shuttle is shown behind the Skylark rocket because the TEXUS experiments were a precursor to those to be flown on the Shuttle.[31]

(University of Bonn)[32]

---

27 For a list of launches from Esrange, go to *www.sscspace.com/Products-Services/rocket-balloon-services/launch-services-esc/esrange-space-center* , and click on "List of all rocket launches". (Last accessed August 2014).

28 In 1989 the DFVLR (German Test and Research Institute for Aviation and Space Flight) became the DLR (German Research Institute for Aviation and Space Flight), and DARA (German Agency for Space Flight Affairs) was created.

29 Röhrig & Roth (1997), 'Scientific Sounding Rocket and Balloon Activities in Germany', p.17.

30 ESA EEA database - TEXUS 21, (last accessed July 2014).

31 In particular, a green alga Chara experiment was amongst the 41 microgravity experiments flown on the IML2 (Second International Microgravity Laboratory Mission), (STS-65), launched July 1994. See ESA EEA database\ Space Shuttle\ STS-65, IML-2, 'Gravireaction of Chara' (Sievers & Buchen), (last accessed July 2014).

32 See *www.spacebio.uni-bonn.de/ahp/Sounding/Texus.htm*, last accessed August 2014. Image reproduced with permission.

33 ESA EEA database - TEXUS 21, 'Cytoplasma Streaming and Oriented Movement of Statoliths in Chara Rhizoids' (Sievers *et al*), (last accessed July 2014).

 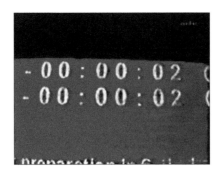 

  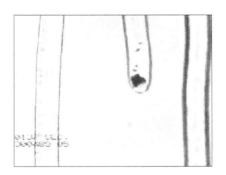

Figures 16.9, 16.10 & 16.11, and 16.12, 16.13 & 16.14. Six stills from the video footage of the TEXUS 21 flight.
(Swedish Space Corporation / University of Bonn) [35]

There is an interesting 60 seconds of video available via the internet,[34] showing the TEXUS 21 launch from Esrange, interspersed with "views through the microscope" of their experiment as it underwent the flight, see above.

25 May 1989   TEXUS 22

TEXUS 22 was launched the following month. The ESA database reveals only three experiments, although there were probably more.[36] Those documented were from Germany, and comprised one materials science and two life science experiments.

TEXUS 22 saw a significant new facility introduced, the monitoring and remote control of microgravity experiments by users outside the Esrange launch site.[37] At this stage, real time data, audio and video communications links were provided by satellite links and wide area and public telephone networks, but as the remote control facility matured, newly available digital lines were used. (See TEXUS 34 below).

On this occasion, the TEXUS 22 materials science experiment used the new facility. The experiment involved growing crystals of the semi-conductor silicon, and the process was remotely observed by means of a CCD video camera from which images were transmitted in real time to the ground.[38] This allowed the investigators to control the experiment from Cologne in Germany as the experiment underwent microgravity in space.[39]

25 November 1989   TEXUS 23

In addition to the two TEXUS flights in the spring of 1989, there were two late autumn flights.[40] In November, a minimum of five experiments were launched on board **TEXUS 23**; these were from a wide range of countries – two from Germany, one each from Holland, Italy and Spain. Three were materials science, and two were life science, experiments.[41]

34   University of Bonn website, section on TEXUS/MAXUS, *www.spacebio.uni-bonn.de/ahp/Sounding/Texus.htm* , (last accessed August 2014).

35   See *www.spacebio.uni-bonn.de/ahp/Sounding/Texus.htm* , last accessed August 2014.

36   The ESA EEA database - TEXUS 22, (last accessed August 2014), lists only three, but the MICREX database (coverage only up to TEXUS 20) indicates that the ESA EEA database does not always include all the experiments launched on the TEXUS missions. This may be because the ESA database lists only ESA sponsored experiments, not those from national programmes.

37   Limburger *et al.* (1996), 'Cost Efficient ISDN-Based Remote Operation of TEXUS 34 Sounding Rocket Experiments', Introduction.

38   ESA EEA database - TEXUS 22, 'Floating-Zone Growth of Silicon with a Partially Free Melt Surface' (Benz *et al*), (last accessed August 2014).

39   Ibid., "Due to the lack of convective cooling of the lamp filament and the sample, the lamp power had to be reduced 8 times by telecommanding to keep the zone length within the desired range of 13 +- 1 mm."

40   Esrange launches tended to take place in winter or spring because the snow helped avoid damage to the payload when landing. (Franke, (2001)).

41   ESA EEA database - TEXUS 23, (last accessed August 2014).

Jan.	Feb.	March	April	May	June	July	Aug.	Sept.	Oct.	Nov.	Dec.
		SISSI 1		TEXUS 25		SISSI 2	SISSI 3			TEXUS 27	
				TEXUS 26						MAXUS	
										TEST	

Table 16.6 The seven Skylark Launches in 1990. (For full details see Appendix 3)

(Key: red = German national)

The remote control facility was used again, this time the Italian experiment was remotely observed and controlled from Naples.[42]

---

06 December 1989   TEXUS 24

Less than two weeks later, TEXUS 24 was launched. This had at least three experiments on board, two from Germany and one from Japan. Two of these were materials science experiments and one a life science experiment.[43]

The life science experiment was one of a series investigating the effect of gravity on a process called free-flow electrophoresis, a technique for separating cells. "In an experiment on

Figure 16.15 The TEXUS 25 logo created by the Bonn experimenters.

(University of Bonn)[48]

TEXUS 24 we demonstrated beyond doubt the significantly enhanced resolution and throughput of this technique under µg conditions".[44]

SKYLARK LAUNCHES AND SCIENCE IN 1990

1990 was almost like the old days for Skylark; with seven launches, it was the busiest year since 1978. However this was not to be repeated; in the years to follow, the maximum annual number of launches would only be three.

---

06 March 1990   SISSI 1

The SISSI aeronomy programme involved the launch of four Skylark payloads from Esrange over the period spring 1990 to spring 1991. SISSI stood for "**S**pectroscopic **I**nfrared **S**tructure **S**ignatures **I**nvestigation", and on each flight the main instrument was a liquid helium cooled infrared spectrometer.[45] This measured emissions of carbon dioxide, ozone, water vapour, nitric oxide, atomic oxygen and methane in the mesosphere and lower thermosphere.[46]

The rockets used refurbished payloads left over from two earlier programmes (Energy Balance, 1980/81 and MAP/WINE, 1984), each payload being used twice more during the SISSI campaign. They were equipped with seven experiments, and included systems for attitude measurement, attitude control and land recovery.[47] As well as having economic benefits, reusing them in this way meant that the SISSI results could readily be compared with those from the earlier campaigns.

---

[42] Limburger *et al.* (1996), Introduction.
[43] ESA EEA database - TEXUS 24, (last accessed August 2014).
[44] Zimmermann *et al.* (1997), 'Biotechnology on Sounding Rockets: Development of Techniques for Space Biotechnology'.
[45] Grossmann *et al.* (1991), 'Rocket-borne infrared measurements in the Arctic upper atmosphere'.
[46] Vollmann & Grossmann (1997), 'Excitation of 4.3 µm CO_2 emissions by O (1D) during twilight'.
[47] Auchter *et al.* (1991), 'Payload SISSI. Sounding rocket program Final report'.
[48] See *www.spacebio.uni-bonn.de/ahp/Sounding/Texus.htm* , last accessed August 2014. Reproduced with permission.

SISSI 1 was launched from Esrange in the dawn twilight of Tuesday 6th March 1990, and the Skylark 6 successfully carried its Fl scientific payload to an apogee of 178 km (111 miles).

This first launch also formed part of the DYANA campaign (**DY**namics **A**dapted **N**etwork for the **A**tmosphere), which took place from January to March 1990 in the northern hemisphere. A large number of ground-based, balloon and rocket borne experiments were carried out to study various aspects of middle atmosphere dynamics (10–100 km). In turn, DYANA was part of the Solar Terrestrial Energy Program (STEP).[49]

May 1990   TEXUS 25, TEXUS 26

May saw the launch from Esrange of two TEXUS missions in quick succession. **TEXUS 25** was launched during the early hours of the morning of Sunday the 13th; it had at least six experiments on board, five from Germany and one from France. Three were materials science and three were life science experiments.[50] One of the life science experiments was a continuation of that flown by the University of Bonn on TEXUS 21, as before it studied the response of the green algae Chara to microgravity.[51]

As with TEXUS 22 and 23, a remote control facility was used,[52] allowing investigators the convenience of controlling at least one of the experiments from the Microgravity User Support Centre (MUSC) in Cologne "During flight, this experiment was directly observed by video-downlink and telemanipulated from the ground." [53]

TEXUS 26 followed just two days later. It also carried at least six experiments, four from Germany and two from Sweden. Four were materials science and two life science experiments, most of them a continuation of earlier work.[54]

---

25 July & 2 August 1990   SISSI 2 & SISSI 3

Two more SISSI vehicles (payloads F2 and F3) were launched during summer twilight conditions from Esrange in July and August. SISSI F2 was launched during a fading noctilucent cloud event, and powered by a Skylark 6 (Raven VI and Goldfinch), it reached a modest altitude of 168 km (104 miles), similar to SISSI 1.

SISSI F3 was launched a week later during a solar proton event,[55] and with the more powerful Skylark 7 (Raven XI and Goldfinch) reached a greater altitude of 239 km (149 miles).

---

15 November 1990   TEXUS 27

The end of the year saw one more TEXUS launch. **TEXUS 27** carried at least five experiments, including three from Germany and one each from the UK and France. Three of these were materials science experiments, two life science experiments.

That from France was a biotechnology experiment observed by a camera, for which a remote control capability was implemented to allow the camera to be moved sideways and be focussed on the sample. The images were sent to the ground in real time and recorded.[56] Very different from the early days of Skylark!

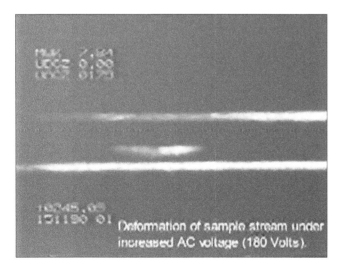

Figure 16.16 A still from the video of the TEXUS 27 French biotechnical experiment.[57]

---

[49]   Offermann (1994), 'The DYANA campaign: A survey'.
[50]   ESA EEA database - TEXUS 25, (last accessed August 2014).
[51]   ESA EEA database - TEXUS 25, 'Functions of Statoliths in the Rhizoids of Chara' (Sievers *et al*).
[52]   Limburger *et al.* (1996), 'Cost Efficient ISDN-Based Remote Operation of TEXUS 34 Sounding Rocket Experiments', Introduction.
[53]   ESA EEA database - TEXUS 25, 'Electrofusion of plant protoplasts' (Hampp), (last accessed August 2014).
[54]   ESA EEA database - TEXUS 26, (last accessed August 2014).
[55]   Ratkowski *et al.* (1993), 'Rocket measurements of high-latitude summer mesospheric [O], OH, O2 Delta and spacecraft glow'.
[56]   ESA EEA database - TEXUS 27, 'Electrophoresis Visualisation' (Roux-de Balmann and Sanchez), (last accessed August 2014).
[57]   ESA EEA database - TEXUS 27, 'Electrophoresis Visualisation' (Roux-de Balmann and Sanchez), attachments, video 2, (last accessed August 2014).

The British experiment was from the University of Bristol, and investigated how the lack of gravity affected a salt solution in a supercritical condition at about 350°C.[58]

---

25 November 1990   MAXUS TEST

As described at the start of this chapter, the European MAXUS sounding rocket development programme aimed to increase the microgravity time achievable with a sounding rocket up to 15 minutes.

The TEXUS microgravity programme had been running successfully since December 1977, but with the grounding of the Space Shuttle fleet after the Challenger disaster in January 1986, and in preparation for the anticipated European Space Station Columbus,[59] the microgravity research community was looking for longer experiment flight opportunities. The Swedish Space Corporation (SSC) proposed a Long Duration Sounding Rocket to ESA for these demands and received a study contract. As noted before, Skylark 17 had been bid in competition by BAe Space Systems against a vehicle based on the larger Castor motor[60] for this purpose. Unfortunately, the internal pricing policy prevalent in Royal Ordnance at the time meant that commercially it was no match for the Castor.[61]

The outcome was an agreement in 1988 between MBB-ERNO[62] and SSC for the development of a single-stage rocket based on the Castor strap-on boosters for the Delta 2 launch vehicle. This larger version of the **MA**SER/TE**XUS** rockets became known as MAXUS.[63]

As part of the development, a three-stage Skylark 12 **MAXUS TEST** vehicle was launched successfully in November 1990 to an altitude of 534 km. The main objective was to verify MAXUS guidance and control systems and safety operations systems onboard and on the ground.[64] Another purpose was to qualify Skylark 12 for use at Esrange, using the SPINRAC control system to reduce dispersion.[65] This latter

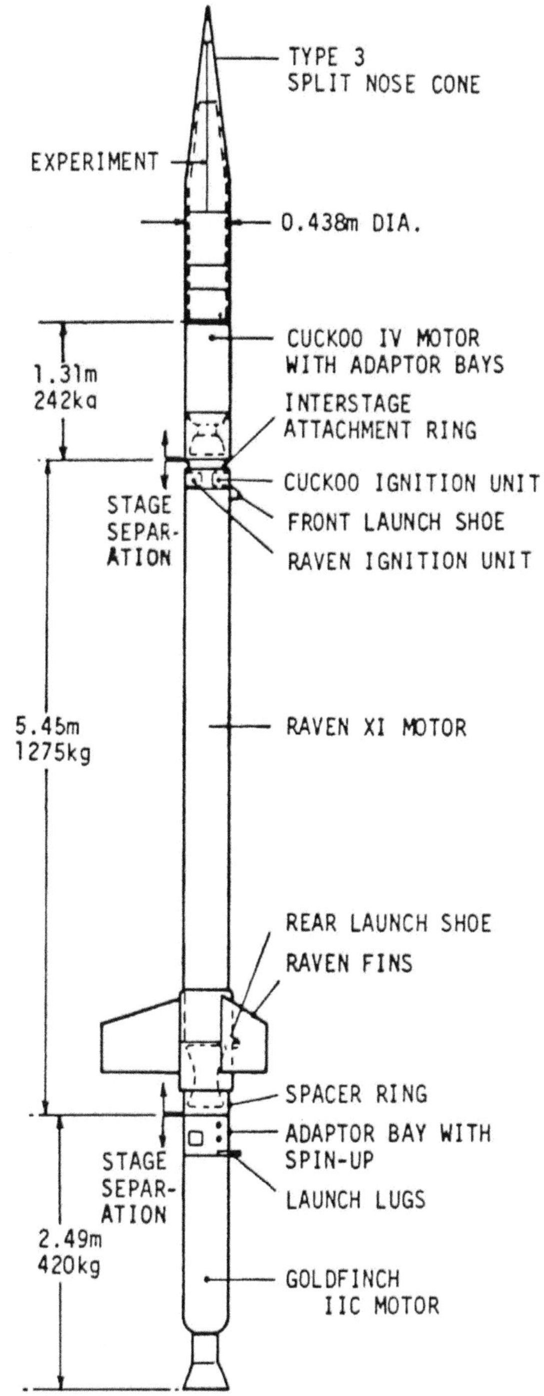

Figure 16.17 The Skylark 12 'Maxus Test' vehicle.

(Dreier (1990), p.12)

---

[58] ESA EEA database - TEXUS 27, 'Pressures of Supercritical Salt Solutions' (Turner).

[59] Originally conceived in the early 1980s as an independent space station, the Columbus laboratory ended up as ESA's biggest single contribution to the International Space Station. Eventually launched in February 2008, the 4.5-metre diameter cylindrical module provides internal payload accommodation for experiments in material science, fluid physics and life science.

[60] The Castor family of solid-fuel rocket stages and boosters were built by Thiokol in the USA and used on a variety of launch vehicles, including the 'Scout' that launched Ariel III in 1967. In 1974 Thiokol won the contract to build the solid rocket booster (SRB) for the Space Shuttle, but in 1986 a fault in an SRB destroyed the Space Shuttle Challenger in flight, and the company was found at fault for the explosion and the deaths of the astronauts.

[61] As noted before, "the pricing policy reflected the poor price competitiveness of plastic propellant motors, and as a direct consequence, the solid propellant business at Westcott suffered a series of major blows". Harlow (2000), p.13.

[62] MBB had taken over its fellow German company ERNO in 1982. As part of a continuing series of aerospace mergers (paralleling those in the UK), in 1989 MBB was in turn acquired by 'Deutsche Aerospace AG' (DASA), which was renamed 'Daimler-Benz Aerospace' in 1995.

[63] Stefan Zenker, *www.zenker.se/Space/Jubilee/jubilee-c.shtml*, last accessed August 2014.

[64] Stefan Zenker, *www.zenker.se/Space/Jubilee/jubilee-c.shtml*, last accessed August 2014. See also Dreier (1990).

[65] Dreier (1990), *Plan for the MAXUS-TEST campaign at Esrange November 1990*, p.4.

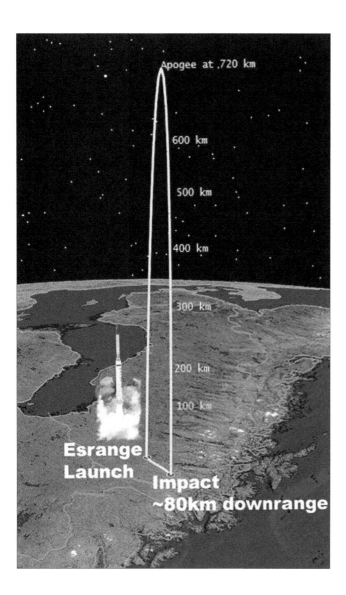

Figure 16.18 This unusual viewpoint from the north shows the trajectory of the Maxus sounding rocket, and illustrates how at Esrange the allowable impact distance was very short compared to the altitude reached. With an apogee of 534 km, the Skylark 12 'Maxus Test' vehicle trajectory was similar.

(Swedish Space Corporation)

Figure 16.19 A comparison of ESA sounding rocket maximum altitudes compared to the Shuttle and ISS, (not to scale!)

(Ceglia (2005), figure 5-5)

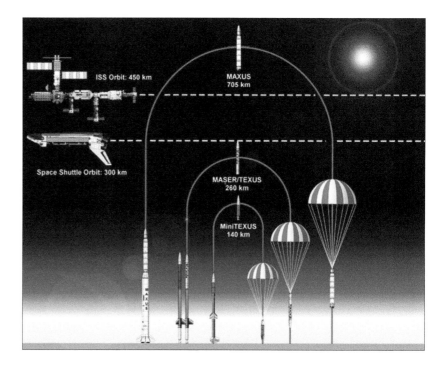

1991	1992	1993	1994	1995
SISSI 4 (Apr)	TEXUS 29 (Nov)	TEXUS 30 (May)	TEXUS 32 (May)	-
TEXUS 28 (Nov)		MASER 6 (Nov)	TEXUS 33 (Nov)	
		TEXUS 31 (Nov)		

Table 16.7 Skylark launches from 1991 to 1995.

(Key: red = German national, pink = ESA)

was very successful, as the payload landed with an impact point only five km from that predicted. Unfortunately, this first Skylark 12 launch from Esrange was also the last, as the MAXUS TEST would prove to be the final launch for the three-stage Skylark 12. All subsequent Skylark missions would use the two-stage Skylark 7 (Raven XI +Goldfinch).

In due course, the first MAXUS launch proper took place in May 1991. However, because of bad workmanship in the 'Thrust Vector Control System' delivered by Thiokol, the rocket disintegrated at 40 km altitude and fell in pieces to the ground. The reflight in November 1992 (MAXUS 1B) was successful, and the rocket reached 716 km. A second successful flight occurred in 1995.[66]

Since then launches have occurred at a rate of one every three or four years, about half the rate for the parallel TEXUS programme which continues. At the time of writing (2014), the most recent launch was MAXUS 8 in 2010, with MAXUS 9 due to be launched in 2014.

SKYLARK LAUNCHES AND SCIENCE 1991 – 1995

In 1991 the number of Skylark launches slumped to only two, compared to seven the year before. This did not reflect a lack of activity at Esrange, as during the year 31 sounding rocket launches took place. However all these other launches were of smaller sounding rockets; most reached about 100 km, none except the Skylark powered SISSI 4 and TEXUS 28 reached higher than 200 km.[67]

In 1994, the recently formed Matra Marconi Space Company (MMS)[68] acquired British Aerospace Space Systems. Thus, it inherited the Skylark production facility at Filton, Bristol, although this did not last very long, as described later.

In another sign of the times, in November 1994 BAe ceased production of Skylark motors, as described under the '1995' heading below.

Figure 16.20 Return to Sardinia – in July 1994 about 30 technicians, engineers, scientists and others who had been involved in the early ESRO Sounding Rocket Programme, returned to commemorate the 30th anniversary of the first Skylark/pan-European space launch.

(ESA Bulletin **Nr. 80,** *November 1994)*

---

[66] Stefan Zenker, *www.zenker.se/Space/Jubilee/jubilee-c.shtml*, last accessed August 2014.

[67] For a list of launches from Esrange, go to *www.sscspace.com/Products-Services/rocket-balloon-services/launch-services-esc/esrange-space-center* , and click on "List of all rocket launches". (Last accessed August 2014).

[68] Matra Marconi Space (MMS) had been established in 1990 as a joint venture between the space and telecommunication divisions of the Lagardère Group (Matra Espace) and the GEC-Marconi group. In July 1994, MMS acquired British Aerospace Space Systems Ltd. (a subsidiary of BAe Dynamics with 900 workers) to create Europe's (then) leading space company and largest satellite manufacturer.

Figure 16.21 The logo for TEXUS 29.
(University of Bonn) [71]

---

09 April 1991   SISSI 4

This fourth SISSI launch brought the campaign investigating the arctic middle atmosphere to a successful conclusion. As with SISSI 3, **SISSI 4** utilised the more powerful Skylark 7, and reached a similar altitude of 245 km (152 miles).

---

23 November 1991   TEXUS 28

TEXUS 28 carried at least six microgravity experiments, five from Germany and one from France. For the first time the majority were life science experiments, five in all, leaving just one materials science experiment.[69]

---

22 November 1992   TEXUS 29

1992 saw a new low in Skylark's fortunes, the renaissance was over. Almost exactly twelve months to the day after TEXUS 28, the launch of TEXUS 29 took place. Never before had there been only one Skylark launch in a calendar year.

There were at least eight experiments flown on board **TEXUS 29**, seven from Germany and one from Japan. Six of these were materials science experiments, this time just two were life science experiments.[70]

---

01 May 1993   TEXUS 30

With three launches taking place, 1993 was a slightly better year for Skylark. **TEXUS 30** was an all-German affair, with at least six German experiments. Three were materials science, three were life science experiments.

November 1993   MASER 6, TEXUS 31

The Swedish MASER (**MA**terials **S**cience **E**xperiment **R**ocket) had been first launched in back in 1987. It had practically the same capabilities as the German Texus vehicle, however:

> The reason for starting the Maser program was simple. Back in those days Texus was a purely German programme and ESA did not have a programme of its own. We offered them one. [72]

The MASER missions were (and are) managed by the Swedish Space Corporation (SSC), although MASER 6 to 10 were 100% funded by ESA to meet the increasing demand for capacity, [73] and offered as an alternative for flying ESA microgravity experiments.

MASER payloads had originally been powered by a Terrier-Black Brant 5 rocket, and so have not been included in this book until now. But from Maser 6 onwards, the vehicle used instead the same Skylark 7 rocket motor combination as TEXUS, and would include the last ever Skylark launch as Maser 10, on 2 May 2005.

---

[69] ESA EEA database - TEXUS 28, (last accessed August 2014).
[70] ESA EEA database - TEXUS 29, (last accessed August 2014).
[71] See *www.spacebio.uni-bonn.de/ahp/Sounding/Texus.htm* , (last accessed August 2014).
[72] Sven Grahn, personal communication, March 2010.
[73] Ceglia (2005), *European Users Guide to Low Gravity Platforms*, p.5-6.

As with TEXUS, the MASER vehicle could carry payloads of about 250 kg up to apogees typically 250-300 km, yielding 5-7 minutes of microgravity with a residual acceleration of less than 10^{-4} g. Each payload consists of 4-6 modules housing up to a few dozen samples. In the same way that the TEXUS vehicle used experiment specific TEM modules (**T**exus **E**xperiment **M**odules), the MASER payload used CIS (**C**ell **I**n **S**pace) autonomous modules, each with its own power supply and electronics unit.

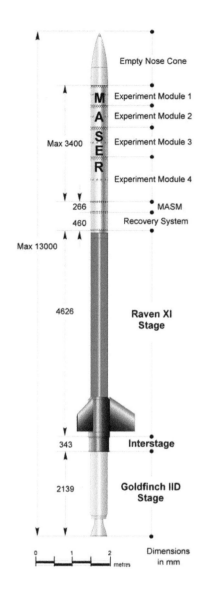

Figure 16.22 The MASER sounding rocket as propelled by 'Skylark 7'.

(after Ceglia (2005), figure 5-3)

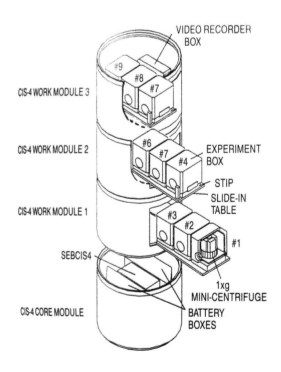

Figures 16.23 and 16.24 The CIS-4 payload module developed for MASER 6. (ESA SP-1206)

MASER 6 was launched on the 4th November, and successfully reached an altitude of 243 km (151 miles) with a total of at least five microgravity experiments, two each from France and Holland, and one from Italy. Two of these were materials science and three life science experiments.[74]

TEXUS 31 was launched from Esrange on the 26th, three weeks after MASER 6. The launch proved to be the last time that two Skylark rockets were launched in the same month. It carried at least four materials science experiments, one each from France, Holland, Belgium and Germany.[75]

05 May 1994	TEXUS 32

TEXUS 32 carried at least seven microgravity experiments, five from Germany and one each from France and Holland. Four were materials science experiments, and three were life science experiments.[76] Several were continuations of previous TEXUS experiments, one life science experiment was a variation of a Space Shuttle IML-2 experiment to be performed in two month's time,[77] and one[78] was a precursor to an electronics materials experiment to be flown on the SPACEHAB-4 module on board Shuttle mission STS-77 in May 1996.[79]

30 November 1994	TEXUS 33

TEXUS 33 carried at least three microgravity experiments, including one each from Germany, Italy and Spain.[80] All were materials science experiments. That from Spain was a complicated long liquid column experiment, the eleventh in a series flown on TEXUS and Shuttle Spacelab missions since 1983.[81] The original experiments had been recorded using 16mm cine film,[82] now technology had moved on, this time a CCD video camera was used.

1995	-

1995 marked the beginning of the end for Skylark. It was the first year since it was first tested in 1957 that no launches

had taken place; it was even a quiet year for Esrange, with only six sounding rocket launches.

Also a month or two previously, in November 1994, the production of the motors for Skylark had ended. A 'last time buy' of motors produced a small stockpile for future use, allowing twelve more launches, but the clock was now ticking for the end of Skylark.

> … when British Aerospace ended up taking on Skylark or Skylark motors they had a another kind of fixed mindset and that was to make profit on every single line item, on any part, any of the processes, any of the hardware, that was used to support Skylark motor production. As you can imagine, some of the sites that they then had were very expensive to run and if you were the only project on that site you took the whole overhead. That effectively killed the production of Skylark, because of the pricing policy.[83]

> …When BAC took over the prime contractorship of the Skylark programme, we were in fact lumbered I guess is the word with a 5% levy by MoD on the price. We had to levy back to MoD 5% of the price that we charged, to cover the costs of so-called development, which was long lost by the way, but it was just a cash cow as far as the MoD were concerned. And I have to say that as far as British Aerospace were concerned, that is the way it ended up. Motor production was a cash cow. It was going nowhere, we weren't going to reinvest in new propellant, new designs, nothing. Westcott was going to close. That was another nail in the coffin of Skylark.[84]

However, the era of the scientific sounding rocket was not over. In the USA, NASA sounding rocket launches were still taking place at a rate of two or three a month.[85] Even at Woomera, in October and November 1995 NASA launched a series of seven Black Brant V vehicles at the rate of one a week to study astronomical events.[86]

[74] ESA EEA database – MASER 6, (last accessed August 2014).

[75] ESA EEA database - TEXUS 31, (last accessed August 2014).

[76] ESA EEA database - TEXUS 32, (last accessed August 2014).

[77] ESA EEA database - TEXUS 32, 'Gravitactic orientation in the flagellate Euglena gracilis' (Haeder). The Space Shuttle IML-2 (Second International Microgravity Laboratory) mission, (STS-65), was launched July 1994.

[78] ESA EEA database - TEXUS 32, 'Growth of highly doped GaSb' (Benz *et al.*), (last accessed July 2014).

[79] The SPACEHAB-04 pressurised research module included a Commercial Float Zone Furnace (CFZF), designed to produce large ultra-pure crystals of semiconductor materials such as gallium arsenide.

[80] ESA EEA database - TEXUS 33, (last accessed July 2014).

[81] The website *http://webserver.dmt.upm.es/~isidoro/lc1/index.html* provides a good summary of this work, (last accessed August 2014).

[82] TEXUS 12, 18, 23 & 29. For instance, see the description of TEXUS 12, (1985), in the previous chapter.

[83] John Harlow in 2001, CCBH (2005), *Skylark Sounding Rockets 1957-1972*, p.55, & *Prospero* No.2, p.120.

[84] John Harlow in 2001, CCBH (2005), p.61, & *Prospero* No.2, p.126.

[85] See for instance Jonathan McDowell's list at *www.planet4589.org/space/lvdb/lis/S.lis* (Last accessed August 2014). (Warning - this file is very large!)

[86] The author's information comes from a series of 'First Day Covers' released at Woomera to commemorate the launches.

1996	1997	1998	1999	2000
TEXUS 34 (Mar)	-	TEXUS 36 (Feb)	MASER 8 (May)	TEXUS 37 (Mar)
MASER 7 (May)				TEXUS 38 (Apr)
TEXUS 35 (Nov)				

Table 16.8 1996 provided a temporary respite for Skylark, with three launches, but it was very quiet at Esrange,where these three were the only sounding rocket launches that year!

(Key: red = German national, pink = ESA)

SKYLARK LAUNCHES AND SCIENCE 1996 – 2000

In 1997, Germany's DARA announced that in the near future, because of decreasing budgets, it would not be able to fund more than one TEXUS mission per year.[87] This fact is reflected in the number of Skylark launches from then onwards.

2 March 1996   TEXUS 34

TEXUS 34 carried four experimental modules.[88] These included two from Germany and one from Italy, all with materials science experiments.

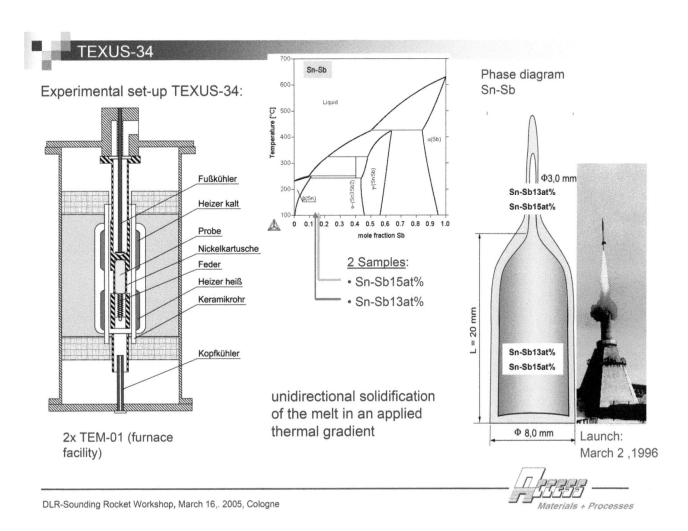

Figure 16.25 This diagram of one of the German material science experiments (solidification of a metal alloy) on board TEXUS 34 is taken from a later presentation. The apparatus was not very successful, so the experiment was repeated on TEXUS 37.

(Kammler *et al.* (2005), p.4)

---

[87] Röhrig & Roth (1997), 'Scientific Sounding Rocket and Balloon Activities in Germany', p.20.
[88] List of "TEXUS/MiniTEXUS/MAXUS-Missions 1977 to 2011", *www.raumfahrt-archiv-bremen.de/download/texmaxus.pdf*, last accessed August 2014.

This was the first TEXUS mission during which ISDN (Integrated Services Digital Network) communications were used, which allowed remote operation from other countries during flight.[89] As described above, remote operation had been first used on TEXUS 22 in May 1989, but the advantage of the new ISDN service was that reliable video, audio and data links were much easier to implement.[90] This was a pioneering use of international digital networks, and there were teething troubles as the telecommunication organisations of Sweden, Germany and Italy learnt to use the new equipment.[91] However, in the end, the links to TEXUS 34 did work successfully, and remote in-flight operations from MUSC[92] at Cologne in Germany and the MARS[93] Centre at Naples in Italy were successful.

From this time, ISDN became a standard facility, with the advantage that some experimenters no longer had to travel to Sweden. Unlike Woomera, Esrange did not have the benefit of nearly continuous clear skies and good weather. Hence, launch delays were common, with consequent inconvenience and cost. In this instance, TEXUS 34 was launched eight days late, mainly because of local weather problems.[94] Thus, the fact that fewer experimenters had to wait around in Sweden was a significant benefit.

---

03 May 1996   MASER 7

MASER 7 carried at least five microgravity experiments. These were flown in four specialised experimental modules 'EMEC', 'LPE', 'GABRIEL' and 'CIS-5'.[95] Two were physical science experiments, and three life science experiments. Three were from Italy, with one each from Germany and Sweden.

The GABRIEL (**G**ravity **A**ssessment for **B**oiling **R**esearch and **I**nvestigations with **El**ectric Field) module was an example of the ESA funded and owned reusable sounding rocket experiment modules. It was first used on this MASER 7 flight, and comprised two chambers for boiling experiments using high voltage electrodes, each chamber having a CCD camera for observations, and weighed 58 kg (128 lbs).[96]

The CIS-5 (**C**ells **I**n **S**pace) module was the updated version of CIS-4 shown previously.

Figure 16.26 The classic view of a Skylark launch from Esrange – MASER 7 leaves the tower on 3rd May 1996.
(Before firing, the exhaust doors in the enclosed base were opened.)
(Swedish Space Corporation)

---

[89] Limburger *et al.* (1996), 'Cost Efficient ISDN-Based Remote Operation of TEXUS 34 Sounding Rocket'.
[90] For instance expensive satellite communication links did not have to be held open whilst awaiting launch.
[91] Limburger *et al.* (1996), section 4.
[92] MUSC – Microgravity User Support Centre, (Cologne, Germany).
[93] MARS – Microgravity Advanced Research and Support, (Naples, Italy).
[94] Limburger *et al.* (1996), section 5.
[95] Seibert & Herfs (1997), 'Microgravity Science from ESA's Microgravity Sounding Rocket Projects (Life and Physical Sciences)', Table 1.
[96] Ceglia (2005), *European Users Guide to Low Gravity Platforms*, p.5-25.

 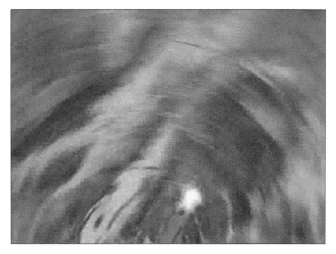

Figures 16.27 and 16.28 Left: MASER clears the tower. The extent of the brown exhaust clouds indicates this was taken from the altitude of MASER 7 in Figure 16.26. Right: Some five seconds later, the Goldfinch boost motor drops away. (Swedish Space Corporation)[97]

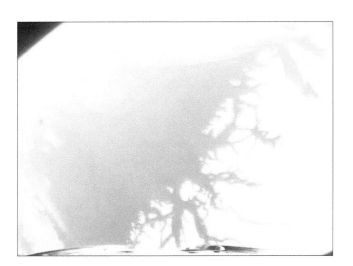 

Figures 16.29 and 16.30 Left: The snow covered coast of Norway viewed during the microgravity phase. Right: The parachute deploys during re-entry. (Swedish Space Corporation)

A MASER external on-board camera

On one of the MASER missions, an onboard video camera was used to take a film of the view from the outside the MASER rocket vehicle. It operated throughout the flight, see the stills above.

24 November 1996	TEXUS 35

By now, TEXUS was the world's longest running sounding rocket programme for microgravity research, and was regarded as being the most successful. With the programme

having been initiated in 1976 and TEXUS 1 launched in 1977, a 20th anniversary symposium took place in Bonn in September 1996 attended by 120 participants.[98]

The programme continued with TEXUS 35, although the mission is a bit of a mystery, as no mention is made of it in any of the ESA documents the author has consulted.[99] It was probably a wholly German funded mission, as the launch certainly took place successfully, as an article appeared confirming that "TEXUS 35 was launched in autumn 1996, leading to promising results in the research areas plasma physics, gravitational biology and semiconductor crystal growth".[100]

---

[97] To view the video from which these stills are taken, visit *http://spaceflight.esa.int/impress/text/multi_video.html* , and click on "MASER Sounding Rocket", (last accessed October 2014).

[98] Röhrig & Roth (1997), 'Scientific Sounding Rocket and Balloon Activities in Germany', p.20.

[99] For instance, table 1 of Seibert & Herfs (1997), 'Microgravity Science from ESA's Microgravity Sounding Rocket Projects (Life and Physical Sciences)' lists other 1996 missions, but not TEXUS 35.

[100] Röhrig & Roth (1997), p.20.

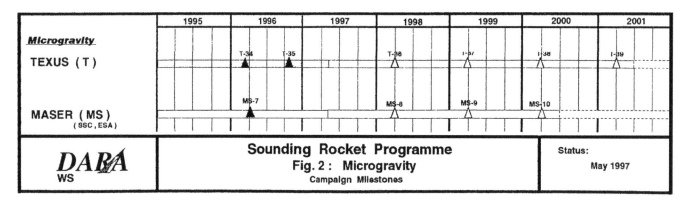

Figure 16.31 Milestones in the German/ESA sounding rocket microgravity programme, as at May 1997. The solid triangles in the 1996 column show the TEXUS 34, MASER 7 and TEXUS 35 missions of that year, but subsequent columns reveal the anticipated reduction in TEXUS launches to only one a year. (From Röhrig & Roth (1997), figure 2)

During the preceding 20 years, there had been up to four TEXUS flights per year, but as noted above, the same paper revealed that because of changing interests and other commitments (small satellites, Spacelab missions etc.); in the future, the German Space Agency (DARA) would only be able to fund one TEXUS mission per year:

1997   -

There were no Skylark launches in 1997, which was ironic, as on 13th February, Skylark became the world's oldest operational 'space launcher', on the 40th anniversary of its first launch from Woomera in 1957.[101]

1997 also marked significant progress in ESA's sounding rocket programme:

> The great potential of sounding rocket experimentation and its attractiveness for the scientific users has been shown. Since 1982, ESA has flown more than five tons of scientific payloads containing 132 experiments on 36 sounding rocket missions (25 Texus, 7 Maser, 2 Maxus, 2 Minitexus). The usefulness of sounding rocket experiments, both as a preparatory step for long-term missions - be it manned or unmanned - and as independent scientific investigations, has been successfully demonstrated in the past. This has been acknowledged by ESA's scientific advisory groups and also by the delegations of the ESA Member States participating in the EMIR Programme. The sounding rocket activities will be continued in the framework of the EMIR-2 Programme. In addition, the sounding rockets will have to take their role in preparing meaningful experiments for the International Space Station.[102]

07 February 1998   TEXUS 36

In 1998, there was only one Skylark launch. The four scientific experiments on board TEXUS 36 dealt with gravitational biology, fundamental physics, metal alloy solidification and crystal growth.[103] As with TEXUS 35, the mission appears to have been funded by Germany rather than ESA,[104] and all were German experiments.

The crystal growth experiment was a continuation of that flown on TEXUS 29 in 1992. It used a special mirror furnace (module TEM-02 ELLI), in which two CCD cameras were used to observe the successful creation of a single silicon crystal during the six minutes of microgravity.[105] When semiconductor crystals are grown on Earth, gravity induced effects cause imperfections, these series of experiments were designed to study such crystal growth with the gravity factor removed.

1999 – Skylark is saved from 'rationalisation'!

As noted earlier in this chapter, in 1994 Matra Marconi Space (MMS) had acquired British Aerospace Space Systems, and hence the Skylark facility at Filton in Bristol. Then, in November 1997, MMS announced that it would close the Filton site in August 1999, with a loss of 400 jobs. Fortunately in 1999 the Skylark manufacturing capability was saved when it was sold to a small private company, "Sounding Rocket Services Ltd." of Bristol. (The year afterwards MMS was itself merged with the space division of DaimlerChrysler Aerospace AG (DASA) to form *Astrium*.)

Thus the last half-dozen or so Skylarks were manufactured by Sounding Rocket Services, and launched in Sweden using the stockpiled motors.

---

[101] Flight International, 26 February – 4 March 1997, p.29.
[102] ESA Microgravity News, Vol.10, No.2, August 1997.
[103] Frings *et al.* (1999), 'Scientific Sounding Rocket and Balloon Activities in Germany', p.26.
[104] For instance, TEXUS 36 does not appear on the list of ESA funded sounding rocket missions for 1997-1999. (Seibert & Herfs (1997), table 2).
[105] Cröll *et al.* (1999), 'Measurement of Temperature Fluctuations and Microscopic Growth Rates in a Silicon Floating Zone on TEXUS 36', p.533.

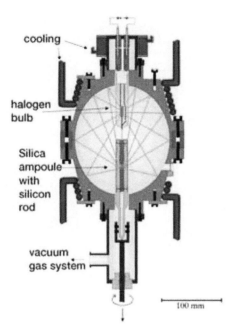

cooling

halogen
bulb

Silica
ampoule
with
silicon
rod

vacuum
gas system

100 mm

Figure 16.32 A cross-section of the mirror furnace as used on TEXUS 36. The restricted space and power available on spacecraft led to the development of these small furnaces. (The internal diameter is only 100 mm / 4 inches).

(Seibert *et al.* (2001), figure 2.3.2.3)

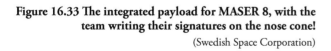

14 May 1999   MASER 8

Originally scheduled for April 1998, MASER 8 was finally launched in May 1999, the delay of one year caused by the loss of a MASER service module on a previous rocket flight.[106] MASER 8 carried four physical science microgravity experiments, flown in the experimental modules GABRIEL-2, JET, CODAG and TRUE.[107] Two were from Italy, one was from Belgium, and one was a pan-European experiment funded by ESA. The CODAG experiment was interesting in that it simulated the early phase of Brownian motion-driven particle aggregation in a proto-planetary dust cloud, and included a live video display of the deployed dust cloud.[108]

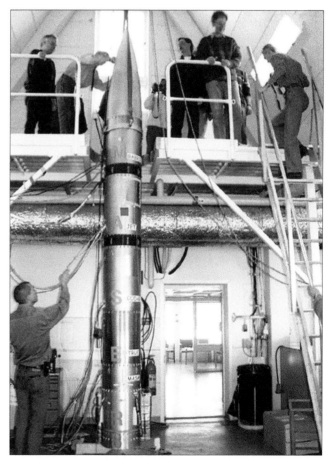

Figure 16.33 The integrated payload for MASER 8, with the team writing their signatures on the nose cone!

(Swedish Space Corporation)

[106] The one year launch delay was caused by the loss of "a required MASER service module in an unfortunate rocket test flight" (Huijser *et al.* (1999), p.511). (Presumably the MERMAID mission on 26 January 1998).

[107] Seibert & Herfs (1997), 'Microgravity Science from ESA's Microgravity Sounding Rocket Projects (Life and Physical Sciences)', Table 2.

[108] Huijser *et al.* (1999), 'Cosmic Dust Aggregation in Microgravity: flight report of the CODAG module on MASER 8'.

Figure 16.34 The MASER 8 payload (complete with signatures!) being loaded into the Skylark launch tower at Esrange. The white Goldfinch boost motor is already in the gantry behind.
(See Figure 16.1 for the next image in this sequence.)

(Swedish Space Corporation)

Launch took place at 13:33 local time. The payload successfully reached an altitude of 260 km (162 miles), and made a safe re-entry and parachute landing 78 km (48 miles) downrange. Recovery took just an hour and 32 minutes, the payload simply being slung underneath the helicopter. All the experiments operated successfully.

Payload Recovery

Figures 16.35, 16.36 and 16.37 Recovery of the MASER 8 payload from 78 km (48 miles) downrange. Very different to recovery conditions at Woomera! The snow helped avoid damage to the payload on landing, which was why these launches took place in winter or spring. [109]

(Swedish Space Corporation)

[109] Franke (2001), 'Program Description and User Scenario TEXUS/MAXUS/MINITEXUS', p.935F/3.

Ten months later, TEXUS 37 and 38 were launched from Esrange only a week apart, so forming a double campaign, the first since TEXUS 25/26 in 1990. TEXUS 37 carried five experiments, three dealing with gravitational biology, one with solidification (all German funded), and one studying fluid physics (ESA funded).[110]

A new technical development was included on these two missions, an adapted low cost GPS (Global Positioning System) receiver[111] for tracking purposes. This had been developed during the preceding years by the DLR (The German equivalent of the RAE), with the expectation of reducing overall system cost compared to conventional radar tracking systems, and to provide the basis for the prediction of an instantaneous impact point (IIP) for range safety purposes.[112] In addition, the telemetry system was vastly improved compared with Skylark's earlier days:

The telemetry is a PCM type of telemetry transmitting all experiment data (analog and digital) in real time to the ground stations and the blockhouse. This telemetry is very powerful and by far sufficient enough to serve 4-5 independent experiment modules as well as status and function of the service systems.....In addition the telemetry system is equipped with a RF-deck which gives the capability to transmit by two independent RF-transmitters 2 TV-images with commercial standard quality real time down to the receiving stations and routed into the blockhouse.[113]

The solidification experiment was a refinement of that launched on TEXUS 34 in 1996, and this time was more successful.[115] It was hoped that this type of research would help with the development of magnetic composite materials

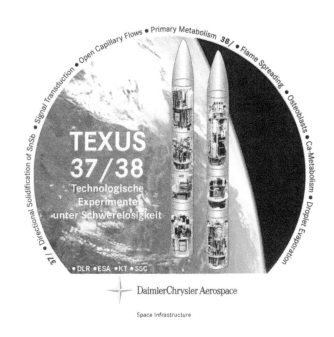

Figure 16.38 The University of Bonn was responsible for two of the life science experiments on TEXUS 37, and produced this logo.
(University of Bonn)[114]

---

[110] Frings *et al.* (1999), 'Scientific Sounding Rocket and Balloon Activities in Germany', p.26.
[111] This provides an interesting illustration of how the performance of electronic devices had outstripped those of rocketry in general. The ARM-60B 32 bit microprocessor based receiver would have had the equivalent of over a million transistors in it, i.e. roughly a million times more processing power in the same space and mass of one valve (vacuum tube) used in the first Skylark experiments. If the Skylark rocket motor had improved by the same factor, it would have had an initial thrust of 12,000,000,000 lbf - greater than 1000 Saturn V moon rockets at lift-off!
[112] Montenbruck *et al.* (2001), 'A GPS receiver for Space Applications'.
[113] Franke (2001), 'Program Description and User Scenario TEXUS/MAXUS/MINITEXUS', p.935F/3.
[114] *www.spacebio.uni-bonn.de/forschung/srocket.htm* , last accessed July 2014.
[115] Kammler *et al.* (1996), 'Unidirectional solidification of a peritectic SnSb-alloy'.

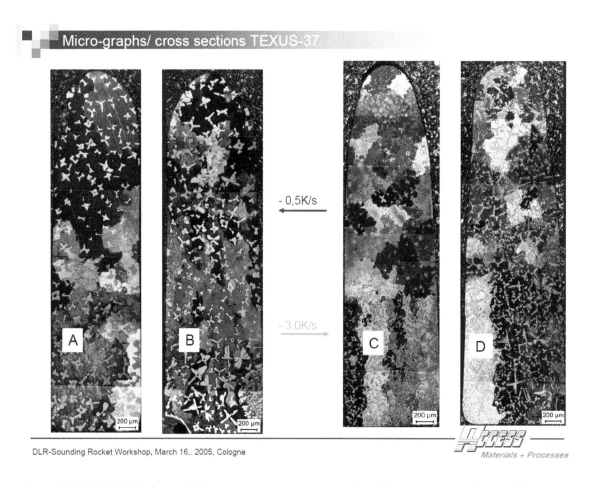

Micro-graphs/ cross sections TEXUS-37

- 0,5K/s

- 3,0K/s

A   B   C   D

200 μm   200 μm   200 μm   200 μm

DLR-Sounding Rocket Workshop, March 16,. 2005, Cologne

Figure 16.39 TEXUS 37 – the solidification experiment: micrographs of the segregation of the two different alloys (antimony and tin) at different cooling rates under micro-gravity.

(Kammler *et al.* (2005), p.9)

---

02 April 2000   TEXUS 38

As noted above, **TEXUS 38** was launched only a week after TEXUS 37. Launch was at 09:34 local time, and the payload successfully reached an altitude of 250 km (155 miles). The payload mass was some 370 kg (816 lb) and microgravity lasted for 5 minutes and 52 seconds.[116] Unusually for a TEXUS mission, it appears to have been funded entirely by ESA.[117] There were three microgravity experimental modules on board, two on the physics of combustion and one on cell and molecular biology: [118]

The Spanish combustion experiment was designed to obtain further knowledge on the basic combustion processes controlling the initiation and spread of fires in spacecraft, such the Shuttle, MIR and International Space Station[119] (Flames behave very differently in microgravity because convection does not carry the hot combustion products away from the fuel source, for instance a match will extinguish itself).

TEM SEN 3: Flame spreading under forced flow conditions; University of Madrid

TEM 06-25: Signal transduction of Osteoblasts (Cell and molecular biology); Universities of Marburg and Leuven

TEM EVA: Droplet combustion experiments; CNRS Orleans.

---

[116] Kayser-Threde GmbH press release on TEXUS-38, 6 April 2000, *www.kayser-threde.de/en/press/news_detail.php?id=37* , last accessed July 2014.

[117] Frings *et al.* (1999), 'Scientific Sounding Rocket and Balloon Activities in Germany', p.26.

[118] ESA EEA database - TEXUS 38, last accessed July 2014.

[119] ESA EEA database - TEXUS 38, 'Flame spreading under forced flow conditions' (Sánchez–Tarifa & Lázaro), last accessed July 2014.

All the experiments worked well during the flight, although after the parachute failed during landing, the payload was severely damaged. This showed one of the benefits of the new communications systems, as by then the experimental data had been transmitted to the ground.

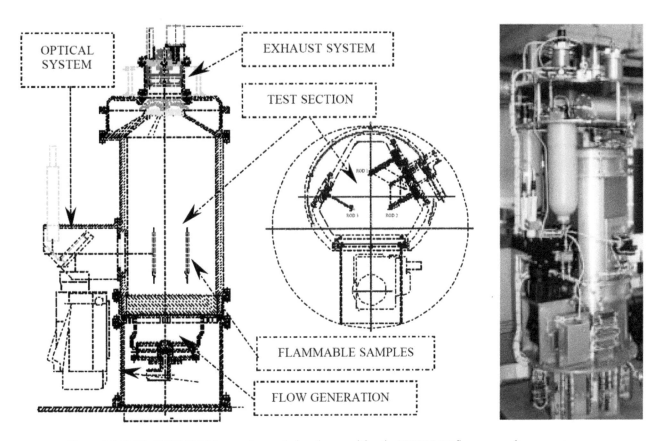

Figure 16.40 The TEM-SEN 3 experimental chamber used for the TEXUS 38 flame spreading experiment. Its complexity is typical of the TEXUS and MASER microgravity modules.

(Sánchez–Tarifa & Lázaro (2001), figure 2)

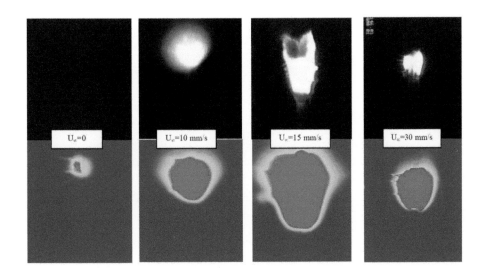

Figure 16.41 The resulting flame visualisation at different flow conditions. Top: visible images. Bottom: IR images. Flow going from bottom to top of the images.

(Sánchez–Tarifa & Lázaro (2001), figure 4)

2001	**2002**	**2003**	**2004**	**2005**
TEXUS 39 (May)	MASER 9 (March)	TEXUS 40 (April)	TEXUS 41 (May)	MASER 10 (March)

Table 16.9 The last five Skylark missions.

(Key: red = German national, pink = ESA programme)

SKYLARK LAUNCHES AND SCIENCE 2001 – 2005

08 May 2001   TEXUS 39

The last five years

As shown above, from 2001 until the last launch in 2005, Skylark launches occurred at the rate of only one a year. This was also a quieter time at Esrange, for instance in the preceding year, (2000), TEXUS 37 and 38 had been the only two sounding rocket launches.[120] Activity picked up a little in 2001, although even then there were only two launches to above 100 km, those of MAXUS 4 and TEXUS 39.

After several launch delays, **TEXUS 39** finally cleared the Skylark launch tower at Esrange at 11:55 local time on the 8th May 2001, a year after its predecessor TEXUS 38. TEXUS 39's microgravity payload successfully reached an altitude of 250 km and landed 69 km downrange.[121] An Orion GPS receiver was flown on the service module for evaluation, and with the exception of a brief gap following lift-off, successfully tracked the position and velocity of the payload from launch to re-entry.[122]

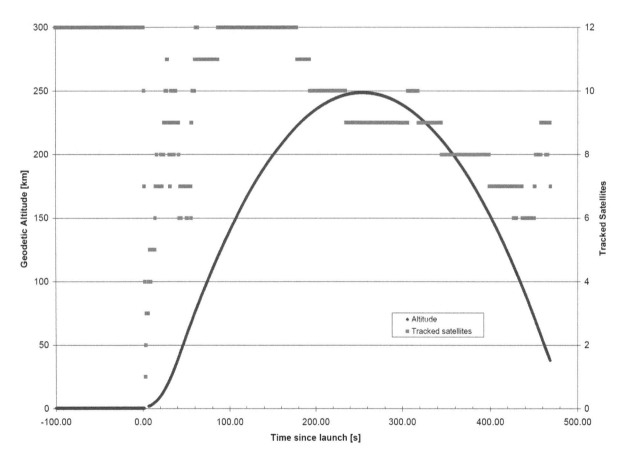

Figure 16.42 The trajectory of TEXUS 39 showing the altitude of the payload and number of tracked GPS satellites - during the flight the GPS receiver tracked between 6 and 12 satellites at any one time. It is interesting to compare this with the 128 km of an early Skylark trajectory such as SL04 (Figure 5.34), and worth a mention that when Skylark SL04 was launched in November 1957, there was only one Earth satellite in orbit (Sputnik 1), and that had flat batteries!

(Montenbruck & Markgraf (2001), figure 2.1)

---

[120] For a list of launches from Esrange, go to *www.sscspace.com/Products-Services/rocket-balloon-services/launch-services-esc/esrange-space-center* , and click on "List of all rocket launches". (Last accessed July 2014).

[121] DLR web page *www.weblab.dlr.de/rbrt/GPSNavPast/Max4Tex39/Max4Tex39.html* (last accessed April 2013), and *www.kayser-threde.de/en/press/news_detail.php?id=46* , last accessed July 2014).

[122] Montenbruck & Markgraf (2001), 'Texus-39 Orion GPS Tracking System - Flight Report', p.3.

Module	Experiment	Institute	Academic Field
TEM 06-21	Second Messenger Levels in Gravitactic Cilates	DLR Cologne	Gravitational biology
Ditto	Primary Metabolism of Plant Cells	University of Tübingen	Gravitational biology
TEM 06-16	Vesicle Transport in Plants	Universities of Hannover and Hamburg	Gravitational Biology
TEM 01-5	Marangoni Migration in Montectic Alloys	TU Chemnitz	Metals
TEM 03-4	ARTEX - Aerogel-Furnace for Metallic Alloys	DLR Cologne	Technology of Metals

Table 16.10 The microgravity experiments flown on TEXUS 39.

(After Preu et al, (2003) and Montenbruck & Markgraf (2001)

TEXUS 39 was launched from Esrange just over a week after ESA's MAXUS 4 high latitude sounding rocket had been launched from the same site. It was therefore part of a 'double campaign', as previously carried out with TEXUS 37 and TEXUS 38. This was done to share the effort of preparation and launching, it reduced the costs significantly,[123] and reflected the way in which Skylark had been launched in 'campaigns' from Woomera and Sardinia in earlier years.

The TEXUS 39 payload comprised five German biological and material sciences experiments in four separate modules, see table 16.10 above.

A report of the time notes that the proportion of sounding rocket life science (especially gravitational biology) experiments was increasing, and by 2003 amounted to over 50% of those flown.[124] The report concluded that sounding rockets were recognised as an essential tool for many experiments in space, as a complementary tool to ground-based and satellite investigations and as an educational and training tool for students and young scientists. Hence, sounding rockets remained an important part of the German microgravity programme.

It also noted that at the time (2003) microgravity research was characterised by a lack of manned long-duration flight opportunities, as the eras of Spacelab and MIR had ended in 1998 and 2001 respectively, and the International Space Station was still under construction. Hence, sounding rockets remained an important part of the German microgravity programme.[125]

---

16 March 2002   MASER 9

The following spring, **MASER 9** was launched from the Esrange Space Centre. The payload successfully reached an altitude of 258 km (160 miles), providing six minutes and five seconds of microgravity.[126] It was quiet at Esrange that year - this was the only sounding rocket launch!

Figures 16.43 and 16.44 MASER 9 launch preparations. As with MASER 8, the team added their signatures to the nose cone.

(Swedish Space Corporation)

---

[123] Preu *et al,* (2003), 'Utilization of Sounding Rockets and Balloons in the German Space Programme'.
[124] Preu *et al,* (2003), p.44.
[125] Preu *et al,* (2003), Conclusion.
[126] Larsson *et al.* (2003), 'Report on the MASER 9 Microgravity Rocket Mission', p.129.

Figure 16.45 MASER 9 launched at Esrange in March 2002.
(Swedish Space Corporation)

The mission was funded by ESA with the SSC as launch contractor. The payload comprised five separate modules containing seven biological and material sciences experiments, provided by a wide range of European research organisations, see table 16.11 below.

To take one example, the ITEL project included the development of a complex new module for MASER 9. Its purpose of was to analyse the fluid dynamics of an evaporating liquid in weightlessness, [127] this being a preliminary step in the preparation of the CIMEX (Convection and Interfacial Mass Exchange) program, foreseen for the ISS (International Space Station).[128]

MASER 9's payload successfully landed 68 km downrange. Two helicopters were used for recovery, one for the biological samples, and one for the payload. The samples were back in the laboratories within one hour and 25 minutes of the launch.[129]

Module	Experiment	Institute	Academic Field
Lymphosig	Signal transduction and Genetic Expression in T-Lymphocytes	ETH Zurich, Switzerland	Gravitational biology
Thyrosig	Responses of in vitro cultures of differentiated, functional Epithelial Follicular Cells from Thyroid	University of Udine, Italy	Gravitational biology
MDB (Modular Bioreactor)	Effect of microgravity on Chondrocytes (Codi)	ETH Zurich, Switzerland	Gravitational Biology
	Effect of microgravity on blood vessel tissue (VeRa)	LEBAO-Hannover, Germany	Gravitational Biology
	Effect of microgravity on Thyroid Cell Clusters (ThyRex)	University of Udine, Italy	Gravitational Biology
ITEL	Interfacial Turbulence in Evaporating Liquids	MRC-ULB, Belgium	Fluid Physics
Cyrène-2	Convective boiling and Condensation of Ammonia	CEA Grenoble, France	Fluid Physics

Table 16.11 The microgravity experiments flown on MASER 9.
(ESA EEA database - MASER 9, and Larsson et al. (2003), p.130)

[127] ESA EEA database - MASER 9, 'Interfacial Turbulence in Evaporating Liquids' (Colinet &Legros), last accessed July 2014.
[128] Colinet et al. (2002), 'Interfacial Turbulence in Evaporating Liquids: Theory and Preliminary Results of the ITEL-MASER 9 Sounding Rocket Experiment'.
[129] Larsson et al. (2003), 'Report on the MASER 9 Microgravity Rocket Mission', p.129.

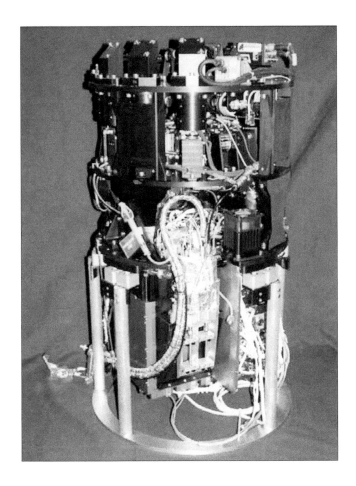

Figure 16.46 The "Interfacial Turbulence in Evaporating Liquids" (ITEL) payload equipment, a complex module first flown on MASER 9.

(Löth *et al.* (2002), figure 1)

The ITEL experiment was reasonably successful, but had a technical problem, which meant that the cell pressure and gas flow rates fluctuated too much for reliable quantitative results to be obtained.[130] However this was a lot better than for two of the other modules. The MDB module (Modular Bioreactor) was slow to perform which affected two of the experiments in it,[131] and an electrical fault on the Thyrosig module meant that no results at all were obtained.[132]

---

08 April 2003   TEXUS 40

In contrast to some of the preceding years, 2003 was a busy year at Esrange, with 54 launches, although 50 of these formed a January meteorological rocket campaign taking wind measurements. Next, on the 1st and 8th April, the MAXUS 5 and **TEXUS 40** sounding rockets were launched, forming another 'double' campaign, as had been carried out two years previously with MAXUS 4 and TEXUS 39.

TEXUS 40 successfully reached an altitude of 246 km (153 miles), and provided over five minutes of microgravity. The payload was soon located using the GPS recovery system, a helicopter transported it back to Esrange, and scientists had access to their experiments only about one hour later.[133] The payload comprised four independent experiment modules as the following rather splendid diagram shows, see figure 16.47 overleaf.

Other events - Mars Express and Beagle 2

Also in 2003, ESA's Mars Express mission was launched from Baikonur in Russia on 2nd June. On board the Mars Express Orbiter was the British Mars Lander, Beagle 2, its purpose to search for signs of life on Mars. After a journey of six months Beagle 2 was released on a ballistic trajectory on 19th December 2003, after which it coasted for six days and was due to enter the Martian atmosphere at over 20,000 km/h on the morning of 25th December.

---

[130] Colinet *et al.* (2002), Conclusion.
[131] More specifically the experiments were "hampered by the failure of the bioreactor to fix the products before the end of weightlessness". ESA EEA database - MASER 9, 'VeRa' and 'ThyRex' experiments. (Last accessed July 2014).
[132] ESA EEA database - MASER 9, 'Responses of in vitro cultures of differentiated, functional epithelial follicular cells from thyroid', last accessed July 2014.
[133] *www.kayser-threde.de/en/press/news_detail.php?id=84*, last accessed July 2014. See also the DLR website page for TEXUS 40, *www.dlr.de/rd/ desktopdefault.aspx/tabid-2284/3422_read-5131/*, last accessed July 2014.

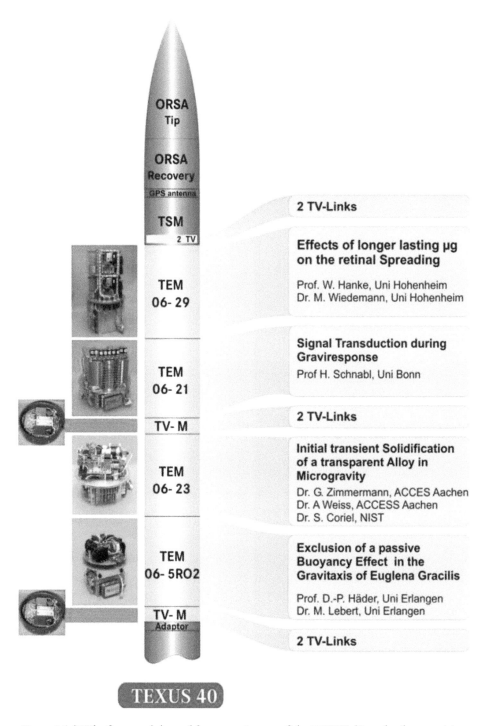

Figure 16.47 The four modules and four experiments of the TEXUS 40 payload, comprising one physics and three biology experiments. Of note is the number of TV links to the ground.

(Astrium)

Sadly, nothing more was heard from Beagle 2, and although the Mars Express Orbiter successfully went into orbit around the planet, Beagle 2 was subsequently declared a loss. At present, it can only be speculated why it failed to land successfully,[134] as ESA refused to give Beagle 2 some of the spare mass available to allow a radio link during the entry phase.[135]

---

[134] The web page *www.beagle2.com/index.htm* included links to summarising and full reports. (Last accessed April 2013).

[135] Pillinger (2010), *My Life on Mars*, p.344. This book is well worth reading, and tells of the incredible amount of political infighting and horse-trading that goes on within ESA, and reveals the forces within ESA that were ranged against Beagle 2.

 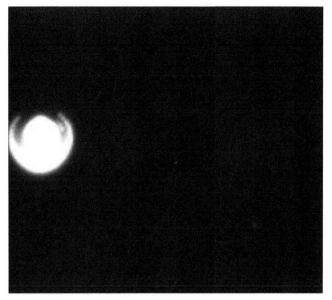

Figures 16.48 and 16.49 Left: A computer generated image of Beagle 2's release from the Mars Express Orbiter. Right: The last actually seen of Beagle 2,[136] a 'webcam' photograph taken after separation on 19 December 2003, with Beagle 2 about 20 metres from the Orbiter. (Copyright ESA, All Rights Reserved Beagle 2)

Many of the academic and industrial organisations that had worked on Skylark were involved with the design of Beagle 2,[137] so it can be said that Beagle 2 was based on the heritage that Skylark had help provide.

| 02 December 2004 | TEXUS 41 |

In contrast to the activity at Esrange in 2003, 2004 was a quiet year, with only three sounding rocket launches. Of these, MAXUS 6 and TEXUS 41 formed another 'double' launch, on the 22nd November and the 2nd December respectively. TEXUS 41 was the 41st [138] and last TEXUS

rocket to be powered by Skylark rocket motors. The first had been TEXUS 1 in 1977, over 25 years earlier, longer than Skylarks had been used for British payloads.[139]

TEXUS 41 successfully reached an altitude of 227 km (141 miles), and landed 85 km (53 miles) downrange to the north of Esrange. The first stage was a Goldfinch IID with a nominal thrust of 189 kN and a burning time of 3.7 seconds, the second a Raven XI with a nominal thrust of 83 kN and a burning time of 39 seconds.[140]

The TEXUS 41 payload carried four German biological and material sciences microgravity experiments:

Module	Experiment	Institute	Academic Field
TEM 06-16	Influences to Transport of Viscles in Endocytosis Pollen Tubes	University of Hanover	Gravitational biology
TEM 06-24	Critical Velocities in Open Capillary Flow	ZARM, University of Bremen	Fluid Physics
TEM 06-29	Effect of Microgravity on the Retinal Spreading Depression	University of Hohenheim	Gravitational Biology
TEM 03-4	Solidification of a Hypo-Eutectic ALSi Alloys under the influence of a Rotating Magnetic Field (ARTEXplus)	DLR Porz	Metals

Table 16.12 The microgravity experiments flown on TEXUS 41.

(Swedish Space Corporation & Steinback *et al.* (2005))

---

[136] This separation photograph was taken by the orbiter's Visual Monitoring Camera (VMC), which four years later was used to provide unique wide-angle views of Mars (Ormston *et al.* (c.2011). There were at least four of these separation images, although apparently not all were released by ESA (Pillinger (2010), p.322).

[137] See for instance *www.beagle2.com/resources/people.htm* , last accessed July 2014.

[138] TEXUS 17 and 18 had been launched by Nike-Black Brant 5B motors, TEXUS 3B and 14B were 'repeats'.

[139] The first British National Progamme launch was in 1957, the last all British use was SL1299 in 1979, a span of 22 years.

[140] SSC webpage *www.ssc.se/?id=7134* , originally accessed March 2010. See also the DLR web page for TEXUS 41, *www.dlr.de/rd/desktopdefault.aspx/ tabid-2282/3421_read-5228/* , last accessed April 2013.

The TEM 06-24 capillary experiment followed on from one on TEXUS 37, the TEM 03-4 'ARTEXplus' was a refinement of that flown on TEXUS 39.[141]

---

02 May 2005   MASER 10

The last ever Skylark launch

There were six sounding rocket launches from Esrange in 2005, the first four being meteorological rockets, and the fifth **MASER 10**. This mission was funded by ESA, with

SSC as launch contractor, and finally launched very early in the morning of Monday 2nd May at 07:00 local time, after a delay caused by high winds.[142]

MASER 10 was the fifth of the MASER series to incorporate a Skylark motor, but also the last ever Skylark launch. Despite having been manufactured some ten years earlier, the final remaining Skylark motor successfully powered the MASER 10 mission by launching the 351 kg (774 lb) payload to an altitude of 252 km (157 miles), providing more than six minutes of microgravity.

Figures 16.50 & 16.51
Above: MASER 10 payload assembly – the parts being weighed. The fully assembled payload had a mass of 370 kg (816 lb). Right: the stacked payload being attended to.
(Swedish Space Corporation)
(See Figure 16.1 for a view of MASER 10 being loaded into the launch tower)

[141] Steinback *et al.* (2005) 'Directional Solidification of Binary AlSi Allays in Diffusive and Convective Regimes'. *ESA SP-590*
[142] Florin *et al.* (2005), 'The MASER-10 Microgravity Rocket Flight', p. 531. *ESA SP-590.* See also *www.esa.int/Our_Activities/Human_Spaceflight/ Research/Successful_flight_of_Maser_10_rocket_marking_the_end_of_a_historic_era_ends_with_a_hard_landing* , (last accessed May 2013).

Figures 16.52 & 16.53 Above: 3, 2, 1, FIRE! - MASER 10 being launched at 07:00 local time. Right: - the last Skylark launch – MASER 10 leaves the Skylark tower at Esrange.

(Swedish Space Corporation)

The payload comprised five experiments housed in four modules:

Module	Experiment	Institute	Academic Field
BIM (Biology in Microgravity)	Role of Microgravity on actin metabolism in mammalian cells (ACTIN)	University, Utrecht	Biology
	Influence of microgravity on the activation of NF-kB (AMUSE)	University of Amsterdam	Biology
TRUE-2	Thermal Radiation forces in Unsteady conditions Experiment	MARS Center, Naples, Italy	Fluid Physics
ITEL-2	Interfacial Turbulence in Evaporating Liquids	MRC-ULB, Belgium	Fluid Physics
CDIC	Chemically Driven Interfacial Convection	T.U. Dresden, Germany MRC-ULB, Belgium	Fluid Physics

Table 16.13 The five microgravity experiments flown on MASER 10. (The TRUE-2 module was based on that that flown on MASER 8, and ITEL-2 was a refight of ITEL on MASER 9).

(ESA EEA database - MASER 10, & Florin et al. (2005), table 2) [143]

[143] Also see *www.esa.int/Our_Activities/Human_Spaceflight/Research/More_about_Maser_10_payload* , (last accessed July 2014).

Figure 16.54 Left: Scientists monitoring the ITEL-2 experiment during flight. Both the ITEL-2 and CDIC modules included video cameras, the images transmitted to the ground during flight.[144]
(Swedish Space Corporation)

Figure 16.55 Right: Scientists monitoring the CDIC experiment during flight. Based on the real time images, they were able to adjust the progress of the experiment by remote control.[145]
(Swedish Space Corporation)

Monitoring during flight

On the MASER 10 mission, more improvements to the in-flight telemetry system were implemented, improving the way scientists could monitor their experiments.

In addition to the local monitoring at Esrange (shown above), scientists in Belgium and Italy were able to follow their experiments live during flight via ISDN links to their countries. A digital video system (DVS) was used as the main video system for the first time, and a digital video transmitter replaced the analogue version used on earlier flights. The video channels shared a 5 Mbit/s link to the ground[146] - a far cry from the 40-120 samples per second of telemetry data available on the first Skylarks!

A bumpy landing

Unfortunately, not all went well at the end of the MASER 10 flight. Because of a fault in the recovery system, the main parachute did not deploy, and after the drogue chute cut, the payload fell more than 3 km onto a frozen lake.[147]

Surprisingly, most of the scientific samples remained intact for further analysis. Overall, the experiments were 100% successful during the flight, and despite the hard payload landing, success was estimated at 90%.[148]

In particular, almost all the biological examples of the ACTIN experiment and three quarters of those from the AMUSE experiments were undamaged, as was the data stored on flash memory. All image data from the three ITEL-2 video tapes

[144] Florin *et al.* (2005), 'The MASER-10 Microgravity Rocket Flight', p.532. *ESA SP-590.*
[145] Florin *et al.* (2005), p.535.
[146] Florin *et al.* (2005), p.536.
[147] Florin *et al.* (2005), pp.352 & 536.
[148] Florin *et al.* (2005), p.531.

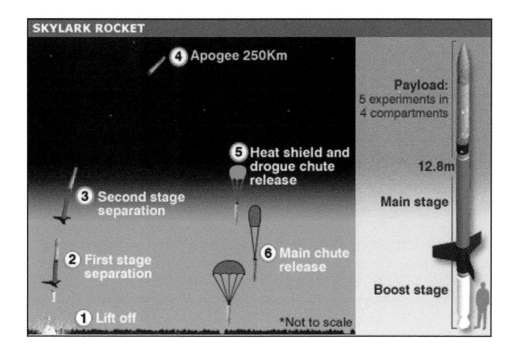

Figure 16.56 MASER 10 – the sequence of Skylark's last flight.
(BBC online News)[149]

and the CDIC on-board flash memory were retrieved, but recovery of high rate sampled experiment data from cracked ITEL-2 flash memory had to be referred to specialists.[150] All data from the TRUE-2 experiment was digitally download-ed during the flight, so the results from this experiment were unaffected by the hard landing, showing the value of the new communication techniques.

Figures 16.57 and 16.58 A scene reminiscent of the early days of Skylark - the sad remains of the MASER 10 payload after landing 96 km (60 miles) downrange. With classic understatement, it was reported, "The impact was very hard and the payload was damaged".
(Swedish Space Corporation)

[149] *http://news.bbc.co.uk/1/hi/sci/tech/4490253.stm*, last accessed July 2014).
[150] Florin *et al.* (2005), 'The MASER-10 Microgravity Rocket Flight', pp.532 & 535. *ESA SP-590*.

Media comments

This last Skylark launch attracted considerable of media attention, for instance the BBC News website reported:[151]

> A hugely successful and largely unsung British space programme is about to draw to a close with the final launch of a Skylark sounding rocket.
>
> The vehicle, which first flew in 1957, became a very inexpensive but effective way of carrying scientific experiments into suborbital space.
>
> It lost official UK government support in the late 1970s but sufficient motors were left to continue research flights. The 441st and last Skylark will blast off from Sweden on Sunday.[152]

Even ESA noted that this was Skylark's last flight:

> Many European scientists and engineers observed this mission not only with a scientific interest, but also with very sentimental personal feelings, as the MASER 10 mission was launched into space by the 441st and last Skylark launcher system, which had marked European scientific research in the upper atmosphere and in open space for nearly half a century. Practically every European researcher involved in space experimentation has been involved at one moment in her or his professional life in a mission employing a Skylark rocket.[153]

A FUTURE WITHOUT SKYLARK

As noted above, MASER 10 was powered by the last remaining Skylark 7 motor assembly. The motor supply had simply run out, because production by ROF Bridgewater had ended in November 1994, and subsequently the stock remaining from the 'last time buy' had been used up. John Harlow:

> Towards the end there were a lot of problems associated with the end-of-production of the motors as materials sourcing became an issue - changes of specification, legislation as to use of materials (especially asbestos used in 'Durestos', adhesives, solvents etc). The design authority for the filled motor was Westcott. Bridgewater

(which is now at last closed - what a slow death!) was 'just' a filling facility and one which did a good job. The last filled motors were at Westcott for a considerable time (in S10 building) before being shipped for use.[154]

Indeed, as noted before, the only reason that Skylark had kept going at all for the final ten years was that production had been taken over by Sounding Rocket Services Ltd in Bristol.

The fact that the Skylark rocket motor was no longer available did not stop the TEXUS and MASER microgravity programmes. By now of course, the payload was no longer made in the UK, and others were happy to fill the gap left by the demise of the Skylark propulsion system. Although Black Brant rocket vehicles (distant cousins of the Skylark) had been used in the past by both the TEXUS and MASER projects, the choice fell on a new rocket vehicle to be developed in conjunction with Brazilian agencies, the VSB-30.[155]

The VSB-30

The Brazilian made VSB-30 sounding rocket vehicle came into existence because of the decision by British Aerospace to discontinue production of Skylark rocket motors.[156] This forced the German DLR[157] to look elsewhere, so they could continue the TEXUS microgravity sounding rocket programme.

The DLR and its predecessors had had a technical relationship with the Brazilian CTA[158] since at least 1996 when it had been proposed that the German Mini-TEXUS payload be fitted to the first stage of the Brazilian SONDA III. This had resulted in a new single stage vehicle, the VS-30.[159]

In common with similar research centres and organisations, the CTA had a small home market for meteorological size sounding rockets, supplemented by the occasional foreign sale. Because of this, "the civilian rocket industry did not blossom due to the limited number of flights".[160] (The same could of course be said of the UK!) However, by 2001 the DLR had drawn up a list of sounding rocket/motor requirements to meet the needs of the TEXUS programme and

---

[151] *http://news.bbc.co.uk/1/hi/sci/tech/4490253.stm*, dateline Friday 29th April 2005, last accessed July 2014.

[152] In the event, high winds delayed the launch until Monday.

[153] *www.esa.int/Our_Activities/Human_Spaceflight/Research/Successful_flight_of_Maser_10_rocket_marking_the_end_of_a_historic_era_ends_with_a_hard_landing*, last accessed July 2014.

[154] John Harlow, personal correspondence, June 2009.

[155] At least Thatcherism was of benefit to the Brazilian aerospace industry!

[156] BAe had become responsible for the motors as well as the Skylark vehicle, after Royal Ordnance (RO) was bought by BAe in 1987. However, RO did not pass to Matra Marconi Space in 1994, when that company acquired British Aerospace Space Systems Ltd.

[157] In 1989 the DFVLR (The German equivalent of the RAE) had been renamed the DFLR (*Deutsche Forschungsanstalt für Luft- und Raumfahrt* / German Research Institute for Aviation and Space Flight"), and in the same year DARA (*Deutsche Agentur für Raumfahrtangelegenheiten* / German Agency for Space Flight Affairs) was formed. In 1997 they were merged to become the DLR (*Deutsches Zentrum für Luft- und Raumfahrt* / German Centre for Aviation and Spaceflight).

[158] The Brazilian CTA (Centro Ténico Aeroespacial) was the research centre of the Brazilian Air Force, and led national rocket development.

[159] Palmerio *et al.* (2003), 'The Development of the VSB-30 Sounding Rocket Vehicle', p.137. *ESA SP-530*.

[160] Palmerio *et al.* (2003), p.137.

improve dispersion compared to Skylark. Hence, in 2001, the CTA had been invited to a meeting in Germany where proposals for the development of such a sounding rocket to replace Skylark were set forth by members of government agencies and private industries.

As a result, the DLR and CTA developed a partnership where they agreed to share in the development of a Skylark replacement vehicle, with the DLR and German industry carrying out much of the vehicle design, and the CTA being responsible for the development and manufacture of a new S31 booster motor. This would be used with the existing Brazilian S30 motor as sustainer; together they would power a new two-stage VSB-30 (VS-30 Boosted) sounding rocket.[161]

The Brazilian rocket motors to be used were some 119 mm (4.7 inches) greater in diameter than Skylark (557 mm compared to 438 mm), so the Germans designed a new payload adapter to enable the existing TEXUS payload and modules (designed for Skylark) to be used. The vehicle retained the three-fin configuration used by Skylark, so that the existing Skylark launcher at Esrange could be used with only minor modifications.[162]

The development of the VSB-30 duly proceeded, during which "… CTA and DLR joined forces in an unprecedented level of cooperation…" [163] However, progress was seri-

ously hampered when in August 2003 a massive explosion destroyed the Brazilian VLS-1 satellite launcher rocket and its pad, prior to the third launch attempt. Twenty-one people died, including the VSB-30 technical manager,[164] and the resulting investigation aggravated the delay. Despite this setback, in October 2004 a successful qualification flight of the VSB-30 was carried out from the Brazilian Alcantara Launch Site.[165]

Thus, following the final Skylark flight in May 2005 (MASER 10), the Skylark tower was modified,[166] and on 1st December that year the TEXUS 42/EML-1 mission was successfully launched by the first VSB-30 fired from Esrange.[167] This established it as the successor to Skylark, and by the end of May 2014, the VSB-30 had been used to successfully launch eleven TEXUS and MASER microgravity missions.[168]

SUMMARY AND CONCLUSION

The Skylark sounding rocket had lasted for nearly fifty years. As described in these pages, design and development had started in 1955, the first flight was in February 1957, the last in May 2005. There were 441 launches in all, with a peak of 35 in 1970. By the end it was the longest running rocket programme of all time,[169] and if longevity is a measure, one of the most successful.

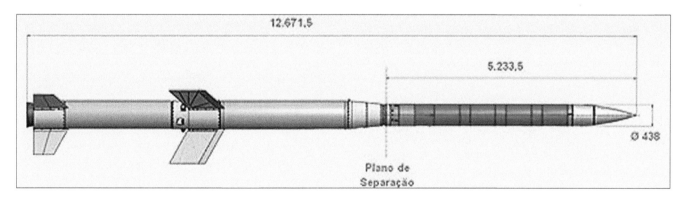

Figure 16.59 The VSB-30 sounding rocket, comprising the S-31and S-30 solid fuel motors and a 'Skylark' payload.
(Centro Ténico Aeroespacial)

[161] Palmerio *et al.* (2003), p.139.
[162] Palmerio *et al.* (2003), p.139.
[163] Palmerio *et al.* (2005), 'Results from the First Flight of the VSB-30 Sounding Rocket', *ESA SP-590*, p.345.
[164] Palmerio *et al.* (2005), p.345.
[165] This was 16 years after the last Skylark flight from Brazil, that of INTERZODIAK II in 1988.
[166] By then the Skylark tower at Esrange had outlasted that at Woomera by 26 years!
[167] For a list of all launches from Esrange, go to *www.sscspace.com/Products-Services/rocket-balloon-services/launch-services-esc* and click on "List of all rocket launches". (Last accessed July 2014).
[168] The eleven comprise TEXUS 42/EML-1, TEXUS 43-50, and MASER 11 & 12.
[169] As described earlier in this book, the rocket that became the Black Brant ('cousin' to Skylark) was first launched in 1959, and later versions are still (in 2014) being manufactured. Thus, it can now claim to have lasted longer than Skylark.
[170] Ken Pounds in 2001, CCBH (2005), *Skylark Sounding Rockets 1957-1972*, & *Prospero* No.2, p.103.

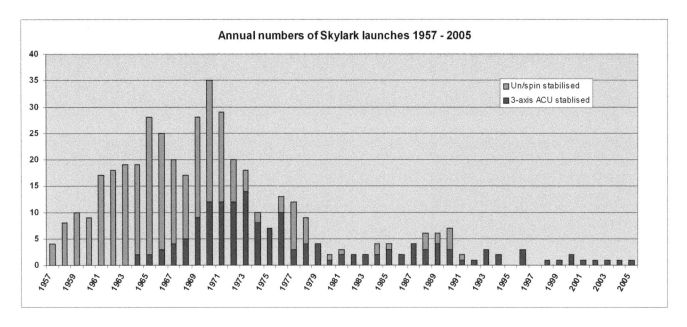

Figure 16.60 The annual numbers of Skylark launches over its full 48 years of use.

Skylark was born from post World War II research into military missile technology, and a scientific desire to explore the unknown. Progress in upper atmosphere research had started after the war in the USA, when captured V-2 rockets were launched with scientific experiments on board. When the V-2 rockets ran out, purpose-made sounding rockets were built. In the UK, the RAE wanted to improve their skills in ballistic missile design, and, spurred on by American achievements, Sir Harrie Massey and the Royal Society were keen to extend their scientific knowledge of the upper atmosphere. This combination resulted in work starting in 1955 on a sounding rocket for civilian purposes, albeit under the auspices of the RAE, and with military uses in mind.

What soon became known as Skylark was nurtured by both military and civilian funding, for instance the rocket range at Woomera had military origins. Hence from the start there was an international dimension, with Australia supplying the range under a joint agreement, and the UK supplying the Skylark vehicles.

On its fourth flight in 1957, Skylark (launched by the Australians) became the first British rocket to leave the atmosphere and reach space. As the diagram above shows, over the next dozen years Skylark rockets were increasingly used to carry a wide range of scientific experiments. At first, these did indeed explore the unknown characteristics of the upper atmosphere, but with the development of the stabilised payload system, experiments became increasingly space oriented, and the field of space science opened up. As the hardware was improved, Skylark became the first sounding

rocket with a payload that could be stabilised in three axes, and for some ten years was the best research vehicle of its kind.[170]

Skylark's international use expanded, with four being used by NASA in 1961, but more importantly, the first European use was by ESRO in 1964. At its peak use of 35 in 1970, half were sponsored by the British National programme, and half by European organisations.

However, Skylark became the victim of the march of progress, in part aided by its own success. The engineering and scientific skills it helped create (and the experiments it flew) were used to build the first British scientific Earth satellites. These began with Ariel I, the world's first international satellite, launched by NASA in 1962. By the early 1970s, it was becoming apparent that for space-based astronomy at least, scientific satellites, funded internationally, were the way forward. Another factor was the vast improvement in electronics, telemetry became much improved, even images could be returned from space, and the sub-orbital sounding rocket's inherent ability to return exposed photographic film to Earth became much less important.

Although sounding rockets remained unparalleled for upper atmosphere research, and despite a successful upper atmosphere auroral activity campaign from Norway in 1977/78, after 21 years the UK's scientific use of Skylark came to a rather abrupt end in 1978. However, by then the production of Skylark rockets had passed to the commercial sector, in the form of BAC (British Aircraft Corporation)[171] in Bristol.

---

[171] Strictly speaking, BAC had been nationalised into British Aerospace (BAe) in 1977.

[172] The author is seeking a volunteer to compile a list!

At this time, in terms of numbers of launches, Skylark was nearly 90% of the way through its operational life, however in terms of years; it was less than half way through! Skylark became increasingly used by the German DFVLR (the equivalent of the RAE). They continued to develop the payload and stabilisation system for their own requirements, particularly in the new field of microgravity research. From 1982 onwards, an increasing number of microgravity sounding rocket activities were funded by the newly formed ESA, both as individual scientific experiments and complete launches.

Skylark's legacy was wide. As far as the original aims were concerned, it did indeed widen the RAE experience in the design of guided weapons. Further, when formed in 1962, the RAE's Space Department was allocated more than half the staff from the Guided Weapons Department, and went on to become the design authority for the Black Arrow satellite launcher. (And that, as they say, is another story!)

On the scientific side, many hundreds of papers were published based on the experiments launched by Skylark over the years,[172] amply repaying the potential Sir Harrie Massey saw in this new tool for scientific research.

In addition, there were benefits unforeseen at the time. The academic pursuit of satellite instrumentation and studies grew out of Skylark work, and the UK's entry into satellite manufacture grew directly out of this.[173]

It provided a unique training ground for scientists, engineers and technicians from the mid 1950s to the 1970s. A PhD student could design an experiment, help built it, fly to Australia, help unpack and re-assemble it, be involved in the excitement of the launch and hopefully have good scientific results at the end. It was viewed as an exceptional way of developing a scientific career, and many such students who were in the right place at the right time have risen to leading positions in their fields. "The nostalgia felt by those who experience[d] a *Skylark* PhD is fuelled by the current lack of any replacement for the horribly realistic management training it provided." [174]

On the wider scene, Skylark and its larger successors were a 'disruptive' technology that had implications in the way that the UK government worked and conducted international relationships, these aspects are of great interest but outside the scope of this book; there are some useful texts for those who wish to learn more.[175]

To sum up, it is worth repeating a phrase from the quotation at the start of this book:

> ... in so large, and so various an *Art* as this of *Experiments,* there are many degrees of usefulness: some may serve for real, and plain *benefit,* without much *delight*: some for *teaching* without apparent *profit*: some for *light* now, and for *use* hereafter; some only for *ornament* and *curiosity*.[176]

[173] Professor Sir Robert Boyd in 2001, CCBH (2005), *Skylark Sounding Rockets 1957-1972*p.40 & *Prospero* No.2, Spring 2005, p.106.
[174] Cruise (2008), *Skylark Ascending*, online article p27, and *Prospero* number 5, Spring 2008, p.61.
[175] Massey & Robins (1986), *History of British Space Science,* and particularly Godwin (2007), *The Skylark Rocket.*
[176] Thomas Sprat (1667), *The History of the Royal Society*, (p.245 of fourth edition).

APPENDIX 1
AN ALPHANUMERIC LIST OF ALL SKYLARK LAUNCHES

(a) UK National Programme

Note: Skylarks missions were numbered long before the launch took place, and if delayed, a mission initiated later on could be launched before one with a lower number.

SL01	1957 Feb.13	SL50	1960 Dec 07	SL137	1964 Sep 01
SL02	1957 May 22	SL51	1960 Apr 12	SL138	1965 May 19
SL03	1957 Jul 23			SL139	1965 May 14
SL04	1957 Nov 13	SL60	1959 Nov 30		
SL05	1958 May 20	SL61	1960 Aug 10	SL140	1965 Mar 17
SL06	1958 Apr 02	SL62	1960 Apr 21	SL141	1965 Mar 25
SL07	1958 Apr 17	SL63	1961 Mar 06		
SL08	1958 Sep 19 (June?)	SL64	1961 Apr 05	SL160	1962 Mar 06
SL09	1958 Jun 19	SL65	1961 Jul 04	SL161	1962 Mar 29
		SL66	1962 Mar 05	SL162	1962 Apr 11
SL10	1960 Jun 16	SL67	1960 Nov 17	SL163	1962 Apr 06
SL11	1958 Dec 03			SL164	1962 Jul 05
SL12	1959 Sep 17	(SL81)	1962 Oct (cancelled)	SL165	1962 Nov 28
SL13	1960 Aug 26	SL81A	1963 Oct 03/02	SL166	1962 Dec 04
SL14	1959 Jul 08	SL82	1962 Oct 15	SL167	1963 Apr 17
SL15	1959 Sep 24	SL83	1961 Nov 24	SL168	1963 Oct 16
SL16	1959 Nov 30	SL84	1963 Mar 01	SL169	1963 Oct 15
SL17	1959 Aug 19	SL85	1963 Mar 11		
SL18	1958 Jun 18	SL86	1963 Aug 02	SL170	1963 Oct 16
SL19	1959 Jul 01	SL87	1963 Sep 05	SL171	1963 Oct 15
		SL87A	1964 Sep 04		
SL20	1964 May 14	SL87B	1965 Mar 03	SL301	1964 Aug 11
SL21	1959 Mar 04	SL88	1964 Feb 04	SL302	1964 Dec 17
SL22	1958 Jun 05	SL88A	1965 Feb 25	SL303	1965 Apr 09
		SL88B	1965 Sep 09	SL304	1966 May 05
SL24	1959 Jul 23	SL88C	1966 Jul 28	SL305	1967 Aug 08
SL25	1961 May 30			SL306	1965 Oct 20
SL26	1961 Jun 07	SL103	1963 Nov 19	SL307	1966 Feb 02
SL27	1962 Nov 22	SL104	1963 Dec 03		
SL28	1962 Aug 29	SL105	1965 Jul 29	SL321	1966 Oct 25
SL29	1963 Jul 25	SL106	1965 Jul 01	SL322	1966 Oct 25
				SL323	1966 Oct 27
SL30	1964 Feb 20	SL108	1962 Sep 20	SL324	1966 Oct 27
SL31	1964 Jul 15	SL109	1962 Aug 15	SL324S	1966 Oct 27
SL32	1964 Jul 17				
SL33	1960 Nov 16	SL114	1962 Nov 13	SL327	1966 Jun 02
SL34	1961 Aug 01	SL115	1963 May 23	SL328	1966 Jun 09
SL35	1961 Nov 08	SL118	1967 Apr 10		
SL35B	1962 Feb 06	SL119	1967 Apr 12	SL361	1965 May 11
SL35C	1962 Jun 06	SL120	1964 Sep 17	SL362	1965 Apr 30
SL36	1961 Feb 13	SL121	1964 Aug 20	SL363	1965 Apr 29
SL37	1961 Oct 24			SL364	1965 Apr 29
SL38	1959 Dec 01	SL126	1963 Jun 18		
SL39	1965 Oct 18	SL127	1963 May 29	SL401	1970 Mar 20
		SL128	1964 Mar 12	SL402	1972 Oct 23
SL40	1961 Sep 27	SL129	1964 Mar 10	SL403	1968 Jul 08
SL42	1961 Dec 06			SL404	1969 May 14
SL43	1961 May 01	SL130	1965 Nov 19	SL405	1966 Dec 08
SL44	1962 Sep 11	SL131	1965 Dec 13	SL406	1967 Mar 14
SL45	1962 Jun 20	SL132	1964 Sep 29	SL407	1967 Nov 01
SL46	1963 Jun 20	SL133	1964 Sep 24	SL408	1968 Mar 20
SL47	1964 Oct 27	SL134	1963 Oct 30		
SL48	1965 Jul 14	SL135	1963 Dec 02	SL421	1966 Jun 23
SL49	1960 Nov 24	SL136	1964 Apr 11	SL422	1966 May 31

SL422A	1967 Dec 01	SL901	1970 Mar 19	SL1221	1974 Nov 01	
SL423	1967 Nov 14	SL902	1971 Aug 05			
SL424	1967 Nov 17	SL903	1971 Dec 10	SL1271	Stability proving round	
		SL904	1970 Nov 20		cancelled 1973	
SL425	1967 Apr 21	SL905	1970 Nov 11	SL1291	1973 Jul 17	
SL426	1967 Apr 04			SL1292	1974 Jul 22	
		SL911	1974 Nov 28	SL1293	1975 Feb 28	
SL461	1965 Apr 29					
SL462	1965 Apr 30	SL921	1970 Mar 12	SL1295	1975 Jul 03	
SL463	1965 Apr 30	SL922	1971 Mar 02	SL1296	1978 Nov 15	
SL464	1965 Apr 29			SL1297	1978 Dec 13	
		SL971	1970 Jul 14	SL1298	1977 Jun 08	
SL481	1966 Nov 18	SL972	1970 Oct 08	SL1299	1979 Mar 01	
		SL973	1971 Oct 07			
SL501	1968 Aug 29	SL974	1971 Oct 24	SL1301	1975 Feb 25	
SL502	1969 Apr 03			SL1302	1976 Jan 30	
SL521	1967 Aug 24	SL1001	1971 Jan 29			
SL522	1967 Aug 29	SL1002	1971 Sep 27	SL1304	1974 Oct 07	
SL523	1968 Jul 23	SL1003	1972 Oct 26	SL1305	1978 May 12	
SL524	1968 Aug 05	SL1004	1973 Mar 14	SL1306	1976 Nov 04	
		SL1005	1972 Dec 11			
SL581	1966 Mar 17			SL1401	discontinued	
SL581A	1966 Dec 14	SL1009	1972 Mar 17	SL1402	1976 Jul 17	
SL581B	1967 Aug 16					
SL582	1966 Apr 10	SL1010	1973 Mar 01/Feb28	SL1421	1977 Nov 17	
SL583	1966 Apr 21	SL1011	1973 Apr 18/17	SL1422	1976 Nov 21	
SL583A	1968 Feb 08	SL1012	1974 Oct 05/04	SL1423	1977 Oct 13	
				SL1424	1978 Nov 10	
SL586	1969 Oct 20	SL1021	1970 Oct 14	SL1425	1976 Dec 11	
		SL1022	1972 Oct 19			
SL601	1968 Dec 04	SL1023	1972 Mar 16	SL1471	1974 Oct 10	
SL602	1969 Nov 18					
SL603	1969 Nov 27	SL1081	1972 Mar 27	SL1501	1976 Jun 17	
SL604	1969 Apr 22	SL1081A	1973 Aug 04	SL1611	cancelled	
SL605	1969 Aug 21					
SL606	1969 Apr 17	SL1101	1971 Nov 30			
		SL1102	1973 Mar 20	**(b) All other launches**		
SL682	1967 Apr 27					
		SL1104	1974 Jun 18	Astro 4-1	1979 Mar 13	
SL721	1969 Jul 25	SL1105	1975 Jun 24	Astro 4-2	1979 Feb 22	
SL722	1969 Jul 15			Astro-Hel	1979 Oct 12	
SL723	1968 Jun 12	SL1111	1973 Jun 16			
SL724	1969 Apr 01	SL1112	1975 Nov 25/24	B-II-1	1976 Jan 04	
SL725	1968 Dec 06			B-II-2	1976 Jan 22	
SL726	1969 Jan 23	SL1114	1976 Dec 03/02			
SL727	1970 Jul 10	SL1115	1976 May 12	CAESAR1	1984 Jan 27	
SL728	1970 Apr 16	SL1115A	1977 Apr 28	CAESAR2	1985 Jan 30	
SL729	1969 Jul 17					
		SL1121	1973 Oct 14	EB1	1980 Nov 16	
SL730	1969 Jul 30	SL1122	1973 Oct 30	EB2	1981 Dec 09	
		SL1123	1973 Nov 16			
SL761	1968 May 31			HRC1	1974 Jan 12	
SL762	1968 May 31	SL1124	1973 Dec 05			
				IMS 1	1977 Oct 13	
SL781	1969 Jan 21	SL1181	1973 Mar 28	IMS 2	1977 Nov 02	
		SL1182	1973 Mar 22	IMS 3	1978 Jan 30	
SL791R	1968 Oct 09	SL1183	1972 Jul 20	IMS 4	1978 Jan 30	
SL801	1969 Nov 20	SL1191	1972 Jul 05	INTERZODIAK	1985 Mar 3	
SL802	1970 Mar 25/24			INTERZODIAK 2	1988 Sep 3	
SL803	1970 Apr 07	SL1202	1972 Dec 07			
SL804	1970 Nov 25	SL1203	1974 Feb 05	LT.1	1971 Jan 14	
				MAP/WINE	1984 Feb 10	
SL811	1970 Jul 16	SL1205	1973 Jan 30			
SL812	1971 May 10	SL1206	1973 Nov 26	MASER 6	1993 Nov 04	
		SL1207	1974 Apr 23	MASER 7	1996 May 03	
SL821	1969 Oct 22			MASER 8	1999 May 14	
		SL1211	1976 May 27	MASER 9	2002 Mar 16	
SL861	1969 Oct 16	SL1212	1976 Jun 11	MASER 10	2005 May 02	
SL862	1969 Oct 17			MAXUS TEST	1990 Nov 25	

PHA2	1977 Jan 22	S54	1971 Feb 26	S103	1975 Oct 09
PHA1	1977 Feb 08	S55	1971 Mar 11	S105	1972 Oct 12/13
PHA3	1977 Feb 20				
PHA4	1977 Mar 16	S56A/1	1970 Jan 24	SN5/1	1970 Mar 22
		S56A/2	1970 Jul 23	SN5/2	1970 Oct 13
PL029	1976 Jan 28	S56B/1	1971 Mar 25		
		S56B/2	1971 May 14	ROSE 1	1988 Nov 26
S01/1	1964 Jul 06			ROSE 2	1988 Dec 05
S01/2	1964 Jul 08	~~S58~~	~~1970 Oct 19~~	ROSE 3	1989 Feb 07
				ROSE 4	1989 Feb 09
S03/1	1965 Mar 31	S61/1	1970 Feb 25		
S03/2	1965 Apr 03	S61/2	1970 Feb 26	SISSI 1	1990 Mar 06
				SISSI 2	1990 Jul 26
S04/1	1965 Sep 30	S63/1	1970 Jul 03	SISSI 3	1990 Aug 02
S04/2	1965 Oct 02	S63/2	1970 Jul 08	SISSI 4	1991 Apr 09
S05/1	1965 Aug 11	S64/1	1969 Jul 06	SUPER NOVA	1987 Aug 24
S05/2	1967 May 26	S64/2	1969 Jul 13		
				TEST FLIGHT	1988 May 9
S08/1	1966 Jun 20	S65/1	1970 Jul 27	(BAe)	
S08/2	1966 Jun 28	S65/2	1970 Jul 24		
				TEXUS 1	1977 Dec 13
S11/2	1967 May 22	S66/1	1970 Apr 02	TEXUS 2	1978 Nov 16
S11/1	1966 Nov 26	S66/2	1970 Feb 14	TEXUS 3A	1980 Apr 28
				TEXUS 3B	1981 Apr 30
S16/1	1968 Mar 27	S67/1	1970 Oct 28	TEXUS 4	1981 May 08
S16/2	1971 Mar 12	S67/2	1970 Oct 29	TEXUS 5	1982 Apr 29
				TEXUS 6	1982 May 08
S17/1	1966 Jun 16	S68/1	1969 Oct 24	TEXUS 7	1983 May 05
S17/2	1966 Jun 18	S68/2	1970 Jun 22	TEXUS 8	1983 May 13
				TEXUS 9	1984 May 03
S18/1	1966 Jul 08	S69	1970 Dec 06	TEXUS 10	1984 May 15
S18/2	1966 Jul 13			TEXUS 11	1985 Apr 27
		S70/1	1970 Feb 24	TEXUS 12	1985 May 06
S19/1	1967 Oct 04	S70/2	1971 Nov 25	TEXUS 13	1986 Apr 30
S19/2	1967 Oct 10			TEXUS 14	1986 May 12
		S72	1970 Feb 11	TEXUS 14B	1987 May 03
S22	1977 Feb 08	S73	1971 Jul 02	TEXUS 15	1987 May 09
		S74	1973 Nov 27	TEXUS 16	1987 Nov 23
S26/1	1967 Sep 27			TEXUS19	1988 Nov 28
S26/2	1967 Oct 07	S75/1	1972 Mar 25	TEXUS 20	1988 Dec 02
		S75/2	1972 Mar 30	TEXUS 21	1989 Apr 30
S26A	1978 Jul 30			TEXUS 22	1989 May 03
S26B	1978 Aug 13	S77/1	1972 Mar 02	TEXUS 23	1989 Nov 25
		S77/2	1972 Sep 24	TEXUS 24	1989 Dec 06
S27/1	1968 Dec 03			TEXUS 25	1990 May 13
		S80/1	1971 Feb 06	TEXUS 26	1990 May 15
S28/1	1970 Apr 04	S80/2	1971 Feb 06	TEXUS 27	1990 Nov 15
		S80/3	1971 Feb 07	TEXUS 28	1991 Nov 23
S29/1	1969 Oct 05			TEXUS 29	1992 Nov 22
S29/2	1969 Oct 17	S81	1971 Oct 12	TEXUS 30	1993 May 01
		S82	1971 Dec 14	TEXUS 31	1993 Nov 26
S38/1	1969 Jul 05	S84	1972 Feb 28	TEXUS 32	1994 May 05
S38/2	1969 Jul 11	S85	1971 Feb 22	TEXUS 33	1994 Nov 30
				TEXUS 34	1996 Mar 02
S41	1968 Nov 22	S87/1	1971 Mar 16	TEXUS 35	1996 Nov 24
		S87/2	1971 Mar 24	TEXUS 36	1998 Feb 07
S43/1	1968 Nov 25			TEXUS 37	2000 Mar 27
S43/2	1969 Mar 15	S89	1971 Oct 20	TEXUS 38	2000 Apr 02
		S90	1972 Feb 28	TEXUS 39	2001 May 08
S44/1	1970 Feb 06			TEXUS 40	2003 Apr 08
S44/2	1971 Nov 16	S91	1972 Jun 25	TEXUS 41	2004 Dec 02
S46/1	1969 Nov 10	S92	1973 Oct 03	US 01	1961 Sep 18
S46/2	1971 Jan 28	S93	1973 Oct 02	US 02	1961 Oct 04
		S94	1972 Sep 20	US 03	1961 Nov 02
S47/1	1968 Oct 07	S95	1972 Dec 02	US 04	1961 Nov 21
S47/2	1971 Sep 30/29				
		S98	1975 Mar 14		
S53	1970 Oct 15				

APPENDIX 2
A SIMPLE CHRONOLOGICAL LIST OF ALL SKYLARK LAUNCHES
(see Appendix 3 for a more detailed list)

SL01	1957 Feb 13	SL35C	1962 Jun 06	SL303	1965 Apr 09
SL02	1957 May 22	SL45	1962 Jun 20	SL464	1965 Apr 29
SL03	1957 Jul 23	SL164	1962 Jul 05	SL363	1965 Apr 29
SL04	1957 Nov 13	SL109	1962 Aug 15	SL364	1965 Apr 29
		SL28	1962 Aug 29	SL461	1965 Apr 29
SL06	1958 Apr 02	SL44	1962 Sep 11	SL462	1965 Apr 30
SL07	1958 Apr 17	SL108	1962 Sep 20	SL463	1965 Apr 30
SL05	1958 May 20	SL82	1962 Oct 15	SL362	1965 Apr 30
SL22	1958 Jun 05	SL114	1962 Nov 13	SL361	1965 May 11
SL18	1958 Jun 18	SL27	1962 Nov 22	SL139	1965 May 14
SL09	1958 Jun 19	SL165	1962 Nov 28	SL138	1965 May 19
SL08	1958 Sep 19 (June?)	SL166	1962 Dec 04	SL106	1965 Jul 01
SL11	1958 Dec 03			SL48	1965 Jul 14
		SL84	1963 Mar 01	SL105	1965 Jul 29
SL21	1959 Mar 04	SL85	1963 Mar 11	S05/1	1965 Aug 11
SL19	1959 Jul 01	SL167	1963 Apr 17	SL88B	1965 Sep 09
SL14	1959 Jul 08	SL115	1963 May 23	S04/1	1965 Sep 30
SL24	1959 Jul 23	SL127	1963 May 29	S04/2	1965 Oct 02
SL17	1959 Aug 19	SL126	1963 Jun 18	SL39	1965 Oct 18
SL12	1959 Sep 17	SL46	1963 Jun 20	SL306	1965 Oct 20
SL15	1959 Sep 24	SL29	1963 Jul 25	SL130	1965 Nov 19
SL16	1959 Nov 30	SL86	1963 Aug 02	SL131	1965 Dec 13
SL60	1959 Nov 30	SL87	1963 Sep 05		
SL38	1959 Dec 01	SL81A	1963 Oct 03/02	SL307	1966 Feb 02
		SL171	1963 Oct 15	SL581	1966 Mar 17
SL51	1960 Apr 12	SL169	1963 Oct 15	SL582	1966 Apr 10
SL62	1960 Apr 21	SL170	1963 Oct 16	SL583	1966 Apr 21
SL10	1960 Jun 16	SL168	1963 Oct 16	SL304	1966 May 05
SL61	1960 Aug 10	SL134	1963 Oct 30	SL422	1966 May 31
SL13	1960 Aug 26	SL103	1963 Nov 19	SL327	1966 Jun 02
SL33	1960 Nov 16	SL135	1963 Dec 02	SL328	1966 Jun 09
SL67	1960 Nov 17	SL104	1963 Dec 03	S17/1	1966 Jun 16
SL49	1960 Nov 24			S17/2	1966 Jun 18
SL50	1960 Dec 07	SL88	1964 Feb 04	S08/1	1966 Jun 20
		SL30	1964 Feb 20	SL421	1966 Jun 23
SL36	1961 Feb 13	SL129	1964 Mar 10	S08/2	1966 Jun 28
SL63	1961 Mar 06	SL128	1964 Mar 12	S18/1	1966 Jul 08
SL64	1961 Apr 05	SL136	1964 Apr 11	S18/2	1966 Jul 13
SL43	1961 May 01	SL20	1964 May 14	SL88C	1966 Jul 28
SL25	1961 May 30	S01/1	1964 Jul 06	SL321	1966 Oct 25
SL26	1961 Jun 07	S01/2	1964 Jul 08	SL322	1966 Oct 25
SL65	1961 Jul 04	SL31	1964 Jul 15	SL324S	1966 Oct 27
SL34	1961 Aug 01	SL32	1964 Jul 17	SL323	1966 Oct 27
US 01	1961 Sep 18	SL301	1964 Aug 11	SL324	1966 Oct 27
SL40	1961 Sep 27	SL121	1964 Aug 20	SL481	1966 Nov 18
US 02	1961 Oct 04	SL137	1964 Sep 01	S11/1	1966 Nov 26
SL37	1961 Oct 24	SL87A	1964 Sep 04	SL405	1966 Dec 08
US 03	1961 Nov 02	SL120	1964 Sep 17	SL581A	1966 Dec 14
SL35	1961 Nov 08	SL133	1964 Sep 24		
US 04	1961 Nov 21	SL132	1964 Sep 29	SL406	1967 Mar 14
SL83	1961 Nov 24	SL47	1964 Oct 27	SL426	1967 Apr 04
SL42	1961 Dec 06	SL302	1964 Dec 17	SL118	1967 Apr 10
				SL119	1967 Apr 12
SL35B	1962 Feb 06	SL88A	1965 Feb 25	SL425	1967 Apr 21
SL66	1962 Mar 05	SL87B	1965 Mar 03	SL682	1967 Apr 27
SL160	1962 Mar 06	SL140	1965 Mar 17	S11/2	1967 May 22
SL161	1962 Mar 29	SL141	1965 Mar 25	S05/2	1967 May 26
SL163	1962 Apr 06			SL305	1967 Aug 08
SL162	1962 Apr 11	S03/1	1965 Mar 31	SL581B	1967 Aug 16
		S03/2	1965 Apr 03	SL521	1967 Aug 24

Code	Date	Code	Date	Code	Date
SL522	1967 Aug 29	S28/1	1970 Apr 04	SL1003	1972 Oct 26
S26/1	1967 Sep 27	SL803	1970 Apr 07	S95	1972 Dec 02
S19/1	1967 Oct 04	SL728	1970 Apr 16	SL1202	1972 Dec 07
S26/2	1967 Oct 07	S68/2	1970 Jun 22	SL1005	1972 Dec 11
S19/2	1967 Oct 10	S63/1	1970 Jul 03		
SL407	1967 Nov 01	S63/2	1970 Jul 08	SL1205	1973 Jan 30
SL423	1967 Nov 14	SL727	1970 Jul 10	SL1010	1973 Mar 01/Feb28
SL424	1967 Nov 17	SL971	1970 Jul 14	SL1004	1973 Mar 14
SL422A	1967 Dec 01	SL811	1970 Jul 16	SL1102	1973 Mar 20
		S56A/2	1970 Jul 23	SL1182	1973 Mar 22
SL583A	1968 Feb 08	S65/2	1970 Jul 24	SL1181	1973 Mar 28
SL408	1968 Mar 20	S65/1	1970 Jul 27	SL1011	1973 Apr 18/17
S16/1	1968 Mar 27	SL972	1970 Oct 08	SL1111	1973 Jun 16
SL761	1968 May 31	SN5/2	1970 Oct 13	SL1291	1973 Jul 17
SL762	1968 May 31	SL1021	1970 Oct 14	SL1081A	1973 Aug 04
SL723	1968 Jun 12	S53	1970 Oct 15	S93	1973 Oct 02
SL403	1968 Jul 08	S58	1970 Oct 19	S92	1973 Oct 03
SL523	1968 Jul 23	S67/1	1970 Oct 28	SL1121	1973 Oct 14
SL524	1968 Aug 05	S67/2	1970 Oct 29	SL1122	1973 Oct 30
SL501	1968 Aug 29	SL905	1970 Nov 11	SL1123	1973 Nov 16
S47/1	1968 Oct 07	SL904	1970 Nov 20	SL1206	1973 Nov 26
SL791R	1968 Oct 09	SL804	1970 Nov 25	S74	1973 Nov 27
S41	1968 Nov 22	S69	1970 Dec 06	SL1124	1973 Dec 05
S43/1	1968 Nov 25				
S27/1	1968 Dec 03	LT.1	1971 Jan 14	HRC1	1974 Jan 12
SL601	1968 Dec 04	S46/2	1971 Jan 28	SL1203	1974 Feb 05
SL725	1968 Dec 06	SL1001	1971 Jan 29	SL1207	1974 Apr 23
		S80/1	1971 Feb 06	SL1104	1974 Jun 18
SL781	1969 Jan 21	S80/2	1971 Feb 06	SL1292	1974 Jul 22
SL726	1969 Jan 23	S80/3	1971 Feb 07	SL1012	1974 Oct 05/04
S43/2	1969 Mar 15	S85	1971 Feb 22	SL1304	1974 Oct 07
SL724	1969 Apr 01	S54	1971 Feb 26	SL1471	1974 Oct 10
SL502	1969 Apr 03	SL922	1971 Mar 02	SL1221	1974 Nov 01
SL606	1969 Apr 17	S55	1971 Mar 11	SL911	1974 Nov 28
SL604	1969 Apr 22	S16/2	1971 Mar 12		
SL404	1969 May 14	S87/1	1971 Mar 16	SL1301	1975 Feb 25
S38/1	1969 Jul 05	S87/2	1971 Mar 24	SL1293	1975 Feb 28
S64/1	1969 Jul 06	S56B/1	1971 Mar 25	S98	1975 Mar 14
S38/2	1969 Jul 11	SL812	1971 May 10	SL1105	1975 Jun 24
S64/2	1969 Jul 13	S56B/2	1971 May 14	SL1295	1975 Jul 03
SL722	1969 Jul 15	S73	1971 Jul 02	S103	1975 Oct 09
SL729	1969 Jul 17	SL902	1971 Aug 05	SL1112	1975 Nov 25/24
SL721	1969 Jul 25	SL1002	1971 Sep 27		
SL730	1969 Jul 30	S47/2	1971 Sep 30/29	B-II-1	1976 Jan 04
SL605	1969 Aug 21	SL973	1971 Oct 07	B-II-2	1976 Jan 22
S29/1	1969 Oct 05	S81	1971 Oct 12	PL029	1976 Jan 28
SL861	1969 Oct 16	S89	1971 Oct 20	SL1302	1976 Jan 30
SL862	1969 Oct 17	SL974	1971 Oct 24	SL1115	1976 May 12
S29/2	1969 Oct 17	S44/2	1971 Nov 16	SL1211	1976 May 27
SL586	1969 Oct 20	S70/2	1971 Nov 25	SL1212	1976 Jun 11
SL821	1969 Oct 22	SL1101	1971 Nov 30	SL1501	1976 Jun 17
S68/1	1969 Oct 24	SL903	1971 Dec 10	SL1402	1976 Jul 17
S46/1	1969 Nov 10	S82	1971 Dec 14	SL1306	1976 Nov 04
SL602	1969 Nov 18			SL1422	1976 Nov 21
SL801	1969 Nov 20	S84	1972 Feb 28	SL1114	1976 Dec 03/02
SL603	1969 Nov 27	S90	1972 Feb 28	SL1425	1976 Dec 11
		S77/1	1972 Mar 02		
S56A/1	1970 Jan 24	SL1023	1972 Mar 16	PHA2	1977 Jan 22
S44/1	1970 Feb 06	SL1009	1972 Mar 17	S22	1977 Feb 08
S72	1970 Feb 11	S75/1	1972 Mar 25	PHA1	1977 Feb 08
S66/2	1970 Feb 14	SL1081	1972 Mar 27	PHA3	1977 Feb 20
S70/1	1970 Feb 24	S75/2	1972 Mar 30	PHA4	1977 Mar 16
S61/1	1970 Feb 25	S91	1972 Jun 25	SL1115A	1977 Apr 28
S61/2	1970 Feb 26	SL1191	1972 Jul 05	SL1298	1977 Jun 08
SL921	1970 Mar 12	SL1183	1972 Jul 20	IMS 1	1977 Oct 13
SL901	1970 Mar 19	S94	1972 Sep 20	SL1423	1977 Oct 13
SL401	1970 Mar 20	S77/2	1972 Sep 24	IMS 2	1977 Nov 02
SN5/1	1970 Mar 22	S105	1972 Oct 12/13	SL1421	1977 Nov 17
SL802	1970 Mar 25/24	SL1022	1972 Oct 19	TEXUS 1	1977 Dec 13
S66/1	1970 Apr 02	SL402	1972 Oct 23		

IMS 3	1978 Jan 30
IMS 4	1978 Jan 30
SL1305	1978 May 12
S26A	1978 Jul 30
S26B	1978 Aug 13
SL1424	1978 Nov 10
SL1296	1978 Nov 15
TEXUS 2	1978 Nov 16
SL1297	1978 Dec 13
Astro 4-2	1979 Feb 22
SL1299	1979 Mar 01
Astro 4-1	1979 Mar 13
Astro-Hel	1979 Oct 12
TEXUS 3A	1980 Apr 28
EB1	1980 Nov 16
TEXUS B	1981 Apr 30
TEXUS 4	1981 May 08
EB2	1981 Dec 09
TEXUS 5	1982 Apr 29
TEXUS 6	1982 May 08
TEXUS 7	1983 May 05
TEXUS 8	1983 May 13
CAESAR1	1984 Jan 27
MAP/WINE	1984 Feb 10
TEXUS 9	1984 May 03
TEXUS 10	1984 May 15
CAESAR2	1985 Jan 30
INTERZODIAK	1985 Mar 3
TEXUS 11	1985 Apr 27
TEXUS 12	1985 May 06
TEXUS 13	1986 Apr 30
TEXUS 14	1986 May 12
TEXUS 14B	1987 May 03
TEXUS 15	1987 May 09
SUPER NOVA	1987 Aug 24
TEXUS 16	1987 Nov 23
TEST FLIGHT (BAe)	1988 May 09
INTERZODIAK 2	1988 Sep 03
ROSE 1	1988 Nov 26
TEXUS19	1988 Nov 28
TEXUS 20	1988 Dec 02
ROSE 2	1988 Dec 05
ROSE 3	1989 Feb 07
ROSE 4	1989 Feb 09
TEXUS 21	1989 Apr 30
TEXUS 22	1989 May 03
TEXUS 23	1989 Nov 25
TEXUS 24	1989 Dec 06
SISSI 1	1990 Mar 06
TEXUS 25	1990 May 13
TEXUS 26	1990 May 15
SISSI 2	1990 Jul 26
SISSI 3	1990 Aug 02
TEXUS 27	1990 Nov 15

MAXUS TEST	1990 Nov 25
SISSI 4	1991 Apr 09
TEXUS 28	1991 Nov 23
TEXUS 29	1992 Nov 22
TEXUS 30	1993 May 01
MASER 6	1993 Nov 04
TEXUS 31	1993 Nov 26
TEXUS 32	1994 May 05
TEXUS 33	1994 Nov 30
TEXUS 34	1996 Mar 02
MASER 7	1996 May 03
TEXUS 35	1996 Nov 24
TEXUS 36	1998 Feb 07
MASER 8	1999 May 14
TEXUS 37	2000 Mar 27
TEXUS 38	2000 Apr 02
TEXUS 39	2001 May 08
MASER 9	2002 Mar 16
TEXUS 40	2003 Apr 08
TEXUS 41	2004 Dec 02
MASER 10	2005 May 02

APPENDIX 3
A Chronological List With Details of All 441
Skylark Launches

Column 1: "Seq. Nos"

A sequential number that is a running total (since the first Skylark flight in 1957) followed in brackets by the running total for that year.

Column 2: "Launch date"

Where two successive dates are given they correspond to GMT-UTC/Australian CST. Woomera is in South Australia, which uses Australian CST (Central Standard Time), GMT +9.30/+10.30 hours. This accounts for (some at least) of the apparent ambiguities which appear in various sources, because a night time/early morning launch that took place between midnight and 9.30/10.30 local time, will have a local date one day ahead of GMT/UTC.

Column 3: "Ref. (sponsor) launch site"

The UK Skylark missions had a simple numbering system (SLXXX), but other designations were more complicated. In this book, the 'common name' has usually been used, for instance 'SISSI 4', rather than 'DLR K-GR-187'.

The (sponsor) in brackets may be the country, or national/international agency concerned.

UK sponsored launches were from Woomera LA2 (Launch Apron 2) unless otherwise noted. Other launch sites used by the UK and others were:

Andøya – Norway

Kiruna (Esrange) - Sweden

El Arenosillo – Spain

Villa Mercedes - Argentina

Centro de Lançamento da Barreira do Inferno (CLBI), near Natal, Brazil

Occasionally an additional field has been added, of the form '(BS227)'. This was the 'Trials Instruction' document number, used as the designation for individual or pairs of similar flight trials (military and civilian) by the WRE at Woomera, and has been included where known.

Column 4: "Configuration"

Type of payload stabilisation, followed by the motor combination

<u>Payload stabilisation - not fully attitude controlled</u>

Un = unstabilised, Spin = spin stabilised, RS = Rate Spin,[1] SPINRAC.[2]

<u>Payload stabilisation - attitude controlled (full 3-axis stabilisation)</u>

Sun = Sun-pointing, Moon = Moon pointing, Star = star pointing, Earth = Earth Resources (horizon sensing), ZR = Zero Rate Control (no rotation in any axis, used on microgravity missions), I/ before Sun, Moon or Star means an inertially based (gyroscope) reference was used.

<u>Motor combination:</u> Rav. = Raven, C = Cuckoo, G = Goldfinch.

---

[1] It is unclear exactly what "Rate Spin" means. The term comes from the document 'BAe (1990), *Record of Skylark Launches 1957-1990"*, but is only used about the ROSE and SISSI missions. The SISSI payloads had an attitude control system of some sort (Auchter *et al.* (1991)), so it may have been a 2-axis control system that controlled the 3rd axis (spin) to some extent.

[2] SPINRAC (**SPIN**ning **R**ocket **A**ttitude **C**ontrol system) was a development of the SAAB Space S19 spin control system, and used cold gas jets instead of aerodynamic control surfaces (canards), to control the attitude of sounding rocket 3rd stages in space. (Hall & Helmersson (1985)). Although a sophisticated system using gyros, the vehicle or stage being controlled maintained its axis spin, so has been classified here as spin stabilised.

Column 5: "Apogee"

The peak altitude reached is stated to the nearest kilometre, followed in brackets rounded to the nearest mile.

Column 6: "Experimenters"

Institutions ("experimenters") (UK based unless otherwise noted) are:

Adel = University of Adelaide, Australia
AL = Appleton Laboratory, UK (see below)
ARD = Astrophysical Research Division, part of RSRS, but located at Culham, UK (see below)
ARU = Astrophysics Research Unit, Culham Laboratory, UK. (See below)
Belfast = Queen's University, Belfast, UK
Bern = Physics Institute, University of Bern, Switzerland
Bonn = Physics Institute, University of Bonn, Germany
Bir = University of Birmingham, UK
Breisach = Ionospharen Institut, Breisach, Germany
Cam = University of Cambridge, UK
Cul = Culham Laboratory, general term for ARU & ARD
CEN = Centre d'Etude Nucleaire, Saclay, France
CES = Centre d'Etudes Spatiale des Rayonnements, Faculté des Sciences de Toulouse, France
DLR = Deutsches Zentrum für Luft- und Raumfahrt (German Research Institute for Aviation and Space Flight)
DSRI = Danish Space Research Institute, Lyngby, Denmark
ESTEC = European Space Technology Centre, Noordwijk, The Netherlands
Freib = Fraunhofer-Institut für Physikalische Mebtechnik (former Fraunhofer-Institut für Physikalische Weltraumforschung), Freiburg, West Germany
GSFC = Goddard Space Flight Center, USA
IAP = Institute of Atmospheric Physics, Paris, France
IASB = Institut d'Aéronomie Spatiale de Belgique, Brussels, Belgium
IC = Imperial College, UK
Kiruna = Kiruna Observatory (Royal Swedish Academy of Science), Kiruna, Sweden.
KTH = Royal Institute of Technology Stockholm, Sweden
Lei = University of Leicester, UK
Liège = Astrophysical Institute, University of Liège, Belgium
Lockheed = Lockheed Palo Alto Research Laboratory, California, USA
MPAe = Max-Planck-Institut für Aeronomie, Germany
MPE = Max Planck Institute for Extraterrestrial physics, Germany
MPI = Max Planck Institute, Germany
MSFC = Marshall Space Flight Center, Alabama, USA
MSSL = Mullard Space Science Laboratory, UK, originally (1967) part of the University College London (UCL) Physics Department, later the UCL's Department of Space and Climate Physics
NDRE = Norwegian Defence Research Establishment, near Oslo, Norway
PIB = Physics Institute, Bologna, Italy
RAE = Royal Aircraft/Aerospace Establishment, UK
ROE = Royal Observatory, Edinburgh, UK
RRS = Radio Research Station, Ditton Park, near Slough, UK (see below).
RSRS = Radio and Space Research Station, UK (see below).
Saclay = Institut de Physique Théorique (IPhT), France
SSD-ESTEC = Space Science Division, ESTEC
Sth = University of Southampton, UK
Sx = University of Sussex, UK
Tas = University of Tasmania, Australia
TU = Toulouse University, France
Tüb = Tübingen University, Germany
UAT = Universities of Adelaide and Tasmania, Australia
UCB = University of California, Berkeley, USA
UCL = University College, London, UK

UCW = University College of Wales (Aberystwyth or Bangor), UK
UoR = University of Reading, Geography Department
Utr = Space Research Laboratory, University of Utrecht, Belgium
Wupp = University of Wuppertal, Germany
(For a detailed list of the principal UK space science groups that existed in 1982 see Massey and Robins, *History of British Space Science,* p.444.)

<u>Notes on the history of some UK government research establishments that used Skylark</u>

Many of the UK government scientific establishments (as listed above) that provided payloads for Skylark have been incorporated into the present (2009) Rutherford Appleton Laboratory, situated at the Harwell Science and Innovation Campus at Chilton near Didcot in Oxfordshire. Their complicated history[3] may be summarised thus:

1965 - the Radio Research Station (RRS)[4] was renamed the Radio and Space Research Station (RSRS), and transferred to the new Science Research Council (SRC).[5] However, the RSRS remained based at Ditton Park near Slough, west of London.
1969 - funding of the Astrophysical Research Unit (ARU) of the UK Atomic Energy Authority's Culham Laboratory in Oxfordshire was transferred to the SRC, although the staff remained at Culham.
1972 - the ARU became the Astrophysical Research Department (ARD) of RSRS, whilst remaining at Culham.[6]
1973 - the RSRS site at Ditton Park was renamed the Appleton Laboratory (AL).
1979 - the AL was merged with the Rutherford Laboratory[7] at Harwell, (just south of Culham) to become the Rutherford Appleton Laboratory (RAL).

The RAL has since consolidated at Harwell and nearby Chilton.[8] The site at Ditton Park was finally vacated in about 1995.

Column 7: "Experiments"

For convenience, the flights and experiments have been classified as follows. Note that to make the best use of each flight, more than one experiment was often flown, although they needed to be compatible; for instance neutral atmosphere experiments with similar launch time and altitude requirements. So sometimes a flight can be classified by the main experiments flown, sometimes not. For scientific experiments, the type of instrument used sometimes follows in brackets.

1. <u>Astronomy</u> – observations beyond the Sun (stars, galaxies etc.)
2. <u>Solar physics</u> – astronomy concerned with observations of the Sun, usually at wavelengths that do not reach the Earth's surface, e.g. X-rays, ultraviolet (UV) light
3. <u>Upper atmosphere</u> experiments – these have been divided into three main and two sub-divisions:
    (1) <u>Neutral atmosphere</u> – studies of the 'ordinary' physical properties of the upper atmosphere, such as temperature, wind velocity and density.
    (2) <u>Aeronomy</u> – in general the study of any atmospheric region where ionisation and photo dissociation processes play a role. However for current purposes, the subdivisions of ionosphere and aurora related experiments have been classified separately, leaving mainly ozone, airglow and studies of the chemical composition of the atmosphere under the 'Aeronomy' heading.
        (2a) <u>Ionosphere</u> – where the experiment is concerned with studying the layers (D, E and F) of the ionosphere, including direct measurements (e.g. using probes) of electrically charged particles such as electrons and ions.
        (2b) <u>Auroral</u> physics
    (3) <u>Geomagnetic</u> fields – studies of the Earth's magnetic and electrical fields
    (4) <u>Geophysics</u> – when a mission covers several of the above aspects, this general classification has sometimes been used
4. <u>Micrometeorites</u> & energetic particles impinging on the upper atmosphere from space
5. <u>Remote sensing</u> – observations of the Earth's surface for Earth resource determination

---

[3]   One is reminded of the maxim "never confuse activity with progress"!
[4]   The RRS had been established in 1920 to try to understand the ionosphere, and advise on radio propagation, very much affected by the ionosphere.
[5]   The SRC (Science Research Council) had been created in 1965 to administer the UK government scientific research budget (e.g. re space research, nuclear and particle physics and astronomy).
[6]   Massey & Robins, *History of British Space Science*, p.221.
[7]   The Rutherford Laboratory had been formed in 1975 when the Atomic Energy Research Establishment (AERE) at Harwell was merged with the Atlas Computer Laboratory on the same site.
[8]   The STFC Rutherford Appleton Laboratory (RAL) now carries out a wide range of space research and technology development, see for instance *www.stfc.ac.uk/ralspace/default.aspx* (last accessed October 2014).

6. <u>Microgravity</u> – experiments that made use of the six or so minutes of very low (10^{-4}g) gravity that can occur during the apogee of Skylark flights[9]
7. <u>Tests</u> & proving flights of various types, for example:
    (1) General vehicle and range facility proving flights
    (2) Skylark technology (e.g. motors, attitude control units)
    (3) Space technology in general (e.g. gyroscopes for the RAE)
    (4) Scientific instrument (particularly during the very early days)

Column 8: "Results"

Results are classified as: S = success, Ps = partial success, F = no experimental results, Ef = experiment failure. Some individual experiments were a technological success, but the required scientific conditions (e.g. the presence of an aurora) were not met. These have been classified as Ps.

Overriding failures caused other than by the experiment have been classified as:

    Mf = rocket motor failure
    Vf = internal rocket vehicle system failure (e.g. ACU failed to acquire, parachute failed)
    Sf = external support system failure (e.g. telemetry)

Column 9: "Sources"

The main sources for the information have been included; see the List of References for further details of individual sources. In addition, some information may have come from scientific papers or other sources, see the corresponding entry in the main part of the book.

BAe = BAe (1990), *Record of Skylark Launches 1957-1990*
Cul = various scientific papers by Burton *et al.* on the stabilised Skylark results
DSTO = Archive of the Australian Defence Science and Technology Organisation (successors to the WRE)
EEA = ESA 'Erasmus Experiment Archive' database
Edin = Original Skylark preparation and results files held by Australian Defence Archives at Edinburgh, South Australia
FDC = First Day Cover – see text description in the appropriate chapter
Flight = Flight magazine (FLIGHT International after 1962)
GW/2320 = RAE GW Dept. (1958), *A Brief Review of the C.T.V.5 Series III Programme*
GW530 = Dorling (1959), *The First Six Skylark Firings,* (RAE Farnborough Technical Note GW 530)
GW589 = Shepherd (1961), *A Recovery System for the Skylark Instrument Head*
Knott = Knott (1961- 66), *The Drift of an Auto-Pilot Gyroscope due to prolonged acceleration in the Skylark Rocket, Parts 1 to 4.*
Jenn = Jennison (1967), 'Some Penetration and Charge Detection Techniques'
M&R = Massey & Robins (1986), *A History of British Space Science,* (Appendices).
McD = Jonathan McDowell's "List of Skylark Launches (2009)"
Micrex = NASA 'Microgravity Research Experiments' database
NAA = National Archives of Australia
SP-76, SP-77, SP-78, SP-79 & SP-80 = ESRO reports SP-76, SP-77, SP-78, SP-79 & SP-80 covering the years 1964-1969
Space Lists = website *www.rocketservices.co.uk* ,[10] sounding rocket section
SRC = Science Research Council (UK), Space Research Report 1969-70 (1972)
SSC = Swedish Space Corporation website, including list of all launches from Esrange near Kiruna, *www.sscspace.com* [11]
UAT = Universities of Adelaide and Tasmania, Australia
UoR = University of Reading, Geography Department, UK

Key to Colour Coding

"Black = UK test launches, blue = UK national programme (unstablised), light blue = Swedish, plum = UK (stablised), pink = NASA, then ESRO/ESA, red = German national

---

[9]   The pull of gravity cannot be escaped at any altitude, for instance at 322 km (200 miles), it is still 90% as strong as at the Earth's surface. However, its effects can be virtually cancelled by remaining in 'free fall', as when the Skylark payload was in 'parabolic' flight.
[10]   Originally accessed July 2010, but the sounding rocket lists were no longer available by July 2014.
[11]   For a list of launches from Esrange, go to *www.sscspace.com/Products-Services/rocket-balloon-services/launch-services-esc/esrange-space-center* , and click on "List of all rocket launches". (Last accessed July 2014).

1957 (4 launches, mainly for test & proving purposes)

Seq. Nos	Launch date	Ref. (sponsor) launch site	Config-uration	Apogee km (miles)	Experi-menters	Experiment(s)	Result	Source
1 (1)	13 Feb. 1957	SL01 (UK) Woomera	Un, Raven 1	12 (9.6)	RAE	Test – general vehicle & range proving, & Black Knight aerial temperature	S	GW530 GW/2320
2 (2)	22 May 1957	SL02 (UK) Woomera	Un, Raven 2A	76 (47)	RAE	Test – ditto	S	"
3 (3)	23 July 1957	SL03 (UK) Woomera	Un, Raven 1A	85 (53)	RAE	Test – ditto	Ps	GW530 GW/2320 M&R
					Belfast	Test – airglow photometer trial	Sf	
					RAE	Test (scientific instrument) – Pirani gauges	Sf	
4 (4)	13 Nov. 1957	SL04 (UK) Woomera	Un, Raven 1A	128 (79)	RAE	Test – vehicle flight proving & Black Knight airborne flash detection		"
					UCL	Neutral atmosphere – temperature, density & wind speed (grenades)	S	
					IC	Neutral atmosphere – wind speed (window/chaff)	S	
					Bir	Ionosphere - electron concentration by rf probe	F	
					RAE	Test (scientific instrument) – Pirani gauges	S	

1958 (5 scientific + 3 proving)

Jan.	Feb.	March	April	May	June	July	Aug	Sept.	Oct.	Nov.	Dec.
			SL06 SL07	SL05	SL22 SL18 SL09			SL08			SL11

Seq. Nos	Launch date	Ref. (sponsor) launch site	Config-uration	Apogee km (miles)	Experi-menters	Experiment(s)	Result	Source
5 (1)	02 April 1958	SL06 (UK) Woomera	Un, Rav.1A	43 (26.5)	RAE	Test (Skylark technology) - thrust interrupter	S	GW530 M&R
					UCL	Test – dummy nose cone probe	S	
6 (2)	17 April 1958	SL07 (UK) Woomera	Un, Rav.2	153 (95)	UCL	Neutral atmosphere – (grenades)	S	GW530 M&R GW/2320
					IC	" " - (window/chaff)	S	
					Bir	Ionosphere - electron concentration	F	
					RAE	Tests (instrument & Skylark technology) – Pirani gauges & B.K. flash & ballistic camera	?	
7 (3)	20 May 1958	SL05 (UK) Woomera	Un, Rav.2	151 (94)	RAE	Test (Skylark technology) - jettisonable nose cone release	Ps	GW530
					Belfast	Test – airglow photometer	Ps	
					RAE	Test (instrument) – flux gate magnetometer	S	
					RAE	Test - sun photocells	S	
8 (4)	5 June 1958	SL22 (UK) Woomera	Un, Rav.2A	153 (95)	RAE	Test – Black Knight command system & long burning high altitude flare	S	GW530 McD GW/2320
9 (5)	18 June 1958	SL18 (UK) Woomera	Un, Rav.2	3 (1.9)	UCL	Neutral atmosphere – (grenades)	Motor failed +4 s.	GW530 M&R McD
					IC	" " - (window/chaff)		
					Bir	Ionosphere – electron concentration		

Seq. Nos	Launch date	Ref. (sponsor) launch site	Config-uration	Apogee km (miles)	Experi-menters	Experiment(s)	Result	Source
10 (6)	19 June 1958	SL09 (UK) Woomera	Un, Rav.2	149 (93)	UCL	Neutral atmosphere – as SL18	F	"
					IC	" "	F	
					Bir	Ionosphere - "	S	
11 (7)	19 June/ Sept. 1958	SL08 (UK) Woomera	Un, Rav.2	157 (98)	UCL	Neutral atmosphere – as SL18	F	"
					IC	" "	F	
					Bir	Ionosphere - "	Sf	
12 (8)	3 Dec. 1958	SL11 (UK) Woomera	Un, Rav.2A	129-137 (80-85)	Belfast	Neutral atmosphere – density & winds > 60 km using sodium vapour	S	"
					RAE	Test – magnetometer & photocells (GW/2320)	S	

1959 (8 scientific & 2 proving)

Jan.	Feb.	March	April	May	June	July	Aug.	Sept.	Oct.	Nov.	Dec.
		SL21				SL19 SL14 SL24	SL17	SL12 SL15		SL16 SL60	SL38

Seq. Nos	Launch date	Ref. (sponsor) launch site	Config-uration	Apogee km (miles)	Experi-menters	Experiment(s)	Result	Source
13 (1)	04 March 1959	SL 21 (UK) Woomera	Un, Rav.2	30 (19)	UCL	Neutral atmosphere – (grenades)	Vf	M&R McD GW/ 2320
					IC	" " - (falling dipoles)		
					Bel	" " - (sodium vapour)		
					RAE	Test - Black Knight type A & B flashes		
14 (2)	01 July 1959	SL19 (UK) Woomera	Un, Rav.2	50 (31)	RAE	Test - probably of new instrumentation. "Suffered propulsion problem"	Ps?	McD Space Lists
15 (3)	08 July 1959	SL14 (UK) Woomera	Un, Rav.2	93 (57)	UCL	Ionosphere – electron & ion concentration (Langmuir probes)	Ps	M&R
					UCL/Lei	Solar physics - X-ray detectors	Ps	
16 (4)	23 July 1959	SL24 (UK) Woomera	Un, Rav.2A	91 (57)	RAE	Test (Skylark technology) - flight test of two magnetic tape recorders	Ef	GW/ 2320 McD
17 (5)	19 Aug. 1959	SL17 (UK) Woomera	Un, Rav.2	144 (89)	UCL	Ionosphere – electron & ion concentration (Langmuir probes)	S	M&R
18 (6)	17 Sept. 1959	SL12 (UK) Woomera	"	132 (82)	Bir	Ionosphere - ion mass spectrometer	F	"
					UCL	Solar physics – Lyman α detectors	Ps	
					UCL	" " - X-ray detectors	S	
					RAE	Test (Skylark technology) - magnetometers & aspect photocells (GW/2320)	?	
19 (7)	24 Sept. 1959	SL15 (UK) Woomera	"	158 (98)	Bir	Ionosphere - ion mass spectrometer	S	M&R GW/ 2320
					UCL	Ionosphere - sporadic E probe	S	
					RAE	Test (Skylark technology) - magnetometers, photocells, reflectometer	?	
20 (8)	30 Nov. 1959	SL16 (UK) Woomera	"	151 (94)	Bel	Neutral atmosphere – (sodium vapour)	S	M&R
					RAE	Test (Skylark technology) - first parachute recovery system proving flight	F	GW589
21 (9)	30 Nov. 1959	SL60 (UK) Woomera	"	163 (101)	UCL	Neutral atmosphere – (grenades)	S	M&R
					IC	" " - (falling dipoles)	F	
22 (10)	01 Dec. 1959	SL38 (UK) Woomera	"	159 (99)	UCL	" " - (grenades)	Ps	"
					IC	" " - (falling dipoles)	F	
					Bir	Ionosphere - dielectric probe	S	

1960 (7 scientific & 2 proving)

Jan.	Feb.	March	April	May	June	July	Aug.	Sept.	Oct.	Nov.	Dec.
			SL51 SL62		SL10		SL61 SL13			SL33 SL67 SL49	SL50

Seq. Nos	Launch date	Ref. (sponsor) launch site	Config-uration	Apogee km (miles)	Experi-menters	Experiment(s)	Result	Source
23 (1)	12 April 1960	SL51 (UK) Woomera	Un, Rav.2 +C	219 (136)	RAE	Test (Skylark technology) - first 2-stage vehicle, used Cuckoo booster	S	BAe
24 (2)	21 April 1960	SL62 (UK) Woomera	Un, Rav.2	141 (88)	UCL	Neutral atmosphere – (grenades)	Ps	M&R
					IC	" " - (falling dipoles)	F	
25 (3)	16 June 1960	SL10 (UK) Woomera	"	129 (80)	Belfast	" " - (sodium vapour)	F	M&R
					Belfast	Micrometeorites – microphone detector	F	
26 (4)	10 Aug. 1960	SL61 (UK) Woomera	"	176 (106)	UCL	Neutral atmosphere – (grenades)	Ps	M & R
					IC	" " - (falling dipoles)	Ps	
27 (5)	26 Aug. 1960	SL13 (UK) Woomera	"	109 (68)	Belfast	" " - (sodium vapour)	S	M & R GW/2320
					Belfast	Micrometeorites – microphone detector	Ps	
					RAE	Test (space technology) – magnetometer	?	
28 (6)	16 Nov. 1960	SL33 (UK) Woomera	"	105 (65)	RAE	Test (space technology) - photographic method of measuring attitude	Ps	Knott McD
					"	Test (Skylark technology) - head roll control	Ps	"
					"	Test (Skylark tech.) – 2nd parachute trial	F	GW589
29 (7)	17 Nov. 1960	SL67 (UK) Woomera	Un, Rav.2 +C	247 (153)	UCL	Neutral atmosphere – (grenades)	S	M&R
					IC	" " - (falling dipoles)	S	
					Belfast	" " - (sodium vapour)	F	
30 (8)	24 Nov. 1960	SL 49 (UK) Woomera	Un, Rav.2	158 (98)	RAE/UCW	Ionosphere - CW radio propagation	S	"
					Lei	Solar physics - soft x-ray detector	S	
					UCL	Ionosphere – positive ion probe	S	
31 (9)	7 Dec. 1960	SL 50 (UK) Woomera	Un, Rav.2	35 (21)	RAE/UCW	Neutral atmosphere – (sodium vapour)	Vf (fin came off)	"
					Leicester	Solar physics - soft x-ray detector		

1961 (11 scientific, 2 proving, 4 mixed)

Jan.	Feb.	March	April	May	June	July	Aug.	Sept.	Oct.	Nov.	Dec.
	SL36	SL63	SL64	SL43 SL25	SL26	SL65	SL34	US01 SL40	US02 SL37	US03 SL35 US04 SL83	SL42

Seq. Nos	Launch date	Ref. (sponsor) launch site	Config-uration	Apogee km (miles)	Experi-menters	Experiment(s)	Result	Source
32 (1)	13 Feb. 1961	SL36 (UK) Woomera	Un, Rav.2	146 (91)	RAE	Test (Skylark tech.) – third parachute trial	Ps	GW589
					UCL	Neutral atmosphere – (grenades)	S	M&R
					IC	" " - (falling dipoles)	S	

No.	Date	Rocket	Vehicle	Altitude	Org.	Experiment	Result	Notes
33 (2)	06 March 1961	SL63 (UK) Woomera	Un, Raven 2 +C	231 (144)	UCL	Neutral atmosphere - (grenades)	S	M&R
					UCL	" " - grenade glows	Ps	
					IC	" " - (falling dipoles)	S	
					Bel	" " - (sodium vapour)	S	
34 (3)	05 April 1961	SL64 (UK) Woomera	Un, Raven 2B	158 (98)	UCL	" " - (grenades)	S	M&R BAe
					UCL	" " - grenade glows	S	
					IC	" " - (falling dipoles)	S	
35 (4)	01 May 1961	SL43 (UK) Woomera	Un, Raven 2	155 (96)	UCL	Astronomy – stellar UV detection (photometers)	S	M&R, BAe
36 (5)	30 May 1961	SL25 UK (Woomera)	Un, Rav.2	149 (92)	RAE	Test (space technology) - interferometer method of measuring attitude	S	BAe, McD Knott
37 (6)	07 June 1961	SL26 (UK) Woomera	Un, Rav.2	184 (114)	RAE	Ditto	Ps	"
38 (7)	04 July 1961	SL65 (UK) Woomera	Un, Rav.2	70 (44)	UCL	Neutral atmosphere - (grenades)	S	M&R, BAe
					UCL	" " - grenade glows	F	
					IC	" " - (falling dipoles)	S	
39 (8)	01 Aug. 1961	SL34 (UK) Woomera	Un, Rav.2	124 (77)	UCL	Astronomy? - UV camera	F	M&R, BAe
					RAE	Test (Skylark technology) - fourth parachute trial	S	
40 (9)	18 Sept. 1961	US 01 (NASA) Woomera	Un, Rav.2 +C	193 (119)	Goddard Space Flight Center, USA	Astronomy - Southern Sky Survey Ultraviolet Astronomy	Ps	NASA BAe
41 (10)	27 Sept. 1961	SL40 (UK) Woomera	Un, Rav.2	152 (95)	UCL/Lei	Solar physics - X-ray photos & spectra	S	M&R BAe
					IC	Geomagnetic - proton magnetometer	S	
					UCL	Ionosphere - sporadic E probe	S	
42 (11)	04 Oct. 1961	US 02 (NASA) Woomera	Un, Rav.2 +C	195 (121)	Goddard Space Flight Center, USA	Astronomy - Southern Sky UV Survey	S	NASA BAe
43 (12)	24 Oct. 1961	SL37 (UK) Woomera	Un, Rav.2	142 (88)	RAE/SRDE	Test (Space technology) – SRDE broadband telemetry	S	M&R BAe Edin
					RAE	Test (Skylark tech.) – parachute recovery	S	
					JB	Micrometeorite – penetration detectors	Ps	
					UCL/Lei	Solar physics – X-ray flux	S	
					UCL	Ionosphere – sporadic E probe	S	
44 (13)	02 Nov. 1961	US 03 (NASA) Woomera	Un, Rav.2 +C	193 (119)	Goddard Space Flight Center, USA	Astronomy - Southern Sky UV Survey	Ps	NASA BAe
45 (14)	08 Nov. 1961	SL35 (UK) Woomera	Un, Rav.2	152 (95)	MO	Aeronomy - ozone distribution	S	M&R BAe Edin
					JB	Micrometeorite – penetration detectors	F	
					UCL	Ionosphere - sporadic E probe	S	
					RAE	Test (Skylark tech.) – parachute recovery	S	
46 (15)	21 Nov. 1961	US 04 (NASA) Woomera	Un, Rav.2 +C	209 (129)	Goddard Space Flight Center, USA	Astronomy - Southern Sky UV Survey	S	NASA BAe
47 (16)	24 Nov. 1961	SL83 (UK) Woomera	Un, Rav.5 +C	-	UCL/Lei	Solar physics - X-ray photos	Vf, broke up	M&R BAe
					UCL	Ionosphere – sporadic E		
					RAE/UCW	" - CW radio experiment		
48 (17)	06 Dec. 1961	SL42 (UK) Woomera	Un, Rav.2 +C	226 (140)	Bir	Ionosphere – RF electron probe	S	M&R BAe
					UCL/Lei	Solar physics - X-ray photos	S	
					UCL	Ionosphere - sporadic E probe	S	

1962 (14 research & 4 proving)

Jan.	Feb.	March	April	May	June	July	August	Sept.	Oct.	Nov.	Dec.
	SL35B	SL66 SL160 SL161	SL163 SL162		SL35C SL45	SL164	SL109 SL28	SL44 SL108	SL82 (SL81)	SL114 SL27 SL165	SL166

Seq. Nos	Launch date	Ref. (sponsor) launch site	Config- uration	Apogee km (miles)	Experi- menters	Experiment(s)	Result	Source
49 (1)	06 Feb. 1962	SL35B (UK) Woomera	Un, Rav.5A +C	215 (133) (est., motor only)	RAE	Test (Skylark tech.) - Raven 5A motor & Cuckoo	Ps	BAE McD Edin
					"	Test (Skylark technology) – parachute recovery	Vf	
					"	Test (") – cameras & flight instruments	Ps	
50 (2)	05 Mar. 1962	SL66 (UK) Woomera	Un, Rav.2 +C	233 (145)	UCL	Ionosphere - sporadic E	Vf	BAe M&R
					UCL	Neutral atmosphere – (grenades)	S	
					UCL	" " - grenade glows	S	
					IC	" " - (falling dipoles)	Ps	
					Bel	" " - (sodium vapour)	F	
51 (3)	06 Mar. 1962	SL160 (UK) Woomera	Un, Rav.2	173 (108)	UCL	Neutral atmosphere – (grenades)	S	M&R, BAe
					UCL	" " - grenade glows	S	
					IC	" " - (falling dipoles)	Ps	
52 (4)	29 Mar. 1962	SL161 (UK) Woomera	Un, Rav.2B	161 (100)	"	Neutral atmosphere – (grenades)	S	M&R, BAe
					"	" " " - grenade glows	S	
					"	" " " - (falling dipoles)	S	
53 (5)	6 April 1962	SL163 (UK) Woomera	Un, Rav.2 +C	238 (148)	"	Neutral atmosphere – (grenades)	S	M&R BAe
					"	" " " - grenade glows	S	
					"	" " " - (falling dipoles)	S	
54 (6)	11 April 1962	SL162 (UK) Woomera	Un, Rav.2	-	"	" " "	Vf	M&R BAe
55 (7)	6 June 1962	SL35C (UK) Woomera	Un, Rav.5A +C	234 (146) (est.)	RAE	Test (Skylark technology) – Raven 5A and Cuckoo combination	S	BAe Edin
					"	Test (Skylark technology) – strengthened split nose cone	S	
56 (8)	20 June 1962	SL45 (UK) Woomera	Un, Rav.5A +C	216 (134)	RAE	Test (Skylark tech.) – strengthened nose cone	F	Edin M&R BAe
					UCL/Lei	Solar physics – X-ray photos	F	
					UCL	" " - Lyman α detectors	Ps	
					UCL	Neutral atmosphere - (grenades)	Ps	
					UCL	" " - falling sphere	F	
					UCL	Ionosphere - positive ion probe	S	
57 (9)	5 July 1962	SL164 (UK) Woomera	Un, Rav.5	111 (69)	UCL	Neutral atmosphere – (grenades)	S	M&R BAe
					IC	" " - falling dipoles	S	
58 (10)	15 Aug. 1962	SL109 (UK) Woomera	Un, Rav.2	111 (69)	Shf/RRS	Ionosphere - electron density by effects on lf radio waves	S	M&R BAe
					UCL	Solar physics – Lyman α detector	S	
					UCL	Ionosphere - positive ion probe	S	
59 (11)	29 Aug. 1962	SL28 (UK) Woomera	Un, Rav.2	110 (68)	RAE	Test (space technology) - gyroscope drift expt.1	Ps	BAe Knott
60 (12)	11 Sept. 1962	SL44 (UK) Woomera	Un, Rav.2	232 (144)	UCL	Ionosphere - electron probe	S	M&R BAe
					UCL	" - ion probe	S	
					UCL	" - Langmuir probe	S	
61 (13)	20 Sept. 1962	SL108 (UK) Woomera	Un, Raven 2B	113 (70)	Shf/RRS	Ionosphere - electron density by effects on lf radio waves (I)	S	BAe, McD

Seq. Nos	Launch date	Ref. (sponsor) launch site	Config-uration	Apogee km (miles)	Experi-menters	Experiment(s)	Result	Source
62 (14)	15 Oct. 1962	SL82 (UK) Woomera	Un, Raven 2	154 (96)	Cam	Ionosphere - deployment of long wire aerial	F	M&R BAe
					Cam	" - measurement of electron density	F	
					UCL	" - sporadic E probe	S	
-	Oct.	(SL81) (UK)	-	n/a	As SL82	As SL82, but cancelled before launch, reflown as SL81A in October 1963	n/a	Edin
63 (15)	13 Nov. 1962	SL114 (UK) Woomera	Un, Raven 7 +C	206 (128)	UCL/Lei	Solar physics - X-ray counter spectrometer	F	M&R BAe
					JB	Micrometeorites – penetration detectors	F	
					MO	Aeronomy - ozone measurements	Ps	
64 (16)	22 Nov. 1962	SL27 (UK) Woomera	Un, Raven 7	114 (70)	RAE	Test (space technology) gyroscope drift expt. 2	S	BAE Knott
65 (17)	28 Nov. 1962	SL165 (UK) Woomera	Un, Rav.7 +C	230 (143)	UCL	Neutral atmosphere – (grenades)	S	M&R BAe
					UCL	" " - grenade glows	S	
					IC	" " - (falling dipoles)	S	
66 (18)	04 Dec. 1962	SL166 (UK) Woomera	Un, Rav.5	105 (65)	"	Neutral atmosphere – (grenades)	S	M&R BAe
					"	" " - grenade glows	S	
					"	" " - (falling dipoles)	S	

1963 (14 research & 5 Proving/Experiments)

Jan.	Feb.	March	April	May	June	July	August	Sept.	Oct.	Nov.	Dec.
		SL84 SL85	SL167	SL115 SL127	SL126 SL46	SL29	SL86	SL87	SL81A SL171 SL169 SL170 SL168 SL134	SL103	SL135 SL104

Seq. Nos	Launch date	Ref. (sponsor) launch site	Config-uration	Apogee km (miles)	Experi-menters	Experiment(s)	Result	Source
67 (1)	01 Mar. 1963	SL84 (UK) Woomera	Un, Rav.7 +C	197 (122)	Bir	Ionosphere - RF probe	S	M&R BAE
					UCW/RAE	Ionosphere - CW propagation	Ps	
					Lei	Solar physics - X-ray counters	S	
					Lei	" " - X-ray cameras	S	
					UCL	" " - Lyman-α telescope	S	
					"	Ionosphere - sporadic E spike probe	F	
68 (2)	11 Mar. 1963	SL85 (UK) Woomera	Un, Rav.7 +C	211 (131)	Bir	Ionosphere – as SL84	S	M&R BAE
					UCW/RAE	" "	S	
					Lei	Solar physics - "	S	
					Lei	" "	S	
					UCL	" "	Ps	
					"	Ionosphere - "	S	
69 (3)	17 April 1963	SL167 (UK) Woomera	Un, Rav.7 +C	235 (146)	UCL	Neutral atmosphere - (grenades)	S	M&R BAe
					"	" " - grenade (glow cloud)	Ps	
					"	" " - falling sphere	S	
					Bel	" " - sodium vapour	F	
70 (4)	23 May 1963	SL115 (UK) Woomera	Un, Rav.7 +C	207 (129)	MO	Aeronomy - ozone distribution	S	M&R, BAE
					JB	Micrometeorites - penetration detector	S	
					Lei	Solar physics - X-ray cameras	S	

No.	Date	Vehicle	Config.	Altitude	Exp.	Experiment	Result	Orgs.
71 (5)	29 May 1963	SL127 (UK) Woomera	Un, Rav.7 +C	207 (129)	RRS	Ionosphere - LF propagation	S	M&R BAE RAE
					"	" - resonance probe	S	
					UCL	" - sporadic E	F	
					Lei	Solar physics - X-ray cameras	S	
					RAE	Test (Skylark technology) – vehicle attitude determination using solar and magnetic sensors	S	
72 (6)	18 Jun 1963	SL126 (UK) Woomera	Un, Rav.7 +C	208 (129)	RRS	Ionosphere – as SL127	S	M&R BAE
					"	" "	Ps	
					UCL	" "	S	
					Lei	Solar physics - "	S	
73 (7)	20 June 1963	SL46 (UK) Woomera	Un, Rav.7 +C	232 (144)	UCL	Ionosphere - Langmuir probe	Ps	M&R BAE
					"	Ionosphere - electron temperature probe	S	
					"	Solar physics - Lyman-α chambers	Ps	
					"	Ionosphere – Sporadic E grid probe	S	
					Lei	Solar physics - X-ray cameras	S	
74 (8)	25 July 1963	SL29 (UK) Woomera	Un, Rav.7	11 (6.6) (est.)	RAE	Test (space technology) gyroscope drift expt.3 (Vehicle broke up after 24s), motor reached 49 km / 30 m)	Vf, Ps	BAE Edin Knott
75 (9)	02 Aug. 1963	SL86 (UK) Woomera	Un, Rav.5A +C	0	RAE	Test (Skylark technology) – test of Cuckoo/Raven 5A combination and strengthened nose cone	Mf	BAE Edin
76 (10)	05 Sept. 1963	SL87 (UK) Woomera	Un, Rav.5A +C	214 (133)	RAE	Test (Skylark technology) – test of Cuckoo/Raven 5A combination	S	BAE McD Edin
77 (11)	3/2 Oct. 1963	SL81A (UK) Woomera	Un, Rav.7	146 (91)	Cam	Ionosphere - long wire aerial impedance	Ps	M&R BAe Edin
					UCL	" - Sporadic E	S	
78 (12)	15 Oct. 1963	SL171 (UK) Woomera	Un, Rav.7 +C	206 (128)	UCL	Neutral atmosphere – (grenades)	S	M&R BAe
					"	" " - grenades (Glow cloud)	Ps	
					Bel	" " - sodium vapour	F	
					UCL	" " - falling sphere	F	
79 (13)	15 Oct. 1963	SL169 (UK) Woomera	Un, Rav.7	136 (85)	UCL	" " - (grenades)	S	M&R BAe
					"	" " - grenades (Glow cloud)	S	
					IC	" " - window/chaff	S	
80 (14)	16 Oct. 1963	SL170 (UK) Woomera	Un, Rav.7	130 (81)	UCL	" " - (grenades)	S	M&R BΛe
					"	" " - grenades (Glow cloud)	S	
					IC	" " - window/chaff	Ps	
81 (15)	16 Oct. 1963	SL168 (UK) Woomera	Un, Rav.7 +C	186 (116)	UCL	" " - (grenades)	S	M&R BAe
					"	" " - grenades (Glow cloud)	Ps	
					Bel	" " - sodium vapour	F	
					UCL	" " - falling sphere	F	
82 (16)	30 Oct. 1963	SL134 (UK) Woomera (BS100)	Un, Rav.7 +C	186 (115)	RAE	Test (space technology) - measurement of the Earth's infra-red radiation, flight test of Moon sensors & tape recorder	Ps	BAE RAE Edin
83 (17)	19 Nov. 1963	SL103 (UK) Woomera (BS94/1)	Un, Rav.7 +C	–	Bir	Ionosphere - RF probe	Vf (MF)	M&R BAe
					UCW/RAE	" - CW propagation (I)		
					Lei	Solar physics - X-ray counters		
					"	" " - X-ray cameras		
					UCL	" - Lyman-α telescope		
					"	Ionosphere – sporadic E spike probe		
84 (18)	02 Dec. 1963	SL135 (UK) Woomera (BS101)	Un, Rav.7 +C	168 (104)	RAE	Test (space technology) - measurement of the Earth's infrared radiation flight test of solar sensors, & tape recorder. (Loss of nose cone at +13 seconds).	F (Vf)	BAE McD RAE Flight

					Bir	Ionosphere – as SL103			
85 (19)	03 Dec. 1963	SL104 (UK) Woomera (BS94/2)	Un, Rav.7 +C	106? (66)	UCW/RAE	" "	Vf	M&R, BAE McD
					Lei	Solar physics - "		
					Lei	" "		
					UCL	" "		
					UCL	Ionosphere - "		

1964 (17 unstabilised & 2 three-axis ACU stabilised)

Jan.	Feb.	March	April	May	June	July	August	Sept.	Oct.	Nov.	Dec.
	SL88 SL30	SL129 SL128	SL136	SL20		S01/1 S01/2 SL31 SL32	SL301 SL121	SL137 SL87A SL120 SL133 SL132	SL47		SL302

Seq. Nos.	Launch date	Ref. (sponsor) launch site	Config- uration	Apogee km (miles)	Experi- menters	Experiment(s)	Result	Source
86 (1)	4 Feb. 1964	SL88 (UK) Woomera (BS103/1)	Un, Rav.5A +C	119 (74)	RAE	Test (Skylark technology) – test of Cuckoo/Raven 5A combination	Ps	BAE Edin
87 (2)	20 Feb. 1964	SL30 (UK) Woomera (BS 92)	Un, Rav.7	105 (65)	RAE	Test (space technology) - gyroscope drift expt. 4.	S	BAE Knott
88 (3)	10 Mar. 1964	SL129 (UK) Woomera (BS106/2)	Un, Rav.7 +C	175 (109)	Soton	Astronomy – galactic γ-rays (spark chamber)	S	M&R BAe
					IC	Geomagnetic - field (magnetometer)	S	
					Lei	Solar physics – X-rays (non-imaging cameras)	S	
					UCL	Ionosphere - sporadic E (probes)	F	
89 (4)	12 Mar. 1964	SL128 (UK) Woomera (BS106/1)	Un, Rav.7 +C	176 (109)	"	Astronomy – as SL129	S	M&R BAe
					"	Geomagnetic - "	S	
					"	Solar physics - "	S	
					"	Ionosphere - "	S	
90 (5)	11 April 1964	SL136 (UK) Woomera (BS108)	Un, Rav.7 +C	202 (126)	MO	Aeronomy - ozone vertical distribution (broad-band detector)	S	M&R BAe
					RAE	Test (Skylark technology) – vehicle attitude determination using solar and magnetic sensors	S	Herbert (1967)
91 (6)	14 May 1964	SL20 (UK) Woomera	Un, Rav.7 +C	182 (113)	RAE	Test (space technology) - study of use of liquid propane in satellite guidance systems	?	RAE BAe Flight
92 (7)	6 July 1964	S01/1 (ESRO) Sardinia	Un, Rav.7 +C	198 (123)	Liège	Aeronomy – spectroscopic study of released ammonia cloud (experiment R12)	S	BAe SP-76
					MPI	Aeronomy - study of ion cloud produced by release of barium in sunlight (experiment R33)	S	
93 (8)	8 July 1964	S01/2 (ESRO) Sardinia	Un, Rav.7 +C	183 (114)	Liège	Aeronomy – as S01/1	S	BAe SP-76
					MPI	" "	S	
94 (9)	15 July 1964	SL31 (UK) Woomera	Un, Rav.7	80 (50)	RAE	Test (space technology) - gyroscope drift expt. 5	S	BAe Knott
95 (10)	17 July 1964	SL32 (UK) Woomera	Un, Rav.7	90 (56)	RAE	Test (space technology) - gyroscope drift expt. 6	S	BAe Knott

No.	Date	Vehicle	Type	Alt.	Estab.	Experiment	Res.	Contractors
96 (11)	11 Aug. 1964	SL301 (UK) Woomera	Sun, Rav.7 +C	145 (91)	RAE	Test (Skylark tech.) – first stabilised (Sun sensors)	S	M&R BAe
					Cul	Test (instrument) - solar image control	S	
					Cul	Solar physics – 2 grazing, 1 norm. incidence spectrograph	Ps	
					Cul	Solar physics - UV (pin-hole camera)	F	
					Lei	" " - X-rays (pin-hole camera)	S	
					Lei	" " - solar X-rays (spectrograph)	S	
97 (12)	20 Aug. 1964	SL121 (UK) Woomera (BS109)	Un, Rav.7 +C	192 (119)	UCW/RAE	Ionosphere - electron density (pulse propagation)	Ps	M&R BAe Edin RAE
					UCW/RAE	Ionosphere - electron density (cw propagation)	Ps	
					Lei	Solar physics – X-rays (2 pin-hole cameras)	S	
					RAE	Test (Skylark technology) – vehicle attitude determination using solar and magnetic sensors	S	
98 (13)	01 Sept. 1964	SL137 (UK) Woomera	Un, Rav.7 +C	211 (131)	MO	Aeronomy - ozone distribution (broad-band detector)	S	M&R BAe
99 (14)	04 Sept. 1964	SL87A (UK) Woomera	Un, Rav.6A +C	182 (113)	RAE	Test (Skylark technology) – first trial of Raven 6A / Cuckoo combination. First test of FPS16 radar transponder.	Ps	BAe Edin
100 (15)	17 Sept. 1964	SL120 (UK) Woomera (BS109)	Un, Rav.7 +C	197 (122)	UCW/RAE	Ionosphere - as SL121	S	M&R BAe Edin RAE
					UCW/RAE	Ionosphere - "	S	
					Lei	Solar physics – "	F	
					RAE	Test (Skylark technology) – as SL121	S	
101 (16)	24 Sept. 1964	SL133 (UK) Woomera	Un, Rav.7 +C	180 (112)	RRS	Ionosphere - plasma environment (Q meter)	S	M&R BAe
					RRS	" - plasma frequency (resonance probes)	S	
					Lei	Solar physics – X-rays (non-imaging cameras)	F	
102 (17)	29 Sept. 1964	SL132 (UK) Woomera	Un, Rav.7 +C	175 (109)	"	Ionosphere – as SL133	S	M&R BAe
					"	" " "	S	
					"	Solar physics - "	Ps	
103 (18)	27 Oct. 1964	SL47 (UK) Woomera	Un, Rav.7 +C	146 (91)	UCL	Ionosphere - sporadic E (probes)	Ps	M&R BAe
					UCL/Lei	Astronomy – non-solar X-ray Background (telescope)	F	
					UCL	Astronomy – stellar UV emission (camera)	F	
104 (19)	17 Dec. 1964	SL302 (UK) Woomera	Sun, Rav.7 +C	167 (104)	RAE	Test (Skylark tech.) – attitude control (Sun sensors)	S	M&R BAe
					Cul	Solar physics - (spectrographs)	S	
					Cul	" " - UV (pin-hole camera)	S	
					Lei	" " - X-rays (pin-hole camera)	S	
					Lei	" " - X-rays (spectrograph)	S	

1965 (26 unstabilised & 2 three-axis ACU stabilised)

Jan.	Feb.	March	April	May	June	July	August	Sept.	Oct.	Nov.	Dec.
	SL88A	SL87B SL140 SL141 S03/1	S03/2 SL303 SL464 SL363 SL364 SL461 SL462 SL463 SL362	SL361 SL139 SL138		SL106 SL48 SL105	S05/1	SL88B S04/1	S04/2 SL39 SL306	SL130	SL131

Seq. Nos	Launch Date	Ref. (sponsor) launch site	Config-uration	Apogee km (miles)	Experi-menters	Experiment(s)	Result	Source
105 (1)	25 Feb. 1965	SL88A (UK) Woomera (BS116/1)	Un, Rav.6A +C	220 (137)	RAE	Test (Skylark technology) – motor/system trial, second test Raven 6A/Cuckoo combination	S	BAe Edin
106 (2)	03 Mar. 1965	SL87B(UK) Woomera (BS116/2)	Un, Rav.6A +C	215 (134)	RAE	Test (Skylark technology) – motor/system trial, third test Raven 6A/Cuckoo combination	S	BAE Edin
107 (3)	17 Mar. 1965	SL140 (UK) Woomera	Un, Rav.7 +C	19 (12)	UCL	Ionosphere - sporadic E (positive ion probes)	Vf	M&R BAe
					Shf	Ionosphere - aerial impedance (probe)	Vf	
					ROE	Astronomy - stellar UV radiation	Vf	
108 (4)	25 Mar. 1965	SL141 (UK) Woomera	Un, Rav.7 +C	174 (108)	UCL	Ionosphere – as SL140	S	M&R BAe
					Shf	" "	S	
					ROE	Astronomy - "	Ps	
109 (5)	31 Mar. 1965	S03/1 (ESRO) Sardinia	Un, Rav.7	45 (27)	Breisach	Ionosphere – electron density in the D-layer (Radio spectrometer) (experiment R19)	Vf	M&R BAe McD SP-76
					Breisach	Ionosphere – electron density in the E-layer (Variable frequency probe) (experiment R21)		
					UCL	Ionosphere – electron temperature profile (Langmuir probe) (experiment R44)		
110 (6)	03 April 1965	S03/2 (ESRO) Sardinia	Un, Rav.7	172 (106)	Ditto	Ionosphere – as S03/1	S	M&R BAe McD SP-76
					Ditto	" "	Ps	
					Ditto	" "	Ps	
111 (7)	09 April 1965	SL303 (UK) Woomera	Sun, Rav.7+C	161 (100)	RAE	Test (space technology) – attitude control (Sun sensors)	S	M&R BAe
					Cul	Solar physics – corona (normal incidence spectrograph)	S	
					Cul	Solar physics - corona (grating pin-hole camera)	S	
					Cul	" " - XUV (pin-hole camera)	S	
					Lei	" " - X-rays (pin-hole camera)	S	
					Lei	" " - X-rays (crystal spectrograph)	S	
112 (8)	29 April 1965	SL464 (UK) Woomera	Un, Rav.7 +C	0	IC	Neutral atmosphere - wind profile (falling dipoles)	Vf	M&R BAe
					Bel	" " - wind velocities (lithium vapour)		
					UCL	" " - wind structure (grenades)		

No.	Date	SL	Config	Apogee	Exp	Experiment	Result	Org
113 (9)	"	SL363 "	Un, Rav.7	137 (85)	IC	" " - wind profile (falling dipoles)	Ps	M&R BAe
					UCL	" " - wind structure (grenades)	S	
114 (10)	"	SL364 "	Un, Rav.7	132 (82)	IC	" " - wind profile (falling dipoles)	S	M&R BAe
					UCL	" " - wind structure (grenades)	S	
115 (11)	"	SL461 "	Un, Rav.7	124 (77)	IC	" " - wind profile (falling dipoles)	Ps	M&R BAe
					UCL	" " - wind structure (grenades)	S	
116 (12)	30 April 1965	SL462 "	Un, Rav.7	140 (87)	IC	" " - wind profile (falling dipoles)	S	M&R BAe
					UCL	" " - wind structure (grenades)	S	
117 (13)	"	SL463 "	Un, Rav.7	135 (84)	IC	" " - wind profile (falling dipoles)	S	M&R BAe
					UCL	" " - wind structure (grenades)	S	
118 (14)	"	SL362 "	Un, Rav.7+C	175 (109)	"	" " - air density (falling sphere)	F	M&R BAe
					"	" " - wind structure (grenades)	Sf	
119 (15)	11 May 1965	SL361 "	Un, Rav.7+C	181 (113)	Bel	" " - wind velocities (lithium vapour)	S	M&R BAe
					UCL	" " - air density (falling sphere)	S	
120 (16)	14 May 1965	SL139 "	Un, Rav.7+C	187 (116)	RSRS	Ionosphere - electron density (lf signal receiver)	S	M&R BAe
					"	" - electron density (current probe)	?	
121 (17)	19 May 1965	SL138 (UK) Woomera	Un, Rav.7 +C	179 (111)	RSRS	Ionosphere - electron density (lf signal receiver)	S	M&R BAe
					"	" - electron density (current probe)	S	
					Lei	Solar physics – X-rays (non-imaging camera)	S	
122 (18)	01 July 1965	SL106 (UK) Woomera	Un, Rav.7 +C	130 (81)	Lei	Solar physics – X-rays (non-imaging camera)	S	M&R BAe
					UCL	Ionosphere - electron & ion concentration (Langmuir & positive ion probes)	S	
					"	Ionosphere- electron temperature (probe)	S	
					"	Aeronomy - effect of rocket on local environment	S	
					"	" - effect of rocket motion & photoemission on probe currents	S	
123 (19)	14 July 1965	SL48 (UK) Woomera	Un, Rav.7 +C	182 (113)	UCL	Astronomy – stellar UV spectra (photometers)	S	M&R BAe RAE Edin
					"	Test (scientific instrument) – attitude measurement (Moon detectors/horizon detectors/fluxgate magnetometers)	S	
					RAE	Test (Skylark technology) – (i) vehicle attitude determination using solar and magnetic sensors (ii) Nose cone gap measurement	S	
124 (20)	29 July 1965	SL105 (UK) Woomera	Un, Rav.7 +C	0	Lei	Solar physics - as SL106		M&R BAe
					UCL	Ionosphere - "	Vf	
					"	" "		
					"	Aeronomy - "		
					"	" "		

No.	Date	Vehicle / Site	Stab.	Altitude km	Exp.	Experiment	Result	Contractor
125 (21)	11 Aug. 1965	S05/1 (ESRO) Sardinia	Un, Rav.7 +C	215 (134)	ROE	Astronomy - stellar UV emission (photometer) (experiment R62)	Sf	M&R BAe SP-76
					"	Astronomy - stellar UV emission (spectrophotometer) (experiment R63)	Sf	
126 (22)	09 Sept. 1965	SL88B (UK) Woomera BS123	Un, Rav.6 +C	221 (137)	RAE	Test (Skylark technology) – motor/system trial, fourth test Raven 6A/Cuckoo combination	S	BAe WRE
127 (23)	30 Sept. 1965	S04/1 (ESRO) Sardinia	Un, Rav.7+C	250 (probably) (155)	MPI	Aeronomy - study of ion cloud produced by release of barium in sunlight (experiment R33)	S	M&R BAe McD SP-76
					UCL	Neutral atmosphere - grenades (experiment R48a)	S	
					"	" " - wind profile by TMA release (expt.R48b)	S	
128 (24)	02 Oct. 1965	S04/2 (ESRO) Sardinia	"	"	MPI	Aeronomy – as S04/1	S	"
					UCL	Neutral atmosphere - as S04/1	S	
					"	" " " "	S	
129 (25)	18 Oct. 1965	SL39 (UK) Woomera	Un, Rav.7 +C	205 (127)	Belfast	Aeronomy – night airglow (photometer)	S	M&R BAe
130 (26)	20 Oct. 1965	SL306 (UK) Woomera	Sun, Rav.6A +C	213 (132)	Lei	Solar physics – X-rays (pinhole cameras)	S	M&R BAe
					Cul	" " - spectra (grating pinhole camera)	S	
					Cul	" " - image in XUV (pinhole camera)	S	
131 (27)	19 Nov. 1965	SL130 (UK) Woomera	Un, Rav.7 +C	138 (86)	Belfast	Neutral atmosphere - wind velocities (lithium vapour)	F	M&R BAe
					Bir	Ionosphere - electron density & temp. (rf probe)	S	
					Lei	Solar physics – X-rays (non-imaging camera)	?	
					IC	Ionosphere - sporadic E field discontinuities (proton precession magnetometer)	S	
					UCL	Ionosphere – sporadic E ionisation (positive ion probes)	S	
132 (28)	13 Dec. 1965	SL131 (UK) Woomera	Un, Rav.7 +C	130 (81)	Bel	Neutral atmosphere – as SL130	S	"
					Bir	Ionosphere - "	S	
					Lei	Solar physics - "	?	
					IC	Ionosphere - "	S	
					UCL	" "	S	

1966 (22 un/spin stabilised & 3 three-axis ACU stabilised)

Jan.	Feb.	March	April	May	June	July	Aug.	Sept.	Oct.	Nov.	Dec.
	SL307	SL581	SL582 SL583	SL304 SL422	SL327 SL328 S17/1 S17/2 S08/1 SL421 S08/2	S18/1 S18/2 SL88C			SL321 SL322 SL324S SL323 SL324	SL481 S11/1	SL405 SL581A

Seq. Nos	Launch date	Ref. (sponsor) launch site	Config-uration	Apogee km (miles)	Experi-menters	Experiment(s)	Result	Source
133 (1)	02 Feb. 1966	SL307 (UK) Woomera	Sun, Rav.6 +C	216 (134)	RAE	Test (Skylark tech.) - attitude control unit (stage 1)	S	M&R BAe Cul
					Lei	Solar physics – X-rays (pin-hole camera)	S	
					Cul	" " - spectra (grating pinhole camera)	Ps	
					Cul	" " - image in XUV (pinhole camera)	Ps	
					Cul	" " - image at very XUV (mirror filter pinhole camera)	S	
134 (2)	17 Mar. 1966	SL581 (UK) Woomera	Un, Rav.6 +C	221 (137)	RAE	Test (Skylark technology) - ignition system reliability, & help qualify Raven 6 for unstabilised payloads	S	BAe McD
135 (3)	10 April 1966	SL582 (UK) Woomera	Un, Rav.8 +C	172 (107)	RAE	Test (Skylark technology) - 1st boosted Raven 8 (also first ever Raven 8)	Ps	BAe McD
136 (4)	21 April 1966	SL583 (UK) Woomera	Un, Rav.8 +C	193 (120)	RAE	Test (Skylark technology) – 2nd boosted Raven 8	Ps	BAe McD
137 (5)	05 May 1966	SL304 (UK) Woomera	Sun, Rav.6 +C	203 (126)	Lei	Solar physics – X-rays (2 crystal spectrometers)	S	M&R BAe
					UCL/Lei	" " - X-rays (scanning spectroheliograph)	S	
					RAE	Test (space tech.) - silicon solar cell performance	S	
138 (6)	31 May 1966	SL422 UK Woomera	Un, Rav.7 +C	161 (100)	MSSL	Aeronomy - plasma waves in rocket wake (probes)	S	M&R BAe
					Shf	Ionosphere - aerial impedance (probes)	S	
139 (7)	02 June 1966	SL327 (UK) Woomera	Un, Rav.7 +C	176 (109)	MO	Aeronomy - ozone concentration (solar absorption detector)	S	M&R BAe
					MO	Solar physics – solar intensity (photo-cells)	S	
					UCW	Ionosphere – electron density profile (cw propagation)	S	
140 (8)	09 June 1966	SL328 (UK) Woomera	Un, Rav.7 +C	184 (114)	"	Aeronomy – as SL327	S	M&R BAe
					"	Solar physics - "	S	
					"	Ionosphere - "	S	
141 (9)	16 June 1966	S17/1 (ESRO) Sardinia	Un, Rav.7 +C	231 (144)	MPI Garching	Aeronomy/Ionosphere – barium release (experiment R33)	S	BAe McD SP-77
142 (10)	18 June 1966	S17/2 (ESRO) Sardinia	Un, Rav.7 +C	220 (137)	MPI Garching	Aeronomy/Ionosphere – barium release (experiment R33)	S	BAe McD SP-77
143 (11)	20 June 1966	S08/1 (ESRO) Sardinia	Un, Rav.7 +C	216 (134)	MPI	Aeronomy/Ionosphere – barium release (expt. R33)	Vf	M&R BAe SP-77
					MO	Aeronomy/Solar physics - ozone concentration by measurement of solar radiation (experiment R47a)		
144 (12)	23 June 1966	SL421 (UK) Woomera	Un, Rav.7 +C	170 (106)	MSSL	Aeronomy - plasma waves in rocket wake	S	M&R BAe
					Shf	Ionosphere - aerial impedance	S	
145 (13)	28 June 1966	S08/2 (ESRO) Sardinia	Un, Rav.7 +C	228 (142)	MPI	Aeronomy/Ionosphere - barium release (expt. R33)	S	BAe M&R SP-77
					MO	Aeronomy/Solar physics - ozone concentration by measurement of solar radiation (experiment R47a)	S	
146 (14)	8 July 1966	S18/1 (ESRO) Sardinia	Un, Rav.7 +C	244 (152)	Liège	Ionosphere/Aeronomy - ammonia release (expt. R85)	S	BAe McD SP-77

147 (15)	13 July 1966	S18/2 (ESRO) Sardinia	Un, Rav.7 +C	249 (155)	Liège	Ionosphere/Aeronomy - ammonia release (expt. R85)	S	BAe McD SP-77
148 (16)	28 July 1966	SL88C, (UK) Woomera	Un, Rav.6+C	213 (132)	RAE	Test (Skylark technology) – fourth test of Raven 6	?	BAe McD
149 (17)	25 Oct. 1966	SL321 (UK) Woomera	Un, Rav.7 +C	211 (131)	Bir	Ionosphere - electron density (39 MHz probe)	S	M&R BAe
					Bir	" - electron temperature (double Langmuir probe)	S	
150 (18)	"	SL322 "	Un, Rav.8	119 (74)	"	Ionosphere - electron density (39 MHz probe)	S	M&R BAe
					"	" - electron temperature (double Langmuir probe)	S	
151 (19)	27 Oct. 1966	SL324S "	Un, Rav.7 +C	173 (108)	"	Ionosphere - electron density (39 MHz probe)	S	M&R BAe
					"	" - electron temperature (double Langmuir probe)	S	
152 (20)	"	SL323 "	Un, Rav.8 +C	212 (132)	"	Ionosphere - electron density (39 MHz probe)	S	M&R BAe
					"	" - electron temperature (double Langmuir probe)	S	
153 (21)	"	SL324 "	Un, Rav.7 +C	200? (124)	"	Ionosphere - electron density (39 MHz probe)		M&R BAe McD
					"	" - electron temperature (double Langmuir probe) (Raven 7 burst in flight)	Mf	
154 (22)	18 Nov. 1966	SL481 (UK) Woomera	Sun, Rav.6 +C	142 (88)	RAE	Test (Skylark technology) - 1st Mk.II build. F? – certainly didn't get very high!	F	BAe McD
155 (23)	26 Nov. 1966	S11/1 (ESRO) Sardinia	Un, Rav.6 +C	2.5 (1.6)	PIB	Ionosphere/Astronomy – study of low energy (X-ray) proton component of cosmic X-rays (expt.R73)	Mf	M&R BAe SP-77
					ROE	Astronomy – night sky random stellar UV survey (experiment R65)		
156 (24)	08 Dec. 1966	SL405 (UK) Woomera	Sun, Rav.6 +C	0?	Cul	Solar physics - corona spectrum (to 500Å)		M&R BAe McD
					Cul	" " - corona spectrum (to 10Å)	Mf	
					Cul	" " - image (pin-hole camera)		
					MO	" " - radiation (as Ariel III)		
					MO	Aeronomy - molecular oxygen concentration		
					Lei	Solar physics - X-Ray spectrum		
157 (25)	14 Dec. 1966	SL581A (UK) Woomera	Spin, Rav.7 +C	164 (102)	RAE	Test (Skylark technology) – improved Raven ignition system & canted fins	S	BAe McD

1967 (16 un/spin stabilised & 4 three-axis ACU stabilised)

Jan.	Feb.	March	April	May	June	July	Aug.	Sept.	Oct.	Nov.	Dec.
		SL406	SL426 SL118 SL119 SL425 SL682	S11/2 S05/2			SL305 SL581B SL521 SL522	S26/1	S19/1 S26/2 S19/2	SL407 SL423 SL424	SL422A

Seq. Nos	Launch date	Ref. (sponsor) launch site	Config-uration	Apogee km (miles)	Experi-menters	Experiment(s)	Result	Source
158 (1)	14 Mar. 1967	SL406 (UK) Woomera	Sun, Rav.6 +C	200 (124)	Cul	Solar physics – XUV spectrum 10-500Å (grazing incidence spectrograph)	Ps	M&R BAe
					Cul	Solar physics - UV spectrum 500-3000Å (normal incidence spectrograph)	S	
					Cul	Solar physics - XUV image	F	
					Lei	" " - solar disc X-ray spectrum	S	
					MO	Aeronomy - solar radiation flux (Ariel III sensor)	S	
					MO	" - molecular oxygen concentration	S	
159 (2)	04 April 1967	SL426 (UK) Woomera	Un, Rav.6 +C	220 (137)	UCW	Ionosphere - electron density profile (cw prop.)	F	M&R BAe UAT
					UCW	" - electron density profile (hf pulse prop.)	S	
					UAT	Astronomy - celestial X-ray scan	S	
160 (3)	10 April 1967	SL118 (UK) Woomera (BS140)	Un, Rav.7 +C	167 (104)	Bel	Aeronomy - altitude & intensity of molecular oxygen (photometers)	S	M&R BAe WRE
					"	Aeronomy - attitude (airglow horizon)	S	
					Lei	Astronomy - cosmic X-ray survey southern sky	S	
					"	Test (space tech.) – infra-red horizon detector	Ps	
					UCW	Ionosphere - rocket induced ionosphere disturbance	S	
161 (4)	12 April 1967	SL119 (UK) Woomera (BS140)	Un, Rav.7 +C	160 (99)	Bel	Aeronomy – as SL118	S	M&R BAe WRE
					"	" " "	S	
					Lei	Astronomy - "	F	
					"	Test - "	Ps	
					UCW	Ionosphere - "	S	
162 (5)	21 April 1967	SL425 (UK) Woomera	Un, Rav.6 +C	218 (135)	UCW	Ionosphere - electron density profile (cw prop.)	F	M&R BAe UAT
					"	" - electron density profile (hf pulse prop.)	S	
					UAT	Astronomy - celestial X-ray scan	S	
163 (6)	27 April 1967	SL682 (UK) Woomera	Sun, Rav.6 +C	203 (126)	RAE	Test (Skylark technology) - special stabilised payload?	?	BAe McD
164 (7)	22 May 1967	S11/2 (ESRO) Sardinia	Un, Rav.6 +C	194 (121)	PIB	Ionosphere/Astronomy – study of low energy (X-ray) proton component of cosmic X-rays (expt.R73)	S	M&R BAe SP-78
					ROE	Astronomy – night sky random stellar UV survey (experiment R65)	S	
165 (8)	26 May 1967	S05/2 (ESRO) Sardinia	Un, Rav.6 +C	239 (149)	ROE	Astronomy - stellar UV emission (photometer) (experiment R62)	S	M&R BAe SP-78
					ROE	Astronomy - stellar UV emission (spectrophotometer) (experiment R63)	S	
166 (9)	08 Aug. 1967	SL305 (UK) Woomera	Sun, Rav.6 +C	182 (113)	MSSL	Solar physics – X-ray spatial resolution (8-18Å) (scanning spectroheliograph)	S	M&R BAe
					MSSL	Solar physics - Lyman-α (ionisation chamber)	?	
					Lei	Solar physics - soft X-ray high res. (counter crystal spectrometer)	S	
167 (10)	16 Aug. 1967	SL581B(UK) Woomera (BS143)	Spin, Rav.7 +C	152 (94)	RAE	Test (Skylark technology) - canted fins & Imp spin-up motors	Ps	BAe McD WRE
168 (11)	24 Aug. 1967	SL521 (UK) Woomera	Un, Rav.7 +C	178 (111)	Oxf	Aeronomy - Lyman-α & Hα night sky brightness, and attitude with respect to the horizon via airglow	F	M&R BAe WRE

169 (12)	29 Aug. 1967	SL522 (UK) Woomera	Un, Rav.7 +C	124 (77)	Oxf	Aeronomy - Lyman-α & Hα night sky brightness, and attitude with respect to the horizon via airglow	Ps	M&R BAe WRE
170 (13)	27 Sept. 1967	S26/1 (ESRO) Sardinia	Un, Rav.7 +C	183 (114)	Bir	Ionosphere - electron density (rf probe) (experiment R105)	S	M&R BAe SP-78
					"	Ionosphere - electron temperature (double Langmuir probe) (experiment R106)	S	
					RSRS	Aeronomy – Lyman-α flux (detector) (expt.R123)	S	
					"	Aeronomy – solar X-rays (detector) (expt.R131)	S	
					"	Ionosphere – D-region electron density (lf propagation/Faraday rotation) (experiment R132)	S	
171 (14)	04 Oct. 1967	S19/1 (ESRO) Sardinia	Un, Rav.7 +C	207 (129)	Breisach	Ionosphere – electron density profile (inverse Seddon expt., 3-channel radio receiver) (experiment R20)	F	M&R BAe SP-78
					MSSL	Ionosphere – electron temperature (Langmuir probe) (experiment R44)	S	
					Bonn	Aeronomy – densities neutral atmosphere components (Two neutral mass spectrometers) (experiment R79)	S	
					IAP	Aeronomy – atmospheric pressure & density (gauges) (experiment R104)	S	
172 (15)	07 Oct. 1967	S26/2 (ESRO) Sardinia	Un, Rav.7 +C	164 (102)	Bir	Ionosphere – as S26/1	S	M&R BAe SP-78
					"	" " "	S	
					RSRS	Aeronomy – as S26/1	S	
					"	" " "	S	
					"	" " "	S	
173 (16)	10 Oct. 1967	S19/2 (ESRO) Sardinia	Un, Rav.7 +C	207 (129)	Breisach	Ionosphere – as S19/1	S	M&R BAe SP-78
					MSSL	" "	S	
					Bonn	Aeronomy – as S19/1	S	
					IAP	" "	S	
174 (17)	01 Nov. 1967	SL407 (UK) Woomera	Sun, Rav.6 +C	206 (128)	Cul	Solar physics - UV spectrum 500-1540Å (normal incidence spectrograph)	S	M&R BAe
					"	Solar physics - XUV spectrum 12-400Å (grazing incidence spectrograph)	F	
					Lei	Solar physics - solar disc X-ray spectrum	S	
					MO	Aeronomy – solar radiation flux (Ariel III sensor)	S	
					"	" - molecular oxygen concentration	S	
175 (18)	14 Nov. 1967	SL423 (UK) Woomera	Un, Rav.7 +C	178 (111)	IC	Ionosphere - E-region current	S	M&R BAe
					RSRS	" - small electron density variation	S	
					"	Aeronomy - absorption of solar Lyman-α	S	
176 (19)	17 Nov. 1967	SL424 (UK) Woomera	Un, Rav.7 +C	181 (112)	IC	Ionosphere – as SL423	S	M&R BAe
					RSRS	" "	S	
					"	Aeronomy - "	S	
177 (20)	01 Dec. 1967	SL422A (UK) Woomera	Un, Rav.7 +C	181 (112)	RAE	Test (Skylark technology) - no Cuckoo fins	S	BAe McD UAT
					UAT	Astronomy - celestial X-ray scan (proportional counters)	Ps	

1968 (12 un/spin stabilised & 5 three-axis ACU stabilised)

Jan.	Feb.	March	April	May	June	July	Aug.	Sept.	Oct.	Nov.	Dec.
	SL583A	SL408 SL16/1		SL761 SL762	SL723	SL403 SL523	SL524 SL501		S47/1 SL791R	S41 S43/1	S27/1 SL601 SL725

Seq. Nos	Launch date	Ref. (sponsor) launch site	Config- uration	Apogee km (miles)	Experi- menters	Experiment(s)	Result	Source
178 (1)	08 Feb. 1968	SL583A (UK) Woomera	Un, Rav.6 +G	300 (186)	RAE	Test (Skylark technology) - first proving flight for Goldfinch II booster	S	BAe McD
179 (2)	20 Mar. 1968	SL408 (UK) Woomera	Sun, Rav.6 +C	217 (135)	CuI	Solar physics – X-ray & XUV spectrums 12-70Å & 140-500Å (2 grazing incidence spectrographs)	S	M&R BAe
					CuI	Solar physics - spectrum 1100Å to 2810Å (normal incidence spectrograph)	S	
					CuI	Solar physics - UV image (pin-hole camera)	F	
					Lei	" " - X-ray image (pin-hole camera)	S	
					MO	Aeronomy - solar radiation flux (detector)	S	
					MO	" - molecular oxygen concentration (attenuation of radiation)	S	
180 (3)	27 Mar. 1968	S16/1 (ESRO) Kiruna	Un, Rav.8	172 (107)	MSSL	Ionosphere - electron temperature (Langmuir probe) (experiment R44)	S	M&R BAe SP-79
					MSSL	Ionosphere - auroral ionisation structure (positive ion probes) (experiment R45)	S	
					IC	Aurora – magnetic fields in aurora (proton magnetometer) (experiment R49)	Ps	
181 (4)	31 May 1968	SL761 (UK) Woomera	Un, Rav.7 +C	238 (148)	UCL	Neutral atmosphere - wind velocity & atmospheric density (grenades & TMA dispenser)	S	M&R BAe
182 (5)	"	SL762 "	"	242 (150)	"	"	S	M&R BAc
183 (6)	12 June 1968	SL723 (UK) Woomera	Un, Rav.5A +C	184 (114)	Lei	Astronomy - cosmic X-ray survey (proportional counters)	S	M&R BAe
184 (7)	8 July 1968	SL403 (UK) Woomera	Moon, Rav.6 +C	177 (110)	RAE	Test (Skylark technology) – 1st flight Stage 3 Attitude Control Unit	S	M&R BAe
					Lei	Astronomy – cosmic X-ray emission (proportional counters scanning M-87 galaxy)	S	
					Lei	Astronomy – cosmic X-ray image (pin-hole camera stabilised on M-87 galaxy)	S	
185 (8)	23 July 1968	SL523 (UK) Woomera	Un, Rav.5A +C	258 (160)	UCW	Ionosphere - electron density profile & layer heights (cw & pulse propagation)	Ps	M&R BAe
186 (9)	05 Aug. 1968	SL524 (UK) Woomera	Un, Rav.5A +C	235 (146)	"	"	S	M&R BAe

187 (10)	29 Aug. 1968	SL501 (UK) Woomera	Sun, Rav.6 +C	210 (131)	MSSL	Solar physics – intensity of solar emission lines (scanning spectrophotometer)	Ps	M&R BAe
					MSSL	Solar physics – extreme UV solar spectrum (grazing incidence spectrograph)	Ps	
					MSSL	Ionosphere - electron temperature (probe)	Ps	
					MSSL	" - positive ion density (probe)	Ps	
					Bir	Ionosphere - electron density (probe)	Ps	
188 (11)	07 Oct. 1968	S47/1 (ESRO) Sardinia	Un, Rav.6 +C	208 (129)	ROE	Astronomy – UV sky brightness (photomultiplier) (experiment R120)	S	M&R BAe SP-79
					ROE	Astronomy – absolute stellar UV emission (twin-channel photometer) (experiment R121A)	F	
					ROE	Astronomy – stellar UV emission (Cassegrain telescope photometer) (experiment R121B)	F	
189 (12)	09 Oct. 1968	SL791R (UK) Woomera	Un, Rav.8	106 (66)	RAE	Test, purpose unknown	S	BAe McD
190 (13)	22 Nov. 1968	S41 (ESRO) Sardinia	Sun, Rav.6 +C	210 (131)	UTR	Solar physics - X-ray spectrometry (experiment R7)	Ps	M&R BAe SP-79
					Lei	Solar physics – crystal X-ray spectrometry (Bragg crystal spectrometer) (experiment R56)	S	
191 (14)	25 Nov. 1968	S43/1 (ESRO) Kiruna	Un, Rav.8 +C	212 (132)	Breisach	Aurora - electron density (experiment R21)	S	BAe SP-79
					Liège	" - UV spectrum (experiment R81)	Ps	
					Kiruna	" – auroral particles (experiment R86)	Ps	
					Bir	" - electron density (experiment R105)	S	
					"	" - electron temperature (experiment R106)	S	
192 (15)	03 Dec. 1968	S27/1 (ESRO) Sardinia	Un, Rav.6 +C	198 (123)	ROE	Astronomy - integrated night sky spectroscopy (Cassegrain telescope) (experiment R65)	S	M&R BAe SP-79
					ROE	Astronomy – stellar UV emission (photometer) (experiment R100)	S	
193 (16)	04 Dec. 1968	SL601 (UK) Woomera	Sun, Rav.6 +C	182 (113)	Cul/Bel	Solar physics - Mg II doublet profile (Fabry- Perot interferometer)	S	M&R BAe
					Cul/Bel	Solar physics - image (imaging camera)	S	
194 (17)	06 Dec. 1968	SL725 (UK) Woomera	Un, Rav.7 +C	146 (91)	MSSL	Ionosphere - positive ion density in Es layer (probes)	S	M&R BAe
					RSRS	Ionosphere – magnetic field in Es layer (Rb magnetometer)	S	
					Bir	Ionosphere - electron density (probe)	S	

1969 (19 un/spin stabilised & 9 three-axis ACU stabilised)

Jan.	Feb.	March	April	May	June	July	Aug.	Sept.	Oct.	Nov.	Dec.
SL781 SL726		S43/2	SL724 SL502 SL606 SL604	SL404		S38/1 S64/1 S38/2 S64/2 SL722 SL729 SL721 SL730	SL605		S29/1 SL861 SL862 S29/2 SL586 SL821 S68/1	S46/1 SL602 SL801 SL603	

Seq. Nos	Launch date	Ref. (sponsor) launch site	Config-uration	Apogee km (miles)	Experi-menters	Experiment(s)	Result	Source
195 (1)	21 Jan. 1969	SL781 (UK) Woomera	Un, Rav.6 +G	~3 (1.8)	RAE	Test (Skylark technology) – 2nd proving flight for Goldfinch booster (Head separated from the sustainer prematurely at 4.8 seconds)	Vf	BAe 9th policy Tuohy
					UAT	Astronomy – X-ray survey of the southern sky	Vf	
196 (2)	23 Jan. 1969	SL726 (UK) Woomera	Un, Rav.7 +C	149 (93)	MSSL	Ionosphere - positive ion density in Es layer (probes)	S	M&R BAe
					RSRS	Ionosphere - magnetic field in Es layer (Rb magnetometer)	S	
					Bir	Ionosphere - electron temperature (probe)	S	
197 (3)	15 Mar. 1969	S43/2 (ESRO) Kiruna	Un, Rav.8 +C	210 (131)	Breisach	Aurora - electron density (experiment R21)	S	BAe SP-80
					Liège	" - UV spectrum (experiment R81)	S	
					Kiruna	" – auroral particles (experiment R86)	Ps	
					Bir	" - electron density (experiment R105)	S	
					"	" - electron temperature (experiment R106)	S	
198 (4)	01 April 1969	SL724 (UK) Woomera	Un, Rav.5A +C	192 (119)	Lei	Astronomy - cosmic X-ray survey (proportional counters) (1st BAC launch)	S	M&R BAe
199 (5)	03 April 1969	SL502 (UK) Woomera	Sun, Rav.6 +G	273 (170)	MSSL	Solar physics - intensity of solar emission lines (scanning spectrophotometer)	S	M&R BAe
					MSSL	Solar physics – extreme UV spectrum (grazing incidence spectrograph)	S	
					MSSL	Ionosphere - electron temperature (probe)	S	
					MSSL	" - positive ion density (probe)	S	
					Bir	Ionosphere - electron density (probe)	S	
200 (6)	17 April 1969	SL606 (UK) Woomera	Sun, Rav.6 +C	202 (126)	Cul	Solar physics – UV spectrum (normal incidence spectrograph)	Sf	M&R BAe
					Cul	Solar physics - UV spectra (grazing incidence spectrographs	Sf	
					Cul	Solar physics - extreme UV image (normal & grating pin-hole camera)	Sf	
					MO	Aeronomy - molecular oxygen concentration (ionisation chambers)	S	
201 (7)	22 April 1969	SL604 (UK) Woomera	Sun, Rav.6 +C	180 (112)	Cul	Solar physics - UV spectrum (échelle grating spectrograph)	S	M&R BAe
202 (8)	14 May 1969	SL404 (UK) Woomera	Moon, Rav.6 +C	178 (111)	Cul	Solar physics - UV spectrum (grazing incidence spectrograph	Vf	M&R BAe
					Cul	Solar physics - extreme UV image (grating pin-hole camera)	Vf	
					Lei	Solar physics - soft x-ray image (pin-hole camera)	Vf	
203 (9)	05 July 1969	S38/1 (ESRO) Sardinia	Spin, Rav.7 +C	c.220 (137)	Liège	Aeronomy – photochemistry of possible cometary parent molecules (propylene release) (experiment R85)	S	BAe SP-80
					BAC/ESRO	Test (Skylark technology) – Imp motor spin-up trial & Raven ignition improvement tests	S	

204 (10)	06 July 1969	S64/1 (ESRO) Sardinia	Un, Rav.6 +C	275 (171)	IASB	Aeronomy – atmospheric temperature & chemical kinetics (methane & oxygen release & burn at 150 & 275 km), (experiment R149)	S	BAe McD SP-80
					BAC/ESRO	Test (Skylark technology) – Imp motor spin-up	S	
205 (11)	11 July 1969	S38/2 (ESRO Sardinia	Spin, Rav.7 +C	203 (126)	Liège	Aeronomy – as S38/1	S	BAe SP-80
206 (12)	13 July 1969	S64/2 (ESRO) Sardinia	Un, Rav.6 +C	285 (177)	IASB	Aeronomy - as S64/1	S	BAe McD SP-80
					BAC/ESRO	Test (Skylark technology) – Imp motor spin-up	S	
207 (13)	15 July 1969	SL722 (UK) Woomera	Un, Rav.5A +C	216 (134)	Shf	Ionosphere - electron density (lf impedance probe)	S	M&R BAe
					UCW	Ionosphere - electron density profile & layer heights (pulse propagation)	Ps	
					UCW	Ionosphere - electron density profile (cw propagation)	Ps	
208 (14)	17 July 1969	SL729 (UK) Woomera	Un, Rav.6 +C	244 (152)	Bel	Aeronomy - day-time airglow (photometer)	S	M&R BAe
					MSSL	Ionosphere - electron temperature (probe)	S	
					UCW	Ionosphere - electron density profile (cw propagation)	S	
209 (15)	25 July 1969	SL721 (UK) Woomera	Un, Rav.5A +C	213 (132)	Shf	As SL722	S	M&R BAe
					UCW	"	S	
					UCW	"	S	
210 (16)	30 July 1969	SL730 (UK) Woomera	Un, Rav.6 +C	262 (163)	Bel	As SL729	S	M&R BAe
					MSSL	"	S	
					UCW	"	S	
211 (17)	21 Aug. 1969	SL605 (UK) Woomera	Sun, Rav.6 +C	197 (122)	Lei	Solar physics - X-ray emission (high resolution crystal spectrometer)	F	M&R BAe SRC
					Lei	Solar physics - X-ray image (pin-hole camera)	S	
212 (18)	05 Oct. 1969	S29/1 (ESRO) Kiruna	Un, Rav.8 +C	225 (140)	Bel	Neutral atmosphere – winds, temperature, diffusion (TMA release) (experiment R37)	S	M&R BAe SP-80
					RSRS	Aurora – particle energy (channel multiplier detector) (experiment R52)	S	
					Bir	Ionosphere – electron density (RF probe) (experiment R105)	S	
					Bir	" - electron temperature (Langmuir probe) (experiment R106)	S	
213 (19)	16 Oct. 1969	SL861 (UK) Woomera	Un, Rav.6 +C	318 (198)	UCL	Neutral atmos. – wind & temperature structure (grenades & TMA release)	S	M&R BAe
					UCL	Ionosphere - electric fields (barium ion cloud dispenser)	S	
214 (20)	17 Oct. 1969	SL862 (UK) Woomera	Un, Rav.6 +C	318 (198)	UCL	As SL861	S	M&R BAe
					UCL	"	S	
215 (21)	17 Oct. 1969	S29/2 (ESRO) Kiruna	Un, Rav.8 +C	225 (140)	Bel	As S29/1	S	M&R BAe SP-80
					RSRS	"	S	
					Bir	"	S	
					Bir	"	S	
216 (22)	20 Oct. 1969	SL586 (UK) Woomera	Sun, Rav.6 +C	223 (139)	RAE	Test (space technology) – performance of horizon sensor for X3 satellite, & various sensors for future spacecraft	S	BAe RAE
217 (23)	22 Oct. 1969	SL821 (UK) Woomera	Un, Rav.6 +C	216 (134)	MSSL	Astronomy – galactic X-ray spectra (proportional counters)	Vf	M&R BAe McD
					MSSL	Solar physics - solar X-ray spectra (calibration of OSO 5 detectors)	Vf	
					MSSL	Ionosphere – monitoring space potential (probes)	Vf	
						Vf – "N/C (nose cone) hit expt." (BAe list)		

Seq Nos	Launch date	Ref. (sponsor) launch site	Config-uration	Apogee km (miles)	Experi-menters	Experiment(s)	Result	Source
218 (24)	24 Oct. 1969	S68/1 (ESRO) Sardinia	Un, Rav.7 +C	184 (114)	ESRO	Test (vehicle & range facility) – flight trial of the RESY sea recovery system	Ps	BAe SP-80
					PIB	Aeronomy – background primary cosmic X-ray measurements (scintillation counters) (expt.R73)	S	
					SSD -ESTEC	Ionosphere – positive-ion density in D-layer, 80-40km (experiment E1)	S	
219 (25)	10 Nov. 1969	S46/1 (ESRO) Kiruna	Un, Rav.8 +C	214 (133)	Breisach	Ionosphere – electron density profile (inverse Seddon expt., 3-channel radio receiver) (expt.R20)	S	M&R BAe SP-80
					CES	Ionosphere – distribution of low-energy electrons (experiment R110)	S	
					Shf	Ionosphere – small scale structure of ionisation in the lower ionosphere (Langmuir probe) (expt. R125)	S	
220 (26)	18 Nov. 1969	SL602 (UK) Woomera	Sun, Rav.6 +C	206 (128)	MSSL	Cosmic X-ray sources (Fresnel shadowgraph camera) (ACU failed - BAe list)	Vf	M&R BAe
221 (27)	20 Nov. 1969	SL801 (UK) Woomera	Sun, Rav.6 +C	274 (170)	Cul	Solar physics - UV spectrum (normal & grazing incidence spectrographs)	Ps	M&R BAe
					MO	Solar physics - UV intensity (ionisation chambers)	Vf	
					MO	Aeronomy - molecular oxygen concentration (ionisation chambers)	Vf	
					Cul	Solar physics - extreme UV image (pin-hole cameras)	Vf	
						(Vf = recovery system failed)		
222 (28)	27 Nov. 1969	SL603 (UK) Woomera	Sun, Rav.6 +C	180 (112)	Cul/Bel	Solar physics - Mg II doublet profile (Fabry- Perot interferometer)	S	M&R BAe
					Cul/Bel	Solar physics - extreme UV image (pin-hole camera)	S	

1970 (23 un/spin stabilised & 12 three-axis ACU stabilised)

Jan.	Feb.	March	April	May	June	July	August	Sept.	Oct.	Nov.	Dec.
S56A/1	S44/1 S72 S66/2 S70 S61/1 S61/2	SL921 SL901 SL401 SN5/1 SL802	S66/1 S28/1 SL803 SL728		S68/2	S63/1 S63/2 SL727 SL971 SL811 S56A/2 S65/2 S65/1			SL972 SN5/2 SL1021 S53 S58 S67/1 S67/2	SL905 SL904 SL804	S69

Seq Nos	Launch date	Ref. (sponsor) launch site	Config-uration	Apogee km (miles)	Experi-menters	Experiment(s)	Result	Source
223 (1)	24 Jan. 1970	S56A/1 (ESRO) Sardinia	Un, Rav.8	100? (62)	RSRS	Aeronomy - solar Lyman-α measurements (experiment R123?)	F?	M&R BAe McD
					"	Ionosphere – D-region electron density (If propagation/Faraday rotation) (expt. R132?)	S?	
					?	?	?	
224 (2)	06 Feb. 1970	S44/1 (ESRO) Sardinia	Star, Rav.8 +C	211 (131)	?	Astronomy - stellar UV emission 'Star-p unit failed' (BAe)	Vf	BAe McD
225 (3)	11 Feb. 1970	S72 (ESRO) Woomera	Star, Rav.6 +C	244 (152)	UCL	Astronomy - stellar UV, high resolution spectroscopy 'Star-p unit failed' (BAe)	Ps	M&R BAe McD

226 (4)	14 Feb. 1970	S66/2 (ESRO) Kiruna	Spin?, Rav.8 +C	210 (131)	UCL	Ionosphere - electron temperature probe	Ps	M&R BAe McD
					KTH/MPE	Ionosphere – simultaneous electric field measurements using several instruments	S	
227 (5)	24 Feb. 1970	S70/1 (ESRO) Kiruna	Spin?, Rav.8 +C	186 (116)	Bir	Ionosphere - electron density & temperature probe	S	M&R BAe McD
					DSRI	Ionosphere - VLF hiss (radio receivers) (probably)	?	
228 (6)	25 Feb. 1970	S61/1 (ESRO) Kiruna	Spin?, Rav.8 +C	220 (137)	MO	Aeronomy - vertical oxygen distribution	S	M&R BAe McD
					?	?	?	
229 (7)	26 Feb. 1970	S61/2 (ESRO) Kiruna	Spin?, Rav.8 +C	225 (140)	MO	Aeronomy - vertical oxygen distribution	S	M&R BAe McD
					?	?	?	
230 (8)	12 Mar. 1970	SL921 (UK) Woomera	Un, Rav.6 +C	247 (154)	MSSL	Astronomy - position and energy spectra of X-ray sources (rotating modulation collimator & proportional counters) (Telemetry failure – BAe)	Sf	M&R BAe
231 (9)	19 Mar. 1970	SL901 (UK) Woomera	Sun, Rav.6 +C	208 (129)	Lei	Astronomy – galactic X-ray line emission from Sco X-1. (Bragg crystal spectrometer)	S	M&R BAe Lei
232 (10)	20 Mar. 1970	SL401 (UK) Woomera	Moon, Rav.6 +C	181 (113)	ROE	Astronomy - UV stellar photography (objective prism Schmidt camera)	S	M&R BAe
					"	Astronomy - in-flight calibration of camera (UV stellar scanning photometer)	S	
233 (11)	22 Mar. 1970	SN5/1 (Germ) Sardinia	Un, Rav.6 +C	0 (0)	Bonn	Aeronomy – measurement neutral gas in the upper atmosphere (helium cooled mass spectrometer)	Vf	BAe McD
234 (12)	25/24 Mar. 1970	SL802 (UK) Woomera	Sun, Rav.6 +C	179 (111)	Lei	Astronomy – celestial X-ray survey in 1-10 KeV energy range (conventional & modulation collimated detectors)	Sf	M&R BAe SRC
					Lei	Astronomy – robot star camera, 5th magnitude	S	
235 (13)	02 April 1970	S66/1 (ESRO) Kiruna	Spin?, Rav.8 +C	198 (123)	UCL/MSSL	Ionosphere - electron temperature probe	S	M&R BAe McD
					KTH/MPE	Ionosphere – simultaneous electric field measurements using several instruments	S	
236 (14)	04 April 1970	S28/1 (ESRO) Kiruna	Spin, Rav.8 +C	203 (126)	Bel / MPE	Neutral atmosphere - sodium releases	S	M&R BAe McD SRC
					Bir	Ionosphere - electron density & temperature probes	S	
237 (15)	07 April 1970	SL803 (UK) Woomera	Sun, Rav.6 +C	204 (127)	ARU (Cul)	Solar physics – UV spectrum 1000Å - 2100Å (échelle diffraction grating spectrograph)	S	M&R BAe
238 (16)	16 April 1970	SL728 (UK) Woomera	Un, Rav.6 +C	210 (131)	MO	Aeronomy - molecular oxygen & ozone concentrations (spectrometer & filter sensors)	S	M&R BAe UAT
					UAT	Astronomy - celestial X-ray spectra & intensities (proportional counters)	S	
239 (17)	22 June 1970	S68/2 (ESRO) Sardinia	Un, Rav.8 +C	3 (1.9)	ESRO	Test (vehicle & range facility) – 2nd flight trial of the RESY sea recovery system	Mf	M&R BAe McD
					?	?		
240 (18)	03 July 1970	S63/1 (ESRO) Sardinia	Un, Rav.8	150 (93)	UCL	Ionosphere - positive ion probes	S	M&R BAe McD
					?	?	?	
241 (19)	08 July 1970	S63/2 (ESRO) Sardinia	Un, Rav.8	149 (93)	UCL	Ionosphere - positive ion probes	S	M&R BAe McD
					?	?	?	

No.	Date	Vehicle	Config	Alt.	Agency	Experiment	Result	Orgs
242 (20)	10 July 1970	SL727 (UK) Woomera	Un, Rav.5A +C	203 (126)	RSRS	Ionosphere - ionospheric currents (rubidium magnetometer)	S	M&R BAe UAT
					MSSL	Ionosphere wind profile (positive ion plate probes)	?	
					MSSL	Ionosphere - ion concentration profile (wire probes)	?	
					UAT	Astronomy - celestial X-ray sources spectra & intensities (gas-filled proportional counters)	Ps	
243 (21)	14 July 1970	SL971 (UK) Woomera	Un, Rav.6 +G	223 (139)	RAE	Test (Skylark technology) – further proving flight for Goldfinch II booster?	S	BAe M&R McD
					MSSL	Astronomy - position and energy spectra of X-ray sources (rotating modulation collimator)	S	
244 (22)	16 July 1970	SL811 (UK) Woomera	Star, Rav.6 +C	164 (102)	RAE	Test (Skylark technology) – 1st flight Stage 5 Attitude Control Unit	Ps	BAe McD
					ARU/MSSL	Astronomy - stellar spectroscopy 900 Å-2300 Å (high resolution objective grating spectrographs)	Ps	
245 (23)	23 July 1970	S56A/2 (ESRO) Sardinia	Un, Rav.8	137 (85)	RSRS	Aeronomy - Lyman-α measurements (expt.R123?)	S	M&R BAe McD
					Lei/RSRS	Solar physics - X-rays (2-8Å)	S	
					RSRS	Ionosphere - Faraday rotation (experiment R132?)	S	
					?	?	?	
246 (24)	24 July 1970	S65/2 (ESRO) Sardinia	Un, Rav.8	125 (78)	Shf	Ionosphere - RF impedance probe	S	BAe McD
					RSRS	Aeronomy – solar Lyman-α measurements (experiment R123?)	S	
					?	?	?	
247 (25)	27 July 1970	S65/1 (ESRO) Sardinia	Un, Rav.8	128 (80)	Shf	Ionosphere - RF impedance probe	S	M&R BAe McD
					RSRS	Aeronomy – solar Lyman-α measurements (experiment R123?)	S	
					?	?	?	
248 (26)	08 Oct. 1970	SL972 (UK) Woomera	Un, Rav.6 +G	232 (144)	RAE	Test (Skylark technology) – further proving flight for Goldfinch II booster?	S	M&R BAe McD SRC
					Lei	Astronomy – cosmic X-ray source measurements (proportional counters) (reflight of C1 & C2 from SL724)	S	
249 (27)	13 Oct. 1970	SN5/2 (Germ) Sardinia	Un, Rav.6 +C	288 (179)	Bonn	Aeronomy – measurement neutral gas in the upper atmosphere (helium cooled mass spectrometer)	S?	BAe McD
250 (28)	14 Oct. 1970	SL1021 (UK) Woomera	Un, Rav.6 +C	270 (168)	MSSL	Astronomy - position and energy spectra of X-ray sources (rotating modulation collimator & proportional counters)	S	M&R BAe
251 (29)	15 Oct. 1970	S53 (ESRO) Woomera	Sun, Rav.6 +C	209 (130)	ESRO	Test (vehicle & range facility) – land trial of the RESY recovery system	Vf	BAe McD
					Cul, Tüb, Utr	Solar physics – "X-ray mission"		
- (-)	19 Oct. 1970	S58 (ESRO) Woomera	Sun, Rav.6 +C ?	200? (124)	ARU	Solar physics - solar line spectrograph	F	M&R McD
252 (30)	28 Oct. 1970	S67/1 (ESRO) Kiruna	Spin?, Rav.8 +C	229 (142)	RSRS	Aurora – electron density (electrostatic analyser)	S	M&R BAe ESA McD
					TU	Aurora – photometer	?	
					?	?	?	
252 (31)	29 Oct. 1970	S67/2 (ESRO) Kiruna	Spin?, Rav.8 +C	234 (145)	RSRS	Aurora – as S67/1	S	M&R BAe McD
					TU	"	?	
					?		?	
254 (32)	11 Nov. 1970	SL905 (UK) Woomera	Sun, Rav.6 +C	183 (114)	MSSL	Astronomy - study of X-ray sources in the energy range 0.5-12 KeV (proportional counter & probe measurements)	Ps	M&R BAe

Seq. Nos	Launch date	Ref. (sponsor) launch site	Config-uration	Apogee km (miles)	Experi-menters	Experiment(s)	Result	Source
255 (33)	20 Nov. 1970	SL904 (UK) Woomera	Sun, Rav.6 +C	209 (130)	Lei	Astronomy - measurement of variation in X-ray background : origin of non X-ray pulses (collimated proportional detectors)	S	M&R BAe
					RAE	Test (space tech.) - Mk.II X3 horizon sensor array	S	RAE
256 (34)	25 Nov. 1970	SL804 (UK) Woomera	Sun, Rav.6 +C	182 (113)	Lei	Solar physics - high resolution spectroscopy of the solar corona at 5-14Å (crystal spectrometer, field of view collimator & pin-hole camera)	Ps	M&R BAe Lei
257 (35)	06 Dec. 1970	S69 (ESRO) Sardinia	Sun Rav.6 +C	187 (116)	Lei	Solar physics - high resolution spectroscopy of the solar corona at 5-23Å (crystal spectrometer, X-ray crystal spectrometer	S	M&R BAe Lei
					?	?	?	

1971 (17 un/spin stabilised & 12 three-axis ACU stabilised)

Jan.	Feb.	March	April	May	June	July	Aug.	Sept.	Oct.	Nov.	Dec.
LT.1 S46/2 SL1001	S80/1 S80/2 S80/3 S85 S54	SL922 S55 S16/2 S87/1 S87/2 S56B/1		SL812 S56B/2		S73	SL902	SL1002 S47/2	SL973 S81 S89 SL974	S44/2 S70/2 SL1101	SL903 S82

Seq. Nos	Launch date	Ref. (sponsor) launch site	Config-uration	Apogee km (miles)	Experi-menters	Experiment(s)	Result	Source
258 (1)	14 Jan. 1971	LT.1(P) (BAC) Aberporth	Un, G	6.4 (4)	BAC/ RAE / DLR	Test (vehicle & range facility) – MAN single rail launcher	S	BAe Flight McD
259 (2)	28 Jan. 1971	S46/2 (ESRO) Kiruna	Spin?, Rav.8 +C	218 (136)	Breisach	Ionosphere – electron density profile (inverse Seddon expt., 3-channel radio receiver) (experiment R20)	S	M&R BAe SP-80
					CES	Ionosphere – distribution of low-energy electrons (experiment R110)	S	
					Shf	Ionosphere – small scale structure of ionisation in the lower ionosphere (Langmuir probe) (experiment R125)	S	
					MPI/ SSD-ESTEC	Ionosphere - barium cloud release re DC electric fields by means of visual observation.(expt.R134)	?	
260 (3)	29 Jan. 1971	SL1001 (UK) Woomera	Sun, Rav.6 +C	203 (126)	MSSL	Astronomy - small spatial fluctuations in the isotropic X-ray background (proportional counter)	S	M&R BAe
					MSSL	Astronomy - isotropic spectrum from 0.25 to 15 keV (photomultipliers)	S	
261 (4)	06 Feb. 1971	S80/1 (ESRO) Sardinia	Un, Rav.6 +C	222 (138)	Bir	Ionosphere - electron density	S	M&R BAe McD
					Bir	Ionosphere - electron temperature	S	
					RSRS	Aeronomy - night-time Lyman-α radiation	S	
					Bonn	?	?	
262 (5)	"	S80/2 (ESRO) Sardinia	Un, Rav.6 +C	226 (140)	Bir	Ionosphere - electron density	S	"
					Bir	Ionosphere - electron temperature	S	
					RSRS	Aeronomy - night-time Lyman-α radiation	S	
					Bonn	?	?	

263 (6)	07 Feb. 1971	S80/3 (ESRO) Sardinia	Un, Rav.6 +C	214 (133)	" " " "	" " " "	S S S ?	"
264 (7)	22 Feb. 1971	S85 (ESRO) Woomera	Star, Rav.6 +C	222 (138)	MSSL / ?	Solar physics - high resolution UV stellar spectroscopy / ?	F / F	M&R BAe Astro
265 (8)	26 Feb. 1971	S54 (ESRO) Sardinia	Sun, Rav.6 +C	250 (155)	MSSL / ?	Solar physics - X-ray spectroheliography (Vf – ACU failed) / ?	Vf	M&R BAe Astro
266 (9)	02 Mar. 1971	SL922 (UK) Woomera	Un, Rav.6 +C	223 (139)	UCL/MSSL/ RSRS/Bir	Ionosphere - joint mission using seven instruments: magnetometer, TMA dispenser, barium gas generators, aluminium grenades, DC electric field probe, Langmuir probe, positive ion density probes	S	M&R BAe
267 (10)	11 Mar. 1971	S55 (ESRO) Sardinia	Sun, Rav.6 +C	159 (99)	Lei / MPE, Tub	Astronomy - stellar X-ray spectra & interstellar absorption / Solar physics - X-ray instruments?	S / S	M&R BAe McD
268 (11)	12 Mar. 1971	S16/2 (ESRO) Kiruna	Spin?, Rav.8 +C	143 (89)	MSSL / MSSL / RSRS	Ionosphere - electron temperature (Langmuir probe) (experiment R44) / Ionosphere - auroral ionisation structure (positive ion probes) (experiment R45) / Ionosphere – currents (magnetometers)	S / S / S	M&R BAe McD
269 (12)	16 Mar. 1971	S87/1 (ESRO) Kiruna	Spin?, Rav.8 +C	188 (117)	KTH/ ESTEC	Ionosphere - electric field measurements	S	BAe McD
270 (13)	24 Mar. 1971	S87/2 (ESRO) Kiruna	Spin?, Rav.8 +C	190 (118)	KTH/ ESTEC	Ditto	S	BAe McD
271 (14)	25 Mar. 1971	S56B/1 (ESRO) Sardinia	Un, Rav.7 +C	130 (81)	Lei/RSRS / RSRS / RSRS /	Solar physics - X-rays from 2-8 Å / Ionosphere - electron density & collisional frequency (Faraday rotation) / Aeronomy - solar Lyman-α / (Sf - telemetry & transponder failed)	Sf / Sf / Sf	M&R BAe McD
272 (15)	10 May 1971	SL812 (UK) Woomera	Star, Rav.6 +G	219 (136)	Lei	Astronomy - X-ray survey (variable spacing modulation collimator) (Vf - Stage 5 ACU failed)	Vf	M&R BAe
273 (16)	14 May 1971	S56B/2 (ESRO) Sardinia	Un, Rav.8	190 (118)	Lei/RSRS / RSRS / RSRS	Solar physics - X-rays from 2-8 Å / Ionosphere - electron density & collisional frequency (Faraday rotation) / Aeronomy - solar Lyman-α	S / S / S	M&R BAe McD
274 (17)	02 July 1971	S73 (ESRO) Sardinia	Sun, Rav.6 +C	224 (139)	MPI / ?	Solar physics – study of Inner zodiacal light (photometer telescopes) (experiment R214) / Solar physics – X-ray instrument?	S / ?	BAe McD
275 (18)	05 Aug. 1971	SL902 (UK) Woomera	Sun, Rav.6 +G	272 (169)	Cul	Solar physics – ultraviolet spectrography (normal & grazing incidence spectrographs) / "1st twin pack ACU" (BAe)	Ps	M&R BAe
276 (19)	27 Sept. 1971	SL1002 (UK) Woomera	Sun, Rav.6 +G	222 (138)	Lei	Astronomy - lunar occultation of cosmic X-ray source GX3+1	S	M&R BAe
277 (20)	30/29 Sept. 1971	S47/2 (ESRO) Woomera	Un, Rav.6 +C	210 (131)	ROE	Astronomy - stellar photometry (Recovery system failed)	Ps	M&R BAe
278 (21)	07 Oct. 1971	SL973 (UK) Woomera (BS192)	Un, Rav.6 +G	230 (143)	MSSL	Astronomy - position of celestial X-ray sources (rotating modulation collimator)	S	M&R BAe
279 (22)	12 Oct. 1971	S81 (ESRO) Woomera	Un, Rav.6 +C	210 (131)	"Rome"	Astronomy – stellar X-ray sources Successful soft landing using land version of Dornier RESY system.	S	BAe McD

280 (23)	20 Oct. 1971	S89 (ESRO) Sardinia	Sun, Rav.6 +C	210 (131)	Lei	Solar physics - X-ray spectra (crystal spectrometer)	Vf	M&R BAe
						"DFVLR parachute fail" (BAe)		McD
281 (24)	24 Oct. 1971	SL974 (UK) Woomera	Un, Rav.6 +G	245 (152)	MSSL	Astronomy - lunar occultation of cosmic X-ray source GX3+1	S	M&R BAe
282 (25)	16 Nov. 1971	S44/2 (ESRO) Sardinia	Star, Rav.8 +C	0 (0)	MPE	Astronomy - UV observations	Mf	BAe McD
					?	?	"	
283 (26)	25 Nov. 1971	S70/2 (ESRO) Kiruna	Spin?, Rav.8 +C	172 (107)	RSRS	Ionosphere - currents (magnetometers)	S	M&R BAe McD
					Bir/ESTEC	Ionosphere - electron density & temp. (probe)	S	
					DSRI	Ionosphere - VLF hiss (radio receivers) (prob.)	S	
284 (27)	30 Nov. 1971	SL1101 (UK) Woomera	Sun, Rav.6 +C	193 (120)	Lei	Solar physics - high resolution solar corona X-ray spectra (crystal spectrometer)	S	M&R BAe
					"	Solar physics - X-ray photography		
					"	Solar physics - white light photography		
285 (28)	10 Dec. 1971	SL903 (UK) Woomera	Sun, Rav.6 +C	198 (123)	MSSL	Solar physics - X-ray spectrometry of small areas of solar disk (collimated Bragg crystal spectrometer)	S	M&R BAe
286 (29)	14 Dec. 1971	S82 (ESRO) Sardinia	Un, Rav.8 +C	151 (94)	Bern	Ionosphere – positive ion composition (mass spectrometer)	S	BAe McD
					?	Micrometeorites – microphone detectors	?	
					?	Probes ?	?	

1972 (8 un/spin stabilised & 12 three-axis ACU stabilised)

Jan.	Feb	March	April	May	June	July	Aug.	Sept.	Oct.	Nov.	Dec.
	S84 S90	S77/1 SL1023 SL1009 S75/1 SL1081 S75/2			S91	SL1191 SL1183		S94 S77/2	S105 SL1022 SL402 SL1003	S95	SL1202 SL1005

Seq. Nos	Launch date	Ref. (sponsor) Launch site	Config-uration	Apogee km (miles)	Experi-menters	Experiment(s)	Result	Source
287 (1)	28 Feb. 1972	S84 (ESRO) Sardinia	Sun, Rav.6 +C	242 (150)	IASB/ Bonn	Aeronomy – simultaneous upper air composition measurements at 115-220 km (UV monochromators & mass spectrometers	S	BAe McD
288 (2)	28 Feb. 1972	S90 (ESRO) Sardinia	Sun, Rav.6 +C	251 (156)	"	Ditto	"	BAe McD
289 (3)	02 Mar. 1972	S77/1 (ESRO) Kiruna	Spin?, Rav.8 +GIIA	237 (147)	RSRS	Aurora – study of particles (separating payload with channel multipliers, electrostatic analysers & Geiger counters)	S	M&R BAe
					?	?	?	
290 (4)	16 Mar. 1972	SL1023 (UK) Woomera	Un, Rav.6 +G	259 (161)	UCL/MSSL/ Bir/ WRE	Ionosphere - comprehensive investigation of the ionosphere's midday Sq current structure, using a wide range of instruments	Ps	M&R BAe MSSL
291 (5)	17 Mar. 1972	SL1009 (UK) Woomera	Sun, Rav.6 +G	237 (147)	RSRS	Solar physics - line profiles in range 100-210 nm (échelle diffraction grating spectrograph). Parachute failed	Ps	M&R BAe

No.	Date	Vehicle	Att.	Alt.	Org.	Experiment	Res.	Contractor
292 (6)	25 Mar. 1972	S75/1 (ESRO) Sardinia	Un, Rav.8 +C	136 (85)	Bonn	Ionosphere – thermospheric densities of gasses (mass spectrometer with cryo-cooled ion source)	S	BAe McD Bonn
293 (7)	27 Mar. 1972	SL1081 (UK) Woomera (BS201)	Earth, Rav.6 +G	297 (185)	RAE	Test (Skylark technology) - remote sensing - proving of zenith pointing attitude control system & Earth resources photographic equipment	S	M&R BAC UoR
294 (8)	30 Mar. 1972	S75/2 (ESRO) Sardinia	Un, Rav.8 +G	133 (83)	Bonn	Ionosphere – as S75/1 Type 6 ignition unit (1st) (BAe)	S	BAe McD Bonn
295 (9)	25 June 1972	S91 (ESRO) Sardinia	Sun, Rav.6 +C	213 (132)	MSSL	Astronomy - cosmic X-ray background (collimated X-ray detectors). Parachute & sea recovery failure	Ps	M&R BAe
296 (10)	05 July 1972	SL1191 (UK) Woomera	Sun, Rav.6 +G	150 (93)	RAE	Test (space technology) – trial S.1 re 'Chevaline' upgrade to Britain's Polaris nuclear weapon delivery system	Ps	BAe McD
297 (11)	20 July 1972	SL1183 (UK) Aberporth	G	5 (3.1)	BAC/ RAE	Test (vehicle & range facility) – trial of simple single rail transportable launcher	S	BAe McD
298 (12)	20 Sept. (Nov?) 1972	S94 (ESRO) Sardinia	Sun, Rav.6 +C	210 (131)	?	Astronomy – "X-ray Crab Nebula"	?	BAe McD
					?	?	?	
299 (13)	24 Sept. 1972	S77/2 (ESRO) Kiruna	Spin?, Rav.8 +G	227 (141)	RSRS	Aurora – study of particles (separating payload with channel multipliers, electrostatic analysers & Geiger counters)	S	M&R BAe
					?	?	?	
300 (14)	12/13 Oct. 1972	S105 (ESRO) Kiruna	Spin?, Rav.8 +C	207 (129)	MSSL	Aurora - measurement of suprathermal electrons during an auroral event (electrostatic analyser)	s	M&R BAe MSSL report
					MSSL?	Aurora - retarding potential analysers, a magnetron gauge and photometers	?	
301 (15)	19 Oct. 1972	SL1022 (UK) Woomera (BS205)	Un, Rav.8 +C	143 (89)	Bel	Aeronomy - resonance scattering of sunlight by upper atmosphere (photometers)	S	M&R BAe McD
					Shf	Ionosphere - ion composition (cryogenic mass spectrometer)	F	
					Tas	Astronomy - X-ray observations?	?	
302 (16)	23 Oct. 1972	SL402 (UK) Woomera (BS206)	Moon, Rav.6 +G	210 (131)	MSSL	Astronomy - soft X-rays from small Magellanic clouds (large area collimated counter)	F	M&R BAe
					MO	Astronomy - lunar UV albedo & night-time ozone concentration	S	
303 (17)	26 Oct. 1972	SL1003 (UK) Woomera	Sun, Rav.6 +C	194 (121)	MSSL	Solar physics - X-rays (crystal spectrometer & rotating collimator)	S	M&R BAe
					MSSL	Solar physics - X-ray photography (pin-hole camera)	S	
304 (18)	02 Nov. 1972	S95 (ESRO) Woomera	Sun, Rav.6 +G	270 (168)	Utr	Solar physics – X-ray imaging on photographic film	S	BAe McD FDC
					CEN	Astronomy - study of X-rays from pulsars	S	
305 (19)	07 Dec. 1972	SL1202 (UK) Woomera	Sun, Rav.6 +C	248 (154)	Lei	Astronomy - lunar occultation of cosmic X-ray source GX5-1 (Vf = despin failure)	Vf	M&R BAe
306 (20)	11 Dec. 1972	SL1005 (UK) Woomera	Sun, Rav.6 +C(III)	195 (121)	Bel	Aeronomy - resonance scattering (photomultipliers)	Ps	M&R BAe FDC
					Shf	Ionosphere - ion composition of lower ionosphere (cryogenic mass spectrometer)	Ps	
					MO	Aeronomy - molecular oxygen concentration (ionisation chambers)	S	
					Adel	?	?	
					RAE	Test (Skylark technology) – 1st flight of Cuckoo III	S	

1973 (4 un/spin stabilised & 14 three-axis ACU stabilised)

Jan.	Feb.	March	April	May	June	July	August	Sept.	Oct.	Nov.	Dec.
SL1205		SL1010 SL1004 SL1102 SL1182 SL1181	SL1011		SL1111	SL1291	SL1081A		S93 S92 SL1121 SL1122	SL1123 SL1206 S74	SL1124

Seq. Nos	Launch date	Ref. (sponsor) launch site	Config-uration	Apogee km (miles)	Experi-menters	Experiment(s)	Result	Source
307 (1)	30 Jan. 1973	SL1205 (UK) Woomera (BS207)	Sun, Rav.6 +C	234 (145)	MSSL	Astronomy - lunar occultation of GX2+5 (X-ray detector)	Ps	M&R BAe
308 (2)	28 Feb./ 01 Mar. 1973	SL1010 (UK) Woomera	Sun, Rav.6 +G	199 (124)	Lei	Astronomy (Solar?) – soft X-ray survey (parabolic reflector telescope & proportional counters)	Ps	M&R BAe
309 (3)	14 Mar. 1973	SL1004 (UK) Woomera	Sun, Rav.6 +G	226 (140)	AL (CuI)	Solar physics - XUV spectrum of limb/disk, (grazing incidence spectrographs with imaging optics)	S	M&R BAe
310 (4)	20 Mar. 1973	SL1102 (UK) Woomera	Sun, Rav.6 +G	225 (140)	AL (CuI)	Solar physics - UV spectrum, (high resolution echelle spectrograph)	S	M&R BAe
311 (5)	22 Mar. 1973	SL1182 (UK) Argentina	Earth, Rav.6 +G	240 (149)	RAE Reading	Remote sensing - Earth observation mission	Ps	BAe UoR
312 (6)	28 Mar. 1973	SL1181 (UK) Argentina	Earth, Rav.6 +G	240 (149)	RAE Reading	Remote sensing - Earth observation mission	S	BAe UoR
313 (7)	18/17 April (Check date) 1973	SL1011 (UK) Woomera	Star, Rav.6 +G	214 (133)	Lei	Astronomy - accurate spacing of X-ray sources in Centaurus & Circinus regions (variable spacing modulation collimator telescope)	S	M&R BAe
314 (8)	16 June 1973	SL1111 (UK) Woomera	Star, Rav.6 +G	227 (141)	AL /UCL	Astronomy - high resolution UV spectroscopy of two bright stars (objective grating spectrographs)	S	M&R BAe
315 (9)	17 July 1973	SL1291 (UK) Woomera	Sun, Rav.6 +C	210 (131)	RAE	Test (space technology) – trial S.2 re 'Chevaline' upgrade to Britain's Polaris nuclear weapon delivery system	Ps	BAe McD
316 (10)	04 Aug. 1973	SL1081A (UK/German/ Sweden) Kiruna	Earth, Rav.8 +G	7 (4.4)	RAE/ DFVLR/ SSC	Remote sensing - Earth observation mission (Vf – Raven sustainer failed to ignite)	Vf	BAe
317 (11)	02 Oct. 1973	S93 (German) El Arenosillo	Ins, Rav.8 +C	186 (116)	MPE/ DFVLR	Astronomy - Test/UV mission (Probably Skylark's 1st inertially controlled ACU)	S	BAe McD
318 (12)	06 Oct. 1973	S92 (German) El Arenosillo	Star, Rav.8 +G	260 (162)	MPE	Astronomy – optical & UV observations	S	BAe McD
319 (13)	14 Oct. 1973	SL1121 (UK) Andøya	Un, Rav.6 +G	266 (165)	AL/ Bir/ MSSL/Sth	Aurora - High latitude campaign - (electron analyser, particle detectors & electric field probe)	S	M&R BAe
320 (14)	30 Oct. 1973	SL1122 (UK) Andøya	Un, Rav.6 +G	230 (143)	AL/ MSSL/Shf/ Sth/Sx	Aurora - High latitude campaign – (plasma wave probe, proton & electron particle detectors, electron analysers & Langmuir probe)	S	M&R BAe
321 (15)	16 Nov. 1973	SL1123 (UK) Andøya	Un, Rav.6 +G	215 (134)	AL/Bir/ MSSL/UCL	Aurora - high latitude campaign – (various probes & particle detectors, TMA dispenser & vector magnetometer)	S	M&R BAe

322 (16)	26 Nov. 1973	SL1206 (UK) Woomera	Sun, Rav.6 +G	238 (148)	Lei	Solar physics – corona spectroscopy, X-ray photography & white light photography (scanning Bragg crystal spectrometers with proportional detectors)	S	M&R BAe
323 (17)	27 Nov. 1973	S74 (German) El Arenosillo	Star, Rav.8 +G	246 (153)	MPE	Astronomy – optical & UV observations	S	BAe McD
324 (18)	05 Dec. 1973	SL1124 (UK) Andøya	Un, Rav.6 +G	222 (138)	Bir/Shf	Aurora - high latitude campaign - (vlf instruments, electron density & temperature probes)	S	M&R BAe

1974 (2 un/spin stabilised & 8 three-axis ACU stabilised)

Jan.	Feb.	March	April	May	June	July	Aug.	Sept.	Oct.	Nov.	Dec.
HRC1	SL1203		SL1207		SL1104	SL1292			SL1012 SL1304 SL1471	SL1221 SL911	

Seq. Nos	Launch date	Ref. (sponsor) Launch site	Config-uration	Apogee km (miles)	Experi-menters	Experiment(s)	Result	Source
325 (1)	12 Jan. 1974	HRC1 (DFVLR) El Arenosillo	Ins, Rav.8 +G	246 (153)	MPE	Astronomy - X-ray observations (Ef – "exp.door failure")	Ef	BAe McD
326 (2)	05 Feb. 1974	SL1203 (UK) Woomera (BS216)	Mag, Rav.6 +G	197 (122) (BAC)	MSSL/ UCB	Astronomy – X-ray background & EUV survey southern skies (proportional counters, EUV telescopes)	S	M&R BAe
327 (3)	23 April 1974	SL1207 (UK) Woomera	Sun. Rav.6 +G	177 (110)	UCL	Ionosphere – currents (magnetometer)	S	M&R BAe
					UCL/MPI	Ionosphere - daytime electric fields (barium ion cloud)	S	
					UCL/WRE	Neutral atmosphere - daytime wind (lithium trail)	S	
					UCL	Neutral atmosphere - thermospheric temperature & winds (interferometer)	S	
328 (4)	18 June 1974	SL1104 (UK) Woomera	Sun, Rav.6 +G	234 (115)	MSSL	Astronomy - Cen X-3 X-ray emissions (proportional counters & memory)	Ps	M&R BAe MSSL
329 (5)	22 July 1974	SL1292 (UK) Woomera	Sun, Rav.6 +C	210 (131)	RAE	Test (space technology) - trial S.3 re 'Chevaline' upgrade to Britain's Polaris nuclear weapon delivery system. (Radar problem)	Ps	BAe McD
330 (6)	4/5 Oct. 1974	SL1012 (UK) Woomera (BS217)	Star, Rav.6 +G	196 (122)	MSSL	Astronomy – X-ray crystal spectrometry of Puppis A	S	BAe Astro
331 (7)	07 Oct. 1974	SL1304 (UK/German) El Arenosillo	Sun, Rav.6 +G	190 (118)	Lei/ MPI/Tüb	Astronomy – Lunar occultation of Crab Nebula	Ps	M&R BAe
332 (8)	10 Oct. 1974	SL1471 (UK) Woomera	Un, Gos.4 +G	270 (168)	AL	Test (Skylark technology) - first Skylark 10A & test of electronic programme unit (receivers & timers)	S	M&R BAe
333 (9)	01 Nov. 1974	SL1221 (UK) Andøya	Un, Rav.6 +G	225 (140)	AL/ KTH	Aurora – study of particle precipitation	S	M&R BAe
334 (10)	28 Nov. 1974	SL911 (UK) Woomera	Star, Rav.6 +G	203 (126)	AL/ UCL	Astronomy – high resolution UV stellar spectroscopy (echelle spectrograph)	F	M&R BAe

1975 (0 un/spin stabilised & 7 three-axis ACU stabilised)

Jan.	Feb.	March	April	May	June	July	August	Sept.	Oct.	Nov.	Dec.
	SL1301 SL1293	S98			SL1105	SL1295			S103	SL1112	

Seq. Nos	Launch date	Ref. (sponsor) launch site	Config-uration	Apogee km (miles)	Experi-menters	Experiment(s)	Result	Source
335 (1)	25 Feb. 1975	SL1301 (UK) Woomera	Sun, Rav.XI +G	282 (175	AL (Cul)	Astronomy - measurement of solar atmospheric structure (Grazing incidence telescope/spectrometer)	S	M&R BAe
336 (2)	28 Feb. 1975	SL1293 (UK) Woomera	Sun Rav.6 +C	210 (131)	RAE	Test (space technology) – trial S.4 re 'Chevaline' upgrade to Britain's Polaris nuclear weapon delivery system	S	BAe McD
337 (3)	14 Mar. 1975	S98 (DFVLR) Woomera	Sun, Rav.6 +G	270? (168)	Tüb/ MPE	Solar physics – X-ray observations? (Dornier recovery system failed)	Ps	BAe McD
338 (4)	24 June 1975	SL1105 (UK) Woomera	Mag, Rav.6 +G	180 (112)	Lei	Astronomy – soft X-ray mapping of Vela-Puppis supernova remnants (one dimensional focussing telescope)	S	M&R BAe
339 (5)	03 July 1975	SL1295 (UK) Woomera	Sun, Rav.6 +G	270 (168)	RAE	Test (space technology) – trial S.5 re 'Chevaline' upgrade to Britain's Polaris nuclear weapon delivery system	S	BAe McD
340 (6)	09 Oct. 1975	S103 (DFVLR) El Arenosillo	Ins, Rav.6 +G	254 (158)	MPI	Solar physics – 'Astro 7' experiment to measure the zodiacal light	S	BAe & scientific paper
341 (7)	24/25 Nov. 1975	SL1112 (UK) Woomera	Star, Rav. X1 +G	251 (156)	Lei/ Saclay	Astronomy – soft X-ray spectrum of Crab Nebula to search for interstellar oxygen edge	S	M&R BAe

1976 (3 un/spin stabilised & 10 three-axis ACU stabilised)

Jan.	Feb.	March	April	May	June	July	August	Sept.	Oct.	Nov.	Dec.
B-II-1 B-II-2 PL029 SL1302				SL1115 SL1211	SL1212 SL1501	SL1402				SL1306 SL1422	SL1114 SL1425

Seq. Nos	Launch date	Ref. (sponsor) launch site	Config-uration	Apogee km (miles)	Experi-menters	Experiment(s)	Result	Source
342 (1)	04 Jan. 1976	B-II-1 (DFVLR) El Arensillo	Ins, Rav.6 +C	116 (72)	Freib	Ionosphere & aeronomy – electron density & profiles (retarding potential analyser) (Western European Winter Anomaly Campaign)	S	BAe McD
343 (2)	22 Jan. 1976	B-II-2 (DFVLR) El Arensillo	Ins, Rav.6 +C	116 (72)	Freib	Ionosphere & aeronomy – electron density & profiles (retarding potential analyser) (Western European Winter Anomaly Campaign)	S	BAe McD
344 (3)	28 Jan. 1976	PL029 (DFVLR) Kiruna	Ins, Rav.8 +G	2 (1.2)	DFVLR/ Koln	Test (space technology) – "Heatpipe I"	Mf	BAe McD
345 (4)	30 Jan. 1976	SL1302 (UK) Woomera	Sun, Rav. XI +G	278 (173)	MSSL /Lockheed	Solar physics – quiet coronal structure (collimated X-ray detector)	Vf	M&R BAe

Seq. Nos	Launch date	Ref. (sponsor) launch site	Config-uration	Apogee km (miles)	Experi-menters	Experiment(s)	Result	Source
346 (5)	12 May 1976	SL1115 (UK) Woomera	Star, Rav. XI +G	231 (144)	Bir/ MSSL/ MSFC	Astronomy – observations to obtain high resolution two dimensional X-ray map of Puppis A supernova remnant (imaging X-ray telescope)	Mf	M&R BAe
347 (6)	27 May 1976	SL1211 (UK) Woomera	Un, Rav. XI +G	254 (158)	RAE/BAC	Test (Skylark technology) – test of new fin design?	S	BAe McD
					UCL/WRE	Neutral atmosphere - daytime wind (lithium trail)	S	
348 (7)	11 June 1976	SL1212 (UK) Woomera	Star, Rav. XI +G	281 (175)	MSSL	Astronomy – measurement of X-ray line emission from the Cygnus Loop (scanning X-ray crystal spectrometer)	S	M&R BAe
349 (8)	17 June 1976	SL1501 (UK) Woomera (BS227)	Sun, Rav. XI +G	258 (160)	Bir	Astronomy – imaging of the galactic centre X-ray source (coded mask telescope)	S	M&R BAe
350 (9)	17 July 1976	SL1402 (UK) El Arensillo	Sun, Rav.XI +G	256 (159)	MSSL/ Tub/MPI	Astronomy – X-ray emission from Cas-A (X-ray crystal spectrometer)	Mf	M&R BAe
351 (10)	04 Nov. 1976	SL1306 (UK) Woomera (BS229)	Sun, Rav.6 +G	191 (119)	Lei	Astronomy – high time resolution study of Cygnus X-1 (large area proportional counter)	Ps (Vf)	M&R BAe
352 (11)	21 Nov. 1976	SL1422 (UK) Andøya	Un, Rav.XI +G+C	715 (444)	MSSL/ AL/Sx/ Sth	Aurora – measurement of supra-thermal electrons & ions in an auroral arc (1976 high latitude campaign)	S	M&R BAe
					RAE	Test (Skylark technology) – first Skylark 12	S	
353 (12)	02/03 Dec. 1976	SL1114 (UK) Woomera (BS228)	Star, Rav. XI +G	263 (163)	ARD	Astronomy – high resolution UV stellar spectroscopy (Cassegrain telescope & echelle spectrograph)	Ef	M&R BAe
354 (13)	11 Dec. 1976	SL1425 (UK) Andøya	Un, Rav. XI +G+C	695 (432)	UCL/AL/ GSFC/ NDRE /MSSL	Aurora – measurement of structure of aurora during strong geomagnetic disturbance (1976 high latitude campaign)	S	M&R BAe

1977 (9 un/spin stabilised & 3 three-axis ACU stabilised)

Seq. Nos	Launch date	Ref. (sponsor) launch site	Config-uration	Apogee km (miles)	Experi-menters	Experiment(s)	Result	Source
355 (1)	22 Jan. 1977	PHA2 (DFVLR) Andøya	Spin, Rav.XI +G	277 (172)	Tüb/ Freib	Aeronomy – (Polar High Atmosphere) 'Eveline' aeronomy mission (EUV spectrometers)	S	BAe McD
356 (2)	08 Feb. 1977	S22 (SSC) Kiruna	Spin, Rav.6 +C	212 (132)	SSC/ Liège	Aurora – auroral arc mission	S	BAe McD
357 (3)	08 Feb. 1977	PHA1 (DFVLR) Andøya	Spin, Rav.XI +G	272 (169)	Tüb/ Freib	Aeronomy – (Polar High Atmosphere) 'Silvia' aeronomy mission (EUV spectrometers)	S	BAe McD
358 (4)	20 Feb. 1977	PHA3 (DFVLR) Andøya	Spin, Rav. XI +G	256 (159)	"	Aeronomy – (Polar High Atmosphere) 'Georgine' aeronomy mission. (Dornier nose cone failure)	Ps	BAe McD
359 (5)	16 Mar. 1977	PHA4 (DFVLR) Andøya	Spin, Rav. XI +G	263 (163)	"	Aeronomy – (Polar High Atmosphere) 'Christ[ina?]' aeronomy mission	S	BAe McD
360 (6)	28 April 1977	SL1115A (UK) Woomera	Star, Rav. XI +G	244 (152)	Bir/ MSSL/ MSFC	Astronomy - observation of Puppis-A in X-ray wavelengths (imaging X-ray telescope)	Vf	M&R BAe McD
361 (7)	08 June 1977	SL1298 (UK) Woomera	Sun, Rav.6 +C	210 (131)	RAE	Test (space technology) - trial S.7 re 'Chevaline' upgrade to Britain's Polaris nuclear weapon delivery system	S	BAe McD

Seq. Nos	Launch date	Ref. (sponsor) launch site	Config-uration	Apogee km (miles)	Experi-menters	Experiment(s)	Result	Source
362 (8)	13 Oct. 1977	IMS1 (DFVLR) Andøya	Spin, Rav.XI +G+C	536 (333)	Tüb/ Freib	Aurora – (International Magnetospheric Study), observations of auroral substorm	S	BAe McD
363 (9)	13 Oct. 1977	SL1423 (UK) Andøya	Spin, Rav. XI +G+C	788 (490)	AL/ MSSL/ Shf/UCL	Aurora - 1976/77 high latitude campaign continued – study of VLF waves, suprathermal electrons, electron & neutral ions, neutral winds	S	M&R BAe
364 (10)	02 Nov. 1977	IMS2 (DFVLR) Andøya	Spin, Rav. XI +G+C	541 (336)	Tüb/ Freib	Aurora – (International Magnetospheric Study), observations of auroral substorm	S	BAe McD
365 (11)	17 Nov. 1977	SL1421 (UK) Andøya	Spin, Rav.XI +G+C	718 (446)	AL/GSFC/ MSSL/Sx	Aurora – 1976/77 high latitude campaign continued – study of supra-thermal electrons & ions, electrons & positive ions	S	M&R BAe
366 (12)	13 Dec. 1977	TEXUS 1 (DFVLR) Kiruna	ZR, Rav. XI +G	265 (165)	11 German 2 Swedish	Microgravity – 13 materials science experiments, mostly involving the study of metal alloys	S	BAe McD Micrex

1978 (5 un/spin stabilised & 4 three-axis ACU stabilised)

Jan.	Feb.	Mar.	Apr.	May	June	July	Aug.	Sept.	Oct.	Nov.	Dec.
IMS3 IMS4				SL1305		S26A	S26B			SL1424 SL1296 TEXUS 2	SL1297

Seq. Nos	Launch date	Ref. (sponsor) launch site	Config-uration	Apogee km (miles)	Experi-menters	Experiment(s)	Result	Source
367 (1)	30 Jan. 1978	IMS3 (DFVLR) Andøya	Spin, Rav.XI +G+C	540 (336)	Tüb/ Freib	Aurora – (International Magnetospheric Study), observations of auroral substorm	S	BAe McD
368 (2)	30 Jan. 1978	IMS4 (DFVLR) Andøya	Spin, Rav. XI +G+C	541 (336)	Tüb/ Freib	Aurora – (International Magnetospheric Study), observations of auroral substorm	S	BAe McD
369 (3)	12 May 1978	SL1305 (UK) Woomera	Sun, Rav.XI +G	283 (176)	AL/ MSSL	Astronomy – H/He abundance ratio in solar corona (UV spectrometer) (Parachute failure - BAe)	S	M&R BAe McD
370 (4)	30 July 1978	S26A (SSC) Kiruna	Spin, Rav.8	114 (71)	SSC	Ionosphere – study of noctilucent clouds	S	BAe McD
371 (5)	13 Aug. 1978	S26B (SSC) Kiruna	Spin, Rav.8	127 (79)	SSC	Ionosphere – study of noctilucent clouds	S	BAe McD
372 (6)	10 Nov. 1978	SL1424 (UK) Andøya	Spin, Rav. XI +G+C	796 (495)	AL/MSSL/ NDRE/ Shf/UCL	Geophysics – Vlf waves in chorus event (receivers and Langmuir probes), Neutral winds (TMA trail)	S	M&R BAe McD
373 (7)	15 Nov. 1978	SL1296 (UK) Woomera	Sun, Rav.6 +C	210? (131)	RAE	Test (space technology) - trial S.8 re 'Chevaline' upgrade to Britain's Polaris nuclear weapon delivery system	S	BAe McD
374 (8)	16 Nov. 1978	TEXUS 2 (DFVLR) Kiruna	ZR, Rav.XI +G	265 (165)	9 German, 1 German/ Austrian, 7(?) Sweden	Microgravity – 17 materials science experiments	S	BAe McD Micrex
375 (9)	13 Dec. 1978	SL1297 (UK) Woomera	Sun, Rav.6 +C	210? (131)	RAE	Test (space technology) - trial S.9 re 'Chevaline' upgrade to Britain's Polaris nuclear weapon delivery system	S	BAe McD

1979 (0 un/spin stabilised & 4 three-axis ACU stabilised)

Jan.	Feb.	March	April	May	June	July	Aug.	Sept.	Oct.	Nov.	Dec.
	Astro-4/2	SL1299 Astro-4/1							Astro-Hel		

Seq. Nos	Launch date	Ref. (sponsor) launch site	Config-uration	Apogee km (miles)	Experi-menters	Experiment(s)	Result	Source
376 (1)	22 Feb. 1979	Astro-4/2 (DFVLR) Woomera	I/Star, Rav.6 +G	192 (119)	Tüb/ MPE	Astronomy – X-ray imaging of Puppis A & Crab Nebula (Wolter telescope)	S	BAe McD
377 (2)	01 Mar. 1979	SL1299 (UK) Woomera	Sun, Rav.6 +G	270? (168)	RAE	Test (space technology) – 9th and final trial re 'Chevaline' upgrade to Britain's Polaris nuclear weapon delivery system	S	BAe McD
378 (3)	13 Mar. 1979	Astro-4/1 (DFVLR) Woomera	I/Sun, Rav.XI +G	258 (160)	Tüb/ MPE	Solar physics – X-ray studies of active coronal regions (zone plate cameras, a Rowland spectrograph and KAP crystal spectrometer)	S	BAe McD
379 (4)	12 Oct. 1979	Astro-Hel (DFVLR) Brazil	I/Sun, Rav.XI +G+C	829 (515)	Tüb	Solar physics – EUV observations of the solar corona (EUV photometer)	S	BAe McD

1980-84 (4 un/spin stabilised & 9 three-axis ACU stabilised)

1980	1981	1982	1983	1984
TEXUS 3A (April) EB1 (Nov)	TEXUS 3B (April) TEXUS 4 (May) EB2 (Dec.)	TEXUS 5 (April) TEXUS 6 (May)	TEXUS 7 (May) TEXUS 8 (May)	CAESAR 1 (Jan.) MAP/WINE1 (Feb.) TEXUS 9 (May) TEXUS 10 (May)

Seq. Nos	Launch date	Ref. (sponsor) launch site	Config-uration	Apogee km (miles)	Experi-menters	Experiment(s)	Result	Source
380 (1)	28 April 1980	TEXUS 3A (DFVLR) Kiruna	ZR, Rav.XI +G	253 (157)	11 German, 1 Swedish	Microgravity – mission failed as low gravity not achieved because of despin failure	F	BAe McD Micrex
381 (2)	16 Nov. 1980	EB1 (DFVLR) Kiruna	Spin, Rav. XI +G	231 (144)	Wupp/ Freib	Aeronomy – (Energy Budget 1) - atmospheric observations by spectrometers & probes	S	BAe McD
382 (1)	30 April 1981	TEXUS 3B (DFVLR) Kiruna	ZR, Rav.XI +G	253 (157)	11 German, 1 Swedish	Microgravity - (Repeat of failed TEXUS 3A), 12 materials science experiments	S	BAe McD Micrex
383 (2)	08 May 1981	TEXUS 4 (DFVLR) Kiruna	ZR, Rav.XI +G	258 (160)	8 German, 1 French	Microgravity - 9 materials science experiments	S	BAe McD Micrex
384 (3)	09 Dec. 1981	EB2 (DFVLR) Kiruna	Spin, Rav. XI +G	237 (147)	Wupp/ Freib	Aeronomy – (Energy Budget 2) - atmospheric observations by spectrometer & probes	S	BAe McD
385 (1)	29 April 1982	TEXUS 5 (DFVLR) Kiruna	ZR, Rav.XI +G	256 (159)	10 German, 3 Swedish	Microgravity – 13 materials science experiments. 8 involved metals and alloys, 3 fluids or capillary action, 1 bubble formation and 1 protein crystal growth	S	BAe McD Micrex

Seq. Nos	Launch date	Ref. (sponsor) launch site	Config-uration	Apogee km (miles)	Experi-menters	Experiment(s)	Result	Source
386 (2)	08 May 1982	TEXUS 6 (DFVLR) Kiruna	ZR, Rav.XI +G	256 (159)	6 German, 1 Belgian, 1 French, 1 Dutch	Microgravity - 9 materials science experiments. Included first ESA funded experiment	S	BAe McD Micrex
387 (1)	05 May 1983	TEXUS 7 (DFVLR) Kiruna	ZR, Rav.XI +G	227 (141)	7 German, 3 Swedish, 1 Belgian, 1 British 1 French	Microgravity - 13 materials science experiments	S	BAe McD Micrex
388 (2)	13 May 1983	TEXUS 8 (DFVLR) Kiruna	ZR, Rav.XI +G	264 (164)	7 German, 1 Belgian, 1 Italian	Microgravity - 9 materials science experiments	S	BAe McD Micrex
389 (1)	27 Jan. 1984	CAESAR 1 (DFVLR) Andøya	Spin, Rav. XI +G+C	700 (435)	MPAe	Aurora – investigation of magnetic substorm phenomena. "Telemetry at 10 secs" (BAe)	F	BAe McD
390 (2)	10 Feb. 1984	MAP/WINE 1 (DFVLR) Kiruna	Spin, Rav.6 +G	180 (112)	3 experiments	Neutral atmosphere – investigation of the middle atmosphere (Part of MAP/WINE project)	S	BAe McD
391 (3)	03 May 1984	TEXUS 9 (DFVLR) Kiruna	ZR, Rav.XI +G	258 (160)	7 German, 2 Belgian, 1 Italian	Microgravity – 10 materials science experiments	S	BAe McD EEA
392 (4)	15 May 1984	TEXUS 10 (DFVLR) Kiruna	ZR, Rav.XI +G	216 (134)	4 German, 3 Swedish, 2 British, 1 Spanish	Microgravity – 7 to 10 materials science experiments	S	BAe McD EEA Micrex

1985-87 (1 un/spin stabilised & 9 three-axis ACU stabilised)

1985	1986	1987
CAESAR 2 (Jan.) INTERZODIAK (Mar.) TEXUS 11 (April) TEXUS 12 (May)	TEXUS 13 (April) TEXUS 14 (May)	TEXUS 14BI(May) TEXUS 15 (May) SUPER NOVA (Aug.) TEXUS 16 (Nov.)

Seq. Nos	Launch date	Ref. (sponsor) launch site	Config-uration	Apogee km (miles)	Experi-menters	Experiment(s)	Result	Source
393 (1)	30 Jan. 1985	CAESAR 2 (DFVLR) Andøya	Spin, Rav.XI +G+C	703 (437)	MPAe	Aurora – repeat of failed CEASAR 1 - investigation of magnetic substorm phenomena	S	BAe McD
394 (2)	03 Mar. 1985 1985	INTERZODIAK (DFVLR) Brazil	I/Sun, Rav.XI +G+C	0? (0)	Bonn	Solar physics – EUV observations of the solar disc & corona (EUV photometer)	F	BAe McD
395 (3)	27 April 1985	TEXUS 11 (DFVLR) Kiruna	ZR, Rav.XI +G	266 (165)	6 German, 1 French	Microgravity – 6 materials science experiments and 1 life science experiment	S	BAe McD EEA
396 (4)	06 May 1985	TEXUS 12 (DFVLR) Kiruna	ZR, Rav.XI +G	253 (157)	5 German, 2 Swedish, 2 British, 1 French, 1 Spanish	Microgravity – 6 to 11 materials science experiments	S	BAe McD EEA Micrex
397 (1)	30 April 1986	TEXUS 13 (DFVLR) Kiruna	ZR, Rav.XI +G	246 (153)	5 German, 1 Belgian, 1 French, 1 Japanese	Microgravity - 6 materials science experiments, 2 biotechnology experiments	S	BAe McD EEA
398 (2)	12 May 1986	TEXUS 14A (DFVLR) Kiruna	ZR, Rav.XI +G	250 (155)	4 German 2 Swedish, 1 Italian, 1 Belgian, 1 British	Microgravity - 8 materials science experiments and 1 life science experiment. Mission failed as low gravity not achieved because of payload instability	F	BAe McD Micrex

399 (1)	03 May 1987	TEXUS 14B (DFVLR) Kiruna	ZR, Rav.XI +G	250 (155)	Ditto with 1 extra German	Microgravity – the TEXUS 14 mission successfully re-flown with 1 extra life science experiment	S	BAe McD FFA
400 (2)	09 May 1987	TEXUS 15 (DFVLR) Kiruna	ZR, Rav.XI +G	252 (157)	5 German, 1 Belgian, 1 Dutch	Microgravity – failed after 2nd stage suffered a lateral burn through	MF	BAe McD Micrex
401 (3)	24 Aug. 1987	SUPER NOVA (DFVLR) Woomera	I/Star, Rav.XI +G	265 (165)	MPE	Astronomy – X-ray imaging of supernova 1987A	. S	BAe McD
402 (4)	23 Nov. 1987	TEXUS 16 (DFVLR) Kiruna	ZR, Rav.XI +G	7? (4)	7 German, 2 Belgian, 1 Swedish	Microgravity – crashed after 2nd stage failed to ignite	MF	BAe McD Micrex

1988 (3 un/spin stabilised & 3 three-axis ACU stabilised)

Jan.	Feb.	March	April	May	June	July	Aug.	Sept.	Oct.	Nov.	Dec.
				BAe TEST				INTER-ZODIAK II		ROSE 1 TEXUS 19	TEXUS 20 ROSE 2

Seq. Nos	Launch date	Ref. (sponsor) launch site	Config-uration	Apogee km (miles)	Experi-menters	Experiment(s)	Result	Source
403 (1)	09 May 1988	BAe Test (BAe) Kiruna	Spin?, Rav.XI +G	262 (163)	BAe	Proving flight – to test Raven XI modifications introduced after TEXUS 15 & 16 failures	S	BAe SSC
404 (2)	03 Sept. 1988	INTERZOD-IAK II (DFVLR) Brazil	Sun/I, Rav.XI +G+C	857 (533)	Bonn	Solar physics – EUV observations of the solar disc & corona (EUV photometer)	S	BAe McD
405 (3)	26 Nov. 1988	ROSE 1 (DFVLR) Andøya	RS, Rav.8 +C	120 (75)	MPI	Ionosphere – the start of the Rockets & Scatter Experiments to investigate the auroral E-region	S	BAe McD
406 (4)	28 Nov. 1988	TEXUS 19 (DFVLR) Kiruna	ZR, Rav.XI +G	244 (152)	6 German 2 Japanese 1 Swedish 1 Belgian	Microgravity – 8 materials science experiments, 2 life science experiments	S	BAe McD EEA
407 (5)	02 Dec. 1988	TEXUS 20 (DFVLR) Kiruna	ZR, Rav.XI +G	238 (148)	6 German, 1 Belgian, 1 Japanese	Microgravity – 6 materials science experiments, 1 life science experiment	S	BAe McD EEA
408 (6)	05 Dec. 1988	ROSE II (DFVLR) Andøya	RS, Rav.8 +C	113 (70)	MPI	Ionosphere – continuation of ROckets & Scatter Experiments to investigate the auroral E-region	S	BAe McD

1989 (2 un/spin stabilised & 4 three-axis ACU stabilised)

Jan.	Feb.	March	April	May	June	July	Aug.	Sept.	Oct.	Nov.	Dec.
	ROSE III ROSE IV		TEXUS 21	TEXUS 22						TEXUS 23	TEXUS 24

Seq. Nos	Launch date	Ref. (sponsor) launch site	Config-uration	Apogee km (miles)	Experi-menters	Experiment(s)	Result	Source
409 (1)	07 Feb. 1989	ROSE III (DFVLR) Kiruna	RS, Rav.8 +C	124 (77)	MPI	Ionosphere – continuation of ROckets & Scatter Experiments to investigate the auroral E-region	S	BAe McD
410 (2)	09 Feb. 1989	ROSE IV (DFVLR) Kiruna	RS, Rav.8 +C	125 (78)	MPI	Ionosphere – continuation of ROckets & Scatter Experiments to investigate the auroral E-region	S	BAe McD
411 (3)	30 April 1989	TEXUS 21 (German) Kiruna	ZR, Rav.XI +G	268 (167)	4 German 1 Belgian	Microgravity – 2 materials science experiments, 3 life science experiments	S	BAe McD EEA
412 (4)	03 May 1989	TEXUS 22 (German) Kiruna	ZR, Rav.XI +G	223 (139)	3 German	Microgravity – 1 materials science experiment, 2 life science experiments	S	BAe McD EEA
413 (5)	25 Nov. 1989	TEXUS 23 (German) Kiruna	ZR, Rav.XI +G	249 (155)	2 German, 1 Dutch, 1 Italian, 1 Spanish	Microgravity – 3 materials science experiments, 2 life science experiments	S	BAe McD EEA
414 (6)	06 Dec. 1989	TEXUS 24 (German) Kiruna	ZR, Rav.XI +G	244 (152)	2 German, 1 Japanese	Microgravity – 2 materials science experiments, 1 life science experiment	S	BAe McD EEA

1990 (4 un/spin stabilised & 3 three-axis ACU stabilised)

Jan.	Feb.	March	April	May	June	July	Aug.	Sept.	Oct.	Nov.	Dec.
		SISSI 1		TEXUS 25 TEXUS 26		SISSI 2	SISSI 3			TEXUS 27 MAXUS TEST	

Seq. Nos	Launch date	Ref. (sponsor) launch site	Config-uration	Apogee km (miles)	Experi-menters	Experiment(s)	Result	Source
415 (1)	06 Mar 1990	SISSI I (DLR) Kiruna	RS, Rav.6 +G	178 (111)	Wupp	Aeronomy – investigation of arctic middle atmosphere dynamics (infrared spectrometer)	S	BAe McD
416 (2)	13 May 1990	TEXUS 25 (German) Kiruna	ZR, Rav.XI +G	234 (145)	5 German 1 French	Microgravity – 3 materials science experiments, 3 life science experiments	S	BAe McD EEA
417 (3)	15 May 1990	TEXUS 26 (German) Kiruna	ZR, Rav.XI +G	235 (146)	4 German 2 Swedish	Microgravity – 4 materials science experiments, 2 life science experiments	S	BAe McD EEA
418 (4)	26 Jul 1989	SISSI 2 (DLR) Kiruna	RS, Rav.6 +G	168 (104)	Wupp	Aeronomy – continued investigation of arctic middle atmosphere dynamics (infrared spectrometer)	S	BAe McD
419 (5)	02 Aug 1990	SISSI 3 (DLR) Kiruna	RS, Rav.XI +G	239 (149)	Wupp	Aeronomy – continued investigation of arctic middle atmosphere dynamics (infrared spectrometer)	S	BAe McD
420 (6)	15 Nov 1990	TEXUS 27 (German) Kiruna	ZR, Rav.XI +G	249 (155)	3 German, 1 French, 1 British	Microgravity – 3 materials science experiments, 2 life science experiments	S	McD EEA
421 (7)	25 Nov 1990	MAXUS Test (German) Kiruna	SPINRAC, Rav.XI +G+C	534 (332)	MBB/SSC	Test – used during MAXUS development to test guidance, control and safety systems	S	McD Dreier

1991-95 (1 un/spin stabilised & 7 three-axis ACU stabilised)

1991	1992	1993	1994	1995
SISSI 4 (Apr) TEXUS 28 (Nov)	TEXUS 29 (Nov)	TEXUS 30 (May) MASER 6 (Nov) TEXUS 31 (Nov)	TEXUS 32 (May) TEXUS 33 (Nov)	-

Seq. Nos	Launch date	Ref. (sponsor) launch site	Config-uration	Apogee km (miles)	Experi-menters	Experiment(s)	Result	Source
422 (1)	09 April 1991	SISSI 4 (DLR) Kiruna	RS, Rav. XI +G	245 (152)	Wupp	Aeronomy – continued investigation of arctic middle atmosphere dynamics (infrared spectrometer)	S	McD
423 (2)	23 Nov. 1991	TEXUS 28 (German) Kiruna	ZR, Rav. XI +G	239 (149)	5 German, 1 French	Microgravity – 1 materials science experiment, 5 life science experiments	S	McD EEA
424 (1)	22 Nov 1992	TEXUS 29 (German) Kiruna	ZR, Rav.XI +G	230 (143)	7 German, 1 Japanese	Microgravity – 6 materials science experiments, 2 life science experiments	S	McD EEA
425 (1)	01 May 1993	TEXUS 30 (German) Kiruna	ZR, Rav. XI +G	234 (145)	6 German	Microgravity – 3 materials science experiments, 3 life science experiments	S	McD EEA
426 (2)	04 Nov. 1993	MASER 6 (ESA) Kiruna	ZR, Rav. XI +G	243 (151)	2 French, 2 Dutch, 1 Italian	Microgravity - 3 materials science experiments, 3 life science experiments	S	McD EEA Ceglia (2005)
427 (3)	26 Nov. 1993	TEXUS 31 (German) Kiruna	ZR, Rav.XI +G	257 (160)		Microgravity –		McD EEA
428 (1)	05 May 1994	TEXUS 32 (German) Kiruna	ZR, Rav.XI +G	235 (146)	5 German, 1 French, 1 Dutch	Microgravity – 4 materials science experiments, 3 life science experiments	S	McD EEA
429 (2)	30 Nov. 1994	TEXUS 33 (German) Kiruna	ZR, Rav.XI +G	267 (166)	1 German, 1 Italian 1 Spanish	Microgravity – 3 materials science experiments	S	McD EEA

1996-2000 (0 un/spin stabilised & 7 three-axis ACU stabilised

1996	1997	1998	1999	2000
TEXUS 34 (Mar) MASER 7 (May) TEXUS 35 (Nov)	-	TEXUS 36 (Feb)	MASER 8 (May)	TEXUS 37 (Mar) TEXUS 38 (Apr)

Seq. Nos	Launch date	Ref. (sponsor) launch site	Config-uration	Apogee km (miles)	Experi-menters	Experiment(s)	Result	Source
430 (1)	02 Mar. 1996	TEXUS 34 (German) Kiruna	ZR, Rav. XI +G	232 (144)	2 German, 1 Italian	Microgravity – 3 or more materials science experiments	S	McD EEA
431 (2)	03 May 1996	MASER 7 (ESA) Kiruna	ZR, Rav. XI +G	252 (157)	3 Italian, 1 German, 1 Swedish	Microgravity – 2 materials science experiment, 3 life science experiments	S	McD EEA Ceglia
432 (3)	24 Nov. 1996	TEXUS 35 (German) Kiruna	ZR, Rav.XI +G	267 (166)	3 German??	Microgravity – 2 or more materials science experiments, 1 or more life science experiments	S	McD Röhrig & Roth

433 (1)	07 Feb. 1998	TEXUS 36 (German) Kiruna	ZR, Rav. XI +G	238 (148)	4 German	Microgravity – 3 materials science, 1 life science experiments	S	McD Frings (1999)
434 (1)	14 May 1999	MASER 8 (ESA) Kiruna	ZR, Rav. XI +G	260 (162)	2 Italian, 1 Belgian, 1 ESA pan- European	Microgravity - 4 materials science experiments	S	McD EEA Ceglia (2005)
435 (1)	27 Mar. 2000	TEXUS 37 (German/ ESA) Kiruna	ZR, Rav.XI +G	243 (151)	5 German	Microgravity – 2 materials science experiments, 3 life science experiments	S	McD Frings (1999)
436 (2)	02 April 2000	TEXUS 38 (ESA) Kiruna	ZR, Rav.XI +G	250 (155)	1 Spanish 1 French, 1 German/ Belgian	Microgravity – 2 physics experiments, 1 biology experiment.	S	McD EEA Frings (1999)

2001-05 (0 un/spin stabilised & 5 three-axis ACU stabilised

2001	2002	2003	2004	2005
TEXUS 39 (May)	MASER 9 (Mar)	TEXUS 40 (Apr)	TEXUS 41 (May)	MASER 10 (Mar)

Seq. Nos	Launch date	Ref. (sponsor) launch site	Config- uration	Apogee km (miles)	Experi- menters	Experiment(s)	Result	Source
437 (1)	08 May 2001	TEXUS 39 (German) Kiruna	ZR, Rav. XI +G	248 (154)	5 German	Microgravity – 2 materials science experiments, 3 life science experiments	S	McD Preu (2003)
438 (1)	16 Mar. 2002	MASER 9 (ESA) Kiruna	ZR, Rav. XI +G	258 (160)	2 Swiss, 2 Italian 1 German, 1 Belgian 1 French	Microgravity – 2 materials science experiment, 5 life science experiments	S	McD EEA Ceglia
439 (1)	08 April 2003	TEXUS 40 (German) Kiruna	ZR, Rav.XI +G	246 (153)	4 German	Microgravity – 1 physics experiment, 3 biology experiments	S	McD DLR
440 (1)	02 Dec. 2004	TEXUS 41 (German) Kiruna	ZR, Rav. XI +G	227 (141)	4 German	Microgravity – 2 materials science experiments, 2 biology experiments	S	McD DLR
441 (1)	02 May 2005	MASER 10 (ESA) Kiruna	ZR, Rav. XI +G	252 (157)	2 Dutch, 1 Belgian 1 German, 1 Italian	Microgravity – 3 fluid physics experiments, 2 biology experiments	S	McD EEA Ceglia

APPENDIX 4

AN EXTRACT FROM THE FIRST SCIENTIFIC PAPER

Upper atmosphere wind and temperature structure by
Skylark rocket-grenade experiments at
Woomera, Australia, 1957–59

BY P. J. BOWEN, R. L. F. BOYD, M. J. DAVIES,* E. B. DORLING,†
G. V. GROVES AND R. F. STEBBINGS‡

Department of Physics, University College London

(*Communicated by Sir Harrie Massey, F.R.S.—Received 6 November 1962—
Revised 20 November 1963*)

[Plates 10 and 11]

An account is presented of the first grenade experiments carried out at the Woomera
rocket range during 1957–59. A description is given of the grenades and their rocket
installation; and of the optical and acoustical instrumentation required to determine their
burst positions and to find the times of travel of the sound waves to the ground. The
method and theory of the experiment are outlined, and details of the firings and results
obtained are presented. The accuracy of the measurements is discussed and comparisons
made with simultaneous measurements by other methods. Determinations of wind speed
and temperature (derived from the speed of sound) have been extended from the upper
balloon limit to about 85 km, and a comparison between summer and winter conditions
has been possible. Wind measurements have been extended to greater heights by means of
the glow phenomenon. Pressure and density profiles have been determined and agree
very closely with the COSPAR International Reference Atmosphere, 1961.

1. INTRODUCTION

In 1954, proposals were made by the Royal Society's Gassiot Committee to the
Ministry of Supply for initiating a programme of upper atmosphere research using
rockets. Although a considerable programme of rocket research had grown up in
the United States during the preceding 8 years, research possibilities were far from
exhausted and the need for observations at different geographical locations encouraged the establishment of a British programme.

American workers had employed various techniques for obtaining temperature
and pressure involving the use of rocket-borne pressure gauges and sound propagation from rocket-borne grenades (Newell 1953). This latter method, known as the
grenade experiment, enables the wind structure, as well as the speed-of-sound structure, to be determined to an altitude of about 90 km. From the speed of sound,
the temperature can be found directly; and by means of the hydrostatic equation
pressure and density may also be deduced.

In 1955 approval was given to a programme of experiments and the design of
a suitable rocket to meet the needs of the various experiments became the responsibility of the Royal Aircraft Establishment (R.A.E.), who also undertook the provision of grenades, grenade bay and associated ejection mechanism. The Skylark

---

* Now at Department of Applied Mathematics, University College of Wales, Aberystwyth.
† Now at Office of the Minister for Science.
‡ Now at General Atomics, Ltd, U.S.A.

[170]

Figure A4.1 This appendix reproduces part of one of the earliest academic papers[1]
resulting from use of the Skylark rocket.

---

[1] Bowen *et al.* (1963), 'Upper atmosphere wind and temperature structure by Skylark rocket-grenade experiments...'.

Upper atmosphere wind and temperature structure   171

rocket, which was first developed for this programme, was 25 ft. in length and 17 in. in diameter and capable of reaching 165 km with a payload of 150 lb. Higher performance Skylark rounds have since been introduced. Being uncontrolled in flight, its dispersion is comparatively large and firings have been required to take place from the Woomera Range in Australia (Jones & Massey 1956).

The firing of Skylark rockets has been undertaken by the Weapons Research Establishment (W.R.E.), Australia; and in the case of the grenade experiment, where a considerable amount of ground equipment such as cameras, flash detectors and sound-recording equipment is involved, these have been operated by W.R.E. personnel. The measurement of winds and temperature up to the 30 km region by balloon methods has been undertaken with very high accuracy by the Meteorological Office, Woomera.

In February 1957 the first Skylark rocket was fired at Woomera and in November of that year the first grenade experiment was successfully staged. The present paper deals with the method and instrumentation of the Woomera grenade experiments, and the results obtained from the first four successful firings are presented.

2. Description of the grenade experiment and interpretation of data

Figure 1 illustrates the principle of the grenade experiment. As the rocket ascends, grenades are ejected and detonated at roughly equal intervals along its flight path. The detonation times are recorded by ground-based flash-detectors, and the arrival of the resulting sound waves at a number of points on the ground are recorded by means of an array of microphones. The co-ordinates of the microphones are known from a ground survey, and the co-ordinates of the bursts are found by means

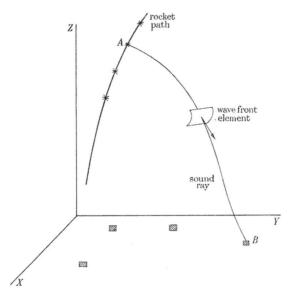

Figure 1. Diagram showing the passage of a sound ray from a grenade explosion A to a microphone B.

11-2

Figure A4.2 The second page from the paper discussed on the previous page.

APPENDIX 5

PLAN OF SATELLITE CLEAN ROOM AT WOOMERA

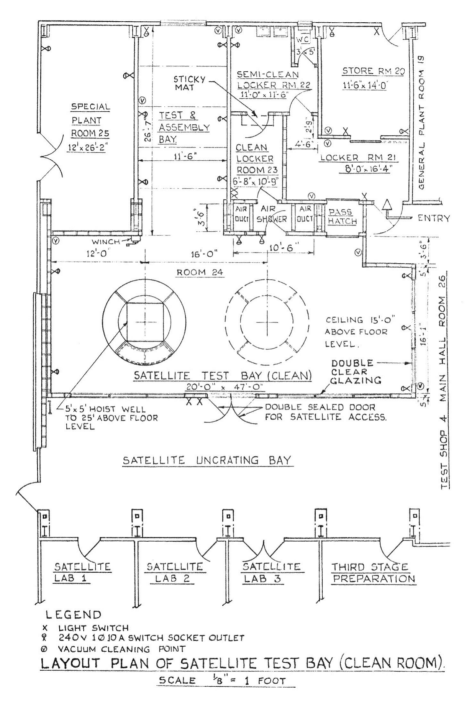

Figure A5.1 Plan of the satellite clean room and test and assembly bay in Test Shop Number 4, Building 206, Range 'E', South Australia.[1]

(For a view of the 'Prospero' satellite in this room, see Figure 12.17.)

[1] Figure 1 of WRE document WR: 30056 produced by Special Projects Group, Facilities Division, Engineering Wing, WRE, Salisbury, S.A., 14/3/1969, copy in possession of author.

APPENDIX 6
PRESERVED SKYLARK ARTEFACTS

This appendix is a guide to where some Skylark artefacts survive. Not all the collections are open to the public, and the list is not exhaustive. The author welcomes fresh information for future editions of this book!

UK

1. The Bristol Aero Collection

This used to be located at Kemble Airfield, near Cirencester in Gloucestershire, and had some noteworthy Skylark exhibits in its missile and spacecraft section. These included a Goldfinch first stage motor and fins recovered after a 500 km mission in Sweden, and all stages of a new Skylark 12, including the main Raven sustainer motor and a payload module.

Unfortunately, the Kemble Airfield venue closed in May 2012, but at the time of writing (July 2014), the collection is due to be re-housed in a new heritage museum, the Bristol Aerospace Centre. Visit *www.bristolaero.com/* for the current situation. (Website last accessed August 2014).

2. The Science Museum, Exhibition Road, South Kensington, London, SW7 2DD

When last visited by the author (October 2008) the Science Museum in London had several Skylark exhibits in the excellent 'Exploring Space' gallery on the ground floor. These included an early Skylark nose cone (see Figure 5.41) , a flight spare of a UCL Langmuir Probe (Figure 6.27), and a Leicester X-ray pinhole camera (Figure 8.64). For general information on the space galley visit the webpage: *www.sciencemuseum.org.uk/visitmuseum/Plan_your_visit/exhibitions/exploring_space.aspx?keywords=space+gallery* (last accessed August 2014).

The Science Museum also holds dozens of other Skylark artefacts, but unfortunately, these are not on public display. Many of the larger objects are located at the storage facility at Wroughton near Swindon in Wiltshire. These include a complete Skylark (at present on loan to the National Space Centre, see below), flown Skylark rocket parts large and small, the remnants of university experiments, and models and paperwork. Much of this material must have been acquired from the RAE,

Figure A6.1 A new Skylark 12 at the Bristol Aero Collection, Kemble Airfield, in 2008. A recovered Goldfinch boost motor can be seen stored underneath.
(Author, 100_1839)

Figure A6.2 A Skylark exhibit at the Science Museum, London.[1]
(Author, 100_2249)

---

[1] Image taken at the London Science Museum, permission granted by Science & Society Picture Library.

**Figures A6.3 and A6.4 The National Space Centre.
Left: an exterior view of the Rocket Tower.
Right: An interior view, Skylark can just be seen at the top left,
behind Blue Streak!**

(Credits National Space Centre, Leicester)

certainly when the RAE Space Department was being closed, "…someone from the Science Museum came down with a van and collected the contents of several filing cabinets." [2]

(Chapters 3 and 7 in this book include several photographs of the Skylark artefacts at Wroughton.)

It is interesting to note that one of the experimenters who worked on Skylark when a post-graduate in 1972 (Chris Rapley, see Right: Figure 12.47), became Director of the Science Museum from 2007 to 2010! [3]

3. National Space Centre, Exploration Drive, Leicester, LE4 5NS

The National Space Centre includes a Skylark on display in the Rocket Tower. (On loan from the Science Museum[4]). This includes a payload, Raven sustainer and Goldfinch boost motor.

Website: *www.spacecentre.co.uk/* (last accessed August 2014).

4. University of Leicester: Department of Physics & Astronomy, University Road, Leicester, LE1 7RH

Although not a public exhibit, a Skylark rocket has been installed as a centrepiece in the foyer of the Physics and Astronomy building at the University of Leicester. (Webpage: www2.le.ac.uk/departments/physics/research/xroa/astronomical-facilities-1/rocket-science-at-leicester/the-skylark-rocket, (last accessed August 2014).

Figure A6.5 The Skylark rocket in the foyer of the Physics and Astronomy building at the University of Leicester.

(University of Leicester)

[2] C.N.Hill, personal correspondence, June 2014.
[3] For instance, see *http://en.wikipedia.org/wiki/Chris_Rapley* , (last accessed July 2014).
[4] Probably item 1967-158.

Figures A6.6 and A6.7 Left: The rocket motor exhibits. Right: The Petrel launch tube.

(Credits Royal Gunpowder Mills Heritage Museum)

5. Royal Gunpowder Mills Heritage Museum, Waltham Abbey, Essex, EN9 1JY

The 'Rocket Vault' exhibition shows the development of rocket motors and propellants from Congreve's gunpowder rocket of the early 19th century through to the Falkland's war. It includes a Raven motor and a model of Skylark, and an example of the Petrel/Skua launch tube.

Website: *www.royalgunpowdermills.com/must-see-attractions/ rocket-vault/* , (last accessed August 2014).

6. Mullard Space Science Laboratory, Surrey

The Mullard Space Science Laboratory (MSSL) is UCL's (University College London) Department of Space and Climate Physics. It is located about 40 miles (64 km) to the south-west of London, and 6 miles (10 km) south-west of the town of Dorking. It is not open to the public.

The laboratory is situated near the village of Holmbury St.Mary, in Holmbury House,[5] an old mansion reached via narrow lanes more reminiscent of the lesser visited parts of Cornwall than Surrey.

Here in the oak panelled hall, neatly tucked into the stair-well, is Skylark SL1302, recovered after being launched from Woomera on 30 January 1976. It certainly makes a change from the traditional country house suit of armour!

As noted above, MSSL is not open to the public as such, but interested visitors may be able to make an appointment to view by phoning reception on +44 (0)1483 204 100.

Website: *www.ucl.ac.uk/mssl/* (last accessed August 2014).

Figure A6.8 Holmbury House.

(Author, 100_3020)

---

[5]   It has been said, "It is no accident that the Mullard Space Science Laboratory at Holmbury House … bears a striking resemblance in various good ways to West Leigh House, Havant, where two of us (D.R.B. and R.L.F.B.) worked with Massey during the war." (Bates, Boyd & Davis (1984), 'Harrie Stewart Wilson Massey, 1908-983', p.491. By coincidence, the author worked for the Plessey Company at the West Leigh site in the 1970s.

Figure A6.9 Holmbury House stairway provides convenient access for viewing the higher bays of SL1302. (Author, 100_3006)

Figure A6.10 In the Holmbury House hall. From left to right the exhibits comprise:
a. **The payload section of SL1302, complete with Stage 1 ACU**
b. **A Goldfinch II boost motor, as used on SL1302**
c. **A Raven XI sustainer motor, as used on SL1302**
(Author, 100_2998)

7. Farnborough, Hampshire

Farnborough was the location of the RAE where Skylark was initially designed and built over 50 years ago. The RAE is no more, but there are still a couple of places worth visiting:

a. *The Farnborough Air Sciences Trust (FAST) Museum, Trenchard House, 85 Farnborough Road, Farnborough, GU14 6TF*

The Farnborough Museum houses a selection from the FAST collection in a historic listed building, and overlooks the runway of Farnborough Airfield - so modern planes can be seen in the air as well as historic planes on display[6] in and around the Museum building. It is a comprehensive museum of the history of British aviation research, although there are only a few items related to Skylark. (See for instance Figure 6.21 and Figure 8.48).

Website: *www.airsciences.org.uk/museum.html* , (last accessed August 2014).

b. *Farnborough Historic Aviation Site / RAE Heritage Quarter*

A Business Park has been developed on the original RAE site, but some historic buildings have been preserved. These include the framework of the 1911 balloon and airship hangar, re-erected close to its original location. Back in 1915, the lower half of the framework was used to construct what be-

Figure A6.11 The re-erected framework of the 1911 balloon and airship hanger.
(Author 100_5723)

---

[6] Including a Jindivik as developed by the WRE and at tested at Woomera.

Figure A6.12 The 'Hub' area, showing refurbished building Q134. Behind this was Q65 where Skylark was originally assembled. In the distance is the tall preserved building, Q121, which houses a 24 foot wind tunnel that was used to test Spitfires and Concorde. To the left of that (on the far right of Q134) is now the National Aerospace Library, which the author visited during research for this book.

(Author 100_5727)

came RAE building Q65, in which Skylark was originally assembled (see Chapter 3). However in 2005, Q65 was demolished, and the frame rebuilt into the hanger.

Also on the Business Park is the original RAE Guided Weapons Department building, or Q134. This building was once the birthplace of the Black Arrow and Black Knight rocket systems. Together with the 'Hub' area Q134 has now been entirely refurbished

Australia

1. The South Australian Aviation Museum, 66 Lipson Street, Port Adelaide, South Australia 5015

The Woomera Rocket collection includes many Skylark artefacts, inherited in January 1996 when the Australian government Defence Science and Technology Organisation (DSTO) loaned their heritage rocket collection to the museum to give the public an opportunity to see more than 30 years of South Australian rocket technology history. The types of rockets on display were all fired from the Woomera rocket range, South Australia, during the 1950-80 era.

Website: *www.saam.org.au/* , (last accessed August 2014).

Figure A6.13 Some of the SAAM sounding rocket collection. On the left is a Skylark with Cuckoo boost motor.

(South Australian Aviation Museum)

Figure A6.14 Part of the South Australian Aviation Museum's fine Woomera rocket collection on loan from the DSTO. It appears to include the original model of the Skylark launch tower, although it depicts the extended version.[7]

(South Australian Aviation Museum)

2. Woomera, South Australia

Today (2014) the Woomera Village is a shadow of its former self, with a permanent population of only a 150-200, a small fraction of the thousands who used to live and work there. Unfortunately, the author has not yet been able to visit, and the following details have mostly been gleaned from the internet:

a. The Woomera Heritage and Visitor Centre, Dewrang Avenue, Woomera, South Australia 5720

The Woomera Heritage Centre contains historical displays relating to the Range and to the closed Joint Defence Facility at Nurrungar. These include an extensive range of rocket parts along with photographs and descriptions of Range activities. Amongst the fine collection of Skylark artefacts is the upper part of the recovered payload from SL728, launched in April 1970.[8] (See Figure 10.48 for an interior view of the museum).

Figure A6.15 A Skylark exhibit at the Woomera Heritage Centre in 2001.

(Roger Henwood)

[7] The Skylark launch tower at Woomera was originally 80 feet (24.4 m) high. In October 1958, this was extended by 25% to 100 feet (31m).
[8] Ian Tuohy, personal correspondence, September 2009.

Figure A6.16 A general view of the Aircraft and Missile Park, showing a Skylark with Cuckoo boost motor. [9]

Figure A6.17 A long-lost Skylark Raven motor case, discovered partially buried in a claypan. It was left in situ and not recovered,[10] so the photo has been included because the remains are still there for the reader to visit!
(Bruce Henderson)

Website: the Heritage Centre Museum appears not to have its own website, but basic details may be found via several tourist information websites, for instance *http://uk.southaustralia.com/info.aspx?id=9001106* , (last accessed August 2014).

b. The nearby outdoor Missile Park

This includes a display of rockets, missiles, aircraft and bombs that have been tested at Woomera over the years. Exhibits include a Canberra bomber, Meteor Jet, Black Arrow and various sounding rockets.

c. The Woomera History Museum

This is located in the ex-St Barbara's Church at the Missile Park which is run (not-for-profit) by volunteers on behalf of the Woomera Board. This museum has an interesting selection of Woomera artefacts both historical and social.

Over the years, many of the missing Skylark rocket payloads and motors have been accidently encountered, and expeditions have taken place to try and recover some of them.

It is a reflection on the nature and size of South Australia that these lost Skylarks should take so long to be found, and that the expeditions have to be carefully organised to avoid danger to the participants. For instance in July 2007 the following report from 1998 appeared in the Woomera local newspaper's 60th anniversary edition:

A recovery team comprising 20 adults, 7 children and 9 vehicles travelled to Anna Creek Station to recover two Skylark rocket motors. One was found approximately 56km from William Creek and the other about 86km away. Searching for the first motor, the team set out on foot to locate its remains, but it wasn't until a young Kerri Nicholls went back to the car for a drink that she made the discovery. The second motor was easily spotted, and the team loaded the two motors and headed back to William Creek Hotel. The 1967 motor was donated to the William Creek Progress Association and is displayed opposite the Hotel. The second motor was delivered back to Woomera.[11]

9   The South Australian Tourist Commission, the Government of South Australia, 9002322-100.jpg, sourced on 15/7/14, *http://uk.southaustralia.com/info.aspx?id=9002322* .
10 Roger Henwood, personal correspondence, April 2013.
11 *Gibber Gabber* community magazine 20 April 2007, 60th anniversary supplement, under '1998'. Reproduced with permission.

Figure A6.18 Two Skylark Raven motor cases safely recovered.
(Bruce Henderson)

3. The Powerhouse Museum, Sydney, NSW 1238

This museum's Space Exhibition includes a Skylark assembled from parts recovered from the Woomera range, and the collections include a Skylark nose cone and Goldfinch II boost motor. For online visitors, the website has an excellent search facility with very well documented results, search under 'Skylark' at:

www.powerhousemuseum.com/collection/database/menu.php (last accessed August 2014).

REFERENCES

Introduction

This section provides full details of the sources noted in the footnotes and text.

It comprises five parts:

1. Acknowledgements for figures
2. Notes on Primary Sources
3. List of References – documents
4. List of References – online databases for microgravity experiments
5. List of References - film, video and audio resources

1. Acknowledgements for figures

In general, the acknowledgements under the figures and photographs are a simplified form of that used in the footnotes. For straightforward cases sourced from archives, the citation is a self-contained indication of where it came from, e.g. (TNA: PRO WO 231/22). Sometimes a footnote type form will be used, e.g. (Freeman and Jones (1970), figure 4), leading back to a full reference in this section. (Alternatively, if the text is too long to fit conveniently under a figure, a footnote will be used).

Sometimes a double credit will appear, this indicates a copyright holder or primary source followed by the secondary source, e.g. (WRE \ Hazell) means originated by the Weapons Research Establishment, sourced via Hazell. If of the form (WRE / Hazell), it means originated by the WRE or Hazell.

2. Notes on Primary Sources (original documents)

(a)   *The [UK] National Archives*

Much of the research for this book has been carried out using original documents held at The National Archives of the UK (TNA), based at Kew in London.

Generally speaking, individual notes, letters and minutes (usually found under a common piece number in 'document files') have been cited only in the footnotes and not in this reference section..

However, in the interest of 'footnote brevity', documents with a piece number of their own, and originally intended for distribution within an organisation (e.g. RAE technical reports), are cited in a shorter form in the footnotes, the full reference is listed below under 'documents'. The same approach has been adopted for minutes of Skylark Policy meetings; see below under MoA / MoD.

The document reference for TNA: PRO[1] documents consists of three parts, the department code, the series number and the piece number (e.g. AVIA 6/21446).[2] Full definitions for the TNA: PRO department codes and series numbers used are provided here, as elsewhere they are only cited without the full description, (e.g. "TNA: PRO AB 16").

---

[1]   The National Archives include both Public Record Office (PRO) and Historical Manuscript Commission (HMC) documents.

[2]   The document reference can be looked up online, see *www.nationalarchives.gov.uk/records/catalogues-and-online-records.htm* , (last accessed July 2014).

AB

16   Ministry of Supply and United Kingdom Atomic Energy Authority, Atomic Energy Division and London Office: Files 1939-1985

AVIA

6   Ministry of Defence and predecessors: Royal Aircraft Factory, later Royal Aircraft Establishment, later Royal Aerospace Establishment: Reports 1908-1991

26   Ministry of Aviation, predecessors and successors: Royal Radar Establishment (later Royal Signals and Radar Establishment) and predecessors: Reports and Memoranda 1921-1991

48   Ministry of Supply and Ministry of Aviation: Guided Projectile Establishment and Rocket Propulsion Establishment: Committee and Research Files 1944-1962

51   Ministry of Supply: Finance, Registered Files (Series 4) 1939-1974

53   Ministry of Supply and predecessor and successors: Contracts, Registered Files (Series 6) 1912-1975

65   Ministry of Supply and successors: Registered Files 1919-1984

67   Ministry of Supply and successors: Explosives Research and Development Establishment: Registered Files 1946-1976

68   Ministry of Supply and Ministry of Aviation: Rocket Propulsion Establishment: Reports and Technical Memoranda 1958-1976

92   Ministry of Aviation and successors: Interdependence, Exports and Electronics Industry Division and successors: Registered Files (ZF Series) 1955-1988

BJ

5   Meteorological Office: Administrative Records 1910-1980

DEFE

16   Ministry of Defence: Australian Royal Commission into United Kingdom Nuclear Weapons Testing in Australia, Photocopies of Proceedings and Documents Presented in Evidence c.1947-1985

72   Ministry of Defence: Procurement Executive: Registered Files, Branch Folders, and Reports 1954-1992

DSIR

23   Department of Scientific and Industrial Research: Aeronautical Research Council: Reports and Papers 1909-1979

INF

6   Central Office of Information and Predecessors: Film Production Documents 1931-1997

OD

6   Directorate of Overseas Surveys: Registered Files 1939-1990

58   Overseas Development Administration and Ministry of Overseas Development: Natural Resources Research Department: Registered Files (NRR Series) 1973-1983

WO

33   War Office: Reports, Memoranda and Papers (O and A Series) 1853-1969

231   War Office: Directorate of Military Training, later Directorate of Army Training: Papers 1940-1978

(b) *Australian Defence Archives (Edinburgh)*

A great deal of unique information has been obtained from the original WRE (Weapons Research Establishment) Skylark Project Trials Preparation and Results files held at the Australian Defence Archive. This archive is located at the Edinburgh RAAF base in South Australia, and is not open to the general public, but the files have been accessed for the author by Roger Henwood. The files were due to have been destroyed decades ago, but most fortunately, many have survived. In the footnotes, these files have been referred to in the format "WRE (1964), SL88 Trials Results file J5555/3/88". Occasionally the file name has been suffixed "Australian Defence Archives (Edinburgh)", but not usually, because it makes the footnotes too long.

(c) *Imperial War Museum*

Several photographs in Chapters 3 and 5 have been reproduced by permission of the Trustees of the Imperial War Museum, London. These have been credited individually, with "IWM", followed by the negative number. They are Crown Copyright, and reproduced by permission of Her Majesty's Stationery Office.

3. List of References - documents

As explained above, for brevity, where appropriate in the footnotes, only the author's name has been provided, (with the year if required to avoid ambiguity), leading the reader to the full details provided here.

Acronyms used for corporate authors etc.:

BAe = 'British Aerospace'
BIS = 'British Interplanetary Society'
BNSC = 'British National Space Centre'
ESA = 'European Space Agency'
ESRO = 'European Space Research Organisation'
MSSL = 'Mullard Space Science Laboratory'
NASA = 'National Aeronautics and Space Administration'
RAE = 'Royal Aeronautical Establishment (until 1988), thereafter 'Royal Aerospace Establishment'
RPE = 'Rocket Propulsion Establishment'
SRC = 'Science Research Council'
TRE = 'Telecommunications Research Establishment'
UKSA = 'United Kingdom Space Agency'
WRE = 'Weapons Research Establishment, Department of Supply, Australian Defence Scientific Service'

To aid the recovery of documents, online (internet) or other access details (e.g. TNA: PRO piece number) are provided as a suffix where known. In this context, the following have been used:

The suffix (ADS) means that the document or abstract is available free online for personal use via the SAO/NASA ADS Digital Library Portal, at *www.adsabs.harvard.edu/* . Unless otherwise noted, the document or abstract was last accessed in August 2014.

Similarly, (NTRS) means that the abstract or document is available free online (2014) via the NTRS (NASA Technical Reports Server), at *http://ntrs.nasa.gov/search.jsp*. (Unless otherwise noted, the document was last accessed August 2014).

The "ESA EEA database" refers to the sounding rocket section, the index page of which is available via the home page *http://eea.spaceflight.esa.int/portal/* and clicking on "Sounding Rockets". Unless otherwise noted, the webpage or attachment was last accessed August 2014).

"MICREX" refers to the NASA Microgravity Research Experiments database, see "4. List of References – online databases for microgravity experiments" below.

A

Abbott, J.K. (1971) *A star-pointing attitude Control System for Skylark*. RAE Technical Report no.71241, December 1971. (TNA: PRO AVIA6/24003).

Ackerman, M. *et al.* (1974), 'Simultaneous upper air composition measurements by means of UV monochromators and mass spectrometers', *Journal of Geophysical Research*, Vol.79, no.31, pp. 4757-4764. (Abstract on ADS).

Acton, E.W.V. (1974), 'Some Aspects of the Management of the Science Research Council's Space Activities', *Journal of the British Interplanetary Society*, Vol.27, no.5 (May 1974), pp.343-348.

Adams, D.J., Cooke, B.A., Evans, K. & Pounds, K.A. (1970), 'Rocket Observations of Virgo XR-1', Non-Solar X- and Gamma-Ray Astronomy, *Proceedings from Symposium no.37 held in Rome, May 8-10, 1969*, International Astronomical Union. (ADS).

Adams, D.J., Janes, A.F. & Whitford, C.H. (1972a), 'A Variable Spacing Modulation Collimator for X-ray Astronomy', *Astronomy and Astrophysics*, Vol.20, p.121. (ADS).

Adams, D.J. and Janes, A.F. (1972b), 'Preliminary Results from the X-ray experiment SL904', *Journal of the British Interplanetary Society*, Vol.25, pp.201-208.

Ahlborn, H. (1983), 'The future of materials science on sounding rocket flights', *Sixth ESA Symposium on European rocket & balloon programmes & related research, 11-15 April 1983*, ESA document SP-183, pp.447-448. (Abstract on ADS).

Alexander, Bowen & Heddle (1964), 'Southern hemisphere observations of ultra-violet radiation from celestial objects. I. Experimental Techniques and Rocket Payload Technology', *Proc. R. Soc. Lond. A 16 June 1964*, Vol. 279 no. 1379, p.510-522.

Aschenbach, B. *et al.* (1981), 'The ROSAT mission', *European Space Agency, ESLAB Symposium on X-ray Astronomy, 15th, Amsterdam, Netherlands, June 22-26, 1981*. Space Science Reviews, Vol. 30, no. 1-4, 1981, p. 569-573. (ADS).

Aschenbach, B. *et al.* (1987), 'A search for soft X-rays from supernova 1987A', *Nature*, Vol. 330, Issue 6145, pp. 232-233. (November 1987). (Abstract on ADS).

Aspinall, R. (1953a), *The development of the supersonic beam riding test missile CTV.1*. TRE Malvern Report T2144, September 1953. (TNA: PRO AVIA 26/1605).

Aspinall, R. (1953b), *The beam riding trials of the supersonic test missile CTV.1*. TRE Malvern Report T2145, September 1953. (TNA: PRO AVIA 26/1606).

Auchter, H., Demharter, H. & Waldmann, H. (1984), 'Sounding rocket program Aeronomie. The payload M-1 in the project MAP-WINE', *Final report, June 1984*, Messerschmitt-Boelkow-Blohm GmbH, Ottobraun (Germany F.R.). Unternehmensbereich Raunfahr. (Abstract on ADS).

Auchter, H, Schlosser, C. & Waldmann, H. (1991), 'Payload SISSI. Sounding rocket program Final report', *report BMFT 50OE8803*. Messerschmitt-Boelkow-Blohm G.m.b.H. (MBB), Muenchen (Germany). Unternehmensbereich Raumfahrt, Kommunikationssysteme und Antriebe. (Abstract available online at *http://hdl.handle.net/10068/77262* , last accessed August 2014).

B

BAC – see under 'British Aircraft Corporation'.

BAe (1990), *Record of Skylark Launches 1957-1990*. (Copy courtesy of Jonathan McDowell).

Barber, Betty (2005), *My War Years 1938 -1947*, (privately printed, 2005).

Barnden, L.R. & Francey, R.J. (1969), 'A New X-ray object at High Galactic Latitude', *Proceedings of the Astronomical Society of Australia*, Vol.1, March 1969, p.236-237. (ADS).

Barnden, L.R. (1972), *Studies of X-rays and Cosmic Rays of Galactic Origin*, PhD thesis, University of Adelaide, March 1971. (Contents & summary available from *http://hdl.handle.net/2440/635566* , last accessed July 2014).

Barnes, M.B. & Kenward, D.R.D. (1972), *Sensor Trials on Skylark 586*. RAE Farnborough Technical Report 72066, 15 March 1972. (TNA: PRO DSIR 23/39703).

Basto, Raitt & Sojka (1976), 'A high resolution, low energy electrostatic analyser for rocket payloads', *Planetary and Space Science*, Vol.24, Feb1976, p.115-129. (Abstract on ADS).

Bates *et al.* (1970), 'Fabry-Pérot Interferograms of the Solar MgII resonance lines', *proceedings from IAU symposium no.36 held in Lunteren, the Netherlands, 1969*. (ADS). See also a similar paper in Nature, Volume 224, issue 5215, pages 161-163 (1969).

Bates *et al.* (1971), 'High Resolution Interferometric Studies of the Solar Magnesium II Doublet Spectral Region', *Phil. Trans. R. Soc. Lond. A 1971 270*, 47-53.

Bates, D. Boyd, R. & Davis, D.G. (1984), 'Harrie Stewart Wilson Massey. 16 May 1908-27 November 1983', *Biographical memoirs of Fellows of the Royal Society (1955-2000)*, Vol. 30, 1 Nov 1984, pp. 444-511.

Batstone, Evans, Parkinson & Pounds (1970), 'Further X-Ray Spectra of Solar Active Regions', *Solar Physics*, Vol. 13, Issue 2, pp.389-400.

Beadell, Len (1975), *Still in the Bush*, Rigby, Australia, ISBN 0 7270 0020 9.

Beadle, B.E. (1961), 'Summary of Discussion' (re RAeS Symposium 11 March 1960), *RAeS Journal* Vol.65 (August 1961), p.550.

Beattie, B.S.E. (1974), 'The Earth Resource Skylark – A Progress Report', *Journal of the British Interplanetary Society*, Vol.27 no.1 (Jan 1974), p.14-17.

Bedford, D.K. & Bryan, H.W. (1974), 'The Micrometeoroid Detector Aboard the Satellite Prospero', *Journal of the British Interplanetary Society*, Vol.27, no.6 (June 1974), pp.459-464.

Bergstralh, T. & Krause, E. (1975), 'Early Upper Atmospheric Research with Rockets', (reprinted as Chapter 11 of Volume 9 of the "History of Rocketry and Astronautics" series, published for the American Astronautical Society by Univelt, San Diego, California, 1989, ISBN 0-87703-3090-9).

Bernard, R. *et al.* (1977), 'Large scale dynamics observed during the Western Europe Winter Anomaly Campaign 1975/76 from wind, temperature and absorption', *COSPAR, 20th Plenary Meeting*, June 7-18 1977. (Abstract on ADS).

Bibbo, Giovanni (1977), *Rocket Studies of the Lower Thermosphere*, PhD thesis, University of Adelaide, September 1977. (Contents & summary available from *http://hdl.handle.net/2440/199544* , last accessed July 2014).

Biltcliffe, D., Thirkettle, A. & Kedar, A. (1962), *A Roll Control System for Skylark*, RAE Farnborough Technical Note no. Space 12, May 1962. (TNA: PRO AVIA 6/19219).

Bjurstrøm, R. & Gundersen, A. (1978), 'Recent and Future Activity at Andøya Rocket Range', *European Sounding-Rocket, Balloon and Related Research, Proceedings of a Symposium 24-29 April 1978*, ESA document SP-135, pp.161-166.

Boksenberg, A. (1972), 'Performance of the UCL image photon counting system', *Proceedings of ESO/CERN conference on auxiliary instrumentation for large telescopes*, p.295-316. (ADS).

Boland et al. (1971a), 'A high resolution solar ultraviolet spectrum between 200 and 220 nm', *P Phil. Trans. R. Soc. Lond. A* July 16, 1971 270:29-46.

Boland, B.C., Jones, B.B. & Engstrom, S.F.T. (1971b), 'An Echelle Spectrograph for High Resolution Studies of the Solar Vacuum Ultraviolet Spectrum', *Solar Physics*, Volume 17, Issue 2, pp.333-354 (04/1971), (ADS).

Boland, B.C., Engstrom, S.F.T., Jones, B.B. & Wilson, R. (1973), 'The Heating of the Solar Corona', *Astronomy and Astrophysics*, Vol. 22, p. 161 (1973), (ADS).

Boland, Dyre, Firth, Gabriel, Jones, Jordan, McWhirter, Monk & Turner, (1975), Further Measurements of Emission Line Profiles in the Solar Ultraviolet Spectrum, *Royal Astronomical Society, Monthly Notices*, Vol. 171, June 1975, p. 697-724, (ADS).

Bosqued et al. (1974), 'Auroral electron fluxes parallel to the geomagnetic field lines', *Journal of Geophysical Research*. Vol. 79, pp. 98-104. 1 Jan.1974. (Abstract on ADS).

Bowen et al. (1963), 'Upper atmosphere wind and temperature structure by Skylark rocket-grenade experiments at Woomera, Australia, 1957-59'. *Proc. R. Soc. Lond. A* July 21, 1964 280:170-184.

Boyd, R.L.F. & Seaton, M.J. (Eds) (1954), *Rocket Exploration of the Upper Atmosphere*, Pergamon Press Ltd, London. (No ISBN).

Boyd, R.L.F. (1960), *Space Research by Rocket and Satellite*, Arrow Books Ltd, London. (No ISBN).

Boyd, R.L.F. (1961), 'The Scientific Programme of Skylark to Mid-1960', *Journal of the Royal Aeronautical Society*, August 1961, Volume 65 (1961), p.531.

Boyd, R.L.F. (1965), 'Techniques for the Measurement of Extra-Terrestrial Soft X-Radiation', *Space Science Reviews*, February 1965, Volume 4, Issue 1, pp.35-90. (ADS).

Boyd, R.L.F. (1967), *Speech by Professor R.L.F.Boyd at the Opening of the Mullard Space Science Laboratory May 3rd 1967*, accessed from website *www.ucl.ac.uk/mssl/about-mssl/heritage/archive-documents/mssl-opening* , click on "Opening Speech by Prof Robert Boyd". (Last accessed August 2014).

Boyd, R.L.F. (1969), 'Future requirements for Cosmic X-ray astronomy', *Proc. R. Soc. Lond. A* November 11, 1969 313 (1514) 381-393.

Brabban, D.H., Glencross, W.M. & Herring, J.R.H. (1970), 'Studies of the Solar X-ray Spectrum as a Function of position on the disk' *New techniques in Space Astronomy. IAU Symposium no. 41*,

Munich Aug. 10-14, 1970. Edited by F. Labuhn and Reimar Lust. International Astronomical Union. Symposium no. 41, Dordrecht, Reidel, p.135, (ADS).

Brabban, D.H. & Glencross, W.M. (1973), 'Crystal spectrometry of active regions on the sun', *Proc. R. Soc. Lond. A.* Vol.334, p.231-239.

Brabban, D.H. (1974), 'A Comparison of three Solar Active Regions based on their Soft X-ray Line Spectra', *Solar Physics*, Vol. 38, Oct. 1974, p. 449-464. (ADS).

Brabban, D.H, Glencross, W.M. and Rosenberg, F.D. (1975), 'Crystal spectrometer studies of the sun employing a rotation modulation collimator', *Solar Physics*, Vol.42, June 1975, p.355-376, (ADS).

Bradley, A., Bullough, K. & Jenkins, C.A.E. (1965), 'A Dipole Aerial System for Rocket Experiments', *Journal of the British Interplanetary Society*, Vol.20, no 6 (November-December 1965), pp.171-176.

Bradt, H.V.D & McClintock, J.E. (1983), 'The optical counterparts of compact galactic X-ray sources', *Annual Review of Astronomy and Astrophysics*.1983.21:13-66. (ADS).

Bramley, E.N., Bain, W.C. & Davies, P.G. (1965), 'Rocket Studies of aerial admittance and resonance rectification', *Planetary and Space Science* Vol. 13, Issue 7, July 1965, pp.723-726.

Briscoe H.M. (1965), 'The choice of propellant for a cold gas propulsion system for a satellite', *Journal of the British Interplanetary Society*, Vol.20, no. 3, (May-June 1965), pp.72-78.

British Aircraft Corporation (c.1966), *skylark upper atmosphere research vehicle*, sales booklet GW/SEB 131, Space and Instrumentation Group, British Aircraft Corporation (Operating) Ltd., Guided Weapons Division, Filton House, Bristol.

Brown, D.J. & Crosse, P.M. (1975), 'The Development of the Skylark 10A Sounding Rocket', *Journal of the British Interplanetary Society*, Vol.28, no.4 (April 1975), pp.227-234.

Brown, D.J. (1976), 'Recent additions to the Skylark family of Sounding Rockets', *European programmes on sounding-rocket & balloon research, Proceedings of a Symposium 3-7 May 1976*, ESA document SP-115, pp.439-453.

Brown, D.J. (1978), 'Recent Advances in Skylark vehicle technology', *European Sounding-Rocket, Balloon and Related Research, Proceedings of a Symposium 24-29 April 1978*, ESA document SP-135, pp.411-416.

Brück, H.A. (1973), *Royal Observatory, Edinburgh. Report for year ending 1973 March 31*. Q.J.R. Astron.Soc,Vol.15, p.36-47 (ADS).

Bryant, D.A. (1981), 'Rocket studies of particle structure associated with auroral arcs', *Proceedings of the Chapman Conference on Formation of Auroral Arcs, Fairbanks, AK, July 21-25, 1980*. (Abstract on ADS).

Burrows, D.N., Nousek, J.A., Berthiaume, G.D. & Garmire, G.P. (1989), 'Search for soft X-ray emission from SN 1987A with a CCD X-ray imaging spectrometer', *Astrophysical Journal*, Part 1, Vol. 347, Dec. 15, 1989, p. 1114-1118. (ADS).

Burrows, K. & Hall, S.H. (1965), 'Rocket Measurements of the Geomagnetic Field above Woomera, South Australia', *Technical Report NASA-TM-X-54957* (Available free online, from the NASA Technical Reports Server [NTRS]). Also available in Journal of Geophysical Research Volume 70, Issue 9, 1 May 1965, pp.2149–2158.

Burton, W.M. & Wilson, R. (1965), 'Observations of the Sun in the Extreme Ultra-violet made from a Stabilized Skylark Rocket', *Nature*, 207, 61-62 (03 July1965). (Abstract on ADS).

Burton, W.M., Ridgeley, A. & Wilson, R. (1967), 'The Ultraviolet Emission Spectrum of the Solar Chromosphere and Corona', *Monthly Notices of the Royal Astronomical Society*, Vol.135, p.207-223. (ADS).

Burton, W.M. (1968), 'Extreme Ultraviolet Observations of Active Regions in the Solar Corona', *Structure and Development of Solar Active Regions*. Symposium no. 35 held in Budapest, Hungary, 4-8 September 1967. Edited by Karl Otto Kiepenheuer. International Astronomical Union. Symposium no. 35, Dordrecht, D. Reidel., p.395. (ADS).

Burton, W.M. (1969), 'Solar Photography in the Extreme Ultraviolet', *Solar Physics*, Vol. 8, Issue 1, pp. 53-71. (ADS).

Burton, W.M. & Ridgeley, A. (1970), 'The Solar Limb Emission Spectrum between 300Å and 2803Å', *Solar Physics*, Vol.14, Issue 1, pp.3-28. (ADS).

Burton, W.M., Jordan, C., Ridgeley, A. & Wilson, R. (1971), 'The structure of the chromosphere-corona transition region from limb and disk intensities', *Phil. Trans. R. Soc. Lond. A* 1971 270:, 81-98.

Burton, W.M., Evans, R.G. & Griffin, W.G. (1974), 'The interstellar medium in the direction of the Gum nebula' *Monthly Notices of the Royal Astronomical Society (1974)*, Vol.169, pp.307-321. (ADS).

Burton, W.M., Evans, R.G. & Griffin, W.G. (1975), 'Skylark Rocket Observations of ultraviolet spectra of γ2 Velorum and ζ Puppis', *Phil. Trans. R. Soc. Lond. A*. 279,355-369.

Burton, W.M., Evans, R.G. & Griffin, W.G. (1976), 'The absolute spectral flux distribution from γ2 Vel', *Monthly Notices of the Royal Astronomical Society (1976)*, Vol.176, Short Communication, 29P-31P3, (1967). (ADS).

Byrne, F.N. & Marsden, D.J. (1975), 'Concentration of metallic neutrals and ions by resonance fluorescence scattering', *MIST (Magnetosphere, Ionosphere & Solar-Terrestrial Environment) meeting at Exeter in March 1975*, as reported in the Quarterly Journal of the Royal Astronomical Society, Vol. 16, p.282. (ADS).

C

Cadbury, D. (2006), *Space Race – The Battle to Rule the Heavens*, Harper Perennial, Harper Collins Publishers, London, ISBN 978-0-00-720994-1.

Cameron, A.M. (1946), Report on Operation "Backfire", (Published in five volumes by The War Office, London, January 1946). (The five volumes are available to read at the British National Archives in London, using references TNA: PRO WO 231/22 to WO 231/26), and also available free online from the US Smithsonian Libraries via *http://library.si.edu/digital-library/book/report-operation-backfire* , last accessed August 2014).

Campbell, J.W. (1970a), 'Absolute Stellar Photometry in the Region 1200 Å – 3000 Å', *Proceedings from IAU Symposium no.36*, D.Reidal Pub.Co., p.135. (ADS).

Campbell, J.W. (1970b), 'Absolute Stellar Photometry in the Region 1900Å - 3000Å', *Astrophysics and Space Science*, Vol. 9, Issue 1, pp.128-145, 10/1970. (ADS).

Campbell, J.W. (1971a), 'Stellar Photometry in the region 1300Å -2000Å. Part I', *Astrophysics and Space Science*, Vol. 11, Issue 3, pp.417-422, 06/1971. (ADS).

Campbell, J.W. (1971b), 'Stellar Photometry in the region 1300Å -2000Å. Part II', *Astrophysics and Space Science*, Vol. 13, Issue 1, pp.189-202, 09/1971. (ADS).

Cannon *et al.* (1980), 'ELF/VLF wavefield measurements made at the time of launch of Skylark SL1424', *ESA European Rocket and Balloon Programs and Related Research*, p.301-307. ESA document SP-152, published 06/1980. (Abstract on ADS).

Carver *et al.* (1972), 'Ultraviolet Ion Chamber Measurements of the Solar Minimum Brightness Temperature', *Solar Physics*, Vol. 27, Issue 2, pp.347-353. (ADS).

CCBH (2005), *Witness Seminar held 7 December 2001, Skylark Sounding Rockets 1957-1972*, Centre for Contemporary British History, 2005, (*www.ccbh.ac.uk/downloads/skylark.pdf* , last accessed July 2014). (Also printed by BROHP in *The Journal of British Rocketry and Nuclear History*, (Prospero), No.2, Spring 2005, p.79).

Ceglia, E. (2005), *European Users Guide to Low Gravity Platforms*, ESA reference USM-ESA-UM-0001, Issue 2 revision 0, Directorate of Human Spaceflight, European Space Agency, Noordwijk. (Available free online via webpage *www.esa.int/SPECIALS/HSF_Research/SEMG2W4KXMF_0.html* , last accessed July 2014).

Chambers, E.W. (1974), *SL1203 Post Firing Report*, (British Aircraft Corporation (Aust.) Pty. Ltd., P.O.Box 180, Salisbury, South Australia, 7th March 1974). (Copy courtesy C.Rapley).

Chambers, E.W. (2000), *Woomera: Its human face*, Seaview Press, Henley Beach, South Australia, ISBN 1 74008 061 0.

Chapman, S. (1954), 'Rockets and the Magnetic Exploration of the Ionosphere', *Rocket Exploration of the Upper Atmosphere*, pp.292-305, Boyd R.L.F. & Seaton M.J. (Eds), Pergamon Press Ltd., London, pp.292-305.

Charles, P.A. & Seward, F.D. (1995), *Exploring the X-ray Universe*, Cambridge University Press, ISBN 0 521 43712 1.

Christiansen, P.J. *et al.* (1976), 'Detection of high-frequency electrostatic signals in the auroral atmosphere', *MIST (Magnetosphere, Ionosphere & Solar-Terrestrial Environment) meeting at Aberystwyth*, (1976), as reported in the Quarterly Journal of the Royal Astronomical Society, Vol.17, p.460. (ADS).

Christiansen, P.J. & Collin, H.L. (1979), *MIST (Magnetosphere, Ionosphere & Solar-Terrestrial Environment) meeting at Southampton, 1978*, as reported in the Quarterly Journal of the Royal Astronomical Society, Vol.20, p.46. (ADS).

Churchill, W. S. (1954), *The Second World War, Volume VI, Triumph and Tragedy*, Penguin Books Ltd., Harmondsworth, 1985. (No ISBN).

Colinet *et al.* (2002), 'Interfacial Turbulence in Evaporating Liquids: Theory and Preliminary Results of the ITEL-MASER 9 Sounding Rocket Experiment', ESA EEA database, MASER 9, 'Interfacial Turbulence in Evaporating Liquids', 1st pdf attachment, (last accessed August 2014).

Cooke, B.A., Pounds, K.A., Stewardson, E.A. & Adams, D.J. (1967), 'A Cosmic X-ray Survey in the Southern Hemisphere', *Astrophysical Journal*, Vol. 150, p.L189. (ADS).

Cooke, B.A., Griffiths, R.E. & Pounds, K.A. (1970), 'Evidence for a Galactic Component of the Diffuse X-ray Background', Non-Solar X- and Gamma-Ray Astronomy, *Proceedings from Symposium no. 37 held in Rome, May 8-10, 1969*. Edited by Livio Gratton. International Astronomical Union. Symposium no. 37, Dordrecht-Holland, D. Reidel Pub. Co., p.280. (ADS).

Cooper, R.D. (2006), *Rocket Man*, Navtech Systems Ltd., Sulby, Welford, Northamptonshire, 2006. Also available online at *www.slideshare.net/Stellvia/rocket-man-roger-cooper* , (last accessed July 2014).

Cope, P.E.G. (1964), 'The Attitude Control System of the Skylark Sounding Rocket', *Journal of the British Interplanetary Society*, Vol.19 no.7 (January-February 1964), pp.285-291.

Corliss, W.R. (1971), *NASA Sounding Rockets 1958-1968, A Historical Summary*. NASA report SP-4401, available free online via the NASA Technical Reports Server (NTRS).

Cox, B. & Cohen, A. (2010), *Wonders of the Solar System*, HarperCollins, London, ISBN 978 0 00 7386901.

Cröll *et al.* (1999), 'Measurement of Temperature Fluctuations and Microscopic Growth Rates in a Silicon Floating Zone on TEXUS 36', *Proceedings 14th ESA Symposium on European Rocket and Balloon Programmes and Related Research*, Potsdam, Germany, 31 May – 3 June 1999, ESA SP-437, September 1999, p.529-534.

Cruise, A.M. (1973), *Rocket studies of cosmic X-ray sources*, Ph.D thesis, University of London. (Abstract on ADS).

Cruise, A.M. (1974), *Some Future Research Tasks For Stabilised Skylarks*, MSSL/UCL Report for the Aeronautical Research Council, ARC 35 530. (TNA: PRO document ref. DSIR 23/41128).

Cruise, A.M. (2008), 'Skylark Ascending', *The Journal of British Rocketry and Nuclear History (Prospero)*, Number 5, Spring 2008), also online at *www.spaceuk.org/journal/prospero5.pdf* (last accessed July 2014).

Cruise, A.M. & Willmore A.P. (1975), 'The analysis of Data from Rotation Modulation Collimators', *Royal Astronomical Society, Monthly Notices*, Vol.170, Jan.1975, p.165-175. (ADS).

D

Dalgarno, A. (1997), 'Sir David Robert Bates. 18 November 1916-5 January 1994'. *Biographical Memoirs of Fellows of the Royal Society*, Vol. 43 (Nov. 1997), pp. 48-71).

Dawton, D.I. (1955), *Performance Estimates for a Single Stage Upper Atmosphere Research Vehicle Powered by a Solid Fuel Rocket Motor*. RAE Farnborough Technical Memo GW 387, October 1955. (TNA: PRO AVIA 6/19785).

Dawton, D.I., Knott, F.R. & Barford, G.S. (1959), *The Technique of Kinetic Heating Measurement in Rocket Test Vehicles: with particular reference to experiments made in CTV.5 series 2*. RAE Farnborough Technical Note GW 509, Feb 1959. (TNA: PRO AVIA 6/21446).

Delury, J.T. (1978), 'Review of the British Scientific Sounding Rocket and Balloon Programmes', *European Sounding-Rocket, Balloon and Related Research, with emphasis on Experiments at High Latitude Research*, ESA document SP-135, pp.45-49.

Delury, J.T. (1980), 'The UK Sounding Rocket and Balloon Programme', *Fifth ESA Symposium on European rocket & balloon programmes & related research, 14-18 April 1980*, ESA document SP-152, pp.29-31.

Delury, J.T. (1983), 'Summary of the 1957-1982 UK Scientific Research Sounding Rocket Programme', *Sixth ESA Symposium on European rocket & balloon programmes & related research, 11-15 April 1983*, ESA document SP-183, pp.21-24.

Department of Supply and Development, Commonwealth of Australia (1949), *The Joint United Kingdom – Australia Long Range Weapons Project in Australia*, April 1949. (TNA: PRO WO 33/2662).

Deudney, F.E. (1950), *Flight Trials measurement on roll control characteristics of C.T.V.3.*, RAE Farnborough Technical note GW 71, May 1950. (TNA: PRO AVIA 6/15365).

Deudney, F.E. & Watts, P.E. (1958), *Wind tunnel tests of several configurations of a model C.T.V.5 at mach numbers 1.58 and 2.02*. RAE Farnborough report AERO 2596, April 1958. (TNA: PRO. AVIA 6/18052).

Dommett, Roy, (2004), 'The First Charles Martin Memorial Lecture', *The Journal of British Rocketry and Nuclear History* (Prospero), Number 1, Spring 2004, p.14.

Dommett, R.L. (2008), 'Engineering the Chevaline Delivery System', *The Journal of British Rocketry and Nuclear History* (Prospero), Number 5, Spring 2008, p.99-121.

Dorado, J.M., Bautista, M. & Sanz-Aránguez, P. (2002), *Spain in Space – a short history of Spanish activity in the space sector*, ESA report HSR-26 (August 2002), ESA Publications Division, ISSN: 1683-4704, ISBN: 92-9092-534-5. (Available online).

Dorling, E.B. (1959), *The First Six Skylark Firings*. RAE Farnborough Technical Note GW 530, October 1959. (TNA: PRO DSIR 23/27687).

Dorling, E.B. (1975), 'Early History of the Skylark Rocket', (reprinted as Chapter 12 of Volume 9 of the "History of Rocketry and Astronautics" series, published for the American Astronautical Society by Univelt, San Diego, California, 1989, ISBN 0-87703-3090-9).

Dorling, E.B. (1991), *Reminiscences of the Mullard Space Science Laboratory to 1991*, (March 1991), available on the MSSL website, *www.ucl.ac.uk/mssl/about-mssl/heritage/Docs/Dorling-book* (last accessed August 2014). See also the similar article 'The Early History of the Mullard Space Science Laboratory, UCL.' in "Prospero", *The Journal of British Rocketry and Nuclear History*, number 5, Spring 2008, p.63.

Dougherty, K. (2006), *The Weapons Research Establishment: an Administrative History*, paper presented at the 57th International Astronautical Congress, Valencia, Spain, Oct. 2006, IAC-06-E4.2.05. (Some pages available free on the Web).

Dreier, L. (1990), *Plan for the MAXUS-TEST campaign at Esrange November 1990*, Swedish Space Corporation September 1990.

DSTO (Australia), (not dated), *Innovations in Defence Science*, pdf document available online at *www.dsto.defence.gov.au/attachments/Innovations%20in%20Defence%20Science.pdf* (last accessed July 2014).

Durney, A.C. *et al.* (1964), 'The Energy Spectrum of the Heavy Primary Cosmic Rays', *Proc. R. Soc. Lond. A*, 6 October 1964 Vol. 281 no. 1387 553-564.

E

Eaton, D. (1972), 'A Survey of the ESRO Sounding Rockets Programme 1964-1971', *Journal of the British Interplanetary Society*, Vol.25, pp.189-200, 1972.

Edwards, T. *et al.* (1975), 'Electric fields and energetic particle precipitation in an auroral arc', *Summer Advanced School on Magnetospheric Particles and Fields, Graz, 4-15 Aug. 1975*. (ADS and available free online).

Edwards, T., Bryant, D.A. & Smith, M.J. (1976), 'Electron intensities and electric fields in a quiet auroral arc', *MIST (Magnetosphere, Ionosphere & Solar-Terrestrial Environment) meeting at Aberystwyth*, (1976), as reported in the Quarterly Journal of the Royal Astronomical Society (1976), Vol.17, p.460. (ADS, under "Royal Astronomical Society MIST meeting at Aberystwyth").

Elliott Brothers (London) Ltd, Weapons Division (1964), *Cold Gas Attitude Control For the Skylark Rocket Payload Stage 1: Solar Pointing Mission*, Technical Report No.T(f)10. (Copy at Cranfield University Library).

Ellis, J.A. (1987), 'Skylark Sounding Rocket Development – Skylark 8', *Proceedings of the 8th ESA Symposium on European Rocket and Balloon Programmes and Related Research, Sunne, Sweden, 17-23 May 1987*. ESA SP-270, pp.437-440.

Ellis, J.A. (1989), 'The Skylark Sounding Rocket Programme and Future Launcher Developments by British Aerospace (Space Systems) Ltd.', *Proc. Ninth ESA/PAC Symposium on 'European Rocket and Balloon Programmes and Related Research', Lahnstein, FRG, 3-7 April 1989*. ESA SP-291, June 1989, p.269.

Ellis, J.A. (1992), 'Skylark Sounding Rockets – Past and Present', *Journal of the British Interplanetary Society*, Vol.45 no.4 (April 1992), pp.179-180.

Encyclopaedia Britannica (1962), (in 24 volumes), Encyclopaedia Britannica Ltd., London, 1962. (No ISBN).

ESRO (1972), *Development, Launch and In-Flight Performance of ESRO Sounding-Rocket Payloads*, Volume 1: Payloads Launched in 1964-1965. ESRO SP-76, November 1972, compiled by Y.P.G.Guérin.

Ibid., Volume II: Payloads Launched in 1966. ESRO SP-77, June 1973.

Ibid., Volume III: Payloads Launched in 1967. ESRO SP-78, November 1973.

Ibid., Volume IV: Payloads Launched in 1968. ESRO SP-79, February 1974.

Ibid., Volume V: Payloads launched in 1969, ESRO SP-80, May 1974.

Evans K. & Pounds K.A. (1968), 'The X-ray Spectrum of a solar active region', The Astrophysical Journal, Vol 152, April 1968. (ADS)

Everest, D. (2006), 'An Armourer at Farnborough', *The Journal of British Rocketry and Nuclear History* (Prospero), Number 3 p.15, Spring 2006.

F

Fabian, A.C. (1974), 'Galactic Contributions to the Isotropy of the Cosmic X-ray Background', *Astronomy and Astrophysics*, Vol. 32, p. 127. (ADS).

Fahleson *et al.* (1971), 'Simultaneous Electric Field Measurements made in the Auroral Ionosphere by Using three Independent Techniques', *Radio Science*, Vol. 6, p.233. (Abstract on ADS).

Fahleson, U., Fälthammar, C.-G, & Pedersen, A. (1974), 'Ionospheric temperature and density measurements by means of spherical double probes', *Planetary & Space Science*, Vol.22, January 1974, pp.41-66. (Abstract on ADS).

Fahr, H.J. & Lay, G. (1979), 'ASTRO-HEL: A new payload for high resolution EUV radiation analysis', *ESA European Sounding Rocket, Balloon and Related Research., with Emphasis on Expt. at High Latitudes*, p 267-275, (Abstract on ADS).

Fahr, H.J, Ripken, H.W. & Lay, G. (1980), 'INTER-ZODIAK: A High-Apogee Rocket Experiment for the Observation of Dust-Generated Neutrals in the Solar Vicinity', *Fifth ESA Symposium on European rocket & balloon programmes & related research, 14-18 April 1980*, ESA document SP-152, pp.449-451.

Farr, C.T. (1971), 'Broadband determination of Sky Brightness from a Skylark Sounding Rocket', *Journal of the British Interplanetary Society*, Vol.24, p.393-407.

Farr C.T. (1975), *Flight Performance of the Skylark SL1011 Starpointing Attitude Control System*, RAE Technical Report 75110, December 1975. (TNA: PRO document ref. AVIA6/25174).

Fearn, D.G. (2005), 'Orbit-Raising Past and Present – the X-Series of Spacecraft and Artemis'. *29th International Electric Propulsion Conference, Princeton University, October 31 – November 4, 2005*. (Available free online, last accessed July 2014).

Firth, J.G. *et al.* (1974), 'Observations of the Solar Spectrum in the Region 150Å to 870Å emitted from the disk and above the limb', *Monthly Notices of the Royal Astronomical Society*, Vol.177, p.543-560. (ADS).

Fischer, F., Stasek, G. & Schmidtke, G. (1980), 'Identification of auroral EUV emissions', Geophys. Res. Lett., Vol. 7, Issue 11, pp. 1003–1002. (Abstract on ADS).

Fisher, W.T. (1975), 'The Use of Sounding Rocket as Targets', *Journal of the British Interplanetary Society*, Vol.28, no.4, (April 1975), pp.245-249.

Flight International magazine – the complete searchable archive from 1909 to 2005 is available free online at *www.flightglobal.com/pdfarchive/index.html* , (last accessed July 2014).

Florin *et al.* (2005), 'The MASER-10 Microgravity Rocket Flight', *Proceedings of the 17th ESA Symposium on European Rocket and Balloon Programmes and Related Research, Sandefjord, Norway,30 May-2 June 2005*, pp531-536, ESA SP-590, August 2005. (Available online)

Fox, J.W. (c.1984), *From Lardner to Massey – A history of physics, space science and astronomy at University College London, 1826 to 1975*, available online at *www.phys.ucl.ac.uk/department/history/BFox1.html#Fox10* , last accessed July 2014).

Francey, Fenton, Harries & McCracken (1968), 'The Variability of Centaurus XR-2', *Proceedings of the Astronomical Society of Australia*, Vol. 1, p.108 (February 1968), (ADS).

Franke (2001), 'Program Description and User Scenario TEXUS/MAXUS/MINITEXUS', *Microgravity Research and Applications in Physical Sciences and Biotechnology, Proceedings of the First International Symposium 10-15 September, 2000 in Sorrento, Italy*. European Space Agency, ESA SP-454, 2001.

Fredriksson (1991), 'The Coalescence Process in Immiscible Alloys'. *In Summary Review of Sounding Rocket Experiments in Fluid Science and Materials Sciences, TEXUS 1 to 20, MASER 1 and 2.* ESA SP-1132, February 1991, pp. 252-253.

Freeman, F.F. & Jones, B.B. (1970), 'Grazing Incidence Spectra of the Sun', *Solar Physics*, Vol.15, Issue 2, pp.288-308, (ADS)

Fredga, K. (2008), 'A life in Space - Jan Stiernstedt, 1925–2008', *ESA Bulletin 136*, November 2008. (Available online, last accessed July 2014).

Friedman, H. (1960), 'Recent Experiments from Rockets and Satellites', *Astronomical Journal*, Vol. 65, p. 264. (ADS).

Friedman, H., Byram, E.T. & Chubb, T.A. (1967), 'Distribution and Variability of Cosmic X-Ray Sources', *Science*, Vol. 156, issue 3773 (21 April 1967), pp. 374-378.

Frings, W., Preu, P. & Röhrig, O. (1999), 'Scientific Sounding Rocket and Balloon Activities in Germany', *Proceedings 14th ESA Symposium on European Rocket and Balloon Programmes and Related Research, Potsdam, Germany, 31 May – 3 June 1999*, ESA SP-437, September 1999, p.23-26. (ADS).

Frischat, G.H., Braedt, M. & Beier, W. (1983), 'Reactions in Glass Melts', *Proceedings of the 4th European Symposium on Materials Sciences Under Microgravity, Madrid, Spain, April 5-8, 1983*, ESA SP-191, pp. 161-165. (ADS).

Froechtenigt, J.F. (1973), *Study of X-ray Optics*, Report MCR-73-317, NASA-CR-139597, November 1973, 'Final Report for Contract NAS 8-29861'. (Available free online via NTRS, last accessed July 2014).

Furst, J.W. (1972), 'Design for High Performance Sounding Rockets', *Journal of the British Interplanetary Society*, Vol.25, no.2 (February 1972), p.153.

Furst J.W. & Brown D.J. (1974), 'Skylark 8 – High Altitude Sounding Rocket", *Journal of the British Interplanetary Society*, Vol.27, no.7 (July 1974), pp.486-498.

G

Geisel, J.E. & Franke, B.J. (1979), 'Experiment modules and facilities in TEXUS 1 and 2', *ESA Mater. Sci. in Space,* p 177-188, pub. 06/1979. (Abstract on ADS).

Gibbons, W., Madahar, B.K. & Woolliscroft, L.J.C. (1981), 'Magnetospheric waves measured on high altitude skylark rockets SL 1423 and SL 1424', *Advances in Space Research*, Vol. 1, Issue 1, 1981, pp.365-368.

Giles, A.B. (1981), 'Observations of sub-millisecond bursts from Cygnus X-1', *Monthly Notices of the Royal Astronomical Society*, Vol. 195, June 1981, p. 721-731. (ADS).

Giles, A.B. (2010a), *A Skylark in Spain (SL-1304), (a contribution to 50 years of Space Physics at Leicester University, UK, 1960-2010)*, available online at *http://space50.star.le.ac.uk/wp-content/uploads/2010/06/Skylark_SL-13041.pdf*, last accessed July 2014.

Giles, A.B. (2010b), *A Skylark in Oz (SL-1306, (a contribution to 50 years of Space Physics at Leicester University, UK, 1960-2010)*, document available online at *http://space50.star.le.ac.uk/wp-content/uploads/2010/06/SL_13061.pdf*, last accessed July 2014.

Gleave, A.G. (1970), *The alignment and photometric calibration of a star and skylight simulator*, RAE Technical Report 70037, March 1970. (TNA: PRO document ref. DSIR 23/38027).

Goddard Space Flight Center (GSFC) (1963), *Ariel I The First International Satellite, The Project Summary*, NASA report SP-43, (NTRS).

Goddard Space Flight Center (GSFC) (1966), *Ariel I The First International Satellite, Experimental Results*, NASA report SP-119. (NTRS).

Godwin, M. (2007), *The Skylark Rocket: British Space Science and the European Space Research Organisation 1957-1972*, Beauchesne, Paris, ISBN 978-2-7010-1511-8.

Goodhew, P. J. & Clyne, D. (1985), *Retention of a Fine Precipitate Dispersion*. In BMFT/DFVLR Texus 11/12 Abschlussbericht, 1985, p. 55. (Post-flight). (MICREX).

Gordon, H.W.B. & Parkin, L.W. (1964), *A Summary of "Black Knight" Flight Data from 1958 to 1962*. RAE Technical Note Space 57 (February 1964, (TNA: PRO doc. ref. DSIR 23/31798).

Grahn S. & Stenmark L. (1980), 'Swedish Materials Science Experiment in the TEXUS 1 and 2 Rockets', *Journal of Spacecraft and Rockets*, Vol.17, p.275, (Abstract on ADS).

Gratton, L. (1969), 'Ground based observations of X-ray sources – a short review', *Proc. R. Soc. London, Ser.A*, Vol.313, p.317-330.

Greer, R.G.H. & Best, G.T. (1967), 'A rocket-borne photometric investigation of the oxygen lines at 5577 Å and 6300 Å, the sodium D-lines, and the continuum at 5300 Å in the night airglow', *Planetary and Space Science*, Vol.15 issue 12, December 1967, pp.1857-1881. (Abstract on ADS).

Griffiths, R.E. (1971), 'A Review of Cosmic X-ray Astronomy', *Journal of the British Interplanetary Society*, Vol.24, no.3 (March 1971), p.129-137.

Griffiths, R.E. (1972), 'A Further High-Resolution Search for Fe XXV Line Emission from Scorpius X-1', *Astronomy & Astrophysics*, 21, 97-103. (ADS).

Grossmann et al. (1991), 'Rocket-borne infrared measurements in the Arctic upper atmosphere', *10th ESA Symposium on European Rocket and Balloon Programmes and Related Research* p 423-427, ESA SP-317. (Abstract on ADS).

Groves, G.V. (1976), 'Rocket studies of atmospheric tides', *Proc. R. Soc. Lond. A*. 351, 437-469.

H

Hall, J.E. & Fooks, Jean (1965), 'The energy distribution in the quiet D-region derived from rocket measurements of low-frequency propagation', *Planetary and Space Science*, Vol. 13, p.1013. (Abstract on ADS).

Hall, L & Helmersson, A. (1985), 'SPINRAC, an attitude control system for obtaining low impact dispersion', *7th ESA Symposium on European rocket & balloon programmes & related research, 5-11 May 1985*, ESA document SP-229, July 1985, pp.361-364.

Hall, S.H. et al. (1971), 'Rocket observations of middle latitude sporadic E, magnetic fields, winds and ionization', *Planetary and Space Science*, Vol. 19, issue 10, October 1971, pp.1319-132. (Abstract on ADS).

Hamilton-Paterson, James (2010), *Empire of the Clouds*, Faber and Faber, London, ISBN 978-0-571-24795-0.

Hampson, Frank (1951), 'Voyage to Venus', Eagle comic, Vol. 2 No.9 (8 June 1951), picture 16. (See for instance the reprint in Dan Dare, Pilot of the Future, Voyage to Venus Part 2, Titan Books, 2004, ISBN 978 184 023 8419).

Hampson, Frank (1955), 'The Man from Nowhere', Eagle comic, Vol.6 No.20 (20 May 1955), picture 10. (See for instance the reprint in Hampson & Slattery (1979).

Hampson, Frank, & Slattery, James (1979), *Dan Dare, Pilot of the Future in The Man From Nowhere*, Dragon's Dream/Book Club Associates. (No ISBN).

Hardy, J.R. (1973), *First estimation of crop area statistics for the area of Argentina photographed by Skylark SL1181, using ground truth data*. University of Reading Remote Sensing Paper No.1, June 1973, (University of Reading Department of Geography).

Hardy, J.R. (1975), *Anglo-Argentinian Geoscopy Experiment Report – December 1975, Section 7*, University of Reading Department of Geography, December 1975.

Harlow, J, (1990), 'Black Knight Upper Stages', *Journal of the British Interplanetary Society*, Vol.43, pp.311-316.

Harlow, J. (1992a), 'A History of the Early Solid Propellant Rocket Motors of Royal Ordnance plc Rocket Motors Division', *28th Joint Propulsion and Exhibit, July 6-8, 1992, Nashville, TN.* , AIAA 92-3613. (Available online via American Institute of Aeronautics and Astronautics).

Harlow, J. (1992b), 'On the many guises of the Rook', *Journal of the British Interplanetary Society*, Vol.45, pp.139-144.

Harlow, J (1998), 'Sustainer propulsion for the UK air defence weapons – The early history', *34th AIAA/ASME/SAE/ASEE Joint Propulsion Conference and Exhibit, Cleveland, OH, July 13-15, 1998*. AIAA-1998-3997. (Available online via American Institute of Aeronautics and Astronautics).

Harlow, J. (2000), 'The Larger Solid Propellant Rocket Motors of the United Kingdom', *51st International Astronautical Congress, October 2000, Rio de Janeiro, Brazil*. IAA-00-IAA.2.3.05.

Harlow, J. (2012), 'Why Composites? The History & Technology of Composite Rocket Propellants', *Space Chronicle: JBIS, Vol.65, Suppl.1, pp.27-42*.

Harmer, R.G. (1972), *Flight-test results for two new versions of the Rook/Raven solid-propellant rocket motor*, RAE Technical Memorandum Aero 1424, 20th June 1972. (TNA: PRO DSIR 23/39711).

Harries, J.R. & Francey, R.J. (1968), 'Observations of CEN XR-2, SCO XR-1, and Terrestrial X-rays', *Australian Journal of Physics*, Vol.21 (October 1968), p.715. (ADS).

Harries, J.R. (1968), *Variable X-ray fluxes from Celestial Objects*, University of Adelaide thesis (October 1968), introduction available online at: *http://digital.library.adelaide.edu.au/dspace/bitstream/2440/20836/1/09phh297.pdf* . (Last accessed July 2014).

Hartog *et al.* (2003), 'Burst-properties as a function of mass accretion rate in GX 3+1', *Astronomy & Astrophys.400:633-642*. (Available free online at *http://arxiv.org/abs/astro-ph/0301245* , last accessed July 2014).

Häuser, H. (1971), 'The Parachute Recovery System RESY', *Journal of the British Interplanetary Society*, Vol.24, pp.203-208.

Hazell, J.F. (1961), 'Skylark', *Journal of the Royal Aeronautical Society*, Vol. 65, no.608 (August 1961), pp.526-530.

Hazell, J.F., Cope, P.E.G. & Walker I.F.M. (1968), 'Development and Operation of the Stabilized Skylark Rocket', *Journal of Spacecraft and Rockets*, Vol.5, no.4, April 1968.

Heddle, D.W.O. (1962), 'Observations in the Southern Hemisphere of Ultra-violet Light from Celestial Objects', *Nature*, Vol. 193, issue 4818, pp. 861 (1962). (Abstract on ADS).

Hemphill, W.J. (1957), *The "Raven" Motor report*, 8th July 1957, RAE Westcott. (TNA: PRO document file AVIA 48/107).

Hemenway, C.L. & Soberman, R.K. (1962), 'Studies of Micrometeorites Obtained from a Recoverable Sounding Rocket', *Astronomical Journal*, Vol.67, p.256. (ADS).

Henkel & Pechstein (1980), 'Astro 4: A sounding rocket programme of the X-ray astronomy', *Fifth ESA Symposium on European Rocket and Balloon Programmes and related research, April 1980, Bournemouth, UK*. ESA publication SP-152, p.147-153.

Henry P., Bowyer S., Rapley C.G. & Culhane J.L. (1976), 'Direction of an Extreme-Ultraviolet Source in the Southern Sky', *Astrophysical Journal*, Vol.209, Oct.1 1976, pt.2, p.L29-L3. (ADS).

Herbert P.J. (1967), *Determination of the Attitudes of the Skylark Rocket in Free Space*, RAE Technical Report No. 67319, December 1967, (TNA: PRO DSIR 23/36132).

Hill, C.N. (2001), *A Vertical Empire*, Imperial College Press, London, ISBN 1-86094-267-9.

Hill, C.N. (2007), *Black Knight – Britain's first ballistic rocket*, a BROHP publication (2007). (No ISBN).

Hill, C.N. (2008), 'The Cancellation of Black Arrow', *The Journal of British Rocketry and Nuclear History* (Prospero), Number 5, Spring 2008, pp.123-132.

Hilton, J.B. (1977), 'Skylark Sounding Rocket for Space Processing Experiments', *Journal of the British Interplanetary Society*, Vol.30, no.10 (October 1977), pp.377-381.

Holliday, C. T. (1950), 'Seeing the Earth from 80 Miles Up', *National Geographic Magazine*, Vol.98, No 4, (October 1950), pp.511-528.

Howarth, I. & Willis, A. (2003), 'Sir Robert Wilson', *RAS Astronomy & Geophysics Journal*, Vol.44, Issue 1, pp 1.34 – 1.35.

Hugill, J. (1965), 'Some Measurements of Aerial Impedance in the Ionosphere', *Astronomical Observations from Space Vehicles*, Proceedings from Symposium no. 23 held in Liège, Belgium, 17 to 20 August 1964. Edited by Jean-Louis Steinberg. International Astronomical Union. Symposium no. 23, Impr. Taffin-Lefort, p.345. (ADS).

Hugill, J. & Smith, F.G. (1965), 'Cosmic radio noise measurements from satellite Ariel II. I, Receiving system and preliminary results', *Monthly Notices of the Royal Astronomical Society*, Vol. 131, p.137. (ADS).

Hummeltenberg, G. (1983), 'E2: A heavy clean payload of the Energy Budget Campaign', *Sixth ESA Symposium on European Rocket and Balloon Programs and Related Research*. ESA SP-183, pp. 111-114. (Abstract on ADS).

Huijser *et al.* (1997), 'CODAG-1: Development of a Sounding Rocket Module to study Cosmic Dust Agglomeration', *Proceedings 13th ESA Symposium on European Rocket and Balloon Programmes and Related Research, Öland, Sweden, 26-29 May 1997*, ESA SP-397 (September 1997), pp.77-84. (ADS)

Huijser *et al.* (1999), 'Cosmic Dust Aggregation in Microgravity, Flight Report of the CODAG Module on MASER 8', *Proceedings 14th ESA Symposium on European Rocket and Balloon Programmes and Related Research, Potsdam, Germany, 31 May-3 June 1999*, ESA SP-437 (September 1999), (ADS).

Hutcheon, R.J., Pye, J.P. & Evans, K.D. (1976),' The spectrum of Fe XVII in the solar corona', *Monthly Notices of the Royal Astronomical Society*, Vol. 175, June 1976, p. 489-499. (ADS).

I

Ingham, M.F. (1969), 'Sources of the Lyman-α emission in the night sky', *Monthly Notices of the Royal Astronomical Society*, Vol. 145 (1969), p.401. (ADS)

J

Jamar *et al,* (1976) 'The E1 experiment aboard S22 payload: Capabilities of the prototype model', *ESA European Programmes on Sounding Rocket and Balloon Research in the Auroral Zone*, pp.343-349. (Abstract on ADS).

Janes, Pounds, Ricketts, Willmore & Morrison (1972), 'Identification of GX3+1 from Lunar Occultations', *Nature*, Vol. 235, issue 5334, pp. 152-155, (Abstract on ADS).

Janes, A.F. (1975), 'Rocket X-ray studies of supernova remnants', *Journal of the British Interplanetary Society*, Vol.28, no.12 (Dec.1975), pp.779-782.

Jennison, R.C. (1967), 'Some Penetration and Charge Detection Techniques', *Smithsonian Contributions to Astrophysics*, Vol.11 (1967), p.253-257. (ADS).

Jessen, F.C. (1959), *Re-design of the Raven Interrupting Device*. RPE Westcott Technical Memorandum No.194, Sept.1959. (TNA: PRO AVIA 68/7).

Joneleit, D. (1976), 'The German Scientific Balloon and Sounding-Rocket Programme', *European programmes on sounding-rocket & balloon research, Proceedings of a Symposium 3-7 May 1976*, ESA document SP-115, pp.23-30.

Jones, F.E. & Massey H.S.W. (1956). 'Rocket Exploration of the Upper Atmosphere', *Nature*, April 7 1956, p.643.

Jones, R.V. (1978), *Most Secret War: British Scientific Intelligence 1939:1946*, Book Club Associates, London, 1978. (No ISBN).

Jordan, C. (2004), 'Sir Robert Wilson CBE. 16 April 1927 - 2 September 2002', *Biogr. Mems Fell. R. Soc.* 1 December 2004 Vol. 50, pp.367-386.

Jude, R.J. (1977), 'An Attitude-Control System for an Earth-Pointing Skylark Rocket', *Journal of the British Interplanetary Society*, Vol.30, no.7 (July 1977), p.272-280.

K

Kammler *et al.* (2005), 'Unidirectional solidification of a peritectic SnSb-alloy', *Presentation at DLR-Sounding Rocket Workshop, March 16, 2005, Cologne*. (ESA EEA archive, TEXUS 34, last accessed July 2014).

Kellogg (1970), 'A Catalog of Soft X-ray Sources, 2nd Edition', *American Science and Engineering Report No. ASE-2357*, February 1970. (As referenced by Griffiths (1971)).

King-Hele, D.G. (1953), *The Limitations of Upper-Atmosphere Research Vehicles Powered by Current British Solid Fuel Rocket Motors*. RAE Technical report GW 291, December 1953. (TNA: PRO AVIA 6/19695 / DSIR 23/22544).

King-Hele, D.G. (1954a), *The Performance of Upper-Atmosphere Research Vehicles Powered by Solid Fuel Rocket Motors*, RAE Technical Note GW 315, May 1954. (TNA: PRO AVIA 6/19719).

King-Hele, D.G. (1954b), *Performance Estimate for Upper-Atmosphere Research Vehicles: Outline of Results*. RAE Technical Memo GW 225, June 1954. (TNA: PRO AVIA 6/18854).

King-Hele, D.G. & Miss D.M.C. Gillmore (1956), *Preliminary assessment of an Earth satellite reconnaissance vehicle*. RAE Technical Note GW 393, January 1956. (TNA: PRO DSIR 23/25364).

King-Hele, Desmond (1992), *A tapestry of orbits*, Cambridge University Press, ISBN 0 521 39323 X.

Klein, R. (1975), 'Equipment and Programme of the Mobile Raketenbasis', *Journal of the British Interplanetary Society*, Vol.28 no.4 (April 1975), pp.250-256.

Knott, F.R. (1964), The *Drift of an Auto-Pilot Gyroscope due to prolonged acceleration in the Skylark Rocket, Part 1: (Instrumentation Systems and Trials Programme)*, RAE Technical Report No. 64096, December 1964, (TNA: PRO AVIA 6/22374).

Knott, F.R. (1965), *The Drift of an Auto-Pilot Gyroscope due to prolonged acceleration in the Skylark Rocket, Part 2: Results from Skylarks SL27/28*. RAE Technical Report No. 65162, August 1965, (TNA: PRO AVIA 6/22510 / DSIR 23/33326).

Knott, F.R. (1966a), *The Drift of an Auto-Pilot Gyroscope due to prolonged acceleration in the Skylark Rocket, Part 3: Results from Skylarks SL29/30*. RAE Technical Report No. 66132, April 1966, (TNA: PRO AVIA 6/22726).

Knott, F.R. (1966b), *The Drift of an Auto-Pilot Gyroscope Due to Prolonged Acceleration in the Skylark Rocket, Part 4: Results from Skylarks SL31/32 and general conclusions from programme*. RAE Technical Report No. 66133, April 1966, (TNA: PRO AVIA 6/22727 / DSIR 23/34450).

Knott, F.R. (1968), *The Drift of an Auto-Pilot Gyroscope Due to Prolonged Acceleration in the Skylark Rocket (Abridged Version)*, Ministry of Aviation Supply Aeronautical Research Council Current Paper C.P. No. 1147 (September 1968), HMSO 1971.

Kopp, E. *et al.* (1985), 'Positive ion composition of the high-latitude summer D region with noctilucent clouds', *Journal of Geophysical Research* (ISSN 0148-0227), Vol. 90 (Dec. 20, 1985), pp.13,041-13,053. (Abstract on ADS).

Kunkel *et al.* (1970), 'An Optical Search for the X-Ray Sources GX3+1, GX5-1, GX9+1, and GX17+2', *Astrophysical Journal*, Vol. 161, p.L169. (ADS).

L

Ladd, A.C. & Smith, J.F (1969), 'An introduction to the Ariel III Satellite Project', *Proc. R. Soc. Lond. A*, August 12, 1969 311:479-487.

Larsson *et al.* (2003), 'Report on the MASER 9 Microgravity Rocket Mission', *Proceedings of the 16th ESA Symposium on European Rocket and Balloon Programmes and Related Research, 2-5 June 2003*, ESA SP-530, August 2003, p.129-134. (Abstract on ADS).

Lay, G., Fahr, H.J. & Nass, H.U. (1989), 'Interzodiak 2: Observation of EUV-resonance radiation', *Ninth ESA/PAC Symposium on European Rocket and Balloon Programmes and Related Research*, April 1989. ESA SP-291, June 1989, p.173. (Abstract on ADS).

Leinert, C., Link, H. & Pitz, E. (1974), 'Rocket Photometry of the Inner Zodiacal Light', *Astronomy and Astrophysics*, Vol. 30, p. 411, 02/1974. (ADS).

Lewis, G.G.E. (1972), 'Recent Developments in the Skylark Sounding Rocket', *Journal of the British Interplanetary Society*, Vol.25, no.2 (February 1972), pp.175-182.

Lloyd, K.H & Sheppard, L.M. (1966), 'Atmospheric Structure at 130–200 km Altitude from Observations on Grenade Glow Clouds during 1962-63', *Australian Journal of Physics*, Vol. 19 (June 1966), p.323. (ADS).

Lloyd, K.H. *et al.* (1971), 'Thermospheric Observations combining chemical seeding and ground based techniques…', *Planetary and Space Science*, Vol.20, issue 5 (May 1972), pp. 761-78. (Abstract on ADS).

Lloyd, K.H., Low, C.H. & Hind, A.D. (1977), *Daytime Observations of Lower Thermospheric Wind Profiles at Woomera*, Australian DSTO Technical Report WRE-TR-1809(W), April 1977. (Available free online via DSTO webpage *http://dspace.dsto.defence.gov.au/dspace/handle/1947/9394* , last accessed July 2014).

Lloyd, K.H. (1978), Upper Atmosphere Research at WRE – a Review, Australian DSTO Technical Report WSRL-0012-TR, May 1978. (Available free online via DSTO webpage *http://dspace.dsto.defence.gov.au/dspace/handle/1947/8724* , last accessed July 2014.)

Löth *et al.* (2002), 'ITEL Experiment Module and its Flight on MASER 9', *ESA EEA database, MASER 9, 'Interfacial Turbulence in Evaporating Liquids', attachment 2*. (Last accessed July 2014).

Limburger *et al.* (1996), 'Cost Efficient ISDN-Based Remote Operation of TEXUS 34 Sounding Rocket Experiments', *Space Mission Operations and Ground Data Systems - SpaceOps '96, Proceedings of the Fourth International Symposium held 16-20 September 1996 in Munich, Germany*. Edited by T.-D. Guyenne. ESA SP-394, p.1508. (ADS).

Luyendyk, A.P.J., Fenton, K.B., Fenton, A.G., Broderick, A.J., Tuohy, I.R. & Harries, J.R. (1973), 'An X-ray Observation of the Norma-Lupus Region', *Proceedings of the 13th International Conference on Cosmic Rays, held in Denver, Colorado*, Volume 5, p.3039. (ADS).

Lyons, D.J. (1961), 'Ballistic Research Rockets with Particular Reference to Black Knight', *Journal of the Royal Aeronautical Society*, Vol.65, no.603 (March 1961), pp.171-187.

M

MacKenzie, E.C. & Sayers, J. (1966), 'A radio frequency electron density probe for rocket investigation of the ionosphere', Planetary and Space Science, Vol.14, issue 8 (August 1966), pp.731-740.

Mallett, E.S., Perkins, R.E. & Knapp, H.W.P. (1965), *Bramble, an Automatic Processing System for Telemetry Data*, RAE Technical Report 65053, March 1965. (TNA: PRO AVIA 6/22420).

Mandell, N. & Leverone, H.W. (1964), *Electronic performance of the S-52 flight 1 spacecraft under thermal-vacuum exposure*, report NASA-TM-X-55167, October 26 1964. (NTRS).

Martin, Charles H. (2002), *De Havilland Blue Streak: an illustrated story*, British Interplanetary Society, London, ISBN 0-9506597-7-0.

Martínez, I. & Sanz, A. (1985). 'Long Liquid Bridges Aboard Sounding Rockets', *ESA Journal*, Vol. 9, No. 3, 1985, pp. 323-328. (Available free online, last accessed July 2014).

Massey, H.S.W. (1958), *Memorandum on Rocket Research*, Royal Society Gassiot Committee memorandum dated 5/11/1958 in UK Ministry of Supply document file 'Upper Atmosphere Research Policy and Financial Control – Skylark' (TNA: PRO AVIA 65/671).

Massey, Professor Sir Harrie (1963), 'Upper Atmosphere Experiments with Particular Reference to Black Knight and Skylark', *Eighth Anglo-American Aeronautical Conference, 1961, London*, Bradbrooke, Joan (Ed), Royal Aeronautical Society, pp.55-78.

Massey, Sir Harric (1966), *Space Travel and Exploration*, A "Contemporary Physics" reprint, Taylor & Francis Ltd., 1966. (No ISBN).

Massey, Sir Harrie & Robins, M.O. (1986), *History of British Space Science*, Cambridge University Press, Cambridge, 1986, ISBN 0 521 30783 X.

McCartney, Mark, & Whitaker, Andrew, (Editors), *Physicists of Ireland: Passion and Precision*, Institute of Physics Publishing, 2002, ISBN 978-0750308663.

McCracken, Ken (2008), *Blast Off*, New Holland Publishers (Australia) Pty Ltd., 2008, ISBN 78174110 6442 (pbk.).

McDowell, J (2009), *List of Skylark Launches*, extracted from his suborbital space launches database, and sent to author on 26/6/09.

Similar results may be obtained via *http://planet4589.org/space/lvdb/list.html* and clicking on Raven. (Last accessed July 2014).

McIntosh, R., Ollendorf, S., Harwell, W. (1976), 'The International Heatpipe Experiment', *ESA Heatpipes*, p.589-591. (Abstract on ADS).

Merchant, D.G. (1959), *Pitch Roll Resonance - with reference to Skylark 21*, RAE Technical Memorandum No. G.W. 364, November 1959 (TNA: PRO DSIR 23/27646).

Millard, Douglas (2001), *The Black Arrow Rocket: A history of a satellite launch vehicle and its engines*, Science Museum, London (NMSI Trading Ltd.) 2001, ISBN 1-900747-41-3.

Millard, Douglas (2005), *An Overview of United Kingdom Space Activity 1957-1987*, ESA report HSR-36, ISBN: 90-9092-547-7 (Available free online as an ESA document, last accessed July 2014).

Miller, D.E. & Stewart, K.H. (1965), 'Observations of atmospheric ozone from an artificial Earth satellite', Proceedings of the Royal Society of London, Series A, Vol. 288, No. 1415 (Nov. 30, 1965), pp. 540-544. (Abstract on ADS).

Miller, D.E. and Ryder, P. (1973), 'Measurement of the ozone concentration from 55 to 95 km at sunset', *Planetary and Space Science*, Vol. 21, issue 6, pp.963-970 (06/1973). (Abstract on ADS).

Ministry of Aviation / Ministry of Technology / Ministry of Defence (UK) – Skylark Policy Meeting Minutes – those for the period 1966 to 1971, (meetings 1 to 18) are in TNA: PRO document file AVIA 92/144, those for the period 1971 to 1972 (meetings 20 to 24) are in TNA:PRO document file AVIA 92/145.

Ministry of Aviation, Space 1(c) (1966), 'Skylark Policy and Programme', review document ref. DS/55/01, Issue 1 dated 28 March 1966, distributed before the first Skylark Policy Meeting on 4 April 1966. (TNA: PRO document file AVIA 92/144).

Ministry of Aviation, Space 1(c) (1967), 'Skylark Policy and Programme', review document ref. DS/55/01, Issue 2 dated 06 November 1967, distributed before the fifth Skylark Policy Meeting on 28 November 1967. (TNA: PRO document file AVIA 92/144).

Mirtov, B.A, and Vedeshin, L.A. (1975), 'Early Upper Atmospheric Research with Rockets', reprinted as Chapter 15 of Volume 9 of the "History of Rocketry and Astronautics" series, published for the American Astronautical Society by Univelt, San Diego, California, 1989, ISBN 0-87703-3090-9.

MIST (Magnetosphere, Ionosphere & Solar-Terrestrial Environment) meetings – see under Royal Astronomical Society.

Montenbruck & Markgraf (2001), 'Texus-39 Orion GPS Tracking System Flight Report', TEX39-DLR-RP-0001, 18 July 2001, DLR Oberpfaffenhoffen (2001). (Available free online at *www.dlr.de/rb/en/Portaldata/38/Resources/dokumente/gsoc_dokumente/rt/TEX39-DLR-RP-0001.pdf*, last accessed July 2014).

Montenbruck *et al.* (2001), 'A GPS Receiver for Space Applications', ION-GPS-2001, Salt Lake City, 12-14 Sept. 2001. (Available free online at *www.dlr.de/rb/Portaldata/38/Resources/dokumente/gsoc_dokumente/rt/ION_01B1Ax.pdf*, last accessed July 2014).

Moore, J.K. (1965), *The Measurement of the Earth's Infra-red Radiation from a Skylark Rocket*, RAE Technical Report 65166, August 1965. (TNA: PRO AVIA 6/22512).

Moore, P.O. (1992), 'Stonechat', *Journal of the British Interplanetary Society*, Vol.45, no.4 (April 1992), pp.145-148.

Morton, Peter (1989), *Fire across the Desert: Woomera and the Anglo-Australian Joint Project, 1946-1980*, Australian Government Publishing Service, Canberra, ISBN 0 644 06068 9.

MSSL (1967), *Opening of the MSSL laboratory on 3rd May 1967*, – programme, press information and copies of speeches available online via links on the following webpage: *www.ucl.ac.uk/mssl/about-mssl/heritage/archive-documents/mssl-opening* , (last accessed August 2014).

MSSL (1967), *MSSL general information*, available as above via *www.ucl.ac.uk/mssl/about-mssl/heritage/archive-documents/mssl-opening* , (last accessed August 2014).

MSSL (1972), *Report of the Mullard Space Science Laboratory for the period 1st January – 30 September 1972*. The Department of Physics and Astronomy, University College London. (Original accessed at MSSL).

MSSL (1973), *Report of the Mullard Space Science Laboratory for the period 1st October 1972 – 30 September 1973*. The Department of Physics and Astronomy, University College London. (Original accessed at MSSL).

MSSL (1974), *Report of the Mullard Space Science Laboratory for the period 1st October 1973 – 30 September 1974*. The Department of Physics and Astronomy, University College London. (Original accessed at MSSL).

MSSL (1975), *Report of the Mullard Space Science Laboratory for the period 1st October 1974 – 30 September 1975*. The Department of Physics and Astronomy, University College London. (Original accessed at MSSL).

(For MSSL annual reports released under the auspices of UCL, see under "U" below).

N

Naylor, T., Charles, P.A. & Longmore, A. J. (1991), 'Infrared observations of low-mass X-ray binaries. I - Candidates for bright bulge sources', *Monthly Notices of the Royal Astronomical Society*, Vol. 252, Sept. 15, 1991, p. 203-209. (ADS).

Negus, C.R., Glencross, W.M. and Pounds, K.A. (1970), 'A Scanning X-ray Spectroheliograph', *Proc. R. Soc. Lond. A*, May 26, 1970 317:101-112.

Neuman, G., Boison, M. & Henkel, R. (1983), 'INTER -ZODIAC: 'A sounding rocket project for high resolution of EUV radiations', *ESA Sixth Symposium on European Rocket and Balloon Programs and Related Research*, ESA SP-183, p.421-427. (Abstract on ADS).

Newell, H.E. (1953), *High altitude rocket research*, New York, Academic Press Inc.

Newey, D. & Carlson, W. (1980), *Bristol Aerospace Limited: 50 Years of Technology 1930-1980, Volume 2*, Bristol Aerospace Ltd., Canada, 1980.

Nicolson, H. (2009), *Summerfield: The history of a rocket research establishment*, a British Rocketry Oral History Programme (BROHP) publication, 2009 (second edition). (No ISBN).

O

Offermann, D. & Trinks, H. (1971), 'A Rocket Borne Mass Spectrometer with Helium Cooled Ion Source', *Review of Scientific Instruments*, Vol. 42, p.1836.

Offermann, D., and Grossmann, K.U. (1973), 'Thermospheric Density and Composition as Determined by a Mass Spectrometer with Cryo Ion Source', *J. Geophys. Res.*, 78(34), 8296–8304.

Offermann, D. (1980), 'A Winter Anomaly Campaign in Western Europe', *Phil. Trans. R. Soc. Lond. A*, 6 March 1980, Vol. 296, no. 1418, 261-268.

Offermann, D. (1985), 'The energy budget campaign 1980 – Introductory review', *Journal of Atmospheric and Terrestrial Physics*, (ISSN 0021-9169), Vol. 47, Jan-Mar. 1985, p.1-26. (Abstract on ADS).

Offermann, D. (1994), 'The DYANA campaign: A survey', *Journal of Atmospheric and Terrestrial Physics*, (ISSN 0021-9169), Vol. 56, no.13-14, p.1, 639-1,657. (Abstract on ADS).

Ormston, T. *et al.* (c.2011), *From Monitoring Camera to Mars Webcam – Producing Outreach from Ops*, available via the ESA website *www.esa.int/Our_Activities/Operations/Mars_Express_VMC/About_the_Visual_Monitoring_Camera_VMC* . (Last accessed July 2014).

Owen-Jones, N.E. & Custance, N.D.E. (1974), 'Digitised Analysis of Skylark Rocket Imagery', *Journal of the British Interplanetary Society*, Vol.27 no.1 (January 1974), pp.18-22.

Owen-Jones, E.S. & Chandler, B.J. (1977), 'The Use of Photographic Imagery in Earth Resources Studies', *Journal of the British Interplanetary Society*, Vol.30 no.5 (May 1977), pp.163-167.

P

Palmerio *et al.* (2003), 'The Development of the VSB-30 Sounding Rocket Vehicle', *Proceedings of the 16th ESA Symposium on European Rocket and Balloon Programmes and Related Research, St.Gallen, Switzerland, 2-5 June 2003*, ESA SP-530, August 2003, p.137-140). (ADS).

Palmerio *et al.* (2005), 'Results from the First Flight of the VSB-30 Sounding Rocket', *Proceedings of the 17th ESA Symposium on European Rocket and Balloon Programmes and Related Research, Sandefjord, Norway, 30 May-2 June 2005*, pp.345-349. ESA SP-590, August 2005. (Contents free online via *www.esa.int/esapub/conference/toc/tocSP590.pdf* , last accessed July 2014).

Parker, W.G. & Smith, T.L. (1955), *Note on a visit to U.S.A. in June, 1955 to discuss Rocket Vehicles Suitable for Upper Atmosphere Research*, RAE Technical note RPD 134, Nov. 1955. (TNA: PRO AVIA 6/19188).

Parkinson J.H., Evans K. & Pounds K.A. (1972), 'Recent High Resolution X-ray Spectra of the Sun', *Ultraviolet and X-ray Spectroscopy of Astrophysical and Laboratory Plasmas, Proceedings of IAU Colloq. 14, held in Utrecht, August, 1971*, Space Science Review 13, p.740. (ADS).

Parkinson, J.H. (1975), 'The analysis of a high-resolution X-ray spectrum of a solar active region', *Solar Physics*, Vol.42, May 1975, p.183-207. (ADS).

Parsons, Stephen (1993), *Shadow to Shadow: A History of the Bristol Aeroplane Banwell Shadow Factory and Bristol Aerojet (BAJ) 1941-1991*, BAJ Coatings Ltd., Weston-Super-Mare, ISBN 0-9522471-0-0.

Paxton, H.J.B. & Turner, R.F. (1974), 'An Engineering Profile of a Sounding Rocket Payload for Observation of the Sun', *Journal of the British Interplanetary Society*, Vol.27 no.11 (November 1974), p.849-859.

Pillinger, C. (2010), *My Life on Mars – The Beagle 2 Diaries*, British Interplanetary Society, London, 2010. ISBN 978-0-9506597-3-2.

Pitz, E., Leinert, A., Schulz, A. & Link, H. (1978), 'Ultraviolet Zodiacal Light Observed by the Astro 7 Rocket Experiment', *Astronomy and Astrophysics*, Vol. 69, p. 297 (1978), (ADS).

Pooley, S.J. (1976), 'Petrel 3 and Skua 4 – Earth Resources Survey Rockets', *European programmes on sounding-rocket & balloon research, Proceedings of a Symposium 3-7 May 1976*, ESA document SP-115, pp.485-495.

Pounds, K., & Bowen, P.J. (1962), 'A simple rocket-borne X-radiation monitor – its scope and results of an early flight', 1962, *Monthly Notices of the Royal Astronomical Society*, Vol.123, p.347-357. (ADS).

Pounds, K.A. (1971), 'Measurement of the Polarisation, Spectra and Accurate Locations of Cosmic X-Ray Sources', *New techniques in Space Astronomy. IAU Symposium no. 41, held in Munich, Aug. 10-14, 1970*. Edited by F. Labuhn and Reimar Lust, Reidel, p.165. (ADS).

Pounds, K.A. (1986), 'British X-ray Astronomy', *Quarterly Journal Royal Astronomical Society*, (ISSN 0035-8738), Vol.27, Sept.1986, pp.435-444. (ADS).

Pounds, K. (2002), 'Forty Years on from Aerobee 150: a personal perspective', Philosophical Transactions of the Royal Society of London, series A, Vol. 360, number 1798, September 15 2002, pp. 1905-1921.

Pounds, K.A. & Cooke, B.A. (1971), 'Rocket Observations of galactic X-ray sources in Norma and Centaurus', *Bulletin of the American Astronomical Society*, Vol.3, p.351, March 1971. (Abstract on ADS).

Preu *et al.* (2003), 'Utilization of Sounding Rockets and Balloons in the German Space Programme', *Proceedings 16th ESA Symposium on European Rocket and Balloon Programmes and Related Research, St.Gallen, Switzerland, 2-5 June 2003*, ESA SP-530, August 2003, p.39-44). (ADS).

Privett, Grant (2001), 'The dome on Ball Hill – the RAE observatory', *Journal of the British Astronomical Association*, Vol.111, no.6, pp.316-320 (Dec 2001). (ADS).

Proctor, R.J., Skinner, G.K. & Willmore, A.P. (1978), 'X-ray emission from the region of the Galactic Centre', *Monthly Notices of the Royal Astronomical Society*, Vol.185, p.745-754. (ADS).

Pye, J.P. *et al.* (1978), 'The Structure of the X-ray Bright Corona above Active Region McMath 12628 and Derived Implications for the Description of Equilibria in the Solar Atmosphere', *Astronomy and Astrophysics*, Vol. 65, no. 1, Apr. 1978, pp.123-138. (ADS).

R

RAE GW Dept. (1958), *A Brief Review of the C.T.V.5 Series III Programme*, document ref. GW/S, 2320/EBD, August 1958. (TNA: PRO AVIA 65/671 - document file 'Upper Atmosphere Research Policy and Financial Control 1955-1959).

RAE GW Dept. (1961), *Organisation of the Royal Society Upper Atmosphere Research Programme using Skylark*, document ref. GW/2320/AWL, 2nd February 1961. (National Archives of Australia online digitised document file A1945: 128/1/41, pp.216-219).

Rapley, C.G. (1974), *A Report on the Design and Performance of SL1203*. (MSSL/UCL internal document 1974, copy courtesy C.G.Rapley).

Rapley, C.G. (1976), *New Techniques and observations in Soft X-ray astronomy*, (Thesis submitted to University of London, May 1976, copy courtesy C.G.Rapley). (Abstract on ADS).

Rapley, C.G., Bell Burnell, S.J. & Culhane, J.L. (1976), 'Observations of the Soft X-ray Diffuse Background', *Space Research XVI* – Akademie-Verlag, Berlin 1976. (Copy courtesy C.G.Rapley). (Abstract on ADS).

Ratkowski *et al.* (1993), 'Rocket measurements of high-latitude summer mesospheric [O], OH, O2 Delta and spacecraft glow', *Proc. SPIE* Vol. 2050, p. 2-14, Airglow and Aurora, Sergej Leontyev; Ed. (Abstract on ADS).

Reed, J.W. (1974), *An Historical Review of Stabilisation Systems for the Skylark Rocket*. Appleton Laboratory report, reference A 1101, September 1974. (TNA: PRO DSIR 23/41125).

Rees, D., Roper, R.G., Lloyd, K.H. & Low, C.H. (1972) 'Determination of the structure of the atmosphere between 90 and 250 km by means of contaminant releases at Woomera, May 1968', *Phil. Trans. R. Soc. Lond. A*, February 17, 1972 271:631-663.

Rees, D., Dorling, E.B., Lloyd, K.H. & Low C. (1976), 'The role of neutral winds and ionospheric electric field in forming stable sporadic E-layers', *Planetary and Space Science*, Vol.24, issue 5, p.475-478, 05/1976. (Abstract on ADS).

Rees, D. *et al.* (1976), 'Structure of the auroral upper atmosphere and its response to substorm activity', *MIST (Magnetosphere, Ionosphere & Solar-Terrestrial Environment) meeting at Aberystwyth, as reported in the Quarterly Journal of the Royal Astronomical Society*, (1976), Vol.17, p.463. (ADS).

RèMe, H. & Bosqued, J.M (1973), 'Rocket Observations of Electron Precipitation in a Westward-Travelling Surge', *Journal of Geophysical Research*, Volume 78, Issue 25, pp. 5553-5558. (Link to Abstract on ADS).

Robins, M.O. (1949), *Interim note on the Roll Stabilisation of a Supersonic Control Test Vehicle C.T.V.2.*, RAE Technical note GW 61, Dec. 1949. (TNA: PRO AVIA 6/15356 / DSIR 23/19046).

Roper, R.G. & Edwards, H.D. (1980), *Theoretical and Experimental Investigations of Upper Atmosphere Dynamics, Final Report E-16-605*, Georgia Inst. of Tech., Atlanta. School of Aerospace Engineering. (Abstract on ADS or full report via NTRS).

Roper, R.G. (1995), 'Rocket vapour trail releases revisited: Turbulence and the scale of gravity waves: Implications for the imaging Doppler interferometry/incoherent scatter radar controversy', *Journal of Geophysical Research*, Vol.101, issue D3, p.7013-7018. (Abstract on ADS).

Röhrig, O. & Roth, M. (1997), 'Scientific Sounding Rocket and Balloon Activities in Germany', *Proceedings 13th ESA Symposium on European Rocket and Balloon Programmes and Related Research, Öland, Sweden, 26-29 May 1997*, ESA SP-397 (September 1997), pp.17-23. (ADS).

Rose, G. (1989), 'Preliminary Results of the Rocket and Scatter Experiments "Rose" – measurements with the newly designed spherical probe', *Proc. Ninth ESA/PAC Symposium on 'European Rocket and Balloon Programmes and Related Research', Lahnstein, FRG, 3-7 April 1989*. ESA SP-291, June 1989, p.141.

Royal Astronomical Society (1975), 'MIST Meeting at Exeter' (March 1975), *Quarterly Journal of the Royal Astronomical Society*, Vol.16, pp.282-297. (ADS).

Royal Astronomical Society (1976), 'MIST Meeting at Aberystwyth' (April 1976), *Quarterly Journal of the Royal Astronomical Society*, Vol.17, pp.457-471. (ADS)

Royal Astronomical Society (1979), 'MIST Meeting at Southampton' (April 1978), *Quarterly Journal of the Royal Astronomical Society*, Vol.20, pp.42-46. (ADS).

RPE Westcott (1961), *Solid Motor Data Sheet for Raven Va*. (TNA: PRO document file AVIA 48/130).

RPE Westcott, (1968), *Index to Solid Propellant Motors*, Technical Memorandum 465, March 1968. (TNA: PRO document AVIA 68/111).

Ridgeley, A. & Burton, W.M. (1972), 'Further Observations of the Solar-Limb Spectrum in the region 550-2000 Å', *Solar Physics*, Volume 27, Issue 2, pp.280-285 (12/1972), (ADS).

Ridgeway, R.B. & Hardy, J.R. (1973), 'Skylark over Woomera', *Geographical Magazine*, Vol.45 (4), January 1973, pp.289-297.

Russell, P.C. & Pounds, K.A. (1966), 'Improved Resolution X-ray photographs of the Sun', *Nature*, Volume 209, Issue 5022, pp. 490-491 (1966). (Abstract on ADS).

S

Salatun, A.S. (1979), 'An Earth Survey System Design using the Kappa-8 Rocket', *Proceedings ITB* [Institut Teknologi Bandung], Vol.12, No.3.

Salway, F.C. (1975), 'Recovery of Skylark Payloads using an Air Snatch System', *Journal of the British Interplanetary Society*, Vol.28 no.4 (April 1975, p.257-262.

Sánchez-Tarifa, C. & Lázaro, B. (2001), 'Experiments Conducted on Combustion of a Solid at Microgravity in the Texus-38 Sounding Rocket. Results and Conclusions', *Microgravity Research and Applications in Physical Sciences and Biotechnology, Proceedings of the First International Symposium held 10-15 September 2000 in Sorrento, Italy*. Edited by O. Minster and B. Schürmann. European Space Agency, ESA SP-454, 2001, p.267. (Available free online, also a summary on ESA-EEA database, under TEXUS 38).

Savigear, R.A.G., Hardy, J.R., Mitchell, C.W., Ridgeway, R.B. & Parsons, A.J. (1974), "Rocket Photography for Earth Resources Surveys", *Journal of the British Interplanetary Society*, Vol.27 no. 5 (May 1974), p.359-372.

Savigear, Hardy, Townshend *et al.* (1975), *Anglo-Argentinian Geoscopy Experiment Report – December 1975*, in nine sections, University of Reading Department of Geography.

Savigear, R.A.G., Ridgway, R.B., Jude, R., Mitchell, C.W., Owen Jones, E.S., Custance, N.D.E. (1977), *The Appraisal of Photography from Skylark SL1081 over Woomera, Australia, for Land Resource Evaluation*, in two volumes, University of Reading Geography Department.

Sayers, Prof. J. (1959), 'Self-Contained Measuring Equipment for Electron Density and Ionic Mass Spectrum', *Proc. R. Soc. Lond. A*, December 29, 1959 253:522-525.

Schrieder, W. & Henkel, R. (1983), 'Coordinated Auroral Experiment using Scatter and Rockets (CAESAR): A sounding rocket project to study the ionosphere', *Sixth ESA Symposium on European Rocket and Balloon Programs and Related Research*, ESA SP-183, pp.355-358. (Abstract on ADS).

Science Research Council – see under SRC.

Schmidt, K., Schneider, K. & Todd, G.E. (1978), 'The Space Processing Mission of TEXUS-1 with respect to Micro-G Environment and Recovery', *European Sounding-Rocket, Balloon and Related Research, Proceedings of a Symposium 24-29 April 1978*, ESA document SP-135, pp.475-481.

Seibert, G. & Herfs, W. (1997), 'Microgravity Science From ESA's Microgravity Sounding Rocket Projects (Life and Physical Sciences)', *Proceedings 13th ESA Symposium on European Rocket and Balloon Programmes and Related Research, Öland, Sweden, 26-29 May 1997*, ESA SP-397 (September 1997), pp65-72. (ADS).

Seibert, G. *et al.* (2001), *A World without Gravity*, ESA publication SP-1251, ESA Publications Division, ESTEC, Noordwijk, The Netherlands, June 2001. (Available free online).

Seibert, G. (2006), *The History of Sounding Rockets and Their Contribution to European Space Research*, ESA report HSR-38, ESA Publication Division, The Netherlands, November 2006, ISBN: 92-9092-550-7.

Sell, P.J., Maisch, E. & Siekmann, J. (1991), 'Liquid motion in capillary tubes (TEXUS 3)', in ESA, *Summary Review of Sounding Rocket Experiments in Fluid Science and Materials Sciences: TEXUS 1 to 20; MASER 1 and 2*, p.20-21., (Abstract on ADS).

Shmelz, J.T. *et al.* (2005), 'Neon lights up a Controversy: the Solar NE/O abundance', *The Astrophysical Journal*, 634:L197–L200, 2005 December 1. (ADS).

Simmons, N. (1974), 'Rockets for Earth Environment Monitoring', *Journal of the British Interplanetary Society*, Vol.27 no.1 (January 1974), pp.1-9.

Sharpe, Mitchell (1976), 'Operation Backfire: England launches the V2', reprinted as Chapter 10 of Volume 9 of the "History of Rocketry and Astronautics" series, published for the American Astronautical Society by Univelt, San Diego, California, 1989, ISBN 0-87703-3090-9.

Shepherd, J.V. (1961). *A Recovery System for the Skylark Instrument Head*. RAE Farnborough Technical Note GW 589, October 1961. (TNA: PRO AVIA 6/21507).

Skinner, G.K. (1979), 'The galactic centre', *Proc.R.Soc.Lond.A*. 366, 345-355 (1979).

Smith, M.J. & Bryant D.A. (1975), 'Evidence for stretching of geomagnetic field-lines', *MIST (Magnetosphere, Ionosphere & Solar-Terrestrial Environment) meeting at Exeter in March 1975, as reported in the Quarterly Journal of the Royal Astronomical Society*, Vol. 16, p.282. (ADS).

Sojka, J.J. & Raitt, W.J. (1976), 'Secondary electron production in the upper atmosphere during auroral activity', *MIST (Magnetosphere, Ionosphere & Solar-Terrestrial Environment) meeting at Aberystwyth, as reported in the Quarterly Journal of the Royal Astronomical Society*, Vol.17, p.465. (ADS).

Southall, Ivan (1962), *Woomera*, Angus and Robertson, Sydney, 1962. (No ISBN).

Southall, Ivan (1964), *Rockets in the Desert*, Angus and Robertson, Sydney, 1964. (No ISBN).

Spenner, K. *et al.* (1977), 'Plasma measurements during the Western European Winter Anomaly Campaign', *Journal of Geophysics-Zeitschrift fuer Geophysik*, Vol.44, no.1-2, 1977, p.81-90. (Abstract on ADS).

Sprat, Thomas (1667), *The History of the Royal Society of London.* (Fourth edition (1734) available free online via Google (last accessed July 2014).

SRC (1972), *Space Research Report 1969-70*, HMSO, London, 1972.

SRC (Appleton Laboratory) (c.1980), *Radio and Space Research 1977-1979*, HMSO, London.

Stark, J.P.W. & Culhane, J.L. (1978), 'A search for X-ray line emission in the spectrum of the Cygnus loop', *Monthly Notices of the Royal Astronomical Society*, Vol.184 (August 1978), pp.509-522. (ADS).

Staubert *et al.* (1975), 'The Crab Nebula: High Energy X-ray Observation of a Lunar Occultation', *The Astrophysical Journal*, 201, L15–L19, 1975 October 1. (ADS).

Stecher *et al.* (1962), 'Stellar Spectrophotometry from above the Atmosphere', *Astrophysical Journal*, Vol.136, p.1. (ADS).

Steinbach, Ratke & Masslow (2005), 'Directional Solidification of Binary AlSi Alloys in Diffusive and Convective Regimes', *Proceedings of the 17th ESA Symposium on European Rocket and Balloon Programmes and Related Research, Sandefjord, Norway, 30 May-2 June 2005*, pp521-526. ESA SP-590, August 2005.

Stephens, W.H. (1958), 'British Upper Atmosphere Sounding Rocket', paper delivered at 'High Altitude and Rockets Symposium 1957', published under the same name by The Royal Aeronautical Society, 1958.

Stewart K.H. & Wildman P.J.L. (1969), 'Preliminary Results of Molecular Oxygen Observations from the Ariel III Satellite', Proc. R. Soc. Lond. A, August 12, 1969 311:591-600.

Stroud, William G. (1975), 'Early Scientific History of the Rocket Grenade Experiment', (reprinted as Chapter 16 of Volume 9 of the "History of Rocketry and Astronautics" series, published for the American Astronautical Society by Univelt, San Diego, California, 1989, ISBN 0-87703-3090-9).

Swedish Space Corporation (2011), *User's Handbook – Sounding Rockets & Balloons*. Swedish Space Corporation, Esrange Space Center, Science Services Division, P.O. Box 802, SE-981 28 Kiruna, Sweden. (Available online at *www.sscspace.com/file/usershandbook.pdf*, last accessed July 2014).

T

Tagg, A.E. & Wheeler, R.L. (1989), *From Sea to Air*, Crossprint, Newport, Isle of Wight, ISBN 0 9509739 3 9.

Taylor, Geoff (2000), *Flights of Fancy: A Life Memoir*, self-published, printed by Fyshwick, ACT, (Canberra Australia), 2000, ISBN 0 646 38897 5.

Tharratt, C.E. (1972), 'Personal Profile, Charles E. Tharratt, Rocket Engineer', *Spaceflight*, Vol.14 No.8 (August 1972), British Interplanetary Society, London.

Theile, B. (1976), 'Support of satellite missions by high-latitude rocket campaigns', *Proceedings of the Tenth ESLAB Symposium, Vienna, Austria, June 1975*, Reidel Publishing Co., pp.425-431. (Abstract on ADS).

Theile B. (1978), 'Initial Results of the Sounding Rocket Campaign "Polar High Atmosphere" ', *European Sounding-Rocket, Balloon and Related Research, Proceedings of a Symposium 24-29 April 1978*, ESA document SP-135 , pp.113-118.

Thomas, G.R. & Bryant, D.A (1975), 'Proposed UK high-latitude rocket campaign in late 1976/early 1977', *ESA European Sounding Rocket and Sci. Balloon Activity at High Latitudes*, p.205-210, published 02/1975. (ADS).

Thomas, W.R. (1969), 'Suborbital Probes', *Proc. R. Soc. Lond. A*. 7 January 1969 Vol. 308 no. 1493 243-257.

Townshend, J.R.G., Savigear, R.A.G., Justice, C.O., Hardy, R.J.R., Drennan, D.S.H. & Bray, C.J. (1974), *A Comparison of the Capabilities of ERTS-1 and the Skylark Earth-Resources Rocket for Resources Surveying in Central Argentina*, Department of Geography, Reading University, 1974.

Townshend, J.R.G. (ed.) (1981), *Terrain Analysis and Remote Sensing*, George Allen and Unwin, London. ISBN 0-04-551037-7 Pbk.

Tuohy, I.R. (1972), 'Celestial X-ray Surveys from the Southern Hemisphere', Ph.D. thesis submitted to the University of Adelaide, January 1972, (Contents and summary available online from *http://hdl.handle.net/2440/20435*, last accessed July 2014).

Tuohy, Harries, Broderick, Fenton and Luyendyk (1972), 'An X-ray observation of the Large Magellanic Cloud', *Proceedings of the Astronomical Society of Australia*, Vol. 2, no. 2, March 1972, p.111-112. (ADS).

Turnill, Reginald & Reed, Arthur (1980), *Farnborough: The Story of RAE*, Robert Hale Ltd., London, 1980, ISBN 0 7091 8584 7.

Turner, D. J. (1986), 'Electrolyte Solutions Near the Critical Point of Water'. *In 6th European Symposium on Material Sciences Under Microgravity Conditions, Bordeaux, France, December 2-5 1986*, ESA SP-256, pp. 125-129.

Turner, J. (1989), 'The SN 1987A Attitude Control System', 9th ESA Symposium on European rocket & balloon programmes & related research, 3-7 April 1989, ESA document SP-291, pub. June 1989, pp.117-122.

Twigge, Stephen Robert (1993), *The Early Development of Guided Weapons in the United Kingdom, 1940-1960*, Harwood Academic Publishers, Reading/Switzerland. ISBN 13: 9783718652976.

U

UCL (1974), *University College London, Mullard Space Science Laboratory, Report for the period 1972 September 1 – 1973 September 30*, Quarterly Journal Royal Astronomical Society (1974) 15, 182-192. (ADS).

UCL (1979), *University College London, Mullard Space Science Laboratory, Report for the period 1977 October 1 – 1978 September 30*, Quarterly Journal Royal Astronomical Society (1979) 20, 71-80. (ADS).

(For MSSL annual reports released directly by MSSL, see under "M" above).

UKSA (2014), *UK Registry of Outer Space Objects*, upload available via *https://www.gov.uk/government/uploads/system/uploads/attachment_data/file/319953/UK_Registry_of_space_objects.pdf*. (Last accessed July 2014).

University of Leicester (2010), *Fifty Years of Space Science at Leicester – A brief history*, a pdf document originally available online at *www.star.le.ac.uk/conf50/history50.pdf* , but apparently no longer available July 2014).

V

Vollmann, K & Grossmann, K.U. (1997), 'Excitation of 4.3 µm CO_2 emissions by $O(1D)$ during twilight', *Advances in Space Research*, Vol. 20, issue 6, pp.1185-1189. (Abstract on ADS).

Vonzahn, U. (1989), 'The project Winter in Northern Europe (MAP/WINE): Introduction and outlook', *International Council of Scientific Unions, Middle Atmosphere Program. Handbook for MAP*, Vol. 27, pp.220-225. (Abstract on ADS).

W

Walker, N.K. & Varker, F.A. (1949), *Preliminary note on the proposed new test vehicle, the C.T.V.4.*, RAE Technical note G.W. 57 Nov. 1949. (TNA: PRO AVIA 6/15352 / DSIR 23/18989).

Walker, N.K. & Hazell, J.F. (1950), *Preliminary discussion for Flight Tests at High Incidence and High Altitude – C.T.V.5.* RAE Technical Note GW 99, Dec.1950. (TNA: PRO AVIA 6/15388 / DSIR 23/19661).

Walter, H.U. (1982), 'Striations in Germanium', *Summary review of sounding rocket experiments in fluid science and materials science: Texus 1-20, Maser 1-2*, ESA SP-1132, Vol. 1, pp. 168

Weber & Henkel (1980), 'Astro-Hel – a Sounding Rocket project for High-resolution analysis of Helium EUV radiations', *Fifth ESA Symposium on European rocket & balloon programmes & related research, 14-18 April 1980*, ESA document SP-152, pub. June 1980, pp.155-160.

Weisner, A.G. (1954), 'The Determination of Temperatures and Winds above Thirty Kilometres', *Rocket Exploration of the Upper Atmosphere*, pp.133-142, Boyd R.L.F. & Seaton M.J. (Eds), Pergamon Press Ltd, London, 1954. (No ISBN).

White, E.C. (1960), *The development of the 'Cuckoo' rocket motor.* RPE Westcott Technical Note 194, Sept.1960. (TNA: PRO doc. ref. DSIR 23/28577).

Wildman, P.J.L., Kerley, M.J. & Shaw, M.S. (1969), 'Molecular oxygen measurements from 100 to 150 km at Woomera, Australia', *Journal of Atmospheric and Terrestrial Physics*, Vol. 31, Issue 7, July 1969, pp.951-957. (Abstract on ADS).

Wilhelm, K. *et al.* (1980), 'Sounding Rocket Observations of Field-Aligned Current Sheets', *European Rocket & Balloon Programme and Related Research, 5th ESA Symposium Proceedings*, ESA SP-152 p.279.

Willmore, A.P. (1987), 'Thirty Years of Space Research', *Journal of the British Interplanetary Society*, Vol.40, p.147-148.

Wilson, R. (1965), 'First Launching of the British Stabilized Skylark Rocket', *Astronomical Observations from Space Vehicles, Proceedings from Symposium no. 23 held in Liège, Belgium, 17 to 20 August 1964*. Edited by Jean-Louis Steinberg. International Astronomical Union. Symposium no. 23, Impr. Taffin-Lefort, p.79, also in Annales d'Astrophysique, Vol. 27, p.769. (ADS).

Wilson, R. & Boksenberg, A, (1969), 'Ultraviolet Astronomy', *Annual Review of Astronomy and Astrophysics*, Vol. 7, p.421. (ADS).

Windsor, Richard M. (1963), *The Southern Sky Survey Payload*, Goddard Space Flight Center Technical Note D-1719, February 1963. (NTRS), *http://ntrs.nasa.gov*, accession number 63N13104, document ID 19630003228, report number: NASA-TN-D-1719).

Winter, Ivan (2010), *Those were the days!* Magpie Press, Adelaide, ISBN 978 064 653 0437.

WRE (1974), *Trials Instruction No. BS217 (SL1012)*, (Mar 1974). (Copy courtesy of John Zarnecki, Open University).

Z

Zand, J. & Markwardt (2007), 'Six new candidate ultracompact X-ray binaries', *arXiv:astro-ph/0701810v2*, (Via Google Scholar).

Zarnecki, J.C. & Culhane, J.L. (1977), 'Detection of O VIII line emission in the X-ray spectrum of Puppis A', *Monthly Notices of the Royal Astronomical Society*, Vol. 178, Mar. 1977, p. 57P-61P.

Zbinden *et al.* (1975), 'Mass spectrometer measurements of the positive ion composition in the D and E regions of the ionosphere', *Planetary and Space Science*, Vol. 23, Issue 12, pp.1621-1640.

Zimmermann *et al.* (1997), 'Biotechnology on Sounding Rockets: Development of Techniques for Space Biotechnology', *Life Sciences Experiments Performed on Sounding Rockets (1985-1994): TEXUS 11-32, MASER 3-6 MAXUS 1*. ESA SP-1206, p.14. (ISBN: 92-9092-423-3).

4. List of References – online databases for microgravity experiments

Two large online database archives available via the internet have been consulted for information on microgravity experiments flown by Skylark rockets. They are referred to in the footnotes to Chapters 11 and 12, and basic access details are provided here rather than be repeated there. (These differ from the 'general purpose' NASA ADS database referred at the start of this reference section because they are secondary sources for microgravity information in their own right, as well as listing and including primary sources).

(a) The ESA (European Space Agency) Erasmus Experiment Archive (EEA) sounding rocket section, the index page of which is available via the home page *http://eea.spaceflight.esa.int/portal/* and clicking on "Sounding Rockets" (last accessed August 2014). This is referred to in the footnotes as "ESA EEA database"

(b) The NASA Microgravity Research Experiments (MICREX) database, the home page of which was at *http://exploration.grc.nasa.gov/fcarchive/media/micrex/* and where the TEXUS programme (up to TEXUS 20 only) was listed at *http://exploration.grc.nasa.gov/fcarchive/media/micrex/texus_idx.html* (last accessed March 2013). This is referred to in the footnotes as "NASA MICREX database". However, when the author tried to revisit the online database in April 2014, it appeared to have been closed down. This seems to leave only the following pdf document available via NTRS, but at 374 pages and size 14.8 MB, it is not user friendly! The citation for the MICREX database as a whole is *Winter, C. and Jones, J. C., "The Microgravity Research Experiments (MICREX) Database", NASA TM-108523, November 1996.*

5. List of References – film, video and audio resources

5.1 Films

(a) As explained in Chapter 9, a 15-minute Central Office of Information film "Tomorrow Today and Living Tomorrow No. 117" was made in 1972/73 to promote the use of Skylark's Earth Resources role. There is a copy/draft of the script in the National Archives at Kew, although the film itself was transferred in 1984 to the BFI (British Film Institute), in their National Archive section, 21 Steven Street, London W1T 1LN.

Document: "Tomorrow Today No. 117A" (1973). (TNA: PRO INF 6/1549).

16 mm Film: *Tomorrow Today and Living Tomorrow No.117* (1973), London Television Service, (Contents: Earth Resources Rocket; Atlas of the Earth; Leafless Pea: Water Resources). There is a viewing copy available at BFI, which the author has seen. The film is listed in their online archive, see *http://explore.bfi.org.uk/4ce2b6940caaa* (last accessed August 2014).

(b) IWM film archive – the Imperial War Museum in London lists many films about Woomera in its website catalogue, although most have not yet been digitised for online viewing, and can only be seen by appointment. Three of the films are about Skylark, two of which are similar to others described in this section:

(i) "The Firing of Skylark at Woomera" (1957, catalogue no. 4150). From the description provided, this contains material similar to the BBC documentary and Woomera Rocket Range videos listed below.

(ii) "Living Tomorrow" (1973, catalogue no. COI 1280). This must be similar or the same as the COI film described in (a) above.

However, the third film is the most intriguing:

(iii) "Skylark over Argentina" (1972 (sic), catalogue no. MTE 4207).

This film was produced by BAC and appears to provide a useful account of the first remote sensing User Trials carried out in Argentina in 1973 as described in Chapter 13. The film sequences include preparation, launch, tracking and results from either SL1182 or SL1181, The author has come across no other film like this, and unfortunately, at the time of writing (2014) has not been able to view it.

5.2 Online video resources

In various places in this book, references have been made to films or video clips that are available online via the internet. For convenience, they are listed here:

(a) BBC documentary screened 30 June 1957, (B&W). "The Restless Sphere – the Story of the International Geophysical Year", a programme from the "Television Service of the BBC", presented by the Duke of Edinburgh, running time 1 hour 14 minutes. A static exhibit of Skylark is shown in the introduction, and the preparation and launch of SL01 are shown 1 hour 2 minutes into the programme, which is archived & available online at *www.bbc.co.uk/archive/prince_philip/6012.shtml* (last accessed August 2014).

(b) A documentary film about Woomera, featuring the launch of SL01 in April 1957, (colour). 'Testing Rockets at Woomera Rocket Range' is a 2 minute 16 seconds excerpt from the film *Rocket Range Australia* (19 mins), produced in 1957. It can be viewed online at *www.australiansatwork.com.au/rocket/rocket_sc7-8.php* (last accessed August 2014).

(c) A comprehensive film by BAC 1967/68, (colour), about ESRO Skylark S26, entitled simply "Skylark: Sounding Space", running time 25 minutes. At the time of writing, it can be viewed or downloaded via the ESA website: *http://spaceinvideos.esa. int/Videos/Undated/Skylark_Sounding_Space* (last accessed August 2014).

(d) The beginning of the Open University's 2007 Annual Lecture for the general public, given by Professor John Zarnecki. It describes the launch and results of his experiment on SL1012, fired from Woomera in October 1974. See *www.open2.net/ oulecture2007/five_minutes.html*, (last accessed August 2014). This first part of a much longer lecture lasts seven minutes, and includes a (smuggled!) audio recording of the launch of SL1012.

(e) German TEXUS 21 flight from Sweden - a one-minute silent sequence showing the launch of TEXUS 21 in April 1989, and the operation of one of its biology experiments. See *www.spacebio.uni-bonn.de/ahp/Sounding/Texus.htm* , (last accessed August 2014), and scroll down to "TEXUS 21".

(f) Swedish launch – this video shows some spectacular views from external cameras during launch and in space on a MASER microgravity mission (possibly MASER 7 in November 1996). The sequence is silent and lasts 1 minute 35 seconds. Visit *http://spaceflight.esa.int/impress/text/multi_video.html*, and click on "MASER Sounding Rocket" (last accessed August 2014).

(g) Academic experiment video clips. The ESA EEA database (see above) contains some short (20-30 second) video clips of experiments filmed by static cameras during microgravity flights. See for instance:

(i) TEXUS 9, experiment 10: 'Thermal Maragoni convection in a floating zone' (Monti). Scroll down to "Attachments" and click on "Video 1", (last accessed August 2014).

(ii) TEXUS 14b, experiment 5: 'Experimental results on microgravitational fluid dynamics' (Monti & Fortezza). Scroll down to "Attachments" and click on "Video 1" or "Video 2", (last accessed August 2014).

(iii) TEXUS 27, experiment 1:'Electrophoresis Visualisation' (Roux-de Balmann and Sanchez), Scroll down to "attachments", and click on "Video 2", (last accessed August 2014).

5.3 Online audio resource

As described in Chapter 14, the launch of SL1306 is one of the rare instances from which an audio recording has survived. This came about because although no personal recording devices were allowed at Woomera, the Leicester experimenters had an instrumentation tape recorder to log flight data. This had an audio channel with a microphone that was used to pick up the range intercom so the tape would contain useful time marker information. The audio recoding was preserved for posterity by Leicester scientist Barry Giles, and although never of high quality, it captures the moment. The recording may be accessed from webpage *http://space50.star.le.ac.uk/2010/10/15/unique-sound-recording-of-sl-1306-launch/index.html* (last accessed August 2014), by clicking on "barry-hiss96." The voices are difficult to make out, but a transcription of the main moments is provided in Figure 14.69.

INDEX